ANALYTIC GEOMETRY AND THE CALCULUS

A. W. GOODMAN

UNIVERSITY OF SOUTH FLORIDA

Analytic Geometry and the Calculus

THE MACMILLAN COMPANY, NEW YORK
COLLIER-MACMILLAN LIMITED, LONDON

Ninth Printing, 1967

Library of Congress catalog card number: 63-8395

The Macmillan Company, New York
Collier-Macmillan Canada, Ltd., Toronto, Ontario

Printed in the United States of America

PREFACE FOR THE TEACHER

Recent textbooks on the Calculus have generally three common characteristics: (a) the inclusion of analytic geometry as an integrated part of the course, (b) the use of vectors, and (c) the introduction of more rigor. There are, I believe, good reasons for (a) and (b), and since these are now in style there is no need to repeat here the arguments in their favor. As the title indicates, this book is a unified treatment of Analytic Geometry and the Calculus. Further, we introduce vectors as early as possible and use vectors whenever we can.

But item (c) is quite different. It seems to me that a really rigorous book on the Calculus would begin with the axioms of set theory, derive the Peano axioms, and then reproduce most of Landau's great *Foundations of Analysis*. After this preparation, the class (if there are any students left) would have no trouble following the proofs needed in the Calculus. Since a completely rigorous presentation of the Calculus is obviously neither practical nor desirable, the central question is which theorems should be proved and which should be left to the intuition of the student. It is my hope that this book comes somewhere near the correct answer for the majority of students.

I have attempted to encourage the proper attitude toward rigor by stating definitions and theorems clearly. In this connection, I contend that one should not try to state all of the hypotheses in a theorem, because the statement can become so long as to be incomprehensible to the average student. Certain hypotheses are tacitly understood by both author and reader and hence, for brevity, should be omitted. As an illustration of the problems involved, consider the following:

THEOREM *S*. *If* $y = f(u)$ *and* $u = g(x)$, *then the derivative of the composite function* $y = f(g(x))$ *is given by*

$$\frac{dy}{dx} = \frac{dy}{du}\frac{du}{dx}.$$

v

Here is a statement that is brief and simple, and the average student has a reasonable chance of understanding it. Now let us look at the same theorem when stated in a rigorous fashion.

> THEOREM R. *Let f and g be two real-valued functions of a real variable and suppose that the range of g is a subset of the domain of f. Let $h = fg$ be the composite function defined over the domain of g by setting $h(x) = f(g(x))$ for each x in the domain of g. If x_0 is an interior point of an interval contained in the domain of g, and g is a differentiable function at x_0, and if f is a differentiable function at $u_0 = g(x_0)$, then h is a differentiable function at x_0, and further the derivative is given by the formula*
>
> $$h'(x_0) = f'(u_0)u'(x_0).$$

There is no doubt that R is the correct statement and S is full of gaps. However, the average student can learn and use S, but when R is presented he will either fall asleep or totally ignore it. It is just too complicated for him to master at this stage of his mathematics study. The presentation of R rather than S does real harm because it serves to repel many students who are originally attracted to mathematics and who might turn out to be capable technicians or teachers (if not creative thinkers) if they are given a reasonable chance to develop.

In this book we always give the short, simple, attractive, and perhaps erroneous statement in preference to the long, complicated, unattractive, but certainly correct version. For the very bright student (say one out of every twenty-five in the average university) who wants a rigorous treatment, it is a simple matter for the teacher to assign additional outside reading, such as Landau's *Foundations of Analysis*, his *Differential and Integral Calculus*, Hardy's *Pure Mathematics*, the two-volume work by Courant and McShane, *Differential and Integral Calculus*, Blachie and Don, Std. London, 1934, or the teacher's favorite book on Advanced Calculus.

The content of a course in Analytic Geometry and the Calculus, is reasonably standard, and a glance at the table of contents of this book will show that all of the essentials have been included, and these items do not require any further discussion. However, this book does have several minor innovations, which are listed here for convenience, together with a word or two of explanation.

1. The appendix contains short chapters on (a) mathematical induction, (b) inequalities, and (c) determinants. A student beginning the Calculus should know this material. It is included for the convenience and use of the poorly prepared student, but it is relegated to the appendix in order to avoid breaking into the natural sequence of ideas in the text proper.

2. Chapter 4 contains a detailed explanation of the summation notation and a list of problems devoted exclusively to this topic.

3. Centroids and moments of inertia have been postponed until Chapter 15. It has been my experience that students always have difficulty with this material, and the trouble may well disappear if we first allow them to develop more maturity. As a bonus for this postponement, we are able to amuse the student with a collection of weighted points that does not possess a center of gravity.

4. Chapter 9 contains some material on the computation of integrals by the method of undetermined coefficients.

5. In Chapter 13, on infinite series, we begin by stressing the computation and use of series, and postpone most of the theorems and proofs till the later part of the chapter. In this way the student can see the need for, and value of, the theorems before he tackles the proofs.

6. Chapter 16 includes a very brief introduction to the descriptive properties of point sets, together with a list of problems.

All topics are important in mathematics, but it must be admitted that some are more important than others. In order to devote enough space to a decent and detailed development of the essential ideas, and still hold this book to a reasonable length, it was necessary to omit certain items. The following topics were selected (with deep regrets and apologies) for exclusion: (a) equations of the angle bisectors for a pair of lines, (b) the radical axis of two circles, (c) average value of a function, (d) Kepler's laws of planetary motion, (e) contour lines as a method of graphing surfaces, and (f) line integrals and work.

Although the physical labor of organizing and writing this book was mine alone, it is obvious that any merit the book may have is ultimately due to the many persons who from every direction extended their helping hands. Just the list of all the mathematicians who have taught, guided, and inspired me is already too long for inclusion here, but the three who have had the deepest influence on my work are Otto Szasz, Paul Erdös, and Hans Rademacher. Unfortunately Otto Szasz is no longer with us, but Paul Erdös, who was barred from this country for many years, has recently been allowed to re-enter, much to the benefit of our own young mathematical scholars. I must also acknowledge my great debt to my parents who understood and encouraged me in my efforts to study mathematics. Finally, special mention is due my wife, who while raising a family found the time and energy to type the entire manuscript of this book, and two other books as well.

Lexington, Kentucky   A. W. GOODMAN

PREFACE FOR THE STUDENT

The Calculus is not an easy subject, and yet every year thousands of students manage to master it. You can do the same. The real difficulty is that the Calculus deals with *variables*. Because it is hard to give a precise definition of a variable this word is at present in ill-favor with some mathematicians. But the concept is easily understood by anyone who keeps his eyes and mind open while observing nature in action. For example, the distance of a car from some fixed reference point is a constant if the car is not moving, but the distance is a variable as soon as the car is in use. In the hands of a steady driver the speed will be constant, at least over short intervals of time, but in the vast majority of cases the speed is a variable. The height of a tree in a windstorm is a variable. The length of a steel bar changes as it is heated or cooled. The pressure of the gas in the cylinder of an automobile varies quite violently. The distance from the moon to Mars changes in a very complicated way.

The Calculus is a branch of mathematics that deals with variable quantities, and it is here that the student has his troubles. In trigonometry the student learns to solve triangles that are fixed (at least while he is solving them), or to prove identities (that are also fixed). In Algebra he learns how to solve a fixed equation for its fixed roots, or to find the value of a certain fixed determinant, etc. In the Calculus, however, we consider a variable quantity and ask such questions as "How fast is the quantity varying?", "What is the maximum value of the quantity?", "When is it increasing, and when is it decreasing?," etc.

As a result of this enlarged viewpoint, we can use the Calculus to solve problems that are very difficult or almost impossible by the means previously at our disposal. Probably the outstanding example is the computation of the area of the region bounded by a given curve. As long as the region is *fixed*, we are powerless to find the area, as all of the mathematicians prior to Newton and Leibniz (with the possible exception of Archimedes) will testify. But once we are willing to let one boundary of the region be variable, then the computation of the area becomes almost trivial. (See Chapter 4.)

The basic concept of the Calculus is expressed by the mysterious looking collection of symbols

$$\lim_{x \to a} y = b,$$

(read, the limit of y, as x approaches a, is b).   Here y depends on x, and as x changes y also changes.   Equation (1) tells us that as x gets closer to a, then y gets closer to b.   How close is y to b? As close as we please.   This means that if we select any small number, usually denoted by ϵ (the Greek letter epsilon) then we can make y within ϵ of b, in symbols

$$|y - b| < \epsilon, \tag{1}$$

by taking x sufficiently close to a.

To feel at home with (1) and its definition, you must have some knowledge of inequalities, and to assist you a brief treatment of this subject is given in Appendix 1.   It is not necessary to master this material before starting the Calculus, but you should have some familiarity with the ideas and the symbols $<$ and $>$.   You should also have some feeling for the relative magnitude of quantities.   For example, it should be immediately obvious that if x is very large then $1/x$ is very small.   This concept is expressed by the symbols

$$\lim_{x \to \infty} \frac{1}{x} = 0. \tag{2}$$

Here x is a variable that is growing without bound ($x \to \infty$), and (2) merely states that as x grows without bound $1/x$ gets closer and closer to zero.   More examples and details will be found in §3 and 4 of Chapter 2.

Every author hopes that his book can be read by the student, and this author is no exception.   The trouble is that the author, in writing his book, cannot raise his voice or pound on the table for emphasis.   You must supply these stage effects for yourself while reading.   The best that we can do is to put the important formulas in boxes, and to put the theorems and definitions in italics so that you can spot the essential items.   It is a good idea for you to memorize all of the theorems, definitions, and boxed formulas.   Memorization is not a substitute for learning, but it frequently happens that once an item is memorized, the subconscious mind will mull it over, and this will hasten eventual understanding.   Naturally, learning and understanding are the ultimate goals, but memorization plays a very important role that is not properly recognized today.   A child who memorizes Lincoln's Gettysburg address, when the words are meaningless will come to understand its meaning and appreciate its beauty far more quickly than the child who does not memorize it.

Most of the exercise lists contain more problems than can be done in one study session. You should be content to work a representative selection (probably the teacher will make a definite assignment) and reserve the rest to be used in review or in studying for examinations. Some problems are more difficult than others, either involving more complicated concepts or more extensive computation. We have marked such problems with stars(★) so that you can be on guard. The double star (★★) means that the problem is even harder than the ones marked with a single star.

The Calculus was discovered almost simultaneously by Isaac Newton (1642–1727) in England and Gottfried Leibniz (1646–1716) in Germany. Parts of the Calculus were anticipated much earlier by Archimedes (287?–212 B.C.) in Syracuse and by Pierre Fermat (1601–1665) in France. As first presented, the material was difficult to understand, but during the second century of its life it was smoothed, polished, simplified, and extended by a host of geniuses. The leaders in this activity were Leonard Euler (1707–1783), Joseph-Louis Lagrange (1736–1813), Pierre-Simon Laplace (1749–1827), and Augustin-Louis Cauchy (1789–1857). With such an array of mental giants contributing to the subject we should expect it to be rich, elegant, and beautiful—but not easy.

As you begin your study of the Calculus, I am tempted to say "Good luck" to you. But it is not luck, just good hard work that will see you safely through. The climb is difficult, but when you reach the peak and look back on the material covered, you will see a mathematical design of great beauty in the mountain "Calculus." There are of course still other mathematical mountains to climb that are even higher and more difficult, and from their tops the scenery is still more beautiful. But the Calculus seems to be the one that separates the men from the boys.

Lexington, Kentucky   A. W. GOODMAN

TABLE OF CONTENTS

CHAPTER 17. MULTIPLE INTEGRALS

CHAPTER 18. DIFFERENTIAL EQUATIONS

ANALYTIC GEOMETRY AND THE CALCULUS

1

INTRODUCTION TO ANALYTIC GEOMETRY

1.   Objective. Before the sixteenth century algebra and geometry were regarded as separate subjects.   It was René Descartes (1596–1650) who first noticed that these two subjects could be united, and that each subject could contribute to the development of the other.   This union, which we now call Analytic Geometry, has been fruitful far beyond the wildest dreams of Descartes.   Our objective in this chapter is to see just how algebra and geometry are brought together.   The unifying element is the rectangular coordinate system, and although the reader is probably already familiar with the coordinate system, a proper presentation requires that we give it a quick review.

2.   Directed distances.   Let AB in Fig. 1 be a line segment to which a particular direction has been assigned as indicated by the arrow. Let C and D be two points on this line three units apart.   By definition the distance between two points is always a positive number, unless the two points coincide.   In this latter case the distance is zero.   But it may happen that we wish to take into account the direction of travel in going from C to D.   If so we can attach a sign to the distance obtaining the *directed distance*.   If the direction of travel coincides with the direction of the line segment AB we attach a plus sign, and if the direction is opposed

Figure 1

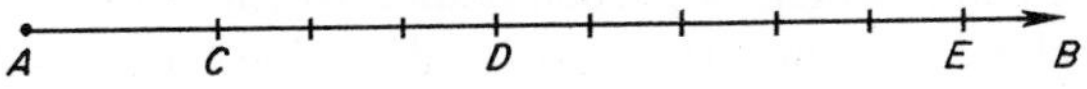

we attach a negative sign.   For example, CD represents the directed distance from C to D in Fig. 1, and hence $CD = 3$.   But DC would represent the distance from D to C and since the direction of travel is now the reverse of the direction from A to B we have $DC = -3$.   Again referring to Fig. 1, we have

$$DE = 5 \qquad\qquad CE = 8$$
$$ED = -5 \qquad\qquad EC = -8.$$

THEOREM 1. *If P, Q and R are any three points on a directed line, then for the directed distances*

$$\overrightarrow{PQ} + \overrightarrow{QR} = \overrightarrow{PR}. \qquad (1)$$

Observe that equation (1) tells us that we can suppress the common letter Q on the left side.   One should not assume that all of the quantities in this equation are positive.   For example, the equation

$$DC + CE = DE \qquad (2)$$

for the points of Fig. 1, states that

$$-3 + 8 = 5 \qquad (3)$$

and this is obviously correct.   The student should test Theorem 1, using Fig. 1, and letting Q be first C, then D and then E.   There are six possible equations of the form (1) with P, Q and R replaced in various ways by C, D, and E and the student should show that each of these six equations leads to a correct numerical result similar to (3).

To complete the proof of Theorem 1 it would be necessary to replace the specific numbers used in the example of Fig. 1, by arbitrary distances, represented by letters.   It is reasonably obvious that equation (1) is always valid, even in this more general situation, so we omit the details of this proof.

3.   The rectangular coordinate system.   The old familiar rectangular coordinate system is just two directed lines meeting at right angles (see Fig. 2).   The point of intersection is called the *origin* and is usually lettered O.   It is customary to make one of these lines horizontal and to take the direction to the right of O as the positive direction on this line. This horizontal line is called the *x-axis*, or the *horizontal axis*.   The other directed line which is perpendicular to the x-axis is called the *y-axis*, or the *vertical axis*, and the positive direction on this axis is upward from O. These two axes divide the plane into four quadrants, which are labeled Q. I, Q. II, Q. III, and Q. IV for convenience, as indicated in Fig. 2.

Once a rectangular coordinate system has been chosen, any point in the plane can be located with respect to it.   Suppose P is some point in the plane.   Let PQ be the line segment from P perpendicular to the x-axis at the point Q, and let PR be the line segment perpendicular to the y-axis at the point R (see Fig. 2).   Then the directed distance OQ is called the *x-coordinate* of P, or the *abscissa* of P.   The directed distance OR is called the *y-coordinate* of *P*, or the *ordinate* of *P*. For example, in Fig. 2, $OQ = 1$ and $OR = 3$, so the *x*-coordinate, the abscissa of *P*, is 1 and the *y*-coordinate, the ordinate of *P*, is 3.

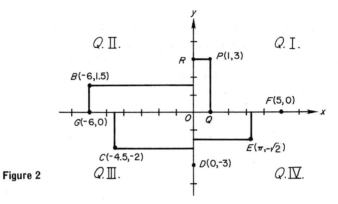

Figure 2

It is customary to enclose this pair of numbers in parentheses thus: (x, y), or in our specific case $(1, 3)$ and these numbers are called the *coordinates* of the point *P*. Since the figure *OQPR* is a rectangle $OQ = RP$ and $OR = QP$, so an alternate definition is possible, namely:

The x-coordinate of P is the directed distance of P from the y-axis,
The y-coordinate of P is the directed distance of P from the x-axis.

Figure 2 shows a number of other points with their coordinates. The student should check each point to see if its coordinates appear to be consistent with the position of the point in the figure.

Of course this procedure can be reversed. Given the coordinates $A(5, -8)$, for example, the point *A* can be located by moving five units to the right of *O* on the *x*-axis and then proceeding downward eight units along a line parallel to the *y*-axis. This discussion proves

THEOREM 2. *With a given rectangular coordinate system each point P in the plane has a uniquely determined pair of coordinates* (x, y). *Conversely each pair of coordinates* (x, y) *determines exactly one point P with these coordinates.*

The distance of a point *P* from the origin is usually denoted by *r*. Since this distance is just the length of the diagonal of a rectangle with sides of length[1] $|x|$, and $|y|$, it is easy to see from the Pythagorean Theorem

---

[1] The symbol $|x|$ denotes the absolute value, or the numerical value of *x*. By definition, if $x \geq 0$ then $|x| = x$, and if $x \leq 0$ then $|x| = -x$. Hence $|x|$ is never negative. For example, $|-3|$ falls in the second case so $|-3| = -(-3) = 3$.

that for any point P with coordinates (x, y) the distance of P from the origin is given by the formula

$$r = \sqrt{x^2 + y^2}. \qquad (4)$$

For example, in Fig. 2 the points OGB are the vertices of a right triangle and OB is the hypotenuse. The directed distances (coordinates) are $OG = x = -6$, and $GB = y = 1.5$. The lengths of the sides of the right triangle are the positive numbers $|-6| = 6$, and $|1.5| = 1.5$. Then by the Pythagorean Theorem

$$r^2 = 6^2 + (1.5)^2 = (-6)^2 + (1.5)^2 = x^2 + y^2, \qquad (5)$$

and this illustrates equation (4). The distance r is not a directed distance, so in (4) the positive square root is indicated. Thus, for the point B in Fig. 2 we have

$$r = \sqrt{36 + 2.25} = 6.184\ldots,$$

an irrational number.

The rectangular coordinate system is frequently called the Cartesian coordinate system in honor of its inventor René Descartes (1596–1650). A brief but highly entertaining account of the life of this genius can be found in *Men of Mathematics* by E. T. Bell (Simon and Schuster, 1937).

EXERCISE 1

1. Let G, H, J be three points in the order named, on a directed line. Let $GH = 5$, and $HJ = 12$. Write all six possible equations of the form of equation (1) for these three points, and check by substituting numbers that each of these equations is correct.

2. Using coordinate paper plot the points $(3, 4)$, $(5, 4\sqrt{6})$, $(-5, 12)$, $(-4, -3)$, $(\sqrt{5}, -2)$, $(0, -7)$, $(\sqrt{2}, \sqrt{3})$. Find r for each of these points.

In problems 3, 4, 5 and 6 use the Pythagorean Theorem to find the missing coordinate of P.

3. $r = 5$, $x = 4$, P is in Q. IV.

4. $r = 13$, $y = -12$, P is in Q. III.

5. $r = \sqrt{29}$, $x = -2$, P is in Q. II.

6. $r = 2\sqrt{7}$, $y = 4$, P is in Q. I.

7. What figure is formed by the set of all points which have (a) y − coordinate equal to 6, (b) x − coordinate equal to -3?

★8. In each of the following state what figure is formed by the set of all points whose coordinates (x, y) satisfy the given equation:

    a. $y = x$,   **b.** $y = -x$,   **c.** $y = x + 1$,

    d. $x^2 + y^2 = 25$,   **e.** $x^2 = y^2$.

⋆**9.** Let A, B, and C be three points, in that order, on a directed line segment, with the distances from A to B equal to a, and the distance from B to C equal to b, so that the distance from A to C is $a + b$. Prove Theorem 1 by considering all six possible ways of writing equation (1) with the letters A, B, and C. For example, prove that $AC + CB = AB$, $BC + CA = BA$, and so on.

10. The square root sign $\sqrt{A}$ always means that positive number whose square is A, if $A \neq 0$. Of course if $A = 0$, then $\sqrt{A} = 0$. For example $\sqrt{(-4)^2}$ is not -4 but is $+4$ by the definition of the symbol. Prove that for all x, $\sqrt{x^2} = |x|$.

4.   The Δ symbol. The Calculus deals with changes in variable quantities, and it is therefore convenient to have at hand a symbol to represent change. Suppose that a point P moving along the x-axis starts at the point $x_1 = 3$ and stops at the point $x_2 = 8$ (see Fig. 3a). What is the change in x, during the motion? Obviously the change in x is 5, and can be computed from x_1 and x_2 by taking the difference: $x_2 - x_1 = 8 - 3 = 5$. The symbol universally used to denote this change is Δx (read "delta x") and by definition[2] if x changes from x_1 to x_2 then

$$\Delta x = x_2 - x_1. \tag{6}$$

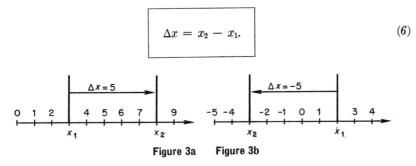

Figure 3a   Figure 3b

If the point is moving in the negative direction on the x-axis, then the x-coordinate is decreasing and we would expect that the change Δx will be negative. This is indeed the case, because in this case x_2 will be less then x_1 in equation (6). For example suppose that the moving point starts at $x_1 = 2$, and stops at $x_2 = -3$, as indicated in Fig. 3b. Then by definition

$$\Delta x = x_2 - x_1 = -3 - 2 = -5$$

and Δx is negative just as we expected. These two examples suggest the following

THEOREM 3. *If $\Delta x = x_2 - x_1$, where x_1 and x_2 are the coordinates of two points on a directed line (the x-axis), then the*

---

[2] The symbol Δ(delta) is the Greek d and is selected because it suggests the word "difference." Indeed, as equation (6) indicates, Δx, the change in x, is just the "difference" between the initial value of x and the final value of x. In words, Δx is the final value of x minus the initial value of x.

numerical value of Δx is the distance between the two points. Further Δx is positive if the direction from x_1 to x_2 coincides with that of the given line, and Δx is negative if the direction from x_1 to x_2 is opposite to that of the given line.

To prove this theorem, we must examine the various possible cases: (a) both x_1 and x_2 positive, i.e., both points to the right of the origin; (b) one coordinate positive and the other negative, i.e., the origin between the two points; and (c) both x_1 and x_2 negative, i.e., both points to the left of the origin. Each of these cases has two subcases according as x_1 precedes x_2, or x_2 precedes x_1 on the x-axis. The reader should complete the proof of the theorem by considering each of the six possible cases that can occur.

Naturally these remarks are not restricted to the x-axis. If a point moves on the y-axis, or more generally if it moves in the plane, then Δy denotes the change in the y-coordinate, i.e.,

$$\Delta y = y_2 - y_1$$

where y_1 is the y-coordinate of the initial position of the point, and y_2 is the y-coordinate of the final position of the point.

But we need not restrict ourselves to moving points and their coordinates. For example if a balloon is being inflated and V denotes the volume of the balloon then ΔV denotes the change in the volume of the balloon. In this case $\Delta V = V_2 - V_1$ where V_1 is the initial volume, and V_2 is the final volume. If h denotes the height of some rocket above the earth, then Δh denotes the change in height.

In all these cases, it may be convenient to think of the change as occurring during some fixed period of time, which would itself be a change in time representable by Δt. For example, suppose that 2 secs after firing, a certain rocket is 5,000 feet above the earth's surface, and that 5 secs after firing it is 20,000 feet above the earth's surface. Then for this data we have

$$\Delta h = h_2 - h_1 = 20,000 - 5,000 = 15,000 \text{ ft,}$$

during the time interval

$$\Delta t = t_2 - t_1 = 5 - 2 = 3 \text{ secs.}$$

5.   A distance formula. Let two points P_1 and P_2 be given in the plane.

If we are given the coordinates (x_1, y_1) and (x_2, y_2) of these points then it is quite easy to compute the distance between the two points. Indeed if we draw a line segment joining the two points and then make this segment the hypotenuse of a right triangle P_1QP_2 as indicated in

Fig. 4 by drawing suitable lines parallel to the axes, the distance[3] $|P_1P_2|$ can be computed by the Pythagorean Theorem:

$$|P_1P_2| = \sqrt{a^2 + b^2}, \tag{7}$$

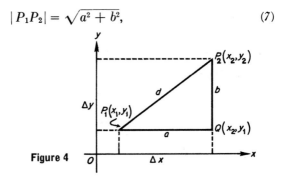

Figure 4

where a is the length of the line segment P_1Q and b is the length of the line segment QP_2.

Now along the line P_1Q, the height above the x-axis does not change, so that $a = |\Delta x|$. Similarly along the line QP_2 the x-coordinate does not change, so that $b = |\Delta y|$. In the case pictured in Fig. 4, both Δx and Δy are positive, but in other cases they may not be, so the absolute value signs are necessary. However on squaring, these absolute values may be dropped because for any number A we have $(A)^2 = (-A)^2$. Substituting for a and b in equation (7) yields

THEOREM 4.   *The distance between the points $P_1(x_1,\ y_1)$ and $P_2(x_2,\ y_2)$ is given by*

$$d = \sqrt{(\Delta x)^2 + (\Delta y)^2} = \sqrt{(x_2 - x_1)^2 + (y_2 - y_1)^2}. \tag{8}$$

We note that this distance is *not* a directed distance, so the positive square root is indicated in (8). Further, given two points in the plane, the distance between them does not depend on the letter assigned, so that either could be called P_1 and the other one P_2. Thus, either logically, or by inspection of equation (8), the quantity d is unchanged if the subscripts 1 and 2 are interchanged.

The formula (8) is easy to memorize because it is just a disguised form of the Pythagorean Theorem.

[3] We use the symbol $|AB|$ to denote the length of the line segment joining the points A and B.

EXAMPLE 1.   Find the distance between $(-3, 7)$ and $(2, -5)$.

SOLUTION.   We select $(-3, 7)$ as P_1, and then $(2, -5)$ is P_2.
Therefore

$$\Delta x = x_2 - x_1 = 2 - (-3) = 5,$$

$$\Delta y = y_2 - y_1 = -5 - 7 = -12,$$

and so by equation (8)

$$d = \sqrt{5^2 + (-12)^2} = \sqrt{25 + 144}$$
$$= \sqrt{169} = 13.$$

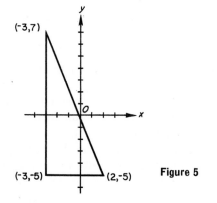

Figure 5

EXAMPLE 2.   A point $P(x, y)$ moves so that it is always the same distance from $A(4, 1)$ and $B(2, 3)$. Find a simple equation that the coordinates (x, y) must satisfy.

SOLUTION.   By equation (8) we have for the distances

$$|PA| = \sqrt{(x - 4)^2 + (y - 1)^2}, \quad |PB| = \sqrt{(x - 2)^2 + (y - 3)^2}. \qquad (9)$$

By the conditions of the problem $|PA| = |PB|$. Squaring both sides and using (9) we have

$$x^2 - 8x + 16 + y^2 - 2y + 1 = x^2 - 4x + 4 + y^2 - 6y + 9.$$

Dropping the terms x^2 and y^2 which appear on both sides, and collecting like terms gives

$$4y = 4x - 4$$

or

$$y = x - 1. \qquad (10)$$

Equation (10) is obviously in as simple a form as possible and hence is the solution of our problem. Conversely it can be shown that if $y = x - 1$, then the point $P(x, y)$ is equidistant from $A(4, 1)$ and $B(2, 3)$, because the steps that lead from (9) to (10) can be reversed to show that $|PA| = |PB|$.

We shall see shortly that an equation like (10) in which x and y appear just to the first degree, always describes a straight line, and this is naturally what we expect to obtain for the perpendicular bisector of the line segment AB.

EXERCISE 2

1. In each of the following compute Δx for the given x_1 and x_2 and make a little drawing similar to Figs. 3a and 3b to check your work. Observe that the six problems illustrate the six possible relative positions of x_1 and x_2 on the x-axis.

  a. $x_1 = 3, \quad x_2 = 12,$ b. $x_1 = -5, \quad x_2 = 4,$

  c. $x_1 = -17, \quad x_2 = -8,$ d. $x_1 = 11, \quad x_2 = 2,$

  e. $x_1 = 2, \quad x_2 = -7,$ f. $x_1 = -6.5, \quad x_2 = -15.5.$

2. In each of the following compute the distance $|AB|$ using formula (8). Then make a careful drawing to scale, and check your answer by measuring the distance with a ruler.

  a. $A(-9, -1), \quad B(3, 4),$ b. $A(-2, 9), \quad B(1, 5),$

  c. $A(7, 1), \quad B(3, 3),$ d. $A(7, 11), \quad B(-9, -5).$

3. Is the quadrilateral with vertices $P(1, 1)$, $Q(4, 11)$, $R(1, 12)$, and $S(-2, 2)$ a parallelogram? Is it a rectangle?

4. Show that equation (8) gives equation (4) in the special case that one of the points is at the origin.

In problems 5 through 10 find a simple equation satisfied by the coordinates of a point $P(x, y)$ subject to the given conditions.

5. $P(x, y)$ is the same distance from $(-1, -3)$ and $(3, 5)$.
6. $P(x, y)$ is the same distance from $(-1, 2)$ and $(-5, 7)$.
7. $P(x, y)$ is five units from the point $(3, -4)$.
8. $P(x, y)$ is nine units from the point $(-4, 5)$.
9. The distance from $P(x, y)$ to the x-axis is equal to the distance from $P(x, y)$ to $(0, 2)$.
10. The distance from $P(x, y)$ to the y-axis is equal to the distance from $P(x, y)$ to the point $(4, 1)$.

6. Graphs of equations and equations of graphs. Let us consider all the pairs of numbers (x, y) that satisfy the equation

$$y = 2x - 1. \tag{11}$$

It is easy to find such pairs. We merely select a particular value for x, say $x = 4$, and using it in (11) we find that $y = 2 \times 4 - 1 = 7$. Thus the pair $(4, 7)$ satisfies equation (11). Corresponding to this pair there is a point in the plane with this pair $(4, 7)$ as coordinates. We can continue to find more pairs, and to mark out more points in the plane. It is desirable to introduce some system into the computations by arranging the work in a little table, selecting values for x for which the computation is easy, and finding the corresponding y. Such a table is shown below, and the corresponding points are marked in Fig. 6.

x	-4	-3	-2	-1	0	1	2	3	4
$y = 2x - 1$	-9	-7	-5	-3	-1	1	3	5	7

The points all seem to lie on a straight line, and we feel reasonably confident that if we continue to select values for x, compute y, and plot the corresponding points, then these new points will also fall on the line deter-

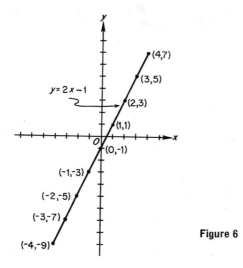

Figure 6

mined by the points already plotted in Fig. 6. Of course this must be proved and we will give a proof in section 8. But first our ideas must be made precise.

> DEFINITION 1. *The graph of an equation is the collection of all points (x, y) whose coordinates satisfy that equation. The graph is also called a curve*[4].

It is obviously impossible to compute all such pairs and mark the corresponding points in the plane, since for most equations there will be

---

[4] Strictly speaking the words "graph" and "curve" do not have the same meaning. The distinction however is rather complicated, and the student need not worry about the distinction at present. In this book we shall regard the two words as synonymous. The graph is also called the *locus* of an equation.

infinitely many such points.   In the case of equation (11) however the matter is simplified because we suspect (and it will be proved later) that the graph is a straight line.   So we can just plot two of the points and then draw the straight line that passes through those two points.

EXAMPLE 1.   Sketch the graph of the equation[5]

$$y = \frac{x^2}{4} + 1. \tag{12}$$

SOLUTION.   In this case we have infinitely many points on the curve so it is impossible to obtain the full graph.   So we compute the coordinates of enough points to enable us to form a good guess as to the appearance of the graph, and then "sketch" the rest of the graph by assuming that the curve is nice and smooth.   The table of values can be condensed by observing that x is squared in (12) so that both x and $-x$ will lead to the same value for y. For example, if $x = 1$ or $x = -1$, we find $y = 5/4$.   The table is shown below and the sketch is shown in Fig. 7.

x	0	± 1	± 2	± 3	± 4	± 5
y	1	$\frac{5}{4}$	2	$\frac{13}{4}$	5	$\frac{29}{4}$

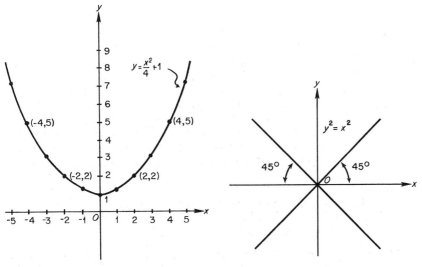

Figure 7   Figure 8

[5] This is the equation of problem 9 in Exercise 2.

EXAMPLE 2. Sketch the graph of the equation $y^2 = x^2$.

SOLUTION. Taking square roots of both sides of the equation we find that either $y = x$, or $y = -x$. We leave it to the reader to make a table of values. The graph of $y = x$ appears to be a straight line through the origin that makes an angle of 45° with the positive x-axis, and the graph of $y = -x$ appears to be a line perpendicular to this line at the origin. Then the graph of $y^2 = x^2$ is the pair of straight lines shown in Fig. 8.

We have seen how each equation in x and y leads to a unique graph, the graph of the equation. One might expect that conversely each graph would lead to a uniquely determined equation. Unfortunately this is not true.

Let us consider the straight line of Fig. 6. Certainly equation (11), $y = 2x - 1$, is an equation for this straight line, since the straight line was plotted from this equation. If we add 1 to both sides of this equation we have

$$y + 1 = 2x. \tag{13}$$

But equation (13) is satisfied whenever equation (11) is, and equation (11) is satisfied whenever equation (13) is. Hence both equation (11) and (13) have the *same* graph. So if we are given the graph, its equation is *not unique*. Indeed we can obtain a large variety of equations, each having the straight line of Fig. 6 for its graph. A few of these are:

$$2y + 2 = 4x, \qquad y - 3 = 2(x - 2),$$
$$3y + 3 = 6x, \qquad y + 5 = 2(x + 2),$$
$$1 = 2x - y, \qquad y^3 = 8x^3 - 12x^2 + 6x - 1.$$

Because of the multiplicity of equations that can arise from a given graph, we cannot say "the" equation of a graph, but rather we must say "an" equation of a graph. However we will always try to find among the set of all such equations, a suitably attractive and simple one to call (erroneously) "the" equation of the graph.

DEFINITION 2. *An equation is called an equation for a graph if the coordinates of a point satisfy the equation whenever the point is on the graph, and do not satisfy the equation whenever the point is not on the graph.*

EXAMPLE 3. Find an equation for the graph consisting of all points P such that $|PF| = |PD|$, where F is the point $(0, 2)$ and $|PD|$ denotes the distance from P to the x-axis.

SOLUTION. Let (x, y) be the coordinates of a point on the graph. Then the distance $|PD|$ from the x-axis is $|y|$, and $|PF| = \sqrt{(x - 0)^2 + (y - 2)^2}$. Hence P is on the graph if and only if

$$|y| = \sqrt{x^2 + y^2 - 4y + 4}. \tag{14}$$

This is an equation for the graph. To find a simpler one we square both sides and obtain

$$y^2 = x^2 + y^2 - 4y + 4$$

$$4y = x^2 + 4$$

$$y = \frac{x^2}{4} + 1. \tag{15}$$

Equation (15) stands as the solution because it cannot be simplified further. Observe that all of the steps in going from the graph to equation (15) can be reversed so that a point that satisfies equation (15) must be on the graph. Notice also that equation (15) is identical with equation (12) so that we already have a sketch of this graph in Fig. 7. This type of graph is called a parabola, and we will study it in detail later on.

EXERCISE 3

In problems 1 through 6, the graph of the equation is a straight line. Find two points satisfying the given equation, draw the line, and then check that other points satisfying the equation also seem to lie on the line.

1. $y = 2x + 5$.
2. $y = -3x + 7$.
3. $y = x - 4$.
4. $y = -2x - 5$.
5. $3y = x + 6$.
6. $4y = -x - 8$.

7. Sketch the graphs of the equations (all with the same set of coordinate axes):

a. $y = x^2$,   b. $y = x^2/4$,   c. $y = x^2/10$,

d. $y = -x^2/10$,   e. $y = -x^2$.

8. Sketch the graphs of the equations (all with the same set of coordinate axes):

a. $y = x^2$,   b. $y = x^3$,   c. $y = x^4$.

In problems 9 through 16 sketch the graphs of the given equation.

9. $x^2 + y^2 = 25$.
10. $y^2 = 9x^2$.
11. $y = |x|$.
12. $y = x(x - 2)(x - 4)$.
13. $y = x(x - 1)^2$.
14. $y = x^3 - 4x$.
15. $4y = x^4 - 4x^2$.
16. $4x = y^2$.

In problems 17 through 21 the point $P(x, y)$ is subject to certain given conditions. In each case find a simple equation for the graph consisting of all points P that satisfy the given condition. Then use the equation to sketch the graph.

17. P is equidistant from $A(2, 5)$ and $B(4, 3)$.
18. P is on a circle with center at the origin and radius 3.
19. P is on the x-axis.
20. P is on a line parallel to the y-axis and three units to the right of the y-axis.

21. *P* is seven units from the point (1, 2).

22. Determine the constants *a* and *b* so that the graph of $y = ax + b$ contains the points $(-1, -6)$ and $(4, 5)$.

★23. Determine the constants *a*, *b*, and *c* so that the curve $y = ax^2 + bx + c$ passes through the points $(1, 0)$, $(2, 0)$, and $(3, 2)$.

7.   The slope of a line. Let *l* be a line in the plane and let α be the angle from the *x*-axis to the line, i.e., the angle through which the *x*-axis must rotate in a positive direction (counterclockwise) in order that it coincide with the given line (see Fig. 9). If the line is falling as we progress from left to right then clearly $90° < \alpha < 180°$ and $\tan \alpha$ is negative. If the line is rising then $0 < \alpha < 90°$ and $\tan \alpha$ is positive. If the line is horizontal, then the line need not intersect the *x*-axis. In this case

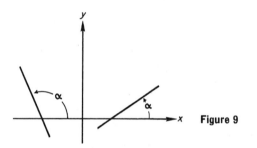

Figure 9

we put $\alpha = 0$. If the line is vertical then $\alpha = 90°$ and $\tan \alpha$ is undefined. However no harm is done if we use the symbol $\tan 90° = \infty$, as long as we keep in mind that ∞ is not a number and do not try to do algebraic manipulations with it. The key idea is that $\tan \alpha$ is a convenient measure for describing the behavior of the line: $\tan \alpha$ is positive for a rising line, negative for a falling line, zero for a horizontal line, and large values for $|\tan \alpha|$ indicate that the line is very steep.

> **DEFINITION 3.** *The slope of a line is denoted by* m *and is defined by*
>
> $$\boxed{m = \tan \alpha} \tag{16}$$
>
> *where* α *is the positive angle from the x-axis to the line. If the line is horizontal* $m = 0$, *and if the line is vertical the slope is undefined.*

It is easy to compute the slope of a line if we know the coordinates of two points on the line. Indeed let $P_1(x_1, y_1)$ and $P_2(x_2, y_2)$ be two distinct points on *l*. We can select the subscripts so that P_2 lies to the right of P_1 and hence $x_2 > x_1$. We construct a right triangle P_1QP_2 (as shown in Figs. 10 and 11) by drawing lines through P_1 and P_2 parallel to the *x*-axis and *y*-axis respectively.

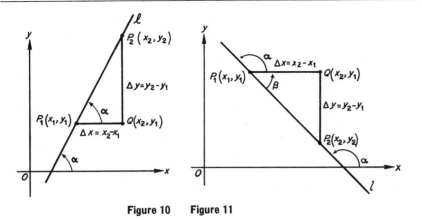

Figure 10   Figure 11

In the case of a rising line, as indicated in Fig. 10, it is obvious that the angle $\alpha = \angle QP_1P_2$ of the right triangle so that $\tan \alpha = QP_2/P_1Q = \Delta y/\Delta x$, and hence,

$$m = \frac{\Delta y}{\Delta x} = \frac{y_2 - y_1}{x_2 - x_1}. \tag{17}$$

In the case of a falling line, formula (17) is still valid but a little twist is needed in the proof to take care of the negative sign. In this case (see Fig. 11)

$$\tan \beta = \frac{P_2Q}{P_1Q} = \frac{|\Delta y|}{\Delta x}$$

where we used $|\Delta y|$ because in this case $\Delta y < 0$, while the length of the side P_2Q of the right triangle is positive. Obviously $\alpha + \beta = 180°$ so $\tan \alpha = -\tan \beta$. Thus $\tan \alpha = -|\Delta y|/\Delta x = \Delta y/\Delta x$.

If the line is horizontal $\Delta y = 0$ and $m = 0$. If the line is vertical $x_1 = x_2$ so that $\Delta x = 0$. In this case formula (17) involves a division by zero, and this is consistent with our agreement that for a vertical line the slope is undefined. This proves

THEOREM 5. *If $P_1(x_1, y_1)$ and $P_2(x_2, y_2)$ are any two distinct points on a line (that is not vertical) then the slope m is given by equation (17).*

EXAMPLE 1. Find the slope of a line through the points $(13, 3)$ and $(-5, 7)$.

SOLUTION. Let $(13, 3)$ be the point P_2 and $(-5, 7)$ be the point P_1. Then by equation (17)

$$m = \frac{y_2 - y_1}{x_2 - x_1} = \frac{3 - 7}{13 - (-5)} = \frac{-4}{18} = -\frac{2}{9}.$$

Since the slope is negative we know that the line is falling. Further we know that for every increase in x of nine units, the line falls two units.

EXERCISE 4

In each of problems 1 through 6 plot the points P and Q and compute the slope of the line through P and Q.

1. $P(2, -1)$, $Q(7, 4)$.
2. $P(13, -3)$, $Q(-7, -4)$.
3. $P(-5, 7)$, $Q(1, -11)$.
4. $P(0, 0)$, $Q(a, b)$, $a \neq 0$.
5. $P(a, b)$, $Q(3a, 7b)$, $a \neq 0$.
6. $P(a, 0)$, $Q(0, b)$, $a \neq 0$.

In each of problems 7 through 10 plot the points P, Q, and R and determine whether they are collinear by computing the slopes of the lines PQ and PR. Check your work by computing the slope of the line QR.

7. $P(-1, -2)$, $Q(5, -5)$, $R(-5, 0)$.
8. $P(2, 4)$, $Q(-3, 2)$, $R(-13, -2)$.
9. $P(-6, 8)$, $Q(4, 2)$, $R(12, -3)$.
10. $P(-2, 5)$, $Q(-12, -11)$, $R(6, 18)$.

Two lines are parallel if they have the same slope. Use this fact in problems 11 and 12 to determine whether $PQRS$ is a parallelogram.

11. $P(-3, -2)$, $Q(8, 1)$, $R(13, 10)$, $S(2, 7)$.
12. $P(13, 7)$, $Q(8, -3)$, $R(-7, 0)$, $S(-1, 12.)$.

$\star$**13.** Prove that if A and B are two distinct points on a straight line, then no matter which one is selected to be P_1 (with the other being P_2) in Theorem 5, the slope computed by equation (17) is the same. *Hint.* Let the coordinates of A be (x_A, y_A) and the coordinates of B be (x_B, y_B). Then observe that

$$\frac{y_B - y_A}{x_B - x_A} \stackrel{?}{=} \frac{y_A - y_B}{x_A - x_B}.$$

8.   Equations for the straight line. Our first task is to find an equation for a line when the slope and one point on the line are given. If m is the given slope, and $P_1(x_1, y_1)$ is the given point on the line, then the variable point $P(x, y)$ is on this line if and only if the slope of the line P_1P is equal to m. Using equation (17) this gives immediately

$$\frac{y - y_1}{x - x_1} = m. \qquad (18)$$

The point $P_1(x_1, y_1)$ is an exceptional point for equation (18) because when we place $x = x_1$ and $y = y_1$, both the numerator and denominator are zero, so the left side is really meaningless. However if we clear fractions we obtain

$$\boxed{y - y_1 = m(x - x_1),} \qquad (19)$$

and the exceptional case disappears. This equation is satisfied if and only if $P(x, y)$ is on the line.

If the line is vertical, so that $m = \infty$, the equations (18) and (19) are both meaningless, but if we divide (19) on both sides by m, and then let m grow indefinitely, so that the left side becomes zero, we obtain the meaningful equation $0 = x - x_1$, or

$$x = x_1. \qquad (20)$$

But a quick inspection of (20) shows that it is indeed the equation of a vertical line through the point $P_1(x_1, y_1)$, even if it was obtained by rather questionable means. This proves

THEOREM 6. *Suppose that a line is given by specifying its slope and one point on the line. If the line is vertical then equation (20) is an equation for the line. In all other cases equation (19) is an equation for the line. Conversely the graph of equation (19) is a straight line with the slope m and passing through P_1.*

For obvious reasons (19) is called the *point-slope form* of the equation of the line with slope m through the point (x_1, y_1).

EXAMPLE 1. Find an equation for the line with slope $3/4$, and passing through the point $(5, -6)$.

SOLUTION. Substituting the given numbers in equation (19), the point-slope form, we find

$$y - (-6) = \tfrac{3}{4}(x - 5)$$

or

$$4y + 24 = 3x - 15$$

or

$$4y = 3x - 39.$$

EXAMPLE 2. Prove that the graph of $3x + 2y = 7$ is a straight line, and find its slope and one point on the line.

SOLUTION. By transposition and division by 2, the given equation is equivalent to

$$y - \tfrac{7}{2} = -\tfrac{3}{2}x. \qquad (21)$$

But (21) has just the form of (19) with $y_1 = 7/2$, $m = -3/2$ and $x_1 = 0$. Therefore, by Theorem 6, the graph is a straight line through the point $(0, 7/2)$ with slope $-3/2$.

If two points are given (instead of the slope and one point) then one can use the two given points to compute the slope. Using this in equation (18) yields

$$\frac{y - y_1}{x - x_1} = \frac{y_2 - y_1}{x_2 - x_1}. \tag{22}$$

The point $x = x_1$, $y = y_1$ is also an exceptional point for (22) just as it is for (18). But this exceptional point disappears after appropriate clearing of fractions. Despite this slight defect, equation (22) is to be preferred because its symmetry makes it easier to memorize. Thus we have

> **THEOREM 7.** *Suppose that the points $P_1(x_1, y_1)$ and $P_2(x_2, y_2)$ are given with $x_1 \neq x_2$. Then equation (22) is an equation for the line passing through P_1 and P_2.*

For obvious reasons (22) is called the *two-point form* of the equation of the straight line.

EXAMPLE 3. Find an equation for the line passing through $(1, -3)$ and $(-4, 5)$.

SOLUTION. Let the given points be P_1 and P_2 respectively. Equation (22) then gives

$$\frac{y - (-3)}{x - 1} = \frac{5 - (-3)}{-4 - 1}.$$

Simplification gives $-5(y + 3) = 8(x - 1)$, or finally $5y + 8x + 7 = 0$, as a suitably simple form for the equation of this line.

Observe that had we selected $(-4, 5)$ as P_1 and $(1, -3)$ as P_2, equation (22) would then give

$$\frac{y - 5}{x - (-4)} = \frac{-3 - 5}{1 - (-4)}.$$

But simplification of this equation also leads to $5y + 8x + 7 = 0$.

> **DEFINITION 4.** *If a line intersects the x-axis at the point $(a, 0)$, then a is called the x-intercept of the line. If the line intersects the y-axis at $(0, b)$ then b is called the y-intercept of the line.*

If we are given the slope and the y-intercept of a line, then using Theorem 6, equation (19), we can write an equation for the line immediately.   Since $(0, b)$ is a point on the line, we have $y - b = m(x - 0)$, or transposing

$$y = mx + b. \tag{23}$$

For obvious reasons (23) is called the *slope-intercept* form of the equation of a straight line.

THEOREM 8.   *If m is the slope and b is the y-intercept of a line, then equation (23) is an equation for the line.*

EXAMPLE 4.   Find an equation for the line with slope 3 that meets the y-axis five units below the origin.

SOLUTION.   Here $m = 3$ and $b = -5$.   So equation (23) gives $y = 3x - 5$.

Using any one of the three Theorems 6, 7, or 8 we see that any straight line has an equation of the form $Ax + By + C = 0$.   We are now in a good position to prove the converse, which we have always suspected to be true anyway.

THEOREM 9.   *If A and B are not simultaneously zero, then the graph of the equation*

$$Ax + By + C = 0 \tag{24}$$

is a straight line.

PROOF.   Suppose $B = 0$.   Then $A \neq 0$, so (24) becomes $Ax + C = 0$, or $x = -C/A$.   But this is just the equation of a vertical line through the point $(-C/A, 0)$.

If $B \neq 0$ then (24) can be written in the form

$$y = -\frac{A}{B}x - \frac{C}{B}.$$

But this is just the slope-intercept form, so the graph is a line with slope $-A/B$ and y-intercept $-C/B$.

EXAMPLE 5.   What is the graph of $-x + 3y + 7 = 0$?

SOLUTION.   This equation is equivalent to $y = x/3 - 7/3$ so the graph is a straight line with slope $1/3$ and y-intercept $-7/3$.

Equations such as (24) that contain only the first power of x and y are called *linear* equations.   We can sloganize our results by saying that every straight line has a linear equation, and every linear equation has a straight line for its graph.

EXERCISE 5

In problems 1 through 5 find a simple equation for the line satisfying the given conditions.

1.   Slope 3, passing through the point $(-1, 2)$.
2.   Slope $-1/4$, passing through the point $(5, -3)$.
3.   Passing through the given pair of points

    a. $(5, 6)$, $(-2, -1)$,   b. $(-1, 6)$, $(13, -1)$,
    c. $(\frac{5}{4}, \frac{1}{2})$, $(-\frac{3}{4}, -\frac{7}{2})$,   d. $(1 - \sqrt{3}, 3)$, $(1 + \sqrt{3}, 5)$.

4.   Slope 10, y-intercept 5.
5.   Slope $-1/3$, y-intercept $7/6$.
6.   Find the slope and y-intercept for each of the following lines.

    a. $2x + 3y + 4 = 0$,   b. $5x - y - 7 = 0$,
    c. $x = 3y + 9$,   d. $57x + 19y = 114$,
    e. $y = 10$,   f. $3x - \sqrt{3}y + 12 = 0$.

7.   Find the angle α from the x-axis to each of the following lines.

    a. $y = x + 2$,   b. $y = x + \pi$,
    c. $y = -x + \sqrt{15}$,   d. $y = \sqrt{3}x - 11$,
    e. $\sqrt{3}y = x - 11$,   f. $x = 100$.

  ★8.   Find the point of intersection of the two lines $2x + 5y = 11$ and $3x - y = -9$.   *Hint:* We want a pair of numbers (x, y) that satisfy both equations simultaneously.

  ★9.   Find the point of intersection of the lines $3x + 7y = -4$ and $5x - 11y = 16$.

  ★10.   Do the straight lines $2x + 3y = 5$ and $6y + 25 = -4x$ intersect? If so find the point of intersection.

  ★11.   Prove that if a line has x-intercept $a \neq 0$ and y-intercept $b \neq 0$, then

$$\frac{x}{a} + \frac{y}{b} = 1$$

is an equation for the line. This is called the *intercept form* of the equation of a straight line. Use this to find a simple equation for the line with x and y intercepts:

    a. $5, -4$,   b. $1, 1$,   c. $2, 7$,   d. $-\frac{1}{3}, \frac{1}{6}$.

  ★12.   What is the graph of $xy + 2 = x + 2y$? *Hint:* The given equation is equivalent to $(y - 1)(x - 2) = 0$.

In problems 13 through 18 find the graph of the given equation.

  13. $(y - x - 2)(y - 3) = 0$.   ★14. $y^2 = x^2 + 4x + 4$.
  ★15. $y = 1 + x + |x|$.   ★16. $y = 2 + |x|$.
  ★17. $y = 2 - |x|$.   ★18. $y = 3 + |x - 2|$.

  ★19.   A line $l: y = mx + b$, divides the plane into two regions, one the set of all points above the line, and the other the set of all points below the line. Show that for the point $P_1(x_1, y_1)$: if $y_1 > mx_1 + b$ then P_1 lies above the line, and if $y_1 < mx_1 + b$ then P_1 lies below the line.

*20. Without making a drawing determine which of the following points lie above the line $y = -x/2 + 5/3$ and which lie below the line:

a. $(10, -3)$,   b. $(50, -23)$,   c. $(-40, 21)$,   d. $(5/2, 2/5)$.

9.   **Parallel and perpendicular lines.** Given two straight lines, can we look at their equations and merely by inspection determine whether the lines are parallel or perpendicular? The answer is yes, and the method is given in

THEOREM 10. *Let l_1 be a line with slope m_1 and let l_2 be a line with slope m_2. Then the lines are parallel if and only if* $\boxed{m_1 = m_2}$ (//) *The lines are mutually perpendicular if and only if*

$$\boxed{m_1 m_2 = -1.} \quad (\perp) \quad\quad\quad\quad (25)$$

PROOF. Two lines are parallel if and only if they make the same angle with the x-axis, and consequently if and only if they have the same slopes.

The perpendicularity criterion is a little harder to prove. Referring to Fig. 12 it is clear that

$$\alpha_2 = \varphi + \alpha_1.$$

If $\varphi = 90°$ then

$$m_2 = \tan \alpha_2 = \tan (90° + \alpha_1) = -\cot \alpha_1 = -\frac{1}{\tan \alpha_1} = -\frac{1}{m_1},$$

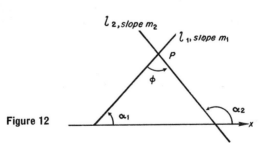

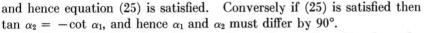

Figure 12

and hence equation (25) is satisfied. Conversely if (25) is satisfied then $\tan \alpha_2 = -\cot \alpha_1$, and hence α_1 and α_2 must differ by 90°.

In Fig. 12, P, the point of intersection of the two lines, lies above the x-axis. We leave it to the reader to make a drawing for the case when P is on, or below the x-axis, and to convince himself that Theorem 10 holds also in this case. A simpler method of completing the proof is indicated in problems 8 and 9 of Exercise 6.

If m_1 or m_2 is undefined, then one of the lines is vertical.   For parallelism, both lines must be vertical, and for perpendicularity one line must be vertical and the other horizontal.   These special cases are rather a nuisance but an accurate presentation requires the above discussion.

EXAMPLE 1.   Find an equation of the line through the point $(5, 1)$, (a) parallel to the line $y = 3x + 7$ and (b) perpendicular to that line.

SOLUTION.   (a) Since the line is to be parallel it must have slope $m = 3$ so we can write

$$y = 3x + b$$

where b is unknown.   Since $(5, 1)$ is on the line its coordinates must satisfy this equation, so we have

$$1 = 3 \times 5 + b.$$

Therefore $b = -14$, and the equation is $y = 3x - 14$.

(b) By equation (25) $3m_2 = -1$ or $m_2 = -1/3$.   Hence the sought equation is

$$y = -\tfrac{1}{3}x + b$$

where again b is an unknown.   Again the point $(5, 1)$ is on the line so that

$$1 = -\tfrac{1}{3} \times 5 + b$$

and consequently $b = 8/3$.   Hence the perpendicular line has as its equation $y = -x/3 + 8/3$, or $3y + x = 8$.

EXERCISE 6

In problems 1 through 5, a point P and a line l are given.   Find an equation for the line through P and (a) parallel to l, and (b) perpendicular to l.

1. $(5, -5)$, $y = x + 10$.
2. $(0, 11)$, $2y = x - 7$.
3. $(0, 0)$, $3y + x = \pi$.
4. $(-1, -1)$, $5y - 2x = 9$.
5. $(100, 200)$, $x - 37 = 0$.

*6.   Prove that the two lines

$$Ax + By + C = 0,$$
$$Ax + By + D = 0,$$

either coincide or are parallel.

*7.   Prove that the two lines

$$Ax + By + C = 0,$$
$$Bx - Ay + D = 0$$

are mutually perpendicular.

*8. Let l_1 and l_2 be the lines $y = mx + b$ and $y = mx + B$, with $B \neq b$. Show that these lines are parallel and that the line l_2 lies above l_1 if and only if $B > b$.

*9. Suppose that the two lines $l_1: y = m_1x + b_1$ and $l_2: y = m_2x + b_2$ intersect in a point below the x-axis. Then by increasing the constants b_1 to B_1 and b_2 to B_2 the two lines can be moved upward so that they intersect above the x-axis. But this does not change either m_1, or m_2, or the angle between the lines l_1 and l_2. Theorem 10 was proved only in case the lines intersect above the x-axis. Show that the above argument extends Theorem 10 to all cases.

*10. Determine the unknown constants, so that the two lines $y = mx + b$ and $y = Mx + 15$ will be mutually perpendicular, and intersect at the point $(4, 13)$.

10. **The circle.** A circle is the collection of all points having a given fixed distance r from a given fixed point C. The distance r is the radius and C is the center. Using our distance formula, it is easy to find a nice equation for a circle.

THEOREM 11. *If (h, k) is the center and r the radius, then*

$$r^2 = (x - h)^2 + (y - k)^2 \qquad (26)$$

is an equation for the circle. Conversely if $r^2 > 0$ the graph of (26) is a circle.

PROOF. In Theorem 4, formula (8), let $d = r$, let P_2 be the **point** (x, y) on the circle, and let P_1 be the center (h, k). Then square both sides.

EXAMPLE 1. Find an equation for the circle of radius 5 and center $(-3, 4)$.

SOLUTION. From equation (26) we have

$$25 = (x - (-3))^2 + (y - 4)^2$$
$$= x^2 + 6x + 9 + y^2 - 8y + 16.$$

The constants can be combined and the terms rearranged to give

$$x^2 + y^2 + 6x - 8y = 0.$$

Obviously this circle passes through the origin. Why?

This procedure can be reversed as illustrated in

EXAMPLE 2. Find the graph of the equation

$$x^2 + y^2 - 4x + 6y + 9 = 0.$$

SOLUTION.   Since this is a quadratic equation and the coefficients of x^2 and y^2 are the same this suggests that the graph is a circle.   Rearranging the terms and completing the squares we have

$$x^2 - 4x \quad + y^2 + 6y \quad = -9$$
$$+ 4 \qquad\qquad + 9 = \qquad + 4 + 9$$
$$\overline{x^2 - 4x + 4 + y^2 + 6y + 9 = \quad 4}$$
$$(x - 2)^2 \qquad + (y - (-3))^2 = \quad 4.$$

Using Theorem 11 our suspicions are confirmed, namely the graph is a circle with center $(2, -3)$ and radius 2.   This example suggests

THEOREM 12.   *The graph of the equation*

$$x^2 + y^2 + Ax + By + C = 0 \tag{27}$$

is either a circle, a point, or has no points at all.   When it is a circle the center is $(-A/2, -B/2)$ and the radius is

$$r = \frac{1}{2}\sqrt{A^2 + B^2 - 4C}. \tag{28}$$

PROOF.   Completing the square in (27) just as in the example we have

$$x^2 + Ax + \frac{A^2}{4} + y^2 + By + \frac{B^2}{4} = \frac{A^2}{4} + \frac{B^2}{4} - C$$

or

$$\left(x + \frac{A}{2}\right)^2 + \left(y + \frac{B}{2}\right)^2 = \frac{1}{4}(A^2 + B^2 - 4C).$$

If the righthand side is positive, the graph is obviously the circle described in the theorem.   Since the square of a real number can never be negative, the lefthand side cannot be negative for any real point (x, y).   So if $A^2 + B^2 - 4C < 0$, there are no points on the graph. If $A^2 + B^2 - 4C = 0$, the only possible point is $x = -A/2$, $y = -B/2$, and the graph consists of a single point (a circle of radius zero).

It does not pay to memorize formula (28), because the process of completing the square is quite simple and leads to r^2 on the righthand side of the equation.

Two points P_1 and P_2 are said to be *symmetric with respect to a line l* if the line l is the perpendicular bisector of the segment P_1P_2.   Each of the points is said to be the *reflection* of the other in the line l.   A curve is said to be *symmetric* with respect to the line l if for every point P_1 on the curve, its reflection in the line l is also on the curve.   In this case the line l is called an *axis of symmetry* for the curve.

Physically, symmetry about a line means that if the curve is drawn carefully on a piece of paper, and if the paper is folded on the line of symmetry, then the two halves of the curve will coincide.

It is intuitively obvious that a circle is symmetric with respect to any line through its center.

* to complete the square of $Ax^2 + Bx + C = 0$,
make $A = 1$
then $C = \left(\frac{1}{2} B\right)^2$
add to both sides of eqn.

EXERCISE 7

In problems 1 through 6 find an equation for the circle with the given center and given radius.

1. $C(5, 12)$, $r = 13$.
2. $C(0, 0)$, $r = 7$.
3. $C(1, -1)$, $r = 2$.
4. $C(-4, -5)$, $r = 6$.
5. $C(a, 2a)$, $r = \sqrt{5}a$.
6. $C(3, b)$, $r = b$.

In problems 7 through 10 find an equation for the circle satisfying the given conditions.

7. Tangent to the x-axis, center at $(3, 2)$. $(x-3)^2+(y-2)^2=(2)^2$
8. Tangent to the y-axis, center at $(-5/2, -3/2)$.
9. Tangent to the line $y = 7$, center at $(5, -2)$.
10. Center at $(1, 1)$, passing through the point $(3, 2)$.

In problems 11 through 14 describe the graph of the given equation.

11. $x^2 + y^2 - 4x + 2y - 20 = 0$.
12. $x^2 + y^2 + 6x + 8y + 24 = 0$.
13. $x^2 + y^2 - 6x - 16y + 73 = 0$.
14. $4x^2 + 4y^2 - 4x + 20y + 36 = 0$.   ie: give $C(x,y)$ & r

★15. Find the equation of the circle through the three points $(0, -2)$, $(8, 2)$, and $(3, 7)$.

★16. Find the equation for the common chord of the two circles $x^2 + y^2 - 2x = 0$ and $x^2 + y^2 - 4x - 4y + 4 = 0$.   *Hint:* If a point satisfies both equations, it satisfies their difference, and this difference is a linear equation.   solve simultaneously

★17. Find the points of intersection of the two circles of problem 16.

★18. The equation $x^2 + y^2 = 2x$ is the equation of a certain circle C. Prove that if x_1, y_1 are real numbers such that $x_1^2 + y_1^2 < 2x_1$ then the point $P(x_1, y_1)$ lies inside the circle C. What can you say about the position of P if $x_1^2 + y_1^2 > 2x_1$?

★★19. Graph the equation $|x| + |y| = 5$.

20. Prove that a circle is symmetric with respect to any diameter.

21. Prove that a square has four axes of symmetry.

22. How many axes of symmetry does a rectangle have if it is not a square?

23. Find the number of axes of symmetry for (a) an equilateral triangle, (b) a regular pentagon, (c) a regular hexagon.

24. Does the figure consisting of two circles have an axis of symmetry if the circles are not concentric, and the circles have different radii?

★25. Prove that if a figure has two distinct axes of symmetry that are parallel, then the figure is unbounded. A *figure* is any collection of points, and the figure is said to be *unbounded* if given any circle, no matter how large, the figure has points outside of the circle.

11.   The conic sections.   The Calculus provides us with a systematic method of studying curves. Hence it would be wise to postpone our study of the conic sections until after we have developed some portions

of the calculus.   But in this very development, it is advantageous to have at hand numerous examples.   For this reason we now give a brief introduction to conic sections.   We will return to a more detailed study of these important curves in Chapter 6.

As the name implies these curves are obtained by cutting a cone with a plane as shown in Fig. 13.   Three types of curves occur: (a) the ellipse, (b) the parabola, and (c) the hyperbola, depending upon the inclination of the cutting plane to the axis of the cone.   However this geometric definition has fallen from favor[6] because the analytic definitions (given below) are easier to use.

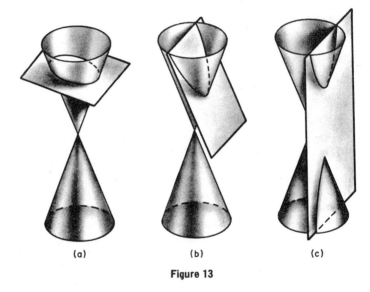

(a)   (b)   (c)

Figure 13

DEFINITION 5.   *A parabola is the curve consisting of all points P that are equidistant from a fixed point F (the focus) and a fixed line d (the directrix).*

In order to find a simple equation for a parabola, we locate the focus and the directrix in a suitably chosen position.   Or if the focus and directrix are not to be moved, then we will place our coordinate axes in an appropriate position.   Whatever point of view we adopt, let us agree that the x-axis is parallel to the directrix and runs midway between the focus and the directrix, and that the focus is on the positive y-axis.   Then the focus F is at $(0, p)$ where p is some positive number, and the equation of the directrix d is $y = -p$ (see Fig. 14).

[6] For a development of the conic sections from their definition as sections of a cone see the author's *The Pleasures of Mathematics* (The Macmillan Company, 1965).

Now by definition $P(x, y)$ is on the parabola if and only if

$$|PF| = |PD| \qquad (29)$$

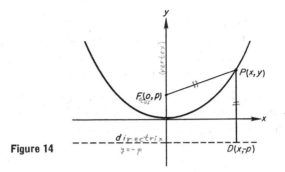

Figure 14

and using our distance formula we have

$$\sqrt{(x - 0)^2 + (y - p)^2} = \sqrt{(x - x)^2 + (y + p)^2}.$$

Squaring both sides and simplifying yields

$$x^2 + y^2 - 2py + p^2 = y^2 + 2py + p^2$$

or

PARABOLA

$$x^2 = 4py. \qquad \boxed{y^2 = 4px} \qquad (30)$$

Each step is reversible, so if (30) is satisfied so is (29) and the point is on the parabola.   We have proved

THEOREM 13.   *The graph of equation (30) is a parabola with focus at* $(0, p)$ *and directrix* $y = -p$.

EXAMPLE 1.   Give an equation for the parabola with focus at $(0, 4)$ and directrix $y = -4$.

SOLUTION.   Here $p = 4$ so by (30) $x^2 = 16y$.

EXAMPLE 2.   What is the distance from the focus to the directrix for the parabola $y = 3x^2$.

SOLUTION.   To match equation (30) we must write

$$x^2 = \tfrac{1}{3}y = 4 \times \tfrac{1}{12}y.$$

Hence $p = 1/12$, and the desired distance is twice this, or 1/6.

The line through the focus and perpendicular to the directrix is called the *axis* of the parabola.   The point of intersection of the axis with the parabola is called the *vertex* of the parabola.   It is obvious from Fig. 14 that with our special choice of the position of the coordinate axes, the vertex turns out to be at the origin.

> **DEFINITION 6.**   *An ellipse is the curve consisting of all points P such that the sum of its distances, $|PF_1|+|PF_2|$, from two fixed points F_1 and F_2 is a constant.   The points F_1 and F_2 are called the foci of the ellipse.*

As before, the task of finding an equation for an ellipse is simplified if the coordinate system is selected judiciously.   Let the x-axis pass through the two foci F_1 and F_2 (as indicated in Fig. 15) and let the y-axis bisect

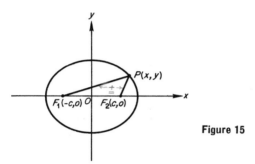

Figure 15

the segment F_1F_2.   If we denote the distance between the two foci by $2c$, then the coordinates for the foci will be $(-c, 0)$ and $(c, 0)$.   It is convenient to denote the constant sum $|PF_1|+|PF_2|$ by $2a$.   Then according to the definition of an ellipse the point P is on the ellipse if and only if

$$|PF_1|+|PF_2| = 2a. \tag{31}$$

Our distance formula, equation (8), gives

$$\sqrt{(x + c)^2 + y^2} + \sqrt{(x - c)^2 + y^2} = 2a.$$

We transpose the second radical to the right side and then square both sides, obtaining

$$x^2 + 2xc + c^2 + y^2 = x^2 - 2xc + c^2 + y^2 - 4a\sqrt{(x - c)^2 + y^2} + 4a^2.$$

If we drop the common terms x^2, y^2, and c^2 from both sides, and then transpose, we obtain

$$4a\sqrt{(x - c)^2 + y^2} = 4a^2 - 4xc. \tag{32}$$

After dividing through by 4 and again squaring, we have

$$a^2(x^2 - 2xc + c^2 + y^2) = a^4 - 2a^2xc + x^2c^2.$$

The terms $-2a^2xc$ drop out and on transposing and grouping we arrive at

$$x^2(a^2 - c^2) + a^2y^2 = a^2(a^2 - c^2),$$

and on dividing by $a^2(a^2 - c^2)$ we have

$$\frac{x^2}{a^2} + \frac{y^2}{a^2 - c^2} = 1. \qquad (33)$$

This suggests that we introduce a new symbol b, defined by the equation $b^2 = a^2 - c^2$. When this is done equation (33) assumes the very simple form

ELLIPSE
$$\boxed{\frac{x^2}{a^2} + \frac{y^2}{b^2} = 1.} \qquad (34)$$

It is not completely obvious that all of the above steps are reversible. Indeed in taking square roots we must assure ourselves that we have taken the positive square root on both sides. Once this subtle point is settled, the proof will be completed for

THEOREM 14.   *Equation (34) is an equation for the ellipse*

$$|PF_1| + |PF_2| = \underline{2a} \quad (\text{major axis}) \qquad (31)$$
$$\underline{2b} \quad (\text{minor axis}$$

where the foci *are* $F_1(-c, 0)$ *and* $F_2(c, 0)$, *and*

$$\boxed{c = \pm\sqrt{a^2 - b^2},} \qquad a > b. \qquad (35)$$

Equation (34) is called the *standard form* for the equation of the ellipse. A sketch of the ellipse $x^2/25 + y^2/16 = 1$ is shown in Fig. 15.

EXAMPLE 3.   Find the graph of $x^2/169 + y^2/25 = 1$.

SOLUTION.   By Theorem 14 the graph is an ellipse with $a = 13$ and $b = 5$. Further for this ellipse, $|PF_1| + |PF_2| = 2a = 2 \times 13 = 26$. Since $c^2 = a^2 - b^2 = 13^2 - 5^2 = 169 - 25 = 144$, we have $c = 12$. Therefore the foci of this ellipse are at $(-12, 0)$ and $(12, 0)$.

If we set $y = 0$ in equation (34) we find that $x = \pm a$. Thus the points $(-a, 0)$ and $(a, 0)$ are points of the ellipse and are indeed the intersection points of the ellipse with the x-axis. Similarly if we set $x = 0$ in (34) we find that $y = \pm b$, so that the points $(0, b)$ and $(0, -b)$ are also on the ellipse and are the intersection points of the ellipse with the y-axis. It is intuitively obvious that the ellipse (34) is symmetric with respect to the x and y-axes. The four points $(-a, 0)$, $(a, 0)$, $(0, b)$ and $(0, -b)$ are known as *vertices* of this ellipse. The segment of length $2a$ between the first pair of vertices is called the *major axis* of the ellipse, and the segment of length $2b$ between the second pair of vertices is known as the *minor axis* of the ellipse (see Fig. 16).

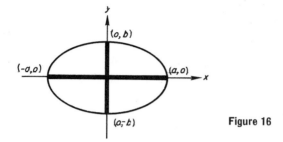

Figure 16

DEFINITION 7. *A hyperbola is the curve consisting of all points P such that the difference of its distances from two fixed points F_1 and F_2 is a constant.   The points F_1 and F_2 are called the foci of the hyperbola.*

Here we should observe that in the definition, the order of the difference is not specified, so there are two possibilities.   To be specific suppose that the constant difference is $2a$, then the point P is on the hyperbola if either

$$|PF_1| - |PF_2| = 2a, \qquad (36)$$

or

$$|PF_2| - |PF_1| = 2a. \qquad (37)$$

To find a simple form for the equation of the hyperbola, we again run the x-axis through the foci F_1 and F_2, and let the y-axis be the perpendicular bisector of the segment F_1F_2 (see Fig. 17).   If the distance between

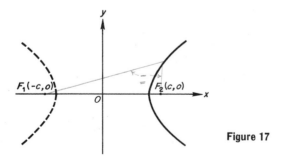

Figure 17

the two foci is $2c$, then the coordinates of the foci will be $(-c, 0)$ and $(c, 0)$.   Let $P(x, y)$ be a point on the hyperbola that satisfies equation (36).   Then by the distance formula (8)

$$\sqrt{(x + c)^2 + y^2} - \sqrt{(x - c)^2 + y^2} = 2a. \qquad (38)$$

We transpose the second radical of (38) to the right side and then square both sides, obtaining

$$x^2 + 2xc + c^2 + y^2 = x^2 - 2xc + c^2 + y^2 + 4a\sqrt{(x - c)^2 + y^2} + 4a^2.$$

If we drop the common terms x^2, y^2, and c^2 from both sides and then transpose we obtain

$$-4a\sqrt{(x - c)^2 + y^2} = 4a^2 - 4xc.$$

Now this equation is almost identical with equation (32) obtained in the derivation of the equation of the ellipse. The only difference is the negative sign in front of the radical, and on squaring this difference disappears. Therefore we can follow that work and arrive again at

$$\frac{x^2}{a^2} + \frac{y^2}{a^2 - c^2} = 1. \tag{33}$$

But for the ellipse the condition $|PF_1| + |PF_2| = 2a$ implied that $a \geq c$, and as a result $a^2 - c^2$ was positive (or zero) and we could set $b^2 = a^2 - c^2$. This time we are dealing with the hyperbola, and $|PF_1| - |PF_2| = 2a$. But since $|F_1F_2| = 2c$ it is obvious that $2a \leq 2c$ and if the equality sign does not hold then $a^2 - c^2$ is negative. Hence, in introducing b^2, we turn the quantity around and write

$$b^2 = c^2 - a^2 \tag{39}$$

(instead of $b^2 = a^2 - c^2$ for the ellipse). Using (39) in (33) we find

HYPERBOLA
$$\frac{x^2}{a^2} - \frac{y^2}{b^2} = 1 \tag{40}$$

as the standard form for the equation of the hyperbola.

If the point P satisfies equation (37) instead of equation (36), a little computation will show that its coordinates still satisfy (40). Conversely, it can be proved that if (x, y) satisfies (40) then P satisfies either equation (36) or (37), but we omit the details.

THEOREM 15. *Equation (40) is an equation for the hyperbola*

$$\pm(|PF_1| - |PF_2|) = 2a$$

where the foci are $F_1(-c, 0)$ *and* $F_2(c, 0)$ *and* $c = \pm\sqrt{a^2 + b^2}$.

The hyperbola $x^2/16 - y^2/9 = 1$ is shown in Fig. 17. The curve falls into two pieces called branches. The righthand branch, shown solid, is the branch for which $|PF_1| - |PF_2| = 2a = 8$. On the lefthand branch, shown dotted, $|PF_2| - |PF_1| = 8$.

EXAMPLE 4. Find an equation of the curve described by a point moving so that the difference of its distances from $(-5, 0)$ and $(5, 0)$ is 8. Sketch this curve.

SOLUTION. The curve is a hyperbola with foci at $(-5, 0)$ and $(5, 0)$. From equation (36) we have $2a = 8$ and hence $a = 4$. Further $c = 5$. Then $b^2 = c^2 - a^2 = 5^2 - 4^2 = 25 - 16 = 9$. Hence $b = 3$ and the equation of this hyperbola is

$$\frac{x^2}{16} - \frac{y^2}{9} = 1.$$

The sketch is shown in Fig. 17. The line through the foci is called the *axis* of the hyperbola. It is intuitively obvious that the hyperbola is symmetric with respect to this axis. It is also symmetric with respect to the perpendicular bisector of the segment F_1F_2. The intersection points of the line F_1F_2 and the hyperbola are called the *vertices* of the hyperbola.

EXERCISE 8
THE PARABOLA

1. Sketch the graph of each of the following parabolas and give the coordinates of the focus, and the equation of the directrix.

   a. $x^2 = 4y$,   b. $y = x^2$,
   c. $y = 4x^2$,   d. $y = x^2/32$.

2. If the focus is on the x-axis at $(p, 0)$, $p > 0$ and if the directrix is the vertical line $x = -p$, then $y^2 = 4px$ is an equation for this parabola. Prove this statement.

3. Suppose the focus is on the y-axis, but below the x-axis, instead of above it. We can still use $(0, p)$ for the focus but this time p is negative. Let the directrix be the line $y = -p$ where now $-p$ is positive and the directrix lies above the x-axis. Prove that $x^2 = 4py$ is an equation for this parabola.

4. Using the results of problems 2 and 3, sketch each of the following parabolas and give the focus and directrix.

   a. $y^2 = 4x$,   b. $x^2 = -4y$,
   c. $y^2 = -4x$,   d. $y = -x^2/8$,
   e. $x = -y^2$,   f. $7y = -5x^2$.

5. Derive a simple equation for the parabola with focus at $(4, 5)$ and directrix $y = 1$. Sketch the parabola from the equation.

6. Repeat problem 5 with the focus at $(-2, -7)$ and directrix the y-axis.

7. The line through the focus of a parabola and perpendicular to the directrix is called the *axis* of the parabola. Prove that any parabola is symmetric with respect to its axis.

8. It can be proved that the graph of $y = Ax^2 + Bx + C$ is a parabola if $A \neq 0$. Determine the constants so that this parabola runs through the three points $(1, 3)$, $(2, 4)$ and $(3, 7)$. Sketch this parabola.

9. The parabola $y = x^2$ divides the plane into two regions, one above the parabola, and one below the parabola. Show that if $y_1 > x_1^2$ then the point $P(x_1, y_1)$ lies in the region above the parabola $y = x^2$.

THE ELLIPSE

10. Write the standard form for the equation of each of the following ellipses and sketch.

  a. Distance sum is 10, and foci at $(\pm 3, 0)$,
  b. distance sum is 20, and foci at $(\pm 6, 0)$,
  c. distance sum is 10, and foci at $(\pm 2\sqrt{6}, 0)$,
  d. distance sum is 10, and foci at $(\pm 1, 0)$.

[handwritten margin: $2a=10$, $a=5$, $c=3$, $b^2=a^2-c^2$, $b^2=25-9$, $b^2=16$, $b=4$, $\frac{x^2}{25}+\frac{y^2}{16}=1$]

11. Let the foci of an ellipse be $(0, c)$ and $(0, -c)$, i.e., on the y-axis instead of on the x-axis. If the distance sum is $2b$, then

$$\frac{x^2}{a^2} + \frac{y^2}{b^2} = 1$$

is still an equation for this ellipse, but now $a^2 = b^2 - c^2$ so that $b > a$. Prove this statement.

12. Find the foci and distance sum for each of the following ellipses, and sketch the graph.

  a. $\dfrac{x^2}{25} + \dfrac{y^2}{9} = 1$,

  b. $\dfrac{x^2}{25} + \dfrac{y^2}{24} = 1$,

  c. $\dfrac{x^2}{9} + \dfrac{y^2}{25} = 1$,   *[handwritten: $b=3 > 2b=6$, $a=5$, $c^2=a^2-b^2$, $=25-9$, $+16$, $c=24$, $F=(0,\pm4)$, $a>b$]*

  d. $\dfrac{x^2}{25} + \dfrac{y^2}{16} = 1$,

  e. $\dfrac{x^2}{4} + \dfrac{y^2}{3} = 1$,

  f. $\dfrac{x^2}{25} + 4y^2 = 1$.

13. Prove that an ellipse is symmetrical with respect to its major axis, and also with respect to its minor axis.

14. Find the ellipse in standard form that passes through the points $(4, -1)$ and $(-2, -2)$.   *[handwritten: $\frac{(4)^2}{a^2}+\frac{(-1)^2}{b^2}=1$; $\frac{(-2)^2}{a^2}+\frac{(-2)^2}{b^2}=1$, solve simultaneously for a^2 & b^2]*

15. Find the ellipse in standard form that passes through the points $(3, \sqrt{7})$ and $(-\sqrt{3}, 3)$.

16. What can be said about the location of a point $P(x_1, y_1)$, if

$$\frac{x_1^2}{9} + \frac{y_1^2}{4} < 1?$$

THE HYPERBOLA

17. Write the standard form for the equation of the hyperbola with:

  a. $\pm(|PF_1| - |PF_2|) = 8$, and foci at $(-5, 0)$ and $(5, 0)$,
  b. $\pm(|PF_1| - |PF_2|) = 6$, and foci at $(-5, 0)$ and $(5, 0)$,
  c. $\pm(|PF_1| - |PF_2|) = 4$, and foci at $(-5, 0)$ and $(5, 0)$,
  d. $\pm(|PF_1| - |PF_2|) = 2$, and foci at $(-5, 0)$ and $(5, 0)$,
  e. $\pm(|PF_1| - |PF_2|) = 1$, and foci at $(-5, 0)$ and $(5, 0)$,
  f. $\pm(|PF_1| - |PF_2|) = 8$, and foci at $(0, -5)$ and $(0, 5)$.

18. Sketch each of the hyperbolas in problem 17. Put the first five on the same coordinate system.

19. Find the foci for each of the hyperbolas:

a. $\dfrac{x^2}{25} - \dfrac{y^2}{144} = 1,$ $c^2 = a^2 + b^2$ $c^2 = 169$ $c = 13$

b. $\dfrac{x^2}{2} - \dfrac{y^2}{2} = 1,$

c. $\dfrac{x^2}{144} - \dfrac{y^2}{25} = 1,$

d. $\dfrac{x^2}{4} - \dfrac{y^2}{5} = 1,$

e. $\dfrac{y^2}{25} - \dfrac{x^2}{144} = 1,$

f. $x^2 - 2y^2 = 6.$

20. Prove that a hyperbola is symmetric with respect to its axis.

21. Prove that a hyperbola is symmetric with respect to the perpendicular bisector of the line segment joining its foci.

★22. Let $K > 0$. Show that the graph of $xy = K^2/2$ is a hyperbola, by showing this equation is the equation of the hyperbola with foci at (K, K) and $(-K, -K)$ and distance difference $2K$.

23. Sketch the hyperbola of problem 22 when $K = \sqrt{2}$.

24. Find the equation of the hyperbola that goes through the point $(2, 3)$ and has foci at $(\pm 2, 0)$.

25. Find the equation of the hyperbola that goes through the points $(\sqrt{6}, 4)$ and $(4, 6)$ if its foci are on the y-axis and the hyperbola has the x-axis as an axis of symmetry.

26. Find the hyperbola described in problem 25 if it goes through the points $(3\sqrt{2}, 2)$ and $(12, 5)$.

12. Functions and function notation

DEFINITION 8. *We say that y is a function of x if whenever x is given, there is a rule, or method, or procedure by which a unique y is determined.*

For example $y = x^2 + 4$ gives y as a function of x. Here the rule or method is to take the number x, multiply it by itself and then add 4, and this gives y.

In some cases the rule may be meaningful for some values of x, and meaningless for other values of x. In this case we say that y is a function of x, only for those values of x for which the rule is meaningful. This is illustrated by the example function $y = \sqrt{25 - x^2}$. If we are working only with real numbers (as we are in this book) then the square root of a negative number has no meaning. Hence y is a function of x only for $-5 \leq x \leq 5$ because for each x in this interval[7] $\sqrt{25 - x^2}$ is a uniquely

---

[7] The collection of x such that $a \leq x \leq b$ is called an *interval*. The points $x = a$ and $x = b$ are called the *end points* of the interval. If the end points are included, the interval is called a *closed interval*. The interval $a < x < b$ is called an *open interval* (the end points have been removed). Intervals such as $a < x \leq b$ or $a \leq x < b$ are called *half-open* or also *half-closed*.

determined real number, while for x outside this interval $25 - x^2$ is negative. It is customary to put such restrictions just after the equation that gives the function; for example we would write in this case

$$y = \sqrt{25 - x^2}, \qquad -5 \leq x \leq 5.$$

As a further illustration, the notation

$$y = \frac{x^2 + 3x + \pi}{x - 6}, \qquad x \neq 6$$

means that y is defined as a function of x by the first equation, for all real values of x except for $x = 6$. The value $x = 6$ must be excluded because when $x = 6$, the denominator is zero, and a real number for y is not determined by the given equation.

In these examples x is called the *independent variable* because it can run freely, and y is called the *dependent variable* because the value of y depends on the value of x. $y = f(x)$

The following examples show that the rule may be very complicated. Examples 2 and 3 illustrate that the rule may be given in several pieces.

EXAMPLE 1. $y = |x|$.   The graph of this function is shown in Fig. 18.

EXAMPLE 2. $y = 4$ if $x \geq 2$, $y = 1$ if $1 \leq x < 2$ and $y = -1$ if $x < 1$. The graph of this function is shown in Fig. 19.   For simplicity such a function is usually written thus:

$$y = \begin{cases} 4, & \text{if} \quad x \geq 2, \\ 1, & \text{if } 1 \leq x < 2, \\ -1, & \text{if} \quad x < 1. \end{cases} \tag{41}$$

EXAMPLE 3. $y = \begin{cases} \sqrt{4 - x^2} + 2, \text{ if } -2 \leq x \leq 2, \\ \quad 2 \quad \text{, for all other } x. \end{cases}$

The graph of this function is shown in Fig. 20.

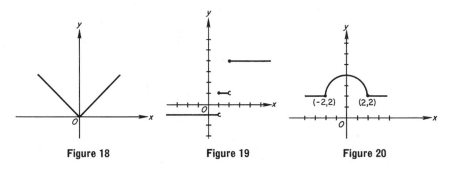

Figure 18   Figure 19   Figure 20

EXAMPLE 4. y is the third digit after the decimal point, in the decimal representation of x. Since $2.000\ldots = 1.9999\ldots$, this function is not well defined, until we agree that in our decimal representation of x we will not permit an infinite sequence of nines. Now our function is well defined, and for this function we have: if x is any integer then $y = 0$, if $x = \sqrt{2}$ then $y = 4$, if $x = \log_{10} 2$ then $y = 1$, and if $x = \pi$ then $y = 1$. For obvious reasons we make no attempt to graph this function, nor do we expect the reader to graph it.

Of what use are such "wild" functions? In the ordinary sense of the word, such functions are not very useful. But in a deeper sense these functions are very useful, because they serve to illustrate the definition of a function, and to show just how "wild" a function can really be.

The graph shown in Fig. 19 has a break or jump at $x = 1$ and another break at $x = 2$. We say that the function is *discontinuous* at $x = 1$ and also discontinuous at $x = 2$. We will give a more careful definition of continuous and discontinuous functions in Chapter 2.

We use x to represent a number in mathematics, without specifying exactly which number we are speaking about. In the same way, we need some notation to represent a function, without specifying exactly which function we are talking about. It frequently happens that we want to talk about an unknown function, or just to talk about functions in general. In such cases we use the symbol.

$$y = f(x)$$

(read "y equals f of x"). Here f does not multiply x but represents the rule or procedure by which we find y when x is given. The symbol f may be thought of as a machine. When we push x into the machine, out pops its corresponding y. Of course in any specific case we must know the function or something about it.

EXAMPLE 5. Suppose that $f(x) = x^2 - x - 1$. Find $f(2)$, $f(3)$, $f(5)$ and prove that $f(2 + 3) \neq f(2) + f(3)$.

SOLUTION. Putting in 2 in place of x we find that

$$f(2) = 2^2 - 2 - 1 = 4 - 2 - 1 = 1.$$

Similarly

$$f(3) = 3^2 - 3 - 1 = 9 - 4 = 5,$$

and

$$f(5) = 5^2 - 5 - 1 = 25 - 6 = 19.$$

Since $19 \neq 1 + 5$, then $f(2 + 3) \neq f(2) + f(3)$.

EXAMPLE 6. If $f(x) = 5^x$ prove that $f(u)f(v) = f(u + v)$.

SOLUTION.   We know that $f(x) = 5^x$, hence $f(u) = 5^u$ and $f(v) = 5^v$.   Multiplying these two equations termwise and using the laws of exponents gives

$$f(u)f(v) = 5^u \times 5^v = 5^{u+v}.$$

But this last expression is just $f(u + v)$.

In the notation for a function, any letter may be used, although some have become standard favorites.   For example, if we wanted to consider three different unknown functions of x, we could denote them by $f(x)$, $g(x)$, and $h(x)$.

EXERCISE 9

1.   Graph each of the following functions:

    a. $y = -|x|$.

    b. $y = |x + 2|$.

    c. $y = |x^2 - 1|$.

    d. $y = 1 + x - |x|$.

    e. $y = \begin{cases} 1, & \text{if } x \geq 1, \\ x, & \text{if } -1 < x < 1, \\ -1, & \text{if } x \leq -1. \end{cases}$

    f. $y = \begin{cases} 2, & \text{if } x \geq 2, \\ 3x - 4, & \text{if } 1 < x < 2, \\ -1, & \text{if } x \leq 1. \end{cases}$

    g. $y = \begin{cases} 4 - x^2, & \text{if } -1 \leq x \leq 1, \\ 2, & \text{for all other } x. \end{cases}$

    h. $y = \begin{cases} x^2, & \text{if } -2 < x < 2, \\ 2x, & \text{for all other } x. \end{cases}$

2.   Which of the functions in problem 1 are discontinuous.   For what values of x do the discontinuities occur.

3.   For each of the following equations give those values of x for which the equation defines y as a function of x.

    a. $y = \sqrt{x(x - 1)(x - 2)}$,

    b. $y = \sqrt[3]{x(x - 1)}$,

    c. $y = \sqrt{4x - x^3}$,

    d. $y = \log x$,

    e. $y = \dfrac{1}{x(x^2 - 9)}$,

    f. $y = \dfrac{1}{\sqrt{x^2 - 4}}$.

4.   If $f(x) = x^3 - 2x^2 + 3x - 4$, show that $f(1) = -2$, $f(2) = 2$, $f(3) = 14$, $f(0) = -4$, and $f(-2) = -26$.

5.   If $f(x) = 2^x$, show that $f(1) = 2$, $f(5) = 32$, $f(0) = 1$, and $f(-2) = 1/4$.

6.   If $f(x) = 11x$ prove that $f(x + y) = f(x) + f(y)$.

7.   If $f(x) = 3x + 5$, prove that $f(4x) = 4f(x) - 15$.

8.   If $f(x) = 7x - 11$, prove that $f(3x) = 3f(x) + 22$.

9.   If $f(x) = x^2$, prove that $f(x + h) - f(x) = h(2x + h)$.

10.   If $f(x) = x^3$, find $f(x + h) - f(x)$.

11.   If $F(x) = \sqrt{x}$, prove that

$$\frac{F(x + h) - F(x)}{h} = \frac{1}{\sqrt{x + h} + \sqrt{x}}, \qquad x > 0, \quad h > 0.$$

12. If $g(x) = \dfrac{x-1}{x+1}$, find $\dfrac{g(x+h) - g(x)}{h}$.

13. If $h(x) = x^2 + 99x + 18$, find those values of x for which $h(2x) = 2h(x)$.

13.   The intersection of pairs of curves.

A point is said to be an intersection point of two curves if it lies on both curves. This means that if (x, y) is the point, the coordinates must satisfy the equations of both curves. Thus (x, y) is simultaneously a solution of both equations. Conversely, any number pair that simultaneously satisfies both equations will be the coordinates of a point that lies on both curves. Therefore all of the techniques for solving simultaneously pairs of equations can be applied to the problem of locating the intersection points of pairs of curves.

EXAMPLE 1.   Find all of the points of intersection of the straight line $y = -x - 3$ and the parabola $y = 3 + 4x - x^2$.

SOLUTION.   At a point of intersection the two x-coordinates are the same and the two y-coordinates are the same, and hence we can equate the two expressions for y, thus

$$-x - 3 = 3 + 4x - x^2.$$

Therefore

$$x^2 - 5x - 6 = 0$$
$$(x - 6)(x + 1) = 0,$$

and hence $x = 6$ or $x = -1$. Substituting these x-values in the equation of the straight line $y = -x - 3$, we find that $y = -6 - 3 = -9$ and $y = -(-1) - 3 = -2$ respectively. The points $(6, -9)$ and $(-1, -2)$ lie on the straight line. We also suspect that they lie on the parabola $y = 3 + 4x - x^2$. To check this we substitute these pairs of numbers in the equation. For $(6, -9)$ we have

$$-9 = 3 + 4 \times 6 - 6^2 = 3 + 24 - 36$$

and this is correct. For the point $(-1, -2)$ we have

$$-2 = 3 + 4(-1) - (-1)^2 = 3 - 4 - 1.$$

Therefore the two points $(6, -9)$ and $(-1, -2)$ are points of intersection of the given line and parabola. The method of working the problem shows that we have found all such points. The two curves and their intersection points are shown in Fig. 21. Observe that for convenience we have used different scales on the x and y axes.

EXAMPLE 2.   Find all of the points of intersection of the two curves $x^2 = 12(y - 1)$ and $12y = x\sqrt{x^2 + 28}$.

SOLUTION.   Let us proceed algebraically, just as before. From the first equation we find that $12y = x^2 + 12$. Equating the two values of $12y$ gives

$$x^2 + 12 = x\sqrt{x^2 + 28}. \tag{42}$$

Squaring both sides of (42) gives

$$x^4 + 24x^2 + 144 = x^2(x^2 + 28) = x^4 + 28x^2 \qquad (43)$$

$$144 = 28x^2 - 24x^2 = 4x^2. \qquad (44)$$

Whence $x^2 = 36$, $x = \pm 6$. From the equation for the parabola we find that $y = x^2/12 + 1 = 3 + 1 = 4$. Thus we suspect that the two points $(6, 4)$, $(-6, 4)$ lie on both curves. Certainly both points lie on the parabola. But a quick glance at Fig. 22 shows that the two curves do *not* intersect at $(-6, 4)$. How did this happen? In the first place the quantity $\sqrt{x^2 + 28}$ is never negative by the definition of the radical sign. Thus the product $x\sqrt{x^2 + 28}$

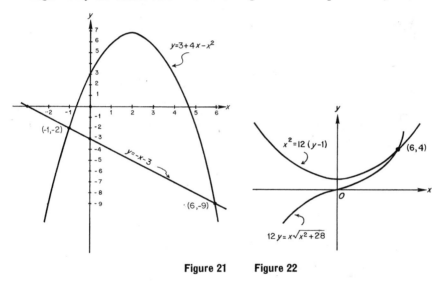

Figure 21   Figure 22

will be negative when the first factor x is negative. This means that for negative x, the curve $y = x\sqrt{x^2 + 28}$ lies below the x-axis just as Fig. 22 shows. Since the curve $y = x^2/12 + 1$ always lies above the x-axis, it is impossible for the two curves to intersect at $(-6, 4)$.

How did we obtain $(-6, 4)$ as a solution? When we squared both sides of equation (42) to obtain equation (43), we introduced the possibility of extra roots (called *extraneous* roots). For example $1 \neq -1$, but on squaring both sides we get $1 = 1$, a true statement. Similarly in equation (42) when $x = -6$ we have $48 = -6\sqrt{64} = -6 \times 8 = -48$, a false assertion. But in equation (44), which was derived from (42) by squaring, the substitution $x = -6$ gives $144 = 4 \times 36$, a true assertion. Thus the extra root $x = -6$ appeared during the squaring operation.

EXERCISE 10

In problems 1 through 14, find all of the points of intersection of the given pair of curves.

1. $2y = x - 5$ and $3y = -2(x + 2)$.   *solve simultaneously*
2. $3y + 5x = 7$ and $y = 4x - 9$.
3. $y = 6x - 2 - x^2$ and $y = 3$.
4. $y = 9 + 2x - x^2$ and $y = -3x + 13$.
5. $y = 1 + x^2$ and $y = 1 + 4x - x^2$.

6. $y = 2x$ and $y = \sqrt{x^2 + 3}$.
*7. $y = 3x + 5$ and $y = x^3 - x^2 - 7x - 3$.
*8. $y = x + 5$ and $y = x^3 - 3x^2 + x + 5$.

*9. $y = -2x + 13$ and $y = 2x + \dfrac{9}{x^2}$.

*10. $2y = x + 3$ and $y = |x|$.
*11. $2y = x + 5$ and $y = |x + 2|$.

12. $\dfrac{x^2}{18} + \dfrac{y^2}{8} = 1$ and $\dfrac{x^2}{3} - \dfrac{y^2}{2} = 1$.

13. $x + y = 1$ and $x^2 + y^2 = 1$.
14. $x + y = 10$ and $x^2 + y^2 = 10$.
**15. What is the largest value of r such that the straight line $x + y = r$ and the circle $x^2 + y^2 = r$ have a point in common?

2

DIFFERENTIATION OF
ALGEBRAIC FUNCTIONS

1.   Objective.   In Chapter 1 we introduced the concept of the slope of
a straight line as a measure of the change in y for a given change in x
[see Theorem 5, equation (17)].   Can a curve have a slope?   At first
glance, the answer would seem to be no, because the change in y for a given
change in x would vary from point to point on the curve.   However if we
fix on one point on the curve, and draw in the line tangent to the curve
at this point (if there is such a line), we might call the slope of the tangent
line, the slope of the curve.   This is indeed the definition.

Our objective is to learn how to compute the slope of a curve, i.e., to
learn how to compute the slope of a line tangent to a given curve at a given
point on the curve.

2.   An example.   Let us consider a specific curve, the parabola
$y = x^2/4$ shown in Fig. 1, and let us concentrate our attention on the
fixed point $P(1, 1/4)$ lying on the curve.   If we select a neighboring point

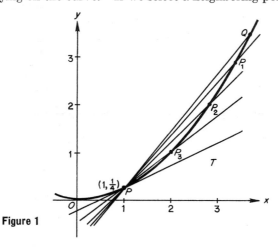

Figure 1

41

Q on the parabola, it is an easy matter to compute the slope of the line PQ. Now we can imagine a succession of different positions P_1, P_2, $P_3, \cdots$, P_n for Q, each on the parabola and each closer to P than the preceding one. For each point P_n we can draw the line PP_n and compute its slope. Or we may imagine the point Q sliding along the curve toward P. In either case the lines seem to tend to a limiting position as Q approaches P and whenever this occurs we call this limiting position the *tangent* to the curve at the point P. Before going further with the theory, let us show how easy it is to find the slope of this tangent line at P for the particular curve of Fig. 1, the parabola. At P, $x = 1$ and $y = 1/4$. Let us suppose that for the neighboring point Q, the x-coordinate has increased by an amount Δx, so that Q has $1 + \Delta x$ for its x-coordinate. Since $y = x^2/4$, the y-coordinate of Q is $(1 + \Delta x)^2/4$. Then for the slope m_{PQ} of the line PQ we have

$$m_{PQ} = \frac{y_2 - y_1}{x_2 - x_1} = \frac{\dfrac{(1 + \Delta x)^2}{4} - \dfrac{1^2}{4}}{1 + \Delta x - 1} = \frac{1}{4} \frac{(1 + \Delta x)^2 - 1}{\Delta x}$$

$$m_{PQ} = \frac{1 + 2\Delta x + (\Delta x)^2 - 1}{4\Delta x} = \frac{2\Delta x + (\Delta x)^2}{4\Delta x} = \frac{1}{4}(2 + \Delta x). \qquad (1)$$

Now as Q approaches P, the difference in the x-coordinates, Δx, gets closer and closer to zero. Hence in equation (1) the slope of the line PQ gets closer to $1/2$. We have proved that:

The line tangent to the curve $y = x^2/4$ at the point $(1, 1/4)$ has slope $m = 1/2$.

The simple process, that we have just illustrated, provides us with the means of computing the slope of the tangent line at any point on any reasonably decent curve. The differential calculus is just a systematic exploitation of the procedure illustrated above. However before we can develop this key idea, we need to lay a firm foundation for the limiting process that we used in going from equation (1) to the conclusion that $m = 1/2$ for the tangent line.

3.   Limits. Let $y = 3x + 7$. When $x = 2$ it is easy to see that $y = 13$. But at this moment we are interested in how y behaves when x is *close* to 2. Is y close to 13? This certainly seems to be the case, and the following two tables of values for x and y support this belief.

x	1.5	1.8	1.9	1.99	1.999	1.9999
$y = 3x + 7$	11.5	12.4	12.7	12.97	12.997	12.9997

Table 1.

x	2.5	2.2	2.1	2.01	2.001	2.0001
$y = 3x + 7$	14.5	13.6	13.3	13.03	13.003	13.0003

Table 2.

In Table 1, the variable x is approaching 2 through values that are less than 2. In this case we say that x is approaching 2 from the left and in symbols we write $x \to 2^-$ (read "x tends to 2 minus" or "x approaches 2 from the left").

In Table 2, the variable x is approaching 2 through values that are greater than 2. In this case we say that x is approaching 2 from the right and in symbols we write $x \to 2^+$ (read "x tends to 2 plus" or "x approaches 2 from the right"). If we wish to indicate that x may approach 2 without restricting its direction of approach we use the symbol $x \to 2$ (read "x approaches 2") leaving off the $\pm$ signs. It is the latter situation that is most common.

Now, how is y behaving as $x \to 2$? It is clear from the tables that as x gets closer to 2, then y gets closer to 13 (in symbols, $y \to 13$).

How close to 13 does y get? Answer: as close as we wish. But in order to make y close to 13, we must insist that x be close to 2. In other words, the two variables x and y are related (in this example by the equation $y = 3x + 7$) and y can be made close to 13 by restricting x to be close to 2.

Summarizing the above discussion: we say that if $y = 3x + 7$ then y approaches 13 as x approaches 2 and we write this in symbols,

$$\lim_{x \to 2} (3x + 7) = 13, \tag{2}$$

(read "the limit of $3x + 7$, as x approaches 2, is 13").

The discussion applies to any function $f(x)$, where the variable x may approach any suitable constant a, and as $x \to a$, the function $y = f(x)$ may approach some suitable limit L. When this occurs we symbolize this by writing,

$$\lim_{x \to a} f(x) = L \tag{3}$$

(read "the limit of $f(x)$, as x approaches a, is L").

We have illustrated the meaning of equation (3) by the example $y = 3x + 7$. But we still need to give the precise definition. The "precise" part of the definition is the part that specifies how close x must be to a, and $f(x)$ must be to L. It is customary to use two Greek letters δ (delta) and ϵ (epsilon) to measure the "closeness" for these two variables.   We need still one more preparation.

What does the condition $|x - a| < \delta$ mean?   From the properties of the absolute value sign, it means that simultaneously

$$-\delta < x - a \quad \text{and} \quad x - a < \delta$$

or equivalently

$$a - \delta < x < a + \delta. \tag{4}$$

From this inequality it is obvious that if $|x - a| < \delta$ then x must lie in the interval (4).   This interval is shown shaded in Fig. 2.   Thus x must lie in the shaded part of Fig. 2 if $|x - a| < \delta$.   Clearly if δ is very small

$a-\delta$ a $a+\delta$ **Figure 2**

this interval is very small, and shrinks to the point a, as $\delta \to 0$.   It is convenient to call the collection of points in the interval (4) a δ-*neighborhood* of a.

Similarly the condition $|f(x) - L| < \epsilon$ means that

$$L - \epsilon < f(x) < L + \epsilon$$

or that $f(x)$ must lie in an ϵ-neighborhood of L.

> DEFINITION 1 (Limit).   *We say that the limit of $f(x)$, as x approaches a, is L and we write*
>
> $$\lim_{x \to a} f(x) = L, \tag{3}$$
>
> *if for each positive ϵ no matter how small, there is a corresponding positive δ such that if*
>
> $$0 < |x - a| < \delta \tag{5}$$
>
> *then*
>
> $$|f(x) - L| < \epsilon. \tag{6}$$

This definition is admittedly complicated and is one of the hardest items in the calculus, so it deserves discussion.   We observe that the condition (5) states that $x \neq a$.   This condition is imposed because we are interested in how $f(x)$ behaves for x *near* a, but not for x *at* a.

Briefly the definition states that we can force $f(x)$ to be in an ϵ-neighborhood of L (no matter how small ϵ may be) if we insist that x lie in a sufficiently small δ-neighborhood of a.   Observe that δ depends on ϵ. The quantity ϵ is given first, and then the value assigned to δ depends on the particular value given to ϵ.

We can picture this situation by drawing the graph of the function $y = f(x)$, as shown in Fig. 3. Here x is plotted as usual along the horizontal axis, and the corresponding function values $y = f(x)$ are plotted along the vertical or y-axis. Now condition (6) has the geometrical interpretation that the point P must lie in the horizontal strip H_ϵ bounded by the lines $y = L + \epsilon$ and $y = L - \epsilon$. The condition (5) means that P

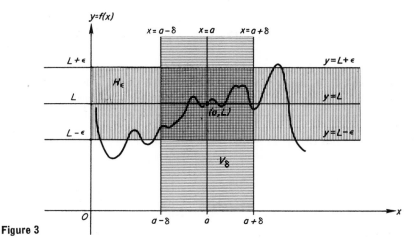

Figure 3

must lie in the vertical strip V_δ bounded by the lines $x = a + \delta$, and $x = a - \delta$. The entire definition states that if the width of H_ϵ is specified no matter how small (i.e., if ϵ is given) then there is a strip V_δ (a $\delta > 0$ can be found) such that when P is in the vertical strip V_δ then it must also be in the horizontal strip H_ϵ. Thus the curve near the point (a, L) must lie in the little box shown shaded in the figure.

EXAMPLE 1.   Start the proof that
$$\lim_{x \to 2} (3x + 7) = 13$$
by finding a suitable δ, (a) when $\epsilon = .1$, (b) when $\epsilon = .01$.

SOLUTION.   (a) Here $|f(x) - L| = |3x + 7 - 13| = |3x - 6|$. In order to force the inequality (6)
$$|3x - 6| < \epsilon = .1$$
we observe that
$$|3x - 6| = 3|x - 2|.$$
Clearly if $|x - 2| < 1/30$, then $3|x - 2| < 1/10$. Hence any $\delta \leq 1/30$ will do. We might set $\delta = .025$ for simplicity. Then the condition on x that $|x - 2| < .025$ gives us that

$$|f(x) - L| = |3x + 7 - 13| = |3x - 6| = 3|x - 2| < 3 \times .025 = .075 < .1.$$

(b) It is obvious from the above analysis that for this particular problem we can just divide the previous δ by 10. Therefore $\delta = .0025$ will insure that $|3x + 7 - 13| < .01$.

EXAMPLE 2.   Prove that

$$\lim_{x \to 2} (3x + 7) = 13.$$

SOLUTION.   The analysis is just as before. Let $\epsilon > 0$ be given. Set $\delta = \epsilon/3$. If now $|x - 2| < \epsilon/3$ then $|f(x) - L| = |3x + 7 - 13| = |3x - 6|$ $= 3|x - 2| < 3 \times \epsilon/3 = \epsilon$. Thus if $|x - 2| < \epsilon/3$, then $|f(x) - L| < \epsilon$.

Q.E.D.

We now state a sequence of important theorems about limits. In illustrating these theorems we use the two example functions $f(x) = 3x + 7$ and $g(x) = 5x + 1$. For these two functions it is obvious that

$$\lim_{x \to 2} (3x + 7) = 13 \quad \text{and} \quad \lim_{x \to 2} (5x + 1) = 11. \tag{7}$$

THEOREM 1.   *If*

$$\lim_{x \to a} f(x) = L \quad and \quad \lim_{x \to a} g(x) = M, \tag{8}$$

then

$$\lim_{x \to a} (f(x) + g(x)) = L + M.$$

In words, the limit of the sum of two functions is the sum of the limits of the functions.

EXAMPLE 3.   Since $8x + 8 = (3x + 7) + (5x + 1)$, Theorem 1 gives

$$\lim_{x \to 2} (8x + 8) = \lim_{x \to 2} (3x + 7) + \lim_{x \to 2} (5x + 1)$$
$$24 \quad = \quad 13 \quad + \quad 11 \quad .$$

THEOREM 2.   *If* $\lim_{x \to a} f(x) = L$ *then for any constant* c

$$\lim_{x \to a} cf(x) = cL.$$

In words, the limit of a constant times a function is the constant times the limit of the function.

EXAMPLE 4.   Since $18x + 42 = 6(3x + 7)$, Theorem 2 gives

$$\lim_{x \to 2} (18x + 42) = 6 \lim_{x \to 2} (3x + 7)$$
$$78 \quad = 6 \quad \times \quad 13.$$

THEOREM 3.   *Under the conditions of Theorem 1 [equation (8)]*

$$\lim_{x \to a} f(x)g(x) = LM.$$

In words, the limit of the product of two functions is the product of the limits of the functions.

EXAMPLE 5.   Since $15x^2 + 38x + 7 = (3x + 7)(5x + 1)$, Theorem 3 gives

$$\lim_{x \to 2} (15x^2 + 38x + 7) = \left\{\lim_{x \to 2} (3x + 7)\right\} \left\{\lim_{x \to 2} (5x + 1)\right\}$$

$$143 \qquad = \qquad 13 \quad \times \quad 11.$$

THEOREM 4.   *Under the conditions of Theorem 1, if $M \neq 0$ then*

$$\lim_{x \to a} \frac{f(x)}{g(x)} = \frac{L}{M}.$$

In words, the limit of the quotient of two functions is the quotient of the limits of the two functions, provided that the limit of the denominator is not zero.

EXAMPLE 6.   By Theorem 4

$$\lim_{x \to 2} \frac{3x + 7}{5x + 1} = \frac{\lim\limits_{x \to 2} (3x + 7)}{\lim\limits_{x \to 2} (5x + 1)} = \frac{13}{11}.$$

THEOREM 5. $\lim\limits_{x \to a} x = a.$

In words, x approaches a, as x approaches a.

What about the proofs of these five theorems?   The proofs follow from Definition 1, but they are a little bit sophisticated.   Like Bach's music, or black olives, one must first develop a taste for this sort of proof, in order to really enjoy it.   So we ask the student to defer the proof until later[1] especially since each of these theorems is really obvious, once its meaning is clear.

A repeated application of the five preceding theorems will prove the next two theorems.   We leave the details of the proofs to the student.

[1] The proofs of these five theorems are given in Appendix 3 of this book.   The student who wants to look deeper into this type of mathematics should consult *Pure Mathematics* by G. H. Hardy (Cambridge University Press, 1938).

THEOREM 6. *If $P(x)$ is any polynomial, that is if[2]*

$$P(x) = a_0x^n + a_1x^{n-1} + a_2x^{n-2} + \cdots + a_{n-2}x^2 + a_{n-1}x + a_n$$

then

$$\lim_{x \to a} P(x) = P(a).$$

THEOREM 7. *If $f(x)$ is any rational function, that is if*

$$f(x) = \frac{N(x)}{D(x)}$$

where $N(x)$ and $D(x)$ are polynomials, and if $D(a) \neq 0$, then

$$\lim_{x \to a} f(x) = \frac{N(a)}{D(a)}.$$

EXAMPLE 7. Find

$$\lim_{x \to -1} \frac{x^3 + 5x^2 + 3x}{2x^5 + 3x^4 - 2x^2 - 1}.$$

SOLUTION. By Theorem 7

$$\lim_{x \to -1} \frac{x^3 + 5x^2 + 3x}{2x^5 + 3x^4 - 2x^2 - 1} = \frac{(-1)^3 + 5(-1)^2 + 3(-1)}{2(-1)^5 + 3(-1)^4 - 2(-1)^2 - 1} = -\frac{1}{2}.$$

EXAMPLE 8. Let $f(x)$ be defined by

$$f(x) = \begin{cases} 5 & \text{if } x \geq 3 \\ 1 & \text{if } x < 3. \end{cases}$$

Find $\lim_{x \to 3} f(x)$.

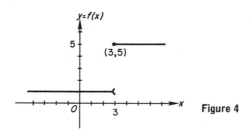

Figure 4

SOLUTION. The graph of this function is shown in Fig. 4. Both from the graph and from the definition of the function, it is obvious that as $x \to 3^+$, $f(x)$ is always 5 and has limiting value 5. But as $x \to 3^-$, $f(x)$ is always 1, and has limiting value 1. Since $1 \neq 5$ we say that the limit of $f(x)$, as $x \to 3$, does not exist for this function.

[2] For a detailed explanation of the three dots that appear in the polynomial $P(x)$, see section 2 of Appendix 2.

EXAMPLE 9. Find

$$\lim_{x \to 4} \frac{x^2 - 16}{x - 4}.$$

SOLUTION. At $x = 4$ both the numerator and denominator are zero, so Theorem 7 is not applicable here. But we can do some preliminary algebra that will be helpful. Indeed when $x \neq 4$, we have

$$\frac{x^2 - 16}{x - 4} = \frac{(x - 4)(x + 4)}{x - 4} = x + 4.$$

Whence it is obvious that

$$\lim_{x \to 4} \frac{x^2 - 16}{x - 4} = \lim_{x \to 4} (x + 4) = 4 + 4 = 8.$$

The notation

$$\lim_{x \to a} f(x) = L \tag{3}$$

can be used with $a = \pm \infty$ or $L = \pm \infty$, or any combination, but of course the meaning of the symbol must be suitably modified. The notation $x \to \infty$ means that x grows without bound, that is, given any M no matter how large x eventually becomes and remains larger than M. The notation $x \to -\infty$ means that x is negative but that $|x|$ grows without bound. Similarly $\lim_{x \to a} f(x) = +\infty$ means that as $x \to a$, $f(x)$ grows without bound. Some of the various possibilities are illustrated in

EXAMPLE 10. Find each of the indicated limits

(a) $\lim_{x \to \infty} \dfrac{x^2 - 7x + 11}{3x^2 + 10{,}000}$ (b) $\lim_{x \to \infty} \dfrac{\pi x - x^2}{\sqrt{2x + 10}}$

(c) $\lim_{x \to \infty} 4000 \dfrac{x^3 + 500x^2}{x^4 + 1}$ (d) $\lim_{x \to 2} \dfrac{3x^2 + 4x + 5}{x^2 + 8x - 20}.$

SOLUTION. In (a) we first divide both the numerator and the denominator by x^2. This gives

$$\lim_{x \to \infty} \frac{x^2 - 7x + 11}{3x^2 + 10{,}000} = \lim_{x \to \infty} \frac{1 - \dfrac{7}{x} + \dfrac{11}{x^2}}{3 + \dfrac{10{,}000}{x^2}}.$$

As x grows without bound each of the terms in this expression tends to zero, except for 1 and 3.   Hence it is obvious that the limit is $1/\dot{3}$.   But if $x \to -\infty$, the same terms tend to zero and we can also write

$$\lim_{x \to -\infty} \frac{x^2 - 7x + 11}{3x^2 + 10{,}000} = \lim_{x \to -\infty} \frac{1 - \dfrac{7}{x} + \dfrac{11}{x^2}}{3 + \dfrac{10{,}000}{x^2}} = \frac{1}{3}.$$

Both (b) and (c) can be worked using the same manipulation of dividing both the numerator and the denominator by a suitable power of x.   For (b) we have

$$\lim_{x \to \infty} \frac{\pi x - x^2}{\sqrt{2x + 10}} = \lim_{x \to \infty} -x \frac{1 - \dfrac{\pi}{x}}{\sqrt{2} + \dfrac{10}{x}}.$$

Now the second factor approaches $1/\sqrt{2}$, as $x \to \infty$, and the first factor approaches $-\infty$.   Hence in (b) the limit is $-\infty$.   However if we let $x \to -\infty$ the limit is changed in sign, and we find that

$$\lim_{x \to -\infty} \frac{\pi x - x^2}{\sqrt{2x + 10}} = \infty.$$

For (c) we have

$$\lim_{x \to \infty} 4000 \frac{x^3 + 500\,x^2}{x^4 + 1} = \lim_{x \to \infty} \frac{4000}{x} \frac{1 + \dfrac{500}{x}}{1 + \dfrac{1}{x^4}} = 0,$$

and the same limit as $x \to -\infty$.

In (d) we factor the denominator and write

$$\lim_{x \to 2} \frac{3x^2 + 4x + 5}{x^2 + 8x - 20} = \lim_{x \to 2} \frac{1}{x - 2} \frac{3x^2 + 4x + 5}{x + 10}.$$

The second factor tends to $25/12$ as $x \to 2$.   The first factor approaches ∞ if $x \to 2^+$, but it reverses sign and tends to $-\infty$ if $x \to 2^-$.   Hence (d) must be separated into two cases, namely

$$\lim_{x \to 2^+} \frac{3x^2 + 4x + 5}{x^2 + 8x - 20} = \infty,$$

and

$$\lim_{x \to 2^-} \frac{3x^2 + 4x + 5}{x^2 + 8x - 20} = -\infty.$$

EXERCISE 1

In problems 1 through 14 find the indicated limit.

1. $\displaystyle\lim_{x \to 0} x^3 + 5x^2 + 1000x.$ 2. $\displaystyle\lim_{x \to 3} x^4 - 27x.$

3. $\lim_{x \to 2} 3x^2 - 10x - 15.$

4. $\lim_{x \to -3} 5x^2 - 7x.$

5. $\lim_{y \to 1} \dfrac{y^2 + 2y + 3}{y - 5}.$

6. $\lim_{z \to -1} \dfrac{z^2 + 5}{z + 5}.$

7. $\lim_{x \to 3} \dfrac{x^2 + 2x - 15}{x - 3}.$

8. $\lim_{x \to -5} \dfrac{x^2 + 2x - 15}{x + 5}.$

9. $\lim_{h \to 0} \dfrac{(x + h)^2 - x^2}{h}.$

10. $\lim_{h \to 0} \dfrac{2(x + h)^3 - 2x^3}{h}.$

11. $\lim_{\Delta x \to 0} \dfrac{(x + \Delta x)^2 - x^2}{\Delta x}.$

12. $\lim_{\Delta x \to 0} \dfrac{2(x + \Delta x)^3 - 2x^3}{\Delta x}.$

13. $\lim_{y \to x} \dfrac{y^3 - x^3}{y - x}. = \dfrac{(y-x)(y^2+xy+x^2)}{(y-x)}$

14. $\lim_{u \to v} \dfrac{u^4 - v^4}{u - v}.$

*15. If $f(x) = 3x^2 + 2x - 7$, find
$$\lim_{h \to 0} \frac{f(x + h) - f(x)}{h}.$$

*16. If $f(x) = \sqrt{x}$, find
$$\lim_{h \to 0} \frac{f(4 + h) - f(4)}{h}.$$

Hint: Rationalize the numerator.

*17. Find $\lim_{\Delta x \to 0} \dfrac{f(x + \Delta x) - f(x)}{\Delta x}$ if

    a. $f(x) = 3x + \dfrac{5}{x}$,

    $\lim_{\Delta x \to 0} \dfrac{[3(x+\Delta x) + \frac{5}{x+\Delta x}] - [3x + \frac{5}{x}]}{\Delta x} = \lim_{\Delta x \to 0} \dfrac{x[3(x+\Delta x)^2 + 5] - [3x^2 + 5][x + \Delta x]}{x \cdot \Delta x \cdot (x + \Delta x)}$

    b. $f(x) = x + 5 - \dfrac{2}{x^2}.$

$= \lim_{\Delta x \to 0} \dfrac{3x^2 + 3x \Delta x - 5 \Delta x - 5}{x^2 + x \Delta x}$

In problems 18 through 27 find the indicated limit.

18. $\lim_{x \to \infty} \dfrac{5x^3 + 1}{20x^3 - 8000x}.$

19. $\lim_{x \to 20^+} \dfrac{5x^3 + 1}{20x^3 - 8000x}.$

20. $\lim_{x \to \infty} \dfrac{50x^{10} + 100}{x^{11} + x^6 + 1}.$

21. $\lim_{x \to -\infty} \dfrac{x^{25} + x}{x^{10}(2x^{15} + \pi)}.$

22. $\lim_{x \to \infty} 2^x.$

23. $\lim_{x \to -\infty} 2^x.$

24. $\lim_{x \to +\infty} 8 \dfrac{10 + 3^x}{20 - 3^x}.$ $\lim_{x \to +\infty} 8 \dfrac{\frac{10 + 3^x}{3^x}}{\frac{20 - 3^x}{3^x}} = \dfrac{\frac{10}{3^x} + 1}{\frac{20}{3^x} - 1}$

25. $\lim_{x \to -\infty} 8 \dfrac{10 + 3^x}{20 - 3^x}.$

26. $\lim_{x \to 1^+} \dfrac{x^2 - 2x + 1}{x^3 - 3x^2 + 3x - 1}.$

27. $\lim_{x \to 5^-} \dfrac{x^{100} - 4x^{99}}{x - 5}.$

28. Suppose that $N(x) = a_0x^n + a_1x^{n-1} + a_2x^{n-2} + \cdots + a_n$ is a polynomial of nth degree, so that $a_0 \neq 0$. Suppose further that $D(x) = b_0x^m + b_1x^{m-1} + b_2x^{m-2} + \cdots + b_m$, with $b_0 \neq 0$. Prove that

$$\lim_{x\to\infty} \frac{N(x)}{D(x)} = \begin{cases} 0, & \text{if } n < m, \\ \dfrac{a_0}{b_0}, & \text{if } n = m, \\ \pm\infty, & \text{if } n > m, \text{ and } \dfrac{a_0}{b_0} \gtrless 0. \end{cases}$$

4. Continuous functions. Let us consider the function defined by

$$y = f(x) = \frac{x^2 - 3x}{2x - 6}, \qquad x \neq 3. \tag{9}$$

This function is defined for all x, except $x = 3$. At $x = 3$, a computation gives $f(3) = 0/0$ and this is meaningless. A proper graph of this function must omit a point corresponding to $x = 3$ (as we have tried to indicate in Fig. 5). Of course it is easy to fill up this gap in the graph. For when $x \neq 3$, we have

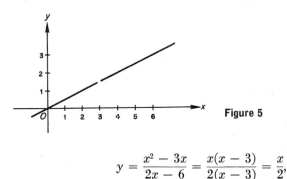

Figure 5

$$y = \frac{x^2 - 3x}{2x - 6} = \frac{x(x - 3)}{2(x - 3)} = \frac{x}{2},$$

so the graph of the function (9) is just the straight line $y = x/2$ minus the single point $(3, 3/2)$. To fill the gap we would merely define $f(3)$ to be $3/2$. But we could fill the gap (in the definition) by being contrary and making the definition $f(3) = 4$ (it is our function to define as we please). With the first definition, $f(3) = 3/2$, the function becomes *continuous*, and the graph has no breaks. With the second definition, $f(3) = 4$, the function becomes discontinuous at $x = 3$, and the graph has a break or jump at $x = 3$. This illustrates the following definition of a continuous function.

> **DEFINITION 2.**   *A function $y = f(x)$ is said to be continuous at a point $x = a$, if*
>
> (A) $y = f(x)$ *is defined at $x = a$,*
>
> (B) $\lim\limits_{x\to a} f(x)$ *is a real number,*
>
> (C) $\lim\limits_{x\to a} f(x) = f(a)$.

Otherwise the function is said to be discontinuous at x = a.

It is customary in writing the definition of a continuous function to write only (C), because the symbols themselves imply that (A) and (B) are satisfied [otherwise (C) would not make any sense]. We have listed all three conditions for clarity.

The function (9) is not continuous at $x = 3$ because condition (A) fails. But observe that condition (B) is satisfied, namely

$$\lim_{x \to 3} \frac{x^2 - 3x}{2x - 6} = \lim_{x \to 3} \frac{x(x - 3)}{2(x - 3)} = \lim_{x \to 3} \frac{x}{2} = \frac{3}{2}.$$

If we make the definition $f(3) = 4$, then conditions (A) and (B) are satisfied at $x = 3$, but not (C). Then the function is not continuous at $x = 3$. But if we make the definition $f(3) = 3/2$, then (A), (B), and (C) are satisfied and hence the revised $f(x)$ is continuous at $x = 3$.

DEFINITION 3. *A function is said to be continuous in an interval if it is continuous at every point of the interval.*

The three preceding definitions may appear to the student as just so much excess luggage, since in his previous courses he has encountered only continuous functions. Furthermore "everyone knows that a continuous function is one whose graph has no breaks or jumps so why all the fuss."

It is true that in this book nearly all of the functions will be continuous, and whenever they are discontinuous, it will be relatively easy to spot the points of discontinuity. However it does pay to be precise in our mathematics, and to be precise it was absolutely necessary for us to give the correct definitions of limit and continuity. But the student can relax because in all our problems relating to limits and continuity, he can rely on his intuition and guess at the answer.

Each of the fundamental theorems on limits (Theorems 1, 2, 3, 4, and 5) has a counterpart in a theorem on continuous functions. For example the sum and product of two continuous functions is a continuous function. The quotient of two continuous functions is also a continuous function if the denominator is not zero. For the convenience of the student who wishes to pursue this matter, Appendix 3 contains precise statements of these theorems and their proofs.

EXERCISE 2

In problems 1 through 6 state whether the function is continuous, and if it is not continuous locate the points of discontinuity.

1. $f(x) = x^3 + 1000x.$ **2.** $f(x) = 50x^{10}.$

3. $f(x) = \begin{cases} \dfrac{x^2 - 16}{x - 4}, & \text{if } x \neq 4, \\ 8, & \text{if } x = 4. \end{cases}$

4. $f(x) = \begin{cases} \dfrac{x^2 + 5x}{10x + 50}, & \text{if } x \neq -5, \\ -1/2, & \text{if } x = -5. \end{cases}$

5. $f(x) = \begin{cases} \dfrac{x^4 - 16}{x - 2}, & \text{if } x \neq 2, \\ 16, & \text{if } x = 2. \end{cases}$

6. $f(x) = \begin{cases} \dfrac{x^3 - x^2 + 2x - 2}{x - 1}, & \text{if } x \neq 1, \\ 4, & \text{if } x = 1. \end{cases}$

7. Let $f(x) = 1/x$, if $x \neq 0$. Is it possible to define $f(0)$, so that $f(x)$ becomes continuous at $x = 0$?

8. Same as problem 7 for

a. $f(x) = \sin(\pi/x)$,   **b.** $f(x) = \cos(\pi/x)$,   **c.** $f(x) = (x^2 - 2x)/x$.

9. Use Theorem 7 to prove that every rational function is continuous for any value of x for which the denominator is not zero. Recall that a rational function is the ratio of two polynomials.

*10. Let

$$f(x) = \begin{cases} 0, & \text{if } x \text{ is a rational number (the ratio of two integers),} \\ 1, & \text{if } x \text{ is an irrational number (not rational).} \end{cases}$$

Discuss the continuity of this function.

11. Let

$$f(x) = \begin{cases} 1, & \text{if } x \leq 3, \\ ax + b, & \text{if } 3 < x < 5, \\ 7, & \text{if } 5 \leq x. \end{cases}$$

Determine the constants a and b, so that this function is continuous, and graph this function.

12. Let

$$f(x) = \begin{cases} Ax^2, & \text{if } x \leq 2, \\ 3, & \text{if } x > 2. \end{cases}$$

Find the constant A, so that this function is continuous, and graph this function.

5.   The derivative. Briefly, the derivative of a function $y = f(x)$ is a second function that gives the slope of the tangent line to the graph of the first function at each point.

But first we will give the analytic definition and postpone the geometric interpretation of the derivative as the slope of a tangent line until the next section.

DEFINITION 4. *If* $y = f(x)$ *and if the limit*

$$\lim_{h \to 0} \frac{f(x_1 + h) - f(x_1)}{h} \qquad (10)$$

exists[3], then that limit is called the derivative of $f(x)$ *at* $x = x_1$, *and is written* $f'(x_1)$ *(read "f prime of x sub one"). When the limit* (10) *exists the function is said to be differentiable at* x_1.

EXAMPLE 1. Find the derivative of $f(x) = 3x^2$ at $x = x_1$.

SOLUTION. Applying the definition to the particular function $3x^2$, we have

$$f'(x_1) = \lim_{h \to 0} \frac{3(x_1 + h)^2 - 3x_1^2}{h} = \lim_{h \to 0} \frac{3x_1^2 + 6x_1 h + 3h^2 - 3x_1^2}{h}$$

$$= \lim_{h \to 0} \frac{6x_1 h + 3h^2}{h} = \lim_{h \to 0} (6x_1 + 3h) = 6x_1 + 3 \times 0 = 6x_1$$

Hence the derivative for this function is $f'(x_1) = 6x_1$.

The subscript on x serves to remind us that x is fixed at x_1 and that it is h that is varying in the limit process. Once these ideas are clear, then we can drop the subscript and write that: if $f(x) = 3x^2$, then $f'(x) = 6x$.

Let us look again at the expression (10). In the numerator we evaluate the function at $x_1 + h$ and also at x_1. Thus h is really the change in x, as x goes from x_1 to $x_1 + h$. It is convenient to use the symbol Δx to denote this change in x, so we set $h = \Delta x$. Further the numerator, $f(x_1 + h) - f(x_1)$, is just the value of the function when x is $x_1 + h$, minus the value of the function at x_1, and this is just the change in $y = f(x)$, so we are justified in calling it Δy. Then the expression (10) takes on the simple form

$$\lim_{\Delta x \to 0} \frac{\Delta y}{\Delta x}. \qquad (11)$$

This form suggests an alternate notation for the derivative which turns out to be very convenient. Indeed in the limiting process, the Greek letters are replaced by their English equivalents and we have (by definition)

$$\frac{dy}{dx} = \lim_{\Delta x \to 0} \frac{\Delta y}{\Delta x}. \qquad (12)$$

This new symbol $\dfrac{dy}{dx}$ is just another symbol for the derivative and is read "the derivative of y with respect to x."

[3.] This means that the ratio in (10) does tend to some limiting value as h approaches zero. There are weird functions for which the ratio oscillates violently as h approaches zero and hence does not have a limit. The student should not worry too much about this fine point because for most of the functions in this book, the limit will exist.

Although $\frac{dy}{dx}$ looks like a fraction, it is not.   It is the limiting value of a fraction, and as such it enjoys many properties of fractions.   The use of this symbol makes many otherwise difficult manipulations become childishly simple.   For this reason, we want to employ the defining equation (12) as frequently as possible.   But whenever there is a suspicion that the notation (12) may be leading us into error, because it looks like a fraction, then we should return to the definition

$$f'(x) = \lim_{h \to 0} \frac{f(x + h) - f(x)}{h} \tag{13}$$

where there is no temptation to treat the derivative $f'(x)$ like a fraction.

In computing derivatives from equation (12), we find it convenient to break the procedure into four steps:

(I)   In $f(x)$, replace x by $x + \Delta x$.   This gives the new y or $y + \Delta y$,

$$y + \Delta y = f(x + \Delta x). \tag{14}$$

(II)   Subtract $y = f(x)$ from (14), obtaining

$$\Delta y = f(x + \Delta x) - f(x). \tag{15}$$

(III)   Divide both sides of (15) by Δx, obtaining,

$$\frac{\Delta y}{\Delta x} = \frac{f(x + \Delta x) - f(x)}{\Delta x}. \tag{16}$$

(IV)   Take the limit in (16) as Δx approaches zero,

$$\frac{dy}{dx} = \lim_{\Delta x \to 0} \frac{\Delta y}{\Delta x} = \lim_{\Delta x \to 0} \frac{f(x + \Delta x) - f(x)}{\Delta x}.$$

EXAMPLE 2.   Find the derivative of $y = 5x^2 + 2x - 7$ using the notation of equation (12).

SOLUTION.   Following the four steps just outlined we have

(I) $y + \Delta y = 5(x + \Delta x)^2 + 2(x + \Delta x) - 7$
$y + \Delta y = 5x^2 + 10x(\Delta x) + 5(\Delta x)^2 + 2x + 2(\Delta x) - 7.$

(II)

$$\begin{array}{l} y \quad\quad = 5x^2 \quad\quad\quad\quad\quad\quad\quad\quad\quad + 2x \quad\quad\quad -7 \\ \hline \Delta y = \quad\quad 10x(\Delta x) + 5(\Delta x)^2 \quad\quad + 2(\Delta x). \end{array}$$

(III) $\dfrac{\Delta y}{\Delta x} = \quad 10x + 5(\Delta x) + 2.$

(IV) $\dfrac{dy}{dx} = \lim\limits_{\Delta x \to 0} \dfrac{\Delta y}{\Delta x} = 10x + 5 \times 0 + 2$

$\dfrac{dy}{dx} = 10x + 2.$

EXAMPLE 3. If $y = \sqrt{x}$ find $\dfrac{dy}{dx}$.

SOLUTION. We use the four steps just outlined.

(I) $y + \Delta y = \sqrt{x + \Delta x}$.

(II) $\dfrac{y \qquad = \sqrt{x}}{\Delta y = \sqrt{x + \Delta x} - \sqrt{x}}$.

(III) $\dfrac{\Delta y}{\Delta x} = \dfrac{\sqrt{x + \Delta x} - \sqrt{x}}{\Delta x}$.

(IV) Letting $\Delta x \to 0$ in the above expression, yields $0/0$, or no information. We must first prepare the way with some clever algebra, which allows cancellation of the Δx. To accomplish our aim we rationalize the numerator. Indeed from (III) we have

$$\frac{\Delta y}{\Delta x} = \frac{\sqrt{x + \Delta x} - \sqrt{x}}{\Delta x} \cdot \frac{\sqrt{x + \Delta x} + \sqrt{x}}{\sqrt{x + \Delta x} + \sqrt{x}} = \frac{x + \Delta x - x}{\Delta x(\sqrt{x + \Delta x} + \sqrt{x})}$$

$$= \frac{\Delta x}{\Delta x(\sqrt{x + \Delta x} + \sqrt{x})} = \frac{1}{\sqrt{x + \Delta x} + \sqrt{x}}.$$

Now we can let $\Delta x \to 0$ comfortably. We find

$$\frac{dy}{dx} = \lim_{\Delta x \to 0} \frac{1}{\sqrt{x + \Delta x} + \sqrt{x}} = \frac{1}{\sqrt{x} + \sqrt{x}} = \frac{1}{2\sqrt{x}}.$$

Thus if $y = \sqrt{x}$ then $\dfrac{dy}{dx} = \dfrac{1}{2\sqrt{x}}$.

In Example 1 we saw that if $y = f(x) = 3x^2$, then the derivative is $6x$. This fact can be written with symbols in a variety of ways all of which are equivalent:

$$f'(x) = 6x \qquad y' = 6x \qquad \frac{dy}{dx} = 6x$$

$$\frac{d}{dx} y = 6x \qquad \frac{d}{dx}(3x^2) = 6x.$$

In the last two expressions the symbol $\dfrac{d}{dx}$ (read, "the derivative with respect to x of") may be thought of as an operator or machine that produces a new function, the derivative, by operating on the original or primitive function.

Computing derivatives from the definition can be a very tedious process if the given $f(x)$ is complicated. But very shortly we will prove some formulas for finding derivatives that will greatly shorten the labor. But first the student must serve his apprenticeship by finding derivatives in the manner illustrated above.   One formula (that will be proved later) is that if $y = ax^n$ then $\dfrac{dy}{dx} = nax^{n-1}$.   It is clear that this formula does give the correct answers in the three examples just worked.

EXERCISE 3

In each of problems 1 through 8 compute the derivative, either by the method of Example 1 or by the method of Example 2.   Then check your answer by the formula $\dfrac{d}{dx} ax^n = nax^{n-1}$, wherever this formula is applicable.

1. $y = \dfrac{x^2}{4}$.

2. $y = \dfrac{x^3}{9}$

3. $y = 4 - x^2$.

4. $y = x^2 - 4x$.

5. $y = x^3 - 12x + 2$.

6. $y = \dfrac{x + 2}{x - 5}$, $x \neq 5$.

7. $y = \dfrac{6}{1 + x^2}$.

8. $y = \dfrac{4x}{1 + x^2}$.

*9.   Graph the function

$$y = \begin{cases} x, & 0 \leq x \leq 1, \\ 2 - x, & 1 \leq x \leq 2. \end{cases}$$

Prove that at $x_1 = 1$ this function does not have a derivative.   *Hint:* Use equation (10) and first take h positive, obtaining one limiting value, then take h negative, obtaining a different limiting value.   In a case of this type we say that the function has a *righthand derivative*, and a *lefthand derivative* but not a derivative.

6.   The tangent line to a curve. We select a point $P(x_1, y_1)$ on the curve $y = f(x)$, and a neighboring point $Q(x_2, y_2)$, and draw in the secant line as shown in Fig. 6.

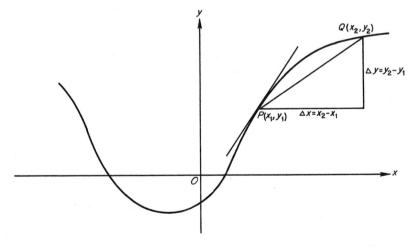

Figure 6

DEFINITION 5. *The tangent line to the curve $y = f(x)$ at the point $P(x_1, y_1)$ is defined to be the limiting position of the secant PQ as the point Q slides toward the point P along the curve.*

Of course the curve may be so bumpy near the point P, that the secant line may jiggle violently as Q approaches P, and it may not have a limit position. If this does occur[4] then we say that the curve does not have a tangent line at P.

Figure 6 shows the point Q approaching the point P from the right ($x_2 > x_1$ and Δx is positive). It could also approach from the left ($x_2 < x_1$ and Δx is negative). For a curve to have a tangent line, the limiting position of the secant must be the same whether Q approaches P from one side or the other.

We can find the equation of the tangent line if we know one point on the line and its slope. We have already selected the point (x_1, y_1) on the curve so that all that remains is to compute the slope. Now let Δx be the change in x in going from x_1 to x_2. Then $\Delta x = x_2 - x_1$, or $x_2 = x_1 + \Delta x$. For the y-coordinate of Q we have $y_2 = f(x_2) = f(x_1 + \Delta x)$, and the change in the y-coordinate is just $\Delta y = y_2 - y_1 = f(x_1 + \Delta x) - f(x_1)$. Then the slope of the secant PQ is given by

$$m_{PQ} = \frac{\Delta y}{\Delta x} = \frac{f(x_1 + \Delta x) - f(x_1)}{\Delta x}. \tag{17}$$

If we take the limit as $Q \to P$, namely as $\Delta x \to 0$, the right side of (17) is identical with the right side of (12) in the definition of the derivative. This proves

THEOREM 8. *Let $y = f(x)$ be the equation of a curve. Then the derivative $f'(x_1)$ is the slope of the line tangent to the curve at the point $P(x_1, y_1)$ on the curve.*

EXAMPLE 1. Find the slope of the line tangent to the curve

$$y = \frac{x^2}{2} - 2x + 3 \tag{18}$$

at the point $(4, 3)$.

SOLUTION. First we should check that the given point is on the curve, for otherwise the computation would be meaningless. At $x = 4$, equation (18) gives

$$y = 16/2 - 2 \times 4 + 3 = 8 - 8 + 3 = 3.$$

---

[4] Nearly all of the curves in this book will be nice smooth curves that always have a tangent. Neither Newton nor Leibniz, the creators of the Calculus, worried about curves without tangents, so there is no reason for us to do so at this stage of the development.

Hence (4, 3) is on the curve.

We next want the derivative at $x_1 = 4$, but it is just as easy to find the derivative for any x, and then set $x = 4$. Following the method of the preceding section we have

(I) $y + \Delta y = \dfrac{(x + \Delta x)^2}{2} - 2(x + \Delta x) + 3$

$y + \Delta y = \dfrac{x^2}{2} + x\Delta x + \dfrac{(\Delta x)^2}{2} - 2x - 2\Delta x + 3.$

(II)

$$\begin{array}{c} y \quad\quad = \dfrac{x^2}{2} \quad\quad\quad\quad - 2x \quad\quad + 3 \\ \hline \Delta y = \quad\quad x\Delta x + \dfrac{(\Delta x)^2}{2} - \quad\quad 2\Delta x. \end{array}$$

(III) $\dfrac{\Delta y}{\Delta x} = \quad x + \dfrac{\Delta x}{2} - 2.$

(IV) Taking the limit as $\Delta x \to 0$ we have for the derivative

$$f'(x) = \frac{dy}{dx} = x - 2. \tag{19}$$

At $x = 4$, the slope m of the tangent line is $f'(4) = 4 - 2 = 2$.

EXAMPLE 2. Sketch the curve of Example 1, by plotting a few points and the tangent lines at those points.

SOLUTION. From Example 1 we have $f'(x) = x - 2$. For each x we can compute the corresponding y and also the slope of the tangent line at the point (x, y). The results of several such computations using equations (18) and (19) are shown in Table 3.

x	-4	-2	0	2	4	6	8
$y = \dfrac{x^2}{2} - 2x + 3$	19	9	3	1	3	9	19
$m = f'(x) = x - 2$	-6	-4	-2	0	2	4	6

Table 3

This data is used to plot the points and the tangent lines shown in Fig. 7. From these points and lines the curve is easily visualized, because at each point plotted we now know the direction of the curve.

EXAMPLE 3. Find the low point on the curve of Example 1.

SOLUTION. Since $f'(x) = x - 2$, we know that $f'(x)$ is negative for $x < 2$. This means that the slope of the tangent line is negative, and this in turn means that the curve is falling as x increases. On the other hand $f'(x)$ is positive for $x > 2$. This means that the slope of the tangent line is positive, and this means that the curve is rising as x increases.   Since the curve falls until $x = 2$ and then rises, it is obvious that $(2, 1)$ is a low point on the curve. Such a point is called a *minimum point* on the curve, and the value for y (in this case 1) is called a *minimum* for the function.

We notice that the minimum occurs, in this example, at $x = 2$ where the derivative is zero.   A value of x for which the derivative $f'(x)$ is zero is called

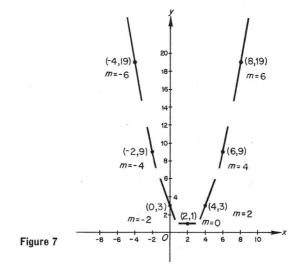

Figure 7

a *critical point* for the function $f(x)$.   The student should plot a few more points and complete the sketch of the curve of Fig. 7, and convince himself that the function

$$y = \frac{x^2}{2} - 2x + 3$$

is never less than 1.

Similarly a curve can have a high point or a maximum.   We will discuss these high and low points more carefully and more thoroughly in Chapter 3.

EXERCISE 4

For each of the problems 1 through 8 of Exercise 3 (where the student has already computed the derivative) sketch the curve by plotting a few points together with the tangent lines at those points.   Find all of the critical values for the function.   Find the high and low points (if any) on each curve.

7.   Differentiation formulas. We have just seen how helpful the derivative is in sketching curves.   But this is only one of the many important uses of the derivative.   However, before we examine some of the other applications, we want to simplify the actual computation of the derivative by proving some useful formulas.

THEOREM 9.   *The derivative of a constant is zero,*

$$\frac{d}{dx} c = 0.$$

(20)

PROOF.   Let $y = c$.   Then if x is increased by an amount Δx, y, being constant, remains unchanged.   Hence $\Delta y = 0$.   The same fact is expressed symbolically by

(I) $y + \Delta y = c$.

(II) $\dfrac{y \qquad\qquad = c}{\Delta y = 0.}$

(III) $\dfrac{\Delta y}{\Delta x} = 0.$

(IV) $\dfrac{dy}{dx} = \lim\limits_{\Delta x \to 0} \dfrac{\Delta y}{\Delta x} = \lim\limits_{\Delta x \to 0} 0 = 0.$ Q.E.D.

THEOREM 10.   *If n is a positive integer and c is a constant, then*

$$\frac{d}{dx} cx^n = cnx^{n-1}.$$

(21)

This formula is easy to memorize.   In differentiating, the exponent n becomes a multiplier in front, and the exponent on x is decreased by one. A nice feature of this formula is that it is true for all values of n, whether an integer or not.   The proof of this formula for any n will be given later on.

PROOF.   Let $y = cx^n$.   Then if x is increased by an amount Δx, the binomial theorem gives

(I) $y + \Delta y = c(x + \Delta x)^n$

$y + \Delta y = cx^n + cnx^{n-1}(\Delta x) + c\dfrac{n(n-1)}{2}x^{n-2}(\Delta x)^2 + \cdots + c(\Delta x)^n.$

(II) $\dfrac{y \qquad\quad = cx^n}{\Delta y = \qquad cnx^{n-1}(\Delta x) + c\dfrac{n(n-1)}{2}x^{n-2}(\Delta x)^2 + \cdots + c(\Delta x)^n.}$

(III) $\dfrac{\Delta y}{\Delta x} = \qquad cnx^{n-1} \qquad + c\dfrac{n(n-1)}{2}x^{n-2}(\Delta x) + \cdots + c(\Delta x)^{n-1}.$

(IV) $\dfrac{dy}{dx} = \lim\limits_{\Delta x \to 0} \dfrac{\Delta y}{\Delta x} = cnx^{n-1}.$ Q.E.D.

EXAMPLE 1.   If $y = 10x^7$, then $\dfrac{dy}{dx} = 70x^6$.

EXAMPLE 2.   If $y = x$, then $\dfrac{dy}{dx} = \dfrac{d}{dx} x^1 = 1 \cdot x^0 = 1 \cdot 1 = 1$.

THEOREM 11.   *The derivative of the sum of two differentiable functions is the sum of the derivatives of the two functions,*

$$\frac{d}{dx} (u + v) = \frac{du}{dx} + \frac{dv}{dx}. \tag{22}$$

PROOF.   Let $y = u(x) + v(x)$. If x is changed by an amount Δx, then u and v will change. If we denote these changes by Δu and Δv then we have for the new value of y

(I) $y + \Delta y = u(x) + \Delta u + v(x) + \Delta v.$

(II) $\dfrac{y \qquad\quad = u(x) \qquad\quad + v(x)}{\Delta y = \qquad \Delta u + \qquad\qquad \Delta v.}$

(III) $\dfrac{\Delta y}{\Delta x} = \qquad \dfrac{\Delta u}{\Delta x} + \qquad \dfrac{\Delta v}{\Delta x}.$

(IV) $\lim\limits_{\Delta x \to 0} \dfrac{\Delta y}{\Delta x} = \lim\limits_{\Delta x \to 0} \dfrac{\Delta u}{\Delta x} + \lim\limits_{\Delta x \to 0} \dfrac{\Delta v}{\Delta x}.$

$$\frac{dy}{dx} = \frac{du}{dx} + \frac{dv}{dx} \qquad\qquad \text{Q.E.D.}$$

EXAMPLE 3.   If $y = 10x^7 + \pi x^3$, then

$$\frac{dy}{dx} = 70x^6 + 3\pi x^2.$$

Theorem 11 can be extended to the sum of any finite number of functions, as stated in

THEOREM 12.   *The derivative of the sum of any finite number of differentiable functions is the sum of the derivatives of the functions,*

$$\frac{d}{dx} (u_1 + u_2 + \cdots + u_n) = \frac{du_1}{dx} + \frac{du_2}{dx} + \cdots + \frac{du_n}{dx}. \tag{23}$$

PROOF.   We use mathematical induction.[5] When $n = 1$ the assertion is meaningless. When $n = 2$, this equation coincides with equation

[5] Mathematical induction is explained in detail in Appendix 2 of this book.

(22) of Theorem 11 and this has already been proved.   Assume that equation (23) has been proved for $n = 2, 3, 4, \cdots, k$.   We will then prove that it is also true for $n = k + 1$.   By grouping, the sum of $k + 1$ functions can be written as the sum of two functions, thus

$$\frac{d}{dx} (u_1 + u_2 + \cdots + u_k + u_{k+1}) = \frac{d}{dx} ([u_1 + u_2 + \cdots + u_k] + u_{k+1}).$$

Then by Theorem 11 for two functions this gives

$$\frac{d}{dx} (u_1 + u_2 + \cdots + u_k + u_{k+1}) = \frac{d}{dx} [u_1 + u_2 + \cdots + u_k] + \frac{d}{dx} u_{k+1}.$$

But by hypothesis (23) is true for $n = k$.   Applying this to the first member on the righthand side we can write

$$\frac{d}{dx} (u_1 + u_2 + \cdots + u_{k+1}) = \frac{du_1}{dx} + \frac{du_2}{dx} + \cdots + \frac{du_k}{dx} + \frac{du_{k+1}}{dx}.$$

Hence if the theorem is true for $n = k$ it is also true for $n = k + 1$.   Starting with $n = 2$ we can proceed by steps to prove the theorem for any larger integer n.   Q.E.D.

EXAMPLE 4.   If $y = 3x^4 - 8x^3 + 6x^2 - 5x + 18$ find $\frac{dy}{dx}$.

SOLUTION.   Observe that a subtraction such as $-8x^3$ can be written as $+(-8)x^3$, so that Theorem 12 can be applied to this sum.   This together with the earlier theorems gives

$$\frac{dy}{dx} = \frac{d}{dx} 3x^4 + \frac{d}{dx}(-8)x^3 + \frac{d}{dx} 6x^2 + \frac{d}{dx}(-5)x + \frac{d}{dx} 18$$
$$= 12x^3 + (-8)3x^2 + 12x + (-5)$$
$$= 12x^3 - 24x^2 + 12x - 5.$$

EXAMPLE 5.   If $y = (2x - 5)^3$ find $\frac{dy}{dx}$.

SOLUTION.   None of the theorems proved so far handles this function directly, although later on we will prove a formula that will be applicable here. In the meantime we must first expand by the binomial theorem.   This gives

$$y = 8x^3 - 60x^2 + 150x - 125.$$

Then by our differentiation formulas

$$\frac{dy}{dx} = 24x^2 - 120x + 150.$$

EXAMPLE 6. If $s = 16t^2 + 64t$, find $\dfrac{ds}{dt}$.

SOLUTION. Although x and y are standard and convenient letters for the independent and dependent variables respectively, there is no law that says these letters, and these only, must be used. In computing the derivative we are computing the limiting value of the ratio of the change in the dependent variable to the change in the independent variable. Hence the formulas are valid no matter what letters are used. Thus if

$$s = 16t^2 + 64t$$

then

$$\frac{ds}{dt} = 32t + 64.$$

EXERCISE 5

In problems 1 through 12 use the formulas to compute the derivative of the dependent variable with respect to the independent variable.

1. $y = 3x^8 - 4x^6$.
2. $y = x^5 + x^4 + x^3 + x^2 + x$.
3. $y = 2x^{1000} + 10x^{200}$.
4. $y = x^{12} - 2x^6 + 4x^3 - 6x^2 + 12x$.
5. $y = -x + 1{,}000{,}000$.
6. $s = 3t^8 - 4t^6$.
7. $u = 3v^8 - 4v^6$.
8. $w = 8z^2 - 5z + 91$.
9. $V = \frac{4}{3}\pi r^3$.
10. $\alpha = 8\beta^2 - 5\beta + 91$.
11. $y = (5x + 2)^3$.
12. $z = (2w - 1)^4$.

In problems 13 through 18 compute the derivative and use the information to sketch the curve of the given equation. Find all of the critical values of the function and the coordinates of the high and low points (if any) on the curve.

13. $y = x^2 + 6x + 5$.
14. $y = 9 + 8x - x^2$.
15. $y = \dfrac{x^3}{9} - \dfrac{x^2}{2} + 5$.
16. $y = \dfrac{1}{10}(12 + 15x - 6x^2 - x^3)$.
17. $y = x(x^2 - 9)$.
18. $y = x^4 - 5x^2 + 4$.

★19. Prove Theorems 9, 10, and 11 using Definition 4.

★20. Find the points on the curve $y = x^3 + x^2 + x$ where the tangent line is parallel to $y = 2x + 3$.

★21. Determine the constants a, b, and c so that the curve $y = ax^2 + bx + c$ will go through the origin and the point $(1, 1)$, and have slope 3 at the point $(1, 1)$.

★22. Determine the constants a, b, and c so that the two curves $y = x^2 + ax + b$ and $y = cx - x^2$ will be tangent to each other at the point $(1, 3)$.

★23. A line is said to be *normal* (perpendicular) to a curve if it is perpendicular to the tangent line to the curve at the point of intersection of the line and the curve. Show that the line $2y + x = 3$ is normal to the parabola $y = x^2$ at one of the points of intersection, but not at the other.

★24. Find an equation for the line through the point $(4, 1)$ normal to the parabola $y = x^2/2$, and prove that there is only one such line.

★25. From the point $P(-6, 9)$ on the parabola $y = x^2/4$ a line PQ is drawn to another point Q on the parabola. Find the two points Q, distinct from P, such that PQ is normal to the parabola at Q. Find the equations of these lines.

**26.   Find equations for the three lines through $(-4, 23/2)$ normal to the parabola $y = x^2/9$.

*27.   Let Q be the point of intersection of the x-axis and the line tangent to the parabola $y = ax^2$ at $P(x, y)$.   Prove that the abscissa of Q is $x/2$.   Show how this information can be used to construct a tangent line, given the coordinate axes and the point P.

*28.   Let R be the intersection of the tangent line of problem 27 and the y-axis. Prove that the ordinate of R is $-y$.

*29.   Let F be the focus of the parabola of problem 27.   Prove that FQ is normal to PQ whenever P is not at the origin.

8.   The product and quotient formulas.

THEOREM 13.   *The derivative of the product of two differentiable functions is the first times the derivative of the second plus the second times the derivative of the first,*

$$\frac{d}{dx}\, uv = u\,\frac{dv}{dx} + v\,\frac{du}{dx}. \tag{24}$$

PROOF.   Let $y = u(x)v(x)$.   If x is changed by an amount Δx, then u and v will change and these changes can be denoted by Δu and Δv respectively.   Then for the new value of y we have

(I) $y + \Delta y = [u(x) + \Delta u][v(x) + \Delta v]$

$y + \Delta y = u(x)\, v(x) + u(x)\, \Delta v + v(x)\, \Delta u + \Delta u\, \Delta v.$

(II) $\dfrac{y \qquad\quad = u(x)\, v(x)}{\Delta y = \qquad\qquad u(x)\, \Delta v + v(x)\, \Delta u + \Delta u\, \Delta v.}$

(III) $\dfrac{\Delta y}{\Delta x} = \qquad u(x)\,\dfrac{\Delta v}{\Delta x} + v(x)\,\dfrac{\Delta u}{\Delta x} + \Delta u\,\dfrac{\Delta v}{\Delta x}.$

(IV) $\dfrac{dy}{dx} = \lim_{\Delta x \to 0}\left(u(x)\,\dfrac{\Delta v}{\Delta x} + v(x)\,\dfrac{\Delta u}{\Delta x} + \Delta u\,\dfrac{\Delta v}{\Delta x}\right)$

$\dfrac{dy}{dx} = \qquad u(x)\,\dfrac{dv}{dx} + v(x)\,\dfrac{du}{dx} + 0 \times \dfrac{dv}{dx}.$

But this last equation is just (24).   Q.E.D.

EXAMPLE 1.   If $y = (x^4 + 3)(3x^3 + 1)$ find $\dfrac{dy}{dx}$.

SOLUTION.   By the formula just proved

$$\frac{dy}{dx} = (x^4 + 3)(9x^2) + (3x^3 + 1)(4x^3)$$

$$= 9x^6 + 27x^2 + 12x^6 + 4x^3$$

$$\frac{dy}{dx} = 21x^6 + 4x^3 + 27x^2 \tag{25}$$

when the terms are arranged with decreasing powers of x. But notice that we could first multiply the two factors and then differentiate. This method gives

$$y = (x^4 + 3)(3x^3 + 1) = 3x^7 + x^4 + 9x^3 + 3. \tag{26}$$

Then using the right side of (26) we have

$$\frac{dy}{dx} = 21x^6 + 4x^3 + 27x^2. \tag{27}$$

We observe that equations (25) and (27) are identical, and hence our formulas are consistent. This is certainly what we must expect.

Since this problem could be solved without formula (24), this formula may seem to be useless. At present this is indeed so, but further on we will see that (24) is an extremely useful formula.

THEOREM 14. *The derivative of the quotient of two differentiable functions is the denominator times the derivative of the numerator minus the numerator times the derivative of the denominator all divided by the square of the denominator, if the denominator is not zero,*

$$\frac{d}{dx}\frac{u}{v} = \frac{v\dfrac{du}{dx} - u\dfrac{dv}{dx}}{v^2}, \qquad v \neq 0. \tag{28}$$

PROOF. As before let the change Δx in x induce changes of Δu, Δv, and Δy in u, v, and y respectively. Then

(I) $\qquad y + \Delta y = \dfrac{u(x) + \Delta u}{v(x) + \Delta v}.$

(II) $\qquad \begin{aligned} y \quad &= \dfrac{u(x)}{v(x)} \\[1em] \hline \Delta y &= \dfrac{u(x) + \Delta u}{v(x) + \Delta v} - \dfrac{u(x)}{v(x)} \\[1em] &= \dfrac{\cancel{u(x)\,v(x)} + v(x)\,\Delta u - \cancel{u(x)\,v(x)} - u(x)\,\Delta v}{[v(x) + \Delta v]v(x)} \\[1em] &= \dfrac{v(x)\,\Delta u - u(x)\,\Delta v}{[v(x) + \Delta v]v(x)}. \end{aligned}$

(III) $\qquad \dfrac{\Delta y}{\Delta x} = \dfrac{v(x)\dfrac{\Delta u}{\Delta x} - u(x)\dfrac{\Delta v}{\Delta x}}{[v(x) + \Delta v]v(x)}.$

(IV) $\qquad \dfrac{dy}{dx} = \lim_{\Delta x \to 0}\dfrac{\Delta y}{\Delta x} = \dfrac{v(x)\dfrac{du}{dx} - u(x)\dfrac{dv}{dx}}{[v(x) + 0]v(x)}.$

But this is identical with (28).   Q.E.D.

EXAMPLE 2.   If $y = \dfrac{x}{x^2 - 3x + 5}$, find $\dfrac{dy}{dx}$.

SOLUTION.   By the quotient formula

$$\frac{dy}{dx} = \frac{(x^2 - 3x + 5)\dfrac{d}{dx}x - x\dfrac{d}{dx}(x^2 - 3x + 5)}{(x^2 - 3x + 5)^2}$$

$$= \frac{(x^2 - 3x + 5)1 - x(2x - 3)}{(x^2 - 3x + 5)^2} = \frac{x^2 - 3x + 5 - 2x^2 + 3x}{(x^2 - 3x + 5)^2}$$

$$= \frac{-x^2 + 5}{(x^2 - 3x + 5)^2} = -\frac{x^2 - 5}{(x^2 - 3x + 5)^2}.$$

EXAMPLE 3.   Prove that the formula for differentiating $y = cx^n$ (Theorem 10) is valid when n is a negative integer.

SOLUTION.   Since we are assuming n is negative we want to bring out this negative character where it can be seen.   So we let $n = -m$, where now m is a positive integer.   Hence $y = cx^n = cx^{-m}$.   Using (28) on this latter expression gives

$$\frac{dy}{dx} = \frac{d}{dx}cx^{-m} = \frac{d}{dx}\frac{c}{x^m} = \frac{x^m \cdot 0 - cmx^{m-1}}{(x^m)^2}$$

$$= \frac{-cmx^{m-1}}{x^{2m}} = -cmx^{-m-1} = c(-m)x^{-m-1}.$$

But $n = -m$, so substituting in the last expression we obtain

$$\frac{dy}{dx} = cnx^{n-1}$$

But this is just equation (21).   As an illustration, if $y = 5x^{-3}$, then

$$\frac{dy}{dx} = 5(-3)x^{-3-1} = -15x^{-4}.$$

EXAMPLE 4.   Sketch the curve of $y = \dfrac{8x}{x^2 + 4}$.

SOLUTION.   The derivative will yield valuable information.   Indeed for this function

$$\frac{dy}{dx} = \frac{(x^2 + 4)8 - 8x \cdot 2x}{(x^2 + 4)^2} = \frac{8x^2 + 32 - 16x^2}{(x^2 + 4)^2}$$

$$= \frac{-8x^2 + 32}{(x^2 + 4)^2} = -8\frac{x^2 - 4}{(x^2 + 4)^2}.$$

We first remark that in this last expression the denominator $(x^2 + 4)^2$ is always positive (in fact it is always greater than or equal to 16). Therefore the sign of the derivative is the sign of $-8(x^2 - 4)$. We see immediately that:

If $x > 2$, then $x^2 - 4 > 0$, and hence $\dfrac{dy}{dx}$ is negative,

If $x < -2$, then $x^2 - 4 > 0$, and hence $\dfrac{dy}{dx}$ is negative,

If $-2 < x < 2$, then $x^2 - 4 < 0$, and hence $\dfrac{dy}{dx}$ is positive.

Consequently, as x steadily increases from $-\infty$ to $+\infty$ the curve is first falling $\left(\dfrac{dy}{dx} \text{ negative}\right)$ until x reaches -2, then the curve begins to rise $\left(\dfrac{dy}{dx} \text{ positive}\right)$ until x reaches $+2$, and then the curve again falls. At $x = -2$, the equation $y = 8x/(x^2 + 4)$ gives $y = -2$ so the point $(-2, -2)$ is a low point on the curve. At $x = 2$, $y = 2$, so the point $(2, 2)$ is a high point on the curve.

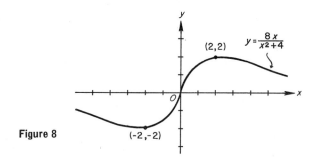

(2,2) $y = \dfrac{8x}{x^2 + 4}$

(-2,-2)

Figure 8

To find the behavior of y as x becomes very large we notice that in the numerator of

$$y = \frac{8x}{x^2 + 4},$$

x occurs to the first power, while in the denominator x is squared. Hence y is very close to zero for x large (try $x = 1{,}000{,}000$). A similar remark applies when x is negative but has large absolute value. These facts suggest that the curve must have the form shown in Fig. 8, and this is easily confirmed by plotting a few more points.

EXERCISE 6

In problems 1 through 10 use the appropriate formulas to compute the derivative of the dependent variable with respect to the independent variable. Simplify the result as much as possible.

1. $y = (x - 1)(x^4 + x^3 + x^2 + x + 1)$.   **2.** $y = \dfrac{x^5}{x - 1}$.

3. $y = (x^2 + 2x + 1)(x^2 - 2x + 1)$.   **4.** $y = \dfrac{x^2 + 2x + 1}{x^2 - 2x + 1}$.

5. $y = \dfrac{ax + b}{cx + d}$.

6. $y = \dfrac{ax^2 + bx + c}{dx + e}$.

7. $y = z^2 + 1 + z^{-2}$.

8. $r = \dfrac{\theta}{\theta^2 + 1}$.

9. $u = \dfrac{3t + 5}{7t + 9}$.

10. $v = \dfrac{t + t^{-1}}{t - t^{-1}}$.

In problems 11 through 16 compute the derivatives and use them to sketch the curve of the given equation. Find all of the critical values of the function, and the high and low points on the curve if any.

11. $y = 2x + \dfrac{1}{x^2}$.

12. $y = \dfrac{2 + 5x^2}{1 + x^2}$.

13. $y = \dfrac{2x + 3}{x - 1}$.

14. $y = \dfrac{1}{x^2} + x^2$.

15. $y = \dfrac{3x}{1 + 2x^2}$.

★16. $y = -\dfrac{21 - 20x + 5x^2}{x^2 - 4x + 5}$.

★17. Test the consistency of the product formula with the formula for differentiating $y = cx^n$, by computing the derivative of $y = x^7 = x^2 \cdot x^5$ in two ways and showing that both ways give the same result. Do the same for $y = 3x^{13} = 3x^9 \cdot x^4$.

★18. Repeat problem 17 for the more general function $y = cx^{m+n} = cx^m \cdot x^n$. Are the formulas still consistent when $n = -m$, so that $m + n = 0$?

★19. Extend Theorem 13 to the product of three differentiable functions by proving that

$$\frac{d}{dx} uvw = uv \frac{dw}{dx} + uw \frac{dv}{dx} + vw \frac{du}{dx}.$$

★20. State the formula for differentiating the product $y = tuvw$ of four functions of x.

★21. There are two points P on the curve $y = \dfrac{x - 4}{x + 5}$ such that the line from the origin to P is tangent to the curve. Find the coordinates of these two points and sketch the curve.

★22. Find all those points P on the curve $y = \dfrac{2}{1 + x^2}$ such that the line OP from the origin to P is normal to the curve. Sketch the curve.

★23. Solve problem 22 for the curve $y = \dfrac{10\sqrt{5}}{1 + x^2}$.

24. Use the formula for differentiating a product to prove the following theorem. *If $u(x)$ is any differentiable function and c is a constant, then*

$$\frac{d}{dx} cu = c \frac{du}{dx};$$

in words, the derivative of a constant times a function is the constant times the derivative of the function.

9. Composite functions and the chain rule. If we wanted to compute the derivative of the function

$$y = (x^2 - 3x + 5)^{25} \qquad (29)$$

we could do so with the formulas developed so far. We would just compute the twenty-fifth power of $x^2 - 3x + 5$, and then differentiate the resulting expression. But what an unpleasant task! Fortunately the chain rule (Theorem 15 below) will give us the derivative

$$\frac{dy}{dx} = 25(x^2 - 3x + 5)^{24}(2x - 3)$$

immediately.

Let us examine the structure of the function (29). We see that it is made up of two parts; first we have a function (let us call it u)

$$u = x^2 - 3x + 5 \qquad (30)$$

and then y is an appropriate function of u, namely

$$y = u^{25}. \qquad (31)$$

The original function (29) is obtained by composing (30) and (31), i.e., substituting the expression for u given in (30) into (31). Such a function is called a *composite function*. In general if y is some function of u, say $y = f(u)$, and if u is simultaneously some function of x, say $u = g(x)$, then y is a function of x. For each time x is given, $u = g(x)$ determines a unique value of u and then this particular value of u determines a corresponding value of y through the function $y = f(u)$. The two functions together, $y = f(u)$ and $u = g(x)$ form the composite function

$$y = f(g(x)) \qquad \text{(read "} f \text{ of } g \text{ of } x\text{")} \qquad (32)$$

obtained by substituting $g(x)$ for u in $y = f(u)$. In our example $f(u)$ is u^{25} and $g(x)$ is $x^2 - 3x + 5$, and $f(g(x)) = (x^2 - 3x + 5)^{25}$.

To differentiate such a function we give x an increment of amount Δx. This causes a change in u of amount Δu, and this in turn induces a change in y, that we denote as usual by Δy. By definition

$$\frac{dy}{dx} = \lim_{\Delta x \to 0} \frac{\Delta y}{\Delta x}.$$

If Δu is not zero we can multiply on the right hand side by $\Delta u / \Delta u$, since $\Delta u / \Delta u = 1$. A slight shuffle then gives

$$\frac{dy}{dx} = \lim_{\Delta x \to 0} \frac{\Delta y}{\Delta u} \frac{\Delta u}{\Delta x}. \qquad (33)$$

If y is a differentiable function of u, then

$$\lim_{\Delta u \to 0} \frac{\Delta y}{\Delta u} = \frac{dy}{du},$$ (34)

and if u is a differentiable function of x, then

$$\lim_{\Delta x \to 0} \frac{\Delta u}{\Delta x} = \frac{du}{dx}.$$ (35)

Finally we must remark that as Δx approaches zero, the induced change in u, Δu also approaches zero.   Using (34) and (35) in (33) we obtain

$$\frac{dy}{dx} = \lim_{\Delta x \to 0} \frac{\Delta y}{\Delta u} \frac{\Delta u}{\Delta x} = \left(\lim_{\Delta u \to 0} \frac{\Delta y}{\Delta u} \right) \left(\lim_{\Delta x \to 0} \frac{\Delta u}{\Delta x} \right)$$ (36)

$$= \frac{dy}{du} \frac{du}{dx}.$$

This suggests the following

> **THEOREM 15.** THE CHAIN RULE.   *If $y = f(u)$ and $u = g(x)$, are two differentiable functions, then the derivative of the composite function $y = f(g(x))$ is given by*
>
> $$\boxed{\frac{dy}{dx} = \frac{dy}{du} \frac{du}{dx}.}$$ (37)

Unfortunately the argument that led us to Theorem 15 has a slight error that would surely go unnoticed by anyone but an expert.   Indeed in this procedure we may have inadvertently divided by zero, and such an operation is not allowed.   In computing the derivative through the definition

$$\frac{dy}{dx} = \lim_{\Delta x \to 0} \frac{\Delta y}{\Delta x}$$

the denominator Δx is small and getting close to zero, but it is never equal to zero.   On the other hand Δy, the change in y, could be zero without any harm since it is in the numerator.

Now let us look at equation (33).   The change Δx may induce no change in u, so that $\Delta u = 0$.   Then equation (33) falls because it contains a forbidden division by zero.   This pulls down with it equation (34) and indeed the entire proof.   But Theorem 15 is true.   The reader may accept this fact on intuitive grounds, or read through the following proof.

From equation (34), the difference quotient $\Delta y/\Delta u$ is close to the derivative when Δu is close to zero, so we can write (34) in the equivalent form

$$\frac{\Delta y}{\Delta u} = \frac{dy}{du} + \epsilon, \qquad \Delta u \neq 0, \tag{38}$$

where ϵ is small and ϵ approaches zero as Δu approaches zero. If we multiply equation (38) by Δu we have

$$\Delta y = \frac{dy}{du} \Delta u + \epsilon \, \Delta u. \tag{39}$$

Although (38) is meaningless when $\Delta u = 0$, equation (39) is meaningful and also correct even when $\Delta u = 0$. For if u does not change ($\Delta u = 0$) then y does not change either ($\Delta y = 0$) and equation (39) merely states that $0 = 0$ in this case. If we divide both sides of equation (39) by Δx ($\Delta x \neq 0$) we have

$$\frac{\Delta y}{\Delta x} = \frac{dy}{du} \frac{\Delta u}{\Delta x} + \epsilon \frac{\Delta u}{\Delta x}. \tag{40}$$

Now take the limits in (40) as Δx approaches zero. Since ϵ tends to zero, equation (40) gives equation (37). Q.E.D.

EXAMPLE 1. Find $\dfrac{dy}{dx}$ if $y = (x^4 - 5x^3 + 3)^{50}$

SOLUTION. The given function becomes a composite function if we let $u = x^4 - 5x^3 + 3$, and $y = u^{50}$. Then by (37)

$$\frac{dy}{dx} = \frac{dy}{du} \frac{du}{dx} = 50u^{49} (4x^3 - 15x^2).$$

Since $u = x^4 - 5x^3 + 3$, this is equivalent to

$$\frac{dy}{dx} = 50(x^4 - 5x^3 + 3)^{49} (4x^3 - 15x^2). \tag{41}$$

In working problems of this type the student may find it helpful at first to put in the intermediate steps. But after a certain amount of practice, he should be able to write the answer, equation (41), immediately.

Sometimes the chain rule must be used in conjunction with other formulas, as illustrated in

EXAMPLE 2. Find $\dfrac{dy}{dx}$ if $y = \left(\dfrac{x^2 - 1}{x^2 + 1}\right)^5$.

SOLUTION. Here we have $y = u^5$ where u is a quotient of two functions of x. Then

$$\frac{dy}{dx} = \frac{dy}{du}\frac{du}{dx} = 5u^4 \frac{d}{dx}\left(\frac{x^2-1}{x^2+1}\right)$$

$$= 5\left(\frac{x^2-1}{x^2+1}\right)^4 \frac{(x^2+1)2x - (x^2-1)2x}{(x^2+1)^2}$$

$$= \frac{20x(x^2-1)^4}{(x^2+1)^6}.$$

EXERCISE 7

In problems 1 through 6 compute the derivative of the given function.

1. $y = (3x + 5)^{10}$

2. $y = (4x^3 + 3x^2 + 2x)^2$

3. $y = \left(\frac{ax+b}{cx+d}\right)^7$

4. $y = (x^2 - 1)^{10}(x^2 + 1)^{15}$

5. $y = (7x + 3)^4(4x + 1)^7$

6. $y = \frac{(x^2+1)^3}{(x^3-1)^2}$

7. The function $y = (x + 3)^8(x - 4)^8$ can be differentiated by two methods: first by considering it as the product of two composite functions, and second by performing the multiplication and differentiating the resulting $y = (x^2 - x - 12)^8$. Show that both methods give the same result for the derivative.

8. The function

$$y = \frac{1}{x^3 + 6x^2 - 7x + 8}$$

can be differentiated as a quotient, or can be written as $y = (x^3 + 6x^2 - 7x + 8)^{-1}$ and then differentiated as a composite function. Show that both methods give the same result.

★9. A polynomial $P(x)$ is said to have an nth order zero at $x = a$, if it can be written in the form

$$P(x) = (x - a)^n Q(x)$$

where $Q(x)$ is a polynomial and $Q(a) \neq 0$. Prove that if $P(x)$ has an nth order zero at $x = a$, then its derivative has a zero of order $n - 1$ at $x = a$.

★10. Prove that if $y = \frac{P(x)}{(x - a)^n}$

where $P(x)$ is a polynomial with $P(a) \neq 0$, then

$$\frac{dy}{dx} = \frac{Q(x)}{(x - a)^{n+1}}$$

where $Q(x)$ is an appropriate polynomial and $Q(a) \neq 0$.

Problems 9 and 10 show that differentiation decreases the order of a zero by one, but it increases the order of an "infinity" by one.

10.   Implicit functions.   Suppose that in the equation

$$y^7 + x^7 = 4x^5y^5 - 2 \tag{42}$$

we select a fixed value for x.   Then (42) becomes a seventh-degree polynomial in y.   In general a seventh-degree polynomial has seven roots, although some of the roots may be complex (involve $\sqrt{-1}$).   If at least one of these roots is real, and we select one of the real roots, then equation (42) defines y as a function of x.   Now it is known (but the proof is difficult) that for the general polynomial of degree greater than 4, there is no explicit formula that gives the roots in terms of the coefficients.   Applying this to (42), we see that it is impossible to solve for y explicitly in terms of x.   But y does depend on x.   In such a case we say that (42) gives y as an *implicit function* of x.

Can we find the derivative of y with respect to x for such a function? Yes, quite simply!   We merely differentiate both sides of equation (42) with respect to x, keeping in mind that y is a function of x.   We will need our formula for differentiating a composite function, since y^7 is now a composite function of x.   For this derivative we find

$$\frac{d}{dx} y^7 = 7y^6 \frac{dy}{dx}.$$

On the righthand side of (42), we have a product, in which one of the factors is the composite function y^5.   For the derivative of this product we have

$$\frac{d}{dx} 4x^5y^5 = 20x^4y^5 + 4x^5 \cdot \left(5y^4 \frac{dy}{dx}\right) = 20x^4y^5 + 20x^5y^4 \frac{dy}{dx}$$

Hence if we differentiate both sides of (42) with respect to x, we find

$$7y^6 \frac{dy}{dx} + 7x^6 = 20x^4y^5 + 20x^5y^4 \frac{dy}{dx}. \tag{43}$$

Solving for $\frac{dy}{dx}$ we find

$$\frac{dy}{dx} (7y^6 - 20x^5y^4) = 20x^4y^5 - 7x^6$$

$$\frac{dy}{dx} = \frac{20x^4y^5 - 7x^6}{7y^6 - 20x^5y^4}, \tag{44}$$

and this is the derivative of y with respect to x, when y and x are related by equation (42).   The procedure used in going from (42) to (43) is called *implicit differentiation*.

What right did we have to differentiate equation (42) with respect to x? The work looks correct, but is it?   If we recall the old slogan "Equals added to equals gives equals," this suggests the corresponding new slogan "Equals differentiated with respect to the same variable gives equals." Making this slogan precise, we have

THEOREM 16.   *If two differentiable functions are equal, their derivatives with respect to the same variable are equal.*

The difficulty here is that the proof of this theorem is too simple. Indeed, differentiation is a uniquely defined operation so that to each differentiable function there is exactly one corresponding function, its derivative.   So if two functions are equal, they are merely different forms for the same function, and hence the derivative of either form must be the same function.   Hence the derivatives are equal.   Q.E.D.

For example the equation (42) really states that $y^7 + x^7$ and $4x^5y^5 - 2$ are merely different forms of one and the same function, so the two different forms for the derivative of this function, given by the two sides of equation (43) are equal.

EXAMPLE 1.   Find the slope of the tangent line to the graph of equation (42) at the point (1, 1).

SOLUTION.   Notice that $x = 1$, $y = 1$ satisfy the given equation.   We compute the derivative just as before and obtain equation (44).   Putting $x = 1, y = 1$ in (44) yields

$$m = \frac{dy}{dx} = \frac{20 - 7}{7 - 20} = \frac{13}{-13} = -1$$

so the slope is -1.   Is it not surprising that we can find the tangent to this curve so easily, when the task of plotting this curve itself is very difficult?

How about the slope at the point (2, 2)?   Equation (44) again yields $m = -1$ when $x = 2$ and $y = 2$.   This computation is merely a manipulation with numbers, and has *no meaning*.   The point (2, 2) is not on the curve. For if $x = 2$ and $y = 2$, the left side of (42) is $2^7 + 2^7 = 256$, while the right side is $4 \times 2^{10} - 2 = 4094$ and these are not equal.   Summarizing: the expression for the derivative found in equation (44) is valid only for pairs (x, y) that satisfy (42).

EXAMPLE 2.   Find the derivative of $y = \sqrt{1 - x^2}$.

SOLUTION.   By squaring and transposing this is equivalent to

$$x^2 + y^2 = 1, \qquad\qquad y \geqq 0.$$

Hence by implicit differentiation

$$2x + 2y \frac{dy}{dx} = 0.$$

$$\frac{dy}{dx} = -\frac{x}{y}$$

But $y = \sqrt{1 - x^2}$, so

$$\frac{dy}{dx} = -\frac{x}{\sqrt{1 - x^2}}.$$

EXAMPLE 3.   Prove that the formula of Theorem 10

$$\frac{d}{dx} cx^n = cnx^{n-1}$$

is valid when n is a rational number.

SOLUTION.   Let $n = p/q$ where p and q are integers and set

$$y = cx^n = cx^{p/q}.$$

Then raising both sides to the qth power

$$y^q = c^q x^p.$$

By implicit differentiation

$$qy^{q-1}\frac{dy}{dx} = c^q px^{p-1}$$

$$\frac{dy}{dx} = c^q \frac{p}{q}\frac{x^{p-1}}{y^{q-1}}.$$

But $y^q = c^q x^p$ and $y^{-1} = 1/cx^{p/q}$.   Substitution gives

$$\frac{dy}{dx} = c^q \frac{p}{q}\frac{x^{p-1}}{c^q x^p}cx^{p/q} = c\frac{p}{q}x^{\frac{p}{q}-1} = cnx^{n-1}. \qquad\qquad \text{Q.E.D.}$$

EXAMPLE 4.   Solve Example 2 without implicit differentiation.

SOLUTION.   Set $u = 1 - x^2$, then

$$y = \sqrt{1-x^2} = (1-x^2)^{1/2} = u^{1/2}$$

$$\frac{dy}{dx} = \frac{1}{2}u^{\frac{1}{2}-1}\frac{du}{dx} = \frac{1}{2\sqrt{u}}(-2x) = \frac{-x}{\sqrt{u}}$$

$$= -\frac{x}{\sqrt{1-x^2}}.$$

EXERCISE 8

In problems 1 through 16 find $\dfrac{dy}{dx}$.

1. $y = x^{3/2} + x^{1/2}$.

2. $y = (x^2 - 1)^{4/7}$.

3. $y = \sqrt{\dfrac{x^2+1}{x^2-1}}$.

4. $y = (x^2 + 1)^{1/3}(x^3 - 1)^{1/2}$.

5. $y = (6 + 5\sqrt{x})^9$.

6. $y = \dfrac{x^2}{\sqrt{1-x^2}}$.

7. $y = \sqrt{4 + \sqrt{4-x}}$.

8. $y = \dfrac{\sqrt{x}+1}{\sqrt{x}-1}$.

9. $\sqrt{x} + \sqrt{y} = 4$.

10. $x^3 + y^3 = 6xy$.

11. $x^3 - 2xy^2 + 3y^3 = 7$.

12. $x^4 + x^3y + y^4 = 3$.

13. $y^2 = \dfrac{x^2 - 4}{x^2 + 4}$.

14. $x^4y^4 = x^4 + y^4$.

15. $x = y + y^5$.

16. $(x + y)^4 = x^4 + y^4$.

17. Show that for the "curve" $x^2 + 2x + 6 + y(y + 4) = 0$, formal manipulation gives

$$\frac{dy}{dx} = -\frac{x + 1}{y + 2}.$$

But this result is meaningless because there are no points on this "curve."

★18. Formal differentiation of $\sqrt{\dfrac{x}{y}} + \sqrt{\dfrac{y}{x}} = 10$ gives $\dfrac{dy}{dx} = \dfrac{y}{x}$. Show that

actually this "curve" consists of two straight lines running through the origin, so that on each of these lines the derivative is a constant.

★19. Similarly show that the "curve" of problem 16 consists of the x and y axes.

20. In elementary geometry it is proved that a tangent line to a circle is perpendicular to the radial line at the point of contact. Give a new proof of this theorem using implicit differentiation on the function $x^2 + y^2 = r^2$.

★21. The graph of $25x^2 + 25y^2 - 14xy = (24)^2$ is an ellipse with center at the origin and vertices at $(4, 4)$ $(-4, -4)$, $(3, -3)$ and $(-3, 3)$. One would expect that these four points would be the only points at which the line from the origin is normal to the curve. Use implicit differentiation to prove this fact.

11.   Higher order derivatives.

The derivative of $y = x^5$ is $5x^4$. But we can differentiate $5x^4$. If we do, we obtain $20x^3$, and this new function is called the *second derivative* of y with respect to x. Repeating the process again we obtain $60x^2$, the *third derivative* of y with respect to x. We may continue this process indefinitely. All that is needed is a notation for these derivatives of higher order. A variety of notations are in current use. If $y = f(x)$, the derivatives can be written as follows:

First derivative	$\dfrac{dy}{dx}$	$\dfrac{d}{dx}y$	y'	$f'(x)$
Second derivative	$\dfrac{d^2y}{dx^2}$	$\dfrac{d^2}{dx^2}y$	y''	$f''(x)$
Third derivative	$\dfrac{d^3y}{dx^3}$	$\dfrac{d^3}{dx^3}y$	y'''	$f'''(x)$
nth derivative	$\dfrac{d^ny}{dx^n}$	$\dfrac{d^n}{dx^n}y$	$y^{(n)}$	$f^{(n)}(x)$

The reader should observe the peculiar location of the superscripts in the first two columns. The reason for this choice of notation, is that the second derivative is the derivative of the first derivative, and hence it is natural to write

$$\frac{d}{dx}\left(\frac{dy}{dx}\right) = \frac{d^2y}{dx^2}.$$

In other words, in the numerator it is the differentiation that is repeated twice, so we expect d^2, but in the denominator it is the variable x that is repeated, i.e., we have differentiated twice with respect to x.

The entries in the third column are read y prime, y double prime, y triple prime, and y upper n, and similarly the entries in the fourth column are read f prime of x, f double prime of x, etc.

It may well appear that there are too many different notations for the derivative, but this is not the case. Each notation has its own particular appeal, and each is very useful in certain situations, as the reader will discover as he goes further and deeper into mathematics.

We shall postpone a study of the uses of the higher order derivatives until later on in the book. For the present we will practice the technique of computing them.

EXAMPLE 1. Find the derivatives of all orders for $y = x^4$.

SOLUTION. From our power formula we have

$$\frac{dy}{dx} = 4x^3 \qquad\qquad\qquad \frac{d^4y}{dx^4} = 24$$

$$\frac{d^2y}{dx^2} = 12x^2 \qquad\qquad\qquad \frac{d^5y}{dx^5} = 0$$

$$\frac{d^3y}{dx^3} = 24x \qquad\qquad\qquad \frac{d^ny}{dx^n} = 0 \qquad \text{for } n \geq 5.$$

EXAMPLE 2. Discover and prove a formula for the nth derivative of

$$y = \frac{1}{1-x}.$$

SOLUTION. To discover a general formula we must examine a few of the earlier cases. Computation gives

$$\frac{dy}{dx} = \frac{d}{dx}(1-x)^{-1} = -1(1-x)^{-2}(-1) = (1-x)^{-2} = \frac{1}{(1-x)^2}.$$

$$\frac{d^2y}{dx^2} = \frac{d}{dx}(1-x)^{-2} = -2(1-x)^{-3}(-1) = 2(1-x)^{-3} = \frac{2}{(1-x)^3}.$$

$$\frac{d^3y}{dx^3} = \frac{d}{dx}2(1-x)^{-3} = -2 \cdot 3(1-x)^{-4}(-1) = 6(1-x)^{-4} = \frac{6}{(1-x)^4}.$$

A study of the first and last columns, and the method of obtaining the derivatives suggests at once the general formula

$$\frac{d^n y}{dx^n} = \frac{n!}{(1-x)^{n+1}}.$$ (45)

Indeed a little thought shows that this formula is really obvious, but if a proof is demanded, we must use mathematical induction. We have already proved that (45) is correct when $n = 1$. In fact it checks when $n = 2$, and $n = 3$ as well. Assuming now that (45) is true when $n = k$, and computing the next higher derivative we have

$$\frac{d^{k+1} y}{dx^{k+1}} = \frac{d}{dx}\left(\frac{d^k y}{dx^k}\right) = \frac{d}{dx}\frac{k!}{(1-x)^{k+1}} = \frac{d}{dx} k!(1-x)^{-(k+1)}$$

$$= -(k+1)k!(1-x)^{-(k+1)-1}(-1) = \frac{(k+1)!}{(1-x)^{k+2}}$$

But this is just equation (45) for the index $n = k + 1$.   Q.E.D.

EXAMPLE 3. Use implicit differentiation to obtain a simple form for y'' for the ellipse $b^2 x^2 + a^2 y^2 = a^2 b^2$.

SOLUTION. For the first derivative we have

$$2b^2 x + 2a^2 y \frac{dy}{dx} = 0$$

or

$$\frac{dy}{dx} = -\frac{b^2 x}{a^2 y}.$$ (46)

Using the quotient formula, and remembering that y is a function of x

$$\frac{d^2 y}{dx^2} = -\frac{a^2 y b^2 - b^2 x a^2 \dfrac{dy}{dx}}{a^4 y^2}.$$

Substituting from (46) we have

$$\frac{d^2 y}{dx^2} = -\frac{a^2 b^2 y - a^2 b^2 x\left(-\dfrac{b^2 x}{a^2 y}\right)}{a^4 y^2} = -\frac{a^4 b^2 y^2 + a^2 b^4 x^2}{a^6 y^3}$$

$$= -\frac{b^2(a^2 y^2 + b^2 x^2)}{a^4 y^3}.$$

But (x, y) must lie on the ellipse $a^2 y^2 + b^2 x^2 = a^2 b^2$. Hence

$$\frac{d^2 y}{dx^2} = -\frac{b^2(a^2 b^2)}{a^4 y^3} = -\frac{b^4}{a^2 y^3}.$$

EXERCISE 9

In problems 1 through 6 find the second derivative.

1. $y = x^{10} + 3x^6$.

2. $y = \sqrt{x^3 + 1}$.

3. $y = \dfrac{x}{(1 - x)^2}$.

4. $u = \dfrac{(1 - v)^3}{v}$.

5. $s = t^2(t - 1)^5$.

6. $w = (z^2 + 2)^{5/2}$.

In problems 7 through 10 find $f^{(n)}(x)$ for the given function.

7. $y = \dfrac{1}{2 + x}$.

8. $y = \dfrac{1}{1 - 2x}$.

9. $y = \dfrac{a}{(b + cx)^2}$.

★10. $y = \sqrt{1 - x}$

In problems 11 through 16 use implicit differentiation to find a simple form for y''.

11. $b^2x^2 - a^2y^2 = a^2b^2$.

12. $x^2 + y^2 = r^2$.

13. $x^3 + y^3 = 1$.

14. $y^2 = 4px$.

15. $x^{1/2} + y^{1/2} = a^{1/2}$.

★16. $x^n + y^n = a^n$.

★17. Show that problem 16 contains problems 12, 13, and 15 as special cases, and check the answers to these earlier problems by setting $n = 2$, 3, and $1/2$ in the answer to problem 16.

★18. The notation $f'(1)$ means the derivative $f'(x)$ computed when $x = 1$. Determine the constants in the function $f(x) = ax^3 + bx^2$ so that $f'(1) = 5$ and $f''(2) = 32$.

★19. Find a formula for $\dfrac{d^2}{dx^2}(uv)$ and $\dfrac{d^3}{dx^3}(uv)$ where u and v are functions of x.

12.   Inverse functions. Suppose that the function $f(x)$ relating x and y is $y = x^2 + 2x + 2$. For each x this function gives a specific y. It would be nice if for each y this same function would also give a specific x, but mathematics is not always so simple. Solving for x as a function of y, we have in this case

$$0 = x^2 + 2x + 2 - y$$

$$x = \frac{-2 \pm \sqrt{4 - 4(2 - y)}}{2}$$

$$x = -1 \pm \sqrt{y - 1}. \tag{47}$$

Thus it appears that for each y there are two values of x. Actually this is true only if $y > 1$. If $y = 1$ there is only one x, and if $y < 1$ there are no real values of x since then the quantity under the radical is negative.

These statements naturally have a graphical interpretation. The curve for $f(x) = x^2 + 2x + 2$ is shown in Fig. 9. Given x_0, we find the corresponding y by erecting a vertical line at $x = x_0$, and noting the y-coordinate of the point of intersection of this line and the curve. Thus if $x_0 = -2$, the line V of Fig. 9 indicates that the corresponding y is 2. Similarly, given y_0 we find the corresponding x by erecting a horizontal line H at $y = y_0$ and noting the x-coordinate of the point of intersection of this line and the curve. But from the figure it is obvious that for this curve there may be two points of intersection and hence two values of x for a given y. Thus, the horizontal line H of Fig. 9 shows that if $y = 5$ the two

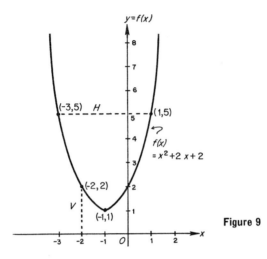

Figure 9

corresponding x values are -3 and 1. Clearly the horizontal line $y = 1$ just touches the curve at $(-1, 1)$ and the horizontal line $y = y_0$ does not meet the curve whenever $y_0 < 1$.

An inverse function is simply a function that preserves the original correspondence between pairs of numbers, but interchanges the independent and dependent variables. If $y = f(x)$ denotes the original or primitive function, we may let $x = g(y)$ denote its inverse function. But we have just had an example for which this inverse is not unique, but indeed falls into two parts. For if $y = f(x) = x^2 + 2x + 2$, then $x = g(y)$ may be either $g(y) = -1 + \sqrt{y - 1}$ or $g(y) = -1 - \sqrt{y - 1}$. Each one of these is called a *branch* of the inverse function. In a more complicated function the inverse function may have more than two branches.

> DEFINITION 6.   *A function* $x = g(y)$ *is called an inverse function of* $y = f(x)$ *if*
>
> $$f(g(y)) = y. \tag{48}$$

EXAMPLE 1.   Use Definition 6 to prove that $g(y) = -1 + \sqrt{y - 1}$ is an inverse function for $f(x) = x^2 + 2x + 2$.

SOLUTION.   We are to compute $f(g(y))$. Thus we replace x by $g(y)$ in $x^2 + 2x + 2$. This gives

$$f(g(y)) = (-1 + \sqrt{y-1})^2 + 2(-1 + \sqrt{y-1}) + 2$$
$$= 1 - 2\sqrt{y-1} + y - 1 - 2 + 2\sqrt{y-1} + 2$$
$$= y. \hspace{4cm} \text{Q.E.D.}$$

Our objective is to find a formula for differentiating the inverse function of a given function.

THEOREM 17. *Let $y = f(x)$ be a differentiable function and suppose that $f'(x_0) \neq 0$. If $x = g(y)$ is an inverse function and $x_0 = g(y_0)$ then*

$$g'(y_0) = \frac{1}{f'(x_0)}. \hspace{3cm} (49)$$

As it stands formula (49) is not easy to recall, but if we use the symbols dx/dy and dy/dx for $g'(y)$ and $f'(x)$ respectively, then (49) becomes

$$\boxed{\frac{dx}{dy} = \frac{1}{\dfrac{dy}{dx}}.} \hspace{3cm} (50)$$

It is understood that in (50) the derivatives are computed at corresponding points. Formula (50) is easy to remember because it resembles a familiar manipulation with fractions in which the denominator on the right side is inverted in order to obtain the left side.

PROOF. Let $y_0 = f(x_0)$ and $y_1 = f(x_1)$ where x_1 is close to x_0. If $\Delta x = x_1 - x_0$, then $\Delta y = y_1 - y_0$. Now

$$f'(x_0) = \frac{dy}{dx} = \lim_{\Delta x \to 0} \frac{\Delta y}{\Delta x} \hspace{2.5cm} (51)$$

and

$$g'(y_0) = \frac{dx}{dy} = \lim_{\Delta y \to 0} \frac{\Delta x}{\Delta y}. \hspace{2.5cm} (52)$$

But in (51) and (52) Δx and Δy have the same meaning so by the laws of fractions we can write

$$\frac{\Delta x}{\Delta y} = \frac{1}{\dfrac{\Delta y}{\Delta x}} \hspace{3cm} (53)$$

Taking the limit in (53) as $\Delta x \to 0$, gives (50) and hence its equivalent (49).

EXAMPLE 2. Check equation (50) for the function $y = x^2 + 2x + 2$ at the point (1, 5).

SOLUTION. Of the two possible branches for the inverse function given by (47), the branch that passes through (1, 5) is $g(y) = -1 + \sqrt{y - 1}$. Then

$$g'(y) = \frac{dx}{dy} = \frac{1}{2\sqrt{y-1}}$$

and at $y = 5$, $g'(y) = 1/4$. But $f'(x) = 2x + 2$ and at $x = 1$, $f'(x) = 4$. Since 4 and 1/4 are reciprocals, these numbers satisfy (50).

There is a simple rule for obtaining the graph of the inverse function of a given function. If $y = f(x)$ is the given function and $x = g(y)$ is a branch of the inverse function, the same pair $x = a$, $y = b$ satisfies both equations, i.e., $b = f(a)$ and $a = g(b)$.

In graphing $x = g(y)$ we regard y as the independent variable and it is represented on the horizontal axis. Similarly x is the dependent variable and is represented on the vertical axis. To conform to standard usage we interchange these letters and write $y = g(x)$, instead of $x = g(y)$, for the inverse function. Thus if the point (a, b) is on the graph of $y = f(x)$ then for some branch of the inverse function $a = g(b)$ and the point (b, a) is on the graph of this branch. But the points (a, b) and (b, a) are symmetrical with respect to the line $y = x$ that passes through the origin and makes a 45° angle with the positive x-axis. This discussion gives

THEOREM 18. *Let $\mathfrak{F}$ be the graph of $y = f(x)$ and let $\mathfrak{G}$ be the graph formed by taking together the graphs of all of the branches of the inverse function $y = g(x)$. Then $\mathfrak{G}$ can be obtained by reflecting $\mathfrak{F}$ around the line $y = x$.*

For example if $\mathfrak{F}$ is the graph of $y = x^2 + 2x + 2$ shown in Fig. 9, then $\mathfrak{G}$ is the graph shown in Fig. 10, and is obtained by rotating the parabola of Fig. 9 about the line $y = x$. The portion of $\mathfrak{G}$ that lies above the line

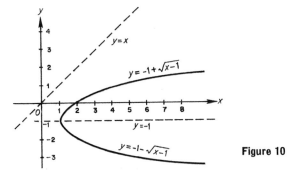

Figure 10

$y = -1$ is the graph of the branch $y = -1 + \sqrt{x - 1}$, and the portion of $\mathfrak{G}$ that lies below the line $y = -1$ is the graph of the branch $y = -1 - \sqrt{x - 1}$. The point $(1, -1)$ belongs to both branches.

EXERCISE 10

In problems 1 through 6, $y = f(x)$ is given. Find one branch of the inverse function, $x = g(y)$ and check your solution by showing that $f(x)$ and $g(y)$ satisfy equation (48). In problems 1, 2, and 5, sketch the graph $\mathcal{G}$ of the inverse function using the technique of Theorem 18.

1. $y = 3x + 11.$

2. $y = 2x^2 - 5x + 3.$

3. $y = x^3 + 6.$

4. $y = x^4 - 2x^2 - 1.$

5. $y = \dfrac{3x + 5}{x - 7}.$

6. $y = \dfrac{2x + 3}{7x - 2}.$

7. For each of the functions given in problems 1 through 6, compute $f'(x)$ and $g'(y)$ at the given point and observe that Theorem 17 holds: 1. $(0, 11)$; 2. $(1, 0)$; 3. $(1, 7)$; 4. $(2,7)$; 5. $(8, 29)$; 6. $(2, 7/12)$.

*8. Give an alternate proof of Theorem 17 directly from Definition 6, by differentiating equation (48) implicitly with respect to y.

**9. Suppose that $f(x)$ has the property that it is its own derivative; that is, for every x, $f'(x) = f(x)$. Show that if $g(y)$ is the inverse function of this $f(x)$ then $g'(y) = 1/y$.

3

APPLICATIONS OF THE DERIVATIVE

1.   **Objective.** The derivative has been introduced as an aid to curve sketching, namely as a method of finding the line tangent to a given curve at a fixed point on the curve.   But the derivative is useful in other problems.   Some of these uses will be considered in this chapter.

2.   **Motion on a straight line.** We suppose a particle P is moving on a straight line.   For simplicity we assume that the line is horizontal. The motion of the particle is completely determined if we specify where the particle is at each instant of time.   This is easy to do if we select some point on the line as the origin and introduce a coordinate system.   In place of the usual x, we use the letter s, to denote the directed distance on this line.   Let $s = f(t)$ be the particular function that gives the directed distance from the origin to the moving particle P at time t.   Whenever such a function is given the motion of the particle is completely specified.

For example let $s = t^2 - 4$ in some convenient units.   To be specific let s be in feet and t in seconds.   This equation states that when $t = 0$ then $s = -4$, so the particle is 4 ft to the left of the origin.   We indicate this in Fig. 1, where the lower line is the directed line on which the particle moves,

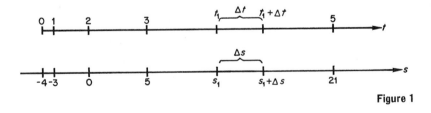

Figure 1

and the upper line indicates the motion of the particle, but is drawn distinct from the lower line for clarity.   The time values are on the upper line, while the corresponding s values are on the lower line.

86

When $t = 2$, $s = 0$, so the particle passes through the origin 2 seconds after starting.   When $t = 5$, the particle is 21 ft to the right of the origin.

The velocity of a moving particle is usually found by taking the directed distance it travels and dividing by the time required to cover that distance.   This is quite satisfactory if the particle is moving uniformly, that is if it doesn't go faster or slower at different times.   If the motion is not uniform as is the case in our example, then this ratio gives only an average velocity, and this average need not be a constant.   To illustrate this statement, suppose that $s = t^2 - 4$.   In the 2 second interval between $t = 1$ and $t = 3$ the particle moves from the point $s = -3$ to the point $s = 5$ and thus travels a distance $\Delta s = 5 - (-3) = 8$ ft.   The average velocity during this 2 second interval is $\Delta s/\Delta t = 8/2 = 4$ ft/sec.   In the two second interval between $t = 3$ and $t = 5$, the particle moves from the point $s = 5$ to the point $s = 21$, a distance of 16 ft.   The average velocity during this two second interval is $\Delta s/\Delta t = 16/2 = 8$ ft/sec.   If we moved the time interval, or changed its length we would obtain still different values for the average velocity.   It is clear from these considerations that what is wanted is an instantaneous velocity at some fixed value of t, and this instantaneous velocity is just the limiting value of the ratio $\Delta s/\Delta t$, as the time interval tends to zero.

DEFINITION 1.   *If* $s = f(t)$ *gives the location of a particle moving on a straight line, then* $v = v(t_1)$, *the instantaneous velocity at* $t = t_1$, *is defined by the equation*

$$v(t_1) = \lim_{\Delta t \to 0} \frac{f(t_1 + \Delta t) - f(t_1)}{\Delta t} = \lim_{\Delta t \to 0} \frac{\Delta s}{\Delta t}. \qquad (1)$$

The speed[1] of the particle is the absolute value of its velocity.

It is clear that the velocity is just the derivative and indeed we may write

$$v = v(t) = f'(t) = \frac{ds}{dt} \qquad (2)$$

selecting whichever notation seems most suitable.

By definition the *acceleration* of a particle is just the instantaneous rate of change of the velocity.   Using $a = a(t)$ to denote this quantity, we have by definition

---

[1] The words *speed* and *velocity* are frequently confused.   The difference is that velocity is a signed quantity, and hence on occasion may be negative.   Thus if the particle is moving from left to right on the line of Fig. 1, then the velocity is positive, while if it is moving from right to left, then s is decreasing and the velocity is negative. But in either case the speed is positive since it is the absolute value of the velocity.

$$a = a(t_1) = \lim_{\Delta t \to 0} \frac{v(t_1 + \Delta t) - v(t_1)}{\Delta t} = \lim_{\Delta t \to 0} \frac{\Delta v}{\Delta t} = \frac{dv}{dt}. \tag{3}$$

Since $v = \dfrac{ds}{dt}$ it follows that

$$a = \frac{d}{dt}\left(\frac{ds}{dt}\right) = \frac{d^2s}{dt^2}. \tag{4}$$

In words, the acceleration of a particle is just the second derivative with respect to time of the function that gives the directed distance of the particle from some fixed origin.

EXAMPLE 1.   Discuss the motion of a particle moving on a straight line if its position is given by $s = t^2 - 12t$ where s is in feet and t is in seconds.

SOLUTION.   At $t = 0$, the equation gives $s = 0$, so the particle starts at the origin.   The velocity at any time is given by

$$v = \frac{ds}{dt} = \frac{d}{dt}(t^2 - 12t) = 2t - 12 = 2(t - 6). \tag{5}$$

Hence at $t = 0$, $v = -12$ ft/sec, so the particle is moving to the left.   These facts are recorded schematically in Fig. 2.   Although the particle is moving on the s-axis, the lower line on the figure, its motion is indicated on the upper curve for clarity.   The arrow indicates the direction of motion, and just as before we place the t values on the upper curve.

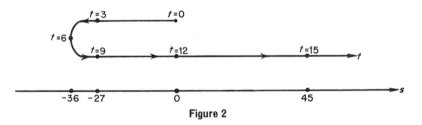

Figure 2

As long as $t < 6$, the second factor on the right side of (5) is negative and hence the velocity is negative.   Thus in the interval $0 \leq t < 6$ the particle is moving to the left.   At $t = 6$, $v = 0$ and the particle is momentarily at rest. For $t > 6$, the velocity is positive, and for these values of t the particle is moving to the right.   Consequently at $t = 6$, the particle attains its extreme position to the left of the origin.   In other words s is a minimum at $t = 6$. An easy computation gives $s = 6^2 - 12 \times 6 = -36$ for this minimum value of s.   To find the time when the particle is again at the origin we solve the equation $s = t^2 - 12t = 0$.   This gives $t = 0$ and $t = 12$.

Finally we compute the acceleration.   From (5)

$$a = \frac{dv}{dt} = \frac{d}{dt}(2t - 12) = 2.$$

In other words the velocity is steadily increasing at the rate of 2 feet/sec each second (written 2 ft/sec²). Thus the velocity starts at -12 ft/sec; in 6 seconds it has increased to 0, and in 6 more seconds it has increased to 12 ft/sec. During this same period the speed has at first decreased from 12 ft/sec down to 0, and then increased back to 12 ft/sec.

3.　　**Motion under gravity.** It is an experimental fact that near the surface of the earth a free falling object has a downward acceleration[2] that is constant at 32 ft/sec², provided that we neglect air resistance. If we select the positive direction upward then the basic equation governing the motion of a body falling under the influence of gravity is

$$a = -32. \tag{6}$$

Since acceleration is the derivative of the velocity with respect to time, equation (6) leads to

$$v = -32t + C_1 \tag{7}$$

where C_1 is some constant. The process of going from equation (6) to equation (7) is the inverse of differentiation. Instead of differentiating a given function, we are given its derivative and asked to find its primitive, i.e., the original function. Such a process is called *integration* (sometimes called *antidifferentiation*) and this process will be studied systematically in the next chapter. For the present we notice that the derivative of v given by (7) does yield (6) no matter what value is assigned to the constant C_1.

To find an expression for s, we recall that $v = \dfrac{ds}{dt}$, so we look for a function whose derivative gives the right side of (7). Inspection shows that

$$s = -16t^2 + C_1 t + C_2 \tag{8}$$

is such a function, where C_2 is any constant. For the derivative of (8) does give (7), and the derivative of (7) does give (6).

What can be said about the constants C_1 and C_2? If we put $t = 0$, in equation (7) we see that $v = C_1$ at the time $t = 0$. We call this velocity the initial velocity, and symbolize it with v_0. Therefore $C_1 = v_0$, the initial velocity. Similarly if we put $t = 0$ in equation (8) we find $s = C_2$. We call this the initial position, and symbolize it with s_0. Therefore $C_2 = s_0$, the location of the moving object at $t = 0$. Then equation (8) has the form

$$s = -16t^2 + v_0 t + s_0. \tag{9}$$

Summarizing: *Equation (9) is the equation of an object falling under the influence of gravity, when air resistance is neglected.*

　[2] Actually a is closer to 32.2 ft/sec², but we will use 32 ft/sec² for simplicity.

$$s = V_0 t - 16 t^2$$
$$V_f = V_0 + at$$
$$a = V_f^2 = V_0^2 + 2as$$

EXAMPLE 1.   A stone is thrown upward from the top of a building 192 ft high with an initial velocity of 64 ft/sec.   Find the maximum height the stone attains.   At what time does it pass the top of the building on the way down? When does it hit the ground?

SOLUTION.   With the positive direction upward and the origin on the ground we have $s_0 = 192$ and $v_0 = 64$.   Equation (9) gives

$$s = -16t^2 + 64t + 192. \tag{10}$$

Differentiating gives for the velocity

$$v = \frac{ds}{dt} = -32t + 64 = -32(t - 2).$$

For $t < 2$ the velocity is positive, and the stone is traveling upward.   At $t = 2$, the velocity is zero, and the stone is stationary for an instant.   Then it starts to descend.   Therefore the maximum height of the stone is obtained by putting $t = 2$ into equation (10).   Thus $s = -16 \times 4 + 64 \times 2 + 192 = 256$ ft is the maximum height.

The stone is at the top of the building when $s = 192$.   Equation (10) gives then

$$-16t^2 + 64t + 192 = 192$$
$$-16(t^2 - 4t) = 0$$
$$t(t - 4) = 0.$$

Hence $t = 0$ or $t = 4$.   So the stone passes the top of the building 4 seconds after it is thrown.

The stone hits the ground when $s = 0$.   Equation (10) gives

$$-16t^2 + 64t + 192 = 0$$
$$-16(t^2 - 4t - 12) = 0$$
$$-16(t - 6)(t + 2) = 0.$$

Thus $s = 0$ when $t = 6$, or $t = -2$.   The second answer is physically meaningless and may be rejected.   Therefore the stone hits the ground 6 seconds after being thrown.

EXERCISE 1

In problems 1 through 4, a particle is moving on a horizontal line in accordance with the given equation.   Find the velocity and acceleration and determine any extreme positions for $t \geq 0$.   Make a graph similar to Fig. 2 showing the motion for $t \geq 0$.

1. $s = 10 + 6t - t^2$.   2. $s = 2t^2 - 20t + 5$.

3. $s = t^3 - 9t - 7$.   4. $s = t^3 + 3t^2 - 45t + 8$.

5.   A stone is thrown upward from the top of a building 48 ft high with an initial velocity of 32 ft/sec.   Find the maximum height of the stone, and when it hits the ground.   Where is the stone when the velocity is -64 ft/sec?

(a) $V_f^2 = V_0^2 + (-2as)$

$0 = (32)^2 - 2(32)s$

$S = \frac{(32)^2}{2(32)} = 16\ ft$

S from the ground $= 48' + 16' = 64\ ft$

(b) $64 = \overset{(v_0)}{0} - 16t^2$

$t^2 = 4$

$t = 2\ sec + 1\ sec = 3\ sec$

(c) $(-64)^2 = 0 - 2(32)s$

$S = \frac{-(64)^2}{64} = 64\ ft$ (dist traveled)
(as it hits ground)

6. A bomb is dropped from a plane 1600 feet above the ground. How much time does it take to reach the ground, and what is the speed of the bomb just before it hits the ground? Neglect the air resistance, and any horizontal motion of the bomb due to the motion of the plane. Actually the bomb will travel along a parabola (as we will learn in Chapter 10) but assume here that the drop is vertical.

7. A man standing on the ground throws a rock vertically upward. Find a formula giving the maximum height of the stone in terms of the initial velocity v_0. Neglect the height of the man. What is the least value of v_0 that will suffice for the stone to land on top of a 100-ft building?

8. A stone is dropped from the roof of a building 144 ft high. One second later a second stone is thrown downward from the top of the same building with an initial speed $|v_0|$. What must be the value of $|v_0|$ in order that both stones hit the ground at the same time?

9. A ball is dropped from a height of H feet above the ground. Show that it strikes the ground in $\sqrt{H}/4$ secs.

10. If the ball of problem 9 is thrown downward with an initial speed of $|v_0|$ ft/sec, show that it hits the ground in $(\sqrt{v_0^2 + 64H} - |v_0|)/32$ secs.

11. A man standing on a bridge throws a stone upward. Exactly 3 seconds later the stone passes the man on the way down, and 2 seconds after that it lands in the water below. Find the initial velocity of the stone, and the height of the bridge above the water.

$(a)\ V_f = V_0 + at$ $\qquad$ $(b)\ s = V_0 t - 16 t^2$
$\quad 0 = V_0 + (32)(1.5)$ $\qquad\quad = (48)(2) - 16(2)^2$
$\quad V_0 = 48\ ft/sec$ $\qquad\qquad = -160\ ft$

4.   **Related rates.** The location of a particle is not the only quantity that can depend on time. Indeed any physical quantity Q that is changing gives rise to a function $Q(t)$, and the derivative $Q'(t)$ gives the instantaneous rate of change of Q with respect to t. For example Q might be the volume of a balloon into which gas is being pumped, or Q might be the concentration of acid in a vat in which a chemical reaction is taking place, or Q might be the quantity of electrical charge on a condenser, or Q might be the stress in a certain steel beam in a bridge, over which a truck is passing. It may be difficult or even impossible to determine $Q(t)$ and hence its derivative, but in all cases the procedure is the same. We set up an equation relating Q, the quantity in question, and other quantities for which we know the rate of change. We then differentiate this equation with respect to t. We can then solve the resulting equation for $Q'(t)$.

EXAMPLE 1. Gas is being pumped into a spherical balloon at the rate of 8 in.³/sec. Find the rate of change of the radius of the balloon when the radius of the balloon is 1/2 ft.

SOLUTION. The known formula for the volume of a sphere is

$$V = \frac{4}{3}\pi r^3. \tag{11}$$

Differentiating both sides of (11) with respect to t (Theorem 16, Chapter 2) gives

$$\frac{dV}{dt} = 4\pi r^2 \frac{dr}{dt}.$$

We are given that $\frac{dV}{dt} = 8$ and that $r = \frac{12}{2} = 6$ in.   Hence

$$\frac{dr}{dt} = \frac{8}{4\pi 36} = \frac{1}{18\pi} = .01768\cdots\text{in./sec.}$$

In working problems of this type many students try to substitute $r = 6$ directly in equation (11) and then differentiate.   When this is done the right side of equation (11) becomes a constant and then $\frac{dV}{dt} = 0$.   This is of course a ridiculous answer.   We leave it to the reader to explain to himself what is erroneous about this computation.

EXAMPLE 2.   A man is standing on the top rung of a 13-ft ladder which is leaning against a wall, when a scientific minded joker starts to pull the bottom of the ladder away from the wall steadily at the rate of 6 ft/min.   At what rate is the man on the ladder descending (he remains standing on the top rung) when the bottom of the ladder is 5 ft from the wall?   When the bottom is 12 ft from the wall?

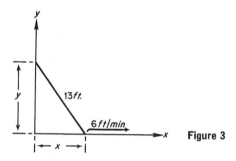

Figure 3

SOLUTION.   We introduce a coordinate system as indicated in Fig. 3.   Then no matter what the position of the ladder

$$x^2 + y^2 = 13^2 = 169. \tag{12}$$

Differentiating both sides of this equation with respect to t gives

$$2x \frac{dx}{dt} + 2y \frac{dy}{dt} = 0,$$

or

$$\frac{dy}{dt} = - \frac{x}{y} \frac{dx}{dt}. \tag{13}$$

When $x = 5$, equation (12) gives $y = \sqrt{169 - 25} = 12$.   Then from (13)

$$\frac{dy}{dt} = - \frac{5}{12} 6 = -2.5 \text{ ft/min,}$$

or the man is descending at the rate of 2.5 ft/min. When $x = 12$, then $y = \sqrt{169 - 144} = 5$ and in this case

$$\frac{dy}{dt} = -\frac{12}{5}6 = -14.4 \text{ ft/min},$$

and this is somewhat faster.

Margin handwritten:
t ↑ A
14 ft | 14 mph
35 mi |
35-14t | 20t →
B 20 mph

(a) $s = \sqrt{(35-14t)^2 + (20t)^2}$

(b) $\frac{ds}{dt} = \frac{d}{dt}\left[(35-14t)^2 + (400t^2)\right]^{1/2}$

$= \frac{1}{2}\left[(35-14t^2) + 400t^2\right]^{-1/2} \cdot \left[2(35-14t)(-14) + 600t\right]$

EXERCISE 2

1. A snowball is melting at the rate of 1 ft³/hr. If it is always a sphere how fast is the radius changing when the snowball is 18 in. in diameter?

Margin handwritten:
@ $t = 1$ hr
$\frac{dx}{dt} = \frac{21^2}{2\sqrt{13\pi}} = \frac{106}{\sqrt{74\pi}} = \frac{16}{2}$

2. How fast is the surface area changing for the snowball of problem 1?

3. At noon a certain ship A is 35 miles due north of a ship B. The ship A is travelling south with a speed of 14 miles/hr., and the ship B is travelling east with a speed of 20 mi./hr. Find a general expression for the distance between these two ships at any time t. How fast is this distance increasing at 1:00 P.M.?

4. A conical tank full of water is 20 ft high and 10 ft in diameter at the top. If the water is flowing out at the bottom at the rate of 2 ft³/min, find the rate at which the water level is falling (a) when the water level is 16 ft above the bottom, (b) when the water level is 2 ft above the bottom.

5. Sand is being poured onto a conical pile at the rate of 9 ft³/min. Friction forces in the sand are such that the slope of the sides of the conical pile is always 2/3. How fast is the altitude increasing when the radius of the base of the pile is 6 ft?

Margin handwritten:
$\frac{h}{r} = \frac{a}{6} \to h = \frac{ar}{6} \to \frac{dh}{dt} = $ $t \frac{dr}{dt} = $

Right margin:
$Vol = \frac{1}{3}\pi r^2 h$
differentiate
w/rt - t

6. A man 6 ft tall walks away from the base of a street light at a rate of 3.5 ft/sec. If the light is 20 ft above the ground find the rate of change of the length of the man's shadow (a) when he is 10 ft from the base of the light, (b) when he is 50 ft from the base of the light.

7. In problem 6 how fast is the farther end of his shadow moving?

8. A boat is fastened to a rope that is wound about a windlass 20 ft above the level at which the rope is attached to the boat. If the boat is moving away from the dock at the rate of 5 ft/sec, how fast is the rope unwinding when the boat is 40 ft from the point at water level directly under the windlass?

9. A point P moves on the curve $y = x^3$ in such a way that the x-coordinate changes 5 units/sec. (a) How fast is the y-coordinate of P changing? (b) What is the rate of change of the slope of the curve at P?

10. The surface of a cube is changing at the rate of 8 in.²/sec. How fast is the volume changing when the surface is 60 in.².

5.   **Increasing and decreasing functions.** The student will recall that an interval means the collection of numbers x between two given numbers, and is usually denoted by $a < x < b$. The numbers a and b are called the *end points* of the interval. For example the interval $3 < x < 5$ is the collection of all numbers that are greater than 3 but less than 5. Thus 3.1 is in the interval but 6 is not. If we wish to add the end points a and b to the set we call the new set a *closed interval* and denote it by $a \leq x \leq b$.

The interval $a < x < b$ is frequently called an *open interval*, because the end points have been deleted.

Naturally the phrase "increasing function" means what it says, but we must be precise about where it is increasing. The function graphed in Fig. 4 is increasing in $a < x < b$.

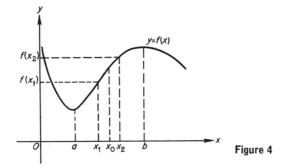

Figure 4

DEFINITION 2.   *A function $f(x)$ is said to be increasing in the interval $a < x < b$ if, whenever x_1 and x_2 are in this interval, and $x_1 < x_2$, then*

$$f(x_1) < f(x_2). \tag{14}$$

The function is increasing at a point x_0 if there is an interval around x_0, such that in that interval

$$x_0 < x_2 \tag{15}$$

implies that

$$f(x_0) < f(x_2), \tag{16}$$

and

$$x_1 < x_0 \tag{17}$$

implies that

$$f(x_1) < f(x_0). \tag{18}$$

An easy test for an increasing function is given by

THEOREM 1.   *If the derivative $f'(x)$ is positive at x_0 then $f(x)$ is increasing at x_0. If the derivative is positive in an interval then $f(x)$ is increasing in that interval.*

PROOF.   The definition of the derivative at x_0 can be written in the form

$$f'(x_0) = \lim_{x_2 \to x_0} \frac{f(x_2) - f(x_0)}{x_2 - x_0} \tag{19}$$

because the numerator is just the difference Δy as x changes from x_0 to

x_2 and the denominator is just Δx. By hypothesis the derivative is positive so that if x_2 is close to x_0, then

$$\frac{f(x_2) - f(x_0)}{x_2 - x_0} > 0. \tag{20}$$

If $x_0 < x_2$, the denominator of (20) is positive and hence the numerator must also be positive. Therefore $f(x_0) < f(x_2)$. This proves that (15) implies (16). To prove that (17) implies (18), replace x_2 by x_1 in (20) obtaining

$$\frac{f(x_1) - f(x_0)}{x_1 - x_0} > 0 \tag{21}$$

for x_1 close to x_0. Now suppose $x_1 < x_0$. Then the denominator in (21) is negative, so the numerator must also be negative. Therefore $f(x_1) < f(x_0)$. This proves that (17) implies (18). Hence if $f'(x_0) > 0$, the function is increasing at x_0.

Finally if $f'(x)$ is positive in an interval, it is positive at each point in the interval, and hence it is increasing at each point of the interval. Therefore it is increasing in the interval. Q.E.D.

The definition of a decreasing function should be obvious, and it is clear that if the derivative $f'(x)$ is negative in an interval, then $f(x)$ is decreasing in that interval. The student may accept this on intuitive grounds, or write out the definition and proof for himself.

EXAMPLE 1. In what intervals is the function $y = 13 - 15x + 9x^2 - x^3$ increasing? In what intervals is this function decreasing?

SOLUTION. Computing the derivative we find

$$\frac{dy}{dx} = -15 + 18x - 3x^2 = -3(5 - 6x + x^2)$$

$$\frac{dy}{dx} = -3(x - 5)(x - 1). \tag{22}$$

Clearly the derivative is zero when $x = 1$ and $x = 5$, and only for those values. These two points, where the derivative is zero, break the x-axis into three intervals.

$$I_1: \quad -\infty < x < 1,$$

$$I_2: \quad 1 < x < 5,$$

$$I_3: \quad 5 < x < \infty.$$

In each of these intervals we may expect the derivative to have constant sign. Let us look first at I_3. When $x > 5$, the last two factors in (22) are positive. Hence $dy/dx < 0$ and the function is decreasing in I_3. A similar type discussion gives the sign of the derivative in the other two intervals. The work may be arranged systematically as in the following table.

	Range of x	Sign of $-3(x - 5)(x - 1)$	Sign of $\dfrac{dy}{dx}$	Function is
I_1	$-\infty < x < 1$	$(-)(-)(-)$	$-$	decreasing
I_2	$1 < x < 5$	$(-)(-)(+)$	$+$	increasing
I_3	$5 < x < \infty$	$(-)(+)(+)$	$-$	decreasing

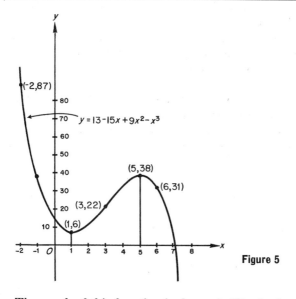

Figure 5

The graph of this function is shown in Fig. 5 where for convenience we have used different scales on the two axes. It is clear from the picture that the function increases and decreases as predicted by the entries in the table.

6.   Extreme values of a function. Briefly the maximum value of a function is its largest value, and the minimum value is its smallest. But to be precise we must specify the interval we are considering. In other words it must be clear which values of x are allowed to enter the competition for making $f(x)$ maximum or minimum.

DEFINITION 3. *The function $f(x)$ is said to have a maximum value in the closed interval $a \leq x \leq b$ at x_0 if x_0 is in the interval and if $f(x_0) \geq f(x)$ for all x in that interval. The number $f(x_0)$ is said to be the maximum of $f(x)$ in that interval. Similarly $f(x_0)$ is the minimum if $f(x_0) \leq f(x)$ for all other x in the interval under consideration.*

The graph of a function may have several high points, one of which may be higher than all of the others. To distinguish among such high points, the highest one is called the *maximum* or the *absolute maximum* while each of the others is called a *relative maximum*. Precisely we have

DEFINITION 4. *The function $f(x)$ is said to have a relative maximum at x_0 if there is an interval with x_0 in the interior, such that in that interval, $f(x_0)$ is the maximum value of the function.*

Similarly we may define the *minimum value* of a function in an interval, and *relative minimum* values. All such values, whether maximum or minimum, (absolute or relative), are called *extreme* values. One expects that extreme values occur where the derivative is zero. The precise statement is

THEOREM 2. *If $f(x)$ has a relative maximum at $x = x_0$, and if $f(x)$ is differentiable at x_0, then $f'(x_0) = 0$.*

PROOF. Let us compute the derivative of $y = f(x)$ at x_0. By definition,

$$f'(x_0) = \lim_{h \to 0} \frac{f(x_0 + h) - f(x_0)}{h}. \tag{23}$$

By hypothesis $f(x_0)$ is a relative maximum value so $f(x_0) \geq f(x_0 + h)$ when $|h|$ is sufficiently small. Whence the numerator of (23) is always negative or at most zero. Now if h approaches 0 through positive values, the ratio on the right in (23) is always negative (or zero) and hence the limit process gives

$$f'(x_0) \leq 0. \tag{24}$$

On the other hand if h is negative and approaching zero in (23) then the quotient on the right side of (23) is always positive (or zero) and hence the limit process gives

$$f'(x_0) \geq 0. \tag{25}$$

Now the two conditions on the derivative, (24) and (25), are incompatible unless $f'(x_0) = 0$.   Q.E.D.

Naturally a similar theorem holds for a relative minimum.

THEOREM 3. *If $f(x)$ has a relative minimum at x_0, and if $f(x)$ is differentiable at x_0, then $f'(x_0) = 0$.*

The proof is similar to that of Theorem 2 and is left for the reader.

EXAMPLE 1. Find the extreme values of the function $y = 13 - 15x + 9x^2 - x^3$ (a) for all real x,   (b) in the interval $-2 \leqq x \leqq 6$ and   (c) in the interval $3 \leqq x \leqq 6$.

SOLUTION. (a) This function is the same as the one treated in the example of the preceding section and the graph is shown in Fig. 5. We first locate all the relative extreme points. By Theorems 2 and 3 this means that we must compute the derivative, and then find the values of x for which the derivative is zero. Since $y = 13 - 15x + 9x^2 - x^3$,

$$\frac{dy}{dx} = -15 + 18x - 3x^2 = -3(5 - 6x + x^2)$$
$$= -3(x - 5)(x - 1). \ .$$

Therefore relative extreme values can occur only at $x = 1$ and $x = 5$. Since $f(x)$ is decreasing for $x < 1$, and increasing if $x > 1$, and $x < 5$, it is clear that the curve descends, stops at $x = 1$, then rises, so that a relative minimum occurs at $x = 1$, and this minimum value is $f(1) = 13 - 15 + 9 - 1 = 6$. Similarly the function is increasing as x runs from 1 to 5, stops at $x = 5$, and thereafter is decreasing; hence a relative maximum occurs at $x = 5$, and this maximum value is $f(5) = 13 - 15 \times 5 + 9 \times 25 - 125 = 38$. Thus $(1, 6)$ is a relative minimum point and $(5, 38)$ is a relative maximum point.

Is 6 the absolute minimum value of the function? No! For if we put $x = 10$ we find $f(10) = 13 - 150 + 900 - 1000 = -237$ and this is less than 6. But this is not the minimum either, because $f(100) = 13 - 1500 + 90,000 - 1,000,000 = -911,487$, and this is still less than -237. Indeed we have seen that for $x > 5$, the function $f(x)$ is steadily decreasing as x increases, and hence there is no absolute minimum. Thus 6 is a relative minimum, but not a minimum.

Similarly, by letting x approach $-\infty$ we see that 38 is a relative maximum, but not an absolute maximum value for the function. For example $f(-10) = 13 + 150 + 900 + 1000 = 2063$ and $2063 > 38$. Since $f(x)$ is decreasing, as x increases for $x < 1$, we can reverse the direction of x, and say that $f(x)$ is increasing as x decreases toward $-\infty$. Hence $f(x)$ has no maximum.

(b) The situation changes when we restrict x to lie in some interval. Suppose now that x must lie in the interval $-2 \leqq x \leqq 6$. It is clear that we only need to compare the relative maximum and minimum with the values of $f(x)$ at the end points. Now $f(-2) = 13 + 30 + 36 + 8 = 87 > 38$. Hence the maximum value of $f(x)$ in the interval $-2 \leqq x \leqq 6$ is 87 and it occurs at $x = -2$. At the other end point $x = 6$ we have $f(6) = 13 - 90 + 324 - 216 = 31$. Hence 6 is the minimum value of $f(x)$ in this interval. In this case the relative minimum and absolute minimum are the same.

(c) In the interval $3 \leq x \leq 6$, the point $(5, 38)$ is the only relative extreme point. At the end points we have $f(3) = 13 - 45 + 81 - 27 = 22$ and $f(6) = 31$. Comparing these two values with $f(5) = 38$, we can conclude that in the interval $3 \leq x \leq 6$, the minimum value of $f(x)$ is 22 and the maximum value is 38.

EXAMPLE 2. Find the extreme values for the function $y = x^3$.

SOLUTION. First we find where the derivative vanishes:

$$\frac{dy}{dx} = 3x^2 = 0, \qquad \text{at } x = 0.$$

At $x = 0$, $y = 0$, and this is the only possible relative maximum or minimum. But if x is positive then y is positive, and if x is negative, y is negative, so near $x = 0$ this function assumes values greater than zero, and also values that are

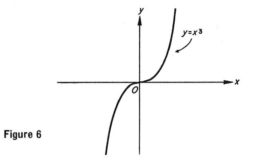

Figure 6

less than zero. Therefore $x = 0$ is neither a relative maximum, nor a relative minimum. Indeed the derivative is always positive, except at $x = 0$, and hence the function is everywhere increasing (it is an increasing function also at $x = 0$). Therefore $y = x^3$ has neither an absolute maximum, nor an absolute minimum, nor a relative maximum or minimum.

This second example shows that the vanishing of the derivative is a necessary condition for a relative extreme point, but it is not a sufficient condition. The meaning of these new technical terms "necessary" and "sufficient" has already been illustrated in the preceding work. However for clarity we recapitulate:

The condition is necessary. If $f(x_0)$ is a relative extreme, then (necessarily) the derivative must vanish at x_0. This is the content of Theorems 2 and 3.

The condition is sufficient. If the derivative vanishes at x_0 then (this is sufficient to insure that) the function has a relative extreme at x_0. But actually in this situation, the *condition is not sufficient*. For as shown in Example 2, the derivative of the function $y = x^3$ vanishes at $x = 0$ but the function does not have a relative extreme at $x = 0$.

EXERCISE 3

In problems 1 through 10 find all the intervals on which the given function is increasing, and find all of the relative maximum and minimum points.

1. $y = x^2 + 2x - 5.$ 2. $y = 10 - 6x - 2x^2.$

3. $y = 2x^3 - 3x^2 - 36x + 7.$ 4. $y = 1 - 12x - 9x^2 - 2x^3.$

*5. $y = 5 - (x + 2)^3(x - 3)^2.$ *6. $y = (x + 1)^3(x - 3)^3.$

*7. $y = 20 - 6x + 9x^2 - 5x^3.$ *8. $y = x^3 + 6x^2 + 12x + 8.$

*9. $y = \dfrac{9 + 2x - x^2}{1 + x}.$ *10. $y = \dfrac{5 - 3x}{1 - x}.$

In problems 11 through 14 find the absolute minimum and the absolute maximum for the given function in the given interval.

11. $f(x) = \dfrac{3x + 1}{x^2 + x + 3}, \qquad -4 \leqq x \leqq -1.$

12. $f(x) = \dfrac{x^2}{1 + x^2}, \qquad 9 \leqq x \leqq 10.$

13. $f(x) = \dfrac{2 - x}{5 - 4x + x^2}, \qquad -100 \leqq x \leqq 2.$

14. $f(x) = \dfrac{1 + x + x^2 + x^3}{1 + x^3}, \qquad 2 \leqq x \leqq 5.$

15. Discuss the character of the point $(0, 0)$ on the curve $y = x^n$ for each positive integer n.

16. Without using the calculus find the minimum value of $y = (x - 3)^4 + 7$.

*17. Without using the calculus find the minimum value of $x^4 + 4x^3 + 6x^2 + 4x + 12$.

*18. Find the maximum value of the derivative of the function $y = x/(1 + x^2)$.

19. Find constants a, b, and c so that the curve $y = ax^2 + bx + c$ goes through the point $(0, 3)$ and has a relative extreme at $(1, 2)$.

20. Show that the condition that the integer n is even, is a necessary condition, but not a sufficient condition for n to be divisible by 4.

21. Let the number n be expressed in decimal notation. Show that the condition that the last digit is a 5 is a sufficient condition, but not a necessary condition for n to be divisible by 5.

22. Show that if n is a prime greater than 2, then it is odd, but not conversely. Thus n being odd is a necessary condition, but not a sufficient condition for n to be a prime greater than 2.

7.   Rolle's Theorem. We know that the derivative of a constant is zero. How about the converse? If the derivative of a function is zero for all x in a certain interval, does it follow that the function is constant in that interval? This seems to be obviously true, and we could simplify matters by merely stating "this is an obvious fact." But we can also give a proof, and we shall do so shortly (Theorem 7). The real question at issue is this: which assertions can be accepted as obvious, and which assertions demand a proof? Unfortunately we cannot stop to prove all of the theorems required for the calculus, because to do so starting from a bare minimum of axioms would require so much time and energy that the reader would lose all interest before he arrived at the calculus.

As a practical way out of this dilemma we start somewhere in the middle rather than at the beginning[3]. Thus we take, without proof, certain theorems that are obviously true anyway and use them as axioms. One such theorem, that will be particularly useful in this section is

THEOREM 4. *If $f(x)$ is a continuous function of x in the closed interval $a \leq x \leq b$ then it has a maximum value at some point of the interval. It also has a minimum value at some (other) point of the interval.*

As already mentioned we do not propose to prove this theorem[4]. The following examples illuminate its content. Consider the function

$$f(x) = \begin{cases} x, \text{ if } 0 \leq x < 1, \\ 0, \text{ if } x = 1. \end{cases} \tag{26}$$

The graph of this function is shown in Fig. 7. This function does not have

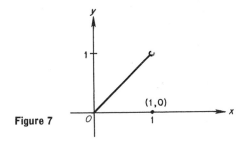

Figure 7

a maximum in the closed interval $0 \leq x \leq 1$. Certainly any number less than 1 cannot be a maximum because $f(x)$ can be as close to 1 as we please, by taking x close to 1. But 1 is not a maximum either because $f(x)$ does not assume this value, for by definition $f(1) = 0$. This does not contradict Theorem 4, because in Theorem 4 the function $f(x)$ is required to be continuous, while our example function is discontinuous at $x = 1$. We

[3] In the author's opinion, the beginning consists of Peano's five axioms for the positive integers. Anyone who wants to start at the beginning can find an excellent presentation in the book by E. Landau, *Foundations of Analysis*, Chelsea Publishing Co., New York, 1951. However, I recommend that the reader defer this material until he has mastered at least the calculus.

[4] The interested reader can find a proof of this theorem in *Pure Mathematics* by G. H. Hardy, Cambridge University Press, 1938, p. 194.

might try to construct a counter example to Theorem 4, by removing the discontinuity. Indeed if we consider $f(x)$ defined by (26) in the open interval $0 < x < 1$, then $f(x)$ is continuous in this open interval and does not have a maximum in this interval. In fact it also does not have a minimum in this interval. But this is an open interval, while Theorem 4 requires that $f(x)$ is to be considered in a closed interval.

THEOREM 5.   (Rolle's Theorem.)   *Suppose that the function $f(x)$ is defined in the closed interval $a \leq x \leq b$ and that*

1. $f(a) = f(b) = 0$,
2.   *It is continuous in $a \leq x \leq b$.*
3.   *It is differentiable in $a < x < b$.*

Then there is some point ξ (Greek letter xi) in the open interval $a < \xi < b$, such that $f'(\xi) = 0$.

PROOF.   If $f(x) = 0$ for all x in $a \leq x \leq b$ then $f'(x) = 0$ for all x in that interval, and then any ξ will do. Suppose now that $f(x)$ is not zero for some value of x. By Theorem 4, $f(x)$ has a maximum and a minimum in that interval. Let M and m be the maximum and minimum values respectively of $f(x)$. Then either $M > 0$ or $m < 0$, or perhaps both (see Fig. 8). Suppose that $M > 0$, and $M = f(\xi_1)$.

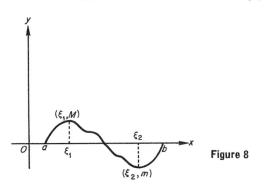

Figure 8

Then $a < \xi_1 < b$, because at the end points the function is zero. Now the conditions of Theorem 2 are satisfied at $x = \xi_1$ and hence $f'(\xi_1) = 0$. If the maximum M is 0, then the minimum $m < 0$. We apply the same argument to ξ_2 where $f(\xi_2) = m$ and find (using Theorem 3) that $f'(\xi_2) = 0$.

Q.E.D.

EXAMPLE 1.   Prove that the equation $g(x) = 4x^3 - 3x^2 + 2x - 1 = 0$ has a root between 0 and 1.

SOLUTION.   The given equation is a cubic and can be solved by Cardan's formula (really Tartaglia's formula). When this is done then it is clear that $g(x) = 0$ has a root in the specified interval. But nowadays nobody is ex-

pected to know Tartaglia's formula, and hence another approach is desirable.
   By inspection we see that if

$$f(x) = x^4 - x^3 + x^2 - x$$

then the derivative of $f(x)$ is $g(x)$, that is

$$f'(x) = 4x^3 - 3x^2 + 2x - 1 = g(x).$$

Now $f(0) = 0$ and $f(1) = 1 - 1 + 1 - 1 = 0$.   Thus condition (1) of Rolle's
Theorem is satisfied with $a = 0$ and $b = 1$.   But the other two conditions are
always satisfied for any polynomial.   Therefore by Rolle's Theorem, $f'(x)$ has
at least one zero in the open interval $0 < x < 1$.   Q.E.D.

   In solving this problem it was necessary to reverse the process of
differentiation, that is, given $g(x)$ we found $f(x)$ such that $f'(x) = g(x)$.
We have already encountered this situation in section 3.   The function
$f(x)$ is called an *integral* of $g(x)$, and the process of going from $g(x)$ to $f(x)$ is
called *integration*.   Thus integration is the inverse operation of differentiation.   In Chapter 4 we will introduce a suitable notation for the process
of integration and we will make a systematic study of this new operation.
For the present we will need only the following formula: If $g(x) = ax^n$ and
$n \neq -1$ then its integral is

$$f(x) = \frac{ax^{n+1}}{n+1} + C,$$

where C is some arbitrary constant.   This is easily checked by differentiating $f(x)$ to obtain $f'(x) = ax^n = g(x)$.

   THEOREM 6.   (The Mean Value Theorem.)   *Suppose that*
$f(x)$ is

   1.   *continuous in the closed interval $a \leq x \leq b$,*
   2.   *differentiable in the open interval $a < x < b$.*

Then there is a point ξ in the open interval $a < \xi < b$ such that

$$f'(\xi) = \frac{f(b) - f(a)}{b - a}. \tag{27}$$

It is frequently convenient to write equation (27) in the equivalent form

$$f(b) - f(a) = (b - a)f'(\xi), \qquad a < \xi < b. \tag{28}$$

   Before proving this theorem we try to picture its meaning.   If we
graph the function $y = f(x)$ then the ratio

$$\frac{f(b) - f(a)}{b - a}$$

is just the slope of the line segment joining the two points $(a, f(a))$ and

$(b, f(b))$, (see Fig. 9). Now $f'(\xi)$ is the slope of the line tangent to the curve at $(\xi, f(\xi))$. So (27) asserts that there is some point on the curve where the tangent line is parallel to the chord line. When equation (27)

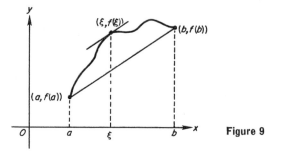

Figure 9

is regarded in this light, it appears obvious that some such point must exist on the curve.

PROOF. We intend to employ Rolle's Theorem in the proof of Theorem 6. We want a function that is zero at $x = a$ and at $x = b$. For the reader who is familiar with third order determinants it is easy to see that the function $F(x)$ defined by the determinant

$$F(x) = \begin{vmatrix} f(x) & x & 1 \\ f(a) & a & 1 \\ f(b) & b & 1 \end{vmatrix}$$

is zero at $x = a$ and at $x = b$, because when $x = a$ the first two rows are identical, and when $x = b$ the first and third rows are identical. Expanding this determinant by minors of the first row gives

$$F(x) = f(x)(a - b) - x[f(a) - f(b)] + bf(a) - af(b). \tag{29}$$

For the reader who is not familiar with determinants, the proof can start with the function $F(x)$ defined by equation (29). It is easy to check from (29) that $F(a) = 0$ and $F(b) = 0$. Further $F(x)$ is continuous in $a \leq x \leq b$ because $f(x)$ is continuous there. Finally $F(x)$ is differentiable in $a < x < b$ because $f(x)$ is differentiable there. Thus the three conditions of Rolle's Theorem are satisfied by $F(x)$. Consequently there is a point ξ in $a < \xi < b$ such that the derivative of $F(x)$,

$$F'(x) = f'(x)(a - b) - [f(a) - f(b)], \tag{30}$$

vanishes at ξ. This means that for $x = \xi$, the equation (30) yields

$$0 = f'(\xi)(a - b) - [f(a) - f(b)]. \tag{31}$$

Solving equation (31) for $f'(\xi)$, yields (27). Q.E.D.

Although these two theorems, Rolle's Theorem and the Mean Value Theorem, look innocent and ineffective, they are in fact fundamental in the theoretical development of the calculus. These two theorems will be used frequently throughout the book, and it would be well for the student to memorize these two theorems. At present we only want to make two applications of the Mean Value Theorem.

THEOREM 7. *If the derivative of $f(x)$ is zero in an interval $a \le x \le b$, then the function is a constant in that interval.*

PROOF. We rewrite equation (27) in the form

$$(b - a)f'(\xi) = f(b) - f(a), \qquad a < \xi < b,$$

or

$$f(b) = f(a) + (b - a)f'(\xi), \qquad a < \xi < b. \tag{32}$$

We now let b be variable, i.e., replace b in (32) by x where x is any number in the interval $a < x \le b$. In this situation ξ is also a variable depending on x, but we always have $a < \xi < x$. Then (32) becomes

$$f(x) = f(a) + (x - a)f'(\xi), \qquad a < \xi < x. \tag{33}$$

By the hypothesis of Theorem 7, $f'(\xi) = 0$ for every ξ in $a < \xi < b$. Then (33) simplifies to

$$f(x) = f(a), \qquad a < x \le b, \tag{34}$$

and this means that $f(x)$ is the constant number $f(a)$. Q.E.D.

THEOREM 8. *If $f(x)$ and $g(x)$ are two functions each defined in $a \le x \le b$, and having the same derivative there, then they differ by a constant. That is, there is a constant C such that*

$$f(x) = g(x) + C, \qquad a \le x \le b. \tag{35}$$

PROOF. We are given that

$$\frac{d}{dx} f(x) = \frac{d}{dx} g(x), \qquad a \le x \le b, \tag{36}$$

and this means that

$$\frac{d}{dx} (f(x) - g(x)) = 0, \qquad a \le x \le b.$$

Now apply Theorem 7 to the function $f(x) - g(x)$ whose derivative is zero. It follows from Theorem 7 that $f(x) - g(x) = C$, and hence equation (35). Q.E.D.

EXAMPLE 2.   Show that the two functions

$$f(x) = \frac{3x + 5}{x - 7} \quad \text{and} \quad g(x) = \frac{-x + 33}{x - 7}$$

differ by a constant.

SOLUTION.   Of course we could merely compute $f(x) - g(x)$, but this would spoil the fun.   Instead we compute the derivatives.

$$f'(x) = \frac{(x - 7)3 - (3x + 5)1}{(x - 7)^2} \qquad\qquad g'(x) = \frac{(x - 7)(-1) - (-x + 33)1}{(x - 7)^2}$$

$$f'(x) = \frac{-26}{(x - 7)^2} \qquad\qquad\qquad\qquad g'(x) = \frac{-26}{(x - 7)^2}$$

Since $f'(x) = g'(x)$ for all x (except $x = 7$, of course) it follows from Theorem 8, that $f(x) = g(x) + C$.   We leave it to the student to prove that $C = 4$.

One might at first be surprised that these two functions differ by a constant, but a little careful study will dispel this feeling.   Later on in the calculus we will meet pairs of functions that look quite different, but still have the same derivative.   In such cases the surprise will be quite solid and lasting.

EXERCISE 4

*1.   State and prove (a) Rolle's Theorem, (b) The Mean Value Theorem, without peeking at the book.

*2.   The function

$$f(x) = \begin{cases} x, & 0 \leqq x \leqq 1, \\ 2 - x, & 1 \leqq x \leqq 2. \end{cases}$$

(see Fig. 10) is zero at $x = 0$ and $x = 2$.   Therefore by Rolle's Theorem the derivative should be zero at least once in the interval $0 < x < 2$.   But it is not zero, at any point of this interval.   Where lies the trouble?

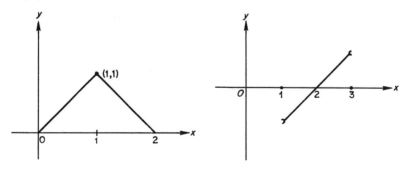

Figure 10   Figure 11

*3.   Repeat problem 2 for the function

$$f(x) = \begin{cases} 0, & x = 1, \\ x - 2, & 1 < x < 3, \\ 0, & x = 3. \end{cases}$$

shown in Fig. 11.

4. For each of the following functions, check that the conditions of Rolle's Theorem are satisfied in the given interval. Then find a suitable value of ξ as predicted by the theorem.

    a. $f(x) = \dfrac{x(x-2)}{x^2 - 2x + 2}$, $0 \le x \le 2$,

    b. $f(x) = x(x-1)(x-2)$, $0 \le x \le 1$,
    c. $f(x) = x(x-1)(x-2)$, $1 \le x \le 2$.

5. Suppose that $B^2 - 4AC > 0$, and $A > 0$. Then the quadratic function $f(x) = Ax^2 + Bx + C$ vanishes at the real points

$$a = \frac{-B - \sqrt{B^2 - 4AC}}{2A} \quad \text{and} \quad b = \frac{-B + \sqrt{B^2 - 4AC}}{2A}.$$

According to Rolle's Theorem $f'(x)$ must vanish once in the open interval $a < x < b$. Show that this is really the case.

6. Find an integral for each of the following functions

    a. $g(x) = 6x^2$,   **b.** $g(x) = x^7 - 5x^4$,
    c. $g(x) = 2x^5 + 5x^2$,   **d.** $g(x) = ax^n + bx^m$.

7. Prove that the equation

$$6x^5 - 5x^4 + 4x^3 - 3x^2 + 2x - 1 = 0$$

has at least one root in $0 < x < 1$.

The Mean Value Theorem states that for a suitable ξ the tangent line at $(\xi, f(\xi))$ is parallel to the chord. In each of the problems 8 through 12 a curve and the end points of a chord are given. Find a value of ξ satisfying the requirements of the Mean Value Theorem. Sketch the curve subtended by the given chord.

    8. $y = x^2$,   (2, 4), (3, 9).
    9. $y = \sqrt{x}$,   (25, 5), (36, 6).
    10. $y = x^3 - 9x + 1$,   (−3, 1), (4, 29).

    11. $y = \dfrac{1}{x-7}$,   (7.1, 10), (7.2, 5)

    12. $y = \dfrac{1}{x-7}$,   (7.01, 100), (7.02, 50).

    13. Show by differentiating

$$f(x) = -\frac{2 + 5x - 10x^2}{1 + 3x - 5x^2 + 4x^3} \quad \text{and} \quad g(x) = \frac{x(1 + 8x^2)}{1 + 3x - 5x^2 + 4x^3}$$

that $f(x) = g(x) + C$. What is C?

    14. If $y = mx + b$ then $y'' = 0$. Prove conversely that if $y'' = 0$ then $y = mx + b$.

    15. Use the Mean Value Theorem to prove that under suitable conditions

$$f'(x_2) - f'(x_1) = (x_2 - x_1)f''(\xi), \quad x_1 < \xi < x_2.$$

What are the conditions?

16.   Use Rolle's Theorem to prove that if $a > 0$ the cubic equation $x^3 + ax + b = 0$ cannot have more than one real root no matter what value is assigned to b.

17.   Is the following assertion correct? A necessary and sufficient condition that a given function $f(x)$ be a constant for all points in an interval, is that $f'(x)$ is zero throughout that interval.

8.   Concave curves and inflection points.   Let us consider a curve, the graph of $y = f(x)$ in an interval $a \leq x \leq b$, and let us pick two values of x, say x_1 and x_2 such that $a \leq x_1 < x_2 \leq b$. Then the line segment joining the points $(x_1, f(x_1))$ and $(x_2, f(x_2))$ on the curve is called a *chord* of the curve (or a chord of the function) in that interval (Fig. 12). Now a chord may either cut the curve in a third point, or it may lie entirely above the curve (except for its end points), or it may lie entirely below the curve (except for its end points). This suggests

> **DEFINITION 5.**   *A curve (or function) is said to be concave upward in an interval if every chord in that interval lies above the curve except for its end points (see Fig. 12). The function is said to be concave downward if every such chord, except for its end points, lies below the curve.*

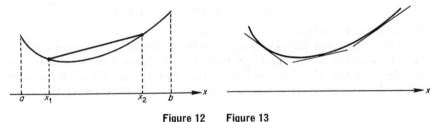

Figure 12   Figure 13

If we look for a criterion for curves that are concave upwards it is easy to find one. Suppose we draw the tangent lines to the curve at a sequence of points along the curve, as shown in Fig. 13. Then it is obvious from the graph that the slope of the tangent line is increasing. For the three lines shown in Fig. 13 the slope of the first is negative, the slope for the second one is positive but small, and the slope of the third one is positive and larger. But if the slope is increasing, the derivative of the slope,

$$\frac{dm}{dx} = \frac{d}{dx}\left(\frac{dy}{dx}\right) = \frac{d^2y}{dx^2}$$

should be positive. These geometrical considerations suggest

> **THEOREM 9.**   *If $f''(x) > 0$ in an interval $a \leq x \leq b$, then the curve $y = f(x)$ is concave upward in that interval. If $f''(x) < 0$ in $a \leq x \leq b$, then the curve $y = f(x)$ is concave downward in that interval.*

This result is quite easy to remember using the following mnemonic device:

Second derivative positive.   Second derivative negative.
Bowl will hold water.   Bowl won't hold water.
Curve is concave upward   Curve is concave downward.

Actually we can go a little further and allow the second derivative to be zero at isolated points in the interval, and still further refinement is possible. Also Theorem 9 has a partial converse, namely if the curve $y = f(x)$ is concave upward and if $f(x)$ is twice differentiable then $f''(x) \geq 0$. Similarly if the curve is concave downward then $f''(x) \leq 0$.

We have not yet proved Theorem 9 nor its partial converse Theorem 11 (below). Although these theorems are simple to state, easy to visualize, and have strong intuitive appeal, it turns out that the proofs are a little bit complicated and unusual. The student could well ignore these proofs, and for this reason we turn to an example and a further discussion. Merely for the sake of completeness, we include the proofs at the end of this section.

EXAMPLE 1. Discuss the concavity of the curve

$$y = f(x) = (x^3 - 18x^2 + 81x + 36)/18.$$

SOLUTION. Differentiating we find

$$\frac{dy}{dx} = f'(x) = \frac{1}{18}(3x^2 - 36x + 81) = \frac{1}{6}(x^2 - 12x + 27)$$

$$= \frac{1}{6}(x - 3)(x - 9).$$

So the critical points are $x = 3$, and $x = 9$. Differentiating again

$$\frac{d^2y}{dx^2} = f''(x) = \frac{1}{6}(2x - 12) = \frac{1}{3}(x - 6). \tag{37}$$

For $x > 6$, we have $f''(x) > 0$ and hence for $x > 6$, the curve is concave upward. Similarly for $x < 6$, $f''(x) < 0$, and the curve is concave downward. For the critical points we have

$$f(3) = \frac{1}{18}(3^3 - 6 \times 3^3 + 9 \times 3^3 + 36) = \frac{1}{18}(4 \times 3^3 + 4 \times 3^2) = 8$$

$$f(9) = \frac{1}{18}(9^3 - 2 \times 9^3 + 9^3 + 36) \qquad = \frac{1}{18}(36) = 2.$$

The graph of this curve is shown in Fig. 14.

What can we say about the point $(6, 5)$? From the graph it appears that the tangent line at $(6, 5)$ actually cuts through the curve, part of the curve lying on one side of the tangent line, and part on the other side. It is clear that this occurs because for $x < 6$, the slope is decreasing i.e., the tangent line is turning in a clockwise direction, while for $x > 6$, the slope is increasing, i.e., the tangent line is turning in a counterclockwise direction. Such a point is called an *inflection point*. More precisely we have

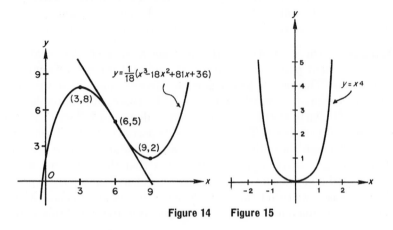

Figure 14   Figure 15

DEFINITION 6.   *A point (x_1, y_1) on the curve $y = f(x)$ is called an inflection point of the curve if there is an interval $a \leq x \leq b$ around x_1 such that in that interval the derivative is increasing on one side of x_1, and decreasing on the other side.*

Two cases are possible, namely:

(I) $f'(x)$ is increasing for $a \leq x < x_1$, and
    $f'(x)$ is decreasing for $x_1 < x \leq b$.

(II) $f'(x)$ is decreasing for $a \leq x < x_1$, and
    $f'(x)$ is increasing for $x_1 < x \leq b$.

THEOREM 10.   *If (x_1, y_1) is an inflection point of the curve $y = f(x)$ and if the second derivative $f''(x)$ is continuous at x_1, then $f''(x_1) = 0$.*

PROOF.   By definition $f'(x)$ is increasing on one side of x_1 so $f''(x)$ is positive on that side of x_1; and $f'(x)$ is decreasing on the other side of x_1 so $f''(x)$ is negative on that side of x_1. Since $f''(x)$ is continuous at x_1 it must be zero at x_1.   Q.E.D.

In Example 1, we suspect that the point $(6, 5)$ is an inflection point. It is clear from equation (37) that $f'(x)$ is decreasing for $x < 6$ and increasing for $x > 6$. Thus by definition 6, this point is indeed an inflection point. But then Theorem 10 asserts that $f''(6) = 0$, and this is certainly the case by inspection of equation (37).

The condition that $f''(x_1) = 0$ is a necessary condition for an inflection point but it is not a sufficient one. Consider for example the function

$y = x^4$, and its graph, shown in Fig. 15. Here we have $f'(x) = 4x^3$, $f''(x) = 12x^2$ and hence $f''(x) = 0$ if $x = 0$. But $(0, 0)$ is not an inflection point on the curve, because the tangent line in this case is just the x-axis, and it lies entirely on one side of the curve, except of course for the point of tangency.

This same curve illustrates another subtle point, namely the second derivative may vanish at points in an interval of concavity. Clearly the curve $y = x^4$ is concave upward for all x. But we cannot say that therefore $f''(x) > 0$ because in this example $f''(0) = 0$.

> THEOREM 11. *If the curve $y = f(x)$ is concave upward in $a \leq x \leq b$ and if the second derivative $f''(x)$ is continuous in $a \leq x \leq b$, then $f''(x) \geq 0$ for $a \leq x \leq b$. If the curve is concave downward then $f''(x) \leq 0$.*

PROOF OF THEOREM 11. It is sufficient to consider the case in which the curve is concave upward, for the second case can be handled in a similar manner, or (still better) we can apply the result of the first case to $g(x) = -f(x)$ which merely turns the curve upside down.

Suppose now that the curve is concave upward and that x_1 is some point in the interval other than the right end point b. We then select a second point x_2 to the right of x_1 but still in the interval so that we have $a \leq x_1 < x_2 \leq b$ (see Fig. 16). Let m be the slope of the chord joining $P_1(x_1, y_1)$ and $P_2(x_2, y_2)$ on the curve, and let m_1 and m_2 be the slopes of the tangent lines to the curve at P_1 and P_2 respectively. If $m_1 > m$ then the curve would lie partly above the chord. Similarly if $m_2 < m$, then the curve would lie partly above the chord. Since we are assuming that the curve is concave upward, these two inequalities cannot occur, so we must have (Fig. 16)

$$m_1 \leq m \leq m_2. \tag{38}$$

Actually the equality sign cannot occur in (38), but we do not need this fact, and since the proof is difficult we omit it. Now $m_1 = f'(x_1)$ and $m_2 = f'(x_2)$. If we apply the Mean Value Theorem to $f'(x)$, we find that there is some number ξ with $x_1 < \xi < x_2$ such that

$$f''(\xi) = \frac{f'(x_2) - f'(x_1)}{x_2 - x_1}. \tag{39}$$

But $f'(x_2) - f'(x_1) = m_2 - m_1 \geq 0$ and $x_2 - x_1 > 0$. Therefore, from (39), $f''(\xi) \geq 0$. Now let x_2 approach x_1. Since ξ is always between x_1 and x_2, we see that ξ approaches x_1 also. Now the second derivative $f''(\xi)$ is continuous and $f''(\xi) \geq 0$, hence $f''(x_1) \geq 0$. But x_1 is any point such that $a \leq x_1 < b$. The continuity of the second derivative shows that also at the right hand end point $f''(b) \geq 0$.   Q.E.D.

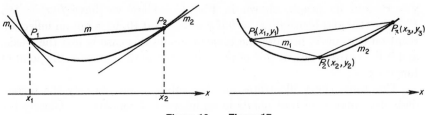

Figure 16   Figure 17

PROOF OF THEOREM 9.   Let P_1, P_2, P_3 be three points on the curve $y = f(x)$, with $x_1 < x_2 < x_3$.   If the point P_2 lies below the chord P_1P_3 then for the slopes (see Fig. 17) we have $m_1 < m_2$ or

$$\frac{y_2 - y_1}{x_2 - x_1} < \frac{y_3 - y_2}{x_3 - x_2}. \qquad (40)$$

But also conversely, if the inequality (40) is satisfied then $m_1 < m_2$ and the point P_2 lies below the chord P_1P_3.   Since $x_2 - x_1 > 0$ and $x_3 - x_2 > 0$ by hypothesis, we can multiply (40) by $(x_2 - x_1)(x_3 - x_2)$ and obtain

$$(x_3 - x_2)(y_2 - y_1) < (x_2 - x_1)(y_3 - y_2) \qquad (41)$$

or

$$0 < (x_2 - x_1)(y_3 - y_2) - (x_3 - x_2)(y_2 - y_1). \qquad (42)$$

Now the points P_1, P_2, P_3 are on the curve so $y_1 = f(x_1)$, $y_2 = f(x_2)$, and $y_3 = f(x_3)$.   Using the Mean Value Theorem, equation (28), we can write

$$y_2 - y_1 = f(x_2) - f(x_1) = (x_2 - x_1)f'(\xi_1), \qquad x_1 < \xi_1 < x_2,$$

and

$$y_3 - y_2 = f(x_3) - f(x_2) = (x_3 - x_2)f'(\xi_2), \qquad x_2 < \xi_2 < x_3.$$

Using these in (42) gives

$$0 < (x_2 - x_1)(x_3 - x_2)f'(\xi_2) - (x_3 - x_2)(x_2 - x_1)f'(\xi_1) \qquad (43)$$

$$0 < (x_2 - x_1)(x_3 - x_2)[f'(\xi_2) - f'(\xi_1)], \quad x_1 < \xi_1 < x_2 < \xi_2 < x_3. \qquad (44)$$

But we can apply the Mean Value Theorem again, this time to $f'(x)$, and find from equation (28) that

$$f'(\xi_2) - f'(\xi_1) = (\xi_2 - \xi_1)f''(\xi_3), \qquad \xi_1 < \xi_3 < \xi_2.$$

Then the righthand side of (44) can be written in the form

$$(x_2 - x_1)(x_3 - x_2)(\xi_2 - \xi_1)f''(\xi_3), \qquad x_1 < \xi_3 < x_3. \qquad (45)$$

Now suppose that in the interval $a \leqq x \leqq b$, $f''(x)$ is positive, and let P_1P_3 be any chord of the curve joining the points (x_1, y_1) and (x_3, y_3), with $a \leqq x_1 < x_3 \leqq b$.   Does this chord lie above the curve? Let $P_2(x_2, y_2)$

be any point on the curve with $x_1 < x_2 < x_3$. Then the expression (45) is positive since each of the four factors is positive. Thus we have (44). But from the inequality (44) we have (43), and hence (42), and hence (41) and finally (40). But the inequality (40) states that P_2 lies below the chord P_1P_3. Q.E.D.

EXERCISE 5

In problems 1 through 10 determine the intervals in which the curve is concave upward, concave downward, and locate all of the points of inflection.

1. $y = x^5$.   **2.** $y = x^6$.

3. $y = x^3 - 3x^2 - 9x + 10$.   **4.** $y = x^4 - 12x^3 + 48x^2 - 25$.

5. $y = \dfrac{1}{1 + x^2}$.   **6.** $y = \dfrac{10x}{1 + 3x^2}$.

7. $y = x + \dfrac{1}{x}$.   **8.** $y = 3x^2 - \dfrac{16}{x^2}$.

★9. $y = x^5(x - 6)^5$.   **★10.** $y = (x + 1)^3(x - 5)^6$.

9.   The second derivative test. The second derivative furnishes a convenient method for determining which of the critical points are relative maximum points, and which are relative minimum points. For if a curve is concave upward in a neighborhood of (x_1, y_1) and if $f'(x_1) = 0$ it is obvious that (x_1, y_1) is a relative minimum point. If the curve is concave downward, then (x_1, y_1) is obviously a relative maximum point. Stated in terms of the second derivative we have

> THEOREM 12. *Suppose that $f''(x)$ is continuous in a neighborhood of x_1 and that $f'(x_1) = 0$. If $f''(x_1)$ is positive then the point (x_1, y_1) is a relative minimum point for the curve, $y = f(x)$, where $y_1 = f(x_1)$. If $f''(x_1)$ is negative then the point (x_1, y_1) is a relative maximum point.*

This criterion is easy to recall if we keep in mind that $f''(x_1)$ positive means the bowl will hold water, and that $f''(x_1)$ negative means the bowl won't hold water.

EXAMPLE 1.   Locate the extreme points for the curve

$$y = x^4 - 4x^3 - 2x^2 + 12x - 5.$$

SOLUTION.   Differentiating gives

$$\frac{dy}{dx} = f'(x) = 4x^3 - 12x^2 - 4x + 12 = 4(x^3 - 3x^2 - x + 3).$$

Differentiating again gives

$$\frac{d^2y}{dx^2} = f''(x) = 4(3x^2 - 6x - 1).$$

The critical values for x are obtained by solving

$$f'(x) = 0, \quad \text{or} \quad x^3 - 3x^2 - x + 3 = 0.$$

Factoring gives

$$x^2(x - 3) - (x - 3) = (x^2 - 1)(x - 3) = (x - 1)(x + 1)(x - 3).$$

Thus the critical values for x are $x = -1$, 1, and 3. The corresponding y values are -14, 2, and -14 respectively. The second derivative computed for these values gives:

$$\begin{aligned}
f''(-1) &= 4\,[3 \times (-1)^2 - 6 \times (-1) - 1] = 32 > 0, \\
f''(1) &= 4\,[3 \times (1)^2 - 6 \times 1 - 1] = -16 < 0, \\
f''(3) &= 4\,[3 \times (3)^2 - 6 \times 3 - 1] = 32 > 0.
\end{aligned}$$

Therefore the two points $(-1, -14)$ and $(3, -14)$ are relative minimum points, and $(1, 2)$ is a relative maximum point.

EXAMPLE 2. Locate the extreme points for the curve $y = x^4$, shown in Fig. 15.

SOLUTION. Since x^4 is always positive or zero, and is zero only at $x = 0$, the curve has an absolute minimum at $x = 0$, as well as a relative minimum there.

If we apply the calculus, we find that $f'(x) = 4x^3$ and this is zero only at $x = 0$. Hence, the only extreme point is the minimum at $(0, 0)$. What does the second derivative test tell us? Since $f''(x) = 12x^2$, and this is zero at $x = 0$, the test gives no information, even though the point $(0, 0)$ is obviously a minimum point.

We conclude from this example that $f''(x_1) > 0$ and $f'(x_1) = 0$ together form a sufficient condition for a relative minimum at x_1, but not a necessary condition.

EXERCISE 6

Use the second derivative test, whenever it is applicable, to locate the relative maximum points and relative minimum points, for each of the functions given in Exercise 5.

10. Applications of the theory of extremes. So far we have been concerned with maximum and minimum points on a curve. Now there are many quite natural problems that arise in the physical world that can be reduced to the problem of finding a maximum or minimum point on a curve. Thus we are in a position to solve such problems quite simply.

We first give a number of concrete examples, and then we will try to formulate some general principles based on the experience gained through the examples.

EXAMPLE 1.   Find two numbers whose sum is 24 and whose product is as large as possible.

SOLUTION.   Let x and y be the numbers.   Then the conditions of the problem state that

$$x + y = 24. \tag{46}$$

If we let P denote the product, then we are to maximize

$$P = xy. \tag{47}$$

One might expect to begin by differentiating P, since we seek its maximum. But be careful! P depends on *two* variables, and so far our calculus has all been developed for a *single* independent variable.   So we must first alter P in some way so that it will depend on just one variable.   Equation (46) gives us the means to do this.   Solving (46) for y we have $y = 24 - x$.   Substituting in (47) gives

$$P = x(24 - x) = 24x - x^2, \tag{48}$$

a function of a single variable.   Differentiating twice gives

$$\frac{dP}{dx} = 24 - 2x, \qquad \frac{d^2P}{dx^2} = -2.$$

Clearly the derivative is zero when $24 - 2x = 0$, or when $x = 12$.   Since the second derivative is negative we have located a maximum point.   When $x = 12$, equation (46) gives $y = 12$.   Thus the point $(12, 144)$ is a relative maximum point on the curve of equation (48).   But more than that it is an absolute maximum.   We leave the proof of this last statement to the student.   Thus the maximum product is 144, and it occurs when 24 is split into 12 and 12.

EXAMPLE 2.   A farmer with a field adjacent to a straight river wishes to fence off a rectangular area for grazing.   If no fence is needed along the river, and he has available 1600 ft of fencing, what should be the dimensions of the field in order that it have a maximum area?

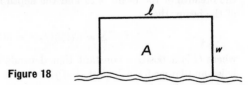

Figure 18

SOLUTION.   Let l and w denote the length and width of the field respectively, and let A be the area (see Fig. 18).   Using all of the fencing available gives

$$l + 2w = 1600. \tag{49}$$

We are to maximize

$$A = lw. \tag{50}$$

This is a function of two variables, but solving (49) for l we get $l = 1600 - 2w$, and using this in (50) gives

$$A = w(1600 - 2w) = 1600w - 2w^2.$$

Then

$$\frac{dA}{dw} = 1600 - 4w, \qquad \frac{d^2A}{dw^2} = -4.$$

The derivative is zero at $w = 400$, and the second derivative is negative, so we have a maximum. The dimension of the field should be 400 ft by 800 ft and the maximum area is $400 \times 800 = 320,000$ ft².

EXAMPLE 3. The strength of a rectangular beam varies directly as the breadth and the square of the depth. What are the dimensions of the strongest rectangular beam that can be cut from a cylindrical log of radius r.

SOLUTION. We place the cross section of the log on a rectangular coordinate system as shown in Fig. 19. Let (x, y) denote the coordinates of the point P

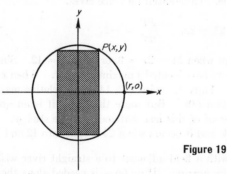

Figure 19

in the first quadrant where the corner of the rectangle lies on the circle. Then the breadth of the beam is $2x$ and the depth is $2y$. If S denotes the strength of the beam, then

$$S = C(2x)(2y)^2 = 8Cxy^2 \tag{51}$$

where C is a positive constant that depends on the type of wood (small for balsa and larger for oak) but is of no interest here. Since P lies on the circle $x^2 + y^2 = r^2$ we have

$$y^2 = r^2 - x^2 \tag{52}$$

and substituting this in equation (51) we find

$$S = 8Cx(r^2 - x^2) = 8C(xr^2 - x^3).$$

Differentiating twice gives

$$\frac{dS}{dx} = 8C(r^2 - 3x^2), \qquad \frac{d^2S}{dx^2} = -48Cx.$$

The first derivative is zero for $x = \pm r/\sqrt{3}$. The negative value for x may be rejected because it has no physical meaning in our problem, since the breadth $2x$ must be positive. At $x = r/\sqrt{3}$, the second derivative is negative so this value gives the maximum strength. For this x we find

$$y = \sqrt{r^2 - x^2} = \sqrt{r^2 - \frac{r^2}{3}} = \sqrt{\frac{2}{3}}\, r.$$

The breadth is therefore $2r/\sqrt{3}$ and the depth is $2\sqrt{2/3}\, r$, for a beam of maximum strength.

EXAMPLE 4. A piece of wire of length L is to be cut into two pieces, and each piece bent so as to form a square. How should the wire be cut if the sum of the areas enclosed by the two squares is to be a maximum?

Figure 20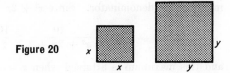

SOLUTION. Let x and y be the lengths of a side of the two squares (Fig. 20). Then for the total area we have

$$A = x^2 + y^2. \tag{53}$$

Since all the material comes from the given wire the perimeter of the two figures must give L so

$$L = 4x + 4y. \tag{54}$$

Solving (54) for x we find $x = L/4 - y$ so equation (53) becomes

$$A = \left(\frac{L}{4} - y\right)^2 + y^2 = \frac{L^2}{16} - \frac{L}{2}y + 2y^2. \tag{55}$$

Differentiating twice gives

$$\frac{dA}{dy} = -\frac{L}{2} + 4y, \qquad \frac{d^2A}{dy^2} = 4.$$

The derivative is zero at $y = L/8$, but this time the second derivative is positive so we have a *minimum* point. In other words if we cut the wire in half and form a square from each piece, the squares will each have sides of length $L/8$ and the total area enclosed will be as *small* as possible. This minimum area is $2(L/8)^2$ or $L^2/32$. To find a maximum value we observe that under the conditions of the problem $0 \leqq y \leqq L/4$. By symmetry it suffices to check one end point, say $y = L/4$. Then $A = (L/4)^2 = L^2/16$. This is the maximum value of A given by (55) for y in this interval. But the problem states that the wire is to be cut into two pieces. If we adhere strictly to the statement of the problem and insist on two pieces then the problem has *no solution*. For no matter how small we make the x square, we can increase the total area by making x still smaller and y still larger because for y near $L/4$ the derivative dA/dy is positive.

EXAMPLE 5.   Find the maximum value of the function

$$f(x) = \frac{10}{x^2 + 2x + 3}. \tag{56}$$

SOLUTION.   In the first three examples, the calculus was quite helpful. In example 4, the calculus followed blindly led to an erroneous result.   In this example we do not even need the calculus.   For the denominator we can write

$$x^2 + 2x + 3 = x^2 + 2x + 1 + 2 = (x + 1)^2 + 2 \geq 2 \tag{57}$$

because $(x + 1)^2$ is never negative. The last equality sign in (57) occurs if and only if $x = -1$. But to maximize $f(x)$ defined by (56) it is sufficient to minimize the denominator.   Since $x^2 + 2x + 3 \geq 2$, then

$$\frac{10}{x^2 + 2x + 3} \leq \frac{10}{2} = 5$$

and this maximum is attained when $x = -1$, and only for that value of x. We have solved a maximum problem without the calculus.

Let us summarize in a general form the procedure used in the first four examples.

STEP 1.   *If Q is the quantity to be maximized or minimized, find an expression for Q involving one or possibly more variables.*

In our examples this expression is given by equations (47), (50), (51), and (53).

STEP 2.   *If the expression for Q involves more than one variable, search for other equations relating the variables.   Use these equations to reduce Q to a function of a single variable.*

In our examples, equations (46), (49), (52), and (54), play the role of auxiliary equations which are used to simplify the expressions for P, A, S, and A respectively.

STEP 3.   *If Q = Q(x) compute the first and second derivatives Q'(x) and Q''(x).   Find the critical values of x; that is, the values of x for which Q'(x) = 0. Then use the second derivative test on each critical point to determine if it gives a relative minimum or a relative maximum.*

In all of these physical problems there is a natural interval for each of the variables, and it is understood that the variables assume only such values as are physically meaningful.   In most problems it is physically obvious that the extreme values exist, and occur for special values inside the natural interval of the variable. But we must be careful, because as we saw in Example 4, an extreme value may occur at the end point of an interval. Hence in all problems one should examine the end points.

To illustrate these vague and general remarks about the natural interval, let us reexamine our examples.

In Example 1, $x + y = 24$ and we are to maximize the product $P = xy$. Here x and y could be any real numbers, but since the product is negative if either x or y are negative (they can't both be negative) it is obvious that no harm is done if we insist that x and y be both non-negative. Then the natural interval is $0 \leq x \leq 24$ for x, and the same for y. At the end points the product $P = 0$, so the end points cannot furnish a maximum.

In Example 2 the length and width of the field must both be positive so the natural intervals are $0 < l < 1600$, and $0 < w < 800$. At either end point of these two intervals, the area, as given by equation (50), is zero.

In Example 3 the natural intervals for the breadth $2x$ and depth $2y$ of the beam are $0 < 2x < 2r$ and $0 < 2y < 2r$ respectively. At either end point of these two intervals $S = 0$.

In Example 4 the natural intervals for the variables x and y are $0 < x < L/4$ and $0 < y < L/4$. But this time the expression to be maximized, $x^2 + y^2$, has a larger value at either end point of these intervals than at any interior point. But since the end points are not admitted in the problem, the problem as stated has no solution.

STEP 4. *Determine the natural intervals for the variables involved in the problem, from the physical meaning of the variables. Check the values of Q at the end points of these natural intervals.*

EXERCISE 7

1. A square piece of tin 18 in. on each side is to be made into a box, without a top, by cutting a square from each corner, and folding up the flaps to form the

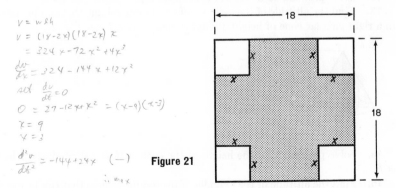

Figure 21

sides (see Fig. 21). What size corners should be cut in order that the volume of the box be as large as possible?

2. Solve problem 1 if the given piece of tin is a rectangle 24 in. by 45 in.

3. Prove that of all rectangles inscribed in a given fixed circle (see Fig. 19) the square has the largest area.

4. Prove that if we maximize the perimeter of the rectangle instead of the area in problem 3, the solution is still the square.

*5. A generalization of problem 4. Let l and w be the length and width of a rectangle inscribed in a circle of fixed radius, and suppose that we are to find the rectangle that maximizes the quantity

$$P = l^n + w^n$$

where n is some fixed positive number. Prove that if $n < 2$, then the square makes P a maximum, but if $n > 2$, then the maximum is given by the degenerate rectangle in which l or w is the diameter of the circle while the other dimension is zero. Notice that if $n = 2$ then P is the same for all rectangles.

6. The stiffness of a rectangular beam varies directly with the breadth and the cube of the depth. Find the dimensions of the stiffest beam that can be cut from a cylindrical log of radius R.

7. Three planks each 12 in. wide are made into a trough. If the cross section of the trough is in the form of a trapezoid, how far apart should the top of the planks be set in order that the cross section have a maximum area. $A = \frac{1}{2}(B_1 + B_2)h$

8. Find the maximum of the area for all circular sectors of given fixed perimeter P. *Hint:* Use radian measure for the angle of the sector.

9. Find two positive numbers whose product is 100 and whose sum is as small as possible.

*10. A closed cylindrical can is to contain a certain fixed volume V. What should be the ratio of the height to the radius of the can in order that the can requires the least amount of material, i.e., in order that the surface area be a minimum.

11. A closed rectangular box has a square base and has a fixed volume. What is the ratio of the height to a side of the base, in order that the surface area of the box is a minimum.

12. Solve problem 11 if the box is open on top.

13. Find the altitude of the cylinder of maximum volume that can be inscribed in a right circular cone of height 12 and radius of base 7 (see Fig. 22).

Figure 22

14. Solve problem 13 if the height of the cone is H and the radius of the base is R.

15. Find the altitude of the cylinder of maximum volume that can be inscribed in a sphere of radius R.

16. Find the altitude of the cone of maximum volume that can be inscribed in a sphere of radius R.

★**17.** Prove that if a right circular cone is circumscribed about a sphere the volume of the cone is greater than or equal to twice the volume of the sphere.

18. Find two positive numbers x and y such that their sum is 60 and the product xy^3 is a maximum.

19. Find two positive numbers x and y such that their sum is 35 and the product x^2y^5 is a maximum. $S = x+y = 35$ $P = x^2 y^2 = x^2(35-x)$

★**20.** Generalization of problems 18 and 19. Let p and q be fixed positive numbers. Show that among all pairs of positive numbers x and y such that $x + y = S$, the maximum of the product $x^p y^q$ is obtained when $x = pS/(p + q)$ and $y = qS/(p + q)$.

21. Find two positive numbers whose sum is 16 and the sum of whose cubes is a maximum.

22. Solve problem 21, if we are to minimize the sum of the cubes.

23. Find two numbers whose sum is 18 and for which the sum of the fourth power of the first and the square of the second is a minimum.

24. Find the point on the parabola $y = x^2$ that is nearest to the point $(10, 2)$.

25. Find the points on the parabola $8y = x^2 - 40$ which are closest to the origin. What is the radius of a circle with center at the origin that is tangent to this parabola?

26. Plans for a new super market require a floor area of 14,400 square feet. The supermarket is to be rectangular in shape with three solid brick walls, and a very fancy all glass front. If glass costs 1.88 times as much as the brick wall per linear foot, what should be the dimensions of the building so that the cost of materials for the walls is a minimum.

27. Suppose that in the supermarket of problem 26 the heat loss across the glass front is seven times as great as the heat loss across the brick per square foot. Neglecting the heat loss across the roof and through the floor, what should be the dimensions of the building so that the heat loss is a minimum.

★**28.** Suppose that the architects for the supermarket of problems 26 and 27 wish to take account of the heat losses across the floor and ceiling and that the ceiling is to be 15 ft. high. Suppose further that the rate of heat loss per square foot of ceiling is K_1 times the rate of heat loss per square foot of brick wall, and that for the floor the multiplier is K_2. Find the dimensions of the supermarket that minimize the heat loss.

29. Let us call space in an attic livable if a 6-ft man can stand upright without

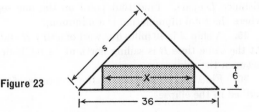

Figure 23

bumping his head. As indicated in Fig. 23 let s be the slant height of the roof and suppose that the cost of building the roof is proportional to the material used and this in turn is proportional to s. If the base is 36 feet find the slope of the roof that minimizes the cost per square foot of livable attic space. *Hint:* Show that this amounts to minimizing s/x.

30. A certain handbill requires 150 sq. in. for the printed message and must have a 3-in. margin at the top and bottom and a 2-in. margin on each side. Find the dimensions of this handbill, if the amount of paper used is a minimum.

★31. A certain stained glass window consists of a rectangle together with a matching semicircle set on the upper base of the rectangle. If the perimeter of the window is fixed at P, find the altitude of the rectangle and the radius of the semicircle for the window that will let in the most light (have maximum area).

32. A man at a point A on one shore of a lake 6 miles wide with parallel shore lines, wishes to reach a point C on the other side 13 miles along the bank of the lake from a point B directly opposite the point A. If he can row 4 miles per hour and walk 5 miles per hour and if he sets out by boat, find how far from B he should land in order to make the trip as quickly as possible. How long does the trip take? How much longer does it take if he rows first to B and then walks to C?

33. If light travels from a point A to a point P on a plane mirror and is then reflected to a point B, the most careful measurements seem to show that the angle of incidence equals the angle of reflection. With the lettering of Fig. 24

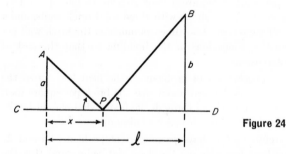

Figure 24

this states that $\angle CPA = \angle DPB$. Make the assumption that light always takes the shortest path (in air) and then prove this law by showing that the path APB is shortest when $a/x = b/(l - x)$.

34. The illumination at a point P due to a light source is directly proportional to the strength of the source and inversely proportional to the square of the distance of P from the source. Two light sources of strength A and B respectively are distance L apart. Find that point on the line segment joining the two sources where the total illumination is a minimum.

35. A ship A is 40 miles due west of a ship B and A is sailing east at 12 mi/hour. At the same time B is sailing north at 16 mi/hour. Find the minimum distance between the ships.

36. Find the dimensions of the rectangle of maximum area that can be inscribed in the ellipse

$$\frac{x^2}{a^2} + \frac{y^2}{b^2} = 1.$$

11.   Differentials. We have already mentioned that the symbolism

$$\frac{dy}{dx},\tag{58}$$

introduced for the derivative, looks like a fraction, but is not one.   It has the appearance of a fraction, and in certain circumstances actually acts like one.   The two most important cases are:

(a)
$$\frac{dy}{du}\frac{du}{dx} = \frac{dy}{d\!\!\!/u}\frac{d\!\!\!/u}{dx} = \frac{dy}{dx}$$

where a valid formula for the derivative of a function of a function is obtained by cancellation as in a fraction, and

(b)
$$\frac{dx}{dy} = \frac{1}{\dfrac{dy}{dx}}$$

where a valid formula for the derivative of the function $x = g(y)$ that is the inverse of the function $y = f(x)$, can be obtained by manipulating as if the derivative were a fraction.

Our present objective is to give a meaning to the pieces of (58), namely a meaning to dy and dx so that their quotient is indeed the derivative $f'(x)$.

Since the derivative $f'(x)$ is the limit value of the ratio $\Delta y/\Delta x$, the difference of these two quantities is tending to zero as $\Delta x \to 0$.   Let ϵ denote this difference.   In other words let

$$\frac{\Delta y}{\Delta x} = f'(x) + \epsilon, \qquad \Delta x \neq 0.\tag{59}$$

where $\epsilon \to 0$ as $\Delta x \to 0$.   Multiplying through by Δx gives

$$\Delta y = f'(x)\Delta x + \epsilon\Delta x.\tag{60}$$

DEFINITION 7.   *The quantity Δx may be any nonzero change in the independent variable x, and is called the differential of x, and written dx.   In symbols $dx = \Delta x$.*

To define the differential of the dependent variable y, we drop the last term in (60) and denote the remaining part by dy instead of Δy.   Thus $dy = f'(x)\,\Delta x$ gives the differential of y.   But since $\Delta x = dx$ this is equivalent to

DEFINITION 8.   *Let y be a differentiable function of x.   Then dy, the differential of the dependent variable, is given by* (mul. both sides by dx)

$$dy = f'(x)\,dx.\tag{61}$$

Why make such a definition? Answer: Now dy and dx each have a meaning and by (61) we see that their quotient is indeed

$$\frac{dy}{dx} = f'(x)$$

the derivative of y with respect to x.

But more important dy, the differential of y, is very close to Δy, the actual change in y. For comparing equations (60) and (61) yields

$$\Delta y - dy = \epsilon \Delta x \tag{62}$$

and the right side of (62) is tending to zero more rapidly than either Δy or dy on the left side of (62). In fact if we divide both sides of (62) by Δx (which is the same as dx) we have

$$\frac{\Delta y}{\Delta x} - \frac{dy}{dx} = \epsilon. \tag{63}$$

On the left side $\Delta y/\Delta x$ tends to a limit not necessarily zero, while the right side tends to zero.

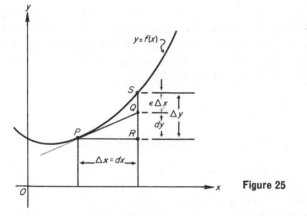

Figure 25

The various quantities are shown graphically in Fig. 25. Here $f'(x)$ is the slope of the line PQ and $\Delta x = dx$ is the adjacent side in the right triangle QPR. Hence from trigonometry $dy = f'(x)dx$ is just RQ, the side opposite. Briefly:

Δy *is the change in y along the curve*, $\Delta y = RS$; dy *is the change in y along the line tangent to the curve*, $dy = RQ$.

Although in Fig. 25, $\epsilon \Delta x$ appears to be of the same order of magnitude as Δx or Δy, it actually tends to zero much more rapidly than Δx or Δy. We illustrate this point in

EXAMPLE 1.   For the function $y = x^2$, find Δy and dy (a) in general, (b) at $x = 3$; (c) at $x = 3$, compute Δy and dy for $\Delta x = .1, .01,$ and $.001$.

SOLUTION.   (a) If $y = x^2$ then at $x + \Delta x$ we have

$$y + \Delta y = (x + \Delta x)^2 = x^2 + 2x\Delta x + (\Delta x)^2.$$

Subtracting $y \qquad\qquad\qquad = x^2 \qquad\qquad\qquad\qquad$ ← $f(x+\Delta x) - f(x)$

$$\Delta y \qquad\qquad = \qquad 2x\Delta x + (\Delta x)^2.$$

By contrast $\qquad dy = f'(x)dx = 2xdx = 2x\Delta x.$

Finally $\qquad\qquad \Delta y - dy \qquad = 2x\Delta x + (\Delta x)^2 - 2x\Delta x = (\Delta x)^2.$

So that in this case $\qquad\qquad \epsilon\Delta x \; = \; (\Delta x)^2$

(b)   In particular at $x = 3$, we have $\Delta y = 6\Delta x + (\Delta x)^2$, $dy = 6\Delta x$, and $\Delta y - dy = (\Delta x)^2$.

(c)   The results for specific values of Δx are presented in the following table

Δx	$\Delta y = 6\Delta x + (\Delta x)^2$	$dy = 6\Delta x$	$\Delta y - dy = \epsilon\Delta x$
.1	.61	.6	.01
.01	.0601	.06	.0001
.001	.006001	.006	.000001

It is clear that the entries in the fourth column are much smaller than the corresponding entries in the second or third columns.   This means that for approximations it is frequently satisfactory to replace Δy by dy if Δx is small.

EXAMPLE 2.   Find an approximate value for $\sqrt[3]{26.5}$, without using tables.

SOLUTION.   We observe that 26.5 is close to 27, a perfect cube, so this suggests the use of differentials.   This will tell us approximately how much $\sqrt[3]{x}$ is changing as x changes from 27 to 26.5.   Since x is decreasing, we will have $dx = -.5$ in this case.   Set

$$y = f(x) = \sqrt[3]{x} = x^{1/3}.$$

Then

$$\frac{dy}{dx} = f'(x) = \frac{1}{3}x^{-2/3} = \frac{1}{3\sqrt[3]{x^2}},$$

$$dy = f'(x)dx = \frac{dx}{3\sqrt[3]{x^2}}.$$

Setting $x = 27$, and $dx = -.5$ we have

$$dy = \frac{-.5}{3\sqrt[3]{27^2}} = \frac{-.5}{3 \times 9} = -\frac{1}{54}.$$

We use the symbol $\approx$ to denote approximate equality.   Then

$$\sqrt[3]{x + \Delta x} = \sqrt[3]{26.5} = \sqrt[3]{27} + \Delta y \approx \sqrt[3]{27} + dy$$

$$\approx 3 - \frac{1}{54} \approx 3 - .0185$$

$$\approx 2.9815.$$

The correct value of $\sqrt[3]{26.5}$ to six significant figures is 2.98137.   The method of differentials gave the first four figures correctly, and this is quite good. The error here is less than .0002.

It would be nice to have some general formulas that tell us how large the error may be whenever this method is used.   Such formulas exist but are a little too complicated to present this early in the game.

Now that differentials have been defined, we can have differential formulas as well as derivative formulas.   For example, the formula

$$\frac{d}{dx} x^2 = 2x$$

can now be written as

$$dx^2 = 2x\,dx.$$

Each formula for differentiating an expression gives rise to a corresponding differential formula, by multiplying through by dx.   Here are the differentiation formulas obtained so far in this book together with the corresponding differential formulas.

DIFFERENTIATIONS   DIFFERENTIALS

$$\frac{dc}{dx} = 0. \qquad\qquad\qquad dc = 0. \qquad\qquad (64)$$

$$\frac{dx^n}{dx} = nx^{n-1}. \qquad\qquad dx^n = nx^{n-1}dx. \qquad (65)$$

$$\frac{dau}{dx} = a\frac{du}{dx}. \qquad\qquad dau = a\,du. \qquad\qquad (66)$$

$$\frac{du^n}{dx} = nu^{n-1}\frac{du}{dx}. \qquad\qquad du^n = nu^{n-1}du. \qquad (67)$$

$$\frac{d(u+v)}{dx} = \frac{du}{dx} + \frac{dv}{dx}. \qquad d(u+v) = du + dv. \qquad (68)$$

$$\frac{d(uv)}{dx} = u\frac{dv}{dx} + v\frac{du}{dx}. \qquad d(uv) = u\,dv + v\,du. \qquad (69)$$

$$\frac{d\left(\dfrac{u}{v}\right)}{dx} = \frac{v\dfrac{du}{dx} - u\dfrac{dv}{dx}}{v^2}. \qquad d\left(\frac{u}{v}\right) = \frac{v\,du - u\,dv}{v^2}. \qquad (70)$$

EXERCISE 8

In problems 1 through 5 obtain expressions for (a) Δy, and (b) $\Delta y - dy$. Show that in each case $(\Delta x)^2$ is a factor of $\Delta y - dy$.

1. $y = 2x^3$.

2. $y = 3x - x^2$.

3. $y = \dfrac{1}{x^2}$.

4. $y = \dfrac{x}{10 + x}$.

5. $y = 3x^2 + 6x + 15$.

In problems 6 through 14 use differentials to find an approximate value for the given quantity. Give each answer to four significant figures.

6. $\sqrt{104}$.

7. $\sqrt{65}$.

8. $\sqrt[3]{65}$.

9. $\sqrt[6]{65}$.

10. $\sqrt[3]{999}$.

11. $\sqrt{141}$.

12. $\sqrt{26.5}$.

13. $\sqrt{4.12}$.

14. $\sqrt{.037}$.

15. The approximations are good, only if Δx is small. Find $\sqrt{111}$ first by regarding 111 as near 100, and second by regarding 111 as near 121, and compare the results. Tables give $\sqrt{111} = 10.5356\cdots$.

16. The derivative of the formula $A = \pi r^2$ for the area of a circle with respect to r gives $2\pi r$, the circumference of the circle. Explain this on the basis of differentials. In the same way explain why the derivative of $\frac{4}{3}\pi r^3$ gives $4\pi r^2$, the surface area of a sphere.

17. The side of a cube is by measurement 8 in. long. If this measurement is subject on each edge to an error of $\pm .05$ in. find an approximation for the maximum error that is made in computing the volume of the cube.

4

INTEGRATION

1.   Objective. Starting from the fact that the area of a rectangle is the product of the lengths of its sides, we soon learn how to find the area of a parallelogram, a triangle, and then the area of any polygon by decomposing it into the sum of a number of triangles.   Thus we are able to find the area of any plane figure, as long as it is bounded by a finite number of straight line segments (for example the shaded area shown in Fig. 1).

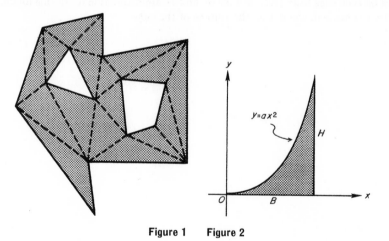

Figure 1   Figure 2

But what shall we do if a part of the boundary of the figure is a curve? For example what is the area of the shaded region shown in Fig. 2, which is bounded by the parabola $y = ax^2$, the x-axis, and the vertical line $x = B$? Fantastic as it may seem this problem was solved more than two thousand years ago by Archimedes (287–212 B.C.) by a very ingenious method.   In

128

fact he showed that $A = BH/3$. Unfortunately the method of Archimedes could not be applied to figures bounded by other curves, and so this general problem of finding the area of a region bounded wholly or in part by curves continued to plague mathematicians for the next eighteen hundred years. One can well imagine the tremendous excitement that was generated when almost simultaneously Newton (1642–1727) and Leibniz (1646–1716) showed how the calculus can be used in a systematic way to obtain the area bounded by any curve or set of curves. Is it any wonder then that in 1669 Isaac Barrow resigned his position as a professor of mathematics at Cambridge, in favor of his student Isaac Newton?

Our purpose in this chapter is to learn just how the calculus is used to find areas. Further we will see that finding areas of regions bounded by curves is more than just a game. Many very practical problems can be reduced to equivalent problems in finding the area of a region bounded by curves. Such, for example, is the problem of finding the total force on the side of a dam due to the water in the reservoir.

2.   The indefinite integral.   We have already mentioned in Chapter 3 that integration is the inverse of differentiation. In other words given

$$\frac{dy}{dx} = f(x) \tag{1}$$

we are to find a function $y = F(x)$ such that on differentiating $F(x)$ we obtain $f(x)$. When we find such a function $F(x)$ it is called an integral of $f(x)$. To introduce a suitable notation for this concept we first write (1) in the differential form

$$dy = f(x)dx \tag{2}$$

and then prefix an integral sign[1] $\int$ in front of both sides, obtaining

$$\int dy = \int f(x)dx. \tag{3}$$

The sign $\int$ is read "the integral of" and merely means to find a function whose differential is the quantity standing after the sign. The function $f(x)$ in (3) is called the *integrand*.

For example, given

$$dy = x^3dx,$$

---

[1] The integral sign is really an elongated S and this symbol was actually used for an S several hundred years ago. The letter S or $\int$ is intended to remind us of the word sum, and as we will learn in section 6, the integral is the limit of a certain sum.

then on integrating both sides we would have

$$\int dy = \int x^3 \, dx \tag{4}$$

$$y = \frac{x^4}{4} + C. \tag{5}$$

The left side of (5) is y because the differential of y is dy and the right side of (5) is $x^4/4 + C$ because the derivative with respect to x of this function is x^3, and so its differential is $x^3 dx$.

Now the differential of any constant C is zero, so the integral is not uniquely determined. To obtain the most general integral we must add an arbitrary constant C. Because of the indefiniteness of this constant, the integral in (3) is called an *indefinite integral*. Later in section 4 we will meet a related concept called the definite integral.

When we perform the indicated integration in equation (4), why not add a constant to each side? The two constants to be added, one on each side may be different, so we must use different symbols for these two constants. Let C_1 and C_2 denote these constants. Then we obtain from (4)

$$y + C_1 = \frac{x^4}{4} + C_2 \tag{6}$$

or

$$y = \frac{x^4}{4} + (C_2 - C_1) \tag{7}$$

$$= \frac{x^4}{4} + C$$

where $C = C_2 - C_1$ is just another constant. Thus (7) and hence (6) are both equivalent to (5), and so there is no advantage or generality to be gained by adding a constant on both sides.

EXAMPLE 1. It is known that a certain curve passes through the point (3, 38) and has slope $m = 2x^3 - x + 5$ for each x. Find the equation of the curve.

SOLUTION. From the conditions of the problem

$$m = \frac{dy}{dx} = 2x^3 - x + 5.$$

Then

$$dy = (2x^3 - x + 5) \, dx.$$

Integrating both sides of this equation gives

$$\int dy = \int (2x^3 - x + 5) \, dx$$

$$y = \frac{x^4}{2} - \frac{x^2}{2} + 5x + C. \tag{8}$$

Since the curve passes through (3, 38) these values must satisfy the equation. Substituting $x = 3$, and $y = 38$ in (8) gives

$$38 = \frac{81}{2} - \frac{9}{2} + 15 + C = 51 + C.$$

Whence $C = 38 - 51 = -13$. Using this in (8) we find that the solution to our problem is

$$y = \frac{x^4}{2} - \frac{x^2}{2} + 5x - 13.$$

The side condition that the curve pass through the point (3, 38) enables us to determine the value of C. Thus we can select from the infinity of indefinite integrals (8), the particular one fitting the conditions of the problem. In any natural problem such side conditions always appear. Frequently these side conditions are called "initial conditions." The idea is that the curve "starts" from the point (3, 38) even though in reality it may "start" somewhere else, or "start" may have no real meaning.

We have already proved (Theorem 8, Chapter 3) that if two functions have the same derivative, then they differ by a constant. This means that if we are integrating a function $f(x)$ and find one suitable integral $F(x)$, then any other integral must differ from $F(x)$ by at most a constant. Thus we obtain the most general integral merely by adding an arbitrary constant C to $F(x)$. Restating this important theorem in terms of integrals we have

THEOREM 1. *If $F'(x) = f(x)$ then*

$$\int f(x)dx = F(x) + C. \tag{9}$$

Since integration is the inverse of differentiation every differentiation formula may be written as an integral formula. For ready reference we collect the important ones below. It may at first seem like a burdensome task to be asked to memorize all of these new formulas, equations (10) through (15), but the perceptive student will quickly recognize that these are all old friends, just dressed up in a new disguise, so that memorization is hardly any trouble at all. For reasons which will appear later, we use the letter u in place of x in certain of the formulas.

$$\int dx = x + C. \tag{10}$$

$$\int du = u + C. \tag{11}$$

$$\int Cf(x)dx = C\int f(x)dx. \tag{12}$$

$$\int dy = \int y^0 \, dy = y' = y$$

$$\int (f(x) + g(x))dx = \int f(x)dx + \int g(x)dx. \tag{13}$$

$$\int x^n dx = \frac{x^{n+1}}{n+1} + C, \qquad \text{if } n \neq -1. \tag{14}$$

$$\int u^n du = \frac{u^{n+1}}{n+1} + C, \qquad \text{if } n \neq -1. \tag{15}$$

The formulas (10) and (11) are really identical. We merely want to emphasize that there is nothing magic about the letter x. Any letter is suitable to indicate a variable quantity.

Formulas (12) and (13) are just the integral forms of the differentiation formulas

$$\frac{d}{dx} C F(x) = C \frac{d}{dx} F(x)$$

and

$$\frac{d}{dx} [F(x) + G(x)] = \frac{d}{dx} F(x) + \frac{d}{dx} G(x),$$

where $\frac{d}{dx} F(x) = f(x)$ and $\frac{d}{dx} G(x) = g(x)$.

The student will observe that in (14) and (15) the value $n = -1$ is forbidden. For if $n = -1$, then the denominator on the righthand side is zero, and the formula is meaningless. We will see that the case $n = -1$, i.e., the determination of the integral

$$\int \frac{dx}{x}$$

is one of the most fascinating little chapters in the calculus. But this must be reserved for Chapter 8.

EXAMPLE 2.   Find the indefinite integrals

a. $\displaystyle\int \left(7x^3 - \frac{3}{x^2} \right) dx,$ and   b. $\displaystyle\int (x^2 + 6)^{3/2} x \, dx.$

SOLUTION.   For (a) using formulas (13), (12), and (14) in turn we have

$$\int \left(7x^3 - \frac{3}{x^2} \right) dx = \int 7x^3 \, dx + \int - \frac{3}{x^2} \, dx$$

$$= 7 \int x^3 \, dx - 3 \int x^{-2} \, dx$$

$$= 7 \frac{x^4}{4} - 3 \frac{x^{-2+1}}{-2+1} + C$$

$$= \frac{7}{4} x^4 + \frac{3}{x} + C.$$

The integral (b) does not fit any of the standard formulas. However if we select u properly it turns out that (b) can be made to fit formula (15). To do this set $u = x^2 + 6$. Then $du = 2x\,dx$. In (b) we have a term $x\,dx$, and this is almost du. In fact it is $du/2$. With these substitutions we have

$$\int (x^2 + 6)^{3/2}\,x\,dx = \int u^{3/2}\frac{du}{2} = \frac{1}{2}\int u^{3/2}\,du.$$

Using formula (15)

$$\frac{1}{2}\int u^{3/2}\,du = \frac{1}{2}\left(\frac{u^{5/2}}{5/2}\right) + C = \frac{1}{2}\left(\frac{2}{5}\,u^{5/2}\right) + C.$$

Replacing u by $x^2 + 6$, we then have

$$\int (x^2 + 6)^{3/2}\,x\,dx = \frac{1}{5}(x^2 + 6)^{5/2} + C.$$

EXAMPLE 3. A differential equation is any equation relating variables and their derivatives. Solve the differential equation

$$\frac{dy}{dx} = y^2 x^2 + \frac{y^2}{x^2}.$$

SOLUTION. In this case the variables x and y can be separated, by factoring the right side. This gives

$$\frac{dy}{dx} = y^2\left(x^2 + \frac{1}{x^2}\right)$$

$$\frac{dy}{y^2} = \left(x^2 + \frac{1}{x^2}\right)dx.$$

Integrating both sides of this equation gives

$$-\frac{1}{y} = \frac{x^3}{3} - \frac{1}{x} + C$$

$$y = -\frac{1}{\dfrac{x^3}{3} - \dfrac{1}{x} + C}$$

$$y = \frac{3x}{3 - x^4 - 3Cx}. \tag{16}$$

Observe that since C is an arbitrary constant, we could replace C by $-C/3$, which is just as arbitrary. Then we could write the solution of our differential equation as

$$y = \frac{3x}{3 - x^4 + Cx}. \tag{17}$$

Equation (17) is just as much a solution as (16) but the symbol C does not have the same value in the two equations.

EXERCISE 1

In problems 1 through 12 find the indefinite integral.

1. $\displaystyle\int (1000x - 5x^4)dx.$ = $1000\int x\,dx - 5\int dx$

2. $\displaystyle\int (\pi x^2 + \sqrt{x})dx.$ = $\pi\int x^2\,dx + \int x^{1/2}\,dx$

3. $\displaystyle\int \left(\sqrt{2}\,x^7 - \frac{3}{2}x^2 + \frac{1}{x^5}\right)dx.$

4. $\displaystyle\int (2x + 7)^3\,dx.$

5. $\displaystyle\int (2x + 7)^{513}\,dx.$ let $u = (2x+7)$ $du = 2\,dx$ $dy = \frac{du}{2}$ $\int u^{513}\frac{du}{2} = \frac{1}{2}\int u^{513}\,du$

6. $\displaystyle\int (1 - 7x)^{1/2}\,dx.$

7. $\displaystyle\int (3 + 11x^2)^{5/2}\,x\,dx.$

8. $\displaystyle\int \frac{t\,dt}{(11 + 7t^2)^2}.$

9. $\displaystyle\int \frac{u^2\,du}{(1 + u^3)^{5/2}}$

10. $\displaystyle\int \frac{\sqrt{z^6 + 5z^4}}{z}\,dz, z \neq 0.$

11. $\displaystyle\int (y^3 + y + 55)^{7/2}(3y^2 + 1)dy.$ u $du = 3y^2+1$

12. $\displaystyle\int \frac{\sqrt{3}(w + 1)dw}{\sqrt{5w^2 + 10w + 11}}.$

In problems 13 through 16 find the equation of the curve, given the derivative and one point P on the curve.

13. $\dfrac{dy}{dx} = 3x^2 + 2x,$ $P(0, 0).$ $dy = 3x^2 + 2x\,dx$ $\int dy = 3\int x^2 + 2\int x\,dx$ $y = x^3 + x^2 + C$ @ $(0,0)$ $0 = 0 + 0 + C$ ∴ $C = 0$ ∴ $y = x^3 + x^2 + 0)$

14. $\dfrac{dy}{dx} = \dfrac{2}{x^3} - \dfrac{3}{x^4},$ $P(1, 2).$

15. $\dfrac{dy}{dx} = x\sqrt{4 + 5x^2},$ $P\left(-1, \dfrac{1}{5}\right).$

16. $\dfrac{dy}{dx} = mx + b,$ $P(-1, 0).$

In problems 17 through 21 solve the given differential equation, subject to the given initial conditions.

17. $\dfrac{ds}{dt} = 32t + 5,$ $s = 100$ when $t = 0.$

18. $\dfrac{dy}{dx} = xy^2,$ $dy = xy^2\,dx$ $\frac{dy}{y^2} = x\,dx$ $-\frac{1}{y} = \frac{x^2}{2} + C$ @$(1,6)$ $C = -\frac{1}{6} - \frac{1}{2} = -$ $y = 6$ when $x = 1.$ ∴ $\frac{1}{y} = -\frac{x^2}{2} + \frac{2}{3}$

★19. $y\dfrac{dy}{dx} = x(y^4 + 2y^2 + 1),$ $y = 1$ when $x = -3.$

20. $\dfrac{dy}{dx} = \dfrac{x}{y},$ $y = 5$ when $x = 2\sqrt{6}.$

21. $\dfrac{du}{dv} = \sqrt{uv},$ $u = 100$ when $v = 9.$

3. **The concept of an area.** Before we compute the area of a plane figure, it is worthwhile to consider carefully just what we mean by area. Of course we have an intuitive idea of what the area of a figure

should be.   We have no intention of disturbing this intuitive idea.   Indeed we will stay very close to it.   All we want to do is to bring this hazy intuitive idea into sharper focus, by expressly stating what it is that we expect of an area.   These statements can be regarded as axioms for the area concept.

   I.   *To each plane figure bounded by curves[2] there corresponds a nonnegative number called the area of the figure.*

   At first glance one might demand that the area should always be positive.   But the length of a point is zero, and hence by analogy we expect that the area of a line segment will also be zero.   In fact this is consistent with the formula for the area of a rectangle $A = ab$.   Thus if the line

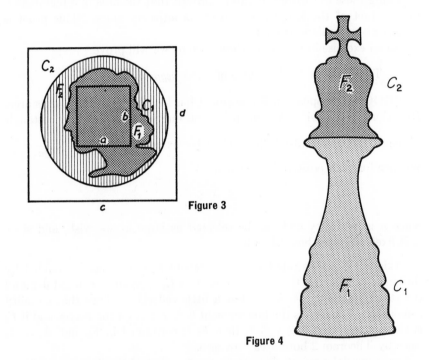

Figure 3

Figure 4

segment is regarded as a rectangle in which two of the sides coincide, then it has zero width, and hence $A = a \times 0 = 0$.   We will prove that $A = 0$ in Theorem 2.

   II.   *Two congruent figures have the same area.*

   [2] The figure may be bounded partly by straight line segments and partly by curves, as in the case of the shaded area of Fig. 2, or even entirely by straight line segments as in Fig. 1.   To simplify the language, we regard a straight line segment as being a special type of curve.

III.   *The area of a square of unit side is 1.*

IV.   *If F_1 and F_2 are plane figures with areas A_1 and A_2 respectively, and if the figure F_1 is contained in the figure F_2 then $A_1 \leqq A_2$ (see Fig. 3).*

V.   *If two figures F_1 and F_2 have no points in common except possibly boundary points or boundary curves, and if F_3 is the figure obtained by taking F_1 and F_2 together (deleting common boundary points or curves if any) then*

$$A_3 = A_1 + A_2,$$

where A_1, A_2, and A_3 are the areas of F_1, F_2, and F_3 respectively (see Fig. 4).

Axiom III is the basis for introducing the unit of measure.   Thus if the side of the square is one foot, then its area is one square foot.   If the side is a yard then its area is 1 square yard, etc.

Using these five axioms it can be proved that the area of a rectangle is the product of the lengths of two of its adjacent sides.   This proof is usually given in plane geometry.

As an exercise in the use of these axioms we will prove

THEOREM 2.   *The area of a line segment is zero.*

PROOF.   Suppose the line segment has length a and let A be its area. By axiom I, $0 \leqq A$.   We can place the line segment inside a rectangle of length $2a$ and width $1/2n$.   Then by axiom IV, $A \leqq 2a \times \dfrac{1}{2n} = \dfrac{a}{n}$. Whence for each positive integer n

$$0 \leqq A \leqq \frac{a}{n}.$$

Since n is arbitrary and can be selected as large as we wish, and since A is fixed we must have $A = 0$.

Axiom IV is illustrated in Fig. 3, where F_1 is the figure bounded by the curve C_1 and F_2 is the figure bounded by C_2.   Again one might demand the strict inequality $A_1 < A_2$, but a little reflection shows that equality can occur.   For if F_1 is the line segment $0 \leqq x \leqq 1$ on the x-axis, and if F_2 is the line segment $0 \leqq x \leqq 2$, then F_1 is contained in F_2, but $A_1 = A_2$ since by Theorem 2 both areas are zero.

As a special case of this axiom we see that if the figure contains a rectangle, then the area of the figure must be greater than or equal to that of the rectangle, and if the figure is contained in a rectangle the inequality goes the other way.   Thus for the figure F_2 bounded by C_2 in Fig. 3 we have

$$ab \leqq A_2 \leqq cd.$$

In fact in this case we expect on intuitive grounds that there will be strict inequality in both places.

4.   Computation of areas by integration.   We are now in a position to compute certain areas quite easily.   Let $y = f(x)$ be the equation of some curve C and suppose that $f(x)$ is continuous and positive in an interval $a \leq x \leq b$.   We construct two vertical lines, one at $x = a$, and a second one for any other fixed value of x in this interval (see Fig. 5). We are interested in the area of the region bounded on top by the curve, on the sides by the two vertical lines, and on the bottom by the x-axis. This is the region shown heavily shaded in Fig. 5. ·

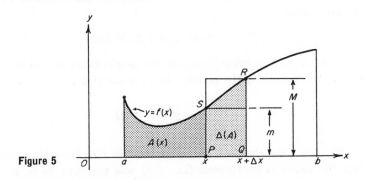

Figure 5

In order to avoid lengthy descriptions we will henceforth speak of the region as *the region under the curve between a and x*, merely naming the two points on the x-axis at which the vertical boundary lines are drawn.   With the top, bottom, and lefthand boundaries fixed, the enclosed area is uniquely determined by the location of the righthand vertical line, namely by the value of x.   Therefore we can use function notation and let $A(x)$ denote the area of the region under the curve between a and x.

> THEOREM 3.   *If $f(x)$ is a positive continuous function in the closed interval $a \leq x \leq b$, then the area $A(x)$ is a differentiable function and*

$$\frac{dA(x)}{dx} = f(x). \tag{18}$$

Here $f(x)$ denotes the y coordinate on the curve corresponding to the value of x selected for the righthand vertical boundary.   In a way this result is not too surprising for if we ask, at what rate is the area increasing as the vertical boundary moves to the right, we might expect that this rate is just the "local" height of the figure.

PROOF of Theorem 3.   Let Δx be a change in x and assume first that Δx is positive.   Then by definition

$$\frac{dA}{dx} = \lim_{\Delta x \to 0} \frac{\Delta A}{\Delta x}. \tag{19}$$

Now by the definition of $A(x)$ we have $\Delta A = A(x + \Delta x) - A(x)$ and obviously (or using Axiom V) this is the area of the slim figure $\Delta F = PQRS$ under the curve between x and $x + \Delta x$, and shown lightly shaded in Fig. 5.

Let m and M denote the minimum and maximum values respectively of $f(x)$ in the closed interval from x to $x + \Delta x$. Then the figure ΔF contains the rectangle with the same base and height m. Further it is contained in the rectangle with the same base and height M. Now ΔA is the area of this figure ΔF, so obviously (or using Axiom IV) we have the inequality

$$m\Delta x \leqq \Delta A \leqq M\Delta x, \tag{20}$$

since the area of a rectangle is just the height times the width. Dividing both sides of (20) by the positive number Δx yields.

$$m \leqq \frac{\Delta A}{\Delta x} \leqq M. \tag{21}$$

We now take the limit as Δx approaches zero through positive values. But the curve is continuous (i.e., $f(x)$ was assumed to be a continuous function), so as Δx shrinks to zero, m and M, the minimum and maximum values of y in that interval must both tend to the common value of y at the fixed point x. In Fig. 5 this is just the length of the line segment PS. Therefore (21) yields

$$f(x) \leqq \lim_{\Delta x \to 0} \frac{\Delta A}{\Delta x} \leqq f(x). \tag{22}$$

Hence, as far as positive values of Δx are concerned, $A(x)$ is differentiable and its derivative is $f(x)$. This is equation (18).

In case Δx is negative, the area $A(x)$ decreases, and so ΔA is negative. But then the quotient $\Delta A/\Delta x$ in the inequality (21) is positive and again this inequality is satisfied, except that this time m and M are the minimum and maximum values of $f(x)$ in a closed interval of length $|\Delta x|$ to the left of the fixed point x. Taking the limit as $\Delta x \to 0$, this time through negative values, again gives (22) and hence (18).   Q.E.D.

To complete the computation, we observe that when $x = a$, the figure becomes just a vertical line segment and obviously (or using Theorem 2) the area is zero. Thus the area satisfies the two conditions

$$\frac{dA(x)}{dx} = f(x) \qquad \text{and} \qquad A(a) = 0. \tag{23}$$

Before continuing with the theory we illustrate with

EXAMPLE 1. Find the area under the parabola $y = x^2$ between $x = 1$ and $x = 2$ (Fig. 6).

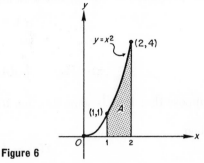

Figure 6

SOLUTION. We first replace the fixed righthand boundary at $x = 2$ by a variable vertical line. Let $A(x)$ denote the area under the parabola between 1 and x. Then by Theorem 3

$$\frac{dA}{dx} = x^2.$$

Hence

$$\int dA = \int x^2 dx$$

$$A(x) = \frac{x^3}{3} + C.$$

But at $x = 1$, $A(1) = 0$, and using these values in this equation we find

$$0 = \frac{1}{3} + C$$

or

$$C = -\frac{1}{3}.$$

Thus the variable area is given by

$$A(x) = \frac{x^3}{3} - \frac{1}{3}$$

and putting in the particular value $x = 2$, we find that the area of the shaded region in Fig. 6 is

$$A = \frac{2^3}{3} - \frac{1}{3} = \frac{8}{3} - \frac{1}{3} = \frac{7}{3}.$$

Our next step is to review the above example in a general setting and formulate our results as a theorem. We suppose again that the upper boundary is a continuous curve with the equation $y = f(x)$, and the sides are the vertical lines $x = a$ and $x = b$, and the lower boundary is the x-axis. Our procedure in finding this area starts with

$$\frac{dA}{dx} = f(x)$$

$$A(x) = \int dA = \int f(x)dx.$$

Suppose that $F(x)$ is some function for which $\dfrac{dF(x)}{dx} = f(x)$.

Then

$$A(x) = F(x) + C \tag{24}$$

At $x = a$, the area is zero.   Using this fact in (24) gives

$$0 = F(a) + C$$

or $C = -F(a)$.   Therefore equation (24) becomes

$$A(x) = F(x) - F(a) \tag{25}$$

and consequently at $x = b$

$$A(b) = F(b) - F(a). \tag{26}$$

This proves

> **THEOREM 4.**   *Let $F(x)$ be any indefinite integral of $f(x)$ and suppose that $f(x)$ is continuous and positive in the interval $a \leq x \leq b$. Then the area of the region under the curve $y = f(x)$ between $x = a$ and $x = b$ is given by*

$$A = F(b) - F(a). \tag{27}$$

Finally we want to introduce a notation that makes the computation mechanically simpler.   We have already seen the symbol

$$\int f(x)dx$$

which is the indefinite integral of $f(x)$.   We now introduce the symbol

$$\int_a^b f(x)dx \tag{28}$$

which is read "the integral from a to b of $f(x)dx$."   The numbers a and b are called the *lower* and *upper* limits of integration respectively, and this entire quantity is called a *definite* integral.

When we have found $F(x)$, an indefinite integral of $f(x)$, we carry along the numbers a and b by writing

$$\int_a^b f(x)dx = F(x)\Big|_a^b \tag{29}$$

and the meaning of the right side of (29) is just

$$F(x)\Big|_a^b = F(b) - F(a). \tag{30}$$

Thus as equation (30) states, we replace x by the upper limit b in the indefinite integral, and then subtract the value of the indefinite integral at the lower limit a. Thus expressing Theorem 4 in our new symbolism we have

> **THEOREM 5.** *The area of the figure described in Theorem 4 is given by*
>
> $$\int_a^b f(x)dx = F(x)\Big|_a^b = F(b) - F(a). \tag{31}$$

EXAMPLE 2. Evaluate

$$\int_{-1}^5 x^3\,dx.$$

SOLUTION. $\displaystyle\int_{-1}^5 x^3\,dx = \frac{x^4}{4}\Big|_{-1}^5 = \frac{(5)^4}{4} - \frac{(-1)^4}{4}$

$$= \frac{625}{4} - \frac{1}{4} = \frac{624}{4} = 156.$$

Notice that in this example the function $f(x) = x^3$ is not positive over the entire interval of integration $-1 \le x \le 5$. We shall return to this situation and study it in detail in the next section.

EXAMPLE 3. Find the area of the figure bounded by the x-axis, the curve $y = x\sqrt{x^2 - 9}$, and the vertical lines $x = 5$ and $x = 7$.

SOLUTION. By Theorem 5

let $u = x^2 - 9$

$\frac{du}{dx} = 2x \qquad du = 2x\,dx$

$$A = \int_5^7 x\sqrt{x^2 - 9}\,dx = \frac{1}{2}\int_5^7 (x^2 - 9)^{1/2} 2x\,dx$$

$$= \frac{1}{2}\int_{x=5}^{x=7} u^{1/2}\,du = \frac{1}{2}\frac{(x^2 - 9)^{3/2}}{3/2}\Big|_5^7$$

$$= \frac{1}{3}(x^2 - 9)^{3/2}\Big|_5^7 = \frac{1}{3}(40)^{3/2} - \frac{1}{3}(16)^{3/2}$$

$$= \frac{80}{3}\sqrt{10} - \frac{64}{3}.$$

Suitable tables give $A = 84.33\cdots - 21.33\cdots \approx 63.00$. Since the given figure is contained in a rectangle of width 2, and height $y = 7\sqrt{49 - 9} = 7\sqrt{40}$, we expect that $A < 2 \times 7\sqrt{40} = 88.54\cdots$ and this is the case. Also we expect that $A > 2 \times 5 \sqrt{25 - 9} = 40$, the area of a rectangle contained in the figure. Such simple checks as these are frequently useful in catching errors.

EXAMPLE 4.   Find the area of the region bounded by the parabola $y = x^2 + 2$, and the straight line $y = x + 4$.

SOLUTION.   We first draw a graph of these two curves in order to obtain a picture of the situation.   A first step in graphing is to solve the two equations

$$y = x^2 + 2$$
$$y = x + 4$$

simultaneously in order to find the points of intersection of the two curves. We have

$$x^2 + 2 = x + 4$$
$$x^2 - x - 2 = 0$$
$$(x + 1)(x - 2) = 0.$$

So the points of intersection are $(-1, 3)$ and $(2, 6)$.   We are to compute the shaded area in Fig. 7.   Clearly this situation is not covered in Theorem 4.

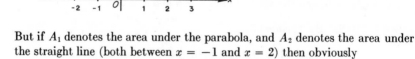

Figure 7

But if A_1 denotes the area under the parabola, and A_2 denotes the area under the straight line (both between $x = -1$ and $x = 2$) then obviously

$$A = A_2 - A_1.$$

Hence

$$A = \int_{-1}^{2} (x + 4)dx - \int_{-1}^{2} (x^2 + 2)dx$$

$$= \left(\frac{x^2}{2} + 4x \right) \Big|_{-1}^{2} - \left(\frac{x^3}{3} + 2x \right) \Big|_{-1}^{2}$$

$$= (2 + 8) - \left(\frac{1}{2} - 4 \right) - \left[\frac{8}{3} + 4 - \left(\frac{-1}{3} - 2 \right) \right]$$

$$= 10 + \frac{7}{2} - \left[\frac{9}{3} + 6 \right] = \frac{9}{2} = 4.5.$$

EXERCISE 2

In problems 1 through 8 evaluate the given definite integral.

1. $\int_1^5 (x+2)dx.$

2. $\int_1^5 (u+2)du.$ $= \int_1^5 u\,du + \int_1^5 2\,du = \frac{u^2}{2}\Big|_1^5 + 2u\Big|_1^5$

$= \frac{(5)^2}{2} - \frac{(1)^2}{2} + 2(5) - 2(1) = 20$

3. $\int_{-2}^2 x^3\,dx.$

4. $\int_{-2}^2 x^4\,dx.$

5. $\int_0^5 \dfrac{x\,dx}{\sqrt{144+x^2}}.$

6. $\int_1^3 \left(x-\dfrac{2}{x}\right)^2 dx.$ $= \int_1^3 \left(x^2 - 4 + \frac{4}{x^2}\right)dx = \int_1^3 x^2\,dx - \int_1^3 4\,dx + \int_1^3 4x^{-2} = \frac{10}{3}$

7. $\int_{-1}^1 (ax^2 + bx + c)dx.$

8. $\int_0^B ax^2 dx.$

In problems 9 through 15 find the area of the figure bounded by the x-axis, the given curve, and the two given vertical lines. In each case first sketch the figure and guess an approximate value for the area by a consideration of suitable rectangles.

9. $y = x^2,\quad x = 0,\quad x = 1.$

10. $y = x^4,\quad x = 0,\quad x = 1.$

11. $y = 2x + 5,\quad x = -1,\quad x = 6.$

12. $y = x^2 + 1,\quad x = -2,\quad x = 2.$

13. $y = x\sqrt{6x^2 + 1},\quad x = 0,\quad x = 2.$

14. $y = \dfrac{1}{x^2},\quad x = 1,\quad x = 100.$

15. $y = \dfrac{x}{\sqrt{x^2 + 1}},\quad x = 1,\quad x = \sqrt{7}.$

★16. The figure bounded by the x-axis, the line $y = mx + b$, and the lines $x = 0$, and $x = a$, is a trapezoid if the constants a, b, and m are all positive. It is known that the area of such a trapezoid is its width a times the average of the two vertical sides b and $ma + b$. Prove this rule by using the calculus to find the area. Show that in the special case that $m = 0$, integration gives the area of a rectangle.

★17. Prove the theorem of Archimedes mentioned in section 1. In other words prove that the area of the figure bounded by the parabola $y = ax^2$, the x-axis, and the lines $x = 0$, and $x = B$ is $BH/3$ where $H = aB^2$ is the height of the parabola.

★18. Prove that if n is a positive even integer then

$$\int_{-a}^a x^n\,dx = 2\int_0^a x^n\,dx$$

and if n is an odd positive integer

$$\int_{-a}^a x^n\,dx = 0.$$

★19. Prove that

$$\int_a^b f(x)dx + \int_a^b g(x)dx = \int_a^b (f(x) + g(x))dx.$$

Hint: If $F(x)$ and $G(x)$ are indefinite integrals of $f(x)$ and $g(x)$ this amounts to proving that

$$F(b) - F(a) + G(b) - G(a) = F(b) + G(b) - [F(a) + G(a)].$$

The result proved here will be useful in simplifying the computations in the following five problems.

In problems 20 through 23 find the area bounded by the given pair of curves.

  20. $y = 6x - 2 - x^2$ and $y = 3$.
  21. $y = 9 + 2x - x^2$ and $y = -3x + 13$.
  22. $y = 1 + 4x - x^2$ and $y = 1 + x^2$.
★23. $y = x^3 - 3x^2 + x + 5$ and $y = x + 5$.
★24. Find the area of the region lying in the first quadrant and bounded by the curves $y = -2x + 13$ and $y = 2x + 9/x^2$.

5.   **The definite integral.** We have just seen that if $F'(x) = f(x)$ then the quantity

$$\int_a^b f(x)dx = F(b) - F(a) \qquad (31)$$

represents a certain area, as long as $f(x)$ is not negative in the interval $a \leq x \leq b$. But suppose $f(x)$ should assume negative values for some values of x in the interval? Then equation (31) still has a meaning. In fact we make

    DEFINITION 1. *If $F'(x) = f(x)$, then the right side of equation (31) gives the definition of the left side. The quantity on the left is called the definite integral from a to b of the given function $f(x)$.*

If $f(x) \geq 0$ in $a \leq x \leq b$, then the definite integral gives the area under the curve for that interval. To discover a meaning for the definite integral when the curve $y = f(x)$ crosses the x-axis, let us look at an example.

Suppose that $y = x^2 - 1$ and we are considering the interval $0 \leq x \leq 3$. By Definition 1 the definite integral of this function over the interval is

$$\int_0^3 (x^2 - 1)dx = \left(\frac{x^3}{3} - x\right)\Big|_0^3 = \frac{27}{3} - 3 - (0 - 0) = 6.$$

Is this the area of the shaded regions in Fig. 8? To check on this possibility let us compute A_2, the area of the shaded region lying under the curve between $x = 1$ and $x = 3$. By Theorem 5 we have

$$A_2 = \int_1^3 (x^2 - 1)dx = \left(\frac{x^3}{3} - x\right)\Big|_1^3 = \frac{27}{3} - 3 - \left(\frac{1}{3} - 1\right)$$

$$= 6 - \left(-\frac{2}{3}\right) = 6\frac{2}{3}.$$

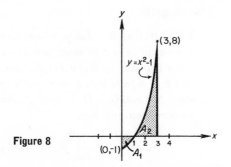

Figure 8

Therefore 6 cannot be the total area, since the area of just a part of it, A_2, is 6-2/3 and this is greater than 6. We may suspect that $A_1 = 2/3$ and that because it is below the axis it makes a negative contribution to the definite integral. Symbolically we suspect that

$$\int_0^3 (x^2 - 1)dx = A_2 - A_1 = 6\frac{2}{3} - \frac{2}{3} = 6.$$

It is easy to prove that this is the case. For if we turn the curve upside down by writing $y = 1 - x^2$ (the negative of $x^2 - 1$) we can compute A_1, in the conventional manner. The resulting graph is shown in Fig. 9.

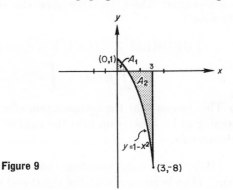

Figure 9

Indeed the area A_1 is the same in both figures and we have, from Fig. 9

$$A_1 = \int_0^1 (1 - x^2)dx = \left(x - \frac{x^3}{3} \right)\Bigg|_0^1 = 1 - \frac{1}{3} = \frac{2}{3}$$

just as we expected. If we wanted the total area of the regions shaded in Fig. 8 (or Fig. 9) we must add A_1 and A_2. We find

$$A = 6\frac{2}{3} + \frac{2}{3} = 7\frac{1}{3}.$$

This suggests

> THEOREM 6.   *Let $y = f(x)$ be the equation of a curve that cuts the x-axis in one or more points in the interval $a \leq x \leq b$.   The figure bounded by this curve, the x-axis, and the vertical lines $x = a$ and $x = b$ falls into several parts, some below the x-axis and some above the x-axis.   If T_1 and T_2 denote the total areas of these two parts respectively then*

$$\int_a^b f(x)dx = T_2 - T_1. \tag{32}$$

Briefly the definite integral automatically counts areas above the x-axis with a positive sign and areas below the x-axis with a negative sign. We will call the quantity $T_2 - T_1$ the *algebraic area* under the curve between a and b, in order to distinguish it from the area $T_1 + T_2$.   When there is a danger of confusion we will call this latter quantity the *geometric area* (or absolute area).   Thus the algebraic area is a "signed" area counting the area of regions above the x-axis with a positive sign, and the area of regions below the x-axis with a negative sign.

This theorem appeals immediately to the intuition, and the student could profitably skip the detailed proof and proceed directly to the following example and the exercises.   The proof is easy to build up from the next two theorems which together give the essential steps for the proof of Theorem 6.

> THEOREM 7.   *If $a \leq b \leq c$, then*

$$\int_a^c f(x)dx = \int_a^b f(x)dx + \int_b^c f(x)dx. \tag{33}$$

This means that the computation of a definite integral over some interval, can be broken up into the sum of definite integrals over suitable subintervals.

PROOF.   We are assuming that we have an $F(x)$ whose derivative is $f(x)$.   Then beginning with the righthand side of (33) we find

$$\int_a^b f(x)dx + \int_b^c f(x)dx = [F(b) - F(a)] + [F(c) - F(b)]$$

$$= F(c) - F(a) = \int_a^c f(x)dx. \qquad \text{Q.E.D.}$$

In order to simplify our thinking, we have required that a, b, and c satisfy the condition $a \leq b \leq c$ and this means that as points on the x-axis they occur in that order.   But the critical student will observe that in Definition 1 of the definite integral no restriction was placed on a and b so that we could have $b < a$.   Further in the proof of Theorem 7 no use was made of the condition $a \leq b \leq c$, so that a, b, and c could be any three numbers.

THEOREM 8. *Let $f(x) \leq 0$ in the interval $a \leq x \leq b$. Then the area of the region bounded by the curve $y = f(x)$, the x-axis, and the lines $x = a$ and $x = b$ is given by*

$$A = \int_a^b -f(x)dx = -\int_a^b f(x)dx. \tag{34}$$

PROOF. The region involved lies below the x-axis as indicated by the shaded portion shown in Fig. 10. But if we take the mirror image of the curve $y = f(x)$ in the x-axis we obtain the curve $y = -f(x)$ and the region bounded by this new curve, the x-axis, and the same vertical lines now lies above the x-axis. But by symmetry the area is unchanged. Hence by Theorem 5 the area is given by the middle term of equation (34). We leave it as a problem (Exercise 3, Problem 8) to show that this is the same as the last term of equation (34).

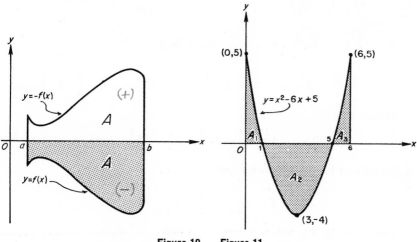

Figure 10   Figure 11

EXAMPLE 1. Find the area bounded by the curve $y = x^2 - 6x + 5$, the two axes and the line $x = 6$. Compute the definite integral of $y = x^2 - 6x + 5$ over the interval $0 \leq x \leq 6$.

SOLUTION. For the definite integral we have

$$I = \int_0^6 (x^2 - 6x + 5)dx = \left(\frac{x^3}{3} - 3x^2 + 5x \right) \Big|_0^6$$

$$= \frac{6 \times 36}{3} - 3 \times 36 + 30 - (0) = -36 + 30 = -6.$$

This is certainly not the area. As Fig. 11 shows the curve intersects the x-axis at $x = 1$ and $x = 5$. Using A_1, A_2, and A_3 to denote the areas of the three pieces shown in the figure, we have

$$A = A_1 + A_2 + A_3$$

where

$$A_1 = \int_0^1 (x^2 - 6x + 5)dx = \left(\frac{x^3}{3} - 3x^2 + 5x \right)\Big|_0^1$$

$$= \frac{1}{3} - 3 + 5 = 2\frac{1}{3},$$

$$A_2 = \int_1^5 (-x^2 + 6x - 5)dx = \left(-\frac{x^3}{3} + 3x^2 - 5x \right)\Big|_1^5$$

$$= -\frac{125}{3} + 75 - 25 - \left(-\frac{1}{3} + 3 - 5 \right)$$

$$= 8\frac{1}{3} - \left(-2\frac{1}{3} \right) = 10\frac{2}{3},$$

$$A_3 = \int_5^6 (x^2 - 6x + 5)dx = \left(\frac{x^3}{3} - 3x^2 + 5x \right)\Big|_5^6$$

$$= \frac{6 \times 36}{3} - 3 \times 36 + 30 - \left(\frac{125}{3} - 75 + 25 \right) = -6 - \left(-8\frac{1}{3} \right) = 2\frac{1}{3}.$$

Therefore

$$A = 2\frac{1}{3} + 10\frac{2}{3} + 2\frac{1}{3} = 15\frac{1}{3}.$$

Notice that for the definite integral I we have

$$I = 2\frac{1}{3} - 10\frac{2}{3} + 2\frac{1}{3} = -6.$$

This illustrates Theorem 6.

EXERCISE 3

In problems 1 through 6 compute (a) the definite integral of the given function over the given interval, and (b) the area of the figure bounded by the curve $y = f(x)$, the x-axis, and the vertical lines at the end points of the interval.

1. $f(x) = 4x - x^2$, $0 \le x \le 5$.
2. $f(x) = 4 - 4x^3$, $0 \le x \le 3$.
3. $f(x) = x^2 - 2x$, $1 \le x \le 4$.
4. $f(x) = x^2 + 3x$, $-1 \le x \le 2$.
5. $f(x) = x^2 - 4x + 3$, $0 \le x \le 4$.
*6. $f(x) = 9 - 3x^2$, $0 \le x \le 3$.

7. Prove that for a definite integral

$$\int_a^b f(x)dx = -\int_b^a f(x)dx.$$

Thus, interchanging the limits changes the sign.

8. Prove that for a definite integral

$$\int_a^b cf(x)dx = c\int_a^b f(x)dx$$

for any constant c.

6. **The summation notation.** We will prove in the next section that the definite integral is really a limit of a certain sum. Since we will be dealing with sums that have many terms, we want a notation that will reduce the labor of writing these sums. This section will be devoted to explaining and illustrating this new notation. The symbol $\sum$ is a capital sigma in the Greek alphabet and corresponds to our English S. Thus it naturally reminds us of the word sum. The symbol

$$\sum f(k)$$

means that we are to sum the numbers $f(k)$ for various integer values of k. The range for the integers is indicated by placing them below and above the $\sum$. For example

$$\sum_{k=1}^{4} f(k)$$

means $f(1) + f(2) + f(3) + f(4)$. Thus we substitute in $f(k)$ successively all of the integers between and including the lower and the upper limits of summation, in this case $k = 1$, 2, 3 and 4, and then add the results.

The sum need not start at 1 nor end at 4. Further any letter can be used instead of k. The following examples should indicate the various possibilities. The new shorthand notation is on the left side, and its meaning is on the right side in each of these equations.

$$\sum_{j=1}^{4} f(j) = f(1) + f(2) + f(3) + f(4).$$

$$\sum_{k=2}^{6} g(k) = g(2) + g(3) + g(4) + g(5) + g(6).$$

$$\sum_{k=1}^{7} k^2 = 1 + 4 + 9 + 16 + 25 + 36 + 49.$$

$$\sum_{j=1}^{8} 1 = 1 + 1 + 1 + 1 + 1 + 1 + 1 + 1 = 8.$$

$$\sum_{k=1}^{n} f(k) = f(1) + f(2) + f(3) + \cdots + f(n).$$

Sometimes the terms to be added involve subscripts, or combinations of functions with subscripts.   These possibilities are illustrated below.

$$\sum_{n=3}^{7} a_n = a_3 + a_4 + a_5 + a_6 + a_7.$$

$$\sum_{n=1}^{5} nb_n = b_1 + 2b_2 + 3b_3 + 4b_4 + 5b_5.$$

$$\sum_{k=1}^{n} \frac{a_k}{k} = a_1 + \frac{a_2}{2} + \frac{a_3}{3} + \cdots + \frac{a_n}{n}.$$

In order to see that this is really a nice notation, the student should consider the task of writing the sum of the squares of the first 100 positive integers.   This would take quite a lot of time and energy.   But with our new notation we can write the same sum as

$$\sum_{k=1}^{100} k^2$$

in just a few seconds.   In order to assist the student to master this new notation, we will frequently use both the new and the old notation together.

To provide both interesting and useful exercises with this summation notation, we will prove a number of formulas by mathematical induction.

EXAMPLE 1.   Prove that the sum of the first n positive integers is $n(n+1)/2$.

SOLUTION.   We are to prove that

$$\sum_{j=1}^{n} j = 1 + 2 + 3 + \cdots + n = \frac{n(n+1)}{2}. \tag{35}$$

The formula is true when $n = 1$, for then we have

$$\sum_{j=1}^{1} j = 1 = \frac{1(1+1)}{2} = 1.$$

Assume that (35) is true when $n = k$.   Thus we assume that

$$\sum_{j=1}^{k} j = 1 + 2 + 3 + \cdots + k = \frac{k(k+1)}{2}.$$

Adding $(k+1)$ to both sides of this equation gives

$$\sum_{j=1}^{k+1} j = 1 + 2 + 3 + \cdots + k + k + 1 = \frac{k(k+1)}{2} + k + 1$$

$$= \frac{k(k+1) + 2(k+1)}{2}$$

$$= \frac{(k+1)(k+2)}{2}.$$

But this is equation (35) when $n = k + 1$.   Q.E.D.

EXAMPLE 2. Prove that if $x \neq 1$ then

$$\sum_{j=0}^{n} x^i = 1 + x + x^2 + x^3 + \cdots + x^n = \frac{1 - x^{n+1}}{1 - x}. \tag{36}$$

SOLUTION. For $n = 1$ we have

$$\sum_{j=0}^{1} x^i = 1 + x = \frac{(1 - x)(1 + x)}{1 - x} = \frac{1 - x^2}{1 - x},$$

and hence the formula is true when $n = 1$.

Assume (36) is true when $n = k$. Thus we assume that

$$\sum_{j=0}^{k} x^i = 1 + x + x^2 + \cdots + x^k = \frac{1 - x^{k+1}}{1 - x}.$$

Adding x^{k+1} to both sides gives

$$\sum_{j=0}^{k+1} x^i = 1 + x + x^2 + \cdots + x^k + x^{k+1} = \frac{1 - x^{k+1}}{1 - x} + x^{k+1}$$

$$= \frac{1 - x^{k+1} + x^{k+1} - x^{k+2}}{1 - x} = \frac{1 - x^{k+2}}{1 - x}.$$

But this is equation (36) when $n = k + 1$. Q.E.D.

EXAMPLE 3. Show by direct computation that

$$\sum_{k=1}^{5} k^2 = 55.$$

SOLUTION. Writing out the lefthand side we have

$$\sum_{k=1}^{5} k^2 = 1 + 4 + 9 + 16 + 25.$$

But the sum of these terms is 55.

EXERCISE 4

1. Show by direct computations that each of the following assertions is true.

a. $\displaystyle\sum_{k=1}^{6} k^2 = 91.$

b. $\displaystyle\sum_{k=1}^{5} k^3 = 225.$

c. $\displaystyle\sum_{n=1}^{10} 2n = 110.$

d. $\displaystyle\sum_{n=0}^{5} \frac{1}{2} n(n - 1) = 20.$

e. $\displaystyle\sum_{n=1}^{5} \frac{1}{n} = \frac{137}{60}.$

f. $\displaystyle\sum_{n=1}^{7} \frac{1}{n(n + 1)} = \frac{7}{8}.$

In problems 2 through 16 a number of assertions are given with the summation notation.   In each case write out both sides of the equation in full and decide whether the given assertion is always true, or sometimes may be false.

2. $c\sum\limits_{k=1}^{n} k^4 = \sum\limits_{k=1}^{n} ck^4.$

3. $c\sum\limits_{k=1}^{n} a_k = \sum\limits_{k=1}^{n} ca_k.$

4. $\sum\limits_{k=1}^{n} b_k + \sum\limits_{k=n+1}^{N} b_k = \sum\limits_{k=1}^{N} b_k, \qquad 1 < n < N.$

5. $\sum\limits_{k=1}^{N} b_k = \sum\limits_{j=1}^{N} b_j.$

6. $\sum\limits_{k=1}^{n} f(k) = \sum\limits_{k=2}^{n+1} f(k).$

7. $\sum\limits_{k=1}^{n} f(k) = \sum\limits_{k=2}^{n+1} f(k-1).$

8. $\left(\sum\limits_{k=1}^{n} a_k\right)\left(\sum\limits_{k=1}^{n} b_k\right) = \sum\limits_{k=1}^{n} a_k b_k.$ $\left(a_1 + a_2 + a_3 + \cdots + a_n\right)\left(b_1 + b_2 + b_3 + \cdots + b_n\right) = \left(a_1 b_1 + a_2 b_2 + \cdots\right)$

9. $\left(\sum\limits_{k=1}^{n} a_k\right)^2 = \sum\limits_{k=1}^{n} a_k^2 + \sum\limits_{k=1}^{n} 2a_k + \sum\limits_{k=1}^{n} 1.$

10. $\sum\limits_{k=1}^{n} a_k + \sum\limits_{k=1}^{n} b_k = \sum\limits_{k=1}^{n} (a_k + b_k).$

11.   If $a_k \leq b_k$ for each positive integer k then $\sum\limits_{k=1}^{n} a_k \leq \sum\limits_{k=1}^{n} b_k.$

12. $\sum\limits_{k=0}^{n} a_k = \sum\limits_{k=0}^{n} a_{n-k}.$

13. $\dfrac{d}{dx}\left(\sum\limits_{k=1}^{n} x^k\right) = \sum\limits_{k=1}^{n} kx^{k-1}.$

14. $\displaystyle\int_0^2\left(\sum\limits_{k=1}^{n} x^k\right) dx = \sum\limits_{k=1}^{n} \dfrac{2^{k+1}}{k+1}.$

15. $\sum\limits_{k=1}^{n} (a_{k+1} - a_k) = a_{n+1} - a_1.$

16. $\sum\limits_{k=1}^{n} [(k+1)^2 - k^2] = \sum\limits_{k=1}^{n} (2k+1) = 2\sum\limits_{k=1}^{n} k + n.$

17.   Combine the results of problems 15 and 16 to get a new proof of the formula (35) of Example 1.

In problems 18 through 23 write out the given assertion in full and then use mathematical induction to prove that the assertion is true for every positive integer n.

18. $\displaystyle\sum_{j=1}^{n} (2j - 1) = n^2.$

19. $\displaystyle\sum_{j=1}^{n} (3j - 1) = \frac{n(3n + 1)}{2}.$

20. $\displaystyle\sum_{j=1}^{n} j(j + 1) = \frac{n(n + 1)(n + 2)}{3}.$

21. $\displaystyle\sum_{j=1}^{n} j^2 = \frac{n(n + 1)(2n + 1)}{6}.$

22. $\displaystyle\sum_{j=1}^{n} \frac{1}{j(j + 1)} = \frac{n}{n + 1}.$

23. $\displaystyle\sum_{j=1}^{n} j^3 = \frac{n^2(n + 1)^2}{4}.$

24. Combine the results of problem 23 and Example 1 [equation (35)] to prove that

$$\sum_{j=1}^{n} j^3 = \left(\sum_{j=1}^{n} j\right)^2.$$

State the result in words.

7.   Area as the limit of a sum.   We have already learned how to compute areas of figures bounded by curves, so it would seem almost pointless to reconsider this problem.   But it turns out that if we look at the computation of areas from a different point of view we obtain a principle that can be applied in a wide variety of situations that are far removed from the problem of computing an area.   This different point of view requires a considerable dose of theory and the student may perhaps find this medicine somewhat tasteless or even unpleasant.   But we can promise that the goal is well worth the effort, and in the end it will appear that this medicine is not only good but also quite tasty.

One advantage that theoretical material has over applications, is that theory deals only with ideas and requires almost no numerical computation.   Hence in this respect theory is really easier and more attractive than applications.

Let us assume for convenience that $f(x)$ is positive and continuous in the interval $a \leq x \leq b$.   Let A denote as usual the area of the region under the curve $y = f(x)$ between $x = a$ and $x = b$.   We will try to get a close approximation for A by considering the areas of certain rectangles. We divide the interval $a \leq x \leq b$ into n subintervals, using $n + 1$ distinct points $x_0, x_1, \cdots, x_n$.   The notation is selected so that $x_0 = a$, $x_n = b$ and all of the points are in order on the line, namely $x_0 < x_1 < x_2 < x_3 < \cdots < x_n$. The situation is pictured both in Fig. 12 and Fig. 13.   We number these subintervals in the natural way, that is, the first subinterval is the interval $x_0 \leq x \leq x_1$, the second subinterval is $x_1 \leq x \leq x_2$, and in general the kth subinterval is the interval $x_{k-1} \leq x \leq x_k$, where k may have any one of the values $k = 1, 2, 3, \cdots, n$. Thus the nth subinterval is the interval $x_{n-1} \leqq x \leqq x_n = b$.

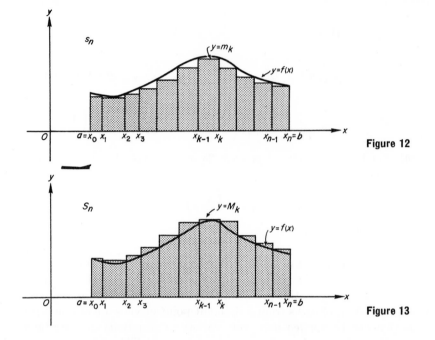

Figure 12

Figure 13

Over each of these subintervals we erect rectangles as shown in Fig. 12 and Fig. 13.   In Fig. 12 the height of the rectangle over the kth subinterval is taken as the minimum value of the function $f(x)$ in that subinterval. We denote this minimum value by m_k.

In Fig. 13, the height of the rectangle over the kth subinterval is taken as the maximum value of the function $f(x)$ in that subinterval.   We denote this maximum value by M_k.

It is now clear that the region below the curve $y = f(x)$ between $x = a$ and $x = b$ will contain all of those rectangles with height m_k as indicated in Fig. 12.   By contrast if we form a new region by collecting together all of the rectangles with height M_k, this new region will contain the region below the curve between $x = a$ and $x = b$, as indicated in Fig. 13.   Obviously (or by Axiom IV) we obtain two estimates for A, one that is smaller than A, and one that is larger than A, by computing the sums of the areas of the rectangles in Fig. 12 and Fig. 13 respectively.

In order to express these sums algebraically we need a notation for the width of the rectangles.   Let $\Delta x_1 = x_1 - x_0$, $\Delta x_2 = x_2 - x_1$, and in general set $\Delta x_k = x_k - x_{k-1}$ for $k = 1, 2, \cdots n$.   Let s_n denote the total area of the inscribed rectangles shown in Fig. 12.

Then

$$s_n = m_1\Delta x_1 + m_2\Delta x_2 + \cdots + m_n\Delta x_n = \sum_{k=1}^{n} m_k\Delta x_k, \qquad (37)$$

since the area of each rectangle is its height times its width. The sum s_n is called a *lower* sum, and as already mentioned, $s_n \leqq A$. Similarly if S_n is the total area of the rectangles that together contain the region under the curve (see Fig. 13) then

$$S_n = M_1\Delta x_1 + M_2\Delta x_2 + \cdots + M_n\Delta x_n = \sum_{k=1}^{n} M_k\Delta x_k. \qquad (38)$$

The sum S_n is called an *upper* sum, and as already mentioned, $A \leqq S_n$. Therefore

$$s_n \leqq A \leqq S_n. \qquad (39)$$

Before going on, we summarize our results in

THEOREM 9. *Let $f(x)$ be positive and continuous in $a \leqq x \leqq b$ and let A be the area of the region under the curve $y = f(x)$ between $x = a$ and $x = b$. Divide the interval into n subintervals with points $a = x_0 < x_1 < x_2 < \cdots < x_n = b$. Let m_k and M_k be the minimum and maximum values of $f(x)$ in the kth interval $x_{k-1} \leqq x \leqq x_k$ and let $\Delta x_k = x_k - x_{k-1}$ for $k = 1, 2, 3, \cdots, n$. Form the lower and upper sums s_n and S_n defined by equations (37) and (38) respectively. Then these sums satisfy the inequality (39).*

We are now going to consider the limit of these upper and lower sums as n tends to infinity. Since the number of subintervals is increasing we might expect that their lengths are tending to zero but this need not happen unless we expressly demand it. Let Δ be the maximum of the lengths $\Delta x_k (k = 1, 2, \cdots, n)$ of the subintervals. Then we require that as $n \to \infty$ the subdivision points shall be chosen[3] so that $\Delta \to 0$. This states that we are not completely free in our selection of the subdivision points, but that

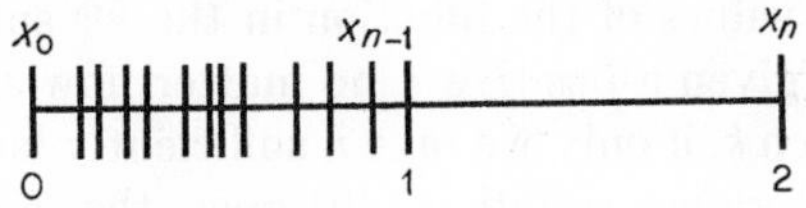

Figure 14

we must distribute them in a decent way throughout the interval. For example if our interval is $0 \leqq x \leqq 2$, the last point x_n must always be 2, but someone might want to put all of the remaining x_k in the interval

---

[3] This situation will occur repeatedly throughout the book. In order to avoid lengthy sentences, we make this hypothesis once and for all, namely whenever an interval is subdivided by n points, and n is increased indefinitely, then Δ, the maximum length of the subintervals, must tend to zero.

$0 \leq x \leq 1$, as shown in Fig. 14.   But this will not be allowed, because if he did this the nth subinterval would have length

$$\Delta x_n = x_n - x_{n-1} \geq 2 - 1 = 1$$

and so Δ would not tend to zero as n approaches infinity.

Our object is to prove that as $n \to \infty$, $s_n \to A$ and $S_n \to A$.   To prove this we consider the difference $S_n - s_n$.   Using (38) and (39) we find that

$$S_n - s_n = M_1 \Delta x_1 + M_2 \Delta x_2 + \cdots + M_n \Delta x_n - (m_1 \Delta x_1 + m_2 \Delta x_2 + \cdots + m_n \Delta x_n)$$
$$S_n - s_n = (M_1 - m_1) \Delta x_1 + (M_2 - m_2) \Delta x_2 + \cdots + (M_n - m_n) \Delta x_n. \quad (40)$$

On the one hand, this quantity must be greater than or equal to zero, because each of the terms in the sum has this property.   To see that this difference $S_n - s_n$ can be made arbitrarily small, by taking n sufficiently large, we look at a geometric interpretation of equation (40).   Each term in equation (40) has the form $(M_k - m_k)\Delta x_k$ and is just the difference in the areas of a certain rectangle in Fig. 13 and the corresponding rectangle standing just above it in Fig. 12.   The situation is illustrated in Fig. 15, where the area of the shaded regions is equal to the sum in equation (40).

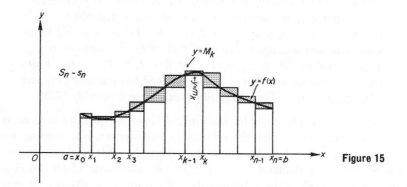

Figure 15

If now we let $n \to \infty$, the length of each subinterval tends to zero, and consequently the difference, $M_k - m_k$, between the maximum and minimum values of the function in the kth subinterval is also tending to zero. Thus given a positive ϵ, no matter how small, we find that $M_k - m_k < \epsilon$ for each k, if only we take n sufficiently large so that Δ is sufficiently small[4]

Therefore equation (40) gives the inequality

$$S_n - s_n < \epsilon \Delta x_1 + \epsilon \Delta x_2 + \cdots + \epsilon \Delta x_n$$
$$< \epsilon(\Delta x_1 + \Delta x_2 + \cdots + \Delta x_n) = \epsilon(b - a),$$

[4] The experienced mathematician will recognize that we are invoking the uniform continuity of a continuous function on a closed interval.   The concept belongs properly in a course in Advanced Calculus, and there is no reason to disturb the student with this delicate detail, especially since the facts appear to be completely reasonable.   The curious student can consult any book on Advanced Calculus and look under the heading "uniform continuity."

if only n is taken sufficiently large.   But ϵ can be made as small as we please, just so long as it is positive.   On the other hand we already know that $S_n - s_n \geqq 0$.   Thus we have $0 \leqq S_n - s_n < \epsilon(b - a)$ for n large, or

$$\lim_{n\to\infty} S_n - s_n = 0. \tag{41}$$

Finally combining (41) and the fact that $s_n \leqq A \leqq S_n$, we see that

$$\lim_{n\to\infty} S_n = A, \tag{42}$$

and

$$\lim_{n\to\infty} s_n = A. \tag{43}$$

This gives

THEOREM 10.   *Under the conditions of Theorem 9 the upper and lower sums S_n and s_n both have the limit A as n tends to infinity.*

Suppose now that in forming a sum, as in equations (37) and (38), we did not select the minimum m_k nor the maximum M_k of the function $f(x)$ in the kth subinterval.   Instead let us select in each subinterval an arbitrary point $x_k^\star$, $x_{k-1} \leqq x_k^\star \leqq x_k$, and use as our multiplier $f(x_k^\star)$ rather than m_k or M_k.   By the definition of m_k and M_k as minimum and maximum values of $f(x)$ in the kth interval we always have

$$m_k \leqq f(x_k^\star) \leqq M_k, \qquad k = 1, 2, \cdots, n, \tag{44}$$

and hence multiplying by the positive number Δx_k,

$$m_k \Delta x_k \leqq f(x_k^\star)\Delta x_k \leqq M_k \Delta x_k, \qquad k = 1, 2, \cdots, n. \tag{45}$$

Let $S_n^\star$ denote the sum with these new multipliers, namely

$$S_n^\star = f(x_1^\star)\Delta x_1 + f(x_2^\star)\Delta x_2 + \cdots + f(x_n^\star)\Delta x_n = \sum_{k=1}^{n} f(x_k^\star)\Delta x_k. \tag{46}$$

Then the inequality (45) gives a parallel inequality for the sums:

$$\sum_{k=1}^{n} m_k \Delta x_k \leqq \sum_{k=1}^{n} f(x_k^\star)\Delta x_k \leqq \sum_{k=1}^{n} M_k \Delta x_k, \tag{47}$$

and using (37), (46), and (38) in turn, this is equivalent to

$$s_n \leqq S_n^\star \leqq S_n, \tag{48}$$

for each n.   Since $s_n \to A$ and $S_n \to A$ as $n \to \infty$, it follows that $S_n^\star \to A$ as $n \to \infty$.   We have proved

THEOREM 11.   *Let $f(x)$ be positive and continuous in $a \leqq x \leqq b$. Subdivide this interval into n subintervals by points $a = x_0 < x_1 < x_2 <$*

$\cdots < x_n = b$, and in the kth subinterval select arbitrarily $x_k^\star$ (for $k = 1, 2, \cdots, n$). Let $\Delta x_k = x_k - x_{k-1}$. Then

$$\lim_{n \to \infty} S_n^\star = \lim_{n \to \infty} [f(x_1^\star)\Delta x_1 + f(x_2^\star)\Delta x_2 + \cdots + f(x_n^\star)\Delta x_n] = A,$$

the area under the curve $y = f(x)$ between $x = a$ and $x = b$.

Finally by Theorem 5, this area is a certain definite integral. Hence we have

THEOREM 12.   *Under the conditions of Theorem 11*

$$\lim_{n \to \infty} [f(x_1^\star)\Delta x_1 + f(x_2^\star)\Delta x_2 + \cdots + f(x_n^\star)\Delta x_n] = \int_a^b f(x)dx. \qquad (49)$$

It is now clear why a symbol $\int$ reminding us of a sum, was chosen for the concept of a definite integral. Indeed the definite integral is just the limit of the sum on the left side of equation (49).

Notice that although the area was a useful concept in leading us to the proof of Theorem 12, it has itself completely disappeared from the statement of this theorem. This is a very important point, and we will return to this later on in the book.

One last remark about Theorem 12. This theorem was proved under the assumption that $f(x) > 0$ in the interval $a \leq x \leq b$. Suppose this is not the case. For example the graph of the function $y = x^2 - 6x + 5$ crosses the x-axis twice, once at $x = 1$ and again at $x = 5$, as indicated in Fig. 11 page 147. What does equation (49) say about such a function? For simplicity we may include the crossing points as points of the subdivision, when the interval $a \leq x \leq b$ is divided into subintervals. Then in each of the subintervals $f(x)$ has a constant sign. What about the sum on the left side of (49)? Some of the terms will be negative and others positive or zero. A negative term will correspond to a rectangle that lies below the x-axis, and will give the negative of the area of such a rectangle. A positive (or zero) term will correspond to a rectangle (possibly degenerate) that lies above (or on) the x-axis and will give the area of the rectangle. Hence the limit of the sum

$$\lim_{n \to \infty} [f(x_1^\star)\Delta x_1 + f(x_2^\star)\Delta x_2 + \cdots + f(x_n^\star)\Delta x_n] \qquad (50)$$

gives the algebraic area of the regions enclosed by the curve, the x-axis, and the line $x = a$ and $x = b$. In other words, if T_2 denotes the total area of the regions below the curve and above the x-axis, and if T_1 denotes the total area of the regions above the curve and below the x-axis (naturally between $x = a$ and $x = b$) then the limit in (50) is just $T_2 - T_1$.

But by Theorem 6, the definite integral on the right of (49) also gives

$T_2 - T_1$. Therefore (49) is valid for any function $f(x)$ continuous in $a \leq x \leq b$. We have

> **THEOREM 13.** *If $f(x)$ is a continuous function in $a \leq x \leq b$, then equation (49) holds. Further, either side of equation (49) gives the algebraic area of the regions bounded by the curve $y = f(x)$, the x-axis, and the lines $x = a$ and $x = b$.*

EXAMPLE 1. Use the methods of this section to find the area under the parabola $y = x^2$, between $x = 0$ and $x = 1$.

SOLUTION. We divide the interval $0 \leq x \leq 1$ into n equal subintervals, as indicated in Fig. 16. Then each subinterval has length $\Delta x_k = 1/n$ and the

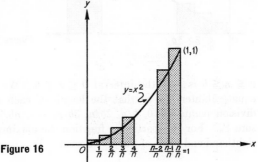

Figure 16

points of subdivision are $0, 1/n, 2/n, 3/n, \cdots, n/n = 1$. We form the upper sum S_n. For this particular function $y = x^2$, the maximum M_k always occurs at the righthand end point of the kth interval. Since this is $x_k = k/n$ we have

$$M_k = \left(\frac{k}{n}\right)^2 = \frac{k^2}{n^2}.$$

Then the upper sum, equation (38), for this specific curve is

$$S_n = \frac{1}{n^2} \cdot \frac{1}{n} + \frac{4}{n^2} \cdot \frac{1}{n} + \frac{9}{n^2} \cdot \frac{1}{n} + \cdots + \frac{n^2}{n^2} \cdot \frac{1}{n}$$

$$= \frac{1}{n^3}(1 + 4 + 9 + \cdots + n^2).$$

By the result of problem 21 Exercise 4 this sum is $\dfrac{n(n + 1)(2n + 1)}{6}$. Hence

$$S_n = \frac{1}{n^3} \cdot \frac{n(n + 1)(2n + 1)}{6} = \frac{1}{6}\left(1 + \frac{1}{n}\right)\left(2 + \frac{1}{n}\right).$$

Taking the limit as $n \to \infty$, the left side approaches A by Theorem 10, and the right side obviously approaches $2/6 = 1/3$. Hence for this figure $A = 1/3$. This result is easy to check by our earlier method

$$A = \int_0^1 x^2 \, dx = \frac{x^3}{3}\Big|_0^1 = \frac{1}{3} - 0 = \frac{1}{3}.$$

EXAMPLE 2. Use the methods of this section to prove the formula $A = bh/2$ for the area of a right triangle.

SOLUTION. We place the triangle on a coordinate system as shown in Fig. 17. The equation of the hypotenuse is then $y = \dfrac{h}{b} x$, and the interval

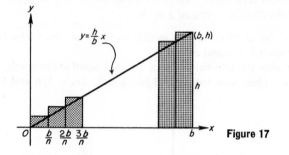

Figure 17

$a \leqq x \leqq b$ is now the interval $0 \leqq x \leqq b$. We divide this interval into n equal subintervals, so that the length of each subinterval is b/n, and the division points are 0, b/n, $2b/n$, $3b/n$, $\cdots$, $nb/n = b$. We form the upper sum S_n. For this particular function the maximum M_k always occurs at the righthand end point of the kth interval. This is $x_k = kb/n$ and the maximum value of the function $y = \dfrac{h}{b} x$ is

$$M_k = \frac{h}{b} \cdot \frac{kb}{n} = \frac{hk}{n}.$$

Then the upper sum, equation (38), for this specific curve is

$$S_n = \frac{h}{n} \cdot \frac{b}{n} + \frac{2h}{n} \cdot \frac{b}{n} + \frac{3h}{n} \cdot \frac{b}{n} + \cdots + \frac{nh}{n} \cdot \frac{b}{n}$$

$$= \frac{bh}{n^2} (1 + 2 + 3 + \cdots + n).$$

By the result of Example 1 of section 6, equation (35), the sum of the first n positive integers is $n(n + 1)/2$, hence

$$S_n = \frac{bh}{n^2} \cdot \frac{n(n + 1)}{2} = \frac{bh}{2} \left(1 + \frac{1}{n}\right).$$

Taking the limit as $n \to \infty$, the left side approaches A by Theorem 10, and the right side obviously approaches $bh/2$. Q.E.D.

EXERCISE 5

1. Show that in example 1 the lower sum is given by

$$s_n = \frac{1}{n^3} (1 + 4 + 9 + \cdots + (n - 1)^2) = \frac{1}{n^3} \frac{(n - 1)n(2n - 1)}{6}$$

and use this to prove that $A = 1/3$.

2. Show that in example 2, the lower sum is given by

$$s_n = \frac{bh}{n^2}(1 + 2 + \cdots + (n-1)) = \frac{bh\,n(n-1)}{2n^2}.$$

3. Use the method of this section to prove that the area under the curve $y = x^3$ between 0 and 1 is 1/4. *Hint:* You will need the result of problem 23, Exercise 4.

4. Use the method of this section to obtain the area under the curve $y = Cx^2$ between 0 and b. Assume C and b are positive. Check your result by the method of section 4.

8. **The definite integral reconsidered.** In section 5 we defined the definite integral of $f(x)$ by the equation

$$\int_a^b f(x)dx = F(b) - F(a) \tag{32}$$

where $F(x)$ is so chosen that its derivative is $f(x)$. But what is the situation, if we cannot think of a $F(x)$ that has the required derivative? Such for example would be the case if we wanted the definite integral

$$\int_a^b x\sqrt{x^6 + 7x^4 + x^2 + 11}\ dx. \tag{51}$$

Try as we may we cannot obtain an expression involving a finite number of algebraic operations[5] on x which will give a $F(x)$ whose derivative is $x\sqrt{x^6 + 7x^4 + x^2 + 11}$. Does this imply that the expression (51) has no meaning? Not at all. We have just seen that if $f(x) = x\sqrt{x^6 + 7x^4 + x^2 + 11}$, the expression

$$\lim_{n\to\infty} [f(x_1^\star)\Delta x_1 + f(x_2^\star)\Delta x_2 + \cdots + f(x_n^\star)\Delta x_n] \tag{50}$$

exists, in the sense that this limit is a number. Indeed this is just the algebraic area of the regions bounded by the curve $y = x\sqrt{x^6 + 7x^4 + x^2 + 11}$, the x-axis, and the lines $x = a$ and $x = b$.

We must modify our definition of the definite integral, because Definition 1 is defective. The defect is of course that we cannot always find explicitly a $F(x)$ whose derivative is $f(x)$. The simple way out is to replace Definition 1 with

DEFINITION 2. *The definite integral of $f(x)$ from a to b is defined to be the limiting value of the sum, as given by equation (50).*

---

[5] The algebraic operations are addition, subtraction, division, raising to a power, and extracting a root.

Of course it is understood that in equation (50) it is the interval $a \leq x \leq b$ that is divided into n subintervals of length $\Delta x_k = x_k - x_{k-1}$ and that the maximum of the lengths of these intervals tends to zero as n tends to infinity. Further $x_k^\star$ is an arbitrarily selected point in the interval $x_{k-1} \leq x \leq x_k$ for $k = 1, 2, \cdots, n$. Quite naturally we use the same symbol

$$\int_a^b f(x)dx \tag{52}$$

for the definite integral of $f(x)$ from a to b.

With our new meaning for this symbol it is necessary to reexamine some of our early results. For one thing the symbol (52) is now defined only if $a < b$. So we extend the definition to include the missing cases, that is, if $a = b$, we make the definition

$$\int_a^b f(x)dx = \int_a^a f(x)dx = 0. \tag{53}$$

If $a > b$ we make the definition

$$\int_a^b f(x)dx = -\int_b^a f(x)dx \tag{54}$$

and this is meaningful because on the righthand side $b < a$ and this case is already covered by Definition 2.

The following results now flow directly from our new definition.

If a, b, and c are any three numbers then

$$\int_a^b f(x)dx + \int_b^c f(x)dx = \int_a^c f(x)dx. \tag{55}$$

If $f(x)$ and $g(x)$ are any two continuous functions, then

$$\int_a^b [f(x) + g(x)]dx = \int_a^b f(x)dx + \int_a^b g(x)dx. \tag{56}$$

If C is any constant, then

$$\int_a^b C f(x)dx = C\int_a^b f(x)dx. \tag{57}$$

The proofs of these three results are not at all difficult, but they are rather tedious and involve considerable care with the details, so we omit these proofs. The curious student can find them in any good book on Advanced Calculus[6]. However a better approach would be for the

---

[6] Almost any book on Advanced Calculus contains an analytic proof that the integral of a continuous function exists. A very careful and detailed account of this material can be found in the book by H. S. Carslaw, *Introduction to the Theory of Fourier's Series and Integrals*, Dover Publications, 1930.

student to restate each of these theorems as a relation between the limits of suitable sums of the form (50), and then the results will be intuitively obvious. Only (55) may give a little trouble because one must first assume that $a < b < c$, and then use (53) and (54) to obtain the general case of arbitrary a, b, and c.

What happens to Definition 1, now that it has been replaced by Definition 2? Answer: It becomes a theorem namely

THEOREM 14. *If $F(x)$ is a function such that its derivative $F'(x) = f(x)$ and if $f(x)$ is continuous in $a \leq x \leq b$, then*

$$\int_a^b f(x)dx = F(b) - F(a). \tag{32}$$

This theorem is called the Fundamental Theorem of the Integral Calculus, and it is easy to understand why it carries this title. We have already proved this theorem in our work on finding areas. But we want an analytic proof, one that does not depend on the concept of area.

ANALYTIC PROOF OF THE FUNDAMENTAL THEOREM.

Divide the interval $a \leq x \leq b$ into n subintervals $\Delta x_k = x_k - x_{k-1}$, $k = 1, 2, \cdots, n$, in the usual manner. In each subinterval we apply the Mean Value Theorem (Theorem 6, Chapter 3). This states that since $F'(x) = f(x)$ there is in each subinterval an $x_k^\star$ such that

$$F(x_k) - F(x_{k-1}) = F'(x_k^\star)(x_k - x_{k-1})$$
$$= f(x_k^\star)\Delta x_k.$$

We write one such equality for each subinterval:

$$F(x_1) - F(a) = f(x_1^\star)\Delta x_1$$
$$F(x_2) - F(x_1) = f(x_2^\star)\Delta x_2$$
$$F(x_3) - F(x_2) = f(x_3^\star)\Delta x_3$$
$$\vdots$$
$$F(x_{n-1}) - F(x_{n-2}) = f(x_{n-1}^\star)\Delta x_{n-1}$$
$$F(b) - F(x_{n-1}) = f(x_n^\star)\Delta x_n.$$

Now add these n equations. On the left side all of the terms cancel pairwise except $F(a)$ and $F(b)$, and we have

$$F(b) - F(a) = f(x_1^\star)\Delta x_1 + f(x_2^\star)\Delta x_2 + \cdots + f(x_n^\star)\Delta x_n. \tag{58}$$

Now take the limit in (58) as $n \to \infty$. The righthand side becomes (50) the definition of the definite integral. But the lefthand side is fixed for all n. Hence from (58) we have

$$F(b) - F(a) = \lim_{n \to \infty} \sum_{k=1}^n f(x_k^\star)\Delta x_k = \int_a^b f(x)dx. \qquad \text{Q.E.D.}$$

One last remark about theory before we return to applications. We started by setting out five axioms that an area function must satisfy. Based on these axioms we made remarkable progress in the computation of areas.   In fact if the figure is bounded by relatively "decent" curves we can compute the area of the figure quite simply.   But a pure logician might well object to our procedure.

"You never defined what you mean by an area" he would argue, "so that all of your work has been based on an intuitive notion that to me is rather vague."   "I must reject your work, or at best accept it provisionally until I have time to give it careful thought."

Fortunately for us this conflict between the rigorous thinkers, and those who accept intuitively obvious arguments, has already been settled, and as is always the case, rigor won out.   It is necessary to define area.   One first proves carefully that if $f(x)$ is a continuous function the limit of the sum given in equation (50) always exists.   One then defines the algebraic area under the curve between a and b to be this limit.   It is then necessary to prove that this limit can be computed by integration, namely by finding an appropriate indefinite integral $F(x)$, and then the limit is $F(b) - F(a)$. But this proof must not use the geometric notion of area.   This is Theorem 14, and in the proof just given neither the word area, nor the concept were used.

Peace is now restored, and we can turn our attention to the many applications of the fundamental theorem, applications that are interesting, useful, and a pleasure to consider.

5

APPLICATIONS OF INTEGRATION

1. **The area between two curves.** Suppose that we have two curves $y = f_1(x)$ and $y = f_2(x)$ and we want to find the area A of the figure bounded by these two curves, and two vertical lines $x = a$ and $x = b$. The situation is illustrated in Fig. 1. Naturally we select the notation so

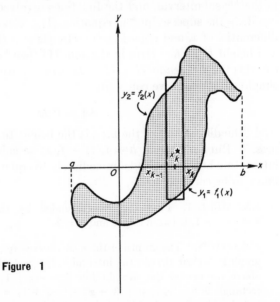

Figure 1

that the curve $y = f_2(x)$ lies above the curve $y = f_1(x)$, and this means that $f_2(x) \geqq f_1(x)$ for $a \leqq x \leqq b$. We approximate this area by summing the areas of suitably selected rectangles. A representative one is shown in the figure. In each subinterval an $x_k^\star$ is selected, and the height h_k of the approximating rectangle is just

$$h_k = y_2 - y_1 = f_2(x_k^\star) - f_1(x_k^\star).$$

The area of the rectangle is $h_k \Delta x_k$ and hence an approximation for the area A bounded by the given curves between $x = a$ and $x = b$ is

$$\sum_{k=1}^{n} [f_2(x_k^\star) - f_1(x_k^\star)] \Delta x_k.$$

In fact by the definition of area

$$A = \lim_{n \to \infty} \sum_{k=1}^{n} [f_2(x_k^\star) - f_1(x_k^\star)] \Delta x_k \tag{1}$$

and by the Fundamental Theorem (Theorem 14, Chapter 4) this is just the definite integral

$$A = \int_a^b [f_2(x) - f_1(x)] \, dx. \tag{2}$$

This same procedure will be used repeatedly so in order to speed up the work we introduce some short cuts in our notation, and in our thought process.

We have already seen that the limit of the sum, given in equation (1) does not depend on the particular $x_k^\star$ selected; just as long as each $x_k^\star$ is in the kth subinterval, and the functions involved are continuous. So we can drop the superscript $\star$ in equation (1). Next we can think of Δx_k as a differential of x, and regard each rectangle as a thin rectangle of width dx and height h. Each term in the sum (1) then has the form $h \, dx$, and we call this the *differential element of the area*. With this simplified view, and simplified notation we can write

$$dA = h \, dx \tag{3}$$

read "the differential of the area is the height times the differential thickness." But for each x, $h = f_2(x) - f_1(x)$ so substituting this in (3) and integrating both sides leads immediately to equation (2) which we already know to be correct.

EXAMPLE 1. Find the area bounded by the curves $y = 3 - x^2$ and $y = -x + 1$, between $x = 0$ and $x = 2$.

SOLUTION. The graphs of these two curves are shown in Fig. 2. From the graph it is clear that in the interval $0 \leq x \leq 2$, the parabola $y = 3 - x^2$ lies above (or meets) the straight line $y = -x + 1$. Hence the height of the rectangle is $h = y_2 - y_1 = 3 - x^2 - (-x + 1) = 2 + x - x^2$. The differential element of area is $dA = h \, dx = (2 + x - x^2) \, dx$ and hence

$$A = \int_0^2 (2 + x - x^2)dx = \left(2x + \frac{x^2}{2} - \frac{x^3}{3} \right) \Bigg|_0^2$$

$$= 4 + \frac{4}{2} - \frac{8}{3} - 0 = \frac{10}{3} = 3\frac{1}{3}.$$

EXAMPLE 2.   Find the area bounded by the curves $y = 3 - x^2$ and $y = -x + 1$.

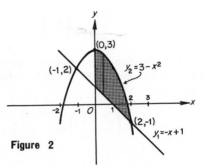

Figure 2

SOLUTION.   Here the terminology implies that the two curves intersect in at least two points, and if they intersect in exactly two points these two points determine a and b, the extreme values of x for the figure.   The case in which there are more than two intersection points for the two curves is illustrated in the next example.

Solving $y = 3 - x^2$ and $y = -x + 1$, leads to $3 - x^2 = -x + 1$ or $x^2 - x - 2 = 0$.   The roots are $x = 2$ and $x = -1$ and the points of intersection are $(2, -1)$ and $(-1, 2)$, just as indicated in Fig. 2.   Then just as in Example 1

$$A = \int_{-1}^{2} h \, dx = \int_{-1}^{2} (y_2 - y_1)dx = \int_{-1}^{2} [3 - x^2 - (-x + 1)] \, dx$$

$$= \int_{-1}^{2} (2 + x - x^2)dx = \left(2x + \frac{x^2}{2} - \frac{x^3}{3} \right) \bigg|_{-1}^{2}$$

$$= 4 + \frac{4}{2} - \frac{8}{3} - \left(-2 + \frac{1}{2} + \frac{1}{3} \right) = \frac{27}{6} = 4\frac{1}{2}.$$

EXAMPLE 3.   Find the area bounded by the curves $y = x^3/2$ and $y = x^5/8$

SOLUTION.   It is easy to prove that these two curves intersect at $(-2, -4)$, $(0, 0)$, and $(2, 4)$ and nowhere else.   The graphs are shown in Fig. 3.

In the interval $0 < x < 2$, the curve $y = x^3/2$ lies above the curve $y = x^5/8$ but in the interval $-2 < x < 0$ their roles are reversed.   Hence

$$A = \int_{-2}^{0} \left(\frac{x^5}{8} - \frac{x^3}{2} \right) dx + \int_{0}^{2} \left(\frac{x^3}{2} - \frac{x^5}{8} \right) dx$$

$$= \left(\frac{x^6}{48} - \frac{x^4}{8} \right) \bigg|_{-2}^{0} + \left(\frac{x^4}{8} - \frac{x^6}{48} \right) \bigg|_{0}^{2}$$

$$= 0 - \left(\frac{4}{3} - 2\right) + \left(2 - \frac{4}{3}\right) - 0$$

$$= \frac{2}{3} + \frac{2}{3} = \frac{4}{3}.$$

In this situation, one could also appeal to the symmetry and say that A is just twice the area of the region bounded by the two curves in the first quadrant. Thus

$$A = 2 \int_0^2 \left(\frac{x^3}{2} - \frac{x^5}{8}\right) dx = 2 \left(\frac{x^4}{8} - \frac{x^6}{48}\right)\Bigg|_0^2 = 2\left(2 - \frac{4}{3}\right) = \frac{4}{3}.$$

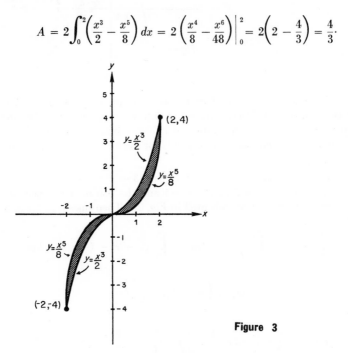

Figure 3

EXAMPLE 4. Find the area in example 3 using horizontal strips rather than vertical strips.

SOLUTION. By symmetry we can restrict ourselves to the region in the first quadrant. If this region is divided into horizontal strips the thickness of each strip is represented by dy and its length by $x_2 - x_1$, so $dA = (x_2 - x_1) \, dy$. For the particular curves under consideration $x_2 = (8y)^{1/5}$ and $x_1 = (2y)^{1/3}$. Hence

$$A = 2 \int_0^4 [(8y)^{1/5} - (2y)^{1/3}] \, dy = 2 \left(\frac{5}{6} 8^{1/5} y^{6/5} - \frac{3}{4} 2^{1/3} y^{4/3}\right)\Bigg|_0^4$$

$$= 2\left(\frac{5}{6} \cdot 8 - \frac{3}{4} \cdot 8\right) = \frac{4}{3}.$$

EXERCISE 1

In problems 1 through 8 find the areas bounded by the given pair of curves.

1. $y = 4x - x^2 - 3$ and $y = -3$.
2. $y = 2x - x^2$ and $y = x - 2$.
3. $x = 4y - y^2 - 3$ and $x = -3$.
4. $x = 2y - y^2$ and $y = x + 2$.
5. $y = x^2$ and $y = x^4$.
6. $y = x$ and $y = x^3$.
★7. $y = x^3$ and $y = 3x + 2$.
★8. $y = x^3 - x^2 - 2x + 2$ and $y = 2$.

★9. Find the area of the triangular shaped region bounded by the parabola $y = x^2$ and the two straight lines $y = 4$ and $y = x + 2$. Do this problem in two ways (a) first using vertical strips or rectangles so that $dA = f(x)\, dx$ with a suitable $f(x)$, and (b) using horizontal strips or rectangles so that $dA = g(y)\, dy$ with a suitable $g(y)$.

10. Use horizontal strips to find the areas in problems 5, 6, and 7.

2.   **Volumes.** If the region below a curve $y = f(x)$ between $x = a$ and $x = b$ is rotated about the x-axis it generates a solid figure called a *solid of revolution*. Because of the symmetrical way in which it is generated (by a rotation of a plane figure) it is easy to compute its volume.

The situation is pictured in Fig. 4 where in order to aid visualization, one-fourth of the solid has been removed. To compute the volume we

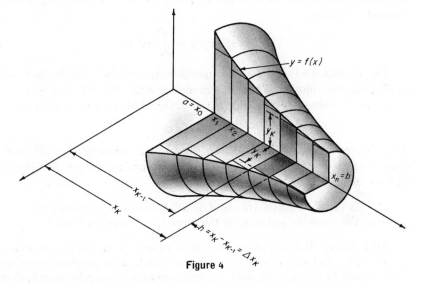

Figure 4

first cut the solid into disks by a number of planes each perpendicular to the x-axis. We notice that each disk is very nearly a right circular cylinder and is like a coin standing on its edge. The height h of the cylinder is the thickness of the slice, and the radius r of the cylinder is the y-coordinate of an appropriate point on the curve. Thus an approximation for the volume of the solid of revolution is obtained by adding the volumes of the approximating right circular cylinders, and the *exact* volume is obtained by taking the limit of this sum.

To carry out this program in detail, divide the interval $a \leq x \leq b$ into n subintervals by selecting points $a = x_0 < x_1 < x_2 \cdots < x_n = b$ and at each point x_k pass a plane perpendicular to the x-axis. If ΔV_k denotes the volume of that portion of the solid contained between the two planes at x_{k-1} and x_k and if the symbol $\approx$ means "approximately equal," then

$$\Delta V_k \approx \pi r_k^2 h = \pi y_k^2 \Delta x_k.$$

Here $h = \Delta x_k$ is the thickness of the disk (the height of the cylinder) and $r_k = y_k$ is a suitably selected radius. Any value of $y = f(x)$, for x in the subinterval $x_{k-1} \leq x \leq x_k$, can be taken for r_k. The picture in Fig. 4, shows the case in which the minimum value of $f(x)$ was selected in each subinterval. Thus an approximation for V is obtained by adding the volume of each of the n disks,

$$V \approx \sum_{k=1}^{n} \pi f^2(x_k)\Delta x_k = \pi[f^2(x_1)\Delta x_1 + f^2(x_2)\Delta x_2 + \cdots + f^2(x_n)\Delta x_n].$$

Taking the limit as $n \to \infty$, the sum tends to the *exact* value of V on the one hand, and on the other hand the limit is the corresponding definite integral. Hence

$$V = \int_a^b \pi f^2(x)dx = \int_a^b \pi y^2 \, dx. \tag{4}$$

The student is advised *not* to memorize this formula. Rather he should recall that the volume of a right circular cylinder is $\pi r^2 h$, and hence the approximate volume of one slice is the differential element of volume

$$dV = \pi r^2 \, dx. \tag{5}$$

Then he can proceed directly from (5) to (4). Because the differential element of volume is a disk, this method of computing volumes is called the *disk method*.

EXAMPLE 1.   Find the volume of the solid of revolution obtained by rotating about the x-axis the region under the curve $y = x^2$ between 0 and 2.

SOLUTION. It is not always necessary to make a perspective drawing of the solid. As indicated in Fig. 5, it is sufficient to draw the plane region that is rotated to generate the solid. A representative rectangular strip is shown in Fig. 5, and on rotation this generates a cylindrical disk of volume

$$dV = \pi r^2 h = \pi y^2 dx.$$

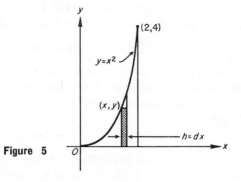

Figure 5

Hence

$$V = \int_0^2 \pi y^2 \, dx = \int_0^2 \pi x^4 \, dx,$$

since in this case $y = x^2$ and so $y^2 = x^4$. Thus

$$V = \pi \frac{x^5}{5} \bigg|_0^2 = \frac{32\pi}{5}.$$

In computing volumes it is frequently convenient to "slice" the solid into "shells" rather than disks. This situation arises when we rotate the plane region around the y-axis instead of around the x-axis. Such a solid is shown in Fig. 6 where one fourth of the resulting solid has been removed

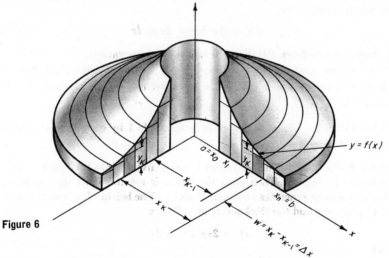

Figure 6

in order to aid visualization. A representative rectangular strip between x_{k-1} and x_k is shown shaded in the figure, and during the rotation this rectangular strip generates a cylindrical shell. If y_k is the height of this shell, then the precise volume of the cylindrical shell is

$$V_k = \pi x_k^2 y_k - \pi x_{k-1}^2 y_k = \pi(x_k + x_{k-1})(x_k - x_{k-1})y_k, \qquad (6)$$

obtained by taking the volume of a solid cylinder, $\pi r^2 y_k$ where $r = x_k$, and subtracting the volume of the hole, $\pi r^2 y_k$ where $r = x_{k-1}$. But x_k and x_{k-1} are approximately equal, so we can replace $x_k + x_{k-1}$ by $2x_k$. Thus (6) becomes

$$V_k \approx 2\pi x_k y_k \Delta x_k. \qquad (7)$$

This formula is easy to remember if we realize that $2\pi x_k$ is the perimeter of the outer circle, y_k is the height of the shell, and Δx_k is its thickness. So formula (7) has the form "length × height × thickness." On adding we have

$$V \approx \sum_{k=1}^{n} 2\pi x_k y_k \Delta x_k$$

and finally, on taking limits

$$V = \int_a^b 2\pi x f(x)\, dx = \int_a^b 2\pi x y\, dx. \qquad (8)$$

Again the student should not memorize this formula. This formula is very similar to (4) and the student who just memorizes will almost certainly confuse the two formulas and most of the time he will use the wrong one. It is much better to recall that the volume of a shell is "length × height × width" when the shell is "cut and flattened out." Then he can write immediately that

$$dV = 2\pi r h w = 2\pi x y\, dx \qquad (9)$$

and then proceed from (9) directly to (8) by integration.

Just as our first method of computing volumes was called the disk method, this procedure is called the *shell method*, or the method of cylindrical shells.

EXAMPLE 2. Check the solution to Example 1 by computing the volume by the shell method.

SOLUTION. This time the region is to be divided into horizontal strips, as indicated in Fig. 7. Then when the region is rotated about the x-axis, each horizontal strip generates a cylindrical shell. The height of each shell is $2 - x$, the radius is y and the thickness is dy. Hence

$$dV = 2\pi y(2 - x)dy$$

and

$$V = \int_0^4 2\pi y(2 - x)dy. \qquad (10)$$

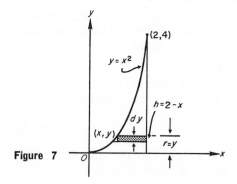

Figure 7

The reader should compare equation (10) with equation (8) and observe how much they differ, although both arise from the method of cylindrical shells. This should be a convincing argument against pure memorization of formulas for this type of problem. A firm grasp of the basic principles is highly recommended.

To complete the computation, we observe that the equation $y = x^2$ for the curve, yields $x = \sqrt{y}$. Hence (10) becomes

$$V = \int_0^4 2\pi y(2 - \sqrt{y})dy = 2\pi \left(y^2 - \frac{2}{5}y^{5/2}\right)\Big|_0^4$$

$$= 2\pi\left(16 - \frac{2}{5} \times 32\right) = \frac{32\pi}{5}.$$

Observe that both the disk and shell methods give the same volume $32\pi/5$.

In computing a volume, the slices need not be disks or shells, but can be any geometric figure that is easy to handle, such as a square, triangle, etc.

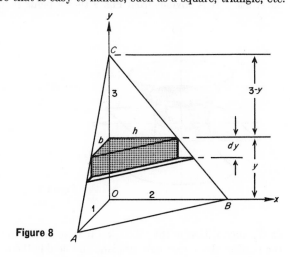

Figure 8

EXAMPLE 3.   Compute the volume of the pyramid $OABC$ shown in Fig. 8. The lines OA, OB, and OC are mutually perpendicular, and have lengths 1, 2, and 3 respectively.

SOLUTION.   We slice the solid by planes perpendicular to the edge OC, obtaining triangular slices.   If we regard OC as on the y-axis with O the origin, then the slices have thickness dy and the differential element of volume is

$$dV = \frac{1}{2} bh\, dy$$

where b and h are the base and height of the triangular face of the slice.   By similar triangles

$$\frac{b}{3 - y} = \frac{1}{3} \quad \text{and} \quad \frac{h}{3 - y} = \frac{2}{3}.$$

Hence $b = (3 - y)/3$ and $h = 2(3 - y)/3$.   Then

$$V = \int_0^3 \frac{1}{2} bh\, dy = \int_0^3 \frac{1}{2}\left(\frac{3 - y}{3}\right)\left(\frac{2(3 - y)}{3}\right) dy = \frac{1}{9} \int_0^3 (3 - y)^2\, dy$$

$$= -\frac{1}{9} \frac{(3 - y)^3}{3} \Bigg|_0^3 = 0 - \left(-\frac{1}{9} \frac{3^3}{3}\right) = 1.$$

Observe that this is consistent with the formula for the volume of any pyramid, namely $V = \frac{1}{3}AH$ where A is the area of the base and H is the altitude of the pyramid.

EXAMPLE 4.   The region bounded by the hyperbola $x^2 - y^2 = 1$ and the lines $y = -2$ and $y = 2$ is rotated about the y-axis.   Find the volume of the resulting solid.

SOLUTION.   Frequently symmetry can be used to simplify numerical computations.   It is obvious from Fig. 9 that a plane perpendicular to the y-axis

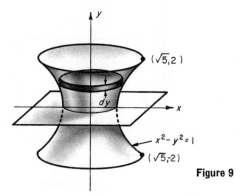

$(\sqrt{5}, 2\,)$

$x^2 - y^2 = 1$

$(\sqrt{5}, -2)$

Figure 9

at the origin, bisects the solid.   So it is sufficient to compute the volume of the portion above that cutting plane and double the result.   Whence

$$V = 2 \int_0^2 \pi r^2 \, dy$$

$$= 2 \int_0^2 \pi x^2 \, dy$$

$$= 2\pi \int_0^2 (1 + y^2) dy$$

$$= 2\pi \left(y + \frac{y^3}{3} \right) \Big|_0^2 = \frac{28\pi}{3}.$$

EXERCISE 2

In problems 1 through 4 the region under the given curve for the given interval is rotated about the x-axis. Use the disk method to find the volume of the solid of revolution so obtained.

1. $y = 2x$, $0 \leq x \leq 5$.   2. $y = x^3$, $0 \leq x \leq 2$.

3. $y = \sqrt{x(2 - x)}$, $0 \leq x \leq 2$.   4. $y = 4x - x^2$, $0 \leq x \leq 4$.

In problems 5 through 8 the region under the curve for the given interval is rotated about the y-axis. Use the shell method to find the volume of the solid of revolution so obtained.

5. $y = 2x$, $3 \leq x \leq 5$.   6. $y = x^3$, $2 \leq x \leq 3$.
7. $y = 4x - x^2$, $0 \leq x \leq 4$.   8. $y = 4x - x^2 - 3$, $1 \leq x \leq 3$.

In problems 9 through 11 the region bounded by the given pair of curves is rotated about the x-axis. Find the volume of the solid (a) by the shell method, and (b) by the disk method and show that the results are the same. Observe that in the disk method each disk will have a circular hole.

9. $y = x^2$ and $y = 2x$.
10. $y = \sqrt{x}$ and $y = x^3$.
11. $y = x^2$ and $y = \dfrac{x^5}{8}$.

12. In the pyramid of Fig. 8, suppose as before that the lines OA, OB, and OC are mutually perpendicular but this time have lengths a, b, and c respectively. Prove the general formula for the volume of such a pyramid, namely $V = \frac{1}{6} abc = \frac{1}{3} AH$, where A is the area of the base and H is the altitude.

13. Prove that the volume of a right circular cone is also $\frac{1}{3} AH$, where A is the area of the base and H is the altitude of the cone. *Hint:* Consider the straight line $y = Rx/H$ for $0 \leq x \leq H$, where R is the radius of the circular base.

14. Prove that the volume of a sphere of radius R is $\frac{4}{3} \pi R^3$ by consideration of a suitable circle.

15. The ellipse $\dfrac{x^2}{a^2} + \dfrac{y^2}{b^2} = 1$ is rotated about the x-axis. Find the volume of the region bounded by the surface of revolution so generated.

16. Find the volume if the ellipse of problem 15 is rotated about the y-axis.

Find all pairs a and b for which this volume is equal to the volume of the solid of problem 15.

17. A certain solid has its base in the xy-plane, and the base is the circle $x^2 + y^2 \leqq r^2$. Each plane perpendicular to the x-axis that meets this solid cuts the solid in a square. Find the volume of the solid.

18. Find the volume of the solid of problem 17 if each of the planes cuts the solid in an equilateral triangle.

*19. A wedge is cut from a cylinder of radius 10 in. by two half-planes, one perpendicular to the axis of the cylinder. The second plane meets the first plane at an angle of 45° along a diameter of the circular cross section made by the first plane. Find the volume of the wedge.

*20. A "hole" is drilled in a solid cylindrical rod of radius r, by a drill also of radius r. The axes of the rod and the drill meet at right angles and because the radii are equal the "hole" just separates the rod into two pieces. Find the volume of the material cut out by the drill.

3.   Fluid pressure. Everyone who swims is familiar with the fact that the pressure of the water on the body increases as one goes deeper under the water. This pressure is most noticeable on the ears which are rather sensitive to such external forces. Careful measurements indicate that for any fluid the pressure at a point is directly proportional to the distance of the point below the surface of the fluid. Further the constant of proportionality is just the density w of the fluid measured in suitable units. Thus if the distance h is measured in feet, then the density w would be measured in pounds per cubic foot, and the pressure, given by the formula

$$P = wh, \qquad\qquad (11)$$

would be in pounds per square foot. Similarly if w is in grams/cm³ and h is in cms then (11) gives P in grams/cm².

Formula (11) is completely reasonable and one could attempt a theoretical proof of (11) by arguing that a flat plate of unit area should support the weight of the column of fluid directly over it. Since most fluids are incompressible the density is a constant, and so equation (11) gives just this weight.

What is not at all obvious, is the fact that this pressure is the same in all directions. This means that if we take a flat metal plate, then no matter how that plate is oriented in the fluid, formula (11) still gives the pressure normal to the face of the plate at each point. Of course this pressure will usually vary as we go from point to point on the plate because h will usually vary.

If h is constant, as it is for a horizontal plate, then the total force F on the plate is just the pressure times the area

$$F = PA = whA.$$

$$F = \int P \, dA = \int wh \, dA \tag{12}$$

When the plate is not horizontal, h is a variable and simple arithmetic fails, but this is just the situation in which the definite integral is useful.

EXAMPLE 1. A vertical dam across a certain small stream has (roughly) the shape of a parabola. It is 36 ft across the top and is 9 ft deep at the center. Find the maximum force that the water can exert on the face of this dam.

SOLUTION. Obviously the maximum force occurs during flood time when the water is at the top of the dam and just about to overflow. The density of water is a variable, depending on the type and amount of dissolved material, but we will suppose for simplicity that for water $w = 62.5$ lbs/cu ft.

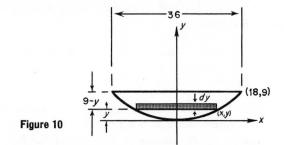

Figure 10

We place the river and the dam on a coordinate system as indicated in Fig. 10. The equation of the parabolic bottom of the dam has the form

$$y = cx^2$$

and since the curve passes through $(18, 9)$ we have

$$9 = c(18)^2$$

$$c = \frac{9}{(18)^2} = \frac{1}{2 \times 18} = \frac{1}{36}.$$

Hence in the first quadrant $x = \sqrt{y/c} = 6\sqrt{y}$. We divide the face of the dam into thin horizontal strips, as indicated in the figure. The representative strip shown is at distance $9 - y$ from the surface of the water. The pressure there is $P = wh = w(9 - y)$. The total force on the strip is

$$dF = P \, dA = w(9 - y) \, dA = w(9 - y) \, 2x \, dy$$

and hence on integration (summing over all such strips, and taking a limit)

$$F = \int_0^9 w(9 - y)2x \, dy. \tag{13}$$

For the particular case in hand $x = 6\sqrt{y}$, so we find

$$F = 12w \int_0^9 (9 - y)\sqrt{y} \, dy = 12w \left(\frac{2}{3} 9y^{3/2} - \frac{2}{5} y^{5/2} \right)\Big|_0^9$$

$$= 12w \left(\frac{2}{3} 3^5 - \frac{2}{5} 3^5 \right) = 24 \times 3^5 w \left(\frac{1}{3} - \frac{1}{5} \right)$$

$$= 24 \times 3^5 \times \frac{2}{15} w = \frac{2^4 \times 3^5 w}{5} \text{ lbs.}$$

Computation with $w = 62.5$ gives $F = 48,600$ lbs or 24.3 tons.

We could develop a general formula, similar to equation (13) for this type of problem.   But it is better not to burden the mind with such a formula.   The student should master the general principles as embodied in equations (11) and (12), and apply these general principles to each particular problem.

EXAMPLE 2.   Suppose that in Example 1 the face of the dam on the water side was slanted at a 45° angle.   Find the total force of the water on the face of the dam.

SOLUTION.   A cross section of the dam is shown in Fig. 11.   The pressure on a representative strip is just the same as before, but now the width of the strip is $\sqrt{2} \, dy$, because of the slant of the face.   Whence the area of the strip, and consequently each subsequent equation in the solution of Example 1

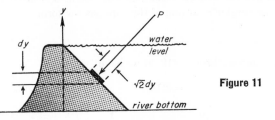

Figure 11

must be multiplied by $\sqrt{2}$.   Then the force of the water on the face of the dam is $\sqrt{2} \times 24.3$ tons or 34.4 tons approximately.   But this force is perpendicular to the face of the dam.   If we resolve this force into horizontal and vertical components, we find that there is a horizontal force of 24.3 tons tending to push the dam down the river, just as before.   The vertical component is also 24.3 tons, and this component is pressing the dam downward against its foundations.   This force would be added to the weight of the concrete, in the computations for the design of the foundation.

4. **Work.** When a constant force F acts in a straight line through a distance s, then the product Fs is called the *work* done by the force, and is denoted by W. This concept of work is introduced in physics, and it turns out to be a very useful one. If the force is a variable, then the arithmetic definition $W = Fs$ is no longer available. If the variable force is acting along a straight line, we make this line an x-axis, and if the force acts from $x = a$ to $x = b$, i.e., if it is pushing some object from $x = a$ to $x = b$ then by *definition* the work done is

$$W = \int_a^b F \, dx. \tag{14}$$

There is nothing to prove here, because this is just a definition of W. But it is clear that the underlying motivation for the definition is the fact that for a small displacement of the object through a distance Δx, the force is nearly constant and hence $F\Delta x$ is a good approximation to the work done during the small displacement. Then W should be the limit of the sum of the work done in each small displacement, as the maximum of the lengths of the small displacements tends to zero. But this is just the definite integral (14), and for this reason (14) is taken as the definition of work.

The compression of a spring furnishes a good illustration of these principles. Each spring has a natural length L, the length of the spring when no external forces are applied other than the gravitational forces. The force required to compress or extend this spring an amount x is directly

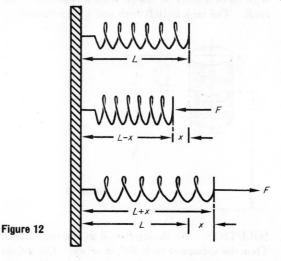

Figure 12

proportional to x, and this proportionality factor is called the spring constant. Thus

$$F = cx \tag{15}$$

where F is the force on the spring and x is the difference in length from the natural length.   The situation is shown in Fig. 12.

EXAMPLE 1.   A spring has a natural length of 20 in. and a 40 lb. force is required to compress it to a length of 18 in.   How much work is done on the spring in compressing it to a length of 17 in.?

SOLUTION.   We must first find the spring constant c from the given data. We know $F = 40$ lbs. when $x = 20 - 18 = 2$ in., whence from (15) $40 = c\,2$ or $c = 20$ lbs/in.   Then to find the work done, equation (14) gives

$$W = \int_a^b F\,dx = \int_0^3 20x\,dx = 10x^2 \Big|_0^3 = 90 \text{ in.-lbs.}$$

If this same spring were stretched from a length of 20 in. to a length of 23 inches, the work done on the spring would be the same.   In each case the work done in compressing or extending the spring appears to be stored in the spring, and can be recovered.   Thus if the spring that has been compressed to a length of 17 in. now pushes some object 2 in., so that the spring extends to a length of 19 in., then the spring does work on the object, and the amount is

$$\int_1^3 F\,dx = \int_1^3 20x\,dx = 10x^2 \Big|_1^3 = 90 - 10 = 80 \text{ in.-lbs.}$$

EXAMPLE 2.   Find the work done in filling a cylindrical tank (Fig. 13) with oil of density 50 lbs/ft³ from a reservoir 15 feet below the bottom of the tank.   The tank is 10 ft high and 8 ft in diameter.

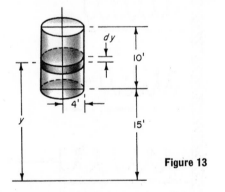

Figure 13

SOLUTION.   We divide the oil in the tank into disks by horizontal planes. Then the volume of each disk is $\pi r^2\,dy$.   The weight of this slice is the density w times the volume, so the work done in lifting this disk from the reservoir to the level y ft above the reservoir is

$$dW = yw\pi r^2\,dy.$$

Integrating between appropriate limits

$$W = \int_{15}^{25} \pi r^2 wy\, dy = \pi r^2 w \left. \frac{y^2}{2}\right|_{15}^{25}$$

$$= \pi r^2 w\, 200$$
$$= \pi \times 16 \times 50 \times 200$$
$$= 160{,}000\, \pi \text{ ft-lbs.}$$

One should observe that we have really computed a minimum value for W. For in actual fact there may be friction losses. Further in a practical case it might be necessary to carry the oil all the way to the top and then discharge it into the tank. In this latter situation all of the oil is lifted 25 ft and the work done on the oil is simply $10\pi r^2 w \times 25 = 10 \times 16 \times 50 \times 25\pi = 200{,}000\pi$ ft–lbs. This is larger than $160{,}000\pi$ ft–lbs as we know it should be.

EXERCISE 3
FLUID PRESSURE

(handwritten notes in margin: $h = 6-y$, $dA = 4dy$, $F = \int_0^6 (62.4)(6-y)\,4dy$, $= 249.6 \int_0^6 (6-y)\,dy = 4500\, lb$)

1. Find the force on one end of a tank if the end is a rectangle 4 ft wide and 6 ft high, and the tank is full of water.

2. Solve problem 1 if the end is an inverted triangle 8 ft wide at the top and 6 ft high.

3. Solve problem 1 if the end is a trapezoid 5 ft wide at the top, 3 ft wide at the bottom, and 6 ft high. Note that the area of the end of the tank is the same in problems 1, 2, and 3. Compare the three forces on the end.

4. A vertical dam has the form of a segment of a parabola 800 ft wide at the top and 100 ft high at the center. Find the maximum force that the water behind the dam can exert on the dam.

5. Find the force on one side of the vertical triangular plate shown in Fig. 14 when the plate is submerged in water.

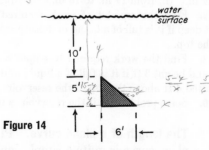

Figure 14

6. A gate for a dam is in the form of an inverted isosceles triangle. The base is 6 ft, the altitude 10 ft, and the base is 10 ft below the surface of the water. Find the force of the water on the gate.

7. A cylindrical drum lying with its axis horizontal is half full of oil. If the density of the oil is 50 lbs/ft³ and the radius of the drum is 9 in., find the force on one end of the drum.

---

8. The cross section of a cylindrical gasoline tank is an ellipse with major axis 3 ft and minor axis 1 ft. Naturally the tank is placed so that the axes of the cylinder and the major axis of the elliptical cross section are horizontal. Find the force on one end of the tank when it is half full of gasoline with a density of 50 lbs/ft³.

9. Solve problem 4 if the dam has the form of half an ellipse, that is the portion of an ellipse lying below the major axis.

10. Solve problem 5 if the base of the triangular plate is B ft instead of 6 ft, all other dimensions being the same.

11. Solve problem 5 if the top of the triangle is H feet below the surface of the water instead of 10 ft.

★12. Find a general formula for the force on one side of a vertical triangular plate submerged in water as shown in Fig. 14, when the base is B ft, the altitude is A ft, and the top is H ft below the surface of the water.

★13. Suppose that in problem 8 the major and minor axes of the ellipse are $2a$ and $2b$ respectively. Prove that the force on the end of the cylinder is $2wab^2/3$ whenever the tank is half full of a liquid of density w.

★14. Suppose that in problem 4 the parabolic segment has width $2a$ and depth b. Show that the force on the dam is $8wab^2/15$.

★15. The bow of a landing barge consists of a rectangular flat plate A ft wide and B ft long. When the barge is floating this plate makes an angle of 30° with the surface of the water. Show that the maximum normal force of the water on this plate is $wAB^2/4$.

WORK

16. If the spring constant is 100 lbs/in. find the work done in compressing a spring of natural length 20 in. from a length of 19 in. to a length of 15 in. $W = \int F \cdot dx$

17. A force of 40 lbs is required to compress a spring of natural length 20 in. to a length of 18 in. Find the work done in compressing this spring (a) from 20 in. to 19 in. (b) from 19 in. to 18 in. (c) from 18 in. to 17 in.

18. Find the amount of work required to empty a hemispherical reservoir 10 ft deep if it is full of a liquid of density w lbs/ft³ and the liquid must be pumped to the top.

19. Find the work required to empty a conical reservoir of radius 6 ft at the top and height 8 ft if it is full of a liquid of density w lbs/ft³ and if the liquid must be lifted 4 ft above the top of the reservoir.

20. Solve problem 19 if the reservoir is filled only to a depth of 4 ft.

5. The length of a plane curve. Physically speaking, the length of a plane curve is quite a simple concept. But mathematically it is a little more complicated. From a physical point of view, we merely take a piece of wire, bend it to fit the curve, snip off the excess, if there is any, straighten out the wire, and measure it with a ruler. What we now want is a solid mathematical definition that will give us just the number which our feelings about the physical nature of the problem demand that we should get.

For simplicity we will assume that the curve is given by an equation $y = f(x)$, and our problem is to define and compute the length of the piece of the curve between the lines $x = a$ and $x = b$. We can approximate the length of the curve by computing the length of a suitable polygon that lies close to the curve. We subdivide the interval $a \leq x \leq b$ into n subintervals with points $x_k, a = x_0 < x_1 < x_2 < \cdots < x_n = b$. Let P_k be the point (x_k, y_k) on the curve, so that $y_k = f(x_k)$. Let L_n be the length of the polygon $P_0 P_1 P_2 P_3 \cdots P_{n-1} P_n$ formed by joining the successive points P_k on the curve with straight line segments (Fig. 15).

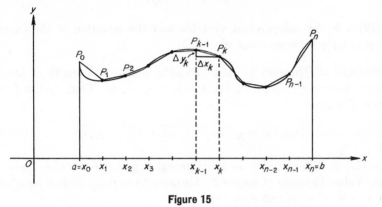

Figure 15

DEFINITION 1. *The length of the curve $y = f(x)$ between $x = a$ and $x = b$ is the limit of L_n, the length of the inscribed polygon, as n tends to infinity.*

If L denotes the length of the curve then by definition

$$L = \lim_{n \to \infty} L_n. \tag{16}$$

THEOREM 1. *If $f'(x)$ is continuous in $a \leq x \leq b$, then the length of the curve $y = f(x)$ between $x = a$ and $x = b$ is given by*

$$L = \int_a^b \sqrt{1 + f'(x)^2} \, dx. \tag{17}$$

At first glance this formula may appear to be hard to memorize. But if we use $\dfrac{dy}{dx}$ for $f'(x)$ we can transform the integrand thus:

$$\sqrt{1 + f'(x)^2} \, dx = \sqrt{1 + \left(\frac{dy}{dx}\right)^2} \, dx = \sqrt{dx^2 + dy^2}$$

so that (17) becomes

$$L = \int \sqrt{dx^2 + dy^2}.$$

(18)

Hence (17) appears as a highly disguised form of the Pythagorean Theorem. Interchanging the role of x and y in (17) or manipulating with (18) we arrive at

$$L = \int_c^d \sqrt{1 + \left(\frac{dx}{dy}\right)^2}\, dy.$$

(19)

In (19) y is the independent variable and the equation of the curve is $x = g(y)$ for y between c and d.

PROOF of Theorem 1. Let $|P_{k-1}P_k|$ denote the length of the line segment joining P_{k-1} and P_k, for $k = 1, 2, 3, \cdots, n$. Then by the Pythagorean Theorem

$$|P_{k-1}P_k| = \sqrt{(x_k - x_{k-1})^2 + (y_k - y_{k-1})^2}.$$

(20)

Since $f(x)$ is differentiable in the interval $a \leq x \leq b$ we can apply the Mean Value Theorem (Chapter 3, Theorem 6) to $f(x)$ and find an $x_k^\star$ such that $x_{k-1} < x_k^\star < x_k$ and such that

$$y_k - y_{k-1} = f'(x_k^\star)(x_k - x_{k-1}) = f'(x_k^\star)\Delta x_k.$$

(21)

Using (21) in (20) we obtain

$$|P_{k-1}P_k| = \sqrt{(\Delta x_k)^2 + [f'(x_k^\star)\Delta x_k]^2} = \sqrt{1 + f'(x_k^\star)^2}\,\Delta x_k.$$

Then on adding the lengths of the individual line segments we have

$$L_n = \sum_{k=1}^n \sqrt{1 + f'(x_k^\star)^2}\,\Delta x_k.$$

(22)

Since $f'(x)$ is continuous, the limit of this sum as $n \to \infty$ exists and is just the definite integral (17).   Q.E.D.

EXAMPLE 1.   Find the length of the curve $y = 2\sqrt{x^3}$ between $x = 1/3$ and $x = 5/3$.

SOLUTION.   By equation (17)

$$L = \int_{1/3}^{5/3} \sqrt{1 + \left(\frac{dy}{dx}\right)^2}\, dx = \int_{1/3}^{5/3} \sqrt{1 + (3\sqrt{x})^2}\, dx$$

$$= \frac{1}{9} \int_{1/3}^{5/3} (1 + 9x)^{1/2} 9\, dx = \frac{1}{9} \frac{2}{3} (1 + 9x)^{3/2} \Big|_{1/3}^{5/3}$$

$$= \frac{2}{27} (64 - 8) = \frac{112}{27}.$$

If the reader will select a curve at random and try to compute its length, he will see that equation (17) frequently leads to integrals that are hard to evaluate. We must select our curves very carefully in order to have $\sqrt{1 + f'(x)^2}$ simplify nicely. This difficulty will partially disappear when we learn more about integration in Chapter 9.

EXERCISE 4

In each of problems 1 through 7 find the length of the arc of the given curve between the given limits.

1. $y^2 = x^3$, $0 \leq x \leq 4$.
2. $3y = 2(1 + x^2)^{3/2}$, $1 \leq x \leq 4$.
3. $3y = (x^2 + 2)^{3/2}$, $0 \leq x \leq 3$.
4. $y = \dfrac{x^3}{3} + \dfrac{1}{4x}$, $1 \leq x \leq 4$.
5. $y = \dfrac{x^3}{6} + \dfrac{1}{2x}$, $1 \leq x \leq 3$.
6. $y = (a^{2/3} - x^{2/3})^{3/2}$, $0 \leq x \leq a$.
7. $x = 2\sqrt{7}\, y^{3/2}$, $0 \leq y \leq 1$.

8. Prove that the length of the arc in problem 7 is greater than the length of the chord joining the end points of the arc.

*9.   Let A be any positive constant.   Show that finding the arc length for the curve

$$y = \frac{1}{3\sqrt{A}} (2 + Ax^2)^{3/2}$$

leads to

$$L = \int_a^b (1 + Ax^2)\, dx.$$

Show that when $A = 2$, this is the curve of problem 2 and when $A = 1$ this is the curve of problem 3.

*10.   Let A and B be positive constants.   Show that finding the arc length of the curve

$$y = Ax^3 + \frac{B}{x}$$

will lead to the integral

$$L = \int_a^b \left(3Ax^2 + \frac{B}{x^2}\right) dx$$

if A and B satisfy the condition $12AB = 1$. Show that when $A = 1/3$ and $B = 1/4$ this is the curve of problem 4, and when $A = 1/6$ and $B = 1/2$ this is the curve of problem 5.

6.   The area of a surface of revolution.   If a curve is rotated about an axis it generates a surface, called a surface of revolution.   Our problem is to find the area of such a surface.   If we consider in particular the curve of Fig. 15, and rotate this curve around the x-axis, then at the same time the inscribed polygon $P_0P_1P_2\cdots P_n$ is also rotated about the same axis, and generates a second surface whose area S_n is very close to the area of the surface generated by the curve.   Each line segment $P_{k-1}P_k$ generates a section or frustum of a cone and the area of the frustum of a cone is known from solid geometry.   Thus we can obtain S_n by adding the areas A_k of each of these sections of a cone.

DEFINITION 2.   *If S denotes the area of the surface of revolution, then*

$$S = \lim_{n \to \infty} S_n. \tag{23}$$

Now the area for the frustum of a cone is

$$A = 2\pi \frac{r_1 + r_2}{2} l = \pi (r_1 + r_2) l$$

where the symbols have the meaning shown in Fig. 16.   Applying this to the frustum generated by the chord $P_{k-1}P_k$ of the curve of Fig. 15 we have

$$A_k = \pi [f(x_{k-1}) + f(x_k)] \sqrt{(\Delta x_k)^2 + (\Delta y_k)^2}. \tag{24}$$

Just as in the derivation of the formula for the length of arc, the Mean

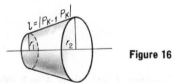

Figure 16

Value Theorem permits us to write that

$$\Delta y_k = f'(x_k^{\star})\Delta x_k \tag{25}$$

where $x_k^{\star}$ is a suitably chosen point in the interval $x_{k-1} < x < x_k$.   Using (25) in (24) and summing we have

$$S_n = \sum_{k=1}^{n} \pi f(x_{k-1}) \sqrt{1 + f'(x_k^{\star})^2}\, \Delta x_k + \sum_{k=1}^{n} \pi f(x_k) \sqrt{1 + f'(x_k^{\star})^2}\, \Delta x_k. \tag{26}$$

It is intuitively clear that as $n \to \infty$ these two sums give the integral

$$S = \int_a^b 2\pi f(x)\sqrt{1 + f'(x)^2}\, dx = 2\pi \int_a^b y \sqrt{1 + \left(\frac{dy}{dx}\right)^2}\, dx \qquad (27)$$

and this is indeed the formula for the area of the surface of revolution generated when the curve $y = f(x)$, between $x = a$ and $x = b$ is rotated about the x-axis.

The fly in the ointment is this: the definition of the definite integral as the limit of a sum requires that the same $x_k^\star$ replace x wherever it occurs in the integrand. But in (26) x_{k-1} appears in one factor, x_k appears in another, and $x_k^\star$ appears in two other factors. Although all three lie in the interval $[x_{k-1},\, x_k]$ they are not equal. It is easy to get around this slight obstacle. The reader may accept (27) on intuitive grounds or complete the proof in the following way.

Rather than handle the particular case of equation (26), it is better and simpler to prove a general theorem that will cover this situation and others as well. The essential feature of (26) is that each term in the sum consists of two factors, each of which is evaluated at points that may be different. So in place of (26) let us consider a sum of the form

$$I_n = \sum_{k=1}^{n} F(x_k')\, G(x_k^\star) \Delta x_k \qquad (28)$$

where the points x_k' and $x_k^\star$ both lie in the interval $x_{k-1} \leq x \leq x_k$ for each k, $k = 1, 2, \cdots, n$. Along with I_n let us consider the sum

$$I_n^\star = \sum_{k=1}^{n} F(x_k^\star)\, G(x_k^\star) \Delta x_k \qquad (29)$$

and compare I_n and $I_n^\star$. The only difference in these two sums is the point at which the first factor $F(x)$ is evaluated.

On the one hand by the definition of an integral

$$\lim_{n \to \infty} I_n^\star = \lim_{n \to \infty} \sum_{k=1}^{n} F(x_k^\star)\, G(x_k^\star) \Delta x_k = \int_a^b F(x)\, G(x)\, dx. \qquad (30)$$

On the other hand we have for the difference $I_n^\star - I_n$

$$D_n = I_n^\star - I_n = \sum_{k=1}^{n} [F(x_k^\star) - F(x_k')]\, G(x_k^\star) \Delta x_k \qquad (31)$$

and consequently

$$|D_n| \leq \sum_{k=1}^{n} |F(x_k^\star) - F(x_k')|\,\|G(x_k^\star)|\, \Delta x_k. \qquad (32)$$

Now as $n \to \infty$, the length of each subinterval $x_{k-1} \leqq x \leqq x_k$, approaches zero, so that $x_k^\star - x_k' \to 0$, both being in the same subinterval. If $F(x)$ is continuous in $a \leqq x \leqq b$, then given any positive ϵ no matter how small, we can find an n sufficiently large that each of the subintervals in the partition will be very small and as a consequence

$$|F(x_k^\star) - F(x_k')| < \epsilon$$

for $k = 1, 2, 3, \cdots, n$. Further if $G(x)$ is continuous in $a \leqq x \leqq b$, there is a constant M, such that $|G(x)| < M$ for all x in $a \leqq x \leqq b$. Then from (32) we have

$$|D_n| < \sum_{k=1}^{n} \epsilon M \Delta x_k = \epsilon M \sum_{k=1}^{n} \Delta x_k$$

$$|D_n| < \epsilon M(b - a). \tag{33}$$

Now M and $b - a$ are fixed, but ϵ may be taken as small as we please. Therefore (33) gives $\lim\limits_{n \to \infty} D_n = 0$.

Using (31) and $\lim\limits_{n \to \infty} D_n = 0$, we see that $\quad \lim\limits_{n \to \infty} I_n = \lim\limits_{n \to \infty} I_n^\star$.

Combining this with (30) and the definition of I_n in equation (28) we have

THEOREM 2. *Let $F(x)$ and $G(x)$ be continuous in $a \leqq x \leqq b$. Then*

$$\lim_{n \to \infty} \sum_{k=1}^{n} F(x_k')G(x_k^\star)\Delta x_k = \int_a^b F(x)G(x)dx, \tag{34}$$

where $a = x_0 < x_1 < \cdots < x_n = b$ is a partition, $\Delta x_k = x_k - x_{k-1}$, and x_k' and $x_k^\star$ both lie in the interval $x_{k-1} \leqq x \leqq x_k$ for $k = 1, 2, \cdots, n$.

The theorem that we have just proved is essentially Duhamel's Theorem. The statement of Duhamel's Theorem found in most books is much more complicated than the version we have presented as Theorem 2. For all practical applications however the two forms of Duhamel's Theorem are the same.

Returning now to the problem of computing the area of a surface of revolution, we apply Theorem 2 by setting $F(x) = 2\pi f(x)$ and $G(x) = \sqrt{1 + f'(x)^2}$. Then for the first sum in equation (26), equation (34) gives

$$\lim_{n \to \infty} \sum_{k=1}^{n} \pi f(x_{k-1}) \sqrt{1 + f'(x_k^\star)^2}\, \Delta x_k = \int_a^b \pi f(x) \sqrt{1 + f'(x)^2}\, dx.$$

A similar result holds for the second sum in (26). Hence Theorem 2 together with equation (26) give

THEOREM 3. *Suppose that $f(x) \geq 0$ and $f'(x)$ is continuous in the interval $a \leq x \leq b$. Then the area of the surface of revolution generated by rotating the curve $y = f(x)$ between $x = a$ and $x = b$ about the x-axis is given by*

$$S = \int_a^b 2\pi y \sqrt{1 + \left(\frac{dy}{dx}\right)^2}\, dx. \tag{35}$$

Naturally if the curve $x = g(y)$ between $y = c$ and $y = d$ is rotated about the y-axis then the area is given by

$$S = \int_c^d 2\pi g(y)\sqrt{1 + g'(y)^2}\, dy = \int_c^d 2\pi x \sqrt{1 + \left(\frac{dx}{dy}\right)^2}\, dy. \tag{36}$$

Finally the curve of Theorem 3 might be rotated about an axis parallel to the x-axis, say the line $y = y_0$. In this case the formula is

$$S = \int_a^b 2\pi(y - y_0) \sqrt{1 + \left(\frac{dy}{dx}\right)^2}\, dx. \tag{37}$$

In formulas (35) and (37) the curve must lie above the axis of rotation, and in (36) it must lie to the right of this axis. We leave it to the reader to discover the reason for this additional restriction (see Exercise 5, problem 12).

EXAMPLE 1. The curve $y = x^3$ lying between $x = 0$ and $x = 2$ is rotated about the x-axis. Find the area of the surface generated.

SOLUTION. By formula (35)

$$S = \int_a^b 2\pi y \sqrt{1 + \left(\frac{dy}{dx}\right)^2}\, dx = \int_0^2 2\pi x^3 \sqrt{1 + (3x^2)^2}\, dx$$

$$= \frac{2\pi}{36} \int_0^2 (1 + 9x^4)^{1/2} 36x^3\, dx = \frac{2\pi}{36} \frac{2}{3} (1 + 9x^4)^{3/2} \Big|_0^2$$

$$= \frac{\pi}{27} [(145)^{3/2} - 1].$$

EXERCISE 5

In problems 1 through 7 find the area of the surface generated by rotating the given arc about the x-axis.

1. $y = 2\sqrt{x}$, $0 \leq x \leq 3$.

2. $y = 4\sqrt{x}$, $5 \leq x \leq 8$.

3. $y = x^3/3$, $0 \leq x \leq \sqrt[4]{15}$.

4. $y = mx$, $a \le x \le b, \quad a \ge 0, \quad m > 0.$

5. $y = \dfrac{x^3}{3} + \dfrac{1}{4x}$, $1 \le x \le 2.$

6. $3y = \sqrt{x}(3 - x)$, $0 \le x \le 3.$

7. $8B^2y^2 = x^2(B^2 - x^2)$, $0 \le x \le B.$

8. The arc of $x = 2\sqrt{15 - y}$ lying in the first quadrant is rotated about the y-axis. Find the area of the surface generated.

9. Prove that the area of the surface of a sphere of radius r is $4\pi r^2$.

10. A zone on a sphere is the portion of the sphere lying between two parallel planes that intersect the sphere. The altitude of the zone is the distance between the two parallel planes. Prove that for a zone of altitude h on a sphere of radius r, the surface area is $2\pi rh$. Notice that this states that the area does not depend on the location of the zone on the sphere.

11. The arc of problem 5 is rotated about the line $y = -C, C > 0$. Find the area of the surface generated.

12. If the line segment $y = x - 3, 1 \le x \le 5$ is rotated about the x-axis it generates a piece of a cone. Show that formal manipulations using equation (35) to compute the surface area, lead to the integral

$$I = \int_1^5 2\pi(x - 3)\sqrt{2}\, dx$$

but that $I = 0$. Find the surface area. and explain why it is not given by I.

6

MORE ANALYTIC GEOMETRY

1.   Translation of axes.   In all of the curves that we have met so far the interesting features of the curves were close to the origin. For example the curve $y = x^2 - 2x + 3$ can be written as $y = (x - 1)^2 + 2$ from which the minimum point is (1, 2) and this is a "reasonable" location for a minimum point.   The student soon learns from experience to expect such nice behavior, and therefore in making a table of values from which to sketch the curve the student starts by using $x = 0, \pm 1, \pm 2$, etc.   And the quizmasters usually keep faith by proposing only "decent" curves for the student to plot.   But suppose we are confronted with a monstrosity such as

$$y = x^2 - 1000x + 252000 \qquad (1)$$

to graph.   We certainly have no desire to put $x = 0, \pm 1, \pm 2$, etc.   If we use calculus to determine the extreme values we find that $y' = 2x - 1000$, and hence the derivative vanishes at $x = 500$.   Since $y'' = 2 > 0$, we easily deduce that (500, 2000) is an absolute minimum point on the curve. Shall we now graph this curve in the usual way?   Of course not.   We would first move our coordinate axes so that the new origin is somewhere near this minimum point, and while we are in the moving business we may as well put the new origin right at the minimum point.   The manipulative technique for accomplishing this objective follows.

$$\begin{aligned} y &= x^2 - 1000x + 252000 \\ &= x^2 - 1000x + 250000 + 2000 \\ &= (x - 500)^2 + 2000 \end{aligned}$$

and hence

$$y - 2000 = (x - 500)^2. \qquad (2)$$

We introduce two new variables X and Y defined by

$$X = x - 500 \qquad Y = y - 2000 \qquad (3)$$

191

and when these new variables are used in equation (2) we have

$$Y = X^2, \tag{4}$$

an old friend.

Let us now analyze just what the substitution (3) does geometrically. Consider two rectangular coordinate systems placed with the corresponding axes parallel and similarly directed, as shown in Fig. 1. Let O' be the origin for the $X-Y$ system, and suppose that (h, k) are the coordinates for O' in the $x-y$ system.

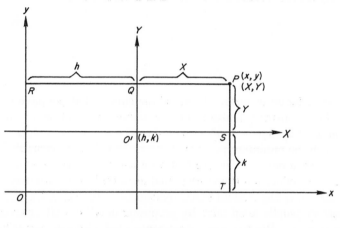

Figure 1

Now each point P in the plane has two sets of coordinates (x, y) when referred to the $x-y$ system and (X, Y) when referred to the $X-Y$ system. From the figure it is obvious that $x = X + h$ and $y = Y + k$, and hence

$$X = x - h, \quad \text{and} \quad Y = y - k. \tag{5}$$

The equations (5) relate the coordinates in the one system to the coordinates in the other. It is convenient to think of the $x-y$ system as the original or primitive system, and to regard the $X-Y$ system as the new system obtained from the original system by shifting (translating) the two axes from their original position to the new position. Then the equations (5) are the equations for the translation of the axes. Keeping in mind that only the axes and the coordinates are changed, but that the points remain just where they were, we have

> **THEOREM 1.** *When the coordinate axes are shifted without turning so that the new origin is on the point with coordinates (h, k) in the original system, then the equation set (5) gives the coordinates of each point P in the new system in terms of its coordinates in the original system.*

PROOF.   It may seem that the proof is obvious from Fig. 1 and that in fact we have already given the proof.   But the figure only shows the very special case that h and k are both positive and P lies in the first quadrant for both coordinate systems.

To complete the proof we must consider all possible locations for O' and all possible positions for the point P.   This is in fact very easy if we recall that coordinates are directed distances, and that with the lettering of Fig. 1 the equation $x = X + h$ is equivalent to the equation

$$RP = RQ + QP. \tag{6}$$

But for directed distances equation (6) is always valid for any three points R, Q, P no matter how the points are distributed on the directed line (see Theorem 1, Chapter 1).   Hence $x = X + h$ in all cases.   Similarly, with the lettering of Fig. 1 $y = Y + k$ is equivalent to

$$TP = TS + SP \tag{7}$$

and again this is always valid, no matter how the points T, S, and P are distributed on the directed line.   Q.E.D.

EXAMPLE 1.   Discuss the graph of equation (1).

SOLUTION.   We have already proved that the substitution $X = x - 500$, $Y = y - 2000$ changes the equation into $Y = X^2$.   But this substitution is just a translation of the coordinate axes so that the new system has its origin at (500, 2000).   Now we already know that the curve $Y = X^2$ is a parabola opening upward with its vertex at (0, 0), its focus at (0, 1/4), and directrix $Y = -1/4$.   Returning to the original coordinate system, the graph of $y = x^2 - 1000x + 252,000$ is a parabola with its vertex at (500, 2000), its focus at (500, 2000.25) and its directrix is the line $y = 1999.75$.

We recall from Chapter 1 the following facts about the conic sections. The standard forms for the equations are:

$$y^2 = 4px \qquad \text{Parabola,} \tag{8}$$

$$x^2 = 4py \qquad \text{Parabola,} \tag{9}$$

$$\frac{x^2}{a^2} + \frac{y^2}{b^2} = 1 \qquad \text{Ellipse,} \tag{10}$$

$$\frac{x^2}{a^2} - \frac{y^2}{b^2} = 1 \qquad \text{Hyperbola,} \tag{11}$$

$$\frac{y^2}{a^2} - \frac{x^2}{b^2} = 1 \qquad \text{Hyperbola.} \tag{12}$$

For the parabola (8) the vertex is at the origin, the focus is at $(p, 0)$ and the directrix is $x = -p$.   For the parabola (9) the focus is at $(0, p)$ and the directrix is $y = -p$.

For the ellipse (10), if $a > b$ the foci are at $(\pm c, 0)$ where $c = \sqrt{a^2 - b^2}$. If $b > a$ the foci are at $(0, \pm c)$ with $c = \sqrt{b^2 - a^2}$.

For the hyperbola (11), the foci are at $(\pm c, 0)$ where now $c = \sqrt{a^2 + b^2}$. For the hyperbola (12) the foci are at $(0, \pm c)$.

EXAMPLE 2.   Discuss the graph of

$$25x^2 - 4y^2 - 150x - 16y + 109 = 0. \tag{13}$$

SOLUTION.   Just as in example 1 we complete the squares by suitably grouping the terms, and adding appropriate constants to both sides.   Equation (13) can be put in the form

$$25(x^2 - 6x \quad) - 4(y^2 + 4y \quad) = -109. \tag{14}$$

We complete the squares inside the parentheses by adding 9 and 4 respectively. This amounts to adding 25×9 and subtracting 4×4 on the left side, and hence the same additions and subtractions must be made on the right side. Equation (14) then gives

$$25(x^2 - 6x + 9) - 4(y^2 + 4y + 4) = -109 + 25 \times 9 - 4 \times 4$$
$$25(x - 3)^2 - 4(y + 2)^2 = -109 + 225 - 16 = 100$$

$$\frac{(x - 3)^2}{4} - \frac{(y + 2)^2}{25} = 1.$$

The translation of axes, $X = x - 3$, $Y = y + 2$ yields

$$\frac{X^2}{2^2} - \frac{Y^2}{5^2} = 1. \tag{15}$$

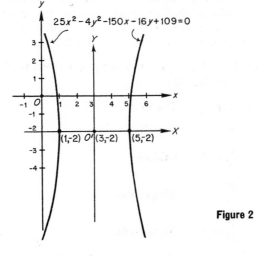

Figure 2

We know that this curve is a hyperbola with foci at $(\pm \sqrt{29}, 0)$ in the $X - Y$ system.   Returning to the original system the curve is still a hyperbola but now the foci are at $(3 \pm \sqrt{29}, -2)$.   Since the X and Y axes are axes of symmetry for the hyperbola (15), it follows that the lines $x = 3$, $y = -2$ are axes of symmetry for the graph of (13). Similarly the points $(1, -2)$ and $(5, -2)$ are vertices of this hyperbola in the original coordinate system. The graph of (13) is shown in Fig. 2.

EXERCISE 1

In problems 1 through 10, put the equation of the given conic into standard form by a translation of the axes, and identify the curve. If it is a parabola give its focus, vertex, and directrix. If it is an ellipse or hyperbola give its foci, vertices, and axes of symmetry.

  1. $y^2 - 4y + 12 = 8x$.
  2. $9x^2 + 25y^2 - 90x - 150y + 225 = 0$.
  3. $16y^2 - 9x^2 - 64y - 54x = 161$.
  4. $x^2 + 2x + 16y + 33 = 0$.
  5. $16x^2 + y^2 - 32x + 4y + 16 = 0$.
  6. $x + 20y^2 + 40y + 27 = 0$.
  7. $y^2 + 20 = x^2 + 10y + 4x$.
  8. $25x^2 + 16y^2 + 100x - 192y + 276 = 0$.
  9. $6x^2 + 84x + 69 = 15y^2 + 90y$.
 10. $2y + 180x = x^2 + 7950$.
 ★11. Prove that if $A \neq 0$ the curve $y = Ax^2 + Bx + C$ is a parabola. Find a formula for the focus of this parabola.
 ★12. Consider the family of parabolas $y = Ax^2 + C$ where C is a constant and A is a variable. Let $(0, F)$ be the focus. Compute dF/dA. What is the limit of F as $A \to 0^+$, as $A \to \infty$? Sketch a few parabolas from this family when $C = 1$.
 ★13. Consider the family of ellipses $x^2 + B^2y^2 = 1$ where B varies. Let $(\pm F, 0)$ be the foci when $B > 1$, with $F > 0$. Compute dF/dB. What is the limit position of the foci as $B \to 0^+$, as $B \to \infty$? Sketch a few ellipses from this family.
 ★14. Consider the family of hyperbolas $x^2 - y^2 = K$, with $K > 0$. With the notation of problem 13, find dF/dK. What is the limit position of the foci as $K \to 0^+$, as $K \to \infty$? Do any two distinct members of this family have points in common? Sketch a few hyperbolas from this family.

2. **Asymptotes.** The graph of the simple equation

$$y = \frac{1}{x} \tag{16}$$

will supply us with suitable examples of asymptotes. The graph can be sketched quite quickly by computing the coordinates of a few points, and the curve obtained is shown in Fig. 3. The important features of this curve are:

(a) At $x = 0$, equation (16) gives no value for y, so the curve does not meet the y axis. For every other value of x, (16) gives a corresponding y, and the function is continuous, so the curve falls into two pieces, separated by the $y -$ axis.

(b)   For a very small positive value of x, the corresponding y is very large.   For example if $x = .001$ then $y = 1000$.   Since y can be made arbitrarily large by taking x sufficiently small, this means that

$$\lim_{x \to 0^+} y = \infty. \tag{17}$$

(c)   For a very small negative value of x, the corresponding y has large absolute value, but is negative.   For example if $x = -.0001$ then $y = -10{,}000$.   Since $|y|$ can be made arbitrarily large by taking x sufficiently small and negative this means that

$$\lim_{x \to 0^-} y = -\infty. \tag{18}$$

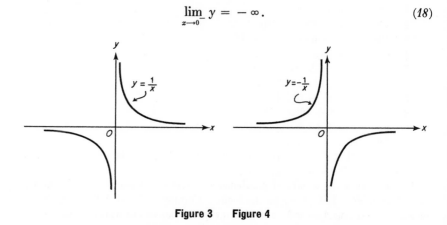

Figure 3   Figure 4

(d)   For a very large positive value of x, the corresponding y is positive and very small.   For example if $x = 100{,}000$, then $y = .00001$.   Clearly we have

$$\lim_{x \to \infty} y = 0. \tag{19}$$

(e)   Similar considerations show that

$$\lim_{x \to -\infty} y = 0. \tag{20}$$

The graph of the function $y = -1/x$ is shown in Fig. 4.   Since the only change in the function, is the factor -1, the curve of Fig. 4 can be obtained from the curve of Fig. 3 either (a) by rotating the curve about the x-axis through an angle of $180°$, or (b) by reflecting the curve across the x-axis.

Let us observe that a point P on the curve of Fig. 3, draws closer and closer to the y-axis as the point travels upward receding further and further from the origin.   If the point travels to the right going further and further from the origin, it draws closer and closer to the x-axis.   These lines, the

x and y axes, are called *asymptotes* of the curve. Similar considerations show that the curve of Fig. 4 has these same lines as asymptotes. This suggests

DEFINITION 1. *Let P be a point on the curve C, let s be the distance of P from a line L, and let r be the distance of P from the origin. If*

$$\lim_{r \to \infty} s = 0 \tag{21}$$

then the line L is called an asymptote of the curve C.

Now that the word asymptote has been given a formal definition, the reader should reexamine the graphs of $y = 1/x$ and $y = -1/x$ and convince himself that the x and y axes are indeed asymptotes for each of these curves.

The asymptote L does not need to be an axis. This is illustrated in

EXAMPLE 1. Find the asymptotes for the graph of

$$y = \frac{3x - 11}{x - 5}. \tag{22}$$

SOLUTION. Taking the limit as $x \to \infty$ we have

$$\lim_{x \to \infty} y = \lim_{x \to \infty} \frac{3x - 11}{x - 5} = \lim_{x \to \infty} \frac{3 - \dfrac{11}{x}}{1 - \dfrac{5}{x}} = \frac{3}{1} = 3.$$

Therefore the line $y = 3$ is a horizontal asymptote. Looking for a vertical asymptote we observe that

$$\lim_{x \to 5+} y = \lim_{x \to 5+} \frac{3x - 11}{x - 5} = \infty$$

and

$$\lim_{x \to 5-} y = \lim_{x \to 5-} \frac{3x - 11}{x - 5} = -\infty.$$

At $x = 5$, y is undefined, so the vertical line $x = 5$ divides the graph into two pieces, and each piece has this line as a vertical asymptote. The curve is shown in Fig. 5.

ALTERNATE SOLUTION. If we divide $x - 5$ into $3x - 11$ we find that

$$y = \frac{3x - 11}{x - 5} = \frac{4}{x - 5} + 3,$$

$$y - 3 = \frac{4}{x - 5}. \tag{23}$$

The substitutions $X = x - 5$, $Y = y - 3$ reduce (23) to the form

$$Y = 4\,\frac{1}{X}, \tag{24}$$

and this is essentially equation (16) except for the factor 4. Hence the graph of $y = (3x - 11)/(x - 5)$ is essentially that of Fig. 3 except that the curve has been stretched by a factor of 4 in the vertical direction, and the origin of the $X-Y$ system is at (5, 3) in the $x - y$ system. The graph is shown in Fig. 5. Since the X and Y axes are asymptotes for the graph of (24), it follows from the theorem on the translation of axes that the lines $x = 5$ and $y = 3$ are asymptotes of the graph of (22).

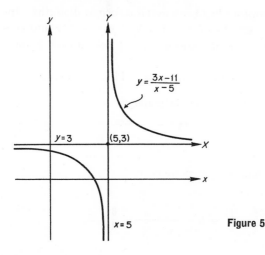

Figure 5

This example suggests that it is easy to locate horizontal and vertical asymptotes by virtue of

THEOREM 2. *Let C be the graph of* $y = f(x)$. *If*

$$\lim_{x \to \infty} f(x) = L_1 \tag{25}$$

then the line $y = L_1$, *is a horizontal asymptote of C as the point P on the curve recedes to the right.   If*

$$\lim_{x \to -\infty} f(x) = L_2 \tag{26}$$

then the line $y = L_2$ *is a horizontal asymptote of C as the point P on the curve recedes to the left.*

If $f(x)$ *can be written in the form*

$$y = \frac{g(x)}{(x - a)^n} \tag{27}$$

*where n is positive, g(a) ≠ 0, and g(x) is continuous at x = a,
then the line x = a is a vertical asymptote.*

This theorem is obvious from the preceding discussion, so we omit the
details of a formal proof. In most applications the limits L_1 and L_2 in
equations (25) and (26) will be the same. Frequently the exponent n in
equation (27) will be 1. When $n = 1$ and $g(a)$ is positive, the graph resembles Fig. 3 with a vertical asymptote at $x = a$, instead of the y-axis.
If $g(a)$ is negative then the curve resembles Fig. 4, with a vertical asymptote
at $x = a$.

EXAMPLE 2. Locate the horizontal and vertical asymptotes for the graph of

$$y = \frac{4x^3}{(x-4)^2(x+2)} \tag{28}$$

SOLUTION. For a horizontal asymptote we divide the numerator and denominator by x^3. This gives

$$\lim_{x\to\infty} \frac{4x^3}{(x-4)^2(x+2)} = \lim_{x\to\infty} \frac{4}{\left(1-\frac{4}{x}\right)^2\left(1+\frac{2}{x}\right)} = 4.$$

The limit is also 4 when $x \to -\infty$. Therefore the line $y = 4$ is a horizontal
asymptote both to the right and to the left. The graph of the function (28)
is shown in Fig. 6. Theorem 2, equation (27) makes it easy to locate the verti-

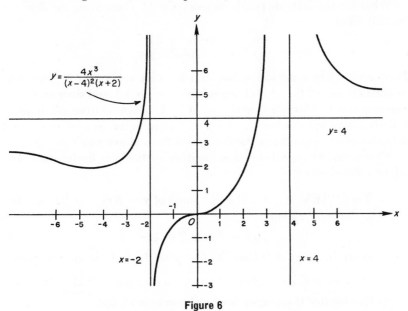

Figure 6

cal asymptotes.   We only need to find the zeros of the denominator.   These
are obviously $x = 4$ and $x = -2$, so the lines $x = 4$ and $x = -2$ are vertical
asymptotes.   For $x = 4$ the function $g(x)$ of the theorem is $4x^3/(x+2)$.
Since $g(4) > 0$, $\lim\limits_{x \to 4^+} y = \infty$, as indicated in Fig. 6.   But $(x - 4)$ occurs
to an even power, hence as $x \to 4^-$ we still have $y \to \infty$.   For $x = -2$ the
function $g(x)$ of the theorem is $4x^3/(x - 4)^2$.   Since $g(-2) < 0$ and since
$n = 1$, the graph is somewhat similar to Fig. 4 in the neighborhood of $x = -2$.
All of these facts are illustrated in Fig. 6.

Does the curve cut the x-axis?   We determine this by setting $y = 0$,
and this leads to the equation $4x^3 = 0$.   So the curve cuts the x-axis only
at the origin, and since $x = 0$ is a triple root of the equation $4x^3 = 0$, we
suspect that the curve has a point of inflection at $(0, 0)$.   Does the curve
meet the horizontal asymptote $y = 4$?   The condition $y = 4$ leads to the
equation

$$4 = \frac{4x^3}{(x - 4)^2(x + 2)}.$$

Hence

$$(x - 4)^2(x + 2) = x^3$$
$$x^3 - 6x^2 + 32 = x^3$$
$$6x^2 = 32.$$

Therefore the curve crosses the horizontal asymptote at

$$x = \pm 4/\sqrt{3} \approx \pm 2.309.$$

What are the extreme points on this curve?   Computing the derivative
for (28) gives

$$\frac{dy}{dx} = \frac{-4x^2(6x + 24)}{(x - 4)^3(x + 2)^2}.$$

Then $x = -4$ is a critical value, and for this value $y = 2$.   Since as x
decreases from -2 to -4, y changes from $+\infty$ to $+2$, and since as $x \to -\infty$,
y approaches 4, it is clear that the point $(-4, 2)$ is a relative minimum and
that the curve approaches the line $y = 4$ from below as $x \to -\infty$.   Similarly the curve approaches the line $y = 4$ from above as $x \to \infty$.

How about asymptotes that are neither vertical nor horizontal?   These
can be located using

> THEOREM 3.   *Let C be the graph of $y = f(x)$.   If $f(x)$ can be
> written in the form*
>
> $$f(x) = Ax + B + g(x) \qquad (29)$$
>
> *where $\lim\limits_{x \to \infty} g(x) = 0$ then the line $y = Ax + B$ is an asymptote
> of the curve C as the point P recedes to the right.   If $\lim\limits_{x \to -\infty} g(x) = 0$
> then the line is an asymptote as P recedes to the left.*

PROOF.   We must distinguish between the coordinates on the curve and on the line.   For a given x, let $y_C = f(x)$ be the corresponding y-coordinate on the curve of $y = f(x)$, and let $y_L = Ax + B$ be the corresponding y-coordinate on the line.   Let P_C and P_L be the points (x, y_C) and (x, y_L).

From equation (29) and the meaning of y_C and y_L we have

$$y_C - y_L = f(x) - (Ax + B) = g(x).$$

Suppose now that $g(x) \to 0$ as $x \to \infty$.   Then $y_C - y_L \to 0$ as $x \to \infty$. But as illustrated in Fig. 7 (the curve for Example 3) the distance s from the point P_C to the line L is less than $|y_C - y_L|$.   Therefore $s \to 0$ as $x \to \infty$.

The proof is just the same, in case $g(x) \to 0$ as $x \to -\infty$.   Q.E.D.

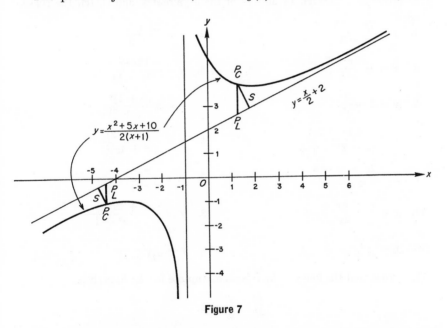

Figure 7

If $y_C - y_L$ is positive then obviously the curve lies above the line.   If $y_C - y_L$ is negative then the curve lies below the line.   But $y_C - y_L$ is just $g(x)$ so it is a simple matter to determine when the curve lies above the asymptote and when it lies below.

EXAMPLE 3.   Find the asymptotes for the graph of

$$y = \frac{x^2 + 5x + 10}{2(x + 1)} \tag{30}$$

SOLUTION.   By Theorem 2 there is a vertical asymptote $x = -1$, since the denominator has a zero at $x = -1$. If we perform the indicated division we find a quotient of $\frac{1}{2}x + 2$ and a remainder of 6.   Therefore

$$y = \frac{x^2 + 5x + 10}{2(x + 1)} = \frac{1}{2}x + 2 + \frac{3}{x + 1}.$$

Comparing this equation with equation (29) we see that $Ax + B$ is $\frac{1}{2}x + 2$ and $g(x)$ is $3/(x + 1)$. Since $\lim\limits_{x \to \pm\infty} 3/(x + 1) = 0$, it follows from Theorem 3 that the line $y = \frac{1}{2}x + 2$ is an asymptote. Further for $x > -1$, $g(x)$ is positive, so for these values of x the curve lies above the asymptote. When $x < -1$, $g(x)$ is negative and the curve lies below the asymptote. The graph of (30) is shown in Fig. 7.

EXERCISE 2

In problems 1 through 14 find all of the asymptotes, and sketch the curve.

1. $y = \dfrac{7x - 18}{x - 3}.$

2. $y = \dfrac{2x + 8}{x + 5}.$

3. $y = -\dfrac{2x + 7}{x + 1}.$

4. $y = \dfrac{-12x + 87}{2x - 14}.$

5. $y = 2 - \dfrac{3}{x^2}.$

6. $y = 5\dfrac{(x + 1)^2}{x(x + 2)}.$

7. $y = \dfrac{4(x^3 - 7x)}{(x - 2)^2(x + 5)}.$

8. $y = \dfrac{-6(x + 2)^4}{(x^2 + 4x)^2}.$

9. $y = \dfrac{2x^2 - x - 8}{2x - 3}.$

10. $y = \dfrac{x^3}{x^2 - 1}.$

11. $y = \dfrac{x^3 - 6x^2 + 6}{2x^2}.$

12. $y = \dfrac{-x^3 + 2x^2 - x + 3}{x^2 + 1}.$

13. $y = \dfrac{x^4}{x^2 + 1}.$

14. $y = \dfrac{x^4}{2x^3 + 16}.$

15.   Prove that the line $y = bx/a$ is an asymptote for the hyperbola.

$$\frac{y^2}{b^2} - \frac{x^2}{a^2} = 1.$$

Hint: This amounts to proving that

$$\lim_{x \to \infty} \left(\frac{bx}{a} - \frac{b}{a}\sqrt{x^2 + a^2} \right) = 0.$$

Notice that

$$\frac{b}{a}(x - \sqrt{x^2 + a^2})(x + \sqrt{x^2 + a^2}) = \frac{b}{a}(-a^2) = -ab.$$

and hence

$$\lim_{x \to \infty} \left(\frac{bx}{a} - \frac{b}{a}\sqrt{x^2 + a^2} \right) = \lim_{x \to \infty} \frac{-ab}{x + \sqrt{x^2 + a^2}} = 0.$$

16. Prove that $y = -bx/a$ is also an asymptote for the hyperbola of problem 15.

17. Prove that the lines $y = \pm bx/a$ are both asymptotes for the hyperbola

$$\frac{x^2}{a^2} - \frac{y^2}{b^2} = 1.$$

18. Does the parabola $y = x^2$ have an asymptote?

3. **Symmetry.** Two points P_1 and P_2 are said to be *symmetric with respect to a line l* if the line l is the perpendicular bisector of the segment P_1P_2. Each of the points is said to be the *reflection* of the other point in the line l. We can think of l as a mirror, and each of the points is an image of the other point in the mirror. A curve is said to be *symmetric with respect to the line l* if for every point P_1 on the curve its reflection P_2 in the line l is also on the curve. In this case the line l is called an axis of symmetry for the curve.

We may also have symmetry with respect to a point. Two points P_1 and P_2 are said to be *symmetric with respect to a point O*, if the point O is the bisector of the segment P_1P_2. Each of the points is said to be the *reflection* of the other in the point O. Of course in this case the physical picture of O acting as a mirror is missing. A curve is said to be *symmetric with respect to a point O* if for every point P on the curve its reflection in the point O is also on the curve. In this case the point O is called a *center of symmetry for the curve*. As an example the center of a circle is a center of symmetry for that curve because every diameter of a circle is bisected by the center.

Our objective is to give an algebraic test for the symmetry of curves. Since we can always translate the axes, we can assume that the line of symmetry is a line through the origin, and the center of symmetry is at the origin.

Just as the symbol $f(x)$ denotes a function of one variable, we can use a similar notation, $F(x, y)$ to denote a function of two variables. Any equation of a plane curve can be put in the form

$$F(x, y) = 0. \tag{31}$$

For example the parabola $y^2 = 16x$ can be written in the form

$$y^2 - 16x = 0 \tag{32}$$

where on comparison with (31) we see that the function of two variables $F(x, y)$ is just $y^2 - 16x$. Actually the graph of (31) may consist of several curves. For example the graph of

$$y^3 - 16xy = 0 \tag{33}$$

consists of the parabola $y^2 = 16x$ and the x-axis since the given function can be factored into the product $y(y^2 - 16x) = 0$, so that either $y = 0$ (the x-axis) or $y^2 - 16x = 0$ (the parabola).

Two equations $F(x, y) = 0$ and $G(x, y) = 0$ are said to be *equivalent* if they have the same graphs.   There is no need for a long discussion of this concept.   The only fact that we will need is the obvious one that if $G(x, y) = C F(x, y)$ where C is some nonzero constant, then the two equations are equivalent.

THEOREM 4.   *If $F(x, -y) = 0$ is equivalent to $F(x, y) = 0$, then the graph of $F(x, y) = 0$ is symmetric with respect to the x-axis.*
If $F(-x, y) = 0$ is equivalent to $F(x, y) = 0$, then the graph of $F(x, y) = 0$ is symmetric with respect to the y-axis.

In simple terms this means that we are to replace one of the variables by its negative and examine the resulting equation.   For example if we replace y by $-y$ in $y^3 - 16xy = 0$ we have $(-y)^3 - 16x(-y) = 0$ or

$$-y^3 + 16xy = 0. \tag{34}$$

Since (33) can be obtained from (34) by multiplying by -1, the two equations are equivalent.   Hence by Theorem 4 the graph of (33) is symmetric with respect to the x-axis.

If we replace x by $-x$ in (33) we obtain $y^3 + 16xy = 0$.   Clearly this equation is not equivalent to (33) and so the graph of (33) is not symmetrical with respect to the y-axis.

PROOF OF THEOREM 4.   Let $P_1(a, b)$ be a point on the curve $F(x, y) = 0$.   If P_2 is the image of P_1 in the x-axis then P_2 has the coordinates $(a, -b)$ (see Fig. 8).   Since P_1 is on the given curve, $F(a, b) = 0$.

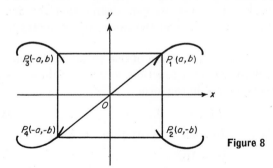

Figure 8

Then the coordinates of P_2 will satisfy the equation $F(x, -y) = 0$.   If $F(x, -y) = 0$ is equivalent to $F(x, y) = 0$, this means that P_2 is on the original curve.   Hence the original curve is symmetric with respect to the x-axis.

Similarly the point $P_3(-a, b)$ is the image of $P_1(a, b)$ in the y-axis. So if $F(-x, y) = 0$ is equivalent to $F(x, y) = 0$, both P_1 and P_3 lie on the curve together, and the curve is symmetric with respect to the y-axis.

Finally the point $P_4(-a, -b)$ is the image of $P_1(a, b)$ in the origin. Hence

THEOREM 5. *If $F(-x, -y) = 0$ is equivalent to $F(x, y) = 0$, then the graph of $F(x, y) = 0$ is symmetric with respect to the origin.*

EXAMPLE 1. Discuss the symmetry of the curve

$$y = \frac{x^3}{x^2 - 1}. \tag{35}$$

SOLUTION. It is not necessary to transpose the terms and obtain the form $F(x, y) = 0$. We can substitute directly in (35). Replacing y by $-y$ gives

$$-y = \frac{x^3}{x^2 - 1}. \tag{36}$$

Replacing x by $-x$ gives

$$y = \frac{-x^3}{x^2 - 1}. \tag{37}$$

Making both replacements we find

$$-y = \frac{-x^3}{x^2 - 1}. \tag{38}$$

Equations (36) and (37) are *not* equivalent to (35), but (38) is equivalent to (35). Hence the curve is symmetric with respect to the origin, but not with respect to either axis. This curve, along with its asymptotes, is shown in Fig. 9. This is the curve of problem 10 of the preceding exercise.

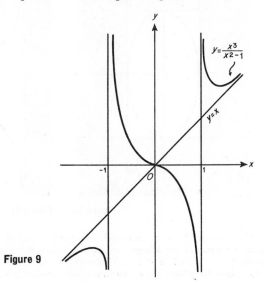

Figure 9

4.   Excluded regions.   In sketching a curve it is frequently helpful to
block out certain regions into which the curve can not enter.   In
most cases such regions occur when we are required to take the square
root of a negative number.   The simplest example is the parabola $y^2 = 16x$.
When x is negative we see that y is the square root of a negative number,
and hence there is *no real* corresponding y.   Thus the parabola does not
enter the half plane to the left of the y-axis.   The half plane[1] $x < 0$ is called
an *excluded region* for this curve.   Of course excluded regions may have
various shapes but for simplicity we consider only half planes and strips.

EXAMPLE 1.   Show   that   the   ellipse $\dfrac{x^2}{a^2} + \dfrac{y^2}{b^2} = 1$ lies   in   the   rectangle
$-a \leqq x \leqq a, \ -b \leqq y \leqq b$.   In   other   words   the   four   half   planes $x > a$,
$x < -a, \ y > b$, and $y < -b$ are excluded regions (see Fig. 10 where the
excluded regions are shaded).

SOLUTION.   Solving for y we find

$$y = \pm b \sqrt{1 - \frac{x^2}{a^2}}.$$

Hence if $|x| > a$, the quantity under the radical is negative, and there is no

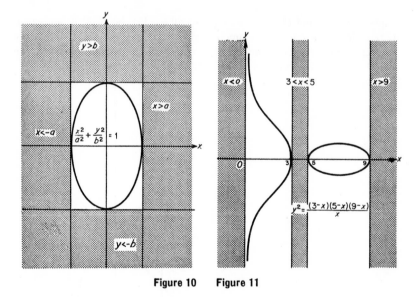

Figure 10   Figure 11

[1] The symbol "$x < 0$" as used here means the set of all those points in the plane for
which the x-coordinate is negative. Clearly this is just the plane to the left of the y-axis.
Similarly the symbol "$a < x < b$" means the vertical strip consisting of all those points
in the plane for which the x-coordinate lies between a and b.

real y. Similarly solving for x we have

$$x = \pm a \sqrt{1 - \frac{y^2}{b^2}}.$$

So if $|y| > b$, the quantity under the radical is negative. Hence the four half planes $x > a$, $x < -a$, $y > b$, and $y < -b$, are excluded regions for this ellipse.

EXAMPLE 2. Sketch the curve

$$y^2 = \frac{(3 - x)(5 - x)(9 - x)}{x} \tag{39}$$

SOLUTION.   Using the tests for symmetry developed in the preceding section we find that the curve is symmetric with respect to the x-axis.   So we can concentrate on that part of the curve above the x-axis.   The line $x = 0$ is a vertical asymptote.   Since

$$y = \sqrt{\frac{(3 - x)(5 - x)(9 - x)}{x}} = \sqrt{Q(x)}$$

we can determine excluded regions by locating those values of x for which the quantity $Q(x) = (3 - x)(5 - x)(9 - x)/x$ is negative.   The sign changes at $x = 0$, $x = 3$, $x = 5$, and $x = 9$.   For $x < 0$, $Q(x)$ is negative.   Therefore we expect that: $Q(x) > 0$ for $0 < x < 3$; $Q(x) < 0$ for $3 < x < 5$; $Q(x) > 0$ for $5 < x < 9$; and $Q(x) < 0$ for $x > 9$.   In other words $Q(x)$ oscillates in sign as we cross the zeros or infinities of $Q(x)$.   Hence the excluded regions are the two half planes $x < 0$ and $x > 9$ and the vertical strip $3 < x < 5$.   The graph of (39) is shown in Fig. 11.   The curve obviously cuts the x-axis at the points $x = 3, 5$, and 9.   We leave it for the reader to compute $\frac{dx}{dy}$ from (39) and show that the tangent to the curve is vertical at these three points.

EXERCISE 3

1. Prove that each of the following curves has the indicated axis or center of symmetry:

a. $\dfrac{x^2}{a^2} + \dfrac{y^2}{b^2} = 1$, x-axis, y-axis, origin.

b. $\dfrac{x^2}{a^2} - \dfrac{y^2}{b^2} = 1$, x-axis, y-axis, origin.

c. $y^2 = 4px$, x-axis.

d. $x^2 = 4py$, y-axis.

e. $xy = C$,   origin.

2. Prove that the strip $-a < x < a$ is an excluded region for the hyperbola of problem 1b.

3. Find excluded regions for $y = x^2/(1 + x^2)$ by solving for x in terms of y.

In problems 4 through 9 examine the given equation for symmetry and excluded regions and sketch the graph of the given equation.

4. $x^2y^2 = 16$.

5. $y^2 = 4\dfrac{x-2}{x-5}$.

6. $y^2 = 4 + x^3$.

7. $y^2 = \dfrac{x^2 - 6x}{x-3}$.

8. $y^2 = x^2(1 - x^2)$.

9. $y^2 = \dfrac{x^2 + 1}{x^2 - x}$.

★10. Prove that if the equation $F(x, y) = 0$ is equivalent to the equation $F(y, x) = 0$, obtained by interchanging the variables, then the graph of $F(x, y) = 0$ is symmetric with respect to the line $y = x$.

11. Test each of the following equations for symmetry about the line $y = x$.

a. $x^n + y^n = r^n$.

b. $xy = 1$

c. $y = \dfrac{x^2 y^2}{x^3 - y^3}$.

d. $x^2 + y^2 = x^3 + y^3$.

★12. By a suitable translation of the coordinate axes, prove that the graph of $y = (3x - 2)/(x - 1)$ is symmetric with respect to the line $y = x + 2$.

5.   The conic sections again.   In Chapter 1 each of the conic sections was defined individually and only the parabola had a directrix. In this section we introduce a directrix for the ellipse and the hyperbola, and show that a single unifying definition can be given for all of the conic sections.

> DEFINITION 2.   *Let e be a fixed positive number, F a fixed point, L a fixed line, and let $|PD|$ denote the distance from a point P to the line L.   The collection of all points P such that*
>
> $$\frac{|PF|}{|PD|} = e \qquad (40)$$
>
> *is called a conic section.   If $e = 1$ the conic section is a parabola. If $0 < e < 1$, the conic section is an ellipse.   If $e > 1$, the conic section is a hyperbola.   The point F is a focus and the line L is a directrix of the conic section.   The number e is called the eccentricity of the conic.*

Although this is a definition, there is something to prove, namely that the curves obtained from this definition are the same ones that we obtained in Chapter 1.   For the parabola this is obvious, because when $e = 1$ in (40) we obtain $|PF| = |PD|$ the same definition used in Chapter 1.

Suppose now that we consider the curve

$$\frac{x^2}{a^2} + \frac{y^2}{b^2} = 1 \qquad (41)$$

where for simplicity we assume that $a > b > 0$.   From Chapter 1 the foci are at $(\pm c, 0)$ where $c = \sqrt{a^2 - b^2}$. To show that this curve is an ellipse (by our new definition) we must show that all of the points $P(x, y)$ that satisfy (41) satisfy (40) and conversely. Of course this requires that the eccentricity, and the directrix be chosen properly. For the curve (41) we set

$$e = \frac{\sqrt{a^2 - b^2}}{a} = \frac{c}{a} \tag{42}$$

and we set

$$d = \frac{a}{e} \tag{43}$$

Then as we shall see e is the eccentricity of the ellipse (41) and the vertical line $x = d$ is a directrix for this ellipse.

THEOREM 6. *If $a > b > 0$, the curve (41) is an ellipse with a focus at $(c, 0)$, a directrix $x = d$, and eccentricity e, where $c = \sqrt{a^2 - b^2}$, $e = c/a$ and $d = a/e$.*

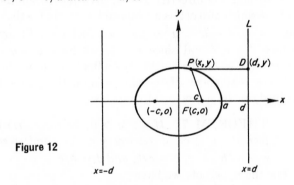

Figure 12

PROOF. Let F be the point $(c, 0)$ and L the line $x = d$. Assume that P satisfies equation (40). From Fig. 12 it is clear that

$$\frac{|PF|}{|PD|} = \frac{\sqrt{(x - c)^2 + y^2}}{|x - d|} = e.$$

On squaring and, observing that $|x - d|^2 = (x - d)^2$, this gives

$$x^2 - 2xc + c^2 + y^2 = e^2x^2 - 2de^2x + e^2d^2. \tag{44}$$

Now $d = a/e$ and $ae = c$, hence $-2de^2x = -2\frac{a}{e}e^2x = -2aex = -2cx$. Thus the terms $-2de^2x$ and $-2cx$ drop out of (44). This gives

$$x^2(1 - e^2) + y^2 = e^2d^2 - c^2. \tag{45}$$

But $e^2d^2 = a^2$ and $a^2 - c^2 = b^2$, so (45) yields

$$\frac{x^2(1 - e^2)}{b^2} + \frac{y^2}{b^2} = 1. \tag{46}$$

Finally $(1 - e^2)/b^2 = (1 - (c/a)^2)/b^2 = (a^2 - c^2)/a^2b^2 = b^2/a^2b^2 = 1/a^2$. Hence (46) yields (41). Therefore every point P that satisfies the condition (40) is on the curve (41). But all of the above steps are reversible, so that any point on the curve (41) satisfies the condition (40). This proves that (41) is the equation of an ellipse with our new definition.

It is clear from equation (42) that if $a > b > 0$, then $0 < e < 1$. Further we may obtain any value of e in this range by selecting a and b suitably. If a is close to b the eccentricity e is near zero, and if a is large compared to b then e is close to 1. In the first case the curve is close to a circle, and in the second case the curve is very flat. Thus the eccentricity measures the amount of distortion of the ellipse from a circle.

Since the curve (41) is symmetric with respect to the y-axis, the focus at $(c, 0)$ and the directrix $x = d$, give rise to another pair $(-c, 0)$ and $x = -d$ which also act as a focus and directrix for the ellipse. We observe that $c = \sqrt{a^2 - b^2} < a$ so the two foci $(\pm c, 0)$ are inside the ellipse. Further $d = a/e$ and since $e < 1$, we have $d > a$ and hence the two directrices $x = \pm d$ lie outside the ellipse, as shown in Fig. 12.

If the major axis of the ellipse is on the y-axis Theorem 6 must be modified, in the following obvious fashion.

THEOREM 7.   *If $b > a > 0$, the curve (41) is an ellipse with foci at $(0, \pm c)$, directrices $y = \pm d$, and eccentricity e. Here $c = \sqrt{b^2 - a^2}$, $e = c/b$, and $d = b/e$.*

For the hyperbola we have

THEOREM 8.   *The curve*

$$\frac{x^2}{a^2} - \frac{y^2}{b^2} = 1 \tag{47}$$

is a hyperbola with focus at $(c, 0)$, directrix $x = d$, and eccentricity e, where $c = \sqrt{a^2 + b^2}$,

$$e = \frac{\sqrt{a^2 + b^2}}{a} = \frac{c}{a} \tag{48}$$

and $d = a/e$.

PROOF.   Down through equation (45) the proof is the same as the proof of Theorem 6, for the only change in the meaning of the symbols is in the definition of c as $\sqrt{a^2 + b^2}$ instead of $\sqrt{a^2 - b^2}$, and this expression for c is not used in obtaining (45).   Now however the right side of (45) gives $e^2d^2 - c^2 = a^2 - c^2 = -b^2$ and hence (45) yields

$$\frac{x^2(1 - e^2)}{-b^2} - \frac{y^2}{b^2} = 1.\qquad(49)$$

But

$$-\frac{(1 - e^2)}{b^2} = -\frac{1 - \left(\frac{c}{a}\right)^2}{b^2} = -\frac{a^2 - c^2}{a^2b^2} = \frac{-(-b^2)}{a^2b^2} = \frac{1}{a^2}.$$

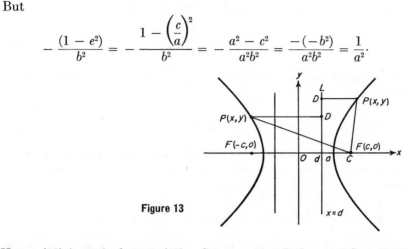

Figure 13

Hence (49) is equivalent to (47).   So any point P that satisfies equation (40) with e given by (48), must lie on the curve (47).   But all the above steps are reversible, so that any point on the curve (47) satisfies the condition (40).   This proves that (47) is the equation of a hyperbola with our new definition.

It is clear from (48) that $e > 1$ and that given any such e, we can always find suitable values of a and b, and obtain a hyperbola with this eccentricity.   Since the curve (47) is symmetric with respect to the y-axis, the focus at $(c, 0)$ and the directrix $x = d$, give rise to another pair $(-c, 0)$, and $x = -d$ that also act as a focus and directrix for the hyperbola.   These are shown in Fig. 13.   Since $e > 1$, we have that $d < a < c$, as indicated in the figure.

For the curve

$$\frac{y^2}{b^2} - \frac{x^2}{a^2} = 1\qquad(50)$$

we must modify Theorem 8 in the following obvious way.

THEOREM 9.   *The curve (50) is a hyperbola with foci at* $(0, \pm c)$, *directrices* $y = \pm d$, *and eccentricity e, where* $c = \sqrt{a^2 + b^2}$, $e = c/b$, *and* $d = b/e$.

Observe that in Theorems 6 and 8 the only difference is in the definition of c.   The same remark is true for Theorems 7 and 9.

EXAMPLE 1. Discuss the graph of

$$3x^2 - y^2 - 18x + 2y = 22. \tag{51}$$

SOLUTION. Completing the square in the usual way gives

$$3(x^2 - 6x + 9) - (y^2 - 2y + 1) = 22 + 27 - 1 = 48$$

or

$$\frac{(x-3)^2}{16} - \frac{(y-1)^2}{48} = 1. \tag{52}$$

The change of variables $X = x - 3$, $Y = y - 1$ reduces (52) to the standard form

$$\frac{X^2}{16} - \frac{Y^2}{48} = 1 \tag{53}$$

and amounts to a translation of the coordinate axes. Thus the graph of equation (51) is just a hyperbola. We apply Theorem 8 to equation (53). Here $a = 4$, $b = \sqrt{48}$, and consequently

$$e = \frac{\sqrt{a^2 + b^2}}{a} = \sqrt{1 + \frac{b^2}{a^2}} = \sqrt{1 + \frac{48}{16}} = \sqrt{1 + 3} = 2.$$

Since $c = \sqrt{a^2 + b^2} = \sqrt{16 + 48} = 8$, the foci are $(\pm 8, 0)$ in the $X-Y$ system. We could also write $c = ae = 4 \times 2 = 8$. Further $d = a/e = 4/2 = 2$ so that $\overline{X} = \pm 2$ gives the directrices. By problem 17 of Exercise 2 the asymptotes are $Y = \pm \sqrt{3}\, X$.

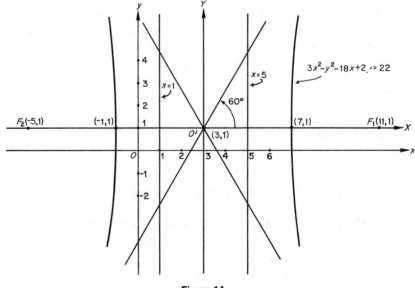

Figure 14

We can now transfer all of this data back to the original $x-y$ system, through the substitutions $X = x - 3$, $Y = y - 1$. We find that in the $x-y$ system, the foci are at $(11, 1)$ and $(-5, 1)$, the directrices are $x = 5$ and $x = 1$, the vertices of the hyperbola are at $(7, 1)$ and $(-1, 1)$ and the asymptotes are $y = \pm\sqrt{3}(x - 3) + 1$. These two asymptotes intersect at $(3, 1)$ the center of the hyperbola, and make angles of $60°$ and $120°$ respectively with the positive x-axis. The curve, together with the important items, is shown in Fig. 14.

EXERCISE 4

In problems 1 through 6 find the eccentricity, foci, and directrices of the given conic section. If the curve is a hyperbola find its asymptotes. It may be helpful to sketch the curve.

1. $3x^2 + 4y^2 - 16y = 92$.
2. $25x^2 + 16y^2 + 200x + 400 = 160y$.
3. $8x^2 + 32x + 23 = y(y + 2)$.
4. $9y^2 + 96x = 16x^2 + 72y + 144$.
5. $2(y^2 - 6y + 3) = x(x + 4)$.
6. $4x(x - 2) + 3y(y + 2) = 41$.
7. Prove that the ellipse of Problem 2 is tangent to both the x- and y-axis.
8. Prove that the hyperbola of Problem 4 is tangent to the x-axis.
9. Let r be the ratio of the minor axis to the major axis in an ellipse. Prove that $r = \sqrt{1 - e^2}$ and hence as $e \to 0$, $r \to 1$.

In problems 10 through 18 find the equation of the conic section with center of symmetry at the origin satisfying the given conditions.

10. Major axis 6, focus at $(2, 0)$.
11. Eccentricity $1/9$, focus at $(1, 0)$.
12. Focus at $(10, 0)$, directrix $x = 8$.
13. Eccentricity 5, directrix $y = 2$.
14. Focus at $(3, 0)$, eccentricity 1.5.
15. Directrix $y = 13$, eccentricity $12/13$.
16. Focus at $(4, 0)$, directrix $x = -9$.
17. Ellipse passing through $(2, 1)$ and $(1, 3)$.
18. Focus at $(\sqrt{5}, 0)$, asymptotes $2y = \pm x$.

19. Prove that for a hyperbola with foci on the x-axis $e = \sqrt{1 + m^2}$ where $\pm m$ is the slope of the asymptotes. Thus the eccentricity measures the deviation of the hyperbola from the x-axis.

★20. Prove that for each fixed $a > 1$ the ellipse

$$\frac{x^2}{a^2} + \frac{y^2}{a^2 - 1} = 1$$

has foci at $(\pm 1, 0)$. If a is large this ellipse resembles a circle $x^2 + y^2 = a^2$. What curve (or figure) does this ellipse approach as $a \to 1^+$?

★21. Prove that for each fixed $M > 2$ the ellipse

$$\frac{(x - M)^2}{M^2} + \frac{y^2}{2M} = 1$$

has center at $(M, 0)$, and vertices at $(0, 0)$, $(2M, 0)$, and $(M, \pm\sqrt{2M})$.   Show that $e = \sqrt{1 - 2/M}$ and the foci are at $(M \pm \sqrt{M^2 - 2M}, 0)$.   Use the vertices to sketch a few of these ellipses for large values of M, for example $M = 50$, $M = 5000$, etc.

★22.   Solve the equation of problem 21 for y^2 and show that as $M \to \infty$ this equation approaches $y^2 = 4x$.   Therefore under certain appropriate conditions the ellipse becomes a parabola as $e \to 1$.   As $M \to \infty$ one focus approaches $(1, 0)$ and one directrix approaches the line $x = -1$.   This is somewhat difficult to prove at present, but becomes easy with L'Hospital's rule covered in Chapter 11.

6.   The angle between two curves.   If L_1 and L_2 are two distinct lines, that are not parallel, they form two angles at their point of intersection and either one is the supplement of the other.   To distinguish between these two angles we will agree to take the least positive angle that the line L_1 must be turned in a counterclockwise direction about the point of intersection, to bring it into coincidence with L_2 (see Fig. 15).   We call

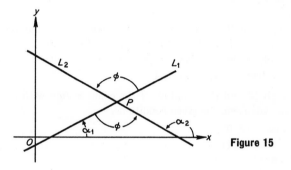

Figure 15

this *the angle from L_1 to L_2* and denote it by φ.   Thus φ is uniquely determined, and if L_1 and L_2 are distinct, φ will lie in the range $0 < \varphi < 180°$. If the lines are given by their equations, it is easy to find φ by computing $\tan \varphi$ using the formula of

THEOREM 10.   *If L_1 and L_2 have slopes m_1 and m_2 respectively and φ is the angle from L_1 to L_2 then*

$$\tan \varphi = \frac{m_2 - m_1}{1 + m_1 m_2}. \tag{54}$$

PROOF.   Assume that the two lines intersect at P as shown in Fig. 15. Then $\alpha_2 = \alpha_1 + \varphi$ or

$$\varphi = \alpha_2 - \alpha_1. \tag{55}$$

Taking the tangent of both sides of (55) gives

$$\tan \varphi = \tan (\alpha_2 - \alpha_1) = \frac{\tan \alpha_2 - \tan \alpha_1}{1 + \tan \alpha_1 \tan \alpha_2} = \frac{m_2 - m_1}{1 + m_1 m_2}. \qquad (56)$$

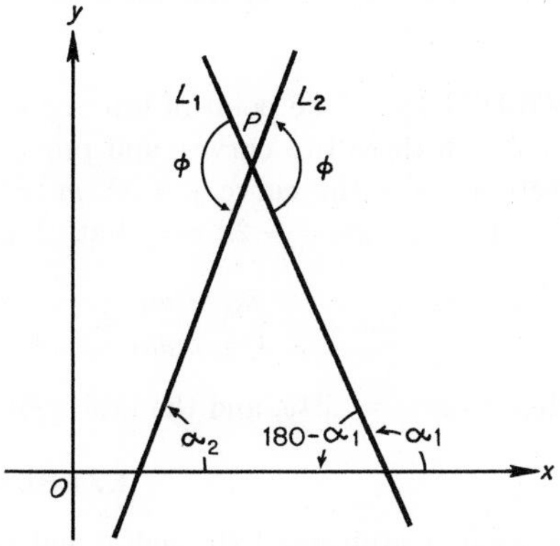

Figure 16

This does not exhaust all cases. In Fig. 15 the point lies above the x-axis, and φ is an interior angle, of the triangle formed by the x-axis and lines L_1 and L_2. Now φ may be an exterior angle as shown in Fig. 16. In this case we have

$$\varphi = \alpha_2 + 180 - \alpha_1.$$

But $\tan (\alpha_2 + 180 - \alpha_1) = \tan (\alpha_2 - \alpha_1)$ and this leads again to equation (56) and hence formula (54).

Finally suppose P the point of intersection lies on or below the x-axis. Then by a suitable translation of the axes, P could be made to appear above the x-axis. But in this translation neither φ nor the slopes m_1 and m_2 of the lines L_1 and L_2 are changed. Therefore formula (54) which has been proved when P lies above the x-axis is valid in all cases.

EXAMPLE 1. Find the angle between the lines L_1: $2y = x + 5$, and L_2: $3y = -x + \sqrt{17\pi}$.

SOLUTION. We have $m_1 = \frac{1}{2}$, $m_2 = -\frac{1}{3}$. If φ denotes the angle from L_1 to L_2, equation (54) gives

$$\tan \varphi = \frac{-\frac{1}{3} - \frac{1}{2}}{1 + \left(-\frac{1}{3}\right)\left(\frac{1}{2}\right)} = \frac{-2 - 3}{6 - 1} = \frac{-5}{5} = -1.$$

Hence $\varphi = 135°$. A computation for θ the angle from L_2 to L_1 will give $\tan \theta = +1$ or $\theta = 45°$. Since the problem did not specify a preferred direction, it is reasonable to present the smaller of the two angles, $45°$, as the answer.

DEFINITION 3.   *The angle between two curves at a point of intersection P is the angle between the tangent lines to the two curves at P.*

EXAMPLE 2.   Find the angle of intersection of the two curves $y = x^3$ and $y = 12 - x^2$.

SOLUTION.   One point of intersection is $(2, 8)$.   We leave it to the student to sketch these two curves, and prove that there are no other points of intersection.   For the curve $y = x^3$, $m_1 = 3x^2 = 12$ at $(2, 8)$, and for the curve $y = 12 - x^2$, $m_2 = -2x = -4$ at $(2, 8)$.   Then

$$\tan \varphi = \frac{m_2 - m_1}{1 + m_1 m_2} = \frac{-4 - 12}{1 + (-4)(12)} = \frac{-16}{-47} = \frac{16}{47}.$$

Hence $\tan \varphi \approx .340$, and the tables give $\varphi \approx 18°47'$.

EXERCISE 5

In each of problems 1 through 6 find $\tan \varphi$ where φ is the angle from the first curve to the second curve, at each point of intersection of the two curves.

1. $3y = x$, $2y = x$.   2. $3y = x$, $3y = -x$.
3. $y = 4x + \pi^2$, $y = 5x - \sqrt{31}$.
4. $y = -2x + 3$, $y = x^3$.
5. $y = x^2$, $y = 2x(x - 1)$.
6. $xy = 8$, $y = 10 - x - x^2$.

★7.   Let P be an arbitrary point on the parabola $x^2 = 4py$, and let F be the focus $(0, p)$ with $p > 0$.   Prove that the line segment PF and the ray through P parallel to the y-axis make equal angles with the tangent line to the parabola at P (see Fig. 17).   Thus a ray of light issuing from F will be reflected by the parabola along a line parallel to the y-axis.   This explains why headlights and searchlights have the form of a paraboloid of revolution with the light source at the focus. Reflecting telescopes have the same type design.

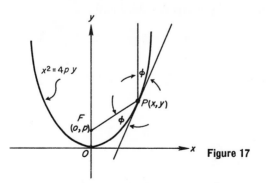

Figure 17

★8.   Prove that a ray of light issuing from one focus of the ellipse $x^2/a^2 + y^2/b^2 = 1$ will pass through the other focus.   In other words if P is any point on the ellipse prove that the line segments PF_1 and PF_2 make equal angles with the tangent to the ellipse at P.   *Hint:* The tangent of each of the angles is b^2/yc.

9.   Prove that the line $y = x$ bisects the angle from the line $y = m_1x$ to the line $y = m_2x$ if and only if $m_1m_2 = 1$.

10.   Prove that the angle from $y = m_1x + b_1$ to $y = m_2x + b_2$ is 45° if and only if $m_2 = (1 + m_1)/(1 - m_1)$.

★7.   Families of curves.   If we consider the equation

$$y = mx + 2 \tag{57}$$

with m constant, the graph is a simple straight line with intercept 2 on the y-axis.   But if m is regarded as a variable, then we get a straight line for each value of m.   Then (57) represents, not a single straight line, but a family of straight lines.   Indeed the family has infinitely many members, one for each value of m, and each of the straight lines passes through the point (0, 2).   A few members of the family are shown in Fig. 18.   The variable m is called a *parameter*.

As another example, the equation

$$(x - 1)^2 + (y - 2)^2 = r^2 \tag{58}$$

represents a family of circles, all with the same center (1, 2).   Here r, the radius of the circle, is the parameter.   A few members of the family are shown in Fig. 19.

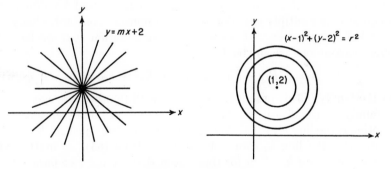

Figure 18   Figure 19

In any equation involving a single parameter all of the members can be transposed to one side, and the equation can be put in the form

$$F(x, y, k) = 0. \tag{59}$$

where k is the parameter.   Such a family is called a *one-parameter family of curves*.   A two-parameter family would be written in the form $F(x, y, h, k) = 0$ where h and k are two parameters.   For example the equation

$$(x - h)^2 + (y - k)^2 - 25 = 0$$

represents the family of all circles with radius 5. This family of circles is a two-parameter family, since h, and k may take on any values.

Suppose now that L_1 and L_2 are two distinct straight lines that intersect at P, and suppose their equations are

$$F_1(x, y) = A_1x + B_1y + C_1 = 0 \tag{60}$$

$$F_2(x, y) = A_2x + B_2y + C_2 = 0 \tag{61}$$

where the capital letters are fixed constants (not parameters). It is an easy matter to find a formula for the family of all straight lines that pass through P. Indeed the equation

$$h(A_1x + B_1y + C_1) + k(A_2x + B_2y + C_2) = 0 \tag{62}$$

defines a two-parameter family of curves, where h and k are parameters. But equation (62) is of first degree in x and y, so each member of the family is a straight line. Further since the coordinates of P satisfy equations (60) and (61), they must also satisfy (62). Hence the point of intersection of L_1 and L_2 lies on each straight line of the family (62). Finally given any point Q in the plane, there is a member of the family passing through Q. For we only need to substitute the coordinates of Q in (62) and then find suitable values of h and k. Therefore (62) is the family of all straight lines through the point of intersection of L_1 and L_2.

The two points P and Q will determine a unique straight line of the family (62) but will not determine the parameters h and k uniquely, for we can always multiply equation (62) by a nonzero constant, changing h and k but not the line. If we set $h = 1$ in equation (62) we have the simpler looking one-parameter family.

$$A_1x + B_1y + C_1 + k(A_2x + B_2y + C_2) = 0. \tag{63}$$

But the family (63) is practically identical with (62) because every line in the family (62) is also in the family (63) with just one exception. This exception is the line L_2. This line is in the family (62), just set $h = 0$, and $k \neq 0$. But the line L_2 cannot be obtained from (63), no matter what value we select for k. It is for this reason that we use two parameters h and k although in most situations we can take either h or k as 1.

EXAMPLE 1. Find the equation of the line joining $Q(2, 3)$ with P, the point of intersection of the two lines $y - 3x - 1 = 0$ and $2y + x + 5 = 0$.

SOLUTION. By our discussion the equation

$$h(y - 3x - 1) + k(2y + x + 5) = 0 \tag{64}$$

represents the family of all lines through P. Since $Q(2, 3)$ is to lie on one such line we put $x = 2$ and $y = 3$ in (64). This gives

$$h(3 - 6 - 1) + k(6 + 2 + 5) = 0$$

or $-4h + 13k = 0$. For simplicity we take $h = 13$, and $k = 4$, although various other combinations are possible. Then (64) yields

$$13(y - 3x - 1) + 4(2y + x + 5) = 0.$$

This gives $21y - 35x + 7 = 0$ or $3y = 5x - 1$. The reader should check this result by finding P and using the two point form of the equation of a straight line to obtain $3y = 5x - 1$.

This technique can be applied to more complicated curves. The very same discussion used for straight lines, will also prove

THEOREM 11. *Let $F_1(x, y) = 0$ and $F_2(x, y) = 0$ be the equations of the curves C_1 and C_2 respectively and let these two curves intersect at points P_1, P_2, $P_3, \cdots$, P_n. Then each curve of the family*

$$hF_1(x, y) + kF_2(x, y) = 0 \tag{65}$$

passes through each one of the points P_1, P_2, $P_3, \cdots$, P_n.

EXAMPLE 2. Find the equation of the common chord of the two circles $x^2 + y^2 + 6x - 41 = 0$ and $x^2 + y^2 - 12x - 6y + 25 = 0$.

SOLUTION. Each curve of the family

$$h(x^2 + y^2 + 6x - 41) + k(x^2 + y^2 - 12x - 6y + 25) = 0 \tag{66}$$

passes through the two points of intersection of the two circles, by Theorem 11. Now set $h = 1$ and $k = -1$. The squared terms in (66) disappear and we find

$$6x - 41 + 12x + 6y - 25 = 0.$$

This gives $18x + 6y - 66 = 0$ or $y = 11 - 3x$. Since this is the equation of a straight line through the two points of intersection of the given circles, this is the equation of the common chord. The reader should now work this problem the long way by first finding the coordinates of the points of intersection of the two circles.

Suppose that the two circles do not intersect. The multipliers h and k can still be selected so that (65) becomes the equation of a straight line. What can be said about this straight line. At first glance one might reply "nothing." But this is far from correct. This line, called the *radical axis* of the two circles, has many interesting properties (whether the circles intersect or not) but this subject must be reserved for a course in higher geometry.

EXAMPLE 3. Find the equation of a circle with radius $2\sqrt{5}$, that passes through the two intersection points of the two circles $x^2 + y^2 - 4x = 0$ and $x^2 + y^2 - 4y = 0$.

SOLUTION. Such a circle should be a member of the family

$$h(x^2 + y^2 - 4x) + k(x^2 + y^2 - 4y) = 0. \tag{67}$$

Completing the square in order to find the radius we have

$$(h + k)x^2 - 4hx + (h + k)y^2 - 4ky = 0$$

$$x^2 - \frac{4h}{h + k}x + \left(\frac{2h}{h + k}\right)^2 + y^2 - \frac{4k}{h + k}y + \left(\frac{2k}{h + k}\right)^2 = \frac{4h^2 + 4k^2}{(h + k)^2}.$$

Therefore if $h + k \neq 0$, equation (67) is the equation of a circle with radius squared equal to $4(h^2 + k^2)/(h + k)^2$. By the conditions of our problem

$$\frac{4(h^2 + k^2)}{(h + k)^2} = (2\sqrt{5})^2 = 20$$

$$h^2 + k^2 = 5(h^2 + 2hk + k^2)$$

$$4h^2 + 10hk + 4k^2 = 0.$$

Naturally this does not determine h and k uniquely, but only their ratio. Solving gives $h/k = -2$ or $h/k = -1/2$. Setting $h = 2$, $k = -1$ in (67) gives $x^2 + y^2 - 8x + 4y = 0$. Setting $h = -1$, $k = 2$ in (67) gives $x^2 + y^2 + 4x - 8y = 0$. Hence we have found two such circles. We leave it to the student to explain why there are exactly two such circles.

EXERCISE 6

In problems 1 through 8 describe geometrically the family of curves defined by the given equation.

1. $y = kx + 2 - 3k$.
2. $2y = x + k^2$.
3. $x^2 + y^2 - 6x + 2ky + k^2 = 7$.
4. $y^2 - k^2x^2 = 0$.
5. $4y = k(x - 2)^2$.
6. $4y = (x - k)^2$.
7. $\dfrac{x^2}{k^2} - \dfrac{y^2}{1 - k^2} = 1$, $\quad 0 < k < 1$.
8. $\dfrac{x^2}{k^2} - \dfrac{y^2}{1 - k^2} = 1$, $\quad 1 < k$.

In problems 9 through 12 find the equation of the line through the point of intersection of the two given lines and satisfying the given condition.

9. $2x + 3y = 4$, $3x + 4y = 5$, and through $Q(3, -2)$.
10. $x + 3y = 5$, $7x + 11y = 13$, and through $Q(6, -2)$.
11. $y = 2x + 5$, $2y = x + 13$, and with slope 3.
12. $y = x + 2$, $y + 2x + 1 = 0$, and with slope m.

13. If the two lines given by (60) and (61) are parallel, but distinct, describe the family defined by (62).

14. Show that if equations (60) and (61) define the same line then the family (62) consists of just one line. Hence a two-parameter family may have only one member (or we must modify the definition of a two-parameter family).

In problems 15 through 17 let P_1 and P_2 be the points of intersection of the two circles $x^2 + y^2 = 100$ and $(x - 11)^2 + (y - 4)^2 = 9$.

15. Find the equation of the straight line through P_1 and P_2.

16. Find the equation of the circle through P_1 and P_2 and the point $Q(8, 8)$.
17. Find the equation of the circle through P_1 and P_2 with center at $(22, 8)$.

18. Find the equation of the ellipse through $(1, 8/3)$ with foci at $(\pm 1, 0)$.
★19. Find the family of all straight lines tangent to the parabola $4y = x^2$.
★20. Find the family of all straight lines tangent to the ellipse $4x^2 + y^2 = 4$.
★21. Find the family of all straight lines that are tangent to the hyperbola $y = 1/(x - 2)$.

★8. **Rotation of axes.** In section 1 we obtained the equations for the change in the coordinates of a point when the axes were translated. We now obtain a similar set of equations when the axes are rotated. Suppose that as indicated in Fig. 20 two rectangular coordinate systems have the same origin and that the $x'-y'$ system can be obtained by rotating the $x-y$ system about the origin in a counterclockwise direction through an angle α. If α is negative then the rotation is understood to be in a clockwise direction through an angle $|\alpha|$. For brevity we merely say that the axes have been rotated through an angle α.

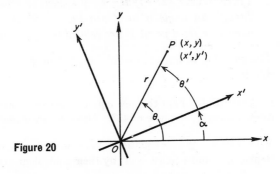

Figure 20

If P is any point in the plane, it has two sets of coordinates (x, y) and (x', y'), one for each coordinate system. To obtain equations relating these four quantities we recall from trigonometry that if $r = |OP|$ is the length of the line segment joining P with the origin and if this line segment makes an angle θ with the positive x-axis then

$$x = r \cos \theta, \qquad y = r \sin \theta. \tag{68}$$

Similarly if the line OP makes an angle θ' with the x' axis, then

$$x' = r \cos \theta', \qquad y' = r \sin \theta'. \tag{69}$$

Now $\theta = \theta' + \alpha$, so using this in (68) we find

$$x = r \cos (\theta' + \alpha) = r \cos \theta' \cos \alpha - r \sin \theta' \sin \alpha$$
and
$$y = r \sin (\theta' + \alpha) = r \sin \theta' \cos \alpha + r \cos \theta' \sin \alpha.$$

Substituting from (69) these equations become

$$\boxed{\begin{aligned} x &= x' \cos \alpha - y' \sin \alpha, \\ y &= x' \sin \alpha + y' \cos \alpha. \end{aligned}} \tag{70}$$

These equations can be solved inversely for x' and y' in the usual way. It is more instructive however to remark that if the $x'-y'$ system is obtained from the $x-y$ system by a rotation through an angle α, then the $x-y$ system is obtained from the $x'-y'$ system by a rotation through an angle $-\alpha$. Then the inverse equations can be obtained by replacing α by $-\alpha$, and shifting the primes to the unprimed letters. Since $\cos(-\alpha) = \cos \alpha$ and $\sin(-\alpha) = -\sin \alpha$, this gives

$$\begin{aligned} x' &= x \cos \alpha + y \sin \alpha \\ y' &= -x \sin \alpha + y \cos \alpha. \end{aligned} \tag{71}$$

THEOREM 12.   *If the $x-y$ system is rotated counterclockwise through an angle α to obtain the $x'-y'$ system, then the coordinates of a fixed point P are related by equations (70) and (71).*

The rotation of axes is useful for putting certain equations into recognizable form.

EXAMPLE 1.   Find the new equation for the curve $xy = A^2$ if the axes are rotated through an angle of 45°.   Use this new equation to discuss the curve.

SOLUTION.   We use equation set (70) with $\sin \alpha = \cos \alpha = \sin 45° = \sqrt{2}/2$. Replacing x and y in $xy = A^2$ by their equivalent expressions (70) we have

$$\left(x'\frac{\sqrt{2}}{2} - y'\frac{\sqrt{2}}{2} \right)\left(x'\frac{\sqrt{2}}{2} + y'\frac{\sqrt{2}}{2} \right) = A^2$$

$$\frac{x'^2}{2} - \frac{y'^2}{2} = A^2.$$

But this is just the equation of a hyperbola with $a^2 = b^2 = 2A^2$ and hence the hyperbola has foci at $(\pm 2A, 0)$ in the $x'-y'$ system. The eccentricity is $\sqrt{2}$, and the directrices are the lines $x' = \pm A$. Then a rotation back to the original coordinate system makes it obvious that the curve $xy = A^2$ is a hyperbola with foci at $(\sqrt{2}\,A, \sqrt{2}\,A)$ and $(-\sqrt{2}\,A, -\sqrt{2}\,A)$. The eccentricity is of course still $\sqrt{2}$, but the directrices are now the lines $x + y = \pm\sqrt{2}\,A$.

The methods used in this example are suitable for removing the xy term in any quadratic expression.   Indeed suppose that

$$Ax^2 + Bxy + Cy^2 + Dx + Ey + F = 0 \tag{72}$$

is the equation of some curve in the $x-y$ plane. Rotating the axes through an angle α, leaves the curve unchanged but changes its equation into

$$A'x'^2 + B'x'y' + C'y'^2 + D'x' + E'y' + F' = 0 \qquad (73)$$

where (73) is obtained by using (70) in (72). We leave it to the student to carry out this substitution and show that the new coefficients, A', B', C', D', and E' are given in terms of the old coefficients by the equations

$$\left\{ \begin{array}{l} A' = A \cos^2 \alpha + B \cos \alpha \sin \alpha + C \sin^2 \alpha, \\ B' = B (\cos^2 \alpha - \sin^2 \alpha) + 2(C - A) \sin \alpha \cos \alpha, \\ C' = A \sin^2 \alpha - B \sin \alpha \cos \alpha + C \cos^2 \alpha, \\ D' = D \cos \alpha + E \sin \alpha, \\ E' = -D \sin \alpha + E \cos \alpha, \\ F' = F. \end{array} \right. \qquad (74)$$

To remove the xy term we merely set $B' = 0$ and have

$$B(\cos^2 \alpha - \sin^2 \alpha) = -2(C - A) \sin \alpha \cos \alpha \qquad (75)$$

or

$$\frac{\cos 2\alpha}{\sin 2\alpha} = \frac{A - C}{B}, \qquad \text{if } B \neq 0.$$

THEOREM 13. *The xy term in any quadratic expression can be removed by a rotation of the coordinate axes through an angle α where*

$$\boxed{\cot 2\alpha = \frac{A - C}{B}} \qquad \text{if } B \neq 0. \qquad (76)$$

Of course if $B = 0$ equation (76) is meaningless, but in this case the xy term is already missing in (72) and so no rotation is necessary. Any other B leads to a unique value for 2α in the interval $0 < 2\alpha < \pi$, and hence determines a unique α in the interval $0 < \alpha < \pi/2$.

We remark for future reference that if we return to equation (75) and divide both sides by $B \cos^2 \alpha$ we find that $\tan \alpha$ is a positive root of

$$\tan^2 \alpha + \frac{2(A - C)}{B} \tan \alpha - 1 = 0. \qquad (77)$$

Hence

$$\tan \alpha = \frac{C - A}{B} + \frac{\sqrt{(C - A)^2 + B^2}}{|B|} \qquad (78)$$

It now seems to be obvious that the curve defined by (72) is always a conic section, but unfortunately, such a simplified statement of the result is false because certain special degenerate cases may arise. For example (72) may be factorable, and hence represent two lines. Or if $A = B = C = 0$, then (72) may represent a single line. Other possibilities can occur, and we leave these to the exercise list. Stated precisely we have

> THEOREM 14. *The graph of (72) is one of the following figures: an ellipse, a circle, a parabola, a hyperbola, two lines, a single line, a point, or no points.*

To prove this theorem, we merely rotate the axes to remove the xy term, and then examine the resulting equation

$$A'x'^2 + C'y'^2 + D'x' + E'y' + F' = 0 \tag{79}$$

If $A' = C' = 0$ then we have either a single line or no points. If $A' = 0$ and $C' \neq 0$ the curve is a parabola. If $C' = 0$ and $A' \neq 0$ the curve is also a parabola. If A' and C' have the same sign the curve is an ellipse, except that the ellipse may degenerate into a circle, or a single point, or no points; for example $x'^2 + y'^2 + F = 0$ where $F = 0$ or $F > 0$. Finally if A' and C' have opposite signs then we have a hyperbola, or two intersecting lines. We are assuming of course that at least one coefficient in (72) and (79) is different from zero. If all the coefficients are zero the equation would be $0 = 0$, and this equation is satisfied for every point in the plane.

It is convenient to have at hand a test that can be applied to the quadratic expression (72) in order to determine the type of conic, without actually performing the rotation. For simplicity, we ignore the various degenerate cases.

> THEOREM 15. *If the graph of (72) is a conic section then:*
>
> (1) *It is a hyperbola if $B^2 - 4AC > 0$,*
> (2) *It is a parabola if $B^2 - 4AC = 0$,*
> (3) *It is an ellipse if $B^2 - 4AC < 0$.*

The quantity $B^2 - 4AC$ is called the *discriminant* of the quadratic expression (72). The proof of Theorem 15 depends upon the fact that $B^2 - 4AC$ is *invariant* under the transformation equations (74), i.e., under a rotation of the axes. The term invariant means in this case, that for every value of α in (74) we have

$$B'^2 - 4A'C' = B^2 - 4AC. \tag{80}$$

Other expressions may also be invariant, and the concept of invariance may be applied to other types of transformations.

PROOF OF THEOREM 15. From equations (74)

$$B'^2 - 4A'C' = [B(\cos^2\alpha - \sin^2\alpha) + 2(C - A)\sin\alpha\cos\alpha]^2 \qquad (81)$$

$$-4(A\cos^2\alpha + B\cos\alpha\sin\alpha + C\sin^2\alpha)(A\sin^2\alpha - B\sin\alpha\cos\alpha + C\cos^2\alpha).$$

A laborious computation with the right side of (81) will reduce it to $B^2 - 4AC$ and hence equation (80) is satisfied.

Now take α so that $B' = 0$. Equation (80) becomes

$$-4A'C' = B^2 - 4AC.$$

If $B^2 - 4AC = 0$, then either A' or C' is zero, and hence the curve is a parabola. If $B^2 - 4AC > 0$, then A' and C' must have opposite signs, and the curve is a hyperbola. If $B^2 - 4AC < 0$, then A' and C' must have the same sign, and the curve is an ellipse.

EXAMPLE 2. Discuss the graph of

$$2x^2 + 3xy + 2y^2 = 7 \qquad (82)$$

SOLUTION. Since $B^2 - 4AC = 9 - 16 = -7 < 0$, the curve is an ellipse. To obtain more information about this ellipse, we must rotate the axes through an angle α where $\cot 2\alpha = (A - C)/B = (2 - 2)/3 = 0$. Whence $2\alpha = 90°$ and $\alpha = 45°$. The transformation equations (70) give $x = (x' - y')\sqrt{2}/2$, $y = (x' + y')\sqrt{2}/2$. Either direct substitution in (82) or using the equation set (74) yields

$$\frac{x'^2}{2} + \frac{y'^2}{14} = 1.$$

Then $c^2 = 14 - 2$, $e = \sqrt{6/7}$, $d = \sqrt{14}/e = 7/\sqrt{3}$. The foci are at $(0, \pm2\sqrt{3})$ and the directrices are $y' = \pm7/\sqrt{3}$.

Using equations (70) and (71) to return to the original coordinate system, the curve is still an ellipse, but now the foci have coordinates $(\sqrt{6}, -\sqrt{6})$ and $(-\sqrt{6}, \sqrt{6})$ and the directrices are $y - x = \pm14/\sqrt{6}$. The vertices at the ends of the major axis are $(\sqrt{7}, -\sqrt{7})$ and $(-\sqrt{7}, \sqrt{7})$ and the other two vertices are $(1, 1)$ and $(-1, -1)$.

EXAMPLE 3. Discuss the graph of

$$6xy + 8y^2 - 12x - 26y + 11 = 0. \qquad (83)$$

SOLUTION. Here $B^2 - 4AC = 36 - 0 > 0$ so the curve is a hyperbola. Now however $\cot 2\alpha = (A - C)/B = -8/6$ so 2α is not one of the "popular" angles. To avoid this difficulty we use equation (77) or its equivalent (78), and find that

$$\tan\alpha = \frac{+8 + \sqrt{64 + 36}}{6} = 3.$$

Whence $\sin \alpha = 3/\sqrt{1 + 3^2} = 3/\sqrt{10}$ and $\cos \alpha = 1/\sqrt{10}$.

Substituting $x = (x' - 3y')/\sqrt{10}$, and $y = (3x' + y')/\sqrt{10}$ in (83) yields

$$6\frac{(x' - 3y')(3x' + y')}{10} + 8\frac{(3x' + y')^2}{10} - 12\frac{x' - 3y'}{\sqrt{10}} - 26\frac{3x' + y'}{\sqrt{10}} + 11 = 0.$$

This simplifies to

$$9x'^2 - y'^2 - 9\sqrt{10}\,x' + \sqrt{10}\,y' + 11 = 0.$$

Completing the squares in the usual manner gives

$$9\left(x'^2 - \sqrt{10}\,x' + \frac{5}{2}\right) - \left(y'^2 - \sqrt{10}\,y' + \frac{5}{2}\right) = 20 - 11 = 9$$

or

$$\frac{X^2}{1} - \frac{Y^2}{9} = 1$$

where $X = x' - \sqrt{10}/2$ and $Y = y' - \sqrt{10}/2$.

In the $X-Y$ coordinate system the curve is a hyperbola with foci at $(\pm\sqrt{10}, 0)$, vertices at $(\pm 1, 0)$, directrices $X = \pm 1/\sqrt{10}$, and asymptotes $Y = \pm 3X$. We leave it to the reader to find these quantities in the $x'-y'$

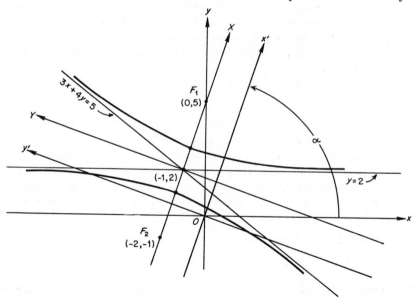

Figure 21 · The graph of $6xy + 8y^2 - 12x - 26y + 11 = 0$.

coordinate system, and then show that in the $x-y$ system the curve has foci at $(0, 5)$, $(-2, -1)$, vertices at $(-1 + 1/\sqrt{10},\ 2 + 3/\sqrt{10})$ and $(-1 - 1/\sqrt{10},\ 2 - 3/\sqrt{10})$, directrices $x + 3y = 6$ and $x + 3y = 4$, and asymptotes $y = 2$ and $3x + 4y = 5$.   The center of the hyperbola is at $(-1, 2)$ and the axes of symmetry are $x + 3y = 5$ and $y - 3x = 5$.   The graph of this curve is shown in Fig. 21.

EXERCISE 7

In problems 1 through 9 identify the conic sections, and then by a rotation of the axis, and a translation (if necessary) find the foci and directrices (or focus and directrix if the curve is a parabola).   Find the asymptotes if the curve is a hyperbola.

1. $x^2 + 2xy + y^2 + 8x - 8y = 0$.
2. $13x^2 - 2\sqrt{3}\, xy + 15y^2 = 192$.
3. $7x^2 - 18xy + 7y^2 = 16$.
4. $5x^2 + 6xy - 3y^2 = 24$.
5. $7x^2 + 6\sqrt{3}\, xy + 13y^2 = 64$.
6. $4x^2 + 4xy + y^2 - 60x + 120y = 0$.
★7. $x^2 - 2xy + y^2 - 14x - 2y + 33 = 0$.
★8. $2xy - 6y - 4x + 11 = 0$.
★★9. $21x^2 + 12xy + 16y^2 - 60x - 60y = 0$.
10. Show by specific examples that the graph of the equation $Ax^2 + Bxy + Cy^2 + Dx + Ey + F = 0$ may be (a) two parallel lines, (b) two intersecting lines, (c) a single line, (d) a point, or (e) no points.
11. Derive equation set (74) by using (70) in (72).
12. Prove that under a translation the equation of a straight line goes into the equation of another straight line with the same slope.   Thus m in $y = mx + b$ is an invariant under a translation.
13. Prove that m in Problem 12 is *not* an invariant under a rotation.
★14. Prove that the distance between two points is an invariant under a translation.
★★15. Prove that the distance between two points is an invariant under a rotation.
★16. Prove that under a rotation: (a) F is an invariant, (b) $A + C$ is an invariant, (c) $D^2 + E^2$ is an invariant, and (d) $B^2 - 4AC$ is an invariant.
★17. Suppose that the coordinate axes are *fixed*, but the *point* $P(x, y)$ *is moved* to a new position $P'(x', y')$ by a rotation of the point through an angle α about the origin.   Naturally in this rotation the point is always on a fixed circle with center at the origin.   Prove that

$$x' = x \cos \alpha - y \sin \alpha$$
$$y' = x \sin \alpha + y \cos \alpha$$

7

THE TRIGONOMETRIC FUNCTIONS

1. **Objective.** Since all of the six trigonometric functions can be expressed in terms of the sine function it is sufficient to find a formula for differentiating $y = \sin \theta$. Then formulas for differentiating the other trigonometric functions will easily follow. We shall see that in order to obtain a simple formula, the unit for measuring θ must be selected properly, and this proper unit turns out to be the radian.

We recall from trigonometry the definition of radian measure. As indicated in Fig. 1, let PS be the arc of a circle with center at O intercepted by the sides of the angle with vertex at O. Let s be the length of this arc, and r the radius of the circle. If θ denotes the measure of $\measuredangle\ SOP$ in radians, then by definition $\theta = s/r$.

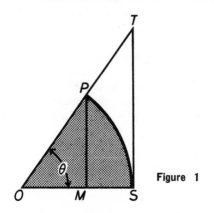

Figure 1

Further we will need a formula for A, the area of the circular sector SOP (shown shaded in Fig. 1). If the radius is fixed and θ varies, it is clear that the area is directly proportional to the magnitude of θ, that is, $A = k\theta$. To determine k, the constant of proportionality we consider the

228

full circle. On the one hand $A = \pi r^2$, and on the other hand the 360° angle (the full circle) has radian measure 2π. Thus $A = k\theta$ becomes $\pi r^2 = k2\pi$, and hence $k = r^2/2$. Using this expression for k in $A = k\theta$ gives

$$A = \frac{r^2\theta}{2} \tag{1}$$

for the area of any circular sector of radius r and angle θ, when θ is expressed in radians.

2. **The derivative of the sine function.** Let SOP be a circular sector, and as indicated in Fig. 1 let the lines PM and TS be perpendicular to the side OS, where T is the point where the line perpendicular to OS at S meets the side OP extended. Then a comparison of the areas of the triangles MOP, and SOT, the first inside the sector and the second containing the sector gives

area of $\triangle MOP$ < area of sector SOP < area of $\triangle SOT$.

For convenience, we take $|OS| = r = 1$. Then $|OM| = \cos\theta$, $|MP| = \sin\theta$, $|ST| = \tan\theta$ and by (1), the area of sector $SOP = \theta/2$. Then the inequalities among the areas give

$$\frac{1}{2}|OM| \times |MP| < \frac{\theta}{2} < \frac{1}{2}|OS| \times |ST|,$$

or

$$\frac{1}{2}\sin\theta\cos\theta < \frac{\theta}{2} < \frac{1}{2}\tan\theta = \frac{1}{2}\frac{\sin\theta}{\cos\theta}.$$

Whence, dividing by $\sin\theta$ and multiplying by 2,

$$\cos\theta < \frac{\theta}{\sin\theta} < \frac{1}{\cos\theta}. \tag{2}$$

Now let $\theta \to 0^+$ in (2). Since $\cos\theta \to 1$ and $1/\cos\theta \to 1$, it follows that $\lim_{\theta\to0^+} \theta/\sin\theta = 1$. Taking reciprocals gives

THEOREM 1. *If θ is measured in radians then*

$$\lim_{\theta\to0} \frac{\sin\theta}{\theta} = 1. \tag{3}$$

Strictly speaking our proof is valid only for positive θ. To complete the proof we observe that if θ is negative and small, then $\sin \theta$ is also negative and since $\sin \theta = -\sin(-\theta)$

$$\frac{\sin \theta}{\theta} = \frac{-\sin(-\theta)}{\theta} = \frac{\sin |\theta|}{|\theta|}.$$

Hence the limit of the ratio is also 1, as $\theta \to 0^-$.

From (3) it is easy to prove that

$$\lim_{\theta \to 0} \frac{\cos \theta - 1}{\theta} = 0. \tag{4}$$

Indeed multiplying the numerator and denominator on the left side by $\cos \theta + 1$, gives

$$\frac{\cos \theta - 1}{\theta} = \frac{(\cos \theta - 1)(\cos \theta + 1)}{(\cos \theta + 1)\theta} = \frac{\cos^2 \theta - 1}{(\cos \theta + 1)\theta} = \frac{-\sin^2 \theta}{(\cos \theta + 1)\theta}$$

$$= -\frac{\sin \theta}{\cos \theta + 1} \cdot \frac{\sin \theta}{\theta}.$$

Now as $\theta \to 0$ the first factor tends to $-0/2$ and the second factor tends to 1. This proves (4). Equations (3) and (4) will now give the main result,

$$\frac{d}{dx} \sin x = \cos x. \tag{5}$$

To prove (5) we recall that by definition

$$\frac{d}{dx} \sin x = \lim_{\Delta x \to 0} \frac{\sin(x + \Delta x) - \sin x}{\Delta x}.$$

Hence

$$\frac{d}{dx} \sin x = \lim_{\Delta x \to 0} \frac{\sin x \cos \Delta x + \cos x \sin \Delta x - \sin x}{\Delta x}$$

$$= \lim_{\Delta x \to 0} \frac{\sin x(\cos \Delta x - 1)}{\Delta x} + \cos x \frac{\sin \Delta x}{\Delta x}.$$

Applying (3) and (4) with θ replaced by Δx yields (5).

If now u is any differentiable function of x, then by the chain rule

$$\frac{d}{dx} \sin u = \cos u \frac{du}{dx}. \qquad (6)$$

To differentiate the cosine function we recall that for any u, $\cos u = \sin \left(\frac{\pi}{2} - u\right)$. Hence

$$\frac{d}{dx} \cos u = \frac{d}{dx} \sin \left(\frac{\pi}{2} - u\right) = \cos \left(\frac{\pi}{2} - u\right) \frac{d}{dx} \left(\frac{\pi}{2} - u\right)$$

$$= \cos \left(\frac{\pi}{2} - u\right) \left(-\frac{du}{dx}\right)$$

$$= -\cos \left(\frac{\pi}{2} - u\right) \frac{du}{dx} = -\sin u \frac{du}{dx}.$$

Hence

$$\frac{d}{dx} \cos u = -\sin u \frac{du}{dx}. \qquad (7)$$

Since each differentiation formula gives rise to a corresponding integral formula, equations (7) and (6) yield

$$\int \sin u \, du = -\cos u + C, \quad (8) \text{ and } \int \cos u \, du = \sin u + C. \quad (9)$$

EXAMPLE 1. Find the derivative for each of the following functions (a) $y = \sin (x^3 + 3x - 5)$, (b) $y = \cos^7 4t$, and (c) $y = (5 + \sin 2x)/\cos^4 3x$.

(a) $\dfrac{dy}{dx} = \cos (x^3 + 3x - 5) \dfrac{d}{dx} (x^3 + 3x - 5)$

$\qquad = (3x^2 + 3) \cos (x^3 + 3x - 5).$

(b) $\dfrac{dy}{dt} = 7 (\cos 4t)^6 \dfrac{d}{dt} \cos 4t = 7 (\cos 4t)^6 (-\sin 4t)4$

$\qquad = -28 \cos^6 4t \sin 4t.$

(c) $\dfrac{dy}{dx} = \dfrac{\cos^4 3x (2 \cos 2x) - (5 + \sin 2x) 4 \cos^3 3x (-\sin 3x)3}{\cos^8 3x}$

$\qquad = \dfrac{2 \cos 2x \cos 3x + 12(5 + \sin 2x)\sin 3x}{\cos^5 3x}.$

EXAMPLE 2.   Compute each of the following integrals

(a) $\displaystyle\int \cos{(3x + 11)}\ dx,$ (b) $\displaystyle\int x^4 \sin{(x^5 + 7)}\ dx,$

(c) $\displaystyle\int_0^{\pi/4} \frac{\sin x}{\cos^3 x}\ dx,$ (d) $\displaystyle\int_0^{\pi/2} \sin t \cos t\ (\sin t + \cos t)\ dt.$

SOLUTION.   In (a) let $u = 3x + 11$, then $du = 3dx$

$$\int \cos{(3x + 11)}\ dx = \frac{1}{3}\int \cos{(3x+11)}(3\ dx) = \frac{1}{3}\int \cos u\ du$$

$$= \frac{1}{3}\sin u + C = \frac{1}{3}\sin{(3x + 11)} + C.$$

(b) $\displaystyle\int x^4 \sin{(x^5 + 7)}\ dx = \frac{1}{5}\int \sin{(x^5 + 7)}\ 5x^4\ dx$

$$= -\frac{1}{5}\cos{(x^5 + 7)} + C.$$

(c) $\displaystyle\int_0^{\pi/4} \frac{\sin x}{\cos^3 x}\ dx = -\int_0^{\pi/4} \cos^{-3} x\ (-\sin x\ dx)$

$$= -\int_{x=0}^{x=\pi/4} u^{-3}\ du = -\frac{u^{-2}}{-2}\Big|_{x=0}^{x=\pi/4}$$

$$= \frac{1}{2}\frac{1}{\cos^2 x}\Big|_0^{\pi/4} = \frac{1}{2}\left(\frac{1}{1/2} - \frac{1}{1}\right) = \frac{1}{2}.$$

(d) $\displaystyle\int_0^{\pi/2} \sin t \cos t\ (\sin t + \cos t)\ dt$

$$= \int_0^{\pi/2} (\sin^2 t \cos t + \cos^2 t \sin t)\ dt$$

$$= \left(\frac{\sin^3 t}{3} - \frac{\cos^3 t}{3}\right)\Big|_0^{\pi/2} = \left(\frac{1}{3} - 0\right) - \left(0 - \frac{1}{3}\right) = \frac{2}{3}.$$

EXERCISE 1

In problems 1 through 8 find the derivative of the given function with respect to the indicated independent variable.

1. $y = \sin 2x \cos 3x.$ 2. $y = \sin^2 x \cos^3 x.$

3. $y = \dfrac{\sin^2 3x}{\cos^3 2x}.$ ★4. $y = \sqrt{\dfrac{1 - \sin^3 x}{1 - \cos^3 x}}.$

5. $z = t \sin^2 (3t^2 + 5).$ 6. $r = (\theta^2 + 2) \sin^2 (5\theta - 1).$

7. $v = \dfrac{1}{u}\sin\dfrac{1}{u^2}.$ 8. $y = (\sin 2x + \cos 2x)^3.$

9. Prove that $\sin^2 u + \cos^2 u$ is a constant by showing that its derivative is zero.

10. Show that the two functions $(\cos^2 u - \sin^2 u)^2$ and $-4 \sin^2 u \cos^2 u$ differ by a constant, by showing that they both have the same derivative.

11. If $f(x) = \sin 3x$ find a formula for $f^{(2n)}(x)$, the $2n^{\text{th}}$ derivative, valid for each positive integer n.

12. If $g(x) = \sin 5x$, find $g^{(2n-1)}(x)$.

13. Find $f^{(2n)}(x)$ if $f(x) = \cos(-2x)$.

In problems 14 through 23 compute the given integral.

14. $\displaystyle\int_0^{\pi/8} \sin 4x \, dx.$

15. $\displaystyle\int_0^{\pi/15} \cos 5t \, dt.$

16. $\displaystyle\int_0^{\sqrt[3]{\pi}} t^2 \sin t^3 \, dt.$

17. $\displaystyle\int (2t + 1) \cos (t^2 + t + 5) \, dt$

18. $\displaystyle\int \sin^3 \theta \, d\theta.$

★19. $\displaystyle\int (\sin \theta + \cos \theta)^3 \, d\theta.$

20. $\displaystyle\int \sqrt{x} \cos x^{3/2} \, dx.$

21. $\displaystyle\int \frac{5 \sin 2\sqrt{x}}{\sqrt{x}} \, dx.$

22. $\displaystyle\int \cos^n ax \sin ax \, dx, \quad n \neq -1.$

23. $\displaystyle\int \frac{\cos cx \, dx}{(a + b \sin cx)^n}, \quad n \neq 1.$

24. Find all of the critical points of $y = x + \sin x$. Prove that this curve is always increasing and hence has neither a relative maximum, nor a relative minimum point. Sketch the curve.

★25. Show that in the interval $0 \leq x \leq \pi/2$ the curve $y = \sin x$ is concave downward and hence always lies above a certain line, joining its end points. Use this fact to prove that in the interval $0 \leq x \leq \pi/2$, we have

$$\sin x \geq \frac{2}{\pi} x.$$

26. Prove that the function $y = A \sin kt + B \cos kt$ satisfies the differential equation

$$\frac{d^2y}{dt^2} + k^2 y = 0.$$

In problems 27 through 30 find all of the relative maximum and minimum points and sketch the curve.

27. $y = 3 \sin x + 4 \cos x.$

28. $y = \sin^4 x.$

29. $y = x - 2 \sin x.$

30. $y = \dfrac{\sin^2 x}{1 + \cos^2 x}.$

★31. Show that for $y = \sin^4 x$ (the curve of problem 28) the second derivative is zero at $x = n\pi/3$ where n is any integer. Prove that the points $(n\pi, 0)$ are not inflection points on the curve, but the points corresponding to the other multiples of $\pi/3$ are inflection points.

32. Using differentials, find an approximate value for (a) sin 32°, (b) sin 44°, (c) cos 59°. Recall that the differentiation formulas are valid only for radian measure and that $1° = \pi/180$ radians. Give your answer to three decimal places.

33. Find the area under one arch of the curve $y = \sin 3x$.

34. Find the area bounded by the curves $y = \cos x$ and $y = \cos^3 x$ between $x = 0$ and $x = \pi/2$.

35. The region under $y = \sin x$ between $x = 0$ and $x = \pi/2$ is rotated about the x-axis. Find the volume of the solid generated. *Hint:* Use the trigonometric identity $\sin^2 x = (1 - \cos 2x)/2$.

36. Find the area bounded by the curves $y = \sin x$ and $y = \cos x$ between any pair of successive intersection points of the two curves.

★37. Find the angle from the curve $y = \sin x$ to the curve $y = \sin 2x$ at each point of intersection of these two curves.

3.   **The trigonometric functions.** The differentiation formulas for all six of the trigonometric functions are given in

THEOREM 2.   *If u is a differentiable function of x then*

$$\frac{d}{dx} \sin u = \cos u \frac{du}{dx}, \qquad (10)$$

$$\frac{d}{dx} \cos u = -\sin u \frac{du}{dx}, \qquad (11)$$

$$\frac{d}{dx} \tan u = \sec^2 u \frac{du}{dx}, \qquad (12)$$

$$\frac{d}{dx} \cot u = -\csc^2 u \frac{du}{dx}, \qquad (13)$$

$$\frac{d}{dx} \sec u = \sec u \tan u \frac{du}{dx}, \qquad (14)$$

$$\frac{d}{dx} \csc u = -\csc u \cot u \frac{du}{dx}. \qquad (15)$$

PROOF. We have already proved (10) and (11), see formulas (6) and (7) of the preceding section. To prove (12) we use the quotient formula in conjunction with (10) and (11). Indeed

$$\frac{d}{dx} \tan u = \frac{d}{dx} \frac{\sin u}{\cos u} = \frac{\cos u \dfrac{d}{dx} \sin u - \sin u \dfrac{d}{dx} \cos u}{\cos^2 u}$$

$$= \frac{\cos u \cos u - \sin u(-\sin u)}{\cos^2 u} \frac{du}{dx} = \frac{1}{\cos^2 u} \frac{du}{dx}$$

$$= \sec^2 u \frac{du}{dx}.$$

To prove (14) we have

$$\frac{d}{dx} \sec u = \frac{d}{dx} (\cos u)^{-1} = -1(\cos u)^{-2}(-\sin u)\frac{du}{dx}$$

$$= \frac{\sin u}{\cos^2 u}\frac{du}{dx} = \frac{1}{\cos u}\frac{\sin u}{\cos u}\frac{du}{dx} = \sec u \tan u \frac{du}{dx}.$$

The proofs of (13) and (15) are similar, and are left for the student as an exercise.

With the four new differentiation formulas we have immediately the four new integration formulas

$$\int \sec^2 u \, du = \tan u + C, \quad (16) \qquad \int \csc^2 u \, du = -\cot u + C, \quad (17)$$

$$\int \sec u \tan u \, du = \sec u + C, \tag{18}$$

$$\int \csc u \cot u \, du = -\csc u + C. \tag{19}$$

EXAMPLE 1. Find the derivative for each of the following functions (a) $y = \tan\sqrt{1 + x^2}$, (b) $y = \tan x \sec^2 x + 2 \tan x$, (c) $y = \csc (\sin x)$, and (d) $y = (1 - \tan^2 t)/(1 + \tan^2 t)$.

SOLUTION.

(a) $\dfrac{dy}{dx} = \sec^2\sqrt{1 + x^2}\,\dfrac{d}{dx}\sqrt{1 + x^2}$

   $= \dfrac{x}{\sqrt{1 + x^2}}\sec^2\sqrt{1 + x^2}.$

(b) $\dfrac{dy}{dx} = \sec^2 x \sec^2 x + \tan x\,(2 \sec x) \sec x \tan x + 2 \sec^2 x$

   $= \sec^4 x + 2 \sec^2 x\,(\tan^2 x + 1)$

   $= \sec^4 x + 2 \sec^2 x \sec^2 x = 3 \sec^4 x.$

(c) $\dfrac{dy}{dx} = -\csc (\sin x) \cot (\sin x)\,\dfrac{d}{dx}\sin x$

   $= -\cos x \csc (\sin x) \cot (\sin x).$

Observe that this expression cannot be simplified.

(d) $\dfrac{dy}{dt} = \dfrac{(1 + \tan^2 t)(-2 \tan t \sec^2 t) - (1 - \tan^2 t)2 \tan t \sec^2 t}{(1 + \tan^2 t)^2}$

$$= \dfrac{-4 \tan t \sec^2 t}{(1 + \tan^2 t)^2} = \dfrac{-4 \tan t \sec^2 t}{(\sec^2 t)^2}$$

$$= -4 \dfrac{\sin t}{\cos t} \cos^2 t = -4 \sin t \cos t = -2 \sin 2t.$$

But the given expression could be simplified before differentiation.   Indeed

$$y = \dfrac{1 - \tan^2 t}{1 + \tan^2 t} = \dfrac{1 - \tan^2 t}{\sec^2 t} = \cos^2 t - \dfrac{\sin^2 t}{\cos^2 t} \cos^2 t$$

$$= \cos^2 t - \sin^2 t = \cos 2t.$$

Hence $\dfrac{dy}{dt} = -2 \sin 2t$

This example shows that it is sometimes advantageous to try to simplify an expression before differentiating it.

EXAMPLE 2.   Compute each of the following integrals.

(a) $\displaystyle\int \tan 3x \sec^2 3x \, dx$ (b) $\displaystyle\int_{\pi/4}^{\pi/2} \csc^8 x \cot x \, dx$

SOLUTION.   (a) Since $d(\tan 3x) = 3 \sec^2 3x \, dx$, we can write

$$\int \tan 3x \sec^2 3x \, dx = \frac{1}{3} \int \tan 3x \, d(\tan 3x) = \frac{1}{6} \tan^2 3x + C.$$

(b) $\displaystyle\int_{\pi/4}^{\pi/2} \csc^8 x \cot x \, dx = - \int_{\pi/4}^{\pi/2} \csc^7 x \, (-\csc x \cot x) \, dx$

$$= - \left. \dfrac{\csc^8 x}{8} \right|_{\pi/4}^{\pi/2} = - \dfrac{1}{8} \left(\csc^8 \dfrac{\pi}{2} - \csc^8 \dfrac{\pi}{4} \right)$$

$$= - \dfrac{1}{8} (1 - (\sqrt{2})^8) = - \dfrac{1}{8} (1 - 16) = \dfrac{15}{8}.$$

EXERCISE 2

In problems 1 through 8 find the derivative of the given function with respect to the indicated independent variable.

1. $y = \sin x \tan x.$

2. $y = 4 \cos x \sin 4x - \sin x \cos 4x.$

3. $s = \tan^3 t + 3 \tan t.$

4. $y = 3\theta + 3 \cot \theta - \cot^3 \theta.$

5. $y = \sec^2 x \csc^3 x.$

6. $r = \tan^3 \theta \cot^4 \theta.$

7. $y = \dfrac{x + \sec 2x}{x + \tan 2x}.$

8. $y = \sqrt{\dfrac{\tan x + \sin x}{\tan x - \sin x}}.$

In problems 9 through 12 find the third derivative of the given function.

9. $y = x^2 \tan x.$ **10.** $y = \sec x^2.$
11. $y = \sin 2x \tan 2x.$ **12.** $y = \tan x \csc x.$

13. Explain why the two functions $y = \tan^2 x$ and $y = \sec^2 x$ both have the same derivative $y' = 2 \sec^2 x \tan x.$

In problems 14 through 21 compute the given integral.

14. $\displaystyle\int \sec^2 5x \tan^3 5x \, dx.$ **15.** $\displaystyle\int \csc^5 6x \cot 6x \, dx.$

16. $\displaystyle\int x^2 \sec^2(5x^3 + 7) dx.$ **17.** $\displaystyle\int (\sec^2 x + \tan^2 x) \, dx.$

18. $\displaystyle\int \frac{\theta d\theta}{\sin^2 4\theta^2}.$ **19.** $\displaystyle\int \sin y \sec^3 y \, dy.$

20. $\displaystyle\int (\sec z + \tan z)^2 \, dz.$ **21.** $\displaystyle\int \sec^4 \theta d\theta.$

22. Find the minimum point on the curve $y = \tan x + \cot x$ in the interval $0 < x < \pi/2.$

23. Solve problem 22 without using the calculus by first proving the identity.

$$\tan x + \cot x = \frac{2}{\sin 2x}.$$

24. Prove that if A is a positive constant then the minimum of $f(x) = \tan x + A \cot x$ is $2\sqrt{A}$ for x in the interval $0 < x < \pi/2.$

25. Use differentials to find approximate values for (a) $\tan 46°48'$, (b) $\tan 44°6'$, (c) $\csc 31°$, (d) $\sec 29°$.

26. Find the area under the curve $y = \sec^2 x$ between $x = 0$ and $x = \pi/4.$

27. The region under the curve $y = \sec x$ between $x = 0$ and $x = \pi/4$ is rotated about the x-axis. Find the volume of the solid generated.

28. Repeat problem 27 for the curve $y = \tan x.$

29. Repeat problem 27 for the curve $y = \sec^2 x.$

30. The region under the curve $y = \sec^2 \pi x^2$ between $x = 0$ and $x = 1/2$ is rotated about the y-axis. Find the volume of the solid generated.

In problems 31 through 34 use implicit differentiation to find $\dfrac{dy}{dx}.$

31. $y + x = \sin y \cos x.$ **32.** $y \tan x + x \sec y = 1.$
33. $yx = \sin y + \cos x.$ **34.** $\sin (x + y) = \tan (x + y).$

35. Prove that the graph of the equation of problem 34 consists of the collection of straight lines $y = -x + n\pi.$

*36. A ladder 27 ft long rests against a wall 8 ft high. On the other side of the wall 12 ft away is a tall building. Prove that with the ladder touching the ground at one end, the other end cannot rest against the building. How close to the wall must the building be, in order that the ladder may just barely reach the building?

4.   The inverse trigonometric functions. We recall from trigonometry
that the function $y = \sin x$ has the graph shown in Fig. 2.   The inverse relation $y = \sin^{-1}x$ (read "y is an angle whose sin is x") preserves the
same correspondence between pairs of numbers, but interchanges the
names of the variables.   Therefore the graph of $y = \sin^{-1} x$ can be obtained from the graph of $y = \sin x$ by rotating the curve of Fig. 2 about the
45° line $y = x$.   This rotation merely interchanges the role of x and y as
independent and dependent variables.   The result of such a rotation is
shown in Fig. 3.

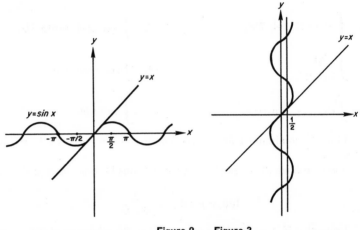

Figure 2   Figure 3

We should like to speak of the "inverse function" $y = \sin^{-1} x$, but in
accordance with the rules of the game a function must be single-valued.
This means that for each fixed x for which $y = \sin^{-1} x$ is defined, there
must be only one corresponding y.   Now a glance at Fig. 3 shows that for
each x in the interval $-1 \leq x \leq 1$, there are many corresponding values
of y.   For example if $x = 1/2$, then $y = \pi/6 + 2n\pi$ and $y = 5\pi/6 + 2n\pi$
(n any integer) all have the property that $\sin y = 1/2$.   For this reason
we call the graph shown in Fig. 3, the graph of a *relation* $y = \sin^{-1} x$,
rather than the graph of a function.

But this difficulty is merely one of terminology.   As soon as we pick
out a specific value of y from among the many possible ones, then
$y = \sin^{-1} x$ becomes a function.   We do this by requiring that y lie in the
interval $-\pi/2 \leq y \leq \pi/2$.   Thus the conditions

$$\sin y = x, \quad \text{and} \quad -\frac{\pi}{2} \leq y \leq \frac{\pi}{2} \tag{20}$$

suffice to *define* the inverse sine function

$$y = \sin^{-1} x. \tag{21}$$

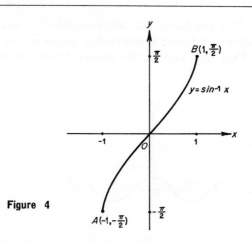

Figure 4

We frequently speak of the function (21) defined by (20) as the *principal branch* of the inverse sine function. The word "principal" is used to emphasize the fact that a definite choice of y has been made, but strictly speaking the word is unnecessary because the function $y = \sin^{-1} x$ will always mean this principal branch. The graph of the function (21) is shown in Fig. 4. Observe that the function is defined only for x in the interval $-1 \leq x \leq 1$.

In a similar manner we can define inverse functions for the remaining five trigonometric functions, by selecting suitable principal branches. For the cosine, tangent, and cotangent functions we make the following definitions:

$y = \cos^{-1} x$ (read "y is the angle whose cosine is x").   (22)
if $x = \cos y$ and $0 \leq y \leq \pi$.

$y = \tan^{-1} x$ (read "y is the angle whose tangent is x")   (23)
if $x = \tan y$ and $-\dfrac{\pi}{2} < y < \dfrac{\pi}{2}$.

$y = \cot^{-1} x$ (read "y is the angle whose cotangent is x")   (24)
if $x = \cot y$ and $0 < y < \pi$.

The inverse cosine function is defined only for $-1 \leq x \leq 1$. The inverse tangent and cotangent functions are defined for all real x. Any number y lying in the indicated intervals in equations (20), (22), (23), and (24) is called a principal value of the inverse function.

The symbol -1 in equations (21), (22), (23), and (24) is not an exponent, but is selected in agreement with the general plan of indicating the inverse function of $f(x)$ by $f^{-1}(x)$. Some authors use arc sin x in place of $\sin^{-1} x$ in order to avoid confusing $\sin^{-1} x$ with $(\sin x)^{-1} = 1/\sin x$.

The graphs of the trigonometric functions, cosine tangent, and cotangent, and their inverse relations are shown in Figs. 5, 6, 7, 8, 9, and 10. In Figs. 6, 8, and 10, the principal branches are shown heavy.

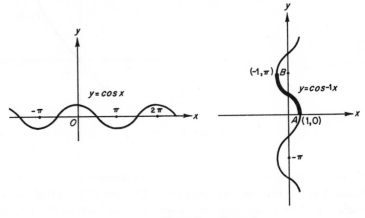

Figure 5   Figure 6

It is quite natural to look for definitions of $\sec^{-1} x$ and $\csc^{-1} x$, and in fact principal branches can be selected for these functions.   However there is no universal agreement on this selection, so we prefer to omit these

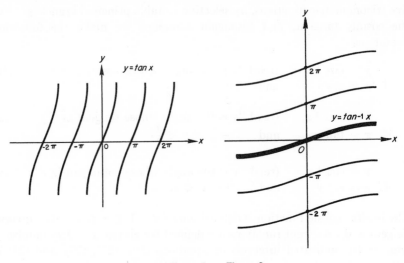

Figure 7   Figure 8

functions completely.   It turns out that there is no practical need for defining $\sec^{-1} x$ and $\csc^{-1} x$, since any natural problem that can be solved using these functions, can be solved just as easily without them.   For the

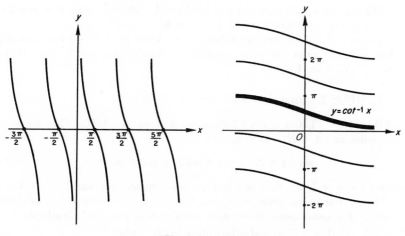

Figure 9   Figure 10

student who is curious about this matter, we have included a sequence of
starred problems in Exercise 4 that exposes the difficulties involved in
selecting a satisfactory principal branch for $\sec^{-1} x$.

EXAMPLE 1.   Find (a) $\sin^{-1} 1$, (b) $\tan^{-1} (-1)$, (c) $\cot^{-1} (-1)$.

SOLUTION.   (a) From trigonometry $\sin \left(\dfrac{\pi}{2} + 2n\pi \right) = 1$ and these are the
only values for y such that $\sin y = 1$.   But among these only $y = \pi/2$ lies in
the required interval $-\pi/2 \leqq y \leqq \pi/2$.   Hence $\sin^{-1} 1 = \pi/2$.

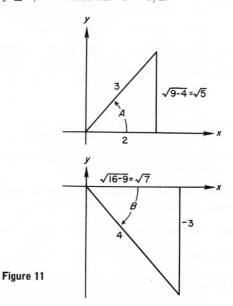

Figure 11

(b) $\tan(3\pi/4 + 2n\pi) = -1$ and $\tan(-\pi/4 + 2n\pi) = -1$. But $-\pi/2 < -\pi/4 < \pi/2$. Whence $\tan^{-1}(-1) = -\pi/4$.

(c) $\cot y = -1$ for the same values of y for which $\tan y = -1$ (see part (b)). But now the principal value must lie in the interval $0 < y < \pi$. Hence $\cot^{-1}(-1) = 3\pi/4$.

EXAMPLE 2. Find $\sin[\cos^{-1} 2/3 + \sin^{-1}(-3/4)]$.

SOLUTION. Let $A = \cos^{-1} 2/3$ and let $B = \sin^{-1}(-3/4)$. Then we are to compute $\sin(A + B)$. Of course we have

$$\sin(A + B) = \sin A \cos B + \cos A \sin B. \tag{25}$$

Since $\cos A = 2/3 > 0$, A is a first quadrant angle. But $\sin B = -3/4 < 0$ so B is a fourth quadrant angle, i.e., $-\pi/2 < B < 0$, since B is a principal value. For convenience these angles are shown in Fig. 11. Clearly $\sin A = \sqrt{5}/3$, $\cos B = \sqrt{7}/4$, and substituting in (25) yields

$$\sin(A + B) = \frac{\sqrt{5}}{3}\frac{\sqrt{7}}{4} + \frac{2}{3}\frac{(-3)}{4} = \frac{\sqrt{35} - 6}{12}$$

We observe that $\sin(A + B)$ is negative but very small. From this we infer that $|B|$ is slightly larger than A.

EXERCISE 3

In problems 1 through 9 give the indicated angle in radians.

1. $\tan^{-1} 0$.   **2.** $\sin^{-1}\left(-\frac{1}{2}\right)$.   **3.** $\cos^{-1} 0$.

4. $\cos^{-1}(-\sqrt{2}/2)$.   **5.** $\tan^{-1}\sqrt{3}$.   **6.** $\tan^{-1}(-1/\sqrt{3})$.

7. $\cot^{-1}(-\sqrt{3}/3)$.   **8.** $\cos^{-1}(-\sqrt{3}/2)$.   **9.** $\sin^{-1}(-\sqrt{3}/2)$.

10. Give a numerical value for:
   a. $\sin(\cos^{-1}(-3/5))$,   **b.** $\cos(\sin^{-1}(-3/5))$,
   c. $\sin(\tan^{-1}(-\sqrt{3}))$,   **d.** $\sin(\cot^{-1}(-\sqrt{3}))$.

11. Give a numerical value for:
   a. $\tan[\sin^{-1} 1/2 + \sin^{-1}(-2/3)]$,
   b. $\cos[\tan^{-1} 1 + \cos^{-1}(-3/4)]$,
   c. $\sin[\cot^{-1} 2/5 + \tan^{-1} 3/7]$.

In problems 12 through 22 identify the statement as true or false in the given domain. If the statement is true prove it.

12. $\sin(\cos^{-1} x) = \sqrt{1 - x^2}$, $-1 \leq x \leq 1$.

13. $\cos(\sin^{-1} x) = \sqrt{1 - x^2}$, $-1 \leq x \leq 1$.

14. $\tan^{-1}\dfrac{\sqrt{1 - x^2}}{x} = \cos^{-1} x$, $0 < x \leq 1$.

15. $\tan^{-1} \dfrac{\sqrt{1-x^2}}{x} = \cos^{-1} x,$ $\qquad\qquad 0 < |x| \leq 1.$

16. $\tan^{-1} u = \cot^{-1} \dfrac{1}{u},$ $\qquad\qquad 0 < |u|.$

17. $\sin^{-1}(-v) = -\sin^{-1} v,$ $\qquad\qquad -1 \leq v \leq 1.$

18. $\cos^{-1}(-w) = \cos^{-1} w,$ $\qquad\qquad -1 \leq w \leq 1.$

19. $\cos^{-1}(-w) = \pi - \cos^{-1} w,$ $\qquad\qquad -1 \leq w \leq 1.$

20. $\cos^{-1} x + \sin^{-1} x = \dfrac{\pi}{2},$ $\qquad\qquad -1 \leq x \leq 1.$

21. $2 \sin^{-1} y = \cos^{-1}(1 - 2y^2),$ $\qquad\qquad -1 \leq y \leq 1.$

22. $\tan^{-1} m + \tan^{-1} n = \tan^{-1} \dfrac{m+n}{1-mn},$ $\qquad mn \neq 1.$

23. For what values of y is the relation of problem 21 true.

24. Find some range for m and n such that the relation of problem 22 is true.

5.   Differentiation of the inverse trigonometric functions. Let $y = \sin^{-1} x$. Then by definition

$$x = \sin y, \qquad -\frac{\pi}{2} \leq y \leq \frac{\pi}{2}. \qquad (20)$$

Differentiating both sides of (20) with respect to x gives

$$1 = \cos y \, \frac{dy}{dx}$$

or

$$\frac{dy}{dx} = \frac{1}{\cos y} \qquad (26)$$

as long as $\cos y \neq 0$. But $\cos y = \pm \sqrt{1 - \sin^2 y} = \pm \sqrt{1 - x^2}$ from equation (20). In the interval $-\pi/2 \leq y \leq \pi/2$, $\cos y$ is never negative, so $\cos y = \sqrt{1 - x^2}$ and (26) becomes

$$\frac{dy}{dx} = \frac{1}{\sqrt{1 - x^2}}. \qquad (27)$$

Finally, since $y = \sin^{-1} x$ we have

$$\boxed{\frac{d}{dx} \sin^{-1} x = \frac{1}{\sqrt{1 - x^2}}.} \qquad (28)$$

Differentiation formulas for the other inverse trigonometric functions can be obtained in the same way.

Let $y = \cos^{-1} x$
       $x = \cos y.$
Differentiating with respect to x gives

$$1 = -\sin y \frac{dy}{dx}$$

$$\frac{dy}{dx} = \frac{-1}{\sin y} = \frac{-1}{\sqrt{1 - \cos^2 y}}$$

$$\frac{dy}{dx} = -\frac{1}{\sqrt{1 - x^2}}.$$

Hence

$$\frac{d}{dx} \cos^{-1} x = -\frac{1}{\sqrt{1 - x^2}} \qquad (30)$$

Let $y = \tan^{-1} x$
       $x = \tan y.$
Differentiating with respect to x gives

$$1 = \sec^2 y \frac{dy}{dx}$$

$$\frac{dy}{dx} = \frac{1}{\sec^2 y} = \frac{1}{1 + \tan^2 y}$$

$$\frac{dy}{dx} = \frac{1}{1 + x^2}. \qquad (29)$$

Hence

$$\frac{d}{dx} \tan^{-1} x = \frac{1}{1 + x^2}. \qquad (31)$$

We leave it as an exercise for the student to prove

$$\frac{d}{dx} \cot^{-1} x = \frac{-1}{1 + x^2}. \qquad (32)$$

Of course these formulas are valid only for suitable values of x. Thus in (28) and (30) x is restricted to the interval $-1 < x < +1$, but in (31) and (32) x can be any real number. Putting $x = \pm 1$ in (28) or (30) yields infinity for the derivative. Of course this is not a number, but the occurrence of the zero in the denominator is consistent with the fact that the curves shown in Figs. 4 and 6 for the principal branches are vertical at the end points A and B. It is also worthwhile to note that the derivatives for $\sin^{-1} x$ and $\tan^{-1} x$ are always positive, so these functions are increasing functions of x. Similarly the derivatives for $\cos^{-1} x$ and $\cot^{-1} x$ are always negative, so these functions are decreasing functions of x. These facts are consistent with the curves shown in Figs. 4, 6, 8, and 10.

If in our differentiation formulas we replace x by an arbitrary function $u(x)$ then the chain rule gives the more general formulas of

THEOREM 3.   *If u is any differentiable function of x,*

$$\frac{d}{dx} \sin^{-1} u = \frac{1}{\sqrt{1 - u^2}} \frac{du}{dx}, \qquad (33)$$

$$\frac{d}{dx} \cos^{-1} u = \frac{-1}{\sqrt{1 - u^2}} \frac{du}{dx}, \qquad (34)$$

$$\frac{d}{dx}\tan^{-1}u = \frac{1}{1+u^2}\frac{du}{dx}, \quad (35)$$

$$\frac{d}{dx}\cot^{-1}u = \frac{-1}{1+u^2}\frac{du}{dx}. \quad (36)$$

Of course in formulas (33) and (34) u must be restricted to lie in the interval $-1 < u < +1$.

Each of these four differentiation formulas leads to a corresponding integration formula, but because the differentiation formulas occur in pairs which differ just by a minus sign [(33), (34), and (35), (36)] only two of the four integration formulas are needed for practical purposes.   These are

$$\int \frac{du}{\sqrt{1-u^2}} = \sin^{-1}u + C, \quad (37)$$

and

$$\int \frac{du}{1+u^2} = \tan^{-1}u + C. \quad (38)$$

EXAMPLE 1.   Find $\dfrac{dy}{dx}$ for the functions

(a) $y = \cos^{-1}x^3$,   **(b)** $y = \sin^{-1}\sqrt{1-x^2}$,   **(c)** $y = x - \dfrac{1}{2}(x^2+4)\tan^{-1}\left(\dfrac{x}{2}\right)$.

SOLUTION.   **(a)** $\dfrac{dy}{dx} = \dfrac{-1}{\sqrt{1-(x^3)^2}}\dfrac{d}{dx}x^3 = \dfrac{-3x^2}{\sqrt{1-x^6}}.$

(b) $\dfrac{dy}{dx} = \dfrac{1}{\sqrt{1-(\sqrt{1-x^2})^2}}\dfrac{d}{dx}\sqrt{1-x^2} = \dfrac{1}{\sqrt{x^2}}\dfrac{1}{2}\dfrac{(-2x)}{\sqrt{1-x^2}}$

$$= -\frac{x}{|x|\sqrt{1-x^2}}.$$

We must write $|x|$ in the denominator because $\sqrt{x^2} = |x|$.   In order to cancel x with $|x|$ as nature seems to impel us to do, we must write that

$$\frac{d}{dx}\sin^{-1}\sqrt{1-x^2} = \frac{\pm 1}{\sqrt{1-x^2}}$$

where the minus sign is to be used if $x > 0$, and the plus sign is to be used if $x < 0$.   A closer investigation will show that the curve $y = \sin^{-1}\sqrt{1-x^2}$

does not have a tangent at the point $(0, \pi/2)$.   The curious student might well sketch the graph of this function.

(c) $\dfrac{dy}{dx} = 1 - x \tan^{-1}\left(\dfrac{x}{2}\right) - \dfrac{1}{2}(x^2 + 4)\dfrac{1}{1 + \dfrac{x^2}{4}}\dfrac{1}{2}$

$\qquad = 1 - x \tan^{-1}\left(\dfrac{x}{2}\right) - \dfrac{x^2 + 4}{x^2 + 4} = -x \tan^{-1}\left(\dfrac{x}{2}\right).$

EXAMPLE 2.   Find each of the following integrals

(a) $\displaystyle\int \dfrac{x^2\, dx}{1 + 4x^6},$ (b) $\displaystyle\int_0^{1/\sqrt{2}} \dfrac{y\,dy}{\sqrt{1 - 2y^4}},$ (c) $\displaystyle\int \dfrac{dx}{\sqrt{6x - x^2}}.$

SOLUTION.   (a) Set $u = 2x^3$. Then $du = 6x^2 dx$, and our given integral can be written in the form

$$\int \frac{x^2\, dx}{1 + 4x^6} = \frac{1}{6}\int \frac{6x^2\, dx}{1 + (2x^3)^2} = \frac{1}{6}\int \frac{du}{1 + u^2}$$

$$= \frac{1}{6}\tan^{-1} u + C = \frac{1}{6}\tan^{-1} 2x^3 + C,$$

by formula (38).

(b) Set $u = \sqrt{2}y^2$. Then $du = 2\sqrt{2}y\, dy$. For the indefinite integral in (b) we can write

$$\int \frac{y\, dy}{\sqrt{1 - 2y^4}} = \frac{1}{2\sqrt{2}}\int \frac{2\sqrt{2}y\, dy}{\sqrt{1 - (\sqrt{2}y^2)^2}} = \frac{1}{2\sqrt{2}}\int \frac{du}{\sqrt{1 - u^2}}$$

$$= \frac{1}{2\sqrt{2}}\sin^{-1}\sqrt{2}y^2 + C.$$

Then for the definite integral we have

$$\int_0^{1/\sqrt{2}} \frac{y\, dy}{\sqrt{1 - 2y^4}} = \frac{1}{2\sqrt{2}}\sin^{-1}\sqrt{2}y^2 \Big|_0^{1/\sqrt{2}}$$

$$= \frac{1}{2\sqrt{2}}\left(\sin^{-1}\frac{\sqrt{2}}{2} - \sin^{-1} 0\right) = \frac{\pi}{8\sqrt{2}}.$$

(c) It is not easy to see that this integral fits the form of either (37) or (38). But if we complete the square under the radical we have

$6x - x^2 = 9 - 9 + 6x - x^2 = 9 - (x^2 - 6x + 9) = 9 - (x - 3)^2.$

Whence we can match this integral with (37) thus:

$$\int \frac{dx}{\sqrt{6x - x^2}} = \int \frac{dx}{\sqrt{9 - (x - 3)^2}} = \frac{1}{3}\int \frac{dx}{\sqrt{1 - \left(\dfrac{x - 3}{3}\right)^2}}$$

$$= \sin^{-1}\frac{x - 3}{3} + C.$$

We should observe that $\sin^{-1}(x-3)/3$ is not defined if $|(x-3)/3| > 1$. This means that x must be restricted to a range in which $-1 \leq (x-3)/3 \leq 1$ or $0 \leq x \leq 6$. This is reasonable because if x is not in this interval the quantity under the radical in the integrand of (c) is negative. Actually we should also exclude the end points $x = 0$ and $x = 6$ because for these values of x the denominator of the integrand is zero. We shall return to this point and discuss it fully when we consider improper integrals in Chapter 11.

EXERCISE 4

In problems 1 through 10 find the derivative of the given function with respect to the independent variable.

1. $y = \cos^{-1} 5x.$

2. $y = \tan^{-1} t^4.$

3. $y = \sin^{-1} \sqrt{x}.$

4. $z = t \cot^{-1}(1 + t^2).$

5. $z = \cot^{-1} \dfrac{y}{1 - y^2}.$

6. $w = \tan^{-1} \dfrac{1}{t}$

7. $x = \sin^{-1} \sqrt{1 - t^4}.$

8. $s = \dfrac{t}{\sqrt{1 - t^2}} + \cos^{-1} t.$

9. $y = (x^2 - 2)\sin^{-1} \dfrac{x}{2} + \dfrac{x}{2} \sqrt{4 - x^2}.$

10. $y = \sqrt{Ax - B^2} - B \tan^{-1} \dfrac{\sqrt{Ax - B^2}}{B}, \quad A > 0, \quad B \neq 0.$

11. Prove that $\sin^{-1} x + \cos^{-1} x$ is a constant by showing that the derivative is zero. What is the constant?

12. Repeat problem 11 for $\tan^{-1} x + \cot^{-1} x.$

13. Sketch the curve $y = \tan^{-1}(1/x)$. Does the curve have any inflection points?

*14. Prove that the derivative of the function $y = \tan^{-1} x + \tan^{-1}(1/x)$ is zero if $x \neq 0$. But y is not a constant. Compare this result with problems 11 and 12. Sketch the graph of this function.

15. A picture 6 ft in height is hung on a wall so that its lower edge is 2 ft above the eye of an observer. How far from the wall should a person stand so that the picture subtends the largest angle at the person's eye?

16. A roadsign 20 ft high stands on a slight rise so that the bottom of the sign is 20 ft above the horizontal plane of the road. If the eye of the driver of an automobile is 4 ft above the road, at what horizontal distance from the sign will the sign appear to be largest to the driver (subtend the largest angle)?

17. An airplane is flying level 2000 ft above ground level at 180 mi/hr. Let θ be the angle between the line of sight from an observer to the plane and a vertical line. How fast is θ changing (a) when the plane is directly overhead, (b) when θ is $\pi/4$? When is the rate of change a maximum?

18. Find the angle of intersection of the two curves $y = \sin^{-1} x$ and $y = \cos^{-1} x.$

19. Prove that if a is any nonzero constant then

$$\int \frac{du}{\sqrt{a^2 - u^2}} = \sin^{-1}\frac{u}{a} + C$$

and

$$\int \frac{du}{a^2 + u^2} = \frac{1}{a}\tan^{-1}\frac{u}{a} + C.$$

These are simple generalizations of (37) and (38) and may be more convenient for practical applications.

In problems 20 through 27 find the given integral.

20. $\displaystyle\int \frac{dx}{\sqrt{25 - 4x^2}}$

21. $\displaystyle\int \frac{dy}{36 + 4y^2}$

22. $\displaystyle\int \frac{z\,dz}{5 + 2z^4}$

23. $\displaystyle\int \frac{\sin x\,dx}{\sqrt{10 - \cos^2 x}}$

24. $\displaystyle\int \frac{dx}{\sqrt{5 + 4x - x^2}}$

25. $\displaystyle\int \frac{7\,dx}{25 - 12x + 4x^2}$

★26. $\displaystyle\int \frac{5\,dt}{9\sqrt{t} + \sqrt{t^3}}$

27. $\displaystyle\int \frac{3\,dy}{\sqrt{5 - 12y - 9y^2}}$

28. Sketch the curve $y = \dfrac{1}{1 + x^2}$. Find the area under this curve between $x = 0$ and $x = M$, where M is a positive constant. Find the limit of this area as $M \to \infty$.

29. Sketch the curve $y = 1/\sqrt{1 - x^2}$ for the interval $0 \leq x < 1$. Find the area under this curve between $x = 0$ and $x = M$ where $0 < M < 1$. Find the limit of this area as $M \to 1^-$.

★30. Sketch the curve $y = \sec x$, and then by a reflection across the line $y = x$, sketch the inverse relation $y = \sec^{-1} x$.

★31. Show that formal manipulation with $y = \sec^{-1} x$ leads to

$$\frac{d}{dx}\sec^{-1} x = \frac{1}{x\sqrt{x^2 - 1}} \tag{39}$$

and hence the function $\sec^{-1} x$ is decreasing when $x < -1$, and increasing when $x > 1$.

★★32. Show that if we select our principal branch for $y = \sec^{-1} x$ by requiring that y be either in the interval $0 \leq y < \pi/2$ or in the interval $\pi \leq y < 3\pi/2$ then for each x such that $|x| \geq 1$ there is exactly one y. Show further that for this selection of the principal value, equation (39) is valid, namely the function is decreasing when $x < -1$ and increasing when $x > 1$. But this selection for the principal branch is unpleasant, because the principal values lie in two disjoint intervals separated by an interval of length $\pi/2$. Show by inspection of the graph, that if equation (39) must hold, then the definition of the principal branch will always require two intervals separated by an interval of length $\pi/2$, at the least.

★★33. If we replace (39) by the equation

$$\frac{d}{dx}\sec^{-1} x = \frac{1}{|x|\sqrt{x^2 - 1}} \qquad (40)$$

then for all x such that $|x| > 1$, the derivative is positive so the function is increasing. Show that we can select the principal branch by requiring that $0 \leq y \leq \pi$, and that on this branch equation (40) is satisfied. Since y is never $\pi/2$ for real x, the principal values again fall into two disjoint intervals, but these intervals are now separated by the single point $y = \pi/2$. But this selection for the principal branch is also unpleasant, because the absolute value sign enters in equation (40) via $|x|$.

8

THE LOGARITHMIC AND EXPONENTIAL FUNCTIONS

1.   Objective. Our natural objective is to obtain differentiation formulas for the functions $y = a^u$ and $y = \log_a u$, where u is a differentiable function of x.

Two paths are open to us: (1) a nonrigorous intuitive approach in which we attain our goals quite quickly while glossing over several difficult points, and (2) a rigorous approach that is correct but somewhat sophisticated and not exactly easy.   Our compromise is to present both approaches, taking the easy intuitive one first in sections 2, 3, 4, and 5 and then presenting the alternate one at the end of the chapter in section 9.   In this way the reader has the advantage of studying the rigorous presentation with a thorough knowledge of the end in view, and some idea of the reasons for the alternate treatment.

2.   Review. The reader is already familiar with the exponential function a^u.   The essential feature here is that the base a is a constant while the exponent u is a variable.   This contrasts sharply with the old familiar u^n in which the base is variable, and the exponent is constant.   Some of the properties of the exponential function are well known to the reader and we list them here for a quick review.   If $a > 0$ and u and v are any pair of real numbers then:

(1) $a^u > 0,$ (2) $a^u a^v = a^{u+v},$

(3) $\dfrac{a^u}{a^v} = a^{u-v},$ (4) $a^{-u} = \dfrac{1}{a^u},$

(5) $(a^u)^v = a^{uv},$ (6) $a^0 = 1,$

(7) $1^u = 1,$ (8) $a^u b^u = (ab)^u,$

(9) $a^{u/v} = \sqrt[v]{a^u} = (a^u)^{1/v} = (\sqrt[v]{a})^u = (a^{1/v})^u, \quad v \neq 0.$

Of course these properties are not all independent. For example (6) can be proved from (1) and (2), and then (4) follows from (3) and (6). Further (1) and (8) are sufficient to prove (7). On the other hand it is impossible to deduce (7) without using (8) or some equivalent.

To gain a feeling for the behavior of the exponential function it is worthwhile to sketch its graph for some fixed base a. In Fig. 1 we show the graph of $y = 2^x$. The student should check a few points on this graph and observe the following features.

a. As $x \to \infty$, the function $y = 2^x \to \infty$.

b. As $x \to -\infty$, the function $y = 2^x \to 0$.

c. For each fixed positive value y_1 of y there is just one value x_1 of x such that $2^{x_1} = y_1$. In other words the function 2^x assumes every positive value exactly once, as x runs through all of the real numbers.

It is customary to define the logarithmic function (to the base a) as the inverse of the exponential function (with the same base). In other words

$$L = \log_a N, \qquad a \neq 1, \quad a > 0, \tag{10}$$

read "L is the logarithm to the base a of N" if and only if

$$N = a^L \tag{11}$$

Since the functions $y = a^x$ and $y = \log_a x$ are inverse functions, the graph of either can be obtained from the other by interchanging x and y, i.e., by rotating the curve about the 45° line through the origin. In this way we can obtain the graph of $y = \log_2 x$ shown in Fig. 2 by a rotation of the graph shown in Fig. 1.

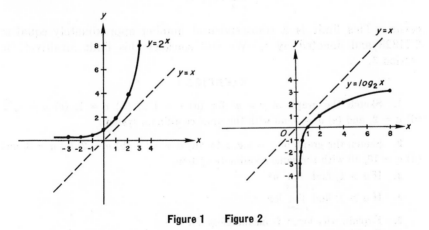

Figure 1   Figure 2

However there is a logical difficulty in proving some of these assertions that would surely pass unnoticed if we did not call attention to it. As long as the exponent u is an integer, and the base a is a rational number the computation of a^u is reasonably easy. For example $(2/5)^6 = 64/15625$. But what can we say about $(\sqrt{2})^{\sqrt{3}}$? Since both $\sqrt{2}$ and $\sqrt{3}$ are irrational numbers, does $(\sqrt{2})^{\sqrt{3}}$ really have some meaning, in the sense that it is a certain number? The answer is yes, but this is by no means obvious. The proof is long and tedious. A rigorous treatment of the exponential and logarithmic functions requires that this point be settled first, namely it must be proved that a^u is well-defined for every $a > 0$ and every real number u. Then equations (1) through (9) must be proved not only when u and v are integers (this case is easy) but for all u and v. Once this sticky point is passed, it is easy to deduce the following properties of the logarithmic function. Suppose $a > 0$, $a \neq 1$, M and N are any positive numbers, and n is any real number. Then

$$\log_a MN = \log_a M + \log_a N, \tag{12}$$

$$\log_a \frac{M}{N} = \log_a M - \log_a N, \tag{13}$$

$$\log_a M^n = n \log_a M, \tag{14}$$

$$\log_a 1 = 0, \qquad \log_a a = 1. \tag{15}$$

We will base our treatment in sections 4 and 5 on the assumption that the properties (1) through (9) and (12) through (15) have already been proved. This is one of the assumptions avoided by the treatment at the end of the chapter. Another such point is the proof that

$$\lim_{t \to 0} (1 + t)^{1/t}$$

exists. This limit is a transcendental number approximately equal to 2.71828 and denoted by e. We will consider this limit intuitively in section 3.

EXERCISE 1

1. Sketch the graph of $y = a^x$ for (a) $a = 1/2$, (b) $a = 1$, (c) $a = \sqrt{2}$, (d) $a = 2$, and (e) $a = 3$, all with the same coordinate system.

2. Sketch the graph of $y = \log_a x$ for (a) $a = \sqrt{2}$, (b) $a = 2$, (c) $a = 3$, and (d) $a = 10$, all with the same coordinate system.

3. If $a > 1$, find $\lim_{x \to -\infty} a^x$.

4. If $a > 1$, find $\lim_{x \to 0+} \log_a x$.

5. Explain why $\log_a N$ is meaningless if $a = 1$.

6. Explain why a^u is not defined for all u if a is negative.

7. Derive equation (6) using (1) and (2).

8. Derive equation (4) using (3) and (6).

9. Derive equation (7) using (1) and (8).

10. If u is an integer and a^u is defined by $a^u = aaa \cdots a$, with u factors, prove that (2) and (3) are true for all positive integers u and v.

★11. Assuming the "laws of exponents," equations (1) through (9), prove the "laws of logarithms," equations (12) through (15).

12. In changing the base of the logarithms from b to a, $\log M$ is changed in accordance with the formula

$$\log_a M = \log_a b \log_b M.$$

Prove this equation. *Hint:* Set $x = \log_a M$ and $y = \log_b M$. Then $a^x = b^y$. Now take the logarithm of both sides to the base a.

13. Prove that $\log_A B \log_B A = 1$.

3. **The number *e*.** This number is defined as the limit of the expression

$$\lim_{t \to 0} (1 + t)^{1/t} = e = 2.718 \tag{16}$$

as $t \to 0$. The proof that this expression tends to a limit is a little difficult and so we omit it temporarily. The proof will be given in section 9. One part of the difficulty is that t may take on irrational values as $t \to 0$. If we are merely trying to obtain a line on the behavior of (16) we can consider the special values $t = 1/n$ where n is an integer. For such values it is easy to do the computation and some values of $(1 + t)^{1/t}$ are recorded in Table 1 to four decimal places. This data is shown graphically in Fig. 3, where the points have been joined by a smooth curve. From the table and the curve it is reasonably clear that as $t \to 0$, the quantity $(1 + t)^{1/t}$ tends to a limit that is roughly 2.7, and it is standard practice to denote this limit number by the letter e. In Chapter 13 we will learn an easy method for computing e to any required degree of accuracy, but for most practical purposes it is sufficient to use $e = 2.71828$. Just like π, the number e is a transcendental number; that is, it is not the root of any polynomial with integer coefficients. The proof that e is transcendental is very difficult, and in fact for many years the question of the nature of e was an unsolved problem. The first proof that e is transcendental was given by Charles Hermite in 1873.

t	$n = 1/t$	$y = (1 + t)^{1/t}$		t	$n = 1/t$	$y = (1 + t)^{1/t}$
1	1	2.0000				
1/2	2	2.2500		$-1/2$	-2	4.0000
1/3	3	2.3704		$-1/3$	-3	3.3750
1/4	4	2.4414		$-1/4$	-4	3.1605
1/5	5	2.4883		$-1/5$	-5	3.0518
1/10	10	2.5937		$-1/10$	-10	2.8680

Table 1

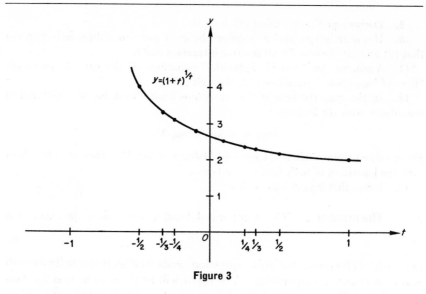

Figure 3

4.   The derivative of the logarithmic function.   Let $y = \log_a x$, and let x be changed by an amount Δx, giving a change of Δy in y. Then we have

$$y + \Delta y = \log_a (x + \Delta x)$$
$$y \quad\quad = \log_a x.$$

On taking the difference and using the laws of logarithms we obtain

$$\Delta y = \log_a (x + \Delta x) - \log_a x = \log_a \frac{x + \Delta x}{x}.$$

Dividing by Δx, and then inserting the factor x/x yields

$$\frac{\Delta y}{\Delta x} = \frac{1}{\Delta x} \log_a \left(1 + \frac{\Delta x}{x}\right) = \frac{1}{x} \frac{x}{\Delta x} \log_a \left(1 + \frac{\Delta x}{x}\right).$$

Applying here equation (14) with $n = x/\Delta x$ gives

$$\frac{\Delta y}{\Delta x} = \frac{1}{x} \log_a \left(1 + \frac{\Delta x}{x}\right)^{x/\Delta x}. \tag{17}$$

We are to let $\Delta x \to 0$ in (17).   For simplicity let us replace $\Delta x/x$ by t in equation (17).   Since $\Delta x \to 0$, then $t \to 0$, and (17) gives

$$\frac{dy}{dx} = \lim_{\Delta x \to 0} \frac{1}{x} \log_a \left(1 + \frac{\Delta x}{x}\right)^{x/\Delta x}$$

$$= \lim_{t \to 0} \frac{1}{x} \log_a (1 + t)^{1/t} = \frac{1}{x} \log_a e$$

by the definition of e in (16). We have proved that if $y = \log_a x$ then

$$\frac{dy}{dx} = \frac{1}{x} \log_a e.$$

Using the chain rule for differentiating a function of a function we can replace x by u, any differentiable function of x, and obtain

THEOREM 1. *If u is any differentiable function of x*

$$\frac{d}{dx} \log_a u = \frac{1}{u} \frac{du}{dx} \log_a e. \tag{18}$$

Equation (18) can be simplified greatly by selecting a suitable number for the base a. Indeed if we select e as the base then $\log_e e = 1$, and the nuisance factor in (18) can be dropped.

Logarithms to the base e are called natural logarithms although at first glance such a base as $2.71828\cdots$ may seem to be most unnatural. But equation (18) does simplify nicely when the base is e. As the student pursues his scientific studies he will find more reasons for regarding e as a natural number, and logarithms to the base e as natural logarithms. A table of natural logarithms is given in the back of the book (Table A).

In order to avoid the subscript a we will use the symbol $\ln u$ to denote the natural logarithm of u, and $\log u$ to denote the logarithm to the base 10 of u. With this notation we have the two special cases of equation (18)

$$\frac{d}{dx} \log u = \frac{1}{u} \frac{du}{dx} \log_{10} e = \frac{1}{u} \frac{du}{dx} \times .434\cdots. \tag{19}$$

and

$$\frac{d}{dx} \ln u = \frac{1}{u} \frac{du}{dx}. \tag{20}$$

EXAMPLE 1. Find the derivative of (a) $y = \ln (x^2 + 1)$, (b) $y = \ln \cos x$, and (c) $y = \ln x^4 (x^2 + 4)^{3/2}$.

SOLUTION. Using equation (20) we have

(a) $\dfrac{dy}{dx} = \dfrac{1}{x^2 + 1} \dfrac{d}{dx} (x^2 + 1) = \dfrac{2x}{x^2 + 1}.$

(b) $\dfrac{dy}{dx} = \dfrac{1}{\cos x} \dfrac{d}{dx} \cos x = \dfrac{-\sin x}{\cos x} = -\tan x.$

(c) The computations are simplified if we first use the laws of logarithms, equations (12) and (14), to simplify the expression for y. Indeed

$$y = \ln x^4(x^2 + 4)^{3/2} = \ln x^4 + \ln(x^2 + 4)^{3/2} = 4 \ln x + \frac{3}{2} \ln(x^2 + 4).$$

Then

$$\frac{dy}{dx} = \frac{4}{x} + \frac{3}{2}\frac{2x}{x^2 + 4} = \frac{4}{x} + \frac{3x}{x^2 + 4} = \frac{4x^2 + 16 + 3x^2}{x(x^2 + 4)} = \frac{7x^2 + 16}{x(x^2 + 4)}.$$

The properties of logarithms can be used to simplify an otherwise complicated problem in differentiation. The method is illustrated in

EXAMPLE 2. Find $\dfrac{dy}{dx}$ if $y = \dfrac{(x^2 + 1)^{1/2}(6x + 5)^{1/3}}{(x^2 - 1)^{1/2}}$.

SOLUTION. We first take the natural logarithm of both sides, and use equations (12), (13), and (14). This gives

$$\ln y = \tfrac{1}{2} \ln (x^2 + 1) + \tfrac{1}{3} \ln (6x + 5) - \tfrac{1}{2} \ln (x^2 - 1).$$

Differentiating both sides with respect to x yields

$$\frac{1}{y}\frac{dy}{dx} = \frac{x}{x^2 + 1} + \frac{2}{6x + 5} - \frac{x}{x^2 - 1}$$

$$= \frac{x(6x + 5)(x^2 - 1) + 2(x^2 + 1)(x^2 - 1) - x(x^2 + 1)(6x + 5)}{(x^2 + 1)(6x + 5)(x^2 - 1)}$$

$$= \frac{2(x^4 - 6x^2 - 5x - 1)}{(x^2 + 1)(6x + 5)(x^2 - 1)}.$$

Finally multiplying through by y and using the expression for y in terms of x we have

$$\frac{dy}{dx} = \frac{(x^2 + 1)^{1/2}(6x + 5)^{1/3}}{(x^2 - 1)^{1/2}} \cdot \frac{2(x^4 - 6x^2 - 5x - 1)}{(x^2 + 1)(6x + 5)(x^2 - 1)}$$

$$= \frac{2(x^4 - 6x^2 - 5x - 1)}{(x^2 + 1)^{1/2}(6x + 5)^{2/3}(x^2 - 1)^{3/2}}.$$

The procedure just illustrated is called *logarithmic differentiation.*

Each differentiation formula leads to an integral formula. Thus equation (20) gives

$$d \ln u = \frac{1}{u} du$$

or

$$\int \frac{du}{u} = \ln u + C. \qquad (21)$$

There is a slight difficulty with (21) because the function $\ln u$ has meaning only if u is positive. Suppose u is negative. Then $-u = |u|$ is positive, and using (21) on $-u$ we can write

$$\int \frac{du}{u} = \int \frac{-du}{-u} = \int \frac{d(-u)}{-u} = \ln(-u) + C = \ln|u| + C.$$

Combining this last formula with (21) we have

THEOREM 2. *If u is not zero then*

$$\int \frac{du}{u} = \ln|u| + C. \tag{22}$$

Of course if $u = 0$ the integrand $1/u$ becomes infinite. In any natural problem this exceptional case will not arise.

EXAMPLE 3. Find the area under the curve $y = 1/x$ between $x = 1$ and $x = 5$.

SOLUTION. Using (22) and Table A in the appendix

$$A = \int_1^5 y\, dx = \int_1^5 \frac{1}{x}\, dx = \ln x \Big|_1^5 = \ln 5 - \ln 1 = 1.609\cdots - 0 \approx 1.609.$$

EXAMPLE 4. Find the indefinite integrals:

(a) $\displaystyle \int \frac{x^3\, dx}{2x^4 + 1}$, (b) $\displaystyle \int \tan x\, dx$, (c) $\displaystyle \int \sec x\, dx$.

SOLUTION. (a) Let $u = 2x^4 + 1$. Then $du = 8x^3\, dx$.

$$\int \frac{x^3\, dx}{2x^4 + 1} = \frac{1}{8} \int \frac{8x^3\, dx}{2x^4 + 1} = \frac{1}{8} \int \frac{du}{u} = \frac{1}{8} \ln(2x^4 + 1) + C.$$

Notice that we have dropped the absolute value signs in $\ln|2x^4 + 1|$ because $2x^4 + 1$ is always positive.

(b) $\displaystyle \int \tan x\, dx = \int \frac{\sin x}{\cos x}\, dx = -\int \frac{d(\cos x)}{\cos x} = -\ln|\cos x| + C.$

(c) We multiply the integrand by $1 = (\sec x + \tan x)/(\sec x + \tan x)$. Then we have

$$\int \sec x\, dx = \int \frac{(\sec x + \tan x)\sec x}{\sec x + \tan x}\, dx = \int \frac{(\sec^2 x + \sec x \tan x)\, dx}{\sec x + \tan x}$$

$$= \int \frac{d(\sec x + \tan x)}{\sec x + \tan x} = \ln|\sec x + \tan x| + C.$$

These last two examples suggest that we expand our list of fundamental integration formulas by adjoining the following:

$$\int \tan u \, du = -\ln|\cos u| + C. \tag{23}$$

$$\int \cot u \, du = \ln|\sin u| + C, \tag{24}$$

$$\int \sec u \, du = \ln|\sec u + \tan u| + C, \tag{25}$$

$$\int \csc u \, du = -\ln|\csc u + \cot u| + C. \tag{26}$$

We have just proved (23) and (25). We leave the proofs of (24) and (26) to the student.

EXERCISE 2

In problems 1 through 15 find $\dfrac{dy}{dx}$.

1. $y = \ln(x^6 + 3x^2 + 1)$.

2. $y = \ln(x + 1)^3. = 3 \ln(x+1)$

3. $y = 3\ln(5x + 5)$.

4. $y = \ln x^2$.

5. $y = \ln^2 x. = (\ln x)^2$

6. $y = \ln \sec x^2$.

7. $y = x^2 \ln x$.

8. $y = x \ln x^2 - 2x$.

9. $y = \ln 2x \sqrt{x^2 + 4}$.

10. $y = [\ln x][\ln(1 - x)]$.

11. $y = \ln \tan x + \ln \cot x$.

12. $y = \ln \dfrac{1 + x^2}{1 - x^2}$.

13. $y = 4x \tan^{-1} 2x - \ln(4x^2 + 1)$.

14. $y = x(\sin \ln x + \cos \ln x)$.

15. $y = x\sqrt{x^2 - 5} - 5 \ln(x + \sqrt{x^2 - 5})$.

Use logarithmic differentiation in problems 16 through 19 to find $\dfrac{dy}{dx}$.

16. $y = \sqrt{(x^2 - 1)(x^2 + 2)}$.

17. $y = \sqrt[3]{(x - 1)(x + 2)(x + 5)}$.

18. $y = 6\dfrac{(3x + 2)^{1/2}}{(2x + 1)^{1/3}}$.

19. $y = \dfrac{\sqrt{x^2 - 5}}{x^6\sqrt{x^2 + 7}}$.

20. Explain why the answers in problems 2 and 3 are the same.

21. Explain why the answer in problem 11 is zero.

In problems 22 through 33 find the given integral

22. $\displaystyle\int \frac{x\,dx}{x^2 + 4}$.

23. $\displaystyle\int \frac{\sin x\,dx}{5 - 3\cos x}$.

24. $\displaystyle\int x\tan x^2\,dx$.

25. $\displaystyle\int \sec 5x\,dx$.

26. $\displaystyle\int \frac{x + 3}{x^2 + 4}\,dx$.

★27. $\displaystyle\int \frac{dx}{\sqrt{x}(1 + x)}$.

★28. $\displaystyle\int \frac{x\,dx}{\sin x^2}$.

★29. $\displaystyle\int \frac{x^3\,dx}{\tan x^4}$.

★30. $\displaystyle\int \frac{\ln x\,dx}{x}$.

★31. $\displaystyle\int \frac{dx}{x\ln x}$.

32. $\displaystyle\int_0^1 \frac{dx}{1 + 5x}$.

33. $\displaystyle\int_0^{\pi/4} \tan x\,dx$.

34. Find the area under the curve:
  a. $y = 1/x$ between $x = 1$ and $x = 7$,
  b. $y = 1/x$ between $x = 4$ and $x = 28$,
  c. $y = 2x/(x^2 + 3)$ between $x = 1$ and $x = 5$.

35. The region bounded by the y-axis and the curve $y = 1/x^2$, between the lines $y = 5$ and $y = 35$ is rotated about the y-axis. Find the volume of the solid generated.

36. Find the length of arc of the curve:

  a. $y = \ln\cos x$,   between $x = 0$ and $x = \pi/4$.

  b. $y = \dfrac{x^2}{2} - \dfrac{1}{4}\ln x$,   between $x = 1$ and $x = 16$.

37. Sketch the curve $y = x^2 - 8\ln x$ for $x > 0$ and locate all extremal points and inflection points on the curve.

38. Prove that for $0 < x < \pi/2$ the functions $\ln(\csc 2x - \cot 2x)$ and $\ln\tan x$ have the same derivative and hence $\ln(\csc 2x - \cot 2x) = \ln\tan x + C$. Find C.

39. Formula (18) is not in a useful form because $\log_a e$ is not available in tables. Use problem 13 of Exercise 1 to show that this factor can be replaced by $1/\ln a$. This factor is easy to compute using Table A.

5.   The exponential function. In order to find a differentiation formula for the function

$$y = a^u \tag{27}$$

it is convenient to first take the natural logarithm of both sides. This yields

$$\ln y = \ln a^u = u \ln a. \tag{28}$$

If we differentiate this equation with respect to x we have, by (20),

$$\frac{1}{y}\frac{dy}{dx} = \frac{du}{dx}\ln a$$

and using (27), this gives

$$\frac{dy}{dx} = y\frac{du}{dx}\ln a = a^u\frac{du}{dx}\ln a. \tag{29}$$

Hence if u is any differentiable function of x

$$\frac{d}{dx}a^u = a^u\frac{du}{dx}\ln a. \tag{30}$$

The most important case occurs when the base a is e. Since $\ln e = \log_e e = 1$, the nuisance factor $\ln a$, in (30), becomes 1, when $a = e$. This gives the special formula

$$\boxed{\frac{d}{dx}e^u = e^u\frac{du}{dx}.} \tag{31}$$

When $u = x$, equation (31) yields

$$\boxed{\frac{d}{dx}e^x = e^x.} \tag{32}$$

Notice that we have here a function that is its own derivative. The simplicity of this formula lends weight to the feeling that e is a natural number. Just as logarithms to the base e are natural logarithms, so e^x is a "natural" exponential function. A table of values for e^x is given in Table B in the Appendix.

Each of the three differentiation formulas (30), (31), and (32) yields an equivalent integration formula. These are

$$\int a^u \, du = \frac{a^u}{\ln a} + C, \tag{33}$$

$$\int e^u \, du = e^u + C, \tag{34}$$

$$\int e^x \, dx = e^x + C. \tag{35}$$

EXAMPLE 1. Find the derivative of (a) $y = e^{3x}$, (b) $y = e^{\tan x^2}$, and (c) $y = (e^{2x} - 1)/(e^{2x} + 1)$.

SOLUTION. (a) $\dfrac{dy}{dx} = e^{3x} \dfrac{d}{dx} 3x = 3e^{3x}.$

(b) $\dfrac{dy}{dx} = e^{\tan x^2} \dfrac{d}{dx} \tan x^2 = e^{\tan x^2} 2x \sec^2 x^2 = 2x \, e^{\tan x^2} \sec^2 x^2.$

(c) $\dfrac{dy}{dx} = \dfrac{(e^{2x} + 1)2e^{2x} - (e^{2x} - 1)2e^{2x}}{(e^{2x} + 1)^2} = \dfrac{4e^{2x}}{(e^{2x} + 1)^2}.$

EXAMPLE 2. Find each of the integrals

(a) $\displaystyle\int_0^2 \frac{dx}{e^x}$, (b) $\displaystyle\int e^x \sin e^x \, dx$, (c) $\displaystyle\int \frac{e^x \, dx}{1 + 5e^x}.$

SOLUTION. (a) $\displaystyle\int_0^2 \frac{dx}{e^x} = \int_0^2 e^{-x} \, dx = -\int_0^2 e^{-x}(-dx)$

$$= -e^{-x} \Big|_0^2 = e^0 - e^{-2} = 1 - e^{-2} = 1 - .1353\cdots \approx .865.$$

(b) $\displaystyle\int e^x \sin e^x \, dx = \int \sin u \, du \qquad \text{(where } u = e^x)$

$$= -\cos u + C = -\cos e^x + C.$$

(c) $\displaystyle\int \frac{e^x \, dx}{1 + 5e^x} = \frac{1}{5} \int \frac{5e^x \, dx}{1 + 5e^x} = \frac{1}{5} \int \frac{du}{u} \qquad \text{(where } u = 1 + 5e^x)$

$$= \frac{1}{5} \ln u + C = \frac{1}{5} \ln (1 + 5e^x) + C.$$

EXAMPLE 3. Find the derivative of $y = x^{x^2}$.

SOLUTION. Since both the base and the exponent are variables none of our formulas cover this case. But logarithmic differentiation will help us to bypass this difficulty. Taking natural logarithms of both sides gives

$$\ln y = x^2 \ln x$$

and now we have a product to differentiate. Hence

$$\frac{1}{y}\frac{dy}{dx} = 2x \ln x + x^2 \frac{1}{x}.$$

$$\frac{dy}{dx} = y(2x \ln x + x) = (x + 2x \ln x)x^{x^2}.$$

EXERCISE 3

In problems 1 through 11 find the derivative.

1. $y = x^2 e^{-3x}$.

2. $y = e^{1/x^2}$.

3. $y = e^{\sin^2 5x}$.

4. $y = \ln(1 + 5e^x)$.

5. $y = \dfrac{x^2}{e^x + x}$.

6. $y = \ln \dfrac{1 + e^{3x}}{1 - e^{3x}}$.

7. $y = x^{\sin x}$.

8. $y = (\sin x)^x$.

9. $y = (1 + 3x)^{1/x}$.

10. $y = (\cos x^2)^{x^3}$.

11. $y = (120 + 120x + 60x^2 + 20x^3 + 5x^4 + x^5)\,e^{-x}$.

In problems 12 through 17 find a formula for the nth derivative.

12. $y = \ln x$.

13. $y = \ln(1 + x)^5$.

14. $y = e^x$.

15. $y = (e^x)^7$.

16. $y = xe^x$.

17. $y = x^2 \ln x$.

In problems 18 through 23 find the indicated integral.

18. $\displaystyle\int e^{-4x}\,dx$.

19. $\displaystyle\int 14xe^{x^2}\,dx$.

20. $\displaystyle\int e^{\tan x}\sec^2 x\,dx$.

21. $\displaystyle\int \frac{6e^x\,dx}{1 + e^{2x}}$.

22. $\displaystyle\int \frac{9e^{3x}\,dx}{1 + e^{3x}}$.

23. $\displaystyle\int \frac{e^x + e^{-x}}{e^x - e^{-x}}\,dx$.

In problems 24 through 28 sketch the graph of the given function and find all of the relative maximum, relative minimum, and inflection points.

24. $y = e^{-x^2}$.

25. $y = e^x + e^{-x}$.

26. $y = e^x - e^{-x}$ **27.** $y = xe^{x/3}$.

★28. $y = e^{-x} \cos x$, for $x > 0$.

29. Find the sides of the largest rectangle that can be drawn with two vertices on the x-axis, and two vertices on the curve $y = e^{-x^2}$.

30. From the point (a, e^a) on the curve $y = e^x$ a line is drawn normal to this curve. Find the x-intercept of this line.

31. Prove that $2x - \ln(3 + 6e^x + 3e^{2x}) = C - 2\ln(1 + e^{-x})$ by showing that both sides have the same derivative. What is C?

32. Find the length of the curve $y = \dfrac{e^x + e^{-x}}{2}$ between $x = 0$ and $x = a$.

33. The curve of problem 32 is rotated about the x-axis. Find the area of the surface generated.

6.   The hyperbolic functions. Certain combinations of the exponential function appear so frequently, both in the applications of mathematics and in the theory, that it is worthwhile to give them special names. We shall see that these functions satisfy identities that are quite similar to the standard trigonometric identities. It is this similarity with the trigonometric functions that accounts for the names attached to the functions.

The function $(e^x - e^{-x})/2$ is called[1] the *hyperbolic sine* of x and is abbreviated sinh x. The function $(e^x + e^{-x})/2$ is called the *hyperbolic cosine* of x and is abbreviated cosh x. The remaining four hyperbolic functions are then defined in terms of sinh x and cosh x, in just the same way that the remaining four trigonometric functions can be defined in terms of sin x and cos x. Precisely we have

DEFINITION 1. *The six hyperbolic functions are*

$$
\begin{aligned}
&\sinh x = \frac{e^x - e^{-x}}{2}, &\qquad &\cosh x = \frac{e^x + e^{-x}}{2}, \\[2mm]
&\tanh x = \frac{\sinh x}{\cosh x} = \frac{e^x - e^{-x}}{e^x + e^{-x}}, &\qquad &\coth x = \frac{\cosh x}{\sinh x} = \frac{e^x + e^{-x}}{e^x - e^{-x}}, \\[2mm]
&\text{sech } x = \frac{1}{\cosh x} = \frac{2}{e^x + e^{-x}}, &\qquad &\text{csch } x = \frac{1}{\sinh x} = \frac{2}{e^x - e^{-x}}.
\end{aligned}
\qquad (36)
$$

For each identity among the trigonometric functions there is a corresponding identity among the hyperbolic functions. We will prove a few of these as our first example, and reserve the rest for Exercise 4.

[1] The relationship between the hyperbolic functions and the hyperbola will be presented in Chapter 10, after we have studied parametric equations.

EXAMPLE 1. Prove that for all x and y

$$\cosh^2 x - \sinh^2 x = 1, \tag{37}$$

$$\operatorname{sech}^2 x + \tanh^2 x = 1, \tag{38}$$

and

$$\sinh (x + y) = \sinh x \cosh y + \cosh x \sinh y. \tag{39}$$

The reader will note that (37) and (38) are similar to $\cos^2 x + \sin^2 x = 1$ and $\sec^2 x - \tan^2 x = 1$ respectively, but there is a change of sign. However (39) coincides completely with its trigonometric counterpart $\sin (x + y) = \sin x \cos y + \cos x \sin y$.

SOLUTION. In proving (37) we will use the fact that $e^x e^{-x} = e^{x-x} = e^0 = 1$. By the very definition of the hyperbolic functions the lefthand side gives

$$\cosh^2 x - \sinh^2 x = \left(\frac{e^x + e^{-x}}{2}\right)^2 - \left(\frac{e^x - e^{-x}}{2}\right)^2$$

$$= \frac{e^{2x} + 2e^0 + e^{-2x}}{4} - \frac{e^{2x} - 2e^0 + e^{-2x}}{4} = \frac{2 + 2}{4} = 1$$

and this completes the proof of (37).

We can prove (38) in a similar fashion, but now that (37) has been established we can use it to give a second and quicker proof. Indeed if we divide both sides of (37) by $\cosh^2 x$ we have

$$\frac{\cosh^2 x - \sinh^2 x}{\cosh^2 x} = \frac{1}{\cosh^2 x}.$$

Then using the definitions of $\tanh x$ and $\operatorname{sech} x$ this gives

$$1 - \tanh^2 x = \operatorname{sech}^2 x,$$

and this is equivalent to (38).

To prove (39) it is simpler to start with the right hand side. By definition

$$\sinh x \cosh y + \cosh x \sinh y = \frac{e^x - e^{-x}}{2} \frac{e^y + e^{-y}}{2} + \frac{e^x + e^{-x}}{2} \frac{e^y - e^{-y}}{2}$$

$$= \frac{e^{x+y} - e^{-x+y} + e^{x-y} - e^{-x-y}}{4} + \frac{e^{x+y} + e^{-x+y} - e^{x-y} - e^{-x-y}}{4}$$

$$= \frac{2e^{x+y} - 2e^{-(x+y)}}{4} = \sinh(x+y).$$

EXAMPLE 2. Prove that $\sinh x$ is an odd function, and $\cosh x$ is an even function.

SOLUTION. Recall that $f(x)$ is an odd function if $f(-x) = -f(x)$. For the hyperbolic sine we have

$$\sinh(-x) = \frac{e^{-x} - e^{-(-x)}}{2} = \frac{e^{-x} - e^{x}}{2} = -\frac{e^{x} - e^{-x}}{2} = -\sinh x.$$

To prove that the hyperbolic cosine is even we have

$$\cosh(-x) = \frac{e^{-x} + e^{-(-x)}}{2} = \frac{e^{-x} + e^{x}}{2} = \frac{e^{x} + e^{-x}}{2} = \cosh x.$$

The graphs of the hyperbolic functions are easy to sketch using the values for e^x from Table B, and the resulting curves are shown in Fig. 4. But in the graphs the similarity between the trigonometric functions and the hyperbolic functions breaks down. For one thing the hyperbolic functions are not periodic. Further $\sin x$ and $\cos x$ are bounded functions, i.e., $|\sin x| \leq 1$ and $|\cos x| \leq 1$. But $\sinh x$ varies from $-\infty$ to $+\infty$ and $\cosh x$ varies between $+1$ and $+\infty$. On the other hand $|\tanh x| < 1$ and $0 < \operatorname{sech} x \leq 1$, while it is their trigonometric counterpart that is unbounded.

The inverse functions of the hyperbolic functions are simpler than the inverse trigonometric functions, because for four of the functions the inverses are naturally single-valued functions. Further these inverse functions can be expressed in terms of the logarithm function.

Let us consider first the inverse hyperbolic sine, written

$$y = \sinh^{-1} x. \tag{40}$$

Equation (40) is equivalent to $x = \sinh y$ and hence

$$x = \frac{e^y - e^{-y}}{2}. \tag{41}$$

If we multiply both sides of this equation by $2e^y$ we have

$$2xe^y = e^{2y} - 1$$

or

$$(e^y)^2 - 2xe^y - 1 = 0.$$

This can be solved as a quadratic equation in e^y, giving

$$e^y = \frac{2x \pm \sqrt{4x^2 + 4}}{2} = x \pm \sqrt{x^2 + 1}. \tag{42}$$

Now taking the natural logarithms of both sides we can write $y = \ln(x \pm \sqrt{x^2 + 1})$.   But this is possible only if $x \pm \sqrt{x^2 + 1}$ is positive.   In other words there is no real value for y in equation (42) unless the

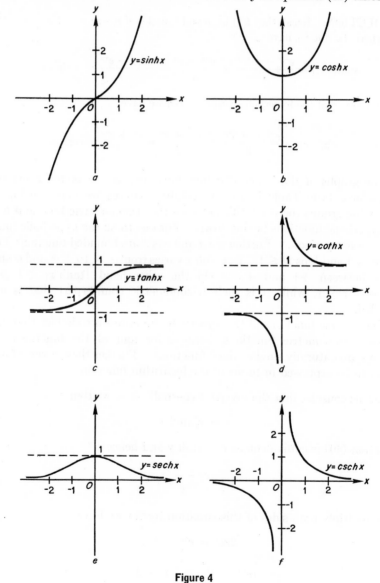

Figure 4

right side is positive.   Hence we must reject the negative sign in (42) and write

$$y = \ln (x + \sqrt{x^2 + 1}). \tag{43}$$

Comparing (40) and (43) we see that

$$\sinh^{-1} x = \ln (x + \sqrt{x^2 + 1}) \tag{44}$$

and we have in fact proved that this inverse relation is a single-valued function.   Of course the single-valuedness was obvious from the graph in Fig. 4a because each horizontal line meets the curve in exactly one point.

We now perform the same manipulations for the inverse hyperbolic cosine

$$y = \cosh^{-1} x. \tag{45}$$

In Fig. 4b, it seems as though each horizontal line above the point $(0, 1)$ meets the curve in two points.   Hence we expect the relation (45) to be double-valued for $x > 1$, and we shall need to select a principal branch. Equation (45) is equivalent to $x = \cosh y$ or

$$x = \frac{e^y + e^{-y}}{2},$$

or

$$2xe^y = e^{2y} + 1,$$

or

$$e^{2y} - 2xe^y + 1 = 0. \tag{46}$$

Now the product of the roots of this quadratic equation in e^y is $+1$, so either both roots are positive or both roots are negative.   Solving (46) for e^y we find

$$e^y = \frac{2x \pm \sqrt{4x^2 - 4}}{2} = x \pm \sqrt{x^2 - 1} \tag{47}$$

Clearly when $x < 1$, e^y is imaginary and there is no real y.   When $x = 1$, $e^y = 1$, and when $x > 1$, equation (46) gives two values for e^y, both of which are positive.   We select for our principal value for e^y, the larger of the two expressions, $x + \sqrt{x^2 - 1}$, and then from (47) we have

$$y = \ln (x + \sqrt{x^2 - 1}). \tag{48}$$

Comparing (45) and (48) yields

$$\cosh^{-1} x = \ln (x + \sqrt{x^2 - 1}), \qquad x \geq 1 \tag{49}$$

Here the principal branch has been chosen so that $\cosh^{-1} x$ is positive or zero, and this corresponds to selecting the right half of the curve in Fig. 4b as the principal branch.

EXERCISE 4

1. Check that the curves shown in Fig. 4 are correct by plotting a few points on each, using Table B.

2. Prove each of the following assertions about the hyperbolic functions, and check that the curves of Fig. 4 illustrate these assertions.

a.	$\cosh x \geq 1$	**b.**	$-1 < \tanh x < 1$
c.	$|\coth x| > 1$	**d.**	$0 < \operatorname{sech} x \leq 1$
e.	$\lim_{x \to \infty} \tanh x = 1$	**f.**	$\lim_{x \to \infty} \operatorname{sech} x = 0$

3. Prove the following assertions.

a. $y = \sinh x$ is an increasing function for all x.
b. $y = \cosh x$ is an increasing function for $x > 0$.
c. $y = \cosh x$ is concave upward for all x.
d. $y = \sinh x$ is concave upward for $x > 0$.

In problems 4 through 11 prove the given identity, and state the corresponding trigonometric identity.

4. $\coth^2 x - \operatorname{csch}^2 x = 1$.   **5.** $\sinh 2x = 2 \sinh x \cosh x$.
6. $\cosh 2x = \cosh^2 x + \sinh^2 x$.   **7.** $2 \cosh^2 x = \cosh 2x + 1$.
8. $2 \sinh^2 x = \cosh 2x - 1$.   **9.** $\cosh (x + y) = \cosh x \cosh y + \sinh x \sinh y$.

10. $\sinh (x - y) = \sinh x \cosh y - \cosh x \sinh y$.

11. $\sinh A + \sinh B = 2 \sinh \dfrac{A + B}{2} \cosh \dfrac{A - B}{2}$.

12. Prove that $\cosh x + \sinh x = e^x$ and $\cosh x - \sinh x = e^{-x}$. Observe that these have no analogue in the trigonometry of a real variable. The student will find a very beautiful trigonometric analogue when he studies the theory of functions of a complex variable.

13. Prove that $(\cosh x + \sinh x)^n = \cosh nx + \sinh nx$.

14. Given that $\sinh x_0 = 4/3$ find the values for the other five hyperbolic functions of x_0.

15. Express in terms of the logarithm function   **a.** $\tanh^{-1} x$,   **b.** $\coth^{-1} x$, **c.** $\operatorname{sech}^{-1} x$,   **d.** $\operatorname{csch}^{-1} x$.   In (c) take the principal branch so that $\operatorname{sech}^{-1} x \geq 0$.

Prove the following identities.

16. $\tanh \ln x = \dfrac{x^2 - 1}{x^2 + 1}$.   **17.** $\tanh x + \coth x = 2 \coth 2x$.

18. $\dfrac{\tanh x + 1}{\tanh x - 1} = -e^{2x}$.   **19.** $8 \sinh^4 x = \cosh 4x - 4 \cosh 2x + 3$.

7. **Differentiation and integration of the hyperbolic functions.** These formulas present a very strong similarity with the formulas for the differentiation and integration of the trigonometric functions. First

$$\frac{d}{dx}\sinh x = \frac{d}{dx}\frac{e^x - e^{-x}}{2} = \frac{e^x + e^{-x}}{2} = \cosh x,$$

and

$$\frac{d}{dx}\cosh x = \frac{d}{dx}\frac{e^x + e^{-x}}{2} = \frac{e^x - e^{-x}}{2} = \sinh x,$$

Using the chain rule we see that if u is any differentiable function of x

$$\frac{d}{dx}\sinh u = \cosh u \frac{du}{dx}, \qquad \frac{d}{dx}\cosh u = \sinh u \frac{du}{dx}. \qquad (50)$$

We leave it as an exercise for the student to derive the following differentiation formulas for the other four hyperbolic functions.

$$\frac{d}{dx}\tanh u = \operatorname{sech}^2 u \frac{du}{dx}, \qquad \frac{d}{dx}\coth u = -\operatorname{csch}^2 u \frac{du}{dx}, \qquad (51)$$

$$\frac{d}{dx}\operatorname{sech} u = -\operatorname{sech} u \tanh u \frac{du}{dx}, \qquad \frac{d}{dx}\operatorname{csch} u = -\operatorname{csch} u \coth u \frac{du}{dx}. \qquad (52)$$

As a memory aid, observe that the derivatives of the first three hyperbolic functions ($\sinh u$, $\cosh u$, and $\tanh u$) carry a positive sign, while the derivatives of the last three carry a negative sign. Otherwise they are identical with the formulas for differentiating the trigonometric functions.

The formulas for differentiating the inverse functions are obtained in the standard way. For example if

$$y = \sinh^{-1} u,$$

then

$$u = \sinh y,$$

$$\frac{du}{dx} = \cosh y \frac{dy}{dx}.$$

Hence

$$\frac{dy}{dx} = \frac{1}{\cosh y}\frac{du}{dx} = \frac{1}{\sqrt{1 + \sinh^2 y}}\frac{du}{dx} = \frac{1}{\sqrt{1 + u^2}}\frac{du}{dx}.$$

This gives the formula

$$\frac{d}{dx}\sinh^{-1} u = \frac{1}{\sqrt{1+u^2}}\frac{du}{dx}. \tag{53}$$

We leave it as an exercise for the student to derive the formulas given below for the derivatives of the other five inverse hyperbolic functions.

$$\frac{d}{dx}\cosh^{-1} u = \frac{1}{\sqrt{u^2-1}}\frac{du}{dx}, \qquad u > 1. \tag{54}$$

$$\frac{d}{dx}\tanh^{-1} u = \frac{1}{1-u^2}\frac{du}{dx}, \qquad |u| < 1. \tag{55}$$

$$\frac{d}{dx}\coth^{-1} u = \frac{1}{1-u^2}\frac{du}{dx}, \qquad |u| > 1. \tag{56}$$

$$\frac{d}{dx}\operatorname{sech}^{-1} u = \frac{-1}{u\sqrt{1-u^2}}\frac{du}{dx}, \qquad 0 < u < 1. \tag{57}$$

$$\frac{d}{dx}\operatorname{csch}^{-1} u = \frac{-1}{|u|\sqrt{1+u^2}}\frac{du}{dx}, \qquad u \neq 0. \tag{58}$$

All of these differentiation formulas lead to integration formulas, but for the present we will use only the eight formulas listed below.

$$\int \sinh u \, du = \cosh u + C. \tag{59}$$

$$\int \cosh u \, du = \sinh u + C. \tag{60}$$

$$\int \operatorname{sech}^2 u \, du = \tanh u + C. \tag{61}$$

$$\int \operatorname{csch}^2 u \, du = -\coth u + C. \tag{62}$$

$$\int \operatorname{sech} u \tanh u \, du = -\operatorname{sech} u + C. \tag{63}$$

$$\int \operatorname{csch} u \coth u \, du = -\operatorname{csch} u + C. \tag{64}$$

$$\int \frac{du}{\sqrt{u^2+1}} = \sinh^{-1} u + C = \ln(u + \sqrt{u^2+1}) + C. \tag{65}$$

$$\int \frac{du}{\sqrt{u^2 - 1}} = \cosh^{-1} u + C = \ln (u + \sqrt{u^2 - 1}) + C, \qquad u > 1. \quad (66)$$

Formulas (55) through (58) also yield integration formulas, but these together with (65) and (66) can be obtained in a more systematic (and hence better) way, as we shall see in the next chapter.

EXAMPLE 1.   Find $\dfrac{dy}{dx}$ for (a) $y = \operatorname{sech}^n x$,

   (b) $y = \cosh^{-1}\sqrt{x^2 + 1}$, $x > 0$.

SOLUTION.   For **(a)** we have

$$\frac{dy}{dx} = n \operatorname{sech}^{n-1} x \frac{d}{dx} \operatorname{sech} x = n \operatorname{sech}^{n-1} x(-\operatorname{sech} x \tanh x)$$

$$= - n \operatorname{sech}^n x \tanh x.$$

(b) $\dfrac{dy}{dx} = \dfrac{1}{\sqrt{x^2 + 1} - 1} \dfrac{d}{dx}\sqrt{x^2 + 1} = \dfrac{1}{\sqrt{x^2}} \dfrac{1}{2} \dfrac{2x}{\sqrt{x^2 + 1}} = \dfrac{1}{\sqrt{x^2 + 1}}.$

EXAMPLE 2.   Find each of the following integrals

(a) $\displaystyle\int x \sinh^n x^2 \cosh x^2 \, dx, \quad n \ne -1,$ (b) $\displaystyle\int \frac{dx}{\sqrt{x^2 - 4x + 3}}.$

SOLUTION.   For **(a)** we set $u = \sinh x^2$, so $du = 2x \cosh x^2 \, dx$.   Then

$$\int x \sinh^n x^2 \cosh x^2 \, dx = \frac{1}{2} \int \sinh^n x^2 (2x \cosh x^2)dx = \frac{1}{2} \int u^n \, du$$

$$= \frac{u^{n+1}}{2(n + 1)} + C = \frac{\sinh^{n+1} x^2}{2n + 2} + C.$$

(b) $\displaystyle\int \frac{dx}{\sqrt{x^2 - 4x + 3}} = \int \frac{dx}{\sqrt{x^2 - 4x + 4 - 1}} = \int \frac{dx}{\sqrt{(x - 2)^2 - 1}}$

$$= \cosh^{-1}(x - 2) + C. \qquad \text{[by (66)]},$$

$$= \ln(x - 2 + \sqrt{x^2 - 4x + 3}) + C, \qquad \text{for } x > 3.$$

EXERCISE 5

1. Derive the formulas (51) and (52).
2. If $f(x) = \cosh 3x$, find $f^{(2n)}(x)$.
3. If $f(x) = \operatorname{sech} x$, find $f''(x)$.
4. Find the interval in which the graph of $y = \operatorname{sech} x$ is concave downward.
5. Find the relative minimum point on the curve $y = 4 \tanh x + \coth x$.
6. Derive the formulas (54) through (58).

7. From (44) we have $\sinh^{-1} u = \ln(u + \sqrt{u^2 + 1})$. Show that the derivative of this function is also the right hand side of (53), as it should be.

★**8.** Show that the function $y = \cosh^{-1}\sqrt{x^2 + 1}$ is decreasing when x is negative, and hence the derivative should be negative. But in Example 1b the derivative for this function turns out to be positive. Where lies the trouble?

In problems 9 through 12 find the derivative of the given function.

9. $y = \ln \sinh x^3$.   **10.** $y = e^x \cosh x$.

11. $y = \cosh^{-1} 1/x$.   **12.** $y = \coth^{-1}\sqrt{1 + x^4}$.

In problems 13 through 22 find the indicated integral.

13. $\displaystyle\int \sinh^3 x \cosh^3 x \, dx$.   **14.** $\displaystyle\int \operatorname{sech} x \tanh^3 x \, dx$.

15. $\displaystyle\int \cosh^2 x \, dx$.   **16.** $\displaystyle\int \coth 5x \, dx$.

17. $\displaystyle\int \operatorname{sech} x \, dx$.   **18.** $\displaystyle\int x^2 \tanh x^3 \, dx$.

19. $\displaystyle\int \frac{dx}{\sqrt{1 + 4x^2}}$.   **20.** $\displaystyle\int \frac{6x \, dx}{\sqrt{x^4 - 1}}$.

★**21.** $\displaystyle\int \frac{dx}{\sqrt{x^2 + 6x + 25}}$.   ★**22.** $\displaystyle\int \frac{4x \, dx}{\sqrt{x^4 + 6x^2 + 5}}$.

23. Generalize formulas (65) and (66) by proving that

$$\int \frac{du}{\sqrt{u^2 + a^2}} = \ln(u + \sqrt{u^2 + a^2}) + C,$$

and

$$\int \frac{du}{\sqrt{u^2 - a^2}} = \ln(u + \sqrt{u^2 - a^2}) + C, \qquad u > a > 0.$$

8.   The derivative of an integral. We now digress in order to present some more material on integration, that will be needed for the rigorous approach to the logarithmic and exponential functions given in the next section. But this material is also of interest in its own right, and is useful both in the further development of the calculus and in applications.

First let us mention that the variable in any definite integral is not a true variable, but is a "dummy" variable, because the value of the integral is a constant, i.e., it does not depend on x. To be specific consider the example

$$I = \int_{-1}^{2} 5x^4 \, dx = x^5 \Big|_{-1}^{2} = 32 - (-1) = 33. \tag{67}$$

Here $I = 33$ is a number, and the question of what value to use for x does not occur, and in fact does not even make sense. To clarify the role of our "dummy" variable x, let us observe that if we replace x by any other letter, for example t, we have

$$I = \int_{-1}^{2} 5t^4 \, dt = t^5 \Big|_{-1}^{2} = 32 - (-1) = 33. \tag{68}$$

To summarize, the value of a definite integral is a constant, and any convenient letter can be used as a variable of integration.

But if we change the integrand, or the end points of the interval of integration, then the value of the definite integral may change. To be specific suppose that the value of b, the upper limit, is changing. Then I changes with b and is thus a proper function of b, and we should write $I(b)$ to denote this function. To emphasize this variability of b, we might use the letter x, and write

$$I(x) = \int_{a}^{x} f(x) \, dx. \tag{69}$$

Now (69) is really in bad taste, although such expressions will be found in many textbooks. It is bad because the letter x is used in one and the same formula with two different meanings, first as the upper limit of the integral, and second as a variable of integration. It is far more accurate to write (69) in the form

$$I(x) = \int_{a}^{x} f(t) \, dt. \tag{70}$$

where it is now clear that it is the upper limit of the integral that is considered as being a variable, the lower end point a and the function $f(t)$ being fixed. As an illustration, replacing 2 by x in (68) leads to the function

$$I(x) = \int_{-1}^{x} 5t^4 \, dt = t^5 \Big|_{-1}^{x} = x^5 + 1. \tag{71}$$

Observe that the derivative of $I(x)$ in (71) is just $5x^4$, the function that appears in the integrand. We shall soon see (Theorem 4) that this is always the case when the integrand is a continuous function. For this we need

THEOREM 3. *Suppose that in the interval $a \le x \le b$, the integrand satisfies the inequality*

$$m \le f(x) \le M. \tag{72}$$

Then

$$m(b - a) \le \int_{a}^{b} f(x) \, dx \le M(b - a). \tag{73}$$

PROOF.   From Chapter 4, Definition 2, the integral is just the limit as $n \to \infty$ of a sum of the form

$$S_n = f(x_1)\Delta x_1 + f(x_2)\Delta x_2 + \cdots + f(x_n)\Delta x_n.$$

Now for each k, we have $\Delta x_k > 0$, and $m \leq f(x_k) \leq M$.   Therefore

$$m\Delta x_1 + m\Delta x_2 + \cdots + m\Delta x_n \leq S_n \leq M\Delta x_1 + M\Delta x_2 + \cdots + M\Delta x_n \text{ or}$$

$$m(\Delta x_1 + \Delta x_2 + \cdots + \Delta x_n) \leq S_n \leq M(\Delta x_1 + \Delta x_2 + \cdots + \Delta x_n).$$

But the interval of integration is just the sum of the subintervals so $\Delta x_1 + \Delta x_2 + \cdots + \Delta x_n = b - a$, and hence

$$m(b - a) \leq S_n \leq M(b - a). \tag{74}$$

Taking the limit as $n \to \infty$ in (74) gives (73).   Q.E.D.

THEOREM 4.   *Let $f(x)$ be a continuous function in the interval $a \leq x \leq b$.   Then for each x in the interval the function*

$$I(x) = \int_a^x f(t)dt \tag{75}$$

is differentiable, and

$$\frac{dI(x)}{dx} = f(x). \tag{76}$$

PROOF.   By definition the derivative of $I(x)$ is

$$\frac{dI(x)}{dx} = \lim_{h \to 0} \frac{I(x + h) - I(x)}{h}$$

where it is understood that h is always selected so that $x + h$ is also in the given interval.   First suppose h is positive.   Then

$$\frac{I(x + h) - I(x)}{h} = \frac{1}{h}\left[\int_a^{x+h} f(t)dt - \int_a^x f(t)dt\right] = \frac{1}{h}\int_x^{x+h} f(t)dt. \tag{77}$$

Let m and M be the minimum and maximum values respectively for $f(t)$ in the interval $x \leq t \leq x + h$.   Then by Theorem 3

$$mh \leq \int_x^{x+h} f(t)dt \leq Mh. \tag{78}$$

Dividing through by the positive number h, and using the result in (77) gives

$$m \leq \frac{I(x + h) - I(x)}{h} \leq M. \tag{79}$$

Now as $h \to 0^+$ both m and M approach $f(x)$, since $f(x)$ is continuous. This proves (76) in the case that $h \to 0$ through positive values.

If h is negative, there is no change in equation (77), but Theorem 3 now gives

$$m|h| \leq \int_{x+h}^{x} f(t)dt \leq M|h| \tag{80}$$

in place of (78). Dividing through by $|h|$ yields

$$m \leq \frac{1}{|h|} \int_{x+h}^{x} f(t)dt = \frac{1}{h} \int_{x}^{x+h} f(t)dt \leq M$$

and when this is used in (77) we get (79) just as before. As $h \to 0^-$, both m and M approach $f(x)$ and this proves (76).   Q.E.D.

We have already illustrated this theorem for the function defined by equation (71). As a second illustration consider the function

$$I(x) = \int_{0}^{x} t \sqrt{t^6 + 7t^4 + t^2 + 11} \, dt.$$

We have no hope of carrying out the indicated integration, and yet we can find the derivative of this function quite easily. Indeed by Theorem 4

$$\frac{dI}{dx} = x \sqrt{x^6 + 7x^4 + x^2 + 11}.$$

EXERCISE 6

1. Prove that $\dfrac{d}{dx} \displaystyle\int_{x}^{b} f(t)dt = -f(x)$.

2. Prove that if u is any differentiable function of x then

$$\frac{d}{dx} \int_{a}^{u} f(t)dt = f(u) \frac{du}{dx}.$$

3. Compute the derivative of the functions

   a. $y = \displaystyle\int_{0}^{x} \sin \theta^2 d\theta$,

   b. $y = \displaystyle\int_{0}^{x^3} e^{v^2} \, dv$,

   c. $y = \displaystyle\int_{6}^{x^2} \ln \cosh u \, du$,

   d. $y = \displaystyle\int_{x}^{x^2} \sqrt{1 + t^5} \, dt$.

4. Find the interval in which the graph of

$$y = \int_{0}^{x} \frac{sds}{\sqrt{128 + s^6}}$$

is concave upward.

5. Repeat problem 4 for the graph of

$$y = \int_5^x (r^2 - 8)e^{-r^2} \, dr.$$

★9.   An alternate definition of the natural logarithm. Let x be any positive number, then we define the natural logarithm of x to be

$$\int_1^x \frac{dt}{t}.$$

We do not know that the function defined by this integral coincides with our old familiar ln x, and so we must use a different symbol, in order to keep matters straight. Let us denote this function by Ln x. In other words, by definition

$$\text{Ln } x = \int_1^x \frac{dt}{t}, \qquad x > 0. \tag{81}$$

We begin to examine the properties of Ln x. Clearly if $x > 1$, then Ln x is just the area under the curve $y = 1/t$ between $t = 1$ and $t = x$, as indicated in Fig. 5.

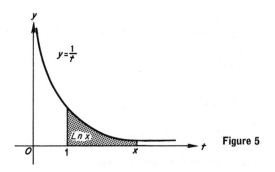

Figure 5

Hence Ln $x > 0$ for $x > 1$ and Ln $1 = 0$. If $x < 1$ then

$$\text{Ln } x = \int_1^x \frac{dt}{t} = -\int_x^1 \frac{dt}{t}$$

and hence is the negative of the area under the curve $y = 1/t$ between $t = x$ and $t = 1$.

THEOREM 5.   *If x and y are any pair of positive numbers then*

$$\text{Ln } xy = \text{Ln } x + \text{Ln } y, \tag{82}$$

$$\text{Ln } \frac{x}{y} = \text{Ln } x - \text{Ln } y, \tag{83}$$

and if r is any rational number

$$\text{Ln } x^r = r \, \text{Ln } x. \tag{84}$$

Naturally we recognize these as old familiar properties of the function $\ln x$.

PROOF. By Theorem 4, applied to equation (81) we have that

$$\frac{d}{dx} \operatorname{Ln} x = \frac{1}{x}$$

and more generally by the chain rule, if u is any differentiable function of x, then

$$\frac{d}{dx} \operatorname{Ln} u = \frac{1}{u} \frac{du}{dx}. \tag{85}$$

We apply (85) when $u = ax$ where a is some constant. Then

$$\frac{d}{dx} \operatorname{Ln} ax = \frac{1}{ax} \frac{d}{dx} ax = \frac{a}{ax} = \frac{1}{x}.$$

But then $\operatorname{Ln} ax$ and $\operatorname{Ln} x$ have the same derivative $1/x$, so these functions differ by a constant. Thus

$$\operatorname{Ln} ax = \operatorname{Ln} x + C, \qquad a > 0, \quad x > 0. \tag{86}$$

Putting $x = 1$ in (86) and recalling that $\operatorname{Ln} 1 = 0$, we find that $\operatorname{Ln} a = 0 + C$ or $C = \operatorname{Ln} a$. Thus

$$\operatorname{Ln} ax = \operatorname{Ln} x + \operatorname{Ln} a \tag{87}$$

for any constant $a > 0$, and all $x > 0$. But since a is arbitrary we can call it y, and then (87) gives (82).

To prove (83) set $y = 1/x$ in (82). Then we have

$$0 = \operatorname{Ln} 1 = \operatorname{Ln} \frac{x}{x} = \operatorname{Ln} x + \operatorname{Ln} \frac{1}{x},$$

and so by transposing

$$\operatorname{Ln} \frac{1}{x} = -\operatorname{Ln} x. \tag{88}$$

Next replace y by $1/y$ in (82) and use (88). This gives

$$\operatorname{Ln} \frac{x}{y} = \operatorname{Ln} x + \operatorname{Ln} \frac{1}{y} = \operatorname{Ln} x - \operatorname{Ln} y$$

and this proves (83).

To prove (84) we apply (85) when $u = x^r$. Hence

$$\frac{d}{dx} \operatorname{Ln} x^r = \frac{1}{x^r} \frac{d}{dx} x^r = \frac{rx^{r-1}}{x^r} = \frac{r}{x}.$$

But also for any constant r

$$\frac{d}{dx} r \operatorname{Ln} x = r \frac{d}{dx} \operatorname{Ln} x = \frac{r}{x}.$$

Since these two functions $\operatorname{Ln} x^r$ and $r \operatorname{Ln} x$ have the same derivative they differ by a constant.   Thus

$$\operatorname{Ln} x^r = r \operatorname{Ln} x + C. \tag{89}$$

Putting $x = 1$ in (89) gives $0 = 0 + C$ and hence $C = 0$.   This proves (84) and completes the proof of Theorem 5.

Let us observe again that the derivative of $\operatorname{Ln} x$ is positive so that $\operatorname{Ln} x$ is a strictly increasing function of x.   In fact we will now prove that $\operatorname{Ln} x \to \infty$ as $x \to \infty$.   For the crudest approximation for the area under the curve $y = 1/t$ between $t = 1$ and $t = 2$ shows that the area is greater than $1/2$ and hence $\operatorname{Ln} 2 > 1/2$.   So from (84) $\operatorname{Ln} 2^n = n \operatorname{Ln} 2 > n/2$ and so can be made arbitrarily large by taking n very large.

Since $\operatorname{Ln} x$ is a continuous function and strictly increasing, it follows that there is exactly one value of x for which $\operatorname{Ln} x = 1$.   We let e' denote this particular value of x, and we will prove

THEOREM 6.   *If* $\operatorname{Ln} e' = 1$, *then*

$$e' = \lim_{h \to 0} (1 + h)^{1/h}. \tag{90}$$

It follows from (90) that $e' = e$ as defined in section 3.   Let us recall that in section 3 we did not prove that the expression $(1 + h)^{1/h}$ had a limit as $h \to 0$.   The proof of Theorem 6, will automatically include a proof that the righthand side of (90) does have a limit, since e' is already defined by the property $\operatorname{Ln} e' = 1$.

PROOF.   By the definition of a derivative

$$\frac{d}{dx} \operatorname{Ln} x = \lim_{h \to 0} \frac{\operatorname{Ln} (x + h) - \operatorname{Ln} x}{h}. \tag{91}$$

In particular at $x = 1$, the left side is $1/x = 1/1 = 1$.   Recalling that $\operatorname{Ln} 1 = 0$, equation (91) gives

$$1 = \lim_{h \to 0} \frac{\operatorname{Ln} (1 + h)}{h}. \tag{92}$$

By the third property in Theorem 5, this becomes

$$1 = \lim_{h \to 0} \operatorname{Ln} (1 + h)^{1/h} \tag{93}$$

Now the fact that Ln x is continuous and strictly increasing permits us to write (93) in the form

$$1 = \text{Ln} \left[\lim_{h \to 0} (1 + h)^{1/h} \right].$$

Comparing this equation with $1 = \text{Ln } e'$ gives (90).   Q.E.D.

THEOREM 7. *For all positive* x

$$\text{Ln } x = \ln x. \tag{94}$$

PROOF.   The statement of this theorem is not really clear. For our contention has been that the function $\ln x$ was not really well defined and it was our purpose in this section to give a rigorous definition. What then are we to prove? We want to prove that if a function denoted by $\ln x$ could be obtained (in any way whatever) with the properties (1) $\ln x$ is defined and continuous for $x > 0$, (2) $\ln x^r = r \ln x$ for all rational r and (3) $\ln e = 1$, then $\ln x$ must be Ln x.

Now Ln x also has just these properties. By properties (2) and (3) we have for any rational value of r

$$\text{Ln } e^r = r \text{ Ln } e = r \cdot 1 = r = r \cdot 1 = r \ln e = \ln e^r.$$

Whence the functions $y = \text{Ln } x$ and $y = \ln x$ agree whenever y is a rational number. But both Ln x and $\ln x$ are continuous functions for $x > 0$ and both give the same y for each x that is a rational power of e. Hence (by continuity) they agree for all $x > 0$.   Q.E.D.

We could now define the exponential function e^x as the inverse of the logarithmic function and proceed to work out all of its properties. The way is clear, although the path may be rocky, especially for a tenderfoot. We have no intention of dragging the reader over this path. There are too many other fields that we must explore.

EXERCISE 7

1. Prove that $\lim_{x \to 0^+} \text{Ln } x = -\infty$.

2. Prove that the graph of $y = \text{Ln } x$ is concave downward for $x > 0$.

3. Prove that $e = \lim_{n \to \infty} \left(1 + \dfrac{1}{n} \right)^n$.

★4. Prove that $\lim_{n \to \infty} \dfrac{(n + 1)^{2n+1}}{n^n (n + 2)^{n+1}} = 1$.

9

METHODS OF INTEGRATION

1. **Objective.** We have learned how to compute the derivative of any combination of the standard functions, and we are now ready to tackle the inverse problem of finding the indefinite integral of such functions. But inverse problems are nearly always more complicated than direct problems. For example the multiplication of two integers always leads to an integer. But to solve the inverse problem of dividing one integer by another, we must introduce new numbers called rational numbers (fractions). Similarly the square of a rational number is always a rational number, but to solve the inverse problem of finding the square root of a rational number we must introduce new numbers called irrational numbers. We should not be surprised therefore to learn that integration sometimes requires the introduction of new functions. We will not prove this fact because the proof is very difficult[1], nor will we introduce any new functions. Our objective is to learn how to recognize those integrals that can be expressed in terms of the functions that we already have.

2. **Some terminology.** The operations of addition, subtraction, multiplication, and division are called the *arithmetic* operations. If we begin with the real numbers and a variable x, and perform these operations (except for division) a finite number of times we obtain a function of the form

$$y = a_0x^n + a_1x^{n-1} + a_2x^{n-2} + \cdots + a_n, \tag{1}$$

where the *coefficients* $a_0, a_1, \cdots, a_n$ are real numbers. Such a function is called a *polynomial* and is usually denoted by the symbol $P(x)$. If we include division among the operations, then a finite number of arithmetic

---

[1] This is proved in the little book by J. F. Ritt, *Integration in Finite Terms* (Columbia University Press, New York 1948).

operations on x and the real numbers will give a function of the form

$$R(x) = \frac{P(x)}{Q(x)} = \frac{a_0 x^n + a_1 x^{n-1} + \cdots + a_n}{b_0 x^m + b_1 x^{m-1} + \cdots + b_m}. \tag{2}$$

Such a function is called a *rational function* and, as indicated in (2), is always the ratio of two polynomials.

If we now add the *algebraic operation* of taking the nth root, where n is any positive integer then we can create still more complicated functions. Thus by a finite number of arithmetic operations together with root extractions we can obtain a function such as

$$f(x) = \frac{\sqrt{x + \sqrt[5]{x^2 + \sqrt[3]{x^7 + 2x^5 + 3x + \ln 17}}}}{\sqrt{x} + \sqrt[3]{x^2 + 1} + \sqrt[5]{\sqrt{x} + \sqrt[3]{2x} + \pi x}}.$$

This is an example of an algebraic function. Because of the large variety of possibilities, we cannot give a simple form for such functions, as we did in formulas (1) and (2) for the polynomials and rational functions.

Let us now enlarge our functions by including the trigonometric functions, and the elementary transcendental functions e^x and $\ln x$, and in addition to the algebraic operations let us include the operation of taking a function of a function. In this way we can create, in a finite number of steps, such functions as $\sin \sqrt{x}$, $\ln (x + e^{\sin x})$, $\sin^4 (e^{\pi x^2})/\ln (\cos x)$, etc. Finally we put all such functions together in one class and denote this class by the symbol $\mathfrak{F}$. In other words $\mathfrak{F}$ consists of those functions of x that can be created by starting with x and the real numbers and performing a *finite number of times* the operations listed above. Every function we have mentioned so far is in $\mathfrak{F}$. We can now state precisely the result mentioned in section 1. *There are functions in $\mathfrak{F}$ whose integral is not in $\mathfrak{F}$.* One such example is e^{x^2}. Surely we feel that there must be some function whose derivative is e^{x^2}, and indeed by Theorem 4 of Chapter 8, the function $F(x)$ defined by

$$F(x) = \int_0^x e^{t^2} \, dt$$

is one such function. But this $F(x)$ is not in $\mathfrak{F}$.

Because the inverse problem of integration is more difficult than differentiation, extensive tables of integrals have been prepared, and such tables are often useful. But no set of tables, no matter how extensive, can cover all of the various possibilities. In the majority of cases a student who is familiar with the various tricks of integration can find an integral much faster than his partner who prides himself on knowing where to look up the material he needs.

The three main tricks for integrating complicated expressions are (1) trigonometric substitutions, (2) partial fractions, and (3) integration by parts. These are covered in sections 6, 7, 8, and 9 of this chapter.

3.   Summary of basic formulas. For reference purposes we summarize the important integration formulas covered so far in this book. Before proceeding further the student should be certain that he has memorized the first twenty formulas [(3) through (22)].

$$\int a\, f(u)du = a \int f(u)du. \tag{3}$$

$$\int (f(u) + g(u))du = \int f(u)du + \int g(u)du. \tag{4}$$

$$\int u^n\, du = \frac{u^{n+1}}{n+1} + C, \qquad n \neq -1. \tag{5}$$

$$\int \frac{du}{u} = \ln|u| + C. \tag{6}$$

$$\int e^u\, du = e^u + C. \tag{7}$$

$$\int a^u\, du = \frac{a^u}{\ln a} + C, \qquad a > 0. \tag{8}$$

$$\int \sin u\, du = -\cos u + C. \tag{9}$$

$$\int \cos u\, du = \sin u + C. \tag{10}$$

$$\int \tan u\, du = -\ln|\cos u| + C. \tag{11}$$

$$\int \cot u\, du = \ln|\sin u| + C. \tag{12}$$

$$\int \sec u\, du = \ln|\sec u + \tan u| + C. \tag{13}$$

$$\int \csc u\, du = -\ln|\csc u + \cot u| + C. \tag{14}$$

$$\int \sec^2 u\, du = \tan u + C. \tag{15}$$

$$\int \csc^2 u\, du = -\cot u + C. \tag{16}$$

$$\int \sec u \tan u \, du = \sec u + C. \tag{17}$$

$$\int \csc u \cot u \, du = -\csc u + C. \tag{18}$$

$$\int \sinh u \, du = \cosh u + C. \tag{19}$$

$$\int \cosh u \, du = \sinh u + C. \tag{20}$$

$$\int \frac{du}{a^2 + u^2} = \frac{1}{a} \tan^{-1} \frac{u}{a} + C. \tag{21}$$

$$\int \frac{du}{\sqrt{a^2 - u^2}} = \sin^{-1} \frac{u}{a} + C. \tag{22}$$

$$\int \frac{du}{\sqrt{u^2 + a^2}} = \ln(u + \sqrt{u^2 + a^2}) + C. \tag{23}$$

$$\int \frac{du}{\sqrt{u^2 - a^2}} = \ln(u + \sqrt{u^2 - a^2}) + C, \qquad u > a > 0. \tag{24}$$

We do not insist that the student memorize (23) and (24), because an alternate method for these two integrals will be presented in section 6.

4.   Algebraic substitutions. Consider the integral

$$I_1 = \int \frac{(2x + 3)dx}{\sqrt{x}(1 + \sqrt[3]{x})}. \tag{25}$$

Clearly this does not fit any of the standard formulas listed in section 3. Our only hope is to find some new variable that on substitution will make (25) more attractive. The difficulty lies in the terms $x^{1/2}$ and $x^{1/3}$ that appear in the denominator. If we select the new variable

$$u = x^{1/6} \tag{26}$$

then $x^{1/3} = u^2$, and $x^{1/2} = u^3$, so that the denominator in (25) will become a polynomial in u. Continuing with this substitution we have from (26)

$$du = \frac{1}{6} x^{-5/6} \, dx = \frac{1}{6x^{5/6}} \, dx = \frac{dx}{6u^5}, \tag{27}$$

or $dx = 6u^5 \, du$. Using this and (26) in (25) gives

$$I_1 = \int \frac{(2u^6 + 3)6u^5 \, du}{u^3(1 + u^2)} = 6 \int \frac{2u^8 + 3u^2}{1 + u^2} \, du. \tag{28}$$

We now have a rational function to integrate. The general rule for a rational function is to divide the numerator by the denominator until the degree of the numerator is less than the degree of the denominator. Following this rule we find that

$$\frac{2u^8 + 3u^2}{1 + u^2} = 2u^6 - 2u^4 + 2u^2 + 1 - \frac{1}{1 + u^2}.$$

Using this in (28) and integrating gives

$$I_1 = 6 \int \frac{2u^8 + 3u^2}{1 + u^2}\, du = 6 \left(\frac{2u^7}{7} - \frac{2u^5}{5} + \frac{2u^3}{3} + u - \tan^{-1} u + C \right).$$

Returning to the original variable x by (26) we find

$$I_1 = 6 \left(\frac{2}{7} x^{7/6} - \frac{2}{5} x^{5/6} + \frac{2}{3} x^{1/2} + x^{1/6} - \tan^{-1} x^{1/6} + C \right).$$

This result is easily checked by showing that the derivative of this expression is just the integrand in (25).

In the case of a definite integral, the work is simplified by making a corresponding change in the limits along with the change in the variable. This is illustrated in

EXAMPLE 1.   Evaluate $\displaystyle\int_0^3 \frac{(x^2 + 2x)dx}{\sqrt{1 + x}}$.

SOLUTION.   Our only hope is to remove the radical sign. We try the substitution.

$$y = \sqrt{1 + x} \tag{29}$$

or $y^2 = 1 + x$. This substitution requires that $2y\, dy = dx$ and $x = y^2 - 1$. Hence for the indefinite integral we have

$$\int \frac{(x^2 + 2x)\, dx}{\sqrt{1 + x}} = \int \frac{(y^2 - 1)^2 + 2(y^2 - 1)}{y} 2y\, dy \tag{30}$$

$$= \int (y^4 - 2y^2 + 1 + 2y^2 - 2)2\, dy = 2 \int (y^4 - 1)\, dy.$$

Now as x increases from 0 to 3 equation (29) dictates that y increases from $\sqrt{1} = 1$ to $\sqrt{1 + 3} = 2$. Putting these limits on the integrals in (30) we have

$$\int_{x=0}^{x=3} \frac{(x^2 + 2x)dx}{\sqrt{1 + x}} = 2 \int_{y=1}^{y=2} (y^4 - 1)dy = 2 \left(\frac{y^5}{5} - y \right) \Big|_1^2 =$$

$$2 \left(\frac{2^5}{5} - 2 - \left(\frac{1}{5} - 1 \right) \right) = \frac{52}{5}.$$

EXERCISE 1

In problems 1 through 8 find the indicated indefinite integral.

1. $\displaystyle\int \frac{8dx}{1 + 4\sqrt{x}}.$

2. $\displaystyle\int \frac{dx}{x^{1/2}(1 + x^{1/4})}.$

3. $\displaystyle\int \frac{dx}{x^{1/2} + x^{1/3}}.$

4. $\displaystyle\int \frac{x^{1/2}dx}{x + x^{4/5}}.$

5. $\displaystyle\int \frac{5x^2 + 20x - 24}{\sqrt{x + 5}}\,dx.$

6. $\displaystyle\int \frac{x^5 - 8x^3}{\sqrt{x^2 - 4}}\,dx.$

7. $\displaystyle\int \frac{dx}{(2x + 5)\sqrt{2x - 3} + 8x - 12}.$

8. $\displaystyle\int \frac{8x + 21\sqrt{2x - 5}}{4 + \sqrt{2x - 5}}\,dx.$

In problems 9 through 12 compute the definite integral.

9. $\displaystyle\int_1^5 \frac{x + 3}{\sqrt{2x - 1}}\,dx.$

10. $\displaystyle\int_0^1 \frac{x^{3/2}\,dx}{1 + x}.$

11. $\displaystyle\int_0^8 \frac{dx}{4 + x^{1/3}}.$

12. $\displaystyle\int_6^{32} \frac{(x - 5)^{2/3}\,dx}{(x - 5)^{2/3} + 3}.$

13. Find the area under the curve $y = 1/(1 + \sqrt{x})$ between $x = 0$ and $x = M$, where $M > 0$.

★14. Find the volume of the solid generated when the region of problem 13 is rotated about the x-axis.

15. Find the volume of the solid generated when the region of problem 13 is rotated about the y-axis.

★16. Let V be the volume of the solid generated when the region of problem 13 is rotated about the line $y = -R$, where $R \geq 0$. Prove that $V = V_0 + 2\pi RA$, where V_0 is the volume of the solid of problem 14, and A is the area of the region of problem 13. Find V when $R = 1/2$.

5.   Trigonometric integrals. We already know how to integrate each of the trigonometric functions [see formulas (9) through (14)]. Since the six trigonometric functions can all be expressed rationally in terms of the sine and cosine function, any rational function of the trigonometric functions can be expressed as a rational function of these functions.   Hence from a theoretical point of view we could restrict ourselves to integrals of the form

$$\int R(\sin x,\ \cos x)dx.$$

However it is frequently convenient to use the other trigonometric functions in certain special circumstances.

We now consider a number of special cases that are still sufficiently general to be of interest.

THEOREM 1.   *If either m or n is a positive odd integer then*

$$\int \sin^n x \cos^m x \, dx \tag{31}$$

can be integrated in $\mathfrak{F}$.

PROOF.   A simple example will suffice to show the general method. Suppose that m is odd.   Indeed, to be specific suppose that we are to compute

$$I_1 = \int \sin^{2/5} x \cos^3 x \, dx.$$

We write $\cos^3 x = \cos^2 x \cos x = (1 - \sin^2 x) \cos x$, and hence

$$I_1 = \int \sin^{2/5} x (1 - \sin^2 x) \cos x \, dx$$

$$= \int \sin^{2/5} x \cos x \, dx - \int \sin^{12/5} x \cos x \, dx$$

$$= \frac{5}{7} \sin^{7/5} x - \frac{5}{17} \sin^{17/5} x + C.$$

If n is odd in (31) then we use the identity $\sin^n x = \sin^{n-1} x \sin x = (1 - \cos^2 x)^p \sin x$ where $p = (n - 1)/2$, and proceed just as in the above example, obtaining a sum of terms of the form

$$\int \cos^q x \sin x \, dx.$$

THEOREM 2.   *If m and n are both even integers then* (31) *can be integrated in* $\mathfrak{F}$.

PROOF.   All that is needed is to alter the powers by a suitable trick so that either m or n or both become odd.   This is done using the two trigonometric identities

$$\sin^2 \theta = \frac{1 - \cos 2\theta}{2}, \quad \cos^2 \theta = \frac{1 + \cos 2\theta}{2}, \tag{32}$$

as illustrated in the following example.   Suppose that we are to compute

$$I_2 = \int \sin^2 3x \cos^2 3x \, dx.$$

We apply (32) with $\theta = 3x$ and have

$$I_2 = \int \frac{1 - \cos 6x}{2} \cdot \frac{1 + \cos 6x}{2}\, dx$$

$$= \frac{1}{4} \int (1 - \cos^2 6x)\, dx.$$

Applying (32) again, this time with $\theta = 6x$, we have

$$I_2 = \frac{1}{4} \int \left(1 - \frac{1 + \cos 12x}{2}\right) dx$$

$$= \frac{1}{8} \int (1 - \cos 12x)\, dx = \frac{1}{8} x - \frac{1}{96} \sin 12x + C.$$

A number of similar theorems can be proved about the integrals of $\tan^m \theta \sec^n \theta$ and $\cot^m \theta \csc^n \theta$. We are content with the following one selected as representative.

THEOREM 3. *If m is a positive odd integer or n is a positive even integer, then*

$$\int \tan^m x \sec^n x\, dx \tag{33}$$

can be integrated in $\mathfrak{F}$.

PROOF. A simple example covering each case will suffice to show the general method.

(a) $\displaystyle \int \tan^3 x \sqrt{\sec x}\, dx = \int \tan x (\sec^2 x - 1) \sqrt{\sec x}\, dx$

$$= \int (\sec^2 x - 1) \frac{1}{\sec^{1/2} x} \sec x \tan x\, dx$$

$$= \int (\sec^{3/2} x - \sec^{-1/2} x)\, d(\sec x)$$

$$= \frac{2}{5} \sec^{5/2} x - 2 \sec^{1/2} x + C.$$

(b) $\displaystyle \int \tan^4 x \sec^6 x\, dx = \int \tan^4 x \sec^4 x \sec^2 x\, dx$

$$= \int \tan^4 x (\tan^2 x + 1)^2 \sec^2 x\, dx$$

$$= \int (\tan^8 x + 2 \tan^6 x + \tan^4 x)\, d(\tan x)$$

$$= \frac{1}{9} \tan^9 x + \frac{2}{7} \tan^7 x + \frac{1}{5} \tan^5 x + C.$$

A perceptive student will observe that in (31) and (33) the same argument "x" occurs in both terms of the product.   Suppose that this does not occur.   Then it may be helpful to recall the trigonometric identities.

$$\sin Ax \cos Bx = \frac{1}{2} [\sin (A + B)x + \sin (A - B)x], \qquad (34)$$

$$\cos Ax \cos Bx = \frac{1}{2} [\cos (A + B)x + \cos (A - B)x], \qquad (35)$$

$$\sin Ax \sin Bx = \frac{1}{2} [\cos (A - B)x - \cos (A + B)x]. \qquad (36)$$

As an example consider the integral

$$I_3 = \int \sin 7x \sin 3x \, dx.$$

Using (36) we can write

$$I_3 = \int \frac{1}{2} [\cos (7 - 3)x - \cos (7 + 3)x] dx$$

$$= \frac{1}{8} \sin 4x - \frac{1}{20} \sin 10x + C.$$

EXERCISE 2

In problems 1 through 10 find the indicated indefinite integral.

1. $\int \sin^5 \theta \, d\theta.$

2. $\int \sin^2 y \cos^3 y \, dy.$

3. $\int \sin^2 x \cos^4 x \, dx.$

4. $\int \tan^2 5x \cos^4 5x \, dx.$

5. $\int \tan^5 x \cos x \, dx.$

6. $\int \cot^2 3x \csc^4 3x \, dx.$

7. $\int \sin 3x \cos 2x \, dx.$

8. $\int \sin^2 3x \sin^2 5x \, dx.$

9. $\int \frac{dx}{\sin^2 6x}.$

10. $\int (\sec 5x + \csc 5x)^2 \, dx.$

In problems 11 through 14, the region below the given curve between the given values for x, is rotated about the x-axis.   Find the volume of the solid generated.

11. $y = \sin x,$ $x = 0$ and $x = \pi.$
12. $y = \sec x,$ $x = 0$ and $x = \pi/4.$
13. $y = \tan 2x,$ $x = 0$ and $x = \pi/8.$
14. $y = \cos^2 x,$ $x = \pi/2$ and $x = \pi.$

15. Let $m \geq 0$ and $n \geq 0$ be any two distinct integers. Prove that

$$\int_0^{2\pi} \sin mx \sin nx \, dx = 0,$$

and

$$\int_0^{2\pi} \cos mx \cos nx \, dx = 0.$$

16. Evaluate the integrals in problem 15 when $m = n$ an integer.

17. Prove that for any two integers m and n,

$$\int_0^{2\pi} \sin mx \cos nx \, dx = 0.$$

★18. Show that the formal substitution $1 - \cos 2\theta = 2 \sin^2\theta$ gives

$$\int_0^{2\pi} (1 - \cos 2\theta)^{3/2} \, d\theta = \int_0^{2\pi} 2\sqrt{2} \sin^3 \theta \, d\theta = 0.$$

But the first integral is not zero. Where lies the trouble?

19. Evaluate the first integral in problem 18.

6. **Trigonometric substitutions.** The integration of certain algebraic expressions is simplified by introducing suitable trigonometric functions. If the integrand[2] involves:

$$\text{(I)} \quad \sqrt{a^2 - u^2}, \quad \text{set} \quad u = a \sin \theta,$$

$$\text{(II)} \quad \sqrt{a^2 + u^2}, \quad \text{set} \quad u = a \tan \theta,$$

$$\text{(III)} \quad \sqrt{u^2 - a^2}, \quad \text{set} \quad u = a \sec \theta.$$

These substitutions are easy to remember if we associate with each of the cases a right triangle whose sides are a, u, and a suitable radical. The labeling of the triangle depends on the particular case at hand. For example in (II) it is clear that the hypotenuse must be $\sqrt{a^2 + u^2}$ while in (I) the hypotenuse must be a, and in (III) the hypotenuse is u. The three triangles and the related quantities are shown in Figs. 1, 2, and 3.

EXAMPLE 1. Find the indefinite integral

$$I_1 = \int \frac{x^2 \, dx}{\sqrt{9 - x^2}}.$$

SOLUTION. This integral is of type (I) with $a = 3$ and $u = x$. We first

---

[2] The radical sign may not be visible. For example if the integrand is $1/(a^2 + u^2)^5$ this comes under case (II) because $1/(a^2 + u^2)^5 = 1/(\sqrt{a^2 + u^2})^{10}$.

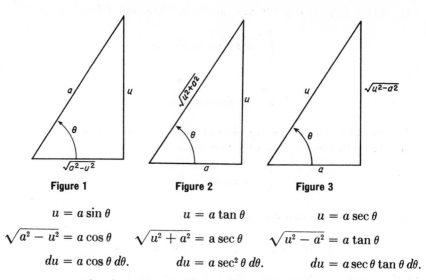

Figure 1   Figure 2   Figure 3

$$u = a \sin \theta \qquad\qquad u = a \tan \theta \qquad\qquad u = a \sec \theta$$

$$\sqrt{a^2 - u^2} = a \cos \theta \qquad \sqrt{u^2 + a^2} = a \sec \theta \qquad \sqrt{u^2 - a^2} = a \tan \theta$$

$$du = a \cos \theta \, d\theta. \qquad\qquad du = a \sec^2 \theta \, d\theta. \qquad\qquad du = a \sec \theta \tan \theta \, d\theta.$$

construct a triangle as shown in Fig. 4.   From this triangle we see immediately that

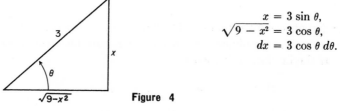

$$x = 3 \sin \theta,$$
$$\sqrt{9 - x^2} = 3 \cos \theta,$$
$$dx = 3 \cos \theta \, d\theta.$$

Figure 4

Using these expressions we have

$$I_1 = \int \frac{x^2 \, dx}{\sqrt{9 - x^2}} = \int \frac{(3 \sin \theta)^2 \, 3 \cos \theta \, d\theta}{3 \cos \theta} = 9 \int \sin^2 \theta \, d\theta$$

$$I_1 = \frac{9}{2} \int (1 - \cos 2\theta) d\theta = \frac{9}{2} \theta - \frac{9}{4} \sin 2\theta + C. \qquad (37)$$

To return to the original variable x, we note that $\theta = \sin^{-1}(x/3)$ and that $\sin 2\theta = 2 \sin \theta \cos \theta$.   Hence

$$I_1 = \frac{9}{2} \sin^{-1} \frac{x}{3} - \frac{9}{2} \frac{x}{3} \frac{\sqrt{9 - x^2}}{3} + C$$

$$I_1 = \frac{9}{2} \sin^{-1} \frac{x}{3} - \frac{1}{2} x \sqrt{9 - x^2} + C. \qquad (38)$$

As a check the student is advised to differentiate I_1 and show that the derivative is indeed $x^2 / \sqrt{9 - x^2}$.

EXAMPLE 2.   Compute $I_2 = \displaystyle\int_{-1.5}^{1.5} \dfrac{x^2 \, dx}{\sqrt{9 - x^2}}$.

SOLUTION.   The integrand here is the same as in Example 1, so we could just substitute the proper limits in equation (38).   Our purpose however is to illustrate the method of changing the limits along with the variable.   Referring to Fig. 4, we see that when $x = 1.5$ then $\theta = 30°$ or $\theta = \pi/6$.   When $x = -1.5$, the relation $x = 3 \sin \theta$ requires θ to be in the fourth quadrant, or $\theta = -\pi/6$.   Thus as x changes continuously from -1.5 to $+1.5$, the angle θ also changes continuously from $-\pi/6$ to $\pi/6$.   Whence from equation (37) we have

$$\int_{-1.5}^{1.5} \frac{x^2 \, dx}{\sqrt{9 - x^2}} = \left(\frac{9}{2} \theta - \frac{9}{4} \sin 2\theta\right)\Bigg|_{\theta=-\pi/6}^{\theta=\pi/6}$$

$$= \frac{9}{2}\frac{\pi}{6} - \frac{9}{4}\frac{\sqrt{3}}{2} - \left[\frac{9}{2}\left(-\frac{\pi}{6}\right) - \frac{9}{4}\left(-\frac{\sqrt{3}}{2}\right)\right]$$

$$= \frac{3}{2} \pi - \frac{9}{4} \sqrt{3}.$$

EXAMPLE 3.   Find $I_3 = \displaystyle\int (4x^2 + 4x + 17)^{-1/2} \, dx$.

SOLUTION.   Since we can write

$$4x^2 + 4x + 17 = 4x^2 + 4x + 1 + 16 = (2x + 1)^2 + 4^2,$$

this integral is of type (II).   We leave it to the student to draw the triangle associated with the substitutions $2x + 1 = 4 \tan \theta$, $\sqrt{(2x + 1)^2 + 4^2} = 4 \sec \theta$, and $2 \, dx = 4 \sec^2 \theta \, d\theta$.   Then

$$I_3 = \int \frac{2 \sec^2 \theta \, d\theta}{4 \sec \theta} = \frac{1}{2} \int \sec \theta \, d\theta = \frac{1}{2} \ln |\sec \theta + \tan \theta| + C$$

$$= \frac{1}{2} \ln \left(\sqrt{4x^2 + 4x + 17} + 2x + 1\right) + C.$$

Observe first that we have dropped the absolute value signs because here the argument of the log function is always positive.   Further a common denominator of 4 has been discarded because $-\dfrac{1}{2} \ln 4$ is just a constant that can be absorbed in C.   The student should differentiate this result and show that the derivative is indeed $1/\sqrt{4x^2 + 4x + 17}$.

EXAMPLE 4.   Find $I_4 = \displaystyle\int \dfrac{\sqrt{9x^2 - 1}}{x} \, dx$.

SOLUTION.   Clearly this integral is of type (III).   We set $3x = \sec \theta$.   Then $\sqrt{9x^2 - 1} = \tan \theta$, and $dx = 1/3 \sec \theta \tan \theta \, d\theta$.   Hence

$$I_4 = \int \frac{\tan\theta \, \tfrac{1}{3}\sec\theta\tan\theta \, d\theta}{\tfrac{1}{3}\sec\theta} = \int \tan^2\theta \, d\theta$$

$$= \int (\sec^2\theta - 1)d\theta = \tan\theta - \theta + C = \sqrt{9x^2 - 1} - \cos^{-1}\frac{1}{3x} + C.$$

EXERCISE 3

In problems 1 through 10 find the indicated indefinite integral.

1. $\displaystyle\int \frac{dx}{(9 - x^2)^{3/2}}.$

2. $\displaystyle\int \frac{dy}{y^2\sqrt{y^2 - 6}}.$

3. $\displaystyle\int \frac{dy}{(25 + y^2)^2}.$

4. $\displaystyle\int \frac{\sqrt{9 - x^2}}{x} \, dx.$

5. $\displaystyle\int \frac{dx}{(x^2 + 5)^{3/2}}.$

6. $\displaystyle\int \frac{\sqrt{4 - y^2}}{y^2} \, dy.$

7. $\displaystyle\int \frac{du}{u^4\sqrt{a^2 - u^2}}.$

8. $\displaystyle\int \frac{du}{u^4\sqrt{u^2 - a^2}}.$

9. $\displaystyle\int \frac{\sqrt{x^2 + 2x - 3}}{x + 1} \, dx.$

10. $\displaystyle\int \frac{(3x + 7)dx}{\sqrt{x^2 + 4x + 5}}.$

11. Use the methods of this section to derive formulas (23) and (24).

12. Find the length of the curve $y = \ln 3x$ between $x = 1$ and $x = \sqrt{8}$.

13. Prove by integration that the area of a circle of radius r is πr^2.

14. In a circle of radius r, a chord b units from the center divides the circle into two parts. Use calculus to find a formula for the area of the smaller part. Observe that if we know the area of the full circle (problem 13) then this problem can also be solved without integration.

15. The region under the curve $y = x^{3/2}/\sqrt{x^2 + 4}$ between $x = 0$ and $x = 4$ is rotated about the x-axis. Find the volume.

16. The region under the curve $y = (4 - x^2)^{1/4}$ between $x = -1$ and $x = 2$ is rotated about the x-axis. Find the volume.

17. If a circle of radius r is rotated about an axis R units from the center of the circle (where $R > r$) the solid generated is called a *torus*, or anchor ring, and resembles a smooth doughnut. Find the volume of the torus.

★Integration by trigonometric substitution has a parallel method, using the hyperbolic functions. Here the identities $\cosh^2\theta - \sinh^2\theta = 1$ and $\operatorname{sech}^2\theta + \tanh^2\theta = 1$ play a fundamental role. These identities suggest the following substitutions:

If the integrand involves $\sqrt{a^2 + x^2}$, set $x = a\sinh\theta$.
If the integrand involves $\sqrt{x^2 - a^2}$, set $x = a\cosh\theta$.
If the integrand involves $\sqrt{a^2 - x^2}$, set $x = a\tanh\theta$.

In problems 18 through 21 use the method of integration by hyperbolic sub-. stitution to obtain the given integration formulas.

★18. $\displaystyle\int \frac{dx}{\sqrt{a^2 + x^2}} = \sinh^{-1}\frac{x}{a} + C.$

★19. $\displaystyle\int \frac{dx}{x^2\sqrt{a^2 + x^2}} = -\frac{1}{a^2}\coth\left(\sinh^{-1}\frac{x}{a}\right) + C.$

★20. $\displaystyle\int \frac{x^2\,dx}{\sqrt{x^2 - a^2}} = \frac{1}{2}x\sqrt{x^2 - a^2} + \frac{a^2}{2}\cosh^{-1}\frac{x}{a} + C.$

★21. $\displaystyle\int \frac{dx}{(a^2 - x^2)^{3/2}} = \frac{1}{a^2}\sinh\left(\tanh^{-1}\frac{x}{a}\right) + C.$

★22. Show that the answer to problem 19 is equal to $-\sqrt{a^2 + x^2}/a^2x + C.$

★23. Show that the answer to problem 21 is equal to $x/a^2\sqrt{a^2 - x^2} + C.$

7. **Partial fractions, distinct linear factors.** Our main objective is

THEOREM 4. *If $R(x)$ is any rational function then*

$$\int R(x)\,dx \qquad\qquad (39)$$

can be integrated in $\mathfrak{F}$.

We will not actually prove this theorem. Instead we will illustrate the method used by a series of examples. At several points, the proof requires a knowledge of higher algebra. However our illustrative examples will certainly convince the student that the theorem is true.

Any rational function is the quotient of two polynomials, so we can write $R(x) = N(x)/D(x)$ where $N(x)$ and $D(x)$ are polynomials. If the degree of $N(x)$ is greater than or equal to the degree of $D(x)$, the first step is to divide the numerator by the denominator obtaining

$$\frac{N(x)}{D(x)} = P(x) + \frac{Q(x)}{D(x)} \qquad\qquad (40)$$

where $P(x)$ and $Q(x)$ are polynomials and $Q(x)$ has degree less than that of $D(x)$.

EXAMPLE 1. Find the indefinite integral

$$I_1 = \int \frac{3x^4 - 8x^3 + 20x^2 - 11x + 8}{x^2 - 2x + 5}\,dx.$$

SOLUTION. Here the numerator is of fourth degree and the denominator is of second degree, so we perform the division as indicated by equation (40). We find that

$$\frac{3x^4 - 8x^3 + 20x^2 - 11x + 8}{x^2 - 2x + 5} = 3x^2 - 2x + 1 + \frac{x + 3}{x^2 - 2x + 5}$$

and hence

$$I_1 = \int \left[3x^2 - 2x + 1 + \frac{x + 3}{x^2 - 2x + 5} \right] dx = x^3 - x^2 + x + \int \frac{x + 3}{x^2 - 2x + 5} \, dx.$$

In the last integral we may absorb x in the differential of the denominator and use the inverse tangent formula for the remaining constant. The details run as follows.

$$\int \frac{(x + 3)dx}{x^2 - 2x + 5} = \frac{1}{2} \int \frac{(2x + 6)dx}{x^2 - 2x + 5} = \frac{1}{2} \int \frac{[(2x - 2) + 8]dx}{x^2 - 2x + 5}$$

$$= \frac{1}{2} \int \frac{(2x - 2)dx}{x^2 - 2x + 5} + \frac{1}{2} \int \frac{8 \, dx}{(x - 1)^2 + 2^2}.$$

Hence

$$I_1 = x^3 - x^2 + x + \frac{1}{2} \ln \left| x^2 - 2x + 5 \right| + 2 \tan^{-1} \frac{x - 1}{2} + C.$$

Continuing our outline of the proof of Theorem 4 we now assume that in (39) the degree of the numerator is less than the degree of the denominator. According to a theorem first proved by Gauss, any polynomial can be factored into a product of linear factors. This means that if the denominator is

$$D(x) = a_0 x^m + a_1 x^{m-1} + a_2 x^{m-2} + \cdots + a_m,$$

then the equation $D(x) = 0$ has m roots $r_1, r_2, \cdots, r_m$ and $D(x)$ can be written in the form

$$D(x) = a_0(x - r_1)(x - r_2) \cdots (x - r_m). \tag{41}$$

Some of these roots may be repeated, and some may be complex. We reserve the discussion of this more complicated situation for the next section and consider now the case in which all of the roots $r_k (k = 1, 2, \cdots, m)$ are real and distinct.

EXAMPLE 2.   Find the indefinite integral

$$I_2 = \int \frac{(2x + 41)dx}{x^2 + 5x - 14}.$$

SOLUTION.   We can find the factors of the denominator by inspection. In this example, equation (41) would read

$$x^2 + 5x - 14 = (x - 2)(x + 7).$$

We now ask, are there numbers A and B such that

$$\frac{2x + 41}{x^2 + 5x - 14} = \frac{A}{x - 2} + \frac{B}{x + 7} \tag{42}$$

is an identity in x? If we can find these unknowns A and B, then the right side of equation (42) is called the *partial fraction decomposition* of the left side of (42). That such numbers can always be found is the statement of a rather complicated algebraic theorem. We now give two methods for finding A and B in (42).

FIRST METHOD. Assuming that numbers A and B exist so that (42) is an identity, multiply both sides of (42) by $(x - 2)(x + 7)$. This gives

$$2x + 41 = A(x + 7) + B(x - 2). \tag{43}$$

Put $x = -7$ in (43). This gives

$$-14 + 41 = A \times 0 + B(-9)$$

and hence $B = 27/(-9) = -3$. Put $x = 2$ in (43). Then

$$4 + 41 = A \times 9 + B \times 0$$

and hence $A = 45/9 = 5$.

SECOND METHOD. We first obtain equation (43) just as before, and then rearrange the right side grouping together the constants, the terms in x, and so on. Thus (43) is equivalent to

$$2x + 41 = (A + B)x + 7A - 2B. \tag{44}$$

In order that (44) be true for all x, the corresponding coefficients must be the same.

Equating coefficients of x yields: $2 = A + B$.
Equating coefficients of 1 yields: $41 = 7A - 2B$.

Thus we have a system of two equations in the two unknowns A and B. We leave it to the reader to solve this system and show that $A = 5$ and $B = -3$. Now returning to equation (42) we have

$$\frac{2x + 41}{x^2 + 5x - 14} = \frac{5}{x - 2} - \frac{3}{x + 7}$$

and hence

$$I_2 = \int \frac{5\,dx}{x - 2} - \int \frac{3\,dx}{x + 7} = 5 \ln|x - 2| - 3 \ln|x + 7| + C$$

$$= \ln\left|\frac{(x - 2)^5}{(x + 7)^3}\right| + C.$$

We may have more than two factors in the denominator. The method is still the same but the algebraic manipulations become more complex.

EXAMPLE 3.   Find the indefinite integral

$$I_3 = \int \frac{(3x^2 + 11x + 4)dx}{x^3 + 4x^2 + x - 6}.$$

SOLUTION.   By inspection the denominator factors into $(x-1)(x+2)(x+3)$. Therefore we search for three numbers A, B, and C such that

$$\frac{3x^2 + 11x + 4}{x^3 + 4x^2 + x - 6} = \frac{A}{x - 1} + \frac{B}{x + 2} + \frac{C}{x + 3} \tag{45}$$

is an identity in x.   Multiplying both sides of (45) by the denominator $(x - 1)(x + 2)(x + 3)$ we have

$$3x^2 + 11x + 4 = A(x + 2)(x + 3) + B(x - 1)(x + 3) + C(x - 1)(x + 2). \tag{46}$$

FIRST METHOD.   Putting $x = 1$ in (46) gives

$$3 + 11 + 4 = A(3)(4)$$
$$A = \frac{18}{12} = \frac{3}{2}.$$

Putting $x = -2$ in (46) gives

$$12 - 22 + 4 = B(-3)(1)$$
$$B = \frac{-6}{-3} = 2.$$

Putting $x = -3$ in (46) gives

$$27 - 33 + 4 = C(-4)(-1)$$
$$C = \frac{-2}{4} = -\frac{1}{2}.$$

SECOND METHOD.   We regroup the terms on the right side of (46), in descending powers of x.

$$3x^2 + 11x + 4 = A(x^2 + 5x + 6) + B(x^2 + 2x - 3) + C(x^2 + x - 2)$$
$$= (A + B + C)x^2 + (5A + 2B + C)x + (6A - 3B - 2C).$$

This is an identity in x if and only if the corresponding coefficients are equal.

Equating coefficients of x^2 yields $A + B + C = 3.$
Equating coefficients of x yields $5A + 2B + C = 11.$
Equating coefficients of 1 yields $6A - 3B - 2C = 4.$

Solving these three simultaneous equations by any of the standard methods gives $A = 3/2$, $B = 2$, and $C = -1/2$.   Naturally these values for A, B, and C are the same as those obtained by the first method.   To compute I_3 we use (45) with the known values for A, B, and C and have

$$I_3 = \frac{3}{2} \int \frac{dx}{x - 1} + 2 \int \frac{dx}{x + 2} - \frac{1}{2} \int \frac{dx}{x + 3}$$

$$= \frac{3}{2} \ln |x - 1| + 2 \ln |x + 2| - \frac{1}{2} \ln |x + 3| + C$$

$$= \frac{1}{2} \ln \left| \frac{(x - 1)^3 (x + 2)^4}{(x + 3)} \right| + C.$$

EXERCISE 4

In problems 1 through 10 find the indicated indefinite integral.

1. $\displaystyle \int \frac{2 \, dx}{x^2 - 1}.$

2. $\displaystyle \int \frac{(5x + 4) \, dx}{x^2 + x - 2}.$

3. $\displaystyle \int \frac{(2x + 7) dx}{x^2 + 4x - 5}.$

4. $\displaystyle \int \frac{(x^2 - 37) dx}{x^2 + x - 12}.$

5. $\displaystyle \int \frac{12x^2 + 4x - 8}{x^3 - 4x} \, dx.$

6. $\displaystyle \int \frac{(3x^2 - 6x - 12) dx}{x^3 + x^2 - 4x - 4}.$

7. $\displaystyle \int \frac{(x^2 - x + 1) dx}{x^3 + 6x^2 + 11x + 6}.$

★8. $\displaystyle \int \frac{(11 + 10x - x^2) dx}{x^3 + 3x^2 - 13x - 15}.$

★9. $\displaystyle \int \frac{2x^5 + 17x^4 + 40x^3 - 3x^2 - 92x - 58}{(x + 1)(x + 2)(x + 3)(x + 4)} \, dx.$

★10. $\displaystyle \int \frac{2x^4 - 2x^3 + x^2 + 13x - 66}{x^4 - 13x^2 + 36} \, dx.$

11. Find the area under the curve $y = 1/(x^2 + 4x + 3)$ between $x = 0$ and $x = 5$.

12. Find the area under the curve $y = 1/(x^2 + 4x + 3)$ between $x = 0$ and $x = M (M > 0)$. What is the limit of this area as $M \to \infty$?

13. The region bounded by the curve $y = 1/\sqrt{x^2 + 6x + 8}$ between $x = -1$ and $x = 4$ is rotated about the x-axis. Find the volume of the solid generated.

14. The region of problem 11 is rotated about the y-axis. Find the volume of the solid generated.

★15. A formal computation for the area under the curve $y = (4x - 10)/(x^2 - 5x + 6)$ between $x = 1$ and $x = 5$ leads to

$$A = \int_1^5 \frac{(4x - 10) dx}{x^2 - 5x + 6} = \ln (x^2 - 5x + 6)^2 \Big|_1^5 = \ln \frac{6^2}{2^2} = \ln 9.$$

Why is this answer incorrect?

★16. Use partial fractions to derive the formula

$$\int \frac{du}{a^2 - u^2} = \frac{1}{2a} \ln \frac{a + u}{a - u} + C, \qquad |u| < a.$$

Compare this result with the formula

$$\int \frac{du}{a^2 - u^2} = \frac{1}{a} \tanh^{-1} \frac{u}{a} + C, \qquad |u| < a,$$

obtained by generalizing formula (55) of Chapter 8. Are these two formulas inconsistent?

8.   Partial fractions, repeated and quadratic factors. If the denominator of the integrand has a factor $(ax + b)$ repeated n times then in the partial fraction decomposition the corresponding term is

$$\frac{A_1}{ax + b} + \frac{A_2}{(ax + b)^2} + \cdots + \frac{A_n}{(ax + b)^n}$$

where $A_1, A_2, \cdots, A_n$ are the unknowns to be determined.

EXAMPLE 1. Find the indefinite integral

$$I_1 = \int \frac{3x^3 + 3x^2 + 3x + 2}{x^3(x + 1)}\, dx.$$

SOLUTION. Since the factor x is repeated three times in the denominator, our partial fraction decomposition must be

$$\frac{3x^3 + 3x^2 + 3x + 2}{x^3(x + 1)} = \frac{A}{x + 1} + \frac{B}{x} + \frac{C}{x^2} + \frac{D}{x^3} \qquad (47)$$

where $A, B, C,$ and D are unknowns to be determined. Multiplying both sides of (47) by $x^3(x + 1)$ we have

$$3x^3 + 3x^2 + 3x + 2 = Ax^3 + Bx^2(x + 1) + Cx(x + 1) + D(x + 1). \quad (48)$$

Here the first method will give A and D directly. For if we set $x = 0$ in (48) we obtain $2 = D$, and if we set $x = -1$ in (48) we obtain $-3 + 3 - 3 + 2 = A(-1)$ or $A = 1$. But B and C are not obtained so readily. Other values of x used in (48) give equations in which both B and C appear. If we use the second method we equate corresponding coefficients in (48).

The coefficients of x^3 yield $A + B$ $= 3.$
The coefficients of x^2 yield $B + C$ $= 3.$
The coefficients of x yield $C + D = 3.$
The coefficients of 1   yield $D = 2.$

Solving this system of four linear equations in four unknowns gives $A = 1$, $B = 2, C = 1,$ and $D = 2$. Hence

$$I_1 = \int \left(\frac{1}{x + 1} + \frac{2}{x} + \frac{1}{x^2} + \frac{2}{x^3} \right) dx = \ln|(x + 1)x^2| - \frac{1}{x} - \frac{1}{x^2} + C.$$

Any polynomial can be factored into linear factors, but some of these factors may involve complex numbers. If the coefficients of the polynomial are real then the complex factors can be paired, each one with a conjugate one, so that the product is a quadratic factor with real coefficients. For example, $[x + (1 + i)][x + (1 - i)] = x^2 + 2x + 2$, where as usual i denotes $\sqrt{-1}$. In such cases it is better to leave the quadratic term unfactored. If $ax^2 + bx + c$ is such a factor of the denominator, then in the partial fraction decomposition the corresponding term is

$$\frac{Ax + B}{ax^2 + bx + c}$$

where A and B are the unknowns.

EXAMPLE 2.   Find the indefinite integral

$$I_2 = \int \frac{(x^2 + 4x + 1)dx}{x^3 + 3x^2 + 4x + 2}.$$

SOLUTION.   The denominator factors into the product $(x + 1)(x^2 + 2x + 2)$. Hence the decomposition is

$$\frac{x^2 + 4x + 1}{(x + 1)(x^2 + 2x + 2)} = \frac{A}{x + 1} + \frac{Bx + C}{x^2 + 2x + 2}. \tag{49}$$

Multiplying both sides of (49) by $(x + 1)(x^2 + 2x + 2)$ gives

$$x^2 + 4x + 1 = A(x^2 + 2x + 2) + (Bx + C)(x + 1)$$
$$= (A + B)x^2 + (2A + B + C)x + (2A + C).$$

The second method leads to the set of equations

$$\begin{array}{llll} x^2: & A + B & & = 1, \\ x: & 2A + B + C & = 4, \\ 1: & 2A & + C & = 1. \end{array}$$

Solving this set gives $A = -2$, $B = 3$, and $C = 5$.   Hence

$$I_2 = \int \left(\frac{-2}{x + 1} + \frac{3x + 5}{x^2 + 2x + 2} \right) dx = -2 \ln|x + 1| + \int \frac{3x + 3 + 2}{x^2 + 2x + 2} dx$$

$$= -2 \ln|x + 1| + \frac{3}{2} \int \frac{(2x + 2)dx}{x^2 + 2x + 2} + \int \frac{2 \, dx}{(x + 1)^2 + 1}$$

$$= -2 \ln|x + 1| + \frac{3}{2} \ln (x^2 + 2x + 2) + 2 \tan^{-1} (x + 1) + C.$$

The only case left to discuss, is that of a repeated quadratic factor.   If the factor is $(ax^2 + bx + c)^n$ then in the partial fraction decomposition the corresponding term[3] is

$$\frac{A_1 x^{2n-1} + A_2 x^{2n-2} + \cdots + A_{2n-1}x + A_{2n}}{(ax^2 + bx + c)^n} \tag{50}$$

where $A_1, A_2, \ldots, A_{2n}$ are unknowns.   The integration of a term such as (50) is then carried out by a suitable trigonometric substitution (see section 6).

EXAMPLE 3.   Find the indefinite integral

$$I_3 = \int \frac{x^3 \, dx}{(x^2 + 4x + 13)^2}.$$

SOLUTION.   Here the decomposition into partial fractions is already accomplished, because the integrand has the form (50).   Since $x^2 + 4x + 13 =$

[3] The procedure followed here is slightly different from that of most textbooks.

$(x + 2)^2 + 3^2$ the trigonometric substitution is dictated by the triangle of Fig. 5.   We have

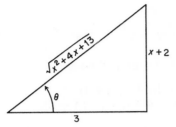

$$x + 2 = 3 \tan \theta$$
$$dx = 3 \sec^2 \theta \, d\theta$$
$$x^2 + 4x + 13 = 9 \sec^2 \theta.$$

Figure 5

$$I_3 = \int \frac{(3 \tan \theta - 2)^3 \, 3 \sec^2 \theta \, d\theta}{(9 \sec^2 \theta)^2}$$

$$= \int \frac{27 \tan^3 \theta - 54 \tan^2 \theta + 36 \tan \theta - 8}{27 \sec^2 \theta} \, d\theta$$

$$= \int \left(\frac{\sin^3 \theta}{\cos \theta} - 2 \sin^2 \theta + \frac{4}{3} \sin \theta \cos \theta - \frac{8}{27} \cos^2 \theta \right) d\theta$$

$$= \int \left[(1 - \cos^2 \theta) \frac{\sin \theta}{\cos \theta} - (1 - \cos 2\theta) + \frac{4}{3} \sin \theta \cos \theta - \frac{4}{27} (1 + \cos 2\theta) \right] d\theta$$

$$= \int \left(\frac{\sin \theta}{\cos \theta} + \frac{1}{3} \sin \theta \cos \theta - \frac{31}{27} + \frac{23}{27} \cos 2\theta \right) d\theta$$

$$= -\ln |\cos \theta| - \frac{1}{6} \cos^2 \theta - \frac{31}{27} \theta + \frac{23}{54} \sin 2\theta + C$$

$$= -\ln \frac{3}{\sqrt{x^2 + 4x + 13}} - \frac{3}{2(x^2 + 4x + 13)} - \frac{31}{27} \tan^{-1} \frac{x + 2}{3}$$

$$+ \frac{23}{27} \left(\frac{3(x + 2)}{x^2 + 4x + 13} \right) + C$$

$$= \frac{1}{2} \ln (x^2 + 4x + 13) + \frac{138x + 195}{54(x^2 + 4x + 13)} - \frac{31}{27} \tan^{-1} \frac{x + 2}{3} + C.$$

In view of the fact that the integration of such an innocent looking function as $x^3/(x^2 + 4x + 13)^2$ leads to such a complicated function, it is easy to surmise that the integral of a more complicated function in $\mathfrak{F}$ may lie outside of $\mathfrak{F}$.

EXERCISE 5

In problems 1 through 11 find the indicated indefinite integral.

1. $\displaystyle\int \frac{(7x + 4)dx}{x^3 - 4x^2}$.

2. $\displaystyle\int \frac{18 - 3x - 2x^2}{x(x - 3)^2}\, dx$.

3. $\displaystyle\int \frac{x^2 - 2x - 8}{x^3 - 4x^2 + 4x}\, dx$.

4. $\displaystyle\int \frac{8x^2 + 4x - 2}{(x^2 - x)^2}\, dx$.

5. $\displaystyle\int \frac{(x^3 + 12x + 14)dx}{(x + 2)^3(x - 1)}$.

6. $\displaystyle\int \frac{(2x^2 + x + 17)dx}{(x - 1)(x^2 + 2x - 3)}$.

7. $\displaystyle\int \frac{(x + 1)(x + 9)}{(x^2 - 9)^2}\, dx$.

8. $\displaystyle\int \frac{2x^2 - 13x + 18}{x(x^2 + 9)}\, dx$.

9. $\displaystyle\int \frac{6x^2\, dx}{(x^2 + 9)^2}$.

10. $\displaystyle\int \frac{8x^3\, dx}{(x^2 + 1)^3}$.

★11. $\displaystyle\int \frac{x^5 - 2x^4 - x^3 + x - 2}{x^6 + 2x^4 + x^2}\, dx$.

9.   Integration by parts. Each differentiation formula leads to an integration formula, but there is one differentiation formula that we have not used as yet. This is the formula

$$d(uv) = u\, dv + v\, du. \tag{51}$$

By transposition we have

$$u\, dv = d(uv) - v\, du$$

and on integrating both sides, this gives

$$\boxed{\int u\, dv = uv - \int v\, du.} \tag{52}$$

This is the fundamental formula for integration by parts. The idea is that the left side may be very complicated, but if we select the part for u and the part for dv quite carefully, the integral on the right side may be much easier.

EXAMPLE 1. Find the indefinite integral

$$I_1 = \int x \ln x\, dx.$$

SOLUTION. Obviously this fits none of the patterns considered so far, so we try to use (52). There are two obvious ways of selecting u and dv.

First possibility.   Let $u = x,$ $dv = \ln x\, dx.$
Second possibility.   Let $u = \ln x,$ $dv = x\, dx.$

In the first selection we cannot find v, so we come to a dead end.   In the second case we can find v.   Following the second possibility we would arrange the work thus:

Let $\qquad\qquad\qquad u = \ln x,$ $\qquad dv = x\, dx.$

Then $\qquad\qquad\qquad du = \dfrac{1}{x}\, dx,$ $\qquad v = \dfrac{x^2}{2}.$

Making these substitutions in (52) we have for the left side

$$\int u\, dv = \int \ln x(x\, dx) = \int x \ln x\, dx,$$

and for the right side

$$uv - \int v\, du = \frac{x^2}{2} \ln x - \int \frac{x^2}{2} \frac{1}{x}\, dx$$

$$= \frac{x^2}{2} \ln x - \frac{1}{2} \int x\, dx.$$

Therefore by (52)

$$I_1 = \int x \ln x\, dx = \frac{x^2}{2} \ln x - \frac{1}{4} x^2 + C.$$

EXAMPLE 2.   Find the indefinite integral

$$I_2 = \int \tan^{-1} 3x\, dx.$$

SOLUTION.   At first it seems as though this integrand cannot be split into two parts, but we can always consider "1" as a factor of any expression.

Let $\qquad u = \tan^{-1} 3x,$ $\qquad\qquad\qquad dv = 1\, dx.$

Then $\qquad du = \dfrac{3\, dx}{1 + 9x^2},$ $\qquad\qquad\qquad v = x.$

From equation (52)

$$I_2 = \int u\, dv = \int \tan^{-1} 3x\, dx = x \tan^{-1} 3x - \int \frac{x\, 3\, dx}{1 + 9x^2}$$

$$= x \tan^{-1} 3x - \frac{1}{6} \ln (1 + 9x^2) + C.$$

EXAMPLE 3.   Find the indefinite integral

$$I_3 = \int e^{2x} \cos 3x\, dx. \tag{53}$$

SOLUTION. Here there is no clear reason for selecting either factor as u. Let us select (at random)

$$u = e^{2x}, \qquad dv = \cos 3x \, dx.$$

Then
$$du = 2e^{2x} \, dx, \qquad v = \frac{1}{3} \sin 3x.$$

From (52)

$$I_3 = \frac{e^{2x}}{3} \sin 3x - \frac{2}{3} \int e^{2x} \sin 3x \, dx. \qquad (54)$$

But this new integral looks just as difficult as the original one. We try integration by parts on this new integral.

Let
$$u = e^{2x}, \qquad dv = \sin 3x \, dx.$$

Then
$$du = 2e^{2x} \, dx, \qquad v = -\frac{1}{3} \cos 3x.$$

$$\int e^{2x} \sin 3x \, dx = -\frac{e^{2x}}{3} \cos 3x + \frac{2}{3} \int e^{2x} \cos 3x \, dx \qquad (55)$$

and we are back with the integral that we started with. But there is still hope. Using (55) in (54) gives

$$I_3 = \frac{e^{2x}}{3} \sin 3x - \frac{2}{3} \left[-\frac{e^{2x}}{3} \cos 3x + \frac{2}{3} I_3 \right] + C_1 \qquad (56)$$

where I_3 has the meaning of (53). But the coefficients of I_3 on the two sides of (56) are different. Transposition gives

$$I_3 + \frac{4}{9} I_3 = \frac{e^{2x}}{3} \sin 3x + \frac{2e^{2x}}{9} \cos 3x + C_1,$$

or multiplying by 9/13

$$I_3 = \frac{e^{2x}}{13} (3 \sin 3x + 2 \cos 3x) + C.$$

EXAMPLE 4. Find $I_4 = \displaystyle\int \sec^3 x \, dx.$

SOLUTION. Let $u = \sec x, \qquad dv = \sec^2 x \, dx.$
Then $du = \sec x \tan x \, dx, \qquad v = \tan x.$

$$\int \sec^3 x \, dx = \sec x \tan x - \int \sec x \tan^2 x \, dx$$

$$= \sec x \tan x - \int \sec x \, (\sec^2 x - 1) \, dx$$

$$= \sec x \tan x - \int \sec^3 x \, dx + \int \sec x \, dx.$$

Therefore by transposition

$$2 \int \sec^3 x \, dx = \sec x \tan x + \int \sec x \, dx.$$

$$I_4 = \int \sec^3 x \, dx = \frac{1}{2} (\sec x \tan x + \ln|\sec x + \tan x|) + C.$$

EXERCISE 6

In problems 1 through 16 find the indicated indefinite integral.

1. $\displaystyle\int x \sin x \, dx.$

2. $\displaystyle\int \theta \cos 3\theta \, d\theta.$

3. $\displaystyle\int x\sqrt{4x + 5} \, dx.$

4. $\displaystyle\int 3x^3\sqrt{x^2 + 2} \, dx.$

5. $\displaystyle\int x^2 \ln x \, dx.$

6. $\displaystyle\int x^n \ln x \, dx, \qquad n \neq -1.$

7. $\displaystyle\int \sin^{-1} 2x \, dx.$

8. $\displaystyle\int x \tan^{-1} x \, dx.$

9. $\displaystyle\int x^2 \tan^{-1} x \, dx.$

10. $\displaystyle\int y^2 \sin 2y \, dy.$

11. $\displaystyle\int xe^{3x} \, dx.$

12. $\displaystyle\int y^2 e^{5y} \, dy.$

13. $\displaystyle\int e^x \sin 2x \, dx.$

★14. $\displaystyle\int e^{ax} \cos bx \, dx.$

★15. $\displaystyle\int \sec^5 x \, dx.$

★16. $\displaystyle\int x^3 \cos 4x \, dx.$

17. The region under the curve $y = e^{-x}$ between $x = 0$ and $x = 2$ is rotated about the y-axis. Find the volume of the solid.

18. The region under the curve $y = \sin x$ between $x = 0$ and $x = \pi$ is rotated about the y-axis. Find the volume of the solid.

19. The region of problem 18 is rotated about the x-axis. Find the area of the surface of the solid.

★10. Rational functions of the trigonometric functions.   In section 6 we learned that the integration of certain algebraic functions can be simplified by introducing trigonometric functions. We shall now prove that the integration of any rational function of the trigonometric functions $\sin x$ and $\cos x$, can be transformed by a suitable substitution, into the integration of a rational function of x, and hence by Theorem 4 (page 293) the integral is in $\mathfrak{F}$.

The magic substitution is

$$z = \tan \frac{x}{2}. \tag{57}$$

We must now show that with (57) $\sin x$, $\cos x$, and $\dfrac{dx}{dz}$ are rational functions of z. First

$$dz = \frac{1}{2} \sec^2 \frac{x}{2} \, dx = \frac{1}{2}\left(\tan^2 \frac{x}{2} + 1\right) dx = \frac{z^2 + 1}{2} \, dx$$

and hence

$$dx = \frac{2}{1 + z^2} \, dz. \tag{58}$$

For $\cos x$ we can write

$$\cos x = \cos^2 \frac{x}{2} - \sin^2 \frac{x}{2} = 2\cos^2 \frac{x}{2} - 1 = \frac{2}{\sec^2 \dfrac{x}{2}} - 1$$

$$= \frac{2}{1 + \tan^2 \dfrac{x}{2}} - 1 = \frac{2}{1 + z^2} - 1 = \frac{1 - z^2}{1 + z^2},$$

$$\cos x = \frac{1 - z^2}{1 + z^2}. \tag{59}$$

Finally

$$\sin x = 2 \sin \frac{x}{2} \cos \frac{x}{2} = 2 \frac{\sin \dfrac{x}{2}}{\cos \dfrac{x}{2}} \cos^2 \frac{x}{2}$$

$$= 2 \tan \frac{x}{2} \frac{1}{1 + \tan^2 \dfrac{x}{2}} = 2z \frac{1}{1 + z^2},$$

$$\sin x = \frac{2z}{1 + z^2}. \tag{60}$$

An inspection of (58), (59), and (60) shows that the substitution (57) transforms any rational function of $\sin x$ and $\cos x$ into a rational function of z.

EXAMPLE 1.   Find $I_1 = \displaystyle\int \frac{dx}{2 + \sin x}$.

SOLUTION.   Using (57), (58), and (60) we have

$$I_1 = \int \frac{\dfrac{2\,dz}{1 + z^2}}{2 + \dfrac{2z}{1 + z^2}} = \int \frac{dz}{z^2 + z + 1} = \int \frac{dz}{\left(z + \dfrac{1}{2}\right)^2 + \left(\dfrac{\sqrt{3}}{2}\right)^2}$$

$$= \frac{2}{\sqrt{3}} \tan^{-1} \frac{2z + 1}{\sqrt{3}} + C$$

$$= \frac{2}{\sqrt{3}} \tan^{-1}\left(\frac{1 + 2\tan \dfrac{x}{2}}{\sqrt{3}}\right) + C.$$

The student should compute the derivative of this answer and show that it is $1/(2 + \sin x)$.

EXAMPLE 2.   Find $I_2 = \displaystyle\int \frac{d\theta}{\cot 4\theta + \csc 4\theta}$.

SOLUTION.   We first change to sines and cosines

$$\int \frac{d\theta}{\cot 4\theta + \csc 4\theta} = \int \frac{d\theta}{\dfrac{\cos 4\theta}{\sin 4\theta} + \dfrac{1}{\sin 4\theta}} = \frac{1}{4}\int \frac{\sin 4\theta(4\,d\theta)}{1 + \cos 4\theta}.$$

We set $x = 4\theta$, $dx = 4\,d\theta$ and use equations (57) through (60).

$$I_2 = \frac{1}{4} \int \frac{\dfrac{2z}{1 + z^2}}{1 + \dfrac{1 - z^2}{1 + z^2}} \cdot \frac{2\,dz}{1 + z^2} = \frac{1}{4}\int \frac{2z\,dz}{1 + z^2}$$

$$= \frac{1}{4}\ln(1 + z^2) + C = \frac{1}{4}\ln\left(1 + \tan^2 \frac{x}{2}\right) + C = \frac{1}{4}\ln\left|\sec^2 \frac{x}{2}\right| + C$$

$$= \frac{1}{2}\ln|\sec 2\theta| + C.$$

EXERCISE 7

In problems 1 through 6 find the indicated indefinite integrals.

1. $\displaystyle\int \frac{dx}{\sin x + \tan x}.$

2. $\displaystyle\int \frac{dx}{1 + \sin 6x + \cos 6x}.$

3. $\displaystyle\int \frac{d\theta}{5 + 4\cos 2\theta}.$

4. $\displaystyle\int \frac{dx}{4\cos x - 3\sin x}.$

5. $\displaystyle\int \frac{dx}{2 + 2\sin x + \cos x}.$

6. $\displaystyle\int \frac{d\theta}{5\sec \theta - 3}.$

⋆11.   Reduction formulas and undetermined coefficients.   It is reasonably clear from our work on integration by parts that an integral such as

$$I_5 = \int x^5 e^{2x}\, dx \tag{61}$$

can be found by a repeated application of integration by parts.   To shorten the labor, however, it is advantageous to consider the more general problem of finding the integral

$$I_n = \int x^n e^{2x}\, dx \tag{62}$$

where for convenience we regard n as being any positive integer.   We integrate (62) by parts.   Let $u = x^n$, $dv = e^{2x}dx$.   Then $du = nx^{n-1}\, dx$, $v = e^{2x}/2$ and hence

$$I_n = \frac{x^n e^{2x}}{2} - \frac{n}{2}\int x^{n-1}e^{2x}\, dx. \tag{63}$$

A formula such as (63) is called a *reduction formula* because it reduces a complicated integral to one that is at least a little simpler (the power on x has decreased by 1).   Using this formula we can express I_5 in terms of I_4, then I_4 in terms of I_3, and so on, eventually computing I_5 explicitly.   In other words, instead of doing an integration by parts 5 times to compute I_5, we do it just once in general terms to obtain (63) and then use (63) repeatedly.

But there is another advantage to having a formula such as (63) that allows us to find I_5 more quickly.   By inspecting the formula we can predict that I_5 has the form

$$I_5 = e^{2x}P(x) \tag{64}$$

where $P(x)$ is a polynomial of degree at most 5.   We set down a polynomial with unknown coefficients in (64) and then differentiate the expression, and determine the unknown coefficients so that the derivative of (64) is $x^5 e^{2x}$.   This is called the method of *undetermined coefficients* and we now illustrate it by finding I_5.

Let

$$I_5 = e^{2x}(a_0x^5 + a_1x^4 + a_2x^3 + a_3x^2 + a_4x + a_5).$$

Then

$$\frac{dI_5}{dx} = 2e^{2x}(a_0x^5 + a_1x^4 + a_2x^3 + a_3x^2 + a_4x + a_5)$$

$$+ e^{2x}(5a_0x^4 + 4a_1x^3 + 3a_2x^2 + 2a_3x + a_4)$$

$$= e^{2x}[2a_0x^5 + (2a_1 + 5a_0)x^4 + (2a_2 + 4a_1)x^3$$

$$+ (2a_3 + 3a_2)x^2 + (2a_4 + 2a_3)x + (2a_5 + a_4)].$$

Since we desire that this expression shall be $e^{2x}x^5$ we want to solve the following set of equations for the unknown coefficients.

$$2a_0 = 1$$
$$5a_0 + 2a_1 = 0$$
$$4a_1 + 2a_2 = 0$$
$$3a_2 + 2a_3 = 0$$
$$2a_3 + 2a_4 = 0$$
$$a_4 + 2a_5 = 0.$$

But these are easy to solve stepwise. We find $a_0 = 1/2$, $a_1 = -5/4$, $a_2 = 5/2$, $a_3 = -15/4$, $a_4 = 15/4$, and $a_5 = -15/8$. Hence

$$\int x^5 e^{2x}\,dx = \frac{e^{2x}}{8}(4x^5 - 10x^4 + 20x^3 - 30x^2 + 30x - 15) + C. \quad (65)$$

The reader should differentiate the right side of (65) and show that the derivative is $x^5 e^{2x}$.

EXERCISE 8

In problems 1 through 9 derive the given reduction formula.

1. $\displaystyle \int x^n e^{ax}\,dx = \frac{x^n e^{ax}}{a} - \frac{n}{a}\int x^{n-1} e^{ax}\,dx.$

2. $\displaystyle \int x^m(\ln x)^n\,dx = \frac{x^{m+1}(\ln x)^n}{m+1} - \frac{n}{m+1}\int x^m(\ln x)^{n-1}\,dx.$

3. $\displaystyle \int x^n \sin ax\,dx = -\frac{x^n \cos ax}{a} + \frac{n}{a}\int x^{n-1}\cos ax\,dx.$

4. $\displaystyle \int x^n \cos bx\,dx = \frac{x^n \sin bx}{b} - \frac{n}{b}\int x^{n-1}\sin bx\,dx.$

5. $\displaystyle \int \sec^n x\,dx = \frac{\sec^{n-2} x \tan x}{n-1} + \frac{n-2}{n-1}\int \sec^{n-2} x\,dx.$

6. $\displaystyle\int \sin^n ax\, dx = -\frac{\sin^{n-1} ax \cos ax}{an} + \frac{n-1}{n}\int \sin^{n-2} ax\, dx.$

7. $\displaystyle\int \cos^n bx\, dx = \frac{\cos^{n-1} bx \sin bx}{bn} + \frac{n-1}{n}\int \cos^{n-2} bx\, dx.$

8. $\displaystyle\int x^n \tan^{-1} x\, dx = \frac{x^{n+1} \tan^{-1} x}{n+1} - \frac{1}{n+1}\int \frac{x^{n+1}}{1+x^2}\, dx.$

9. $\displaystyle\int x^n \sin^{-1} x\, dx = \frac{x^{n+1} \sin^{-1} x}{n+1} - \frac{1}{n+1}\int \frac{x^{n+1}}{\sqrt{1-x^2}}\, dx,$

In problems 10 through 15 find the unknown coefficients.

10. $\displaystyle\int x^4 e^{3x}\, dx = (a_0 x^4 + a_1 x^3 + a_2 x^2 + a_3 x + a_4)\, e^{3x} + C.$

11. $\displaystyle\int x^2 \ln^3 x\, dx = (a_0 \ln^3 x + a_1 \ln^2 x + a_2 \ln x + a_3)\, x^3 + C.$

★12. $\displaystyle\int x^3 \cos 5x\, dx = (a_0 x^3 + a_2 x)\sin 5x + (a_1 x^2 + a_3)\cos 5x + C.$

★13. $\displaystyle\int \sec^8 x\, dx = (a_0 \sec^6 x + a_1 \sec^4 x + a_2 \sec^2 x + a_3)\tan x + C.$

★14. $\displaystyle\int \sin^5 3x\, dx = (a_0 \sin^4 3x + a_1 \sin^2 3x + a_2)\cos 3x + C.$

★15. $\displaystyle\int \cos^6 x\, dx = (a_0 \cos^5 x + a_1 \cos^3 x + a_2 \cos x)\sin x + a_3 x + C.$

16. Use the formulas developed in problems 6 and 7 to prove that if n is a positive even integer then

$$\int_0^{\pi/2} \sin^n x\, dx = \int_0^{\pi/2} \cos^n x\, dx = \frac{1 \cdot 3 \cdot 5 \cdot 7 \cdots (n-1)}{2 \cdot 4 \cdot 6 \cdot 8 \cdots\; n}\; \frac{\pi}{2}.$$

Prove that if n is a positive odd integer then

$$\int_0^{\pi/2} \sin^n x\, dx = \int_0^{\pi/2} \cos^n x\, dx = \frac{2 \cdot 4 \cdot 6 \cdot 8 \cdots (n-1)}{3 \cdot 5 \cdot 7 \cdot 9 \cdots\; n}.$$

EXERCISE 9: REVIEW PROBLEMS FOR CHAPTER 9

Find each of the following integrals using any method you wish.

1. $\displaystyle\int \frac{5x^2 - 3x + 1}{x^2(x^2+1)}\, dx.$

2. $\displaystyle\int \frac{2\, dx}{x(x^2+1)^2}.$

3. $\displaystyle\int \frac{dx}{\sin x \cos x}.$

4. $\displaystyle\int \frac{x\, dx}{1+\sqrt{x}}.$

5. $\displaystyle\int \frac{dx}{e^{2x} - 1}.$

6. $\displaystyle\int \frac{\sin x\, dx}{\sqrt{1 + \cos x}}.$

7. $\displaystyle\int \frac{\sin x\, dx}{1 + \cos^2 x}.$

8. $\displaystyle\int \cosh^3 x\, dx.$

9. $\displaystyle\int \frac{\sin\sqrt{x}}{\sqrt{x}}\, dx.$

10. $\displaystyle\int \frac{d\theta}{\cot \theta - \tan \theta}.$

11. $\displaystyle\int \frac{d\theta}{2 \csc \theta - \sin \theta}.$

12. $\displaystyle\int \frac{x^2}{e^{5x}}\, dx.$

13. $\displaystyle\int \cot^{-1} 2x\, dx.$

14. $\displaystyle\int (\ln x)^2\, dx.$

15. $\displaystyle\int \frac{(\ln x)^7}{x}\, dx.$

16. $\displaystyle\int \frac{5 \cos x\, dx}{6 + \sin x - \sin^2 x}.$

17. $\displaystyle\int \frac{dx}{1 + e^x}.$

18. $\displaystyle\int \frac{(1 + \tan^2 x)\, dx}{1 + 9 \tan^2 x}.$

19. $\displaystyle\int \sinh^3 2x\, dx.$

20. $\displaystyle\int x \sinh x\, dx.$

21. $\displaystyle\int \sin \frac{x}{2} \cos \frac{5x}{2}\, dx.$

22. $\displaystyle\int \frac{dx}{x \ln x}.$

23. $\displaystyle\int e^{\tan y} \sec^2 y\, dy.$

24. $\displaystyle\int \sin^5 x\sqrt{\cos x}\, dx.$

25. $\displaystyle\int \frac{e^{3x}\, dx}{1 + e^{6x}}.$

26. $\displaystyle\int \frac{18\, x\, dx}{9x^2 + 6x + 5}.$

27. $\displaystyle\int \sqrt{1 + \sin \theta}\, d\theta.$

28. $\displaystyle\int 36x^5 e^{2x^3}\, dx.$

29. $\displaystyle\int \ln (x^2 + a^2)^5\, dx.$

30. $\displaystyle\int \frac{\sin t\, dt}{\sec t + \cos t}.$

31. $\displaystyle\int \sqrt{\sec y} \tan y\, dy.$

32. $\displaystyle\int \sin\sqrt{x}\, dx.$

33. $\displaystyle\int \cos 3x \cos 7x\, dx.$

34. $\displaystyle\int \frac{dz}{1 - \tan^2 z}.$

35. $\displaystyle\int \frac{6\, e^{4x}\, dx}{1 - e^x}.$

36. $\displaystyle\int \frac{8\, e^x\, dx}{3 + 2e^x - e^{2x}}.$

37. $\displaystyle\int \theta \sec^2 \theta\, d\theta.$

38. $\displaystyle\int \sqrt{1 - \cos \theta}\, d\theta.$

39. $\displaystyle\int \frac{\tan x\, dx}{\ln (\cos x)}.$

40. $\displaystyle\int \sin \frac{x}{3} \sin \frac{5x}{3}\, dx.$

41. $\displaystyle\int \sinh x \sin x \, dx.$

42. $\displaystyle\int 125 \, x^4 (\ln x)^2 \, dx.$

43. $\displaystyle\int (\tan \theta + \cot \theta)^2 \, d\theta.$

44. $\displaystyle\int e^{ax} \sin bx \, dx.$

45. $\displaystyle\int \frac{24 \, dx}{x(x^2 - 1)(x^2 - 4)}.$

46. $\displaystyle\int \frac{(\tan^{-1} y)^2}{1 + y^2} \, dy.$

47. $\displaystyle\int \cos (\ln x) \, dx.$

48. $\displaystyle\int \frac{\sin \theta \cos^3 \theta \, d\theta}{1 + \sin^2 \theta}.$

49. $\displaystyle\int \tanh (\ln x) \, dx.$

50. $\displaystyle\int e^x \sinh x \cos x \, dx.$

10

VECTORS IN THE PLANE

1.   The algebra of vectors.   Certain quantities in nature possess both a magnitude and a direction.   Force is such a quantity.   For if we add two forces of 10 lbs each we do not necessarily obtain a force of 20 lbs. The resulting force depends on the directions of the individual forces. Similarly the velocity of a moving particle has a magnitude (called its *speed*) and a direction, the direction in which the particle is moving.

In order to handle physical problems involving directed quantities, it is nice to have at hand a mathematical theory for such quantities.   Briefly, these quantities are called *vectors*, and the theory is called *vector analysis*. It is quite natural to denote a force, (or a velocity) by a line segment with an arrow.   The length of the line segment is the magnitude of the force (or the speed of the moving particle) and the arrow and the position of the line segment give the direction of the force (or of the moving particle).

Abstracting from these motivating remarks, the part that is purely mathematical we have

DEFINITION 1.   *A vector is a directed line segment.*

In creating a mathematical theory, we must start by deciding just what is meant by addition, subtraction, multiplication, etc., for our new quantities.   In keeping with this program we have

DEFINITION 2.   *Two vectors are equal if they have the same length and the same direction.*

Observe that two vectors may be equal without being collinear.

To distinguish vectors from numbers, we may use bold face type: thus **A** is a vector and A is a number.   Frequently it is convenient to use letters with arrows to indicate a vector, or double letters giving the beginning

point and ending point of the directed line segment.   Thus in Fig. 1, **B**,
OB, $\vec{B}$, and $\overrightarrow{OB}$ all denote the same vector.

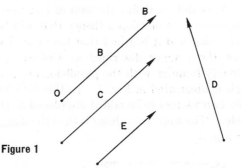

Figure 1

As an illustration of Definition 2, we see that the vectors **B** and **C** of
Fig. 1 are equal (**B** = **C**) because they have the same length and the same
direction.   Thus a given vector is equal to any vector obtained by shifting
the given vector parallel to itself.   The vectors **B** and **D** of Fig. 1 have the
same length but do not have the same direction, so **B** $\neq$ **D**.   Similarly the
vectors $\overrightarrow{OB}$ and $\overrightarrow{BO}$ are not equal because one has exactly the opposite
direction of the other.   The vectors **B** and **E** of Fig. 1 have the same direction but **B** $\neq$ **E** because the lengths are different.

The length, or magnitude, of a vector **B** is frequently denoted by $|\mathbf{B}|$
and is always a nonnegative number.   Sometimes it is convenient to use
the corresponding letter in ordinary type for the length, for example
$B = |\mathbf{B}|$ is the length of the vector **B**.   We also use $|\mathbf{AB}|$ to denote the
length of the vector **AB** from the point A to the point B.

A point can be regarded as a vector of zero length.   Because a point
has no particular direction it is not a vector by our previous definition.
But we can either ignore this slight defect, or more honestly, enlarge our
definition to include the zero vector.   The zero vector will be denoted by **0**.

DEFINITION 3.   *To add the vectors* **AB** *and* **CD**, *place* **CD**
so that its beginning point C falls on the end point B of **AB**.   *The*
sum **AB** $+$ **CD** *is then the vector* **AD**.

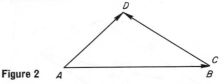

Figure 2

This definition is illustrated in Fig. 2.   Notice that two vectors do *not*
need to be parallel or perpendicular, in order to form their sum.   The sum

of two vectors is frequently called the *resultant*, and each of the vectors in the sum is called a *vector component* of the resultant.

Why did we define the sum of two vectors in this way? Because our objective is to develop a theory that will be useful in studying forces and velocities, and it is a fact that forces, and velocities do indeed combine in just the manner described in Definition 3. The student is probably already familiar with the parallelogram law for adding two forces. This rule is illustrated in Fig. 3. In this definition for the sum of two vectors, the two vectors to be added are placed so that their beginning points coincide. The sum or resultant is then the diagonal of the parallelogram shown in Fig. 3.

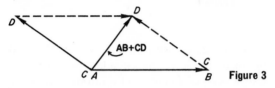

Figure 3

It is clear from Fig. 3 that adding two vectors by the parallelogram method gives the same result as adding the same two vectors by the "tail to head" method of Definition 3. Hence the two definitions are equivalent and we may use whichever definition convenience dictates.

   THEOREM 1.   *Vector addition is commutative, i.e., the sum of two vectors is independent of the order of addition.*

PROOF. We are to prove that for any two vectors **A** and **B**

$$\mathbf{A} + \mathbf{B} = \mathbf{B} + \mathbf{A}. \tag{1}$$

Referring to Fig. 4 it is easy to see that when the vectors **A** and **B** are joined to form the vector sum **A** + **B** they give the lower side of the parallelogram, and when these vectors are joined to form the vector sum **B** + **A**, they give the upper side of the very same parallelogram. Then

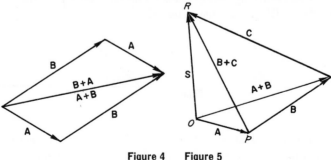

Figure 4   Figure 5

A + **B** and **B** + **A** turn out to be the same diagonal of the same parallelogram and hence are equal.

THEOREM 2.   *Vector addition is associative, i.e., the sum of three vectors is independent of the grouping in forming the sum.*

PROOF.   We are to prove that for any three vectors **A**, **B**, and **C**

$$\mathbf{A} + (\mathbf{B} + \mathbf{C}) = (\mathbf{A} + \mathbf{B}) + \mathbf{C}. \tag{2}$$

This equation is obvious from Fig. 5.   The vector **S** is the sum of **A** and (**B** + **C**) (examine $\triangle OPR$), and it is also the sum of (**A** + **B**) and **C** (examine $\triangle OQR$).   Therefore both sides of equation (2) give the same vector **S** and hence are equal.

THEOREM 3.   *The zero vector* **0** *has the property that for any vector* **A**

$$\mathbf{0} + \mathbf{A} = \mathbf{A} + \mathbf{0} = \mathbf{A}. \tag{3}$$

PROOF.   Obvious.

DEFINITION 4.   *The vector* **B** *is said to be the negative of the vector* **A**, *and we write*

$$\mathbf{B} = -\mathbf{A} \tag{4}$$

if

$$\mathbf{B} + \mathbf{A} = \mathbf{0}. \tag{5}$$

THEOREM 4.   *If* $\mathbf{A} = \overrightarrow{PQ}$, *then the negative of the vector* **A** *is the vector* $\overrightarrow{QP}$.

PROOF.   This is obvious, and is illustrated in Fig. 6 where the sum of the two vectors

$$\overrightarrow{PQ} + \overrightarrow{QP}$$

is obviously the zero vector.

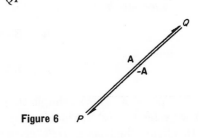

Figure 6

If we add the vector **A** to itself, we obtain a vector in the same direction, but twice as long.   Such a vector would naturally be written as **A**+**A**=2**A**. This suggests

DEFINITION 5.   *If **A** is a vector and c is a number then the product c**A** is a vector whose magnitude is* $|c|\,|\mathbf{A}|$. *The product has the direction of **A** if c > 0, and the opposite direction if c < 0. If c = 0, then c**A** is the zero vector.*

This definition is illustrated in Fig. 7.   It is clear that the product $(-1)\mathbf{A}$ is the same as the negative of the vector as described in Definition 4. In symbols $(-1)\mathbf{A} = -\mathbf{A}$.   Thus the two definitions are consistent.

A number is frequently called a *scalar* to distinguish it from a vector. Definition 5 gives the rules for multiplying a scalar and a vector.   The rules for multiplying two vectors will be given in Chapter 14.

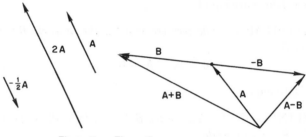

Figure 7   Figure 8

DEFINITION 6 (Subtraction).   *To subtract the vector **B** from the vector **A**, just add the negative of **B** to **A**.   In symbols*

$$\mathbf{A} - \mathbf{B} = \mathbf{A} + (-1)\mathbf{B}.$$

This definition is illustrated in Fig. 8.

THEOREM 5.   *Multiplication of vectors by scalars is distributive, that is, for any two numbers c and d and any two vectors **A** and **B** we have both*

$$c(\mathbf{A} + \mathbf{B}) = c\mathbf{A} + c\mathbf{B} \tag{6}$$

and

$$(c + d)\mathbf{A} = c\mathbf{A} + d\mathbf{A}. \tag{7}$$

The proof of (7) is so simple that we leave it to the reader.   To prove (6) we refer to Fig. 9 which covers the case when c is greater than one. In this figure the triangle OPQ gives the vector sum $\mathbf{A} + \mathbf{B}$.   If $c > 1$, the vectors $c\mathbf{A}$ and $c\mathbf{B}$ will be longer than $\mathbf{A}$ and $\mathbf{B}$ respectively, and their sum is given by the triangle ORS.   From the properties of similar triangles it follows that the points O, Q, and S are collinear and that $c\overrightarrow{OQ} = \overrightarrow{OS}$.   But this is just equation (6).

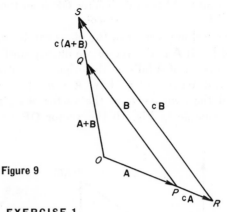

Figure 9

EXERCISE 1

In the following problems, *a* and *b* are any numbers, and **A** and **B** are any vectors.

1. Prove that $1\mathbf{A} = \mathbf{A}$ and $(-1)\mathbf{A} = -\mathbf{A}$.
2. Prove that $(ab)\mathbf{A} = a(b\mathbf{A})$.
3. Prove that $(a + b)\mathbf{A} = a\mathbf{A} + b\mathbf{A}$.   This is equation (7) of Theorem 5.
4. Prove that $(\mathbf{A} - \mathbf{B}) + \mathbf{B} = \mathbf{A}$ and that $\mathbf{A} - \mathbf{B} = -(\mathbf{B} - \mathbf{A})$.
5. Prove that $(\mathbf{A} + \mathbf{B}) - \mathbf{B} = \mathbf{A}$.
6. It is known that in any triangle the length of one side is less than or equal to the sum of the lengths of the other two sides. Use this fact to prove that $|\mathbf{A} + \mathbf{B}| \leq |\mathbf{A}| + |\mathbf{B}|$.
7. Following the methods of problem 6, prove that $|\mathbf{A} - \mathbf{B}| \geq |\mathbf{A}| - |\mathbf{B}|$.
8. Draw a figure for the proof of Theorem 5 in the two cases (a) $0 < c < 1$ and (b) $c < 0$.

2.   Computations with vectors.

While the introduction to vectors presented in section 1, is logically correct and artistically satisfying, the reader may well be left with an uneasy feeling that he still does not know how to compute with vectors, and hence cannot really use them. Given two vectors **A** and **B**, he may well ask "in which direction do they point, which of the two is the larger?" What is needed then is a method of representing a specific vector that will supply this information. A very satisfactory method is given below.

We suppose, for the rest of this chapter, that all of the vectors lie in a plane. We introduce into this plane the usual x and y coordinate axes. Along with this coordinate system we introduce two new elements, namely two vectors **i** and **j** each of unit length. The vector **i** points in the direction of the positive x-axis, and the vector **j** points in the direction of the positive y-axis. Since a vector may be shifted parallel to itself, it is convenient to think of **i** as going from $(0, 0)$ to $(1, 0)$. Similarly **j** can be realized as the vector from $(0, 0)$ to $(0, 1)$. (See Fig. 10.) It is now obvious that if P is the point $(7, 5)$ then the vector **OP** from the origin O to the point P is just $7\mathbf{i} + 5\mathbf{j}$.

Indeed any vector in the plane can be written using these unit vectors **i** and **j**. If **A** is the vector we merely shift it parallel to itself so that the initial point of **A** falls on the origin. If, after the shift, the terminal point of **A** falls on (a_1, a_2) we have $\mathbf{A} = a_1\mathbf{i} + a_2\mathbf{j}$. The quantities a_1 and a_2 are called the *components* of the vector along the x and y axis respectively. For example in Fig. 10 the vector **OP** has the components $a_1 = 7$ and

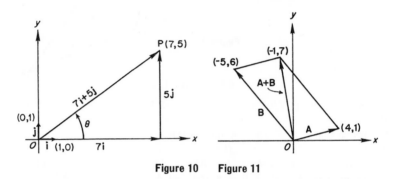

Figure 10   Figure 11

$a_2 = 5$. These components are scalars, and should be distinguished from the vector components which for the vector **OP** are $7\mathbf{i}$ and $5\mathbf{j}$. A component can be negative; for example the components of the vector **B** of Fig. 11 are -5 and 6. Sometimes it is convenient to use letter subscripts for components. Thus we might write $\mathbf{A} = A_x\mathbf{i} + A_y\mathbf{j}$. With this notation the vector **A** of Fig. 11 has the components $A_x = 4$, and $A_y = 1$.

THEOREM 6. *If* $\mathbf{A} = a_1\mathbf{i} + a_2\mathbf{j}$ *and* $\mathbf{B} = b_1\mathbf{i} + b_2\mathbf{j}$ *then*

$$\mathbf{A} + \mathbf{B} = (a_1 + b_1)\mathbf{i} + (a_2 + b_2)\mathbf{j}. \tag{8}$$

PROOF. Using Theorems 1, 2, and 5 we can write

$$\mathbf{A} + \mathbf{B} = (a_1\mathbf{i} + a_2\mathbf{j}) + (b_1\mathbf{i} + b_2\mathbf{j})$$
$$= a_1\mathbf{i} + b_1\mathbf{i} + a_2\mathbf{j} + b_2\mathbf{j}$$
$$= (a_1 + b_1)\mathbf{i} + (a_2 + b_2)\mathbf{j}. \qquad \text{Q.E.D.}$$

In other words, to add two vectors, just add the corresponding components. For example, the vectors shown in Fig. 11 are $\mathbf{A} = 4\mathbf{i} + \mathbf{j}$ and $\mathbf{B} = -5\mathbf{i} + 6\mathbf{j}$ and their sum (by Theorem 6) is $\mathbf{A} + \mathbf{B} = (-5 + 4)\mathbf{i} + (6 + 1)\mathbf{j} = -\mathbf{i} + 7\mathbf{j}$.

In a similar manner Theorem 5 together with problem 2 of Exercise 1 yields

THEOREM 7. *If* $\mathbf{A} = a_1\mathbf{i} + a_2\mathbf{j}$ *then* $c\mathbf{A} = (ca_1)\mathbf{i} + (ca_2)\mathbf{j}$.

For example, $3(-5\mathbf{i} + 6\mathbf{j}) = -15\mathbf{i} + 18\mathbf{j}$.

The Pythagorean Theorem gives immediately the following formula for the length of a vector, namely

$$|\mathbf{A}| = |a_1\mathbf{i} + a_2\mathbf{j}| = \sqrt{a_1{}^2 + a_2{}^2}. \tag{9}$$

We can specify the direction of a nonzero vector, by giving θ, the angle that the vector makes with the positive x-axis. In order that θ be uniquely determined we require that $0 \leq \theta < 2\pi$. A simple formula for θ is not available, but we can write that if $\mathbf{A} = a_1\mathbf{i} + a_2\mathbf{j}$ then

$$\tan \theta = \frac{a_2}{a_1} \tag{10}$$

and then compute θ. Of course (10) fails if $a_1 = 0$, but this causes no difficulty because $\theta = \pi/2$ or $\theta = 3\pi/2$ according as a_2 is positive or negative.

One may be tempted to transform equation (10) into

$$\theta = \tan^{-1}\frac{a_2}{a_1}, \tag{11}$$

but strictly speaking (10) and (11) are not equivalent because (11) requires that $-\pi/2 < \theta < \pi/2$, while we have demanded that $0 \leq \theta < 2\pi$. For example if $\mathbf{C} = -5\mathbf{i} - 5\mathbf{j}$ then $\tan \theta = 1$. Formula (11) gives $\theta = \pi/4$, but it is obvious that this vector $\mathbf{C}$ makes an angle $\theta = 5\pi/4$ with the positive x-axis. If $\mathbf{D} = -3\mathbf{j}$, the x component d_1 is zero, but obviously $\theta = 3\pi/2$.

THEOREM 8. *Any vector* $\mathbf{A}$ *can be written in the form*

$$\mathbf{A} = |\mathbf{A}|\cos\theta\mathbf{i} + |\mathbf{A}|\sin\theta\mathbf{j} \tag{12}$$
$$= |\mathbf{A}|(\cos\theta\mathbf{i} + \sin\theta\mathbf{j}).$$

The proof is almost obvious. The x-component of any vector $\mathbf{A}$ is just the projection of the vector on the x-axis and this is just $|\mathbf{A}|\cos\theta$. Similarly the y-component is the projection on the y-axis and clearly this is $|\mathbf{A}|\sin\theta$.

If $\mathbf{A} = a_1\mathbf{i} + a_2\mathbf{j}$ then equation (12) takes the form

$$\mathbf{A} = \sqrt{a_1{}^2 + a_2{}^2}\,(\cos\theta\mathbf{i} + \sin\theta\mathbf{j})$$

where θ is determined by equation (10).

A *unit vector* is a vector of length one. It is always possible to reduce any given vector to a unit vector with the same direction as the given vector, merely by dividing the given vector by its length (providing the length is not zero).

EXAMPLE 1.   Find a unit vector with the same direction as $\mathbf{E} = 5\sqrt{3}\mathbf{i} - 5\mathbf{j}$.

SOLUTION.   By (9), $|\mathbf{E}| = \sqrt{75 + 25} = 10$.   Then for a unit vector we have

$$\mathbf{e} = \frac{\mathbf{E}}{10} = \frac{\sqrt{3}}{2}\mathbf{i} - \frac{1}{2}\mathbf{j}.$$

Since $\theta = 11\pi/6$, we could also write for this vector

$$\mathbf{e} = \cos\frac{11\pi}{6}\mathbf{i} + \sin\frac{11\pi}{6}\mathbf{j}.$$

The vector from the origin of the coordinate system to a point P is called the *position vector* of the point P.   If P has coordinates (p_1, p_2) it is clear that the position vector $\mathbf{OP}$ has these as components, and indeed $\mathbf{OP} = p_1\mathbf{i} + p_2\mathbf{j}$.   It is easy to find the vector from the point A to the point B by using the position vectors to A and B.   This is the content of

THEOREM 9.   *For any two points A and B*

$$\boxed{\mathbf{AB} = \mathbf{OB} - \mathbf{OA}.}$$

(13)

PROOF.   It is obvious that

$$\mathbf{OA} + \mathbf{AB} = \mathbf{OB}$$

(see Fig. 12).   Then subtract the vector $\mathbf{OA}$ from both sides of this equation and use problem 5 of Exercise 1.   Q.E.D.

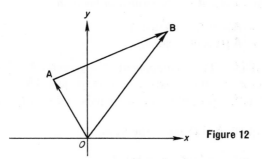

Figure 12

EXAMPLE 2.   Find the length of the vector $\mathbf{AB}$ from the point $A(-3, 5)$ to the point $B(7, 9)$.

SOLUTION.   The position vectors are $\mathbf{OB} = 7\mathbf{i} + 9\mathbf{j}$ and $\mathbf{OA} = -3\mathbf{i} + 5\mathbf{j}$. Therefore by equation (13)

$$\mathbf{AB} = 7\mathbf{i} + 9\mathbf{j} - (-3\mathbf{i} + 5\mathbf{j}) = 7\mathbf{i} + 9\mathbf{j} + 3\mathbf{i} - 5\mathbf{j} = 10\mathbf{i} + 4\mathbf{j}.$$

By equation (9) the length is $|\mathbf{AB}| = \sqrt{10^2 + 4^2} = 2\sqrt{5^2 + 2^2} = 2\sqrt{29}$. If $\mathbf{u}$ denotes a unit vector with the direction of $\mathbf{AB}$ then

$$\mathbf{u} = \frac{\mathbf{i}}{2\sqrt{29}} (10\mathbf{i} + 4\mathbf{j}) = \frac{5}{\sqrt{29}} \mathbf{i} + \frac{2}{\sqrt{29}} \mathbf{j}.$$

EXERCISE 2

1. Let $\mathbf{A} = \mathbf{i} + 2\mathbf{j}$, $\mathbf{B} = 3\mathbf{i} - 5\mathbf{j}$, $\mathbf{C} = -8\mathbf{i} + 7\mathbf{j}$, and $\mathbf{D} = -3\mathbf{i} - 9\mathbf{j}$. Compute each of the following vectors.

  a. $\mathbf{A} + \mathbf{B}$,   b. $\mathbf{A} + \mathbf{C}$,   c. $\mathbf{A} + \mathbf{D}$,
  d. $\mathbf{A} + \mathbf{B} + \mathbf{C}$,   e. $\mathbf{A} + 2\mathbf{B}$,   f. $\mathbf{A} - 3\mathbf{C}$,
   g. $\mathbf{C} + \mathbf{A} + \frac{1}{3} \mathbf{D}$,   h. $8\mathbf{A} - 5\mathbf{B} - 2\mathbf{C} + 3\mathbf{D}$.

2. Compute the length of the vectors $\mathbf{A}$, $\mathbf{B}$, $\mathbf{C}$, and $\mathbf{D}$ of Problem 1.

3. Determine the angle between the positive x-axis, and each of the following vectors: $\mathbf{A} = 2\mathbf{i} - 2\mathbf{j}$, $\mathbf{B} = -4\mathbf{i} + 4\sqrt{3}\mathbf{j}$, $\mathbf{C} = -25\mathbf{i}$, $\mathbf{D} = \pi\mathbf{j}$.

4. Write each of the vectors of problem 3 in the form $r(\cos\theta\mathbf{i} + \sin\theta\mathbf{j})$.

5. In each of the following, find the vector from the first named point to the second named point and find the length of the vector:

  a. $A(11, 7)$, $B(3, 13)$,   b. $C(111, 59)$, $D(141, 99)$,

  c. $E(-5, -7)$, $F(-17, -12)$,   d. $G\left(-\frac{11}{2}, \frac{13}{3}\right)$, $H\left(\frac{13}{2}, -\frac{11}{3}\right)$.

6. For each of the following vectors find a unit vector with the same direction, $\mathbf{A} = 3\mathbf{i} + 4\mathbf{j}$, $\mathbf{B} = 8\mathbf{i} - 15\mathbf{j}$, $\mathbf{C} = -21\mathbf{i} + 20\mathbf{j}$, $\mathbf{D} = 4\mathbf{i} - 7\mathbf{j}$, and $\mathbf{E} = -6\mathbf{i} - 3\mathbf{j}$.

★7. Prove that two vectors $\mathbf{A} = a_1\mathbf{i} + a_2\mathbf{j}$ and $\mathbf{B} = b_1\mathbf{i} + b_2\mathbf{j}$ are equal if and only if $a_1 = b_1$ and $a_2 = b_2$. In other words two vectors are equal if and only if their corresponding components are equal.

★8. Let $\mathbf{OP}$ be the position vector to P the midpoint of the line segment AB where A is (a_1, a_2) and B is (b_1, b_2). Prove that

$$\mathbf{OP} = \frac{1}{2} \mathbf{OA} + \frac{1}{2} \mathbf{OB}.$$

From this deduce the formula for the coordinates of the midpoint

$$\left(\frac{a_1 + b_1}{2}, \frac{a_2 + b_2}{2}\right). \qquad \text{Hint: } \mathbf{OP} = \mathbf{OA} + \tfrac{1}{2} \mathbf{AB}.$$

This formula for the coordinates of the midpoint of a given line segment is important and should be memorized.

9. Find the midpoint of the line segment AB for each of the following pairs of points: (a) $A(3, 2)$, $B(11, 20)$ (b) $A(5, -9)$, $B(9, -5)$ (c) $A(-6, 10)$ $B(8, -6)$ (d) $A(\sqrt{2} + 7, \pi + 3e)$, $B(\sqrt{2} - 7, \pi - e)$.

10. Each vertical line meets the parabola $y = x^2 - 8$ in a point A and the parabola $y = x^2 + 4$ in a second point B. Prove that the collection of midpoints of the line segments AB, forms another parabola. What is the equation of this parabola?

11. Generalize problem 10 by proving that if we start with any two parabolas with vertical axes, the construction of problem 10 will give either another parabola or a straight line.

★12. Let $P_1P_2P_3P_4$ be any quadrilateral and let M_1, M_2, M_3, and M_4 be the midpoints of the segments P_1P_2, P_2P_3, P_3P_4, and P_4P_1 respectively. Prove that $M_1M_2M_3M_4$ is a parallelogram. *Hint:* Use the formula of problem 8 and compute the slopes of the sides.

★★13. Following the methods of problem 8 prove that the point

$$P\left(\frac{2a_1 + b_1}{3}, \frac{2a_2 + b_2}{3}\right)$$

is one of the trisection points of the line segment AB where A is (a_1, a_2) and B is (b_1, b_2). In fact P is that trisection point that is nearer to A. Find a formula for the trisection point nearer to B.

★14. Prove that the three medians of a triangle intersect in a point. *Hint:* If the vertices are (a_1, b_1), (a_2, b_2), and (a_3, b_3) prove that the common intersection point is

$$\left(\frac{a_1 + a_2 + a_3}{3}, \frac{b_1 + b_2 + b_3}{3}\right).$$

15. Prove that if the vector $\mathbf{A} = a_1\mathbf{i} + a_2\mathbf{j}$ is not the zero vector, then the vector $\mathbf{B} = -a_2\mathbf{i} + a_1\mathbf{j}$ is perpendicular to $\mathbf{A}$. *Hint:* $\mathbf{B}$ is 90° in advance of $\mathbf{A}$.

3.   Vectors and parametric equations. Vectors can be very useful in describing curves. Let us suppose that a point P moving in the plane describes some curve. To be specific, let t denote the time, and suppose that for each value of t, the point P has a definite location. Let $\mathbf{R}$ be the position vector of P, i.e., the vector from the origin to the point P. Then for each value of t, the vector $\mathbf{R}$ is specified so that $\mathbf{R}$ is a function, a *vector function*, of the scalar t. We may write $\mathbf{R} = \mathbf{R}(t)$ to indicate this dependence of the vector $\mathbf{R}$ on the scalar t. Of course a vector is specified whenever its components are specified. So the function $\mathbf{R}(t)$ really consists of two scalar functions and we can write

$$\mathbf{R}(t) = f(t)\mathbf{i} + g(t)\mathbf{j} \tag{14}$$

where $f(t)$ is some function that gives the x-component of $\mathbf{R}$ and $g(t)$ is another function that gives the y-component of $\mathbf{R}$.

Actually, equation (14) is just a shorthand way of writing the pair of equations

$$x = f(t), \qquad y = g(t). \tag{15}$$

The pair of equations (15) is called the *parametric equations* of the curve, and t is called the *parameter*.

In order to find a point on the curve, one uses some fixed value t in (15) and one computes for that t the coordinate pair (x, y).   Thus (15) is a set of simultaneous equations.   If we can eliminate t from this pair of equations, by solving simultaneously, we will obtain one equation in the two variables x and y,

$$F(x, y) = 0 \qquad \text{or} \qquad y = f(x) \tag{16}$$

an equation for the curve in its customary form.   To distinguish between these various ways of describing a curve, (16) is called a *Cartesian equation* for the curve, and (14) is called a *vector equation* for the curve.

The vector equation (14), and the parametric equations (15) have an advantage over the Cartesian equation, because they are more flexible, and they give more information, as we shall see later on in this chapter. For one thing (16) merely tells which points are on the curve, but (14) and (15) tell us where the moving point P is at any given time t, that is, how the curve was described.

Further the vector equation or the parametric equations give the curve a direction, namely the direction in which P is traveling as the parameter t increases.   Henceforth when we speak of a positive direction along a curve we mean the direction in which P moves as t increases.   Of course a curve by itself has no direction.   The direction only arises when we give a set of parametric equations.   By changing the functions $f(t)$ and $g(t)$ it is possible to reverse the positive direction on the curve.

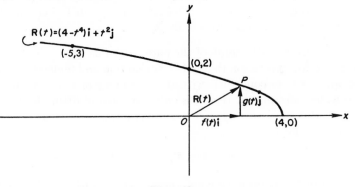

Figure 13

EXAMPLE 1.   Discuss the curve whose vector equation is $\mathbf{R} = (4 - t^4)\mathbf{i} + t^2\mathbf{j}$.

SOLUTION.   This vector equation is equivalent to the pair of parametric equations

$$x = 4 - t^4, \qquad y = t^2. \tag{17}$$

To graph this curve we make a table, selecting convenient values of t and computing the corresponding coordinates of P, the end point of the position vector $\mathbf{R}$.

t	0	1	$\sqrt{2}$	$\sqrt{3}$	2	$\sqrt{5}$
x	4	3	0	-5	-12	-21
y	0	1	2	3	4	5

It is clear that these points $(4, 0)$, $(3, 1)$, $\cdots$ all lie on the curve of Fig. 13. We may gain more information by eliminating t from the pair (17) to obtain a Cartesian equation. Squaring the second equation and substituting in the first, we find

$$x = 4 - y^2,$$

and hence the tip of the vector **R** describes a parabola.

Notice however, that the vector equation does not give the whole parabola, but just the part on and above the x-axis. For, given any real number t, its square is either positive or zero, so from (17) we have $y \geqq 0$ for all t. If we start our moving point P at time $t = 0$, it is at the point $(4, 0)$, and as time passes, the point moves along the upper half of the parabola toward the left steadily getting further away from the vertex $(4, 0)$. Thus for $t \geqq 0$, the vector equation $\mathbf{R} = (4 - t^4)\mathbf{i} + t^2\mathbf{j}$ describes the upper half of the parabola $x = 4 - y^2$ and the positive direction on the parabola is to the left. For $t \leqq 0$, the equation describes the same half of the parabola, but now the positive direction on the parabola is to the right.

It is not necessary to think of the parameter t as time. This is merely a convenient interpretation that aids visualization and understanding. Of course when we are concerned with the trajectory of some moving object such as a shell or a planet, then it is only natural and fitting to let t denote the time. But we are always free to use any letter we wish as a parameter. Thus the equations

$$x = 4 - \theta^4, \qquad y = \theta^2 \tag{18}$$

can be regarded as parametric equations of a curve with θ as the parameter, and when so regarded (18) gives exactly the same curve as (17). The variable θ may have some geometric significance as an angle, but this is not necessary, and in the particular case of the parabola (18) there is no angle in Fig. 13 that is related to the parameter θ.

EXAMPLE 2. A wheel of radius a rolls on a straight line without slipping. Let P be a fixed point on the wheel, at distance b from the center of the wheel. The curve described by the point P is called a *trochoid*. If $b = a$ then the curve is called a *cycloid*. Find parametric equations for the trochoid.

SOLUTION.   For convenience we select the x-axis to be the straight line on which the wheel rolls.   Further we select the initial position of the wheel so that the center C of the wheel is on the y-axis, and the point P is on the y-axis below C (see Fig. 14).   Let Q be that point on the rim of the wheel that lies on the radial line CP.   Then in the initial position of the wheel the point Q coincides with the origin O.

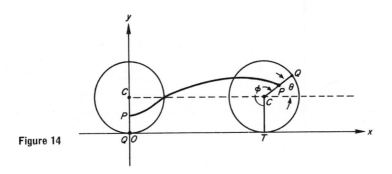

Figure 14

Let us suppose now that the wheel turns through an angle φ (the radial line CQ turns through an angle φ) in going from its initial position to some general position, as shown in Fig. 14.   It is easy to write the vector equation for the point P.   Indeed

$$\mathbf{OP} = \mathbf{OT} + \mathbf{TC} + \mathbf{CP}. \tag{19}$$

Since the wheel rolls without slipping the distance OT is just $a\varphi$, provided that φ is measured in radians.   Whence $\mathbf{OT} = a\varphi\mathbf{i}$.   Clearly $\mathbf{TC} = a\mathbf{j}$.   Finally if θ denotes the angle that the radial line CQ makes with the positive x-axis, then by Theorem 8 $\mathbf{CP} = b(\cos\theta\mathbf{i} + \sin\theta\mathbf{j})$.   Hence equation (19) becomes

$$\begin{aligned} \mathbf{OP} &= a\varphi\mathbf{j} + a\mathbf{j} + b\cos\theta\mathbf{i} + b\sin\theta\mathbf{j} \\ &= (a\varphi + b\cos\theta)\mathbf{i} + (a + b\sin\theta)\mathbf{j}. \end{aligned} \tag{20}$$

But equation (20) contains two parameters φ and θ, and there should only be one.   To eliminate the excess parameter we observe that for any position of the wheel $\varphi + \theta = 3\pi/2$.   Therefore $\cos\theta = \cos(3\pi/2 - \varphi) = -\sin\varphi$ and $\sin\theta = \sin(3\pi/2 - \varphi) = -\cos\varphi$.   Equation (20) now simplifies to

$$\mathbf{OP} = (a\varphi - b\sin\varphi)\mathbf{i} + (a - b\cos\varphi)\mathbf{j}, \tag{21}$$

the vector equation of the trochoid.   Therefore

$$x = a\varphi - b\sin\varphi, \qquad y = a - b\cos\varphi, \tag{22}$$

form a set of parametric equations for the trochoid.   One arch of the trochoid is shown in Fig. 14.

If $b = a$, the curve is called a cycloid.   Obviously the cycloid will meet the x-axis at intervals of length $2\pi a$.   When $b = a$, the equation set (22) becomes

$$x = a(\varphi - \sin\varphi), \qquad y = a(1 - \cos\varphi), \tag{23}$$

the parametric equations for the cycloid.   This curve is shown in Fig. 15.

It is clear from Fig. 15, that y is a function of x, but it is also clear from equation (23) that it is not possible[1] to find a simple expression for this function. Thus for many curves, and in particular the cycloid, the parametric equations are simpler than the Cartesian equations.

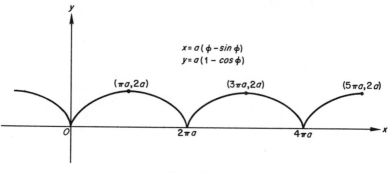

Figure 15

EXERCISE 3

In each of problems 1 through 10 a curve is given by a set of parametric equations. Sketch the curve for the indicated range of the parameter. In problems 1 through 6 obtain a Cartesian equation for the curve by eliminating the parameter, and identify the curve.

1. $x = t$, $y = 1 - t$, $0 \le t \le 1$.
2. $x = 5 \cos t$, $y = 5 \sin t$, $0 \le t \le 2\pi$.
3. $x = 5 \cos^2 t$, $y = 5 \sin^2 t$, $0 \le t \le 2\pi$.
4. $x = 3 \cos \theta$, $y = 5 \sin \theta$, $0 \le \theta \le \pi$.
5. $x = \sin \alpha$, $y = \cos 2\alpha$, $0 \le \alpha \le \pi$.
6. $x = \cosh u$, $y = \sinh u$, $-\infty < u < \infty$.
7. $x = t^3$, $y = t^2$, $-\infty < t < \infty$.
8. $x = t^3 - 3t$, $y = t$, $-\infty < t < \infty$.
★9. $x = t^3 - 3t$, $y = \tan \dfrac{\pi}{4} t$, $-2 < t < 2$.

★10. $x = t^3 - 3t$, $y = 4 - t^2$, $-\infty < t < \infty$.

11. Show that $\mathbf{R} = \mathbf{OP_1} + t\, \mathbf{P_1 P_2}$ is a vector equation for the straight line through P_1 and P_2. Use this vector equation to find parametric equations for the line through (a_1, b_1) and (a_2, b_2).

12. Show that the equations

$$x = a + k \cos \theta$$
$$y = b + k \sin \theta$$

form parametric equations for a circle. What is the center and radius of this circle?

In problems 13 through 17 a curve is described by some geometrical condition

[1] The reader should try his hand at solving the pair of equations (23) for y in terms of x.

on a moving point P. Obtain a vector equation for the position vector $\mathbf{R}$ of the point P. If possible find a Cartesian equation for the curve.

13. From the origin a line OQ is drawn to an arbitrary point Q on a fixed vertical line l, b units to the right of O (see Fig. 16). A line segment QP is then drawn parallel to the x-axis, and to the right of l and such that $|\mathbf{QP}| = |\mathbf{OQ}|^2$. Use the parametric equations to show that the point P describes a parabola.

14. If in Problem 13, $|\mathbf{QP}| = 4|\mathbf{OQ}|$, prove that the point P describes one branch of a hyperbola.

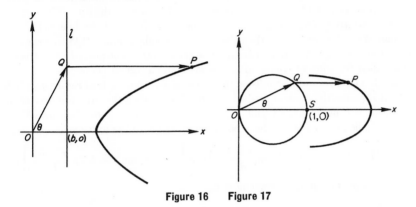

Figure 16   Figure 17

15. We modify the construction of problem 13 by replacing the line l by a circle C. As shown in Fig. 17, C is a circle passing through the origin, with diameter OS of length 1 lying on the positive x-axis. An arbitrary line through the origin meets C again at Q, and the horizontal line segment QP is drawn to the right

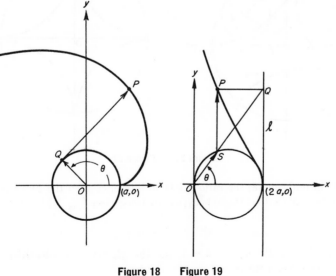

Figure 18   Figure 19

with length $|\mathbf{QP}| = |\mathbf{OQ}|^2$. Use the parametric equations to prove that the moving point P describes an ellipse.   *Hint:* From the right triangle OQS we find $|OQ| = \cos\theta$.

★16.   The *involute* of a circle is the curve described by the end point P of a thread as the thread is unwound from a fixed spool.   For simplicity suppose that the radius of the spool is a, and that when the spool is placed with its center at the origin, the point P starts at $(a, 0)$, (see Fig. 18).   *Hint:* The length of $\mathbf{QP}$ is the amount of thread unwound, namely $a\theta$.

★17.   As shown in Fig. 19, a circle of diameter $2a$ is placed tangent to the y-axis at the origin and at $(2a, 0)$ a line l parallel to the y-axis is drawn.   Through the origin an arbitrary line is drawn meeting the circle at S and the line at Q.   The segment SQ is then made into the hypotenuse of a right triangle PQS by drawing a vertical line through S, and a horizontal line through Q.   The point P then traces a curve called the *witch of Agnesi* after Maria Gaetana Agnesi (1718–99).

★18.   If a circle of radius b rolls on the inside of a second circle of radius a $(a > b)$ without slipping, the curve described by a fixed point P on the circumference of the first circle is called a *hypocycloid*.   Show that if the fixed point P is initially at $(a, 0)$ as indicated in Fig. 20 then the vector equation of the hypocycloid is

$$\mathbf{R} = \left[(a - b) \cos\theta + b \cos\frac{a - b}{b}\theta \right] \mathbf{i} + \left[(a - b) \sin\theta - b \sin\frac{a - b}{b}\theta \right] \mathbf{j}.$$

Hint: If there is no slipping then $a\theta = b\varphi$.

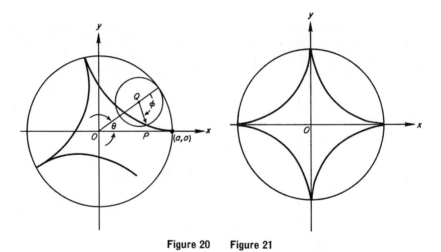

Figure 20   Figure 21

★19.   If in problem 18, the ratio a/b is an integer n, then the hypocycloid will have n cusps.   Show that the hypocycloid of 4 cusps (see Fig. 21) has the Cartesian equation

$$x^{2/3} + y^{2/3} = a^{2/3}.$$

Hint: Use $a - b = 3b$, $(a - b)/b = 3$, and the trigonometric identities $\cos 3\theta = 4\cos^3\theta - 3\cos\theta$ and $\sin 3\theta = 3\sin\theta - 4\sin^3\theta$.

★20. Show that the hypocycloid of 2 cusps obtained from problem 18 when $a = 2b$, is just the straight line segment between $(-a, 0)$ and $(a, 0)$.

21. Sketch the curve $\mathbf{R} = e^t \cos t\mathbf{i} + e^t \sin t\mathbf{j}$.

22. Show that the area bounded by the x-axis and one arch of the cycloid (see Fig. 15) is three times the area of the rolling circle.   *Hint:*

$$A = \int_{x=0}^{x=2\pi a} y \, dx = \int_{\varphi=0}^{\varphi=2\pi} y(\varphi) \frac{dx}{d\varphi} \, d\varphi.$$

23. Use parametric equations $x = a \cos t$, $y = a \sin t$ to compute the area of a circle.

24. Use parametric equations $x = a \cos t$, $y = b \sin t$ to prove that the area enclosed by this ellipse is πab.

★25. Show that the area enclosed by the hypocycloid of 4 cusps (see problem 19) is $3\pi a^2/8$.

★26. If a circle of radius b rolls on the outside of a fixed circle of radius a without slipping, the curve described by a fixed point P on the circumference of the rolling circle is called an *epicycloid*.   If the fixed circle has its center at the origin and if P is initially at $(a, 0)$ show that

$$x = (a + b) \cos \theta - b\cos \frac{a + b}{b} \theta, \qquad y = (a + b) \sin \theta - b\sin \frac{a + b}{b} \theta,$$

are parametric equations for the epicycloid.   Observe that these equations can be obtained from the equations for the hypocycloid (problem 18) by replacing b by $-b$.

4.   Differentiation of vectors.   If $\mathbf{R} = \mathbf{R}(t)$ is a vector function of a scalar t, it should be possible to differentiate this vector function with respect to t.   Suppose that the vector function is given by means of its components $f(t)$ and $g(t)$

$$\mathbf{R}(t) = f(t)\mathbf{i} + g(t)\mathbf{j}. \tag{24}$$

It would be very nice if we could differentiate the vector function by just differentiating its scalar components, thus

$$\frac{d\mathbf{R}(t)}{dt} = \frac{df(t)}{dt}\mathbf{i} + \frac{dg(t)}{dt}\mathbf{j}. \tag{25}$$

For example if

$$\mathbf{R} = t \sin t\mathbf{i} + (t^3 - 3t + e^t)\mathbf{j}$$

then we should like to know that

$$\frac{d\mathbf{R}}{dt} = (t \cos t + \sin t)\mathbf{i} + (3t^2 - 3 + e^t)\mathbf{j}.$$

In order to prove that this is indeed the case, we must first agree on the definition of the derivative of a vector function.   This definition is completely analogous to the definition of the derivative of a scalar function.

DEFINITION 7.   *The derivative of a vector function* $\mathbf{R}(t)$ *is*

$$\lim_{h \to 0} \frac{\mathbf{R}(t + h) - \mathbf{R}(t)}{h} = \frac{d\mathbf{R}}{dt}. \tag{26}$$

Notice that vector subtraction has already been defined and that division by the scalar h is the same as multiplication by the scalar $1/h$. In order for equation (26) to be meaningful we must understand the phrase "the limit of a vector function $\mathbf{V}(h)$ as h approaches zero." If $\mathbf{V}(h)$ is any vector function depending on a scalar h and if $\mathbf{V}_0$ is a constant vector, then we say that $\mathbf{V}(h)$ tends to $\mathbf{V}_0$ as h approaches zero, and we write

$$\lim_{h \to 0} \mathbf{V}(h) = \mathbf{V}_0$$

if the difference of the two vectors, $\mathbf{V}(h) - \mathbf{V}_0$, is getting closer to the zero vector. In terms of scalars this means that the length of this difference, $|\mathbf{V}(h) - \mathbf{V}_0| \to 0$.

As one might expect, the notation $\mathbf{R}'(t)$ is also frequently used to denote the derivative. Since $\mathbf{R}(t + h) - \mathbf{R}(t)$ is just the change $\Delta\mathbf{R}$ in the vector function $\mathbf{R}(t)$ when the independent variable changes by an amount $\Delta t = h$, equation (26) can be written in the equivalent form

$$\frac{d\mathbf{R}}{dt} = \lim_{\Delta t \to 0} \frac{\Delta\mathbf{R}}{\Delta t}. \tag{27}$$

THEOREM 10.   *If the vector function is given by equation (24) then its derivative is given by equation (25).*

PROOF.   By definition

$$\Delta\mathbf{R} = \mathbf{R}(t + h) - \mathbf{R}(t) = [f(t + h)\mathbf{i} + g(t + h)\mathbf{j}] - [f(t)\mathbf{i} + g(t)\mathbf{j}].$$

By Definition 6 and Theorems 6 and 7 we can rearrange the right hand side obtaining

$$\mathbf{R}(t + h) - \mathbf{R}(t) = [f(t + h) - f(t)]\mathbf{i} + [g(t + h) - g(t)]\mathbf{j}.$$

Dividing both sides by h, and again using Theorem 7, gives

$$\frac{\mathbf{R}(t + h) - \mathbf{R}(t)}{h} = \frac{f(t + h) - f(t)}{h}\mathbf{i} + \frac{g(t + h) - g(t)}{h}\mathbf{j}. \tag{28}$$

Now let h approach zero in (28).   This gives

$$\frac{d\mathbf{R}}{dt} = \frac{df}{dt}\mathbf{i} + \frac{dg}{dt}\mathbf{j}. \qquad \text{Q.E.D.}$$

THEOREM 11.   *Let* $\mathbf{R}(t)$ *be the position vector to a point P on a curve C. If* $\mathbf{R}'(t) \neq \mathbf{0}$ *then the derivative* $\mathbf{R}'(t)$ *is a vector tangent* to the curve C, and pointing in the direction of motion of P along the curve C as t increases.

PROOF.   As shown in Fig. 22, the difference vector $\Delta \mathbf{R} = \mathbf{R}(t+\Delta t) - \mathbf{R}(t)$ can be regarded as a vector from the fixed point P on the curve C, to a second point Q on the curve C.   Then

$$\frac{\Delta \mathbf{R}}{\Delta t}$$

is a vector pointing in the same direction if $\Delta t > 0$.   In fact if $\Delta t < 1$, then this vector will be longer than $\Delta \mathbf{R}$, as indicated in the figure.   Now let $\Delta t \to 0$.   The point Q slides along the curve toward the limiting position P, and at the same time, the limiting position of the chord $\Delta \mathbf{R}$ is just the position of a tangent vector, pointing in the direction along C specified by increasing t.   Figure 22 shows several intermediate vectors in this limit process.   Since

$$\lim_{\Delta t \to 0} \frac{\Delta \mathbf{R}}{\Delta t} = \frac{d\mathbf{R}}{dt} = \mathbf{R}'(t)$$

it follows that $\mathbf{R}'(t)$ is a vector with the properties described in the theorem.

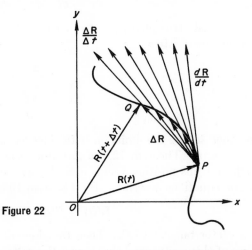

Figure 22

The drawing in Fig. 22 and the proof have been given in the case that Δt is positive.   We leave it to the student to make a suitable drawing and consider the case that Δt is negative.

THEOREM 12.   *Let* $x = f(t)$ *and* $y = g(t)$ *be parametric equa-*

tions for a curve C. *Then* $\dfrac{dy}{dx}$, *the slope of the tangent line to the*

curve C, is given by the formula

$$\frac{dy}{dx} = \frac{g'(t)}{f'(t)} \tag{29}$$

whenever $f'(t) \neq 0$.

Since $x = f(t)$ and $y = g(t)$, this formula is frequently written in the form

$$\frac{dy}{dx} = \frac{\dfrac{dy}{dt}}{\dfrac{dx}{dt}}. \tag{30}$$

In this form, the equation is easy to memorize, for if we regard the right side of (30) as the ratio of a pair of fractions, we can invert the denominator, and multiply. The formal cancellation of dt thus leads from (30) to

$$\frac{dy}{dx} = \frac{dy}{dt} \cdot \frac{dt}{dx} = \frac{dy}{dx}$$

an obviously true identity. In fact this theorem is frequently proved by writing the identity

$$\frac{\Delta y}{\Delta x} = \frac{\dfrac{\Delta y}{\Delta t}}{\dfrac{\Delta x}{\Delta t}}$$

and then taking the limits on both sides as $\Delta t \rightarrow 0$.

To prove Theorem 12, we introduce the position vector $\mathbf{R} = f(t)\mathbf{i} + g(t)\mathbf{j}$, and this position vector describes the same curve C, that the parametric equations describe. By Theorem 10

$$\mathbf{R}'(t) = f'(t)\mathbf{i} + g'(t)\mathbf{j}$$

is a vector tangent to C. Then the slope of the tangent line is just the slope of this vector, and this is just the ratio $g'(t)/f'(t)$ of its y-component to its x-component. On the other hand this slope is also dy/dx. This proves (29) and simultaneously (30). If $f'(t) = 0$ and $g'(t) \neq 0$ then the tangent vector is vertical. We may symbolize this situation by writing $dy/dx = \pm \infty$.

THEOREM 13. *Let s be arc length along the curve C, and suppose the direction for measuring arc length is so chosen that the* *arc length s, and the parameter t increase together. If **R**(t) is the position vector to the curve, then*

$$|\mathbf{R}'(t)| = \frac{ds}{dt}. \tag{31}$$

This equation can be written in a variety of equivalent forms. Using (25) we have

$$\frac{ds}{dt} = \sqrt{\left(\frac{df}{dt}\right)^2 + \left(\frac{dg}{dt}\right)^2} = \sqrt{\left(\frac{dx}{dt}\right)^2 + \left(\frac{dy}{dt}\right)^2}. \tag{32}$$

PROOF. Returning to the proof of Theorem 11 and the associated Fig. 22, we can write

$$\frac{\Delta \mathbf{R}}{\Delta t} = \frac{\Delta \mathbf{R}}{\Delta s} \frac{\Delta s}{\Delta t} \tag{33}$$

merely by inserting the term Δs in two places where it will obviously cancel. Now let Δs denote the length of arc between the two points P and Q, the end points of the vector $\Delta \mathbf{R}$ (Fig. 22). Thus Δs is indeed the change in the arc length as the parameter t changes by an amount Δt. Taking the lengths of the vectors in (33) we have

$$\left|\frac{\Delta \mathbf{R}}{\Delta t}\right| = \left|\frac{\Delta \mathbf{R}}{\Delta s}\right| \frac{\Delta s}{\Delta t} \tag{34}$$

where we have dropped the absolute value signs from the last term, because s and t increase together so the ratio $\Delta s / \Delta t$ is positive. Taking limits as $\Delta t \to 0$ in (34) we have

$$|\mathbf{R}'(t)| = \left|\frac{d\mathbf{R}}{dt}\right| = \left|\frac{d\mathbf{R}}{ds}\right| \frac{ds}{dt}. \tag{35}$$

But $\left|\dfrac{d\mathbf{R}}{ds}\right| = 1$, because it is the limit of the ratio:

chord length, $|\Delta \mathbf{R}|$ /length of the subtended arc, Δs

and by definition of arc length, this ratio tends to 1 as the chord length tends to 0. But then equation (35) gives (31). Q.E.D.

If t is regarded as time, then $\mathbf{R}'(t)$ has a nice interpretation as the velocity of a moving particle. For this we need

DEFINITION 8. *If a particle is moving on a curve C, and s denotes arc length along that curve, measured from some fixed point on the curve C with s increasing in the direction of motion of the*

*particle, then the speed of the particle is defined to be the instan-
taneous rate of change of arc length with respect to time, i.e.,*

$$\text{speed} = \frac{ds}{dt}.$$

*If the speed is not zero, the velocity of the particle is defined to be a
vector **V** that is tangent to the curve, points in the direction of motion
of the particle, and has length equal to the speed. If the speed is
zero, then the velocity is the zero vector.*

THEOREM 14. *If **R**(t) is the position vector of a moving particle, and t is time, then the derivative **R**′(t) is the velocity of the
particle and* $|\mathbf{R}'(t)|$ *is its speed.*

PROOF. We have already proved in Theorem 11 that if $\mathbf{R}'(t) \neq \mathbf{0}$, then
it is tangent to the curve and points in the proper direction. Further from
Theorem 13, $|\mathbf{R}'(t)|$ is the speed of the particle. Hence $\mathbf{R}'(t)$ has all the
required properties of the velocity vector given in definition 8. Whence
$\mathbf{R}'(t) = \mathbf{V}$. In case $\mathbf{R}'(t) = \mathbf{0}$ then by equation (31) the speed is also
zero, and hence by definition 8 we have $\mathbf{V} = \mathbf{0}$. Therefore in both cases
$\mathbf{R}'(t) = \mathbf{V}$. The speed can be zero when the moving particle stops
momentarily and then resumes its motion. The curve may well have a
tangent at such a point, but of course the zero vector does not give the
direction of the tangent to the curve.

DEFINITION 9. *The acceleration vector **A**(t) of a moving particle is defined to be the derivative of the velocity vector, i.e.,*

$$\mathbf{A}(t) = \frac{d}{dt}\mathbf{V}(t) = \frac{d^2}{dt^2}\mathbf{R}(t).$$

EXAMPLE 1. The vector

$$\mathbf{R} = \cos t^2\, \mathbf{i} + \sin t^2\, \mathbf{j}$$

is the position vector of a moving particle, where t denotes the time. Discuss
the motion of the particle.

SOLUTION. The parametric equations are

$$x = \cos t^2, \qquad y = \sin t^2,$$

Since

$$x^2 + y^2 = (\cos t^2)^2 + (\sin t^2)^2 = 1$$

the particle must move on a circle of radius 1 and center at the origin. For
the velocity vector we have

$$\mathbf{V}(t) = \mathbf{R}'(t) = -2t \sin t^2\, \mathbf{i} + 2t \cos t^2\, \mathbf{j}.$$

Hence the speed is given by

$$\frac{ds}{dt} = |\mathbf{V}(t)| = \sqrt{4t^2(\sin t^2)^2 + 4t^2(\cos t^2)^2}$$

$$= 2|t| \sqrt{\sin^2 t^2 + \cos^2 t^2} = 2|t|.$$

Thus at $t = 0$ the speed is 0 and as time goes on the speed steadily increases. The slope of the velocity vector is

$$m_V = \frac{dy}{dx} = \frac{\dfrac{dg}{dt}}{\dfrac{df}{dt}} = \frac{2t \cos t^2}{-2t \sin t^2} = -\frac{\cos t^2}{\sin t^2}$$

whenever the denominator is not zero. We know from Theorem 11, that this vector is tangent to the circle and hence (because the center of the circle is at the origin) it should be perpendicular to the position vector. The slope of the position vector $\mathbf{R}$ is given by

$$m_R = \frac{g(t)}{f(t)} = \frac{\sin t^2}{\cos t^2}.$$

Now

$$m_V m_R = -\frac{\cos t^2}{\sin t^2} \frac{\sin t^2}{\cos t^2} = -1$$

so the vectors $\mathbf{R}$ and $\mathbf{V}$ are indeed perpendicular. Finally the acceleration vector is

$$\mathbf{A}(t) = \frac{d}{dt} \mathbf{V}(t) = (-2 \sin t^2 - 4t^2 \cos t^2)\mathbf{i} + (2 \cos t^2 - 4t^2 \sin t^2)\mathbf{j}.$$

If $t \neq 0$ this acceleration vector can be written in the form

$$\mathbf{A}(t) = \frac{1}{t}(-2t \sin t^2 \mathbf{i} + 2t \cos t^2 \mathbf{j}) - 4t^2(\cos t^2 \mathbf{i} + \sin t^2 \mathbf{j})$$

$$= \frac{1}{t} \mathbf{V}(t) - 4t^2 \mathbf{R}(t).$$

This shows that in this particular motion the acceleration vector has two vector components, one in the direction of the velocity vector, and a second in the direction of a radial line, but pointing inward toward the center.

EXAMPLE 2. Suppose that in describing the involute of Problem 16, Exercise 3, the thread is unwound in such a way that $d\theta/dt = c$, a constant. Find the velocity and acceleration vectors for the end point P of the thread. Show that the velocity vector is never perpendicular to the position vector for $\theta > 0$. When is the tangent to the involute horizontal? When is it vertical?

SOLUTION. The vector equation for the involute (Problem 16 Exercise 3) is

$$\mathbf{R} = (\cos \theta + \theta \sin \theta)\mathbf{i} + (\sin \theta - \theta \cos \theta)\mathbf{j}.$$

Whence

$$\frac{d\mathbf{R}}{dt} = (-\sin\theta + \sin\theta + \theta\cos\theta)\frac{d\theta}{dt}\mathbf{i} + (\cos\theta - \cos\theta + \theta\sin\theta)\frac{d\theta}{dt}\mathbf{j}$$

$$\mathbf{V}(t) = \frac{d\mathbf{R}}{dt} = c(\theta\cos\theta\mathbf{i} + \theta\sin\theta\mathbf{j}).$$

Differentiating again gives the acceleration vector

$$\mathbf{A}(t) = \frac{d^2\mathbf{R}}{dt^2} = c^2\left[(\cos\theta - \theta\sin\theta)\mathbf{i} + (\sin\theta + \theta\cos\theta)\mathbf{j}\right].$$

Now $\mathbf{V}(t) = c\theta(\cos\theta\mathbf{i} + \sin\theta\mathbf{j}) = c\theta\,\mathbf{OQ}$ and therefore $\mathbf{V}(t)$ is parallel to $\mathbf{OQ}$ for $\theta \neq 0$ (see Fig. 18). Suppose that for some location of P, the vector $\mathbf{R}$ is perpendicular to $\mathbf{V}$. This would mean that OP is perpendicular to OQ. But by the construction of the involute curve QP is also perpendicular to OQ. This is impossible. Hence for $\theta > 0$, $\mathbf{R}$ and $\mathbf{V}$ are never perpendicular.

If the y-component of $\mathbf{V}$ is zero while the x-component does not vanish, then the tangent is horizontal. This implies that $\theta\sin\theta = 0$ and $\theta \neq 0$. Hence $\sin\theta = 0$, and the tangent is horizontal when $\theta = \pi,\ 2\pi,\ 3\pi,\ \cdots$. If the x-component of $\mathbf{V}$ is zero while the y-component does not vanish, then the tangent is vertical. This gives $\theta\cos\theta = 0$, $\theta \neq 0$, and hence $\cos\theta = 0$. Therefore the tangent line to the involute is vertical when $\theta = \pi/2,\ 3\pi/2,\ 5\pi/2,\ \cdots$.

In case both of the components of $\mathbf{V} = f'(t)\mathbf{i} + g'(t)\mathbf{j}$ are simultaneously zero at $t = t_0$, the determination of the direction of the tangent vector to the curve is a little more complicated. A good working rule is to consider the slope given by equation (29) for t near to t_0. This situation arises in Problems 7, 8, and 12 in the following exercise. It also arises in this example since both components of $\mathbf{V}$ are zero at $\theta = 0$. Following the rule given above we see that the involute has a horizontal tangent at $\theta = 0$ (see Fig. 18).

EXERCISE 4

In problems 1 through 4 differentiate the given vector function with respect to the independent variable.

1. $\mathbf{R} = \tan t\mathbf{i} + \sec t\mathbf{j}$.   2. $\mathbf{R} = u\cos u\mathbf{i} + u\ln u\mathbf{j}$.
3. $\mathbf{R} = v^3 e^{2v}\mathbf{i} + v^2 e^{-3v}\mathbf{j}$.   4. $\mathbf{R} = \sin^{-1} w\mathbf{i} + \tan^{-1} w\mathbf{j}$.

In problems 5 through 10 the position vector of a moving particle is given for time t. In each case (a) compute the velocity, acceleration, and speed of the moving particle, (b) find the location of the particle when it is stationary (velocity zero), and (c) find the coordinates of those points on the path for which the tangent line is horizontal or vertical.

5. $\mathbf{R} = 5\cos^2 t\mathbf{i} + 5\sin^2 t\mathbf{j}$ (see problem 3 of Exercise 3).
6. $\mathbf{R} = 3\cos t\mathbf{i} + 5\sin t\mathbf{j}$ (see problem 4 of Exercise 3).
7. $\mathbf{R} = \sin t\mathbf{i} + \cos 2t\mathbf{j}$ (see problem 5 of Exercise 3).

8. $R = t^3 i + t^2 j$ (see prob. 7 of Exer. 3).
9. $R = (t^3 - 3t)i + tj$ (see prob. 8 of Exer. 3).
10. $R = (t^3 - 3t)i + (4 - t^2)j$ (see prob. 10 of Exer. 3).
*11. For the cycloid $R = a(\varphi - \sin \varphi)i + a(1 - \cos \varphi)j$ (Example 2, Fig. 15, section 3), find an expression for the speed in terms of $d\varphi/dt$. Assuming $d\varphi/dt$ is a constant, find an expression for the maximum speed. Show that if a car is travelling 60 mi/hr, then the speed of a particle on the tire can be as high as 120 mi/hr.
**12. Locate all horizontal and vertical tangents of the cycloid of problem 11.

13. Prove that the vector $i + \dfrac{dy}{dx} j$ is a vector tangent to the curve $y = f(x)$.

*14. Limit of a vector function. By definition $\lim\limits_{h \to 0} V(h) = V_0$ if

$$\lim_{h \to 0} |V(h) - V_0| = 0.$$

Prove that if $\lim\limits_{h \to 0} V(h) = V_0$ then for any constant c, $\lim\limits_{h \to 0} cV(h) = cV_0$.
*15. Let $V(h) = a(h)i + b(h)j$ and let $V_0 = a_0 i + b_0 j$. Prove that if $\lim\limits_{h \to 0} V(h) = V_0$, then $\lim\limits_{h \to 0} a(h) = a_0$ and $\lim\limits_{h \to 0} b(h) = b_0$.
*16. State and prove the converse of the theorem in problem 15.
**17. In the proof of Theorem 10, we omitted the detailed argument in going from equation (28) to equation (25). Fill the gap by using the theorem of problem 16.

5.   **The motion of a projectile.** It is an experimental fact that bodies falling freely near the earth's surface have a downward acceleration that is constant. Falling freely means that no other forces are acting on the body except the attractive force exerted by the earth. The greatest single disturbing force is the force due to air resistance. This force can be neglected for heavy bodies travelling at low speeds, but otherwise it exerts an influence that is noticeable and rather complicated. For simplicity we will neglect the air resistance throughout the rest of this book.

Our vector calculus can now be used to derive, in a very simple way, the equations for the motion of a projectile. We assume that the projectile is moving in a vertical plane, and we take the x, y-axes in their usual position (Fig. 23). Then the vector expression of the physical law, that the acceleration is constant, is

$$A = \frac{dV}{dt} = -gj \tag{36}$$

where g is the constant value of the acceleration. Direct measurements give $g = 32$ ft/sec^2 (approximately) and this constant is known as the gravitational constant. Integrating the vector equation (36) with respect to t, we have

$$V = -gtj + C_1$$

where $\mathbf{C}_1$ is some suitable vector constant of integration. But at $t = 0$, $\mathbf{V} = \mathbf{V}_0$ the initial vector velocity, hence $\mathbf{C}_1 = \mathbf{V}_0$. Therefore

$$\mathbf{V} = \frac{d\mathbf{R}}{dt} = -gt\mathbf{j} + \mathbf{V}_0,$$

and integrating this equation with respect to t gives the position vector for the projectile,

$$\mathbf{R} = -\frac{gt^2}{2}\mathbf{j} + \mathbf{V}_0 t + \mathbf{C}_2$$

where again $\mathbf{C}_2$ is a vector constant of integration. Putting $t = 0$, we find $\mathbf{C}_2 = \mathbf{R}_0$, the position vector giving the initial position of the projectile. Hence

$$\mathbf{R} = -\frac{gt^2}{2}\mathbf{j} + \mathbf{V}_0 t + \mathbf{R}_0, \qquad (37)$$

and this is the equation that gives the motion of a body falling freely under gravity in terms of its initial position $\mathbf{R}_0$ and its initial velocity $\mathbf{V}_0$.

Of course some simplification can be achieved if we select the origin of the coordinate system to be at the starting point of the projectile. Then $\mathbf{R}_0 = \mathbf{0}$. Further let us write the initial velocity in terms of its components

$$\mathbf{V}_0 = V_1\mathbf{i} + V_2\mathbf{j}$$

and set

$$\mathbf{R} = x\mathbf{i} + y\mathbf{j}.$$

With these conventions, equation (37) can be broken up into its components giving

$$\begin{aligned} x &= V_1 t \\ y &= -\frac{gt^2}{2} + V_2 t \end{aligned} \qquad (38)$$

as the parametric equations for the motion of a projectile. If α is the angle of $\mathbf{V}_0$ then $V_1 = V_0 \cos \alpha$ and $V_2 = V_0 \sin \alpha$.

EXAMPLE 1. The angle of elevation of a gun is 30°. If the muzzle speed is 1600 ft/sec what is the range? How long after firing does the projectile land?

SOLUTION. We are assuming that the gun, and the point of impact of the projectile are in the same horizontal plane (see Fig. 23). The range of the gun means the distance between these two points. We set the coordinate axes

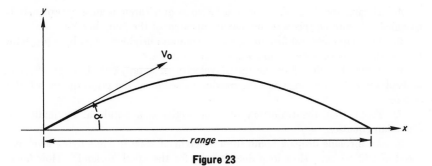

Figure 23

so that the origin is at the muzzle of the gun. Then $R_0 = 0$, and equations (38) are applicable. The projectile hits the earth when $y = 0$. Under this condition equation (38) gives

$$0 = -\frac{g}{2}t^2 + V_2 t = t\left(-\frac{g}{2}t + V_2\right)$$

or

$$t = \frac{2V_2}{g} = \frac{2V_0 \sin \alpha}{32} \tag{39}$$

as the time of flight. Using this in equation (38) we find for x

$$x = V_1 t = V_0 \cos \alpha t = \frac{2V_0^2 \sin \alpha \cos \alpha}{32}$$

$$x = \frac{V_0^2}{32} \sin 2\alpha.$$

This is a general expression for the range of a projectile fired with initial velocity V_0 and angle of elevation α. Using the given data we find that the range is

$$x = \frac{(1600)^2}{32} \sin 60° \approx 69{,}280 \text{ ft} \approx 13.1 \text{ mi.}$$

The time of flight is given by equation (39),

$$t = \frac{V_0 \sin \alpha}{16} = \frac{1600}{16} \frac{1}{2} = 50 \text{ secs.}$$

EXERCISE 5

1. What is the range of a gun if $V_0 = 800$ ft/sec and the angle of elevation is 15°?

2. What is the maximum height reached by a projectile, fired under the conditions of problem 1?

3. Prove that for a given fixed V_0 the maximum range for the gun is obtained by firing the gun at a 45° angle of elevation. Find a formula for this maximum range.

4. During the first World War a German gun threw a shell approximately 64 miles. Assuming this was the maximum range of the gun, find V_0.

5. Develop a general formula for the maximum height reached by a projectile fired with initial velocity V_0 and angle of elevation α.

6. Show that doubling the initial velocity of a projectile has the effect of multiplying both the range and the maximum height of the projectile by a factor of four.

7. Prove that the trajectory of a projectile is a parabola, by finding its Cartesian equation.

8. An airplane drops a bomb from a height of 2500 ft while flying level at a speed of 240 mi/hr. How long does it take for the bomb to land? How far in front of his position, at the time of release, does it land?

9. A boy finds that no matter how hard he tries, he can throw a ball 200 ft, but not further. Find the maximum speed in mi/hr that he can throw a ball.

10. A man standing 30 ft from a tall building throws a ball with an initial velocity of 80 ft/sec. If the angle of elevation of the throw is 60°, how far up the building does the ball hit? Neglect the height of the man, and assume he throws at the building. In what direction is the ball going when it hits the building?

6.   Curvature. Our objective in this section is to obtain a means of measuring how fast a curve is turning. This amounts to finding the rate at which the tangent line is rotating as the point P of tangency travels along the curve. Let φ be the angle that the tangent line at P makes with the x-axis (see Fig. 24). It would seem at first glance that a satisfactory measure of the "curvature" of the curve should be

$$\frac{d\varphi}{dx} \qquad (40)$$

because this gives a rate of turning of the tangent line.

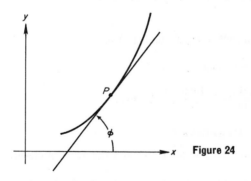

Figure 24

To see that such a definition is not satisfactory, let us consider the "curvature" (40) on the right branch of the parabola $y = x^2$ at the point $(1, 1)$ as indicated in Fig. 25. If we rotate this figure clockwise through an angle $\pi/2$ we obtain the piece of a parabola shown in Fig. 26. Obviously the equation for this curve is $y = -\sqrt{x}$. Now the "curvature" at P should be the same for both curves, because the *rate of turning* of the tangent line should not be altered by this rotation. To check this assertion we compute the "curvature" for both curves at the corresponding point P, using (40).

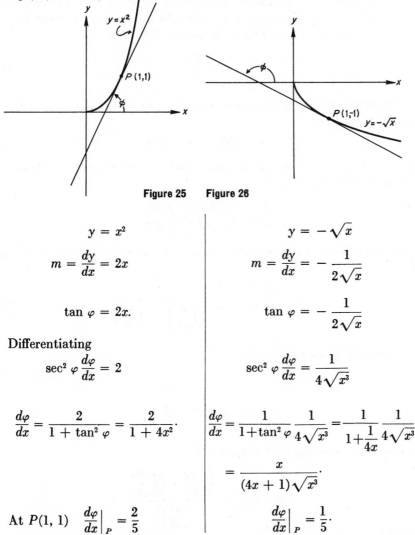

Figure 25   Figure 26

$$y = x^2 \qquad\qquad y = -\sqrt{x}$$

$$m = \frac{dy}{dx} = 2x \qquad\qquad m = \frac{dy}{dx} = -\frac{1}{2\sqrt{x}}$$

$$\tan \varphi = 2x. \qquad\qquad \tan \varphi = -\frac{1}{2\sqrt{x}}$$

Differentiating

$$\sec^2 \varphi \frac{d\varphi}{dx} = 2 \qquad\qquad \sec^2 \varphi \frac{d\varphi}{dx} = \frac{1}{4\sqrt{x^3}}$$

$$\frac{d\varphi}{dx} = \frac{2}{1 + \tan^2 \varphi} = \frac{2}{1 + 4x^2}. \qquad \frac{d\varphi}{dx} = \frac{1}{1+\tan^2 \varphi}\frac{1}{4\sqrt{x^3}} = \frac{1}{1+\frac{1}{4x}}\frac{1}{4\sqrt{x^3}}$$

$$= \frac{x}{(4x + 1)\sqrt{x^3}}.$$

At $P(1, 1)$ $\left.\dfrac{d\varphi}{dx}\right|_P = \dfrac{2}{5}$ $\qquad\qquad \left.\dfrac{d\varphi}{dx}\right|_P = \dfrac{1}{5}.$

Now these two results are not equal. A little thought will show that the "curvature" of the parabola at P did not change during the rotation. What changed was the role that x plays in describing the curve. We do not want to differentiate φ with respect to x. What is wanted is some independent variable whose role is not altered as the curve is moved around.   One such convenient variable is the arc length s, and this is the one that we use.

> DEFINITION 10.   *Let s denote the arc length on a curve, and suppose that a definite direction on the curve has been selected for the direction of increasing s.   Then the curvature of the curve, denoted by the Greek letter κ (kappa), is defined by*

$$\kappa = \frac{d\varphi}{ds}. \tag{41}$$

To obtain a formula for computing κ we suppose that the curve is given parametrically by

$$x = f(t), \qquad y = g(t). \tag{15}$$

For convenience we will assume that s and t increase together.   Then by Theorem 13, equation (32)

$$\frac{ds}{dt} = \sqrt{\left(\frac{dx}{dt}\right)^2 + \left(\frac{dy}{dt}\right)^2}.$$

Now φ is a function of t and t is a function of s so we may write (41) in the form

$$\kappa = \frac{d\varphi}{dt}\frac{dt}{ds} = \frac{d\varphi}{dt} \frac{1}{\sqrt{\left(\frac{dx}{dt}\right)^2 + \left(\frac{dy}{dt}\right)^2}}. \tag{42}$$

To compute $\dfrac{d\varphi}{dt}$ we observe that

$$\tan \varphi = m = \frac{\dfrac{dy}{dt}}{\dfrac{dx}{dt}}$$

and on differentiating with respect to t

$$\sec^2 \varphi \frac{d\varphi}{dt} = \frac{\dfrac{dx}{dt}\dfrac{d^2y}{dt^2} - \dfrac{dy}{dt}\dfrac{d^2x}{dt^2}}{\left(\dfrac{dx}{dt}\right)^2}.$$

But

$$\sec^2 \varphi = 1 + \tan^2 \varphi = 1 + \frac{\left(\dfrac{dy}{dt}\right)^2}{\left(\dfrac{dx}{dt}\right)^2},$$

hence

$$\frac{d\varphi}{dt} = \frac{\dfrac{dx}{dt}\dfrac{d^2y}{dt^2} - \dfrac{dy}{dt}\dfrac{d^2x}{dt^2}}{\left(\dfrac{dx}{dt}\right)^2 + \left(\dfrac{dy}{dt}\right)^2}. \tag{43}$$

Using (43) in (42) gives

THEOREM 15.   *If the curve C is defined parametrically and if the arc length increases with increasing parameter t, then the curvature is given by*

$$\kappa = \frac{\dfrac{dx}{dt}\dfrac{d^2y}{dt^2} - \dfrac{dy}{dt}\dfrac{d^2x}{dt^2}}{\left[\left(\dfrac{dx}{dt}\right)^2 + \left(\dfrac{dy}{dt}\right)^2\right]^{3/2}}. \tag{44}$$

EXAMPLE 1.   Compute the curvature of the parabola $y = x^2$ (a) in general (b) at (1, 1).

SOLUTION.   A convenient parameterization of this parabola is $x = t$ and $y = t^2$.   Then

$$\frac{dx}{dt} = 1 \qquad\qquad\qquad \frac{dy}{dt} = 2t$$

$$\frac{d^2x}{dt^2} = 0 \qquad\qquad\qquad \frac{d^2y}{dt^2} = 2,$$

$$\kappa = \frac{1 \times 2 - 2t \times 0}{[1 + 4t^2]^{3/2}} = \frac{2}{[1 + 4t^2]^{3/2}}.$$

At (1, 1) we must have $t = 1$, and then

$$\kappa = \frac{2}{\sqrt{125}} = \frac{2}{5\sqrt{5}}.$$

As one might expect, this is different from both of the answers obtained using $d\varphi/dx$ (page 341).

It can be proved that the formula (44) is invariant under a rotation of the curve, and also under a change of parameterization.   While these results are intuitively obvious, the actual computations are involved, and so we reserve this important point for the starred problems in the next exercise list.

Two special cases of formula (44) are worth noting. Frequently our curve is given by a formula $y = f(x)$. In this case a convenient parameterization is obtained by setting $x = t$, and $y = f(t)$. Then

$$\frac{dx}{dt} = 1 \qquad \frac{dy}{dt} = \frac{dy}{dx}$$

$$\frac{d^2x}{dt^2} = 0 \qquad \frac{d^2y}{dt^2} = \frac{d^2y}{dx^2}$$

and formula (44) yields the following

COROLLARY. *If $y = f(x)$ then the curvature is given by*

$$\kappa = \frac{\dfrac{d^2y}{dx^2}}{\left[1 + \left(\dfrac{dy}{dx}\right)^2\right]^{3/2}}. \tag{45}$$

If the curve is given by $x = g(y)$ a similar computation shows that

$$\kappa = \frac{-\dfrac{d^2x}{dy^2}}{\left[1 + \left(\dfrac{dx}{dy}\right)^2\right]^{3/2}}. \tag{46}$$

In each of these formulas the direction of increasing arc length is *assumed* to be the same as the direction of increasing parameter. Thus in (45) x and s are both increasing as a point P on the curve moves from left to right, and in (46) y and s are both increasing as a point P moves upward along the curve.

EXAMPLE 2. Show that for a circle the curvature is a constant, and in absolute value is the reciprocal of the radius of the circle.

SOLUTION. One is tempted to use $y = \sqrt{r^2 - x^2}$ and carry out the computations for the upper half of the circle. But it turns out that the computation is simpler if we use the parameterization $x = r \cos t$ and $y = r \sin t$. Then

$$x' = -r \sin t \qquad y' = r \cos t$$
$$x'' = -r \cos t \qquad y'' = -r \sin t$$

and from (44)

$$\kappa = \frac{r^2 \sin^2 t + r^2 \cos^2 t}{[r^2 \sin^2 t + r^2 \cos^2 t]^{3/2}} = \frac{1}{r}.$$

Suppose that we fasten our attention upon a fixed point P on a curve C, and try to draw through P a circle that most closely fits C. We would first require that the circle and the curve be tangent at P, and we might next ask that they have the same curvature. When we do this, the circle is uniquely determined, and we call this circle *the circle of curvature*, or *the osculating circle*, of the curve C at P. The radius of this circle is denoted by the Greek letter ρ (rho) and is called the *radius of curvature* of the curve C at P. From our example, we have $\rho = 1/\kappa$ for any circle and hence for any curve, $y = f(x)$,

$$\rho = \frac{1}{|\kappa|} = \frac{[1 + (y')^2]^{3/2}}{|y''|} \tag{47}$$

provided of course that the denominator y'' is not zero at P.

We did not really prove that this circle of curvature is the "closest" circle to the curve at P, nor could we do so, because we did not define what is meant by "closest" fitting circle. The definition of "closest" is complicated and the proof that the circle of curvature is "closest" is still more complicated. This topic is best reserved for the course in Advanced Calculus.

EXERCISE 6

In problems 1 through 8, find the curvature for the given curve.

1. $y = mx + b$.

2. $y = x^2 + 2x$.

3. $y = e^x$.

4. $x = \sqrt{y}$.

5. $y = \sin 3x$.

6. $x = \ln \cos y$.

7. $x = a(\varphi - \sin \varphi)$,
   $y = a(1 - \cos \varphi)$, $a > 0$.

8. $x = b(\cos \theta + \theta \sin \theta)$,
   $y = b(\sin \theta - \theta \cos \theta)$, $b > 0$.

9. Compute the curvature of $y = -\sqrt{x}$ at $(1, -1)$ and compare this result with the solution to example 1.

10. Show that the curvature of the upper half circle $y = \sqrt{r^2 - x^2}$ is $-1/r$. Notice that this minus sign seems to be inconsistent with the result in example 2 where it was proved that $\kappa = 1/r$. Explain this discrepancy.

11. At what point on the parabola $y = x^2/4$ is the radius of curvature a minimum?

12. Find the minimum value of the radius of curvature for the curve $y = \ln x$.

★13. Find the minimum value of the radius of curvature for the curve $y = x^4/4$.

14. Suppose that a circle C_1 and a curve C_2 are tangent at a point P, and that the equations which give these two curves both have the same second derivative at P. Prove that both curves have the same curvature at P, and hence C_1 is the circle of curvature of C_2 at P.

15. Prove the converse of problem 14, namely that the curve C_2 and its circle of curvature at a point P, both have the same second derivative at their common point of tangency.

16. Prove that at the vertices of an ellipse $x = a \cos t$, $y = b \sin t$ the two values for the curvature are a/b^2 and b/a^2. Notice that when $a = b$, the ellipse is a circle, and both of these formulas give $\kappa = 1/r$, as they should.

***17. Prove that the curvature is invariant under a rotation of the curve about the origin.   Outline of solution: Let $(x, y,)$ be the coordinates in the original position and let (X, Y) be the new coordinates.   Then (from Chapter 6, Exercise 7, problem 17)

$$X = x \cos \alpha - y \sin \alpha$$
$$Y = x \sin \alpha + y \cos \alpha.$$

If the curve C is given parametrically x, y, X, and Y are all functions of t.   Prove that

$$\frac{X'Y'' - Y'X''}{[(x')]^2 + (Y')^2]^{3/2}} = \frac{x'y'' - y'x''}{[(x')^2 + (y')^2]^{3/2}}.$$

The computation can be simplified by considering the numerators and denominators separately, because it turns out that these two pieces are each invariant under a rotation of the curve.

***18. Prove that the curvature is invariant under a change of parameterization. Outline of solution: Let $x = f(t)$, $y = g(t)$ be one parameterization. A new parameter T can be introduced by letting t be a function of T, $t = h(T)$. Prove first that

$$\frac{dx}{dT} = \frac{dx}{dt}\frac{dt}{dT}$$

$$\frac{d^2x}{dT^2} = \frac{d^2x}{dt^2}\left(\frac{dt}{dT}\right)^2 + \frac{dx}{dt}\frac{d^2t}{dT^2},$$

with similar equations for y.   Then use these to prove that

$$\frac{\dfrac{dx}{dT}\dfrac{d^2y}{dT^2} - \dfrac{dy}{dT}\dfrac{d^2x}{dT^2}}{\left[\left(\dfrac{dx}{dT}\right)^2 + \left(\dfrac{dy}{dT}\right)^2\right]^{3/2}} = \frac{\dfrac{dx}{dt}\dfrac{d^2y}{dt^2} - \dfrac{dy}{dt}\dfrac{d^2x}{dt^2}}{\left[\left(\dfrac{dx}{dt}\right)^2 + \left(\dfrac{dy}{dt}\right)^2\right]^{3/2}}.$$

7.   The unit tangent and normal vectors. A *unit vector* is a vector of length one.   We have already introduced two unit vectors **i** and **j** and these vectors have been very helpful.   We now associate with a plane curve two unit vectors **T** and **N** that will be quite useful in the study of the curve.   The vectors **i** and **j** not only have a constant unit length but also a constant direction.   By contrast the new vectors **T** and **N** will have a constant unit length but will have in general a variable direction.

Let C be a directed curve.   Then by definition, **T** is a unit vector tangent to the curve C and pointing in the positive direction along C. Thus if t is a parameter that gives the curve its direction, then the unit tangent vector **T** has the direction of $\mathbf{R}'(t)$, the derivative of the position vector, as long as $\mathbf{R}'(t) \neq \mathbf{0}$.   The vector **N**, is by definition a unit vector normal to the curve, i.e., **N** is perpendicular to **T**.   There are two possible directions for **N**, and we select that direction that is 90° in advance of **T**. In other words, a rotation of 90° of the vector **T** in the counterclockwise direction will bring **T** into coincidence with **N**.   This completes the definition of the unit vectors **T** and **N** for any point on a directed curve.   As

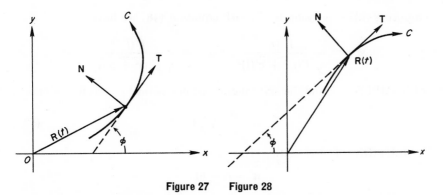

Figure 27   **Figure 28**

mentioned before, both vectors have unit length, but their direction is a variable that depends on the particular point P selected on the curve, and on the particular curve under consideration.   Let us do a little computation with these vectors.

If φ is the angle that gives the direction of **T** then (by Theorem 8)

$$\mathbf{T} = \cos \varphi \mathbf{i} + \sin \varphi \mathbf{j}. \tag{48}$$

Since **N** is 90° in advance of **T** we have

$$\mathbf{N} = \cos (\varphi + 90°)\mathbf{i} + \sin (\varphi + 90°)\mathbf{j}$$

and using the standard trigonometric identities

$$\mathbf{N} = -\sin \varphi \mathbf{i} + \cos \varphi \mathbf{j}. \tag{49}$$

Suppose now that the curve C is given by a position vector $\mathbf{R}(t) = f(t)\mathbf{i} + g(t)\mathbf{j}$, and for simplicity suppose that $\mathbf{R}'(t) \neq \mathbf{0}$.   Then by Theorem 11 **T** has the direction of

$$\mathbf{R}'(t) = f'(t)\mathbf{i} + g'(t)\mathbf{j}. \tag{50}$$

But this vector can be converted into a unit vector merely by dividing by its length $\sqrt{f'(t)^2 + g'(t)^2}$ and hence

$$\mathbf{T} = \frac{f'(t)\mathbf{i} + g'(t)\mathbf{j}}{\sqrt{f'(t)^2 + g'(t)^2}}. \tag{51}$$

Comparing this expression for $\mathbf{T}$ with equation (48) we have

$$\cos \varphi = \frac{f'(t)}{\sqrt{f'(t)^2 + g'(t)^2}}, \quad \sin \varphi = \frac{g'(t)}{\sqrt{f'(t)^2 + g'(t)^2}}.$$

‣ EXAMPLE 1.   Find the unit tangent and unit normal vectors for the curve

$$\mathbf{R} = \frac{t^2}{2}\mathbf{i} + \frac{t^3}{3}\mathbf{j}. \tag{52}$$

SOLUTION.   Differentiating gives

$$\mathbf{R}' = t\mathbf{i} + t^2\mathbf{j},$$

and $|\mathbf{R}'| = \sqrt{t^2 + t^4}$. In this example $\mathbf{R}' = \mathbf{0}$ when $t = 0$, and we may infer that the point $(0, 0)$ is some sort of singular point on the curve at which $\mathbf{T}$ and $\mathbf{N}$ are not defined. For convenience we restrict ourselves to $t > 0$. Then $|\mathbf{R}'| = t\sqrt{1 + t^2}$, and [by equation (51)] the unit tangent is

$$\mathbf{T} = \frac{t\mathbf{i} + t^2\mathbf{j}}{t\sqrt{1 + t^2}} = \frac{\mathbf{i} + t\mathbf{j}}{\sqrt{1 + t^2}}. \tag{53}$$

Although $\mathbf{T}$ is not initially defined at $(0, 0)$ equation (53) shows that the unit tangent vector approaches a definite limit $\mathbf{i}$ as $t \to 0$, and thus $\mathbf{i}$ can be regarded as the unit tangent at $(0, 0)$. Comparing (49) and (48), we see that $\mathbf{N}$ can be obtained from $\mathbf{T}$ by a switch in the components, and an alteration in sign. Performing this operation on (53) we have

$$\mathbf{N} = \frac{-t\mathbf{i} + \mathbf{j}}{\sqrt{1 + t^2}}.$$

8.   Arc length as a parameter.   In many theoretical discussions it is quite convenient to use the length of arc on the curve as parameter. In order to see that this is logically permissible, let us consider as given a fixed curve and a fixed point P_0 on the curve. We suppose further that s is measured from P_0, and that in one direction from P_0 we take s to be positive, and in the opposite direction s is negative. Thus s acts as a directed distance along the curve, and to each number s, there corresponds a unique point P on the curve. But then the coordinates (x, y) of that point P are uniquely determined by s, and this is what we mean when we say that x and y are functions of s. Under the conditions described we can say that s is a parameter, and write $\mathbf{R} = \mathbf{R}(s) = x(s)\mathbf{i} + y(s)\mathbf{j}$ where $x(s)$ and $y(s)$ are the functions of s that give the x and y components of the position vector of the curve.

Although the arc length s can always be introduced as a parameter for a curve, the actual computations are frequently quite messy, and sometimes impossible in terms of our elementary functions. It turns out that this computation is easy for the straight line and for the circle, but even for such an elementary curve as the ellipse, the integrals involved do not lie in $\mathfrak{F}$.

EXAMPLE 1. Find the parametric equations for the curve

$$\mathbf{R} = \frac{t^2}{2}\mathbf{i} + \frac{t^3}{3}\mathbf{j} \qquad t \geq 0 \tag{52}$$

using s, the arc length, as the parameter.

SOLUTION. For convenience we take $(0, 0)$ as the fixed point from which we measure arc length. By Theorem 13

$$\frac{ds}{dt} = |\mathbf{R}'(t)| = \sqrt{t^2 + t^4} = t\sqrt{1 + t^2}$$

and hence

$$s = \int_0^t t\sqrt{1 + t^2}\, dt = \frac{1}{2}\int_0^t (1 + t^2)^{1/2}\, 2t\, dt = \frac{1}{2} \cdot \frac{2}{3} (1 + t^2)^{3/2}\Big|_0^t$$

$$s = \frac{1}{3}(1 + t^2)^{3/2} - \frac{1}{3}. \tag{54}$$

Solving equation (54) for t in terms of s we find

$$t = \sqrt{(3s + 1)^{2/3} - 1}. \tag{55}$$

Using this expression for t in (52) gives

$$x = \frac{1}{2}\left((3s + 1)^{2/3} - 1\right)$$

$$\tag{56}$$

$$y = \frac{1}{3}\left((3s + 1)^{2/3} - 1\right)^{3/2}$$

as parametric equations for the curve (52), where now s is the parameter. We can check our work using

THEOREM 16. *If $\mathbf{R} = \mathbf{R}(s)$ is the vector equation of a curve C, and s is arc length on C, then*

$$\frac{d\mathbf{R}}{ds} = \mathbf{T}, \tag{57}$$

the unit tangent vector.

PROOF. By Theorem 13.

$$|\mathbf{R}'(t)| = \frac{ds}{dt}. \tag{31}$$

But now $s = t$, so the right side is just 1, so $\mathbf{R}'(s)$ is a unit vector. But $\mathbf{R}'$ is a tangent vector for any parameter, as long as $\mathbf{R}' \neq 0$.   Q.E.D.

Written in component form, equation (57) states that

$$\mathbf{T} = \frac{dx}{ds}\mathbf{i} + \frac{dy}{ds}\mathbf{j}, \tag{58}$$

$$\frac{dx}{ds} = \cos\varphi \qquad \frac{dy}{ds} = \sin\varphi, \tag{59}$$

and consequently

$$\left(\frac{dx}{ds}\right)^2 + \left(\frac{dy}{ds}\right)^2 = 1. \tag{60}$$

This last equation (60) can be used to check the computations in the example. To do this differentiate x and y as given by (56), then square and add. The result should be 1. We leave it to the student to carry out this check.

THEOREM 17. *For the unit tangent and normal vectors we have the differentiation formulas*

$$\frac{d\mathbf{T}}{d\varphi} = \mathbf{N}, \tag{61}$$

and

$$\frac{d\mathbf{T}}{ds} = \kappa\mathbf{N}. \tag{62}$$

PROOF. Differentiating the right side of (48) with respect to φ gives the right side of (49). This proves (61). For (62) we have

$$\frac{d\mathbf{T}}{ds} = \frac{d\mathbf{T}}{d\varphi}\frac{d\varphi}{ds} = \mathbf{N}\kappa$$

by using (61), and the definition of the curvature κ, equation (41).

EXERCISE 7

In problems 1 through 8 find the unit normal $\mathbf{N}$ for the given curve.

1. $\mathbf{R} = (a + mt)\mathbf{i} + (b + nt)\mathbf{j}.$
2. $\mathbf{R} = (a + r\cos t)\mathbf{i} + (b + r\sin t)\mathbf{j}, R > 0.$
3. $\mathbf{R} = a\cos t\,\mathbf{i} + b\sin t\,\mathbf{j}.$

4. $R = 2t\,i + t^2 j.$

5. $R = (t^3 - 3t)i + (4 - 3t^2)j.$

6. $R = 2t\,i + (e^t + e^{-t})j.$

★7. $R = a(t - \sin t)i + a(1 - \cos t)j, \ a > 0.$

8. $R = b(\cos u + u \sin u)i + b(\sin u - u \cos u)j, \ b > 0, \ u > 0.$

For each of the curves given in problems 9 through 13 find parametric equations in which the parameter is the arc length measured from the given P_0.   In each case check your answer by showing that $\left(\dfrac{dx}{ds}\right)^2 + \left(\dfrac{dy}{ds}\right)^2 = 1.$

9.   The straight line $R = (a + mt)i + (b + nt)j, \ P_0(a, b).$

10.   The circle $R = (a + r \cos \theta)i + (b + r \sin \theta)j, \ P_0(a + r, b).$

11.   The involute $R = 2(\cos \theta + \theta \sin \theta)i + 2(\sin \theta - \theta \cos \theta)j, \ P_0(2, 0).$

12.   The spiral $R = \dfrac{e^t}{\sqrt{2}}(\cos t\,i + \sin t\,j), \ P_0\!\left(\dfrac{1}{\sqrt{2}}, 0\right).$

13.   One arch of the hypocycloid of 4 cusps $R = \tfrac{2}{3}(\cos^3\theta\,i + \sin^3\theta\,j)$, where $0 \leq \theta \leq \pi/2$ and $P_0(2/3, 0)$.

14.   Find the length of one arch of the cycloid $R = a(t - \sin t)i + a(1 - \cos t)j.$

15.   Show that for the curve $x = 2e^t, \ y = \tfrac{1}{2}e^{2t} - t$, it is possible to find s as an elementary function of t.   Observe that it seems to be difficult to solve for t in terms of s, so that an explicit formula for this curve in terms of elementary functions of s appears to be impossible.

16.   Find an integral expression for the arc length of the ellipse $x = 4 \cos t$, $y = 3 \sin t$, $P_0(4, 0)$.   It is well known that this integral cannot be evaluated in terms of a finite number of the elementary functions.

17.   Show that if $\kappa \neq 0$, then the vector $\kappa\,N$ always points toward the concave side of the curve.   There are four cases to consider.   Two of the cases are shown in Fig. 29 and the other two arise from reversing the positive direction on the curve.

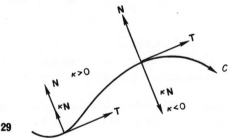

Figure 29

★9.   **Tangential and normal components of acceleration.**   The motion of a particle is completely determined when the x and y coordinates of the particle are given for any time t.   This is done quite simply by giving its position vector.

$$R(t) = f(t)i + g(t)j \tag{63}$$

from which we obtain at once by differentiating the velocity and acceleration vectors.

$$\mathbf{V}(t) = f'(t)\mathbf{i} + g'(t)\mathbf{j}, \tag{64}$$

$$\mathbf{A}(t) = f''(t)\mathbf{i} + g''(t)\mathbf{j}. \tag{65}$$

Now equation (65) gives the components of the acceleration in the
direction of the x and y-axes. Frequently it is important to have the
components of $\mathbf{A}$ along the tangent to the curve and along the normal to
the curve. Using subscripts A_T and A_N to denote these two scalars, they
are defined by the equation

$$\mathbf{A} = A_T\mathbf{T} + A_N\mathbf{N}. \tag{66}$$

Formulas for these components are given in

THEOREM 18. *The velocity and acceleration vectors of a particle moving on a curve* $\mathbf{R}(t)$ *are*

$$\mathbf{V} = \frac{ds}{dt}\mathbf{T} = V\mathbf{T} \tag{67}$$

and

$$\mathbf{A} = \frac{d^2s}{dt^2}\mathbf{T} + \left(\frac{ds}{dt}\right)^2 \kappa\mathbf{N} \tag{68}$$

where $\mathbf{T}$ *and* $\mathbf{N}$ *are the unit tangent and unit normal vectors to the
curve, s is the arc length measured in the direction of the motion, κ
is the curvature, and t is the time.*

Equation (67) states that the normal component of the velocity is zero.
Equation (68) tells us that A_T and A_N are

$$A_T = \frac{d^2s}{dt^2} = \frac{dV}{dt}$$

$$A_N = \left(\frac{ds}{dt}\right)^2 \kappa = \frac{V^2}{\rho}$$

where of course V is the speed of the particle, and ρ, the radius of curvature, is the reciprocal of the curvature.

The importance of the acceleration vector lies in the fact that from all experimental evidence particles in nature move in accordance with the law

$$\mathbf{F} = M\mathbf{A}$$

where $\mathbf{F}$ is the vector force applied to the particle and M is the mass of the particle. Thus $M\mathbf{A}_T$ is the component of the force tangential to the path required to keep the particle moving with the desired speed, and MV^2/ρ is the component of the force normal to the curve required to keep the particle on the curve. This latter force is usually a frictional force, or a restraining force, as in the case of an automobile or a train going around a curve.

PROOF of Theorem 18.   By definition

$$\mathbf{V} = \frac{d\mathbf{R}}{dt},$$

$$= \frac{d\mathbf{R}}{ds}\frac{ds}{dt} = \mathbf{T}\frac{ds}{dt}$$

using Theorem 16, equation (57). This proves (67). Differentiating both sides of (67) with respect to t gives

$$\mathbf{A} = \frac{d\mathbf{V}}{dt} = \frac{d}{dt}\left(\frac{ds}{dt}\mathbf{T}\right) = \frac{d^2s}{dt^2}\mathbf{T} + \frac{ds}{dt}\frac{d\mathbf{T}}{dt}$$

$$= \frac{d^2s}{dt^2}\mathbf{T} + \frac{ds}{dt}\left(\frac{d\mathbf{T}}{ds}\frac{ds}{dt}\right) = \frac{d^2s}{dt^2}\mathbf{T} + \left(\frac{ds}{dt}\right)^2\frac{d\mathbf{T}}{ds}$$

$$= \frac{d^2s}{dt^2}\mathbf{T} + \left(\frac{ds}{dt}\right)^2\kappa\mathbf{N},$$

using Theorem 17.   This proves (68).   Q.E.D.

EXAMPLE 1.   A common amusement device found at large entertainment parks consists of a giant horizontal flat wheel. Volunteers climb onto this wheel while it is stationary. The operator starts the wheel rotating about the fixed center and the volunteers attempt to stay on the wheel as long as possible. Discuss the dynamics of this situation.

SOLUTION.   To be definite let us assume that the wheel has a radius of 20 ft, and that the coefficient of friction μ (Greek letter mu) is 1/10. This latter means that if a person has weight W, then the maximum frictional force that can be exerted between the wheel and the person on it is μW. If the person is pushed horizontally outward with a larger force he will tend to slide off. Thus it is this frictional force μW which provides the person riding on the wheel with the necessary normal component of acceleration to stay in his place on the wheel.

Let us assume that the wheel has a steady motion of ω (Greek letter omega) revolutions per second. Then the speed at any point r ft from the center is $V = 2\pi r\omega$ ft/sec. For the volunteer to stay in place, he needs a normal acceleration (equation (68))

$$A_N = V^2\kappa = \frac{V^2}{r} = 4\pi^2 r\omega^2 \text{ ft/sec}^2.$$

In the equation $F = MA$, the mass in the British system is $M = W/g$, where W is the weight of the body and g is the acceleration due to gravity. Since the wheel is rotating steadily the tangential component of acceleration is zero [see equation (68)], so the frictional force required to keep the volunteer in position is

$$F = MA_N = \frac{W}{g} 4\pi^2 r\omega^2$$

On the other hand $F = \mu W$ is the maximum force that can be exerted by the volunteer in his effort to stay on. Hence the critical ω satisfies the equation

$$\mu W = \frac{W}{g} 4\pi^2 r\omega^2$$

or

$$g\mu = 4\pi^2 r\omega^2. \tag{69}$$

Any greater rate of turning, and the volunteer slides off. Notice that W has cancelled, so a heavy person and a light weight person have equal opportunity.

To be specific, suppose that our volunteer is at the outer edge of the wheel. Then

$$\omega = \sqrt{\frac{g\mu}{4\pi^2 r}} = \sqrt{\frac{32 \times .1}{4\pi^2 20}} = \sqrt{\frac{.04}{\pi^2}}$$

$$= \frac{.2}{\pi} \text{ rev/sec} = \frac{12}{\pi} \text{ rev/min} \approx 3.82 \text{ rev/min.}$$

If the wheel turns more rapidly, the person on the edge must slide off.

EXERCISE 8

1. What is the critical speed for the wheel described in the example if the volunteer is 5 ft from the center of the wheel?

2. Find the critical speed for the wheel described in the example, if the volunteer is only 1 ft from the center of the wheel, and $\mu = 1/4$ (he is wearing gym shoes and has rosin on his hands.)

3. Show that if a person can sit right on the center of the wheel described in the example, then (barring physiological effects) he can stay on indefinitely no matter how fast the wheel turns.

4. A car weighing 3200 lbs going steadily at 60 miles an hour makes a circular turn on a flat road. If the radius of the circular turn is 44 ft, what frictional force is required on the bottom of the tires to keep the car from skidding?

5. What is the least possible value of μ, the coefficient of friction between the tire and the road, that is sufficient to keep the car of problem 4 from slipping.

6. Show that if the driver of the car in problem 4 will cut his speed in half, then the frictional force required to keep his car from slipping will be reduced by a factor of one fourth. Show that the same is true of the minimum value of the coefficient of friction.

7. A locomotive weighing 120 tons is going steadily at 60 miles an hour, along a level track that is at first straight, and then takes a turn. The equation of the curve is $1760y = x^2$ (in feet) and the curved piece joins the straight piece at the vertex $(0, 0)$ of the parabola. Find (approximately) the horizontal thrust of the locomotive on the outer rail just after the locomotive enters on the parabolic turn.

8. A man holds onto a rope to which is tied a pail holding 5 lb of water. He swings the pail in a vertical circle with a radius of 4 ft. If the pail is making 60 r.p.m. what is the pressure of the water on the bottom of the pail at the high point and low point of the swing. Find the least number of r.p.m. in order that the water will stay in the pail.

★9. A popular amusement ride called the Round-Up consists of a flat circular ring with outer radius 16 ft. The ring is at first horizontal and the volunteers stand on the outer edge of the ring each facing the center of the ring. Each person is supported in back by a wire fence that is roughly seven feet high, mounted securely on the outer edge of the ring. When all is ready the ring, fence and volunteers begin rotating. The volunteers are thrown backward against the fence, and when the force is large enough to assure safety the ring, fence, and volunteers are gradually lifted until the collection is rotating in a vertical plane. If the ring rotates in a vertical plane at 21 r.p.m., what force does a man of weight W exert against the wire fence, (a) when he is at the top of the circular path looking downward and (b) when he is at the bottom of the path?

★10. Explain why a Ferris wheel of radius 20 ft should not rotate at more than 12 r.p.m. Actual operating speed is usually about 6 r.p.m.

11. The magnetic drum in the IBM 650 computer is 4 in. in diameter and rotates at about 12,000 r.p.m. Show that the normal acceleration of a particle on the surface of the drum is $80,000\pi^2/3$ ft/sec². Hence the adhesive force necessary to keep the particle from flying off is approximately 8000 W, where W is the weight of the particle.

12. An astronaut is travelling in a circular orbit 440 miles above the surface of the earth. If the radius of the earth is 3960 miles, find his speed. How long does it take for the spaceship to make one circuit around the earth. *Hint:* The ship and the astronaut are both weightless when in orbit. For simplicity assume that at that height g is still 32 ft/sec².

★10.   Geometric interpretation of the hyperbolic functions.   If

$$x = \cos t, \qquad y = \sin t \tag{70}$$

then on squaring and adding, we have

$$x^2 + y^2 = \cos^2 t + \sin^2 t = 1.$$

Hence (70) is a set of parametric equations for the circle of radius 1 with center at the origin.   For brevity we call this circle the *unit circle.*

On the other hand if

$$x = \cosh t \qquad y = \sinh t \tag{71}$$

then on squaring and subtracting we have

$$x^2 - y^2 = \cosh^2 t - \sinh^2 t = 1.$$

Hence (71) is a set of parametric equations for the equilateral hyperbola $x^2 - y^2 = 1$.   We call this hyperbola the *unit hyperbola.*   Observe that as t runs through all real numbers $x = \cosh t$ is always positive so that (71) gives only the right half of the hyperbola, the branch that lies to the right side of the y-axis.

Since the functions $(e^t + e^{-t})/2$ and $(e^t - e^{-t})/2$ provide a nice parameterization for the unit hyperbola it is quite appropriate to name them the hyperbolic cosine, and hyperbolic sine respectively.

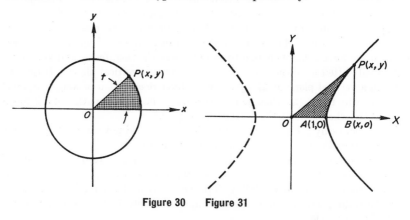

Figure 30   Figure 31

In equation set (70) the variable t has a natural interpretation as the angle between the x-axis and a radial line from O to the corresponding point $P(x, y)$ on the circle (see Fig. 30).   One could not expect the variable t in equation set (71) to appear as an angle in Fig. 31, but there is an analogous interpretation for t as an area that we now derive.

The area of any circular sector is $\frac{1}{2}r^2\theta$ where r is the radius and θ is the central angle measured in radians [Equation (1), Chapter 7].   Applied to the shaded area of Fig. 30, this gives $A = \frac{1}{2}t$, since $r = 1$.   We shall now prove that t has the same meaning for the hyperbolic functions.   In Fig. 31, let $P(x, y)$ be the point given by (71) for a fixed value of t, $(t > 0)$.   *Then the area bounded by the x-axis, the radial line OP, and the arc AP of the hyperbola is* $\frac{1}{2}t$. To prove this observe that

area of sector OAP = area of triangle OBP − area of ABP

$$= \frac{1}{2}\cosh t \sinh t - \text{area of } ABP. \qquad (72)$$

To find this last term, let u be the variable of integration. Then

$$\text{area of } ABP = \int_{X=1}^{X=x} Y dX = \int_{u=0}^{u=t} \sinh u\, d(\cosh u)$$

$$= \int_{0}^{t} \sinh^2 u\, du = \int_{0}^{t} \frac{1}{2}(\cosh 2u - 1) du$$

$$= \frac{1}{4}\sinh 2u - \frac{1}{2}u \Big|_{0}^{t}$$

$$= \frac{1}{4}\sinh 2t - \frac{1}{2}t = \frac{1}{2}\sinh t \cosh t - \frac{1}{2}t.$$

Using this in (72) gives that the area of sector OAP equals $\frac{1}{2}t$. Q.E.D.

11

INDETERMINATE FORMS AND IMPROPER INTEGRALS

1. Indeterminate forms. Suppose that we are to compute

$$\lim_{x \to 1} \frac{x^3 - 1}{e^{1-x} - 1}. \tag{1}$$

Clearly both the numerator and the denominator are 0 at $x = 1$, so that the ratio in (1) has the form $0/0$. We have already met such indeterminate forms before, and in the past we were able to determine the limit by some suitable algebraic manipulations. In the present case no such manipulations present themselves, due to the presence of the exponential function in the denominator. What we need here is a systematic procedure for computing such limits as (1). In section 3 we will prove a theorem, called L'Hospital's rule, that gives just such a method. Briefly the rule states that we should differentiate the numerator and the denominator, and find the limit of the ratio of these two derivatives. Applying this rule in (1) we find that

$$\lim_{x \to 1} \frac{x^3 - 1}{e^{1-x} - 1} = \lim_{x \to 1} \frac{3x^2}{-e^{1-x}} = \frac{3}{-1} = -3, \tag{2}$$

a result that would have been hard to guess.

In order to prove this rule we must first generalize the mean value theorem (Theorem 6 of Chapter 3, p. 103).

2. The generalized mean value theorem. Let us recall Rolle's Theorem (Theorem 5 of chapter 3, p. 102).

ROLLE'S THEOREM. *Suppose that $f(x)$ is a continuous function of x in the closed interval $a \leq x \leq b$, and a differentiable function in the open interval $a < x < b$. If $f(a) = f(b) = 0$*

then there is some point ξ in the open interval $a < \xi < b$ such that
$f'(\xi) = 0$.

We will use Rolle's Theorem to prove

THEOREM 1. (THE GENERALIZED MEAN VALUE THEOREM).
Let $f(t)$ and $g(t)$ be two functions, each continuous in the closed interval $a \le t \le b$, and each differentiable in the open interval $a < t < b$. Suppose further that $f(b) \neq f(a)$, and that the derivatives $f'(t)$ and $g'(t)$ do not vanish simultaneously in $a < t < b$. Then there is some point ξ, with $a < \xi < b$, such that

$$\frac{g(b) - g(a)}{f(b) - f(a)} = \frac{g'(\xi)}{f'(\xi)}. \tag{3}$$

Before proving this theorem let us give a geometric interpretation of this result. Let $x = f(t)$ and $y = g(t)$ be parametric equations for some curve C. As t runs from $t = a$ to $t = b$ the point $P(x, y)$ describes a continuous curve joining the points $A(f(a), g(a))$ and $B(f(b), g(b))$ as indicated in Fig. 1. Now the left side of (3) is just $\Delta y / \Delta x$, the slope of the straight line AB. On the other hand $g'(t)/f'(t)$ is the slope of the tangent line to the curve at the point $P(f(t), g(t))$ on the curve C. Then Theorem 1 states that there is some point P on the curve between A and B such that the tangent line to the curve is parallel to the chord AB. Of course there may be more than one such point, but there is always at least one. The theorem may fail if the curve has a cusp as shown in Fig. 2. This can occur if $f'(t)$ and $g'(t)$ vanish simultaneously, so the hypothesis that they do not vanish simultaneously is necessary in the statement of the theorem. Parametric equations for the curve of Fig. 2 are given in problem 9 of Exercise 1.

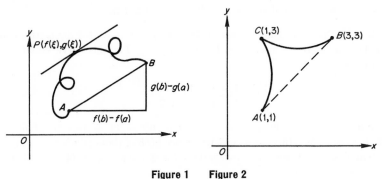

Figure 1   Figure 2

PROOF of Theorem 1. For the reader who is familar with determinants let $F(t)$ be defined by the determinant

$$F(t) = \begin{vmatrix} f(t) & g(t) & 1 \\ f(a) & g(a) & 1 \\ f(b) & g(b) & 1 \end{vmatrix}. \tag{4}$$

When $t = a$ the first and second rows are identical and hence $F(a) = 0$. When $t = b$ the first and third rows are identical and so $F(b) = 0$. It is easy to see that $F(t)$ satisfies the other conditions of Rolle's Theorem. Hence there is some suitable ξ for which $F'(\xi) = 0$. Expanding the determinant in (4) by minors of the first row gives

$$F(t) = f(t)[g(a) - g(b)] - g(t)[f(a) - f(b)] + f(a)g(b) - g(a)f(b). \tag{5}$$

For the reader who is not familiar with determinants, the proof can start with the function $F(t)$ defined by equation (5). A brief computation from (5) will show that $F(a) = F(b) = 0$, and hence Rolle's Theorem can be applied to $F(t)$.

If we differentiate $F(t)$, we have from (5) that

$$F'(t) = f'(t)[g(a) - g(b)] - g'(t)[f(a) - f(b)]. \tag{6}$$

By Rolle's Theorem there is a ξ such that $F'(\xi) = 0$. For this ξ equation (6) gives

$$0 = f'(\xi)[g(a) - g(b)] - g'(\xi)[f(a) - f(b)]. \tag{7}$$

From (7), simple algebraic manipulations give equation (3). However in doing the divisions involved we must be certain that we do not divide by zero. But this is assured by the hypotheses that $f(a) \neq f(b)$ and that $f'(t)$ and $g'(t)$ are not simultaneously zero.   Q.E.D.

EXAMPLE 1. Find a value for ξ as predicted by Theorem 1 for the functions $f(t) = t^2 + 2t + 1$ and $g(t) = t^3 + 3t + 1$ for $0 \leq t \leq 1$.

SOLUTION. The curve $x = t^2 + 2t + 1$, $y = t^3 + 3t + 1$ joins the points $(1, 1)$ and $(4, 5)$ as t runs from $t = 0$ to $t = 1$. For this curve equation (3) leads to

$$\frac{5 - 1}{4 - 1} = \frac{3t^2 + 3}{2t + 2}.$$

Solving for t gives $8t + 8 = 9t^2 + 9$ or $9t^2 - 8t + 1 = 0$. Hence $t = (8 \pm \sqrt{64 - 36})/18 = (4 \pm \sqrt{7})/9$. Since both of these numbers lie in the interval $0 < \xi < 1$ we have two values for ξ namely $\xi_1 = (4 - \sqrt{7})/9$ and $\xi_2 = (4 + \sqrt{7})/9$.

EXERCISE 1

In problems 1 through 8 find all values of ξ satisfying equation (3) (Theorem 1) for the given pair of functions and the given interval. Observe that for each of these problems you have already sketched the curve $x = f(t)$, $y = g(t)$ (see Exercise 3, of Chapter 10).

1. $x = 5 \cos t$, $y = 5 \sin t$, $0 \leq t \leq \pi/2$.
2. $x = 3 \cos t$, $y = 5 \sin t$, $0 \leq t \leq \pi/2$.
3. $x = 3 \cos t$, $y = 5 \sin t$, $0 \leq t \leq \pi$.
4. $x = \sin t$, $y = \cos 2t$, $0 \leq t \leq \pi/2$.
5. $x = \cosh t$, $y = \sinh t$, $0 \leq t \leq 6$.
6. $x = t^3$, · $y = t^2$, $1 \leq t \leq 2$.
7. $x = t^3 - 3t$, $y = t$, $-3 \leq t \leq 3$.
8. $x = t^3 - 3t$, $y = 4 - t^2$, $-3 \leq t \leq 2$.

*9. Sketch the curve $x = 1 + t(t - 1)^2 = f(t)$, $y = 3 + (t - 2)(t - 1)^2 = g(t)$ for $0 \leq t \leq 2$ by plotting a few points. Observe that the curve has a cusp at $(1, 3)$. Show that for this curve $f'(t)$ and $g'(t)$ vanish simultaneously for a suitable value of t. Prove that there is no value of t in the interval $0 < t < 2$ such that

$$\frac{g(2) - g(0)}{f(2) - f(0)} = \frac{g'(t)}{f'(t)}.$$

*10. Repeat problem 9 for the curve $x = t^3$, $y = t^2$ over the interval $-2 < t < 3$.

3.   The form 0/0. If $f(x)$ and $g(x)$ are continuous functions at $x = a$ with $f(a) = 0$ and $g(a) = 0$, then

$$\lim_{x \to a} \frac{g(x)}{f(x)} \qquad (8)$$

is referred to briefly as the *indeterminate form* 0/0. In (8) x can approach a either from the left or from the right. For simplicity we will state our theorem just for the second case, since the first case is handled in exactly the same way. The method of finding a value for the indeterminate form 0/0 is given by

THEOREM 2 (L'HOSPITAL'S RULE). *Suppose that:* $f(a) = g(a) = 0$, $f(x)$ *and* $g(x)$ *are each continuous in* $a \leq x \leq b$, *and differentiable in* $a < x < b$, *and* $f'(x) \neq 0$ *in* $a < x < b$. *Then*

$$\lim_{x \to a^+} \frac{g(x)}{f(x)} = \lim_{x \to a^+} \frac{g'(x)}{f'(x)} \qquad (9)$$

whenever the latter limit exists. If the limit on the right side of equation (9) is $+\infty$, *or* $-\infty$, *then the limit on the left side is* $+\infty$ *or* $-\infty$ *respectively.*

We have already illustrated (8) and (9) in (1) and (2).

PROOF.   We apply Theorem 1, but instead of the interval $a \leq x \leq b$, we use t as the variable and x as the righthand end point.   Thus we consider the interval $a \leq t \leq x$.   Then the generalized mean value theorem states that there is a ξ with $a < \xi < x$ such that

$$\frac{g(x) - g(a)}{f(x) - f(a)} = \frac{g'(\xi)}{f'(\xi)}. \tag{10}$$

But $g(a) = f(a) = 0$, so (10) simplifies to

$$\frac{g(x)}{f(x)} = \frac{g'(\xi)}{f'(\xi)}, \qquad a < \xi < x. \tag{11}$$

Now let $x \to a^+$.   Since $a < \xi < x$, ξ must also approach a^+.   Hence if

$$\lim_{\xi \to a^+} \frac{g'(\xi)}{f'(\xi)} = L$$

then by (11) the left side of (9) has the same limit L.   But this is just the statement of Theorem 2.   Q.E.D.

EXAMPLE 1.   Compute $\lim\limits_{x \to 0} \dfrac{x}{\ln^2 (1 + x)}$

SOLUTION.   At $x = 0$ both the numerator and the denominator are zero, so Theorem 2 is applicable.   By L'Hospital's rule, equation (9)

$$\lim_{x \to 0} \frac{x}{\ln^2 (1 + x)} = \lim_{x \to 0} \frac{1}{\dfrac{2 \ln (1 + x)}{1 + x}} = \lim_{x \to 0} \frac{1 + x}{2 \ln (1 + x)}.$$

If $x > 0$ and $x \to 0$, the denominator of this last fraction is positive and tending to zero.   Hence the fraction grows large without bound and hence the limit is $+\infty$.   When $x \to 0$ and $x < 0$, the denominator is negative and hence the limit is $-\infty$.   This result is symbolized by writing

$$\lim_{x \to 0^+} \frac{x}{\ln^2 (1 + x)} = \infty,$$

and

$$\lim_{x \to 0^-} \frac{x}{\ln^2 (1 + x)} = -\infty.$$

EXAMPLE 2.   Compute $L = \lim\limits_{x \to 2} \dfrac{3 \sqrt[3]{x - 1} - x - 1}{3(x - 2)^2}$

SOLUTION. At $x = 2$, both the numerator and denominator are zero, so Theorem 2 is applicable. Hence

$$L = \lim_{x \to 2} \frac{3\sqrt[3]{x-1} - x - 1}{3(x-2)^2} = \lim_{x \to 2} \frac{\dfrac{1}{(x-1)^{2/3}} - 1}{6(x-2)}. \qquad (12)$$

But in this last fraction the numerator and denominator are both zero at $x = 2$, so we are faced with another indeterminate form $0/0$. But we can apply L'Hospital's rule to this new indeterminate form. Differentiating numerator and denominator gives

$$\lim_{x \to 2} \frac{\dfrac{1}{(x-1)^{2/3}} - 1}{6(x-2)} = \lim_{x \to 2} \frac{-\dfrac{2}{3}\dfrac{1}{(x-1)^{5/3}}}{6} = -\frac{2}{18} = -\frac{1}{9}. \qquad (13)$$

Combining equations (12) and (13) yields $L = -1/9$.

If the original indeterminate form is sufficiently complicated it may be necessary to use L'Hospital's rule a large number of times to obtain a numerical answer.

L'Hospital's rule is exactly the same in case the independent variable x is tending to ∞ instead of some finite number a. Precisely stated we have

THEOREM 3. *Suppose that*[1] $f(\infty) = 0$ *and* $g(\infty) = 0$, $f(x)$ *and* $g(x)$ *are each differentiable in* $M < x < \infty$, *and* $f'(x) \neq 0$ *in* $M < x < \infty$. *Then*

$$\lim_{x \to \infty} \frac{g(x)}{f(x)} = \lim_{x \to \infty} \frac{g'(x)}{f'(x)} \qquad (14)$$

whenever the latter limit exists.

PROOF. We bring the point at infinity into the origin by the substitution $x = 1/t$ and apply L'Hospital's rule with $a = 0$. Clearly as $x \to \infty$, $t \to 0^+$ and conversely as $t \to 0^+$, $x \to \infty$. The details of this program are:

$$\lim_{x \to \infty} \frac{g(x)}{f(x)} = \lim_{t \to 0^+} \frac{g(1/t)}{f(1/t)}$$

$$= \lim_{t \to 0^+} \frac{g'(1/t)(-1/t^2)}{f'(1/t)(-1/t^2)} \qquad \text{(Chain rule for differentiation)}$$

$$= \lim_{t \to 0^+} \frac{g'(1/t)}{f'(1/t)} = \lim_{x \to \infty} \frac{g'(x)}{f'(x)}. \qquad \text{Q.E.D.}$$

EXAMPLE 3. Compute $\lim\limits_{x \to \infty} \dfrac{1/x}{\sin(\pi/x)}$.

[1]This means $\lim\limits_{x \to \infty} f(x) = 0$ and $\lim\limits_{x \to \infty} g(x) = 0$.

SOLUTION. We differentiate the numerator and denominator. By Theorem 3.

$$\lim_{x \to \infty} \frac{1/x}{\sin (\pi/x)} = \lim_{x \to \infty} \frac{-1/x^2}{\cos (\pi/x)(-\pi/x^2)}$$

$$= \lim_{x \to \infty} \frac{1}{\pi \cos (\pi/x)} = \frac{1}{\pi}.$$

EXERCISE 2

Evaluate each of the following limits.

1. $\lim_{x \to 3} \dfrac{x^2 - 4x + 3}{x^2 + x - 12}$.

2. $\lim_{x \to -1} \dfrac{x^2 + 6x + 5}{x^2 - x - 2}$.

3. $\lim_{x \to 1} \dfrac{\sin \pi x}{x^2 - 1}$.

4. $\lim_{x \to 1} \dfrac{\ln x}{x^2 - x}$.

5. $\lim_{x \to 0} \dfrac{e^x - e^{-x}}{\sin 3x}$.

6. $\lim_{x \to \pi} \dfrac{\ln \cos 2x}{(\pi - x)^2}$.

7. $\lim_{x \to 0} \dfrac{e^x - 1 - x}{1 - \cos \pi x}$.

8. $\lim_{x \to 0} \dfrac{\tan 2x - 2x}{x - \sin x}$.

9. $\lim_{x \to 0} \dfrac{\sin x - \sinh x}{x^3}$.

10. $\lim_{x \to 0+} \dfrac{\sin^{-1} x}{\sin^2 3x}$.

11. $\lim_{x \to 0+} \dfrac{\tan^{-1} x}{1 - \cos 2x}$.

12. $\lim_{x \to \pi} \dfrac{1 + \cos x}{\sin 2x}$.

13. $\lim_{x \to 0} \dfrac{b^x - a^x}{x}$, $(b > a > 0)$.

14. $\lim_{x \to 4} \dfrac{4e^{4-x} - x}{\sin \pi x}$.

15. $\lim_{t \to 0} \dfrac{\sin^2 t - \sin t^2}{t^2}$.

16. $\lim_{t \to 0} \dfrac{e^{5t} \sin 2t}{\ln (1 + t)}$.

★17. $\lim_{x \to 0} \dfrac{2 \cos x - 2 + x^2}{3x^4}$.

★18. $\lim_{x \to 0} \dfrac{x \sin(\sin x)}{1 - \cos(\sin x)}$.

19. $\lim_{x \to 1} \dfrac{x^3 - 3x + 1}{x^4 - x^2 - 2x}$.

20. $\lim_{x \to 2} \dfrac{e^{x-2} + 2 - x}{\cos^2 \pi x}$.

21. $\lim_{x \to \infty} \dfrac{e^{3/x} - 1}{\sin (1/x)}$.

★22. $\lim_{x \to \infty} \dfrac{\tan^2 (1/x)}{\ln^2 (1 + 4/x)}$.

4.   The form ∞ / ∞. One of the attractive features of L'Hospital's rule is that it works for the indeterminate form ∞ / ∞ just as it works for $0/0$.

THEOREM 4. Let $\lim_{x \to a} f(x) = \infty$ and $\lim_{x \to a} g(x) = \infty$, and *suppose that $f'(x) \neq 0$ in $a < x < b$. Then*

$$\lim_{x \to a+} \frac{g(x)}{f(x)} = \lim_{x \to a+} \frac{g'(x)}{f'(x)} \tag{15}$$

whenever the latter limit exists.

In other words we can evaluate the indeterminate form

$$\lim_{x \to a^+} \frac{g(x)}{f(x)} = \frac{\infty}{\infty}$$

by just differentiating the numerator and denominator and then taking the limit.

It turns out that a proof of Theorem 4 as stated is somewhat difficult, and so we omit it. The interested reader can find it in any book on Advanced Calculus. But if we add a little to the hypotheses then the proof is easier. Indeed let us suppose that the limit on the left side of (15) does exist and is neither zero nor infinity. In symbols we suppose that

$$\lim_{x \to a^+} \frac{g(x)}{f(x)} = L, \qquad L \neq 0, \quad L \neq \infty. \tag{16}$$

We apply Theorem 2 (or Theorem 3 if $x \to \infty$) to the evaluation of

$$\lim_{x \to a^+} \frac{\dfrac{1}{g(x)}}{\dfrac{1}{f(x)}}$$

which is an indeterminant form $0/0$. Hence

$$\lim_{x \to a^+} \frac{\dfrac{1}{g(x)}}{\dfrac{1}{f(x)}} = \lim_{x \to a^+} \frac{-\dfrac{1}{g^2(x)} g'(x)}{-\dfrac{1}{f^2(x)} f'(x)}.$$

This is equivalent to

$$\lim_{x \to a^+} \frac{f(x)}{g(x)} = \lim_{x \to a^+} \frac{f^2(x)}{g^2(x)} \frac{g'(x)}{f'(x)}$$

$$= \left(\lim_{x \to a^+} \frac{f^2(x)}{g^2(x)} \right) \left(\lim_{x \to a^+} \frac{g'(x)}{f'(x)} \right).$$

Using (16) we have

$$\frac{1}{L} = \frac{1}{L^2} \lim_{x \to a^+} \frac{g'(x)}{f'(x)}$$

and hence

$$L = \lim_{x \to a^+} \frac{g'(x)}{f'(x)}. \qquad\qquad \text{Q.E.D.}$$

EXAMPLE 1.   Compute $\lim\limits_{x\to\infty} \dfrac{\ln^2 x}{x}$.

SOLUTION.   This has the form ∞/∞.   Applying L'Hospital's rule

$$\lim_{x\to\infty} \frac{\ln^2 x}{x} = \lim_{x\to\infty} \frac{2(\ln x)\,\dfrac{1}{x}}{1} = \lim_{x\to\infty} \frac{2\ln x}{x}.$$

This last is still an indeterminate form ∞/∞.   Applying our rule to this new form

$$\lim_{x\to\infty} \frac{2\ln x}{x} = \lim_{x\to\infty} \frac{2\,\dfrac{1}{x}}{1} = 0.$$

EXERCISE 3

In problems 1 through 8 evaluate each of the indeterminate forms.

1. $\lim\limits_{x\to\infty} \dfrac{x}{e^x}$.

2. $\lim\limits_{x\to\infty} \dfrac{\ln x}{\sqrt[3]{x}}$.

3. $\lim\limits_{x\to\infty} \dfrac{x^2 + 3x + 2}{2x^2 + x + 3}$.

4. $\lim\limits_{x\to\infty} \dfrac{e^x}{x^2}$.

★5. $\lim\limits_{x\to\pi/2} \dfrac{\tan x}{\tan 3x}$.

6. $\lim\limits_{x\to\infty} \dfrac{x + \ln x}{x \ln x}$.

7. $\lim\limits_{x\to\pi/2} \dfrac{\sec x + 5}{\tan x}$.

8. $\lim\limits_{x\to 0+} \dfrac{\ln x}{\csc x}$.

9.   Prove that if $P(x)$ and $Q(x)$ are polynomials

$$P(x) = a_0 x^n + \cdots + a_n, \qquad a_0 \neq 0,$$
$$Q(x) = b_0 x^m + \cdots + b_m, \qquad b_0 \neq 0,$$

then

$$\lim_{x\to\infty} \frac{P(x)}{Q(x)} = \begin{cases} \pm\infty & \text{if } n > m, \\ \dfrac{a_0}{b_0} & \text{if } n = m, \\ 0 & \text{if } n < m. \end{cases}$$

10.   Prove that if ϵ is any fixed positive number, no matter how small, then

$$\lim_{x\to\infty} \frac{\ln x}{x^\epsilon} = 0.$$

11.   Prove that if M is any fixed positive number, no matter how large, then

$$\lim_{x\to\infty} \frac{e^x}{x^M} = \infty.$$

Hint: First assume M is an integer.

*12. Without using Theorem 4 prove that

$$\lim_{x \to \infty} \frac{x + \sin x}{x} = 1.$$

Observe that if we differentiate the numerator and denominator we have to consider

$$\lim_{x \to \infty} \frac{\cos x}{1}$$

and this ratio does not tend to any limit. Does this show that Theorem 4 is false?

5. **Other indeterminate forms.** Aside from $0/0$ and ∞/∞ the types of indeterminate forms that occur most frequently are $0 \times \infty$, $\infty - \infty$, 0^0, ∞^0, and 1^∞. Here the meaning of each of these five symbols is obvious, and each is illustrated by an example below. Rather than prove a new theorem for each one of these five types, it is simpler to reduce them by suitable manipulations to a type already treated.

EXAMPLE 1. Compute $L_1 = \lim_{x \to 0^+} x^3 \ln x$.

SOLUTION. This has the form $0 \times (-\infty)$. We transform this into a type ∞/∞ (the negative sign is unimportant here) by writing

$$L_1 = \lim_{x \to 0^+} x^3 \ln x = \lim_{x \to 0^+} \frac{\ln x}{\dfrac{1}{x^3}}.$$

We apply Theorem 4 to the second ratio (∞/∞) and find that

$$L_1 = \lim_{x \to 0^+} \frac{\dfrac{1}{x}}{-\dfrac{3}{x^4}} = \lim_{x \to 0^+} -\frac{x^4}{3x} = \lim_{x \to 0^+} -\frac{x^3}{3} = 0.$$

EXAMPLE 2. Compute $L_2 = \lim_{x \to 0} \left(\frac{1}{x} - \frac{1}{\ln(1+x)} \right)$.

SOLUTION. This has the form $\infty - \infty$. But on adding the fractions,

$$L_2 = \lim_{x \to 0} \frac{\ln(1+x) - x}{x \ln(1+x)}$$

and this has the form $0/0$. L'Hospital's rule gives

$$L_2 = \lim_{x \to 0} \frac{\dfrac{1}{1+x} - 1}{\ln(1+x) + \dfrac{x}{1+x}} = \lim_{x \to 0} \frac{1 - 1 - x}{(1+x)\ln(1+x) + x}.$$

This still has the form 0/0.   Using L'Hospital's rule again

$$L_2 = \lim_{x \to 0} \frac{-1}{1 + \ln(1 + x) + 1} = -\frac{1}{2}.$$

EXAMPLE 3.   Compute $L_3 = \lim_{x \to 0^+} x^{x^3}$.

SOLUTION.   This has the form 0^0.   We let $Q = x^{x^3}$.   Then $\ln Q = \ln x^{x^3} = x^3 \ln x$.   Now as $x \to 0^+$, $x^3 \ln x$ has the form $0 \times \infty$, and in fact this is just the one evaluated in Example 1.   Hence

$$\lim_{x \to 0^+} \ln Q = \lim_{x \to 0^+} x^3 \ln x = 0.$$

Therefore

$$L_3 = \lim_{x \to 0^+} Q = e^0 = 1.$$

EXAMPLE 4.   Compute $L_4 = \lim_{x \to 0^+} \left(1 + \frac{5}{x}\right)^{2x}$.

SOLUTION.   This has the form ∞^0.   We let $Q = \left(1 + \frac{5}{x}\right)^{2x}$.   Then $\ln Q = 2x \ln\left(1 + \frac{5}{x}\right)$, and as $x \to 0^+$ this has the form $0 \times \infty$.   Now

$$\lim_{x \to 0^+} \ln Q = \lim_{x \to 0^+} 2x \ln\left(1 + \frac{5}{x}\right) = \lim_{x \to 0^+} \frac{2\ln\left(1 + \frac{5}{x}\right)}{\frac{1}{x}}.$$

This last limit has the form ∞ / ∞.   Hence

$$\lim_{x \to 0^+} \ln Q = \lim_{x \to 0^+} \frac{2 \dfrac{1}{1 + \dfrac{5}{x}}\left(-\dfrac{5}{x^2}\right)}{-\dfrac{1}{x^2}}$$

$$= \lim_{x \to 0^+} \frac{10}{1 + \dfrac{5}{x}} = 0. \tag{17}$$

Therefore

$$L_4 = \lim_{x \to 0^+} Q = e^0 = 1.$$

EXAMPLE 5.   Compute $L_5 = \lim_{x \to \infty} \left(1 + \frac{5}{x}\right)^{2x}$.

SOLUTION. This has the form 1^∞. The function involved is the same as in Example 4. The only difference is that now $x \to \infty$ instead of $x \to 0^+$. We follow the same pattern up to equation (17) but this time we have

$$\lim_{x \to \infty} \ln Q = \lim_{x \to \infty} \frac{10}{1 + \dfrac{5}{x}} = 10.$$

Hence $L_5 = e^{10}$.

EXERCISE 4

In problems 1 through 18 compute each of the given indeterminate forms.

1. $\lim_{x \to 0} \left(\dfrac{1}{x} - \dfrac{1}{\sin x} \right).$

2. $\lim_{x \to 0} \left(\dfrac{1}{x} - \dfrac{1}{e^x - 1} \right).$

3. $\lim_{x \to \pi/2} (\sec x - \tan x).$

4. $\lim_{x \to 0^+} \sqrt{x} \ln x^2.$

5. $\lim_{x \to \infty} x^3 e^{-x}.$

6. $\lim_{x \to \pi} \left(\dfrac{1}{\sin x} - \dfrac{1}{\pi - x} \right).$

7. $\lim_{x \to \pi/2} (\sin x)^{\tan x}.$

★8. $\lim_{x \to 0^+} x^3 e^{1/x}.$

9. $\lim_{x \to 0} (1 + x^3)^{4/x^3}.$

10. $\lim_{x \to \infty} \left(\cos \dfrac{3}{x} \right)^x.$

★11. $\lim_{x \to 0^+} x^{\ln(1+x)}.$

★12. $\lim_{x \to 0^+} (e^x - 1)^{\sin x}.$

13. $\lim_{x \to \infty} (e^x - 1)^{1/x}.$

14. $\lim_{x \to 1} x^{1/(1-x)}.$

15. $\lim_{x \to 0^+} (\tan x)^{\sin x}.$

16. $\lim_{x \to 0} x^2 \csc(3 \sin^2 x).$

17. $\lim_{x \to \infty} (1 + 2x)^{e^{-x}}.$

18. $\lim_{x \to 1^-} \left(\dfrac{1}{1 - x} \right)^{(1-x)^2}.$

19. The expressions in problems 11, 12, and 15 all have the form 0° and in each case the limit is 1. Prove that for any positive A and n

$$\lim_{x \to 0^+} (Ax)^{x^n} = 1.$$

20. Continuation of 19. Our results seem to indicate that 0^0 is always 1 Explode this conjecture by finding

$$\lim_{x \to 0^+} x^{-k/\ln x}$$

where k is a positive constant.

21. Explain why 1^0, 0^1, and 0^∞ are not indeterminate forms.

22. Explain why the expression in problem 8 is not indeterminate if $x \to 0^-$. What is the limit in this case?

23. Why is the expression

$$\lim_{x \to 2\pi} \left(\frac{1}{\sin x} - \frac{1}{2\pi - x} \right)$$

not an indeterminate form? Compare this with the form in problem 6.

6.   Improper integrals. In our previous work on integration the integrand $f(x)$ was assumed to be bounded over the interval of integration, and that interval was assumed to be finite. If either of these conditions fails to hold then the integral is said to be an *improper integral*. Thus an integral can be improper in two ways: (1) the interval of integration may be infinite, or (2) the integrand $f(x)$ may become infinite at one or possibly more points either inside the interval or at an end point. Suppose that we wish to compute

$$I_1 = \int_2^\infty \frac{1}{x^3}\, dx. \tag{18}$$

The natural thing to do is to compute

$$I(M) = \int_2^M \frac{1}{x^3}\, dx.$$

and then take the limit of $I(M)$ as $M \to \infty$. In fact we make this our definition of (18). In other words we agree by definition that

$$\int_a^\infty f(x)dx = \lim_{M \to \infty} \int_a^M f(x)dx \tag{19}$$

whenever the expression on the right side of (19) has a limit. If the expression on the right side has a limit then the integral is said to be *convergent*, otherwise the integral is said to be *divergent*.

EXAMPLE 1. Compute the integral in (18).

SOLUTION. By definition

$$\int_2^\infty \frac{dx}{x^3} = \lim_{M \to \infty} \int_2^M \frac{dx}{x^3} = \lim_{M \to \infty} \frac{-1}{2x^2}\Big|_2^M = \lim_{M \to \infty} \left(-\frac{1}{2M^2} + \frac{1}{8} \right) = \frac{1}{8}.$$

If the interval of integration is $-\infty < x < b$, equation (19) must be modified in an obvious way. If the interval of integration is $-\infty < x < \infty$, equation (19) is replaced by

$$\int_{-\infty}^\infty f(x)dx = \lim_{L \to -\infty} \int_L^0 f(x)dx + \lim_{M \to \infty} \int_0^M f(x)dx.$$

Integrals of this type will be found in Exercise 5.

As an example of the second type of improper integral consider

$$I_2 = \int_1^3 \frac{dx}{(3-x)^2}. \tag{20}$$

Here the integrand $1/(3-x)^2$ becomes infinite at the upper end point of the interval of integration. The natural thing to do is to compute

$$I(\epsilon) = \int_1^{3-\epsilon} \frac{dx}{(3-x)^2}$$

for $\epsilon > 0$, and then take the limit of $I(\epsilon)$ as $\epsilon \to 0^+$. In fact if $\lim\limits_{x\to b} f(x) = \infty$ we make the definition

$$\int_a^b f(x)dx = \lim_{\epsilon\to 0^+} \int_a^{b-\epsilon} f(x)dx \tag{21}$$

whenever the expression cn the right side of (21) has a limit. When this occurs the integral is said to be *convergent*. If the expression on the right side does not have a limit then the integral is said to be *divergent*. We leave it to the student to frame the proper definition, when $f(x)$ becomes infinite at the lefthand end point, or in the interior, of the interval of integration.

EXAMPLE 2. Compute the integral in (20).

SOLUTION. By definition

$$\int_1^3 \frac{dx}{(3-x)^2} = \lim_{\epsilon\to 0^+} \int_1^{3-\epsilon} \frac{dx}{(3-x)^2} = \lim_{\epsilon\to 0^+} \frac{1}{3-x}\Big|_1^{3-\epsilon} = \lim_{\epsilon\to 0^+} \left(\frac{1}{\epsilon} - \frac{1}{2}\right) = \infty.$$

In this case the integral diverges.

EXAMPLE 3. Compute $I_3 = \int_0^6 \frac{2x\, dx}{(x^2-4)^{2/3}}.$

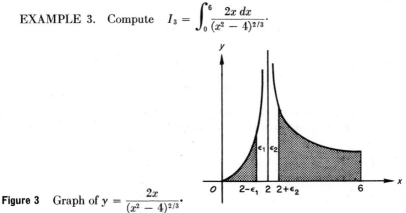

Figure 3   Graph of $y = \dfrac{2x}{(x^2-4)^{2/3}}.$

SOLUTION.   The graph of the curve $y = 2x/(x^2 - 4)^{2/3}$ is shown in Fig. 3. Obviously the function tends to infinity as $x \to 2$, so the curve has a vertical asymptote at $x = 2$.   Since $x = 2$ is inside the interval $0 \leq x \leq 6$ we must break the computation of I_3 into two parts.   Indeed by definition (if the integrals converge)

$$I_3 = \lim_{\epsilon_1 \to 0^+} \int_0^{2-\epsilon_1} \frac{2x\,dx}{(x^2 - 4)^{2/3}} + \lim_{\epsilon_2 \to 0^+} \int_{2+\epsilon_2}^6 \frac{2x\,dx}{(x^2 - 4)^{2/3}}. \tag{22}$$

Thus in (22) we are to compute the area of the shaded regions in Fig. 3 and then take the limit of that area as $\epsilon_1 \to 0^+$ and $\epsilon_2 \to 0^+$.   For simplicity let I' and I'' be the two integrals on the right side of (22).   Then on integrating

$$I' = \lim_{\epsilon_1 \to 0^+} 3(x^2 - 4)^{1/3} \Big|_0^{2-\epsilon_1} = \lim_{\epsilon_1 \to 0^+} (3\sqrt[3]{(2 - \epsilon_1)^2 - 4} + 3\sqrt[3]{4}) = 3\sqrt[3]{4}$$

and

$$I'' = \lim_{\epsilon_2 \to 0^+} 3(x^2 - 4)^{1/3} \Big|_{2+\epsilon_2}^6 = \lim_{\epsilon_2 \to 0^+} (3\sqrt[3]{32} - 3\sqrt[3]{(2 + \epsilon_2)^2 - 4}) = 3\sqrt[3]{32}.$$

Thus $I_3 = I' + I'' = 3\sqrt[3]{4} + 3\sqrt[3]{32} = 9\sqrt[3]{4}$.   Therefore, although the region below the curve $y = 2x/(x^2 - 4)^{2/3}$ between $x = 0$ and $x = 6$ is infinite in extent, it has a finite area, namely $9\sqrt[3]{4}$.

EXAMPLE 4.   Compute $I_4 = \int_0^6 \frac{2x\,dx}{x^2 - 4}$.

SOLUTION.   Following the pattern of Example 3 we have $I_4 = I' + I''$ where

$$I' = \lim_{\epsilon_1 \to 0^+} \ln|x^2 - 4| \Big|_0^{2-\epsilon_1} = \lim_{\epsilon_1 \to 0^+} [\ln \epsilon_1(4 - \epsilon_1) - \ln 4],$$

and

$$I'' = \lim_{\epsilon_2 \to 0^+} \ln|x^2 - 4| \Big|_{2+\epsilon_2}^6 = \lim_{\epsilon_2 \to 0^+} [\ln 32 - \ln \epsilon_2(4 + \epsilon_2)].$$

Clearly $I' = -\infty$ and $I'' = +\infty$, so this integral is divergent.

EXERCISE 5

In problems 1 through 22 evaluate the given improper integral in case it converges.   In each problem interpret the integral as an area under a suitable curve.

1. $\int_1^\infty \frac{dx}{x^2}$.

2. $\int_0^1 \frac{dx}{(1 - x)^2}$.

3. $\int_0^1 \frac{dx}{\sqrt{x}}$.

4. $\int_1^\infty \frac{dx}{\sqrt[3]{x}}$.

5. $\displaystyle\int_0^2 \frac{dx}{4 - x^2}.$

6. $\displaystyle\int_0^3 \frac{x\,dx}{\sqrt{9 - x^2}}.$

7. $\displaystyle\int_1^\infty e^{-2x}\,dx.$

8. $\displaystyle\int_{-\infty}^\infty \frac{x\,dx}{1 + 2x^2}.$

9. $\displaystyle\int_{-\infty}^\infty \frac{dx}{1 + x^2}.$

10. $\displaystyle\int_0^4 \frac{8dx}{\sqrt{16 - x^2}}.$

11. $\displaystyle\int_8^\infty \frac{dx}{x^{4/3}}.$

12. $\displaystyle\int_0^\infty (x - 1)e^{-x}\,dx.$

13. $\displaystyle\int_0^2 \frac{\ln x\,dx}{x}.$

14. $\displaystyle\int_0^2 \frac{\ln x\,dx}{\sqrt{x}}.$

15. $\displaystyle\int_0^{\pi/2} \csc x\,dx.$

16. $\displaystyle\int_{-\infty}^\infty \operatorname{sech} x\,dx.$

17. $\displaystyle\int_{-\infty}^0 \tanh x\,dx.$

18. $\displaystyle\int_0^{\pi/2} \tan x\,dx.$

19. $\displaystyle\int_0^\infty e^{-x}\sin x\,dx.$

20. $\displaystyle\int_{-1}^1 \frac{dx}{\sqrt[3]{x}}.$

21. $\displaystyle\int_{-1}^1 \frac{dx}{x}.$

22. $\displaystyle\int_1^6 \frac{dx}{x^2 - 7x + 12}.$

23. Prove that $\displaystyle\int_1^\infty \frac{dx}{x^k} = \frac{1}{k - 1}$ if $k > 1$, and if $k \le 1$ this integral diverges.

24. State and prove a result similar to that in problem 23 for

$$\int_0^1 \frac{dx}{x^k}.$$

★25. Use mathematical induction to prove that for each positive integer n

$$\int_0^\infty x^n e^{-x}\,dx = n!$$

What is the situation when $n = 0$?

★26. The region bounded by the x-axis and the curve $y = 4/3x^{3/4}$ and to the right of the line $x = 1$ is rotated about the x-axis. Find the volume of the solid generated.

★27. Prove that the surface area of the solid described in problem 26 is infinite. As a result we have a container that can be filled with paint (finite volume) but whose surface cannot be painted (infinite surface). *Hint:* Use the obvious inequality

$$\frac{1}{x^{3/4}}\sqrt{1+\frac{1}{x^{7/2}}} > \frac{1}{x^{3/4}}$$

to prove that

$$S \geqq \frac{8\pi}{3}\int_1^\infty \frac{dx}{x^{3/4}} = \infty \, .$$

**28. A formal computation indicates that the derivative of $-2\sqrt{1-\sin x}$ is $\sqrt{1+\sin x}$. Consequently

$$\int_0^M \sqrt{1+\sin x}\, dx = -2\sqrt{1-\sin x}\,\Big|_0^M = 2 - 2\sqrt{1-\sin M}. \qquad (23)$$

But as $M \to \infty$, the area under the curve $y = \sqrt{1+\sin x}$ between $x = 0$ and $x = M$ becomes infinite (graph the function). On the other hand the right side of (23) is never greater than 2. Where is the error?

12

POLAR COORDINATES

1.   The polar coordinate system.   So far, we have studied exclusively
the rectangular coordinate system.   But there are other coordinate
systems that are frequently useful.   Of these systems, the most important
by far is the polar coordinate system.   In this system a fixed point O is
selected and from this fixed point a fixed ray (half-line) OA is drawn.   The
point O is called the *pole* or *origin*, and the ray OA is called the *polar axis*,
or *polar line*.   All points in the plane are located with respect to the point
O and the ray OA.   For convenience the ray OA is always drawn horizontal and to the right, as shown in Fig. 1.

Figure 1

Now let P be any point in the plane, other than O.   Let r be the distance from P to O, and let θ be the angle from OA to OP.   Then the
numbers r and θ serve as polar coordinates for the point P and these coordinates are written (r, θ).   In this determination of the polar coordinates
for P it is obvious that $r \geq 0$, and $0 \leq \theta < 2\pi$.   However we want to free
our coordinates from this restriction and allow (r, θ) to be any pair of real
numbers.   Hence with each pair of real numbers (r, θ) we associate a
point P by the following procedure.

A ray OL is obtained by turning the polar line through an angle $|\theta|$,
counterclockwise if θ is positive, and clockwise if θ is negative.   Then on
the ray OL a point P is located so that $OP = r$ if r is positive or zero.   If r
is negative, then the ray is extended backward through O, and P is located

375

on this extension so that $OP = |r|$.   This process is illustrated in Fig. 2 where a number of points have been located from their given polar coordinates.

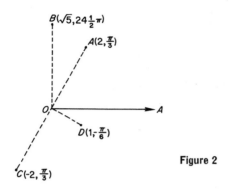

Figure 2

It is clear that to each pair of numbers (r, θ) there corresponds a uniquely determined point P in the plane.   The coordinates (r, θ) are called polar coordinates for P.   But if we are given a point P there may be *many* sets of polar coordinates that correspond to P.   For example if P is at the pole then $r = 0$, but θ can be any real number.   If $r \neq 0$, then θ can be changed by any multiple of 2π.   Or we can replace r by $-r$ and add π to θ to obtain another set of polar coordinates for the point P.   For example the point B in Fig. 2 has the polar coordinates $(\sqrt{5}, (2n + \frac{1}{2})\pi)$ where n is any integer.   The same point B also has the coordinates of $(-\sqrt{5}, (2n + \frac{3}{2})\pi)$.   For this reason we should not speak of *the* polar coordinates of a point because they are not uniquely determined, although for euphony we will frequently make this error.

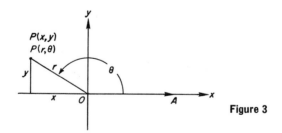

Figure 3

Let us superimpose a rectangular coordinate system on the polar coordinate system, making the origins in both systems coincide and making the positive x-axis fall on the polar line (see Fig. 3).   Then each point P has two types of coordinates, a rectangular set (x, y) and a polar set (r, θ).

We leave it to the student to prove that these coordinates are related by the equations

$$\begin{aligned} x &= r \cos \theta, \\ y &= r \sin \theta, \end{aligned} \tag{1}$$

and

$$\begin{aligned} r^2 &= x^2 + y^2 \\ \tan \theta &= \frac{y}{x}. \end{aligned} \tag{2}$$

The set (1) allows us to pass from the polar coordinates to the rectangular coordinates, and the set (2) takes us in the reverse direction. For example the point $A(2, \pi/3)$ of Fig. 2 has the rectangular coordinates $x = 2 \cos \pi/3 = 1$ and $y = 2 \sin \pi/3 = \sqrt{3}$.

EXERCISE 1

In problems 1 through 9 the polar coordinates of a point are given.   Plot the point and find its rectangular coordinates.

1. $(4, 0)$.
2. $(3, \pi)$.
3. $(-5, -\pi)$.
4. $(2, \pi/2)$.
5. $(4, 3\pi/2)$.
6. $(2, -\pi/6)$.
7. $(8, 3\pi/4)$.
8. $(-8, 5\pi/4)$.
9. $(6, -10\pi/3)$.

In problems 10 through 18 the rectangular coordinates of a point are given. In each case find all possible sets of polar coordinates for the point.

10. $(1, 1)$.
11. $(-\sqrt{3}, \sqrt{3})$.
12. $(2, -2\sqrt{3})$.
13. $(0, -5)$.
14. $(-3, -3)$.
15. $(-4, 0)$.
16. $(3, 4)$.
17. $(-5, 12)$.
18. $(2, -1)$.

19.   Prove that the points (r, θ) and $(r, -\theta)$ are symmetrical with respect to the x-axis.

20.   Prove that the points (r, θ) and $(-r, -\theta)$ are symmetrical with respect to the y-axis.

21.   What can you say about the symmetry of the pair of points (r, θ) and $(-r, \theta)$?

22.   Do problem 21 for the points (r, θ) and $(r, \pi - \theta)$.

23.   Do problem 21 for the points (r, θ) and $(-r, \pi - \theta)$.

24.   Do problem 21 for the points (r, θ) and $\left(r, \dfrac{\pi}{2} - \theta\right)$.

2.   The graph of a polar equation.   Just as in rectangular coordinates, the graph of an equation

$$F(r, \theta) = 0 \tag{3}$$

is by definition the collection of all points $P(r, \theta)$ whose polar coordinates satisfy the equation.   Here the point P has many different sets of coordinates, but P is in the graph if just *one* of its many different sets of coordinates satisfies the equation.

In many cases equation (3) can be solved explicitly for r or θ giving either

$$r = f(\theta) \tag{4}$$

or

$$\theta = g(r). \tag{5}$$

In either of these cases it is easy to sketch the graph.   For example with equation (4), we merely select a sequence of values for θ and compute the associated value for r.

EXAMPLE 1.   Sketch the graph of $r = 2(1 + \cos \theta)$.

SOLUTION.   Since $\cos \theta$ is an even function it is sufficient to make a table for $\theta \geqq 0$.   Selecting the popular angles for θ, and computing r from $r = 2(1 + \cos \theta)$ yields the following table of coordinates for points on the curve.

θ	0	$\pm\dfrac{\pi}{6}$	$\pm\dfrac{\pi}{4}$	$\pm\dfrac{\pi}{3}$	$\pm\dfrac{\pi}{2}$	$\pm\dfrac{2\pi}{3}$	$\pm\dfrac{3\pi}{4}$	$\pm\dfrac{5\pi}{6}$	$\pm\pi$
r	4	$2+\sqrt{3}$	$2+\sqrt{2}$	3	2	1	$2-\sqrt{2}$	$2-\sqrt{3}$	0

The graph of the equation $r = 2(1 + \cos \theta)$ is shown in Fig. 4.   This type of curve is called a *cardioid* because it resembles a heart.

We can also pose the converse problem: given a collection of points, find a polar equation whose graph is the given point set.

EXAMPLE 2.   Find an equation (in polar coordinates) for the circle with center at $(3, 0)$ and radius 3.

SOLUTION.   This circle is shown in Fig. 5.   One diameter of the circle will be the line joining the pole O and the point $R(6, 0)$.   If P is on the circle then $\angle OPR$ is a right angle (inscribed in a semi-circle) and hence $r = |OR| \cos \theta$ or $r = 6 \cos \theta$.   On the other hand it is easy to see that if (r, θ) satisfy $r = 6 \cos \theta$ then P is on the circle.   Therefore this is an equation for the given circle.

To find points of intersection of two given curves we solve their polar coordinate equations simultaneously. But unfortunately this may not give *all* the points of intersection. This peculiar behavior can occur, because the polar coordinates of a point are not unique.

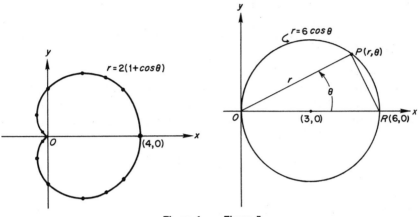

Figure 4   Figure 5

EXAMPLE 3. Find all the points of intersection of the two curves $r = 2(1 + \cos \theta)$ and $r = 6 \cos \theta$.

SOLUTION. These are the curves of Figs. 4 and 5, so the desired points could be found geometrically by superimposing the two sketches.

Suppose that we are to solve this problem analytically. Let (r_1, θ_1) be coordinates of a point P that is on both curves. If (r_1, θ_1) satisfy both of the equations $r = 2(1 + \cos \theta)$ and $r = 6 \cos \theta$ we can write $2(1 + \cos \theta_1) = 6 \cos \theta_1$ since both sides give r_1. Therefore $2 \cos \theta_1 = 1$, and hence $\cos \theta_1 = 1/2$, and $\theta_1 = \pi/3 + 2n\pi$ or $-\pi/3 + 2n\pi$. Using these values for θ in either $r = 2(1 + \cos \theta)$ or $r = 6 \cos \theta$ yields $r_1 = 3$. Therefore $(3, \pi/3)$ and $(3, -\pi/3)$

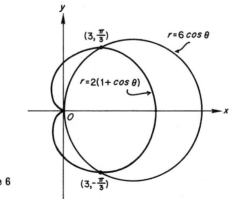

Figure 6

are intersection points of the two given curves. But if we superimpose the two curves as indicated in Fig. 6 we find that the curves also intersect at the origin. How did we miss this point of intersection?

The cardioid passes through the origin because the coordinates $(0, \pi)$ satisfy the equation $r = 2(1 + \cos \theta)$. The curve $r = 6 \cos \theta$ passes through the origin because the coordinates $(0, \pi/2)$ satisfy this equation. Although the point is the same in both cases, the two coordinates $(0, \pi)$ and $(0, \pi/2)$ are different. Hence this point is missed when we solve the pair of equations simultaneously.

There are a number of general rules to handle this situation. One rule is to test the given equation to see if the origin is on both curves, by setting $r = 0$ in each of the equations. A second rule is to replace θ by $\theta + 2n\pi$ in one of the equations. Thus if $r = f(\theta)$ and $r = g(\theta)$ are the equations for the two curves we would solve

$$f(\theta) = g(\theta + 2n\pi)$$

for θ. Such values of θ, would lead to points of intersection of the two curves that may have been missed when we simply set $f(\theta) = g(\theta)$. In most cases however, a sketch of the two curves will be helpful in determining the points of intersection.

*EXAMPLE 4.   Find the points of intersection of the two curves $r = \theta (\theta \geqq 0)$, and $r = 2\theta$, $(\theta \geqq 0)$.

SOLUTION.   We have imposed the restriction that θ is not negative in order to simplify the work.   If we proceed to solve the two equations simultaneously we have $\theta = 2\theta$ or $\theta = 0$ as the only solution.   Therefore a hasty conclusion is that these two curves intersect only at the origin.   But a sketch of the graphs quickly shows that there are *many* other points of intersection.   A portion of the two curves is shown in Fig. 7, where the solid curve represents $r = \theta$ and the dotted curve represents $r = 2\theta$.   To find other points of intersection we replace θ by $\theta_0 + 2m\pi$ in one equation, and by $\theta_0 + 2n\pi$ in the second one.   Here m and n are any pair of positive integers and θ_0 lies in the interval $0 \leqq \theta_0 < 2\pi$.   Then if the corresponding values of r are equal we must have

$$\theta_0 + 2n\pi = 2(\theta_0 + 2m\pi),$$

or

$$\theta_0 = 2\pi(n - 2m).$$

With our restriction on θ, we find that $n = 2m$ so that $\theta_0 = 0$.   The points of intersection have the coordinates $(4m\pi, 4m\pi)$, $m = 0, 1, 2, \cdots$ for the first curve, and $(4m\pi, 2m\pi)$, $m = 0, 1, 2, \cdots$ for the second curve.

Each of the curves in Fig. 7 has the form $r = c\theta$ where c is a constant.   The curve $r = c\theta$ is called a *spiral of Archimedes*.   Clearly these two spirals intersect infinitely often, and all the points of intersection lie on the polar line.

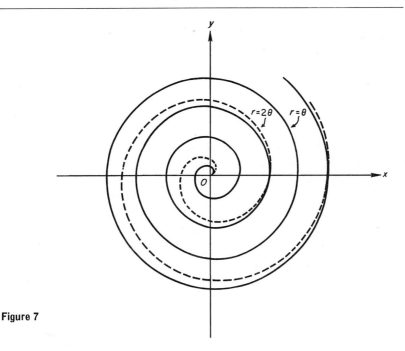

Figure 7

EXERCISE 2

In problems 1 through 10 sketch the curve and if possible give its name. Throughout this chapter a and b denote positive constants.

1. $r = 4$.

2. $\theta = \pi/3$.

3. $r \cos \theta = 5$.

4. $r \sin \theta = 3$.

5. $r = 4(1 + \sin \theta)$.

6. $r = 2 \cos \theta - 1$.

7. $r\theta = \pi$.

8. $r = a \cos 2\theta$.

9. $r^2 = a^2 \sin 2\theta$.

10. $r = a \cos 3\theta$.

11. Prove that the vertical line $x = A$ has $r \cos \theta = A$ as an equation in polar coordinates.

12. Prove that the horizontal line $y = B$ has $r \sin \theta = B$ as an equation in polar coordinates.

13. Find a suitable equation in polar coordinates for the circle $x^2 + y^2 = 2By$.

In problems 14 through 21 find all of the points of intersection of the given pair of curves.

14. $r \sin \theta = 2$, and $r = 4 \sin \theta$.

15. $r \cos \theta = 2$, and $r \sin \theta + 2\sqrt{3} = 0$.

16. $r = a$, and $r = 4a \cos \theta$.

17. $r = a \sin \theta$, and $r = a \cos \theta$.

18. $r = \cos \theta$, and $r = 2/(3 + 2 \cos \theta)$.

19. $r \cos \theta = 1$, and $r = 2 \cos \theta + 1$.

★20. $r^2 = 2 \cos \theta$, and $r = 2(\cos \theta + 1)$.

★21. $r = a \cos 2\theta$, and $4r \cos \theta = a\sqrt{3}$.

★22. Find a suitable equation for the locus of the midpoints of the chords from a given fixed point on a given fixed circle. Identify the curve.

★23. A line segment of fixed length $2a$ slides in such a way that one end is always on the x-axis, and the other end is always on the y-axis. Find an equation in polar coordinates for the locus of points P in which a line from the origin perpendicular to the moving segment intersects the segment. Sketch the curve.

3.   Curve sketching in polar coordinates. We may frequently shorten the labor of sketching a curve, by testing the equation of the curve for symmetries of the curve. We leave it to the student to justify the rules which are given in the following table. Here the variables r and θ are replaced as indicated in the first two columns, and if the equation $F(r, \theta) = 0$ remains unchanged or is transformed into an equivalent equation then the curve has the symmetry indicated in the third column.

Original	Replaced by	Curve is symmetrical with respect to
r, θ	$r, -\theta$	the x-axis[1] $(\theta = 0)$
r, θ	$-r, -\theta$	the y-axis $\left(\theta = \dfrac{\pi}{2}\right)$
r, θ	$-r, \theta$	the origin
r, θ	$r, \pi - \theta$	the y-axis
r, θ	$-r, \pi - \theta$	the x-axis
r, θ	$r, \dfrac{\pi}{2} - \theta$	the line $y = x \left(\theta = \dfrac{\pi}{4}\right)$

Table 1

EXAMPLE 1. Examine the curve $r = 4 \sin 2\theta$ for symmetry.

SOLUTION. Since the sine function is an odd function, $\sin(-2\theta) = -\sin 2\theta$. Hence applying the second test from Table 1 we obtain the equation $-r = 4 \sin(-2\theta)$. But this equation is equivalent to $r = 4 \sin 2\theta$, so the curve is symmetrical with respect to the y-axis. Let us apply the fifth test from Table 1. The altered equation is $-r = \sin 2(\pi - \theta)$. But $\sin 2(\pi - \theta) = \sin(2\pi - 2\theta) = \sin(-2\theta) = -\sin 2\theta$. Hence the equation $-r = \sin 2(\pi - \theta)$ is equivalent to $r = \sin 2\theta$, and the curve is symmetric with respect to the x-axis.

[1] Strictly speaking $\theta = \theta_0$ is not a line but a ray (half of a line). Henceforth the phrase "the line $\theta = \theta_0$" will mean the union of the two rays $\theta = \theta_0$ and $\theta = \theta_0 + \pi$.

Now any curve that is symmetric with respect to the x- and y-axis is also symmetric with respect to the origin. But please note that while the curve has all of these symmetries the first, third, and fourth tests from Table 1 fail to reveal them. Consequently these tests are sufficient to insure the symmetries stated, but are not necessary. We leave it to the student to apply the sixth test from Table 1 and show that the curve is also symmetric with respect to the line $y = x$. As a result of all these symmetries, it is sufficient to sketch the curve, just in the sector between $\theta = 0$ and $\theta = \pi/4$, and then the rest of the curve can be obtained by reflections. The graph of $r = 4 \sin 2\theta$ is shown in Fig. 8 and for obvious reasons the curve is known as the *four-leafed rose.*

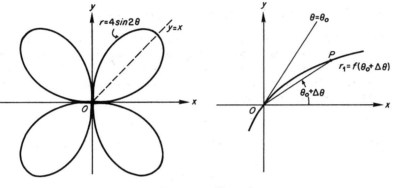

Figure 8 **Figure 9**

In sketching a curve it is helpful to know something about the tangent lines to the curve. We shall consider the general problem in section 5. However when the curve passes through the origin, there is a very simple rule for the tangent line, given in

THEOREM 1. *If $f(\theta)$ is continuous at θ_0 and if $f(\theta_0) = 0$, then the curve $r = f(\theta)$ has the line $\theta = \theta_0$ as a tangent line at the origin.*

PROOF. The origin is on the curve since $r = f(\theta_0) = 0$ by hypothesis. We change θ_0 by a small amount $\Delta\theta$ and consider the point $P(r_1, \theta_0 + \Delta\theta)$ on the curve where $r_1 = f(\theta_0 + \Delta\theta)$. Then the line joining O and P is a secant of the curve. But as $\Delta\theta \to 0$, this secant tends to the line $\theta = \theta_0$. On the other hand, since $f(\theta)$ is continuous at θ_0, r_1 tends to zero as $\Delta\theta \to 0$, so that the point P moves toward O. Thus the limiting position of the secant line $\theta = \theta_0 + \Delta\theta$ is the line $\theta = \theta_0$ as P approaches O. But then the line $\theta = \theta_0$ is a tangent line, by the definition of a tangent line as the limiting position of the secant line. In Fig. 9 where this proof is illustrated, the increment $\Delta\theta$ is negative.

As an example, consider the equation $r = 4 \sin 2\theta$, and its graph as shown in Fig. 8. We have that $r = 0$ whenever $\sin 2\theta = 0$, and this

occurs for $\theta = 0, \pi/2, \pi, 3\pi/2, \cdots$. Hence each of these lines is tangent
to the curve at the origin. In this case however, there are only two distinct tangent lines at the origin, although the curve passes through the
origin four times as θ runs from $-\epsilon$ to $2\pi - \epsilon, \epsilon > 0$.

In sketching a curve, we can always seek help by transforming the
given equation from one coordinate system to another. In changing the
equation from polar coordinates to rectangular coordinates, or in the reverse direction, the equation set (1) $x = r \cos \theta$, and $y = r \sin \theta$ is very
useful.

EXAMPLE 2.   Sketch the curve $r = 2(\sin \theta + \cos \theta)$.

SOLUTION.   We transform this equation into rectangular coordinates to see
if it looks better in that system. If we multiply both sides by r, we introduce
$r = 0$ as a solution, and hence add the origin to the curve. But the origin is
already on the curve (set $\theta = 3\pi/4$ in the original equation) so no harm is
done. After multiplying by r we have

$$r^2 = 2(r \sin \theta + r \cos \theta).$$

But $r^2 = x^2 + y^2$, $r \sin \theta = y$, and $r \cos \theta = x$. Hence this equation is equivalent to

$$x^2 + y^2 = 2y + 2x$$
$$(x - 1)^2 + (y - 1)^2 = 2.$$

So the graph of $r = 2(\sin \theta + \cos \theta)$ is a circle with center $(1, 1)$ and radius $\sqrt{2}$.

EXAMPLE 3.   Sketch the curve $(x^2 + y^2)^3 = 16x^2y^2$.

SOLUTION.   Clearly it would be troublesome to make a table of values for
points (x, y) on the curve. We try transforming the curve into polar coordinates. We have as equivalent equations

$$(r^2)^3 = 16(r \cos \theta)^2 (r \sin \theta)^2$$
$$r^6 = 16 r^4 \sin^2 \theta \cos^2 \theta$$
$$r^2 = 16 \sin^2 \theta \cos^2 \theta$$
$$r = \pm 4 \sin \theta \cos \theta = \pm 2 \sin 2\theta.$$

But this last is exactly the equation of example 1 with the factor 4 replaced
by ± 2. Since the curve $r = 4 \sin 2\theta$ is a four-leafed rose, the graph of $r =
2 \sin 2\theta$ is also a four-leafed rose as shown in Fig. 8 except shrunk by a factor
of $1/2$. Finally the curve is already symmetric with respect to the origin,
so the $\pm$ sign may be dropped in $r = \pm 2 \sin 2\theta$ without changing the curve.

EXERCISE 3

In problems 1 through 10 find the lines of symmetry and sketch the given curve.

1. $r \cos \theta = 5.$ **2.** $r \sin \theta = 3.$

3. $r = 4 + \sin \theta$.

4. $r = 1 + 4 \cos \theta$.

5. $r^2 = 16 \sin 2\theta$.

6. $r = 4 \sin 3\theta$.

7. $r = 4 \cos 3\theta$.

8. $r = 2 \tan \theta \sin \theta$.

9. $r = \dfrac{2}{1 - \sin \theta}$.

*10. $r = \dfrac{1}{\cos 2\theta}$.

11. By transforming to rectangular coordinates prove that the graph $r(A \cos \theta + B \sin \theta) = C$ is always a straight line provided that A and B are not both zero.

12. Prove that the graph of $r = 2A \sin \theta + 2B \cos \theta$ is always a circle through the origin (or a single point). Find the radius and center of the circle.

In problems 13 through 18 transform the given equation into an equation in polar coordinates for the same curve.

13. $x^2 + y^2 - 6y = \sqrt{x^2 + y^2}$.

14. $x^4 + y^4 = 2xy(2 - xy)$.

15. $y^2(1 + x) = x^3$.

16. $x^3 + y^3 = 8xy$.

17. $y^2 = x^2 \dfrac{a + x}{a - x}$.

*18. $x^4 + 2x^2y^2 + y^4 = 6x^2y - 2y^3$.

In problems 19 through 22 transform the given equation into an equation in rectangular coordinates for the same curve.

19. $r = 2 \tan \theta \sin \theta$.

20. $r = \dfrac{8}{1 - \cos \theta}$.

21. $r^2 = \tan \theta \sin^2 \theta$.

22. $r^2 = a^2 \cos 2\theta$.

*23. Sketch the curve $r = a \sin n\theta$ for $0 \leqq \theta \leqq \pi/n$. From this part of the graph deduce the fact that if n is an integer the complete graph is a rose. If n is an even integer the rose has $2n$ petals or loops but if n is an odd integer the rose has only n petals or loops. Prove the same assertion about the graph of $r = a \cos n\theta$, by proving that it is congruent to the graph of $r = a \sin n\theta$. *Hint:* Replace θ by $\theta + 3\pi/2n$ in $r = a \cos n\theta$.

*24. If C_1 is the curve $r = f(\theta)$ and C_2 is the curve $r = kf(\theta)$ where k is a non-zero constant, the curve C_2 is said to be *similar* to C_1 with the origin as the *center of similitude*. (a) Prove that if C_1 is a straight line then C_2 is also a straight line. (b) Prove that if C_1 is a circle through the origin then C_2 is also a circle through the origin. (c) Show that (b) includes the result of problem 22, Exercise 2 as a special case.

*4. Conic sections in polar coordinates.

We recall from Chapter 6 (Definition 2) that a conic section is the collection of all points P such that

$$\frac{|PF|}{|PD|} = e \tag{6}$$

where $|PF|$ is the distance from P to the focus F, $|PD|$ is the distance from P to the directrix, a fixed line L, and e is the eccentricity. If $0 < e < 1$ the curve is an ellipse, if $e = 1$ the curve is a parabola, and if $e > 1$ the curve is a hyperbola. We will use this definition to obtain a nice equation

in polar coordinates for the conic sections.   In order to obtain a simple
result we put the focus F at the origin and we let the directrix be a vertical
line p units $(p > 0)$ to the left of the focus, as shown in Fig. 10.

THEOREM 2.   *Under the conditions just described the equation*

$$r = \frac{ep}{1 - e \cos \theta} \qquad (7)$$

is an equation in polar coordinates for the conic section (6).

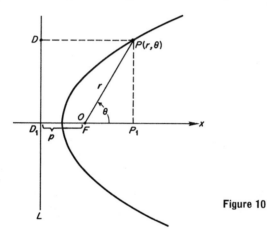

Figure 10

PROOF.   Referring to Fig. 10, the distance $|PD|$ is given by

$$|PD| = |P_1 D_1|$$
$$= D_1 F + F P_1$$
$$= p + r \cos \theta.$$

Further $|PF| = r$, and so if P is on the conic section (6) then

$$\frac{r}{p + r \cos \theta} = e. \qquad (8)$$

Solving equation (8) for r gives (7).   Q.E.D.

EXAMPLE 1.   Describe the graph of $r = \dfrac{8}{1 - 2 \cos \theta}$.

SOLUTION.   Since this equation fits the pattern (7) the graph is a conic
section.   But $e = 2$ so we know that the graph is a hyperbola.   Further
$8 = ep = 2p$, so $p = 4$.   Hence for this hyperbola one focus is at the origin
and its associated directrix is a vertical line 4 units to the left of the origin.

EXAMPLE 2.   Describe the graph of $r = \dfrac{5}{4 - \cos \theta}$.

SOLUTION.   To put this equation in the form (7) we must divide the numerator and denominator by 4, obtaining

$$r = \frac{\dfrac{5}{4}}{1 - \dfrac{1}{4} \cos \theta}.$$

Then $e = 1/4$ and since $5/4 = ep = p/4$ we have $p = 5$.   Hence the graph is an ellipse with one focus at the origin and its associated directrix is a vertical line five units to the left.   What is the major axis of this ellipse?   The fraction $5/(4 - \cos \theta)$ is a maximum (minimum) when the denominator is a minimum (maximum).   If we set $\theta = 0$, $\cos \theta = 1$, then $r = 5/(4 - 1) = 5/3$, its maximum value.   If we set $\theta = \pi$, $\cos \theta = -1$ and $r = 5/(4 + 1) = 1$ its minimum value.   Then the length of the major axis is $1 + 5/3 = 8/3$.   (Why did we add these two numbers?)

EXERCISE 4

In problems 1 through 4 identify the particular conic, and give its eccentricity and the distance of the directrix from the origin.

1. $r = \dfrac{7}{1 - \cos \theta}$.

2. $r = \dfrac{5}{1 - 3 \cos \theta}$.

3. $r = \dfrac{10}{4 - 3 \cos \theta}$.

4. $r = \dfrac{10}{3 - 4 \cos \theta}$.

5.   Derive a standard form similar to equation (7) for a conic with one focus at the origin O, and its associated directrix:

    a.   vertical and p units to the right of O,

    b.   horizontal and p units above O,

    c.   horizontal and p units below O.

6.   Describe the conic $r = \dfrac{12}{2 + \sin \theta}$ and sketch its graph.

7.   Suppose $e < 1$.   Use differential calculus to find the polar coordinates of that point on the ellipse $r = ep/(1 - e \cos \theta)$ that is (a) closest to the origin, (b) furthest from the origin.

8.   Find a formula for the length of the major axis for the ellipse of problem 7. Find the polar coordinates of its center.

★9.   Let (r_0, θ_0) be the polar coordinates for the upper end point of the minor axis of the ellipse of problem 7.   Recall that in rectangular coordinates $c = ae$, $d = a/e$.   Combine this with $p = d - c$ and $c = r_0 \cos \theta_0$ to prove that $r_0 \cos \theta_0 = e^2 p/(1 - e^2)$.

★10. Combine the result of problem 9 with the formula $r = ep/(1 - e \cos \theta)$ to find θ_0. Find the coordinates of the end points of the minor axis. Find its length.

★11. Show that $r \sin \theta$ is a maximum for points on the ellipse, when the point is the upper end point of the minor axis. Use this fact and the calculus to rederive the result of problem 10.

12. Apply the results of problems 7, 8, and 9 to the ellipse $r = 12/(2 - \cos \theta)$. Find the coordinates of its vertices, and the length of its major and minor axes.

13. Prove that the graph of $r = a \sec^2(\theta/2)$ is a parabola and find the polar coordinates of its vertex.

14. A focal chord of a conic section is a chord that passes through one focus of the conic. Let the focus F divide the chord into two segments of lengths d_1 and d_2. Prove that for a fixed ellipse or parabola $1/d_1 + 1/d_2$ is a constant. What is this constant?

★15. Prove that for a hyperbola the assertion of problem 14 is false unless we stay on one branch. Consider for example the particular hyperbola $r = 15/(1 - 4 \cos \theta)$ and first set $\theta = 0$ and then $\theta = \pi/3$.

5.   Differentiation in polar coordinates. Of course the differentiation formulas for $r = f(\theta)$ are just the same as for $y = f(x)$, only the names of the variables have been altered. But the geometric interpretation of the derivative must be different because we are now using a different coordinate system. Our first impulse is to search for a formula for the slope of a line tangent to the curve $r = f(\theta)$. This is given in

THEOREM 3.   *If m is the slope of the line tangent to the curve $r = f(\theta)$ in polar coordinates then*

$$m = \frac{r \cos \theta + \dfrac{dr}{d\theta} \sin \theta}{\dfrac{dr}{d\theta} \cos \theta - r \sin \theta}. \tag{9}$$

PROOF.   The rectangular coordinates of a point on the curve can be obtained from the polar coordinates through the equation set

$$x = r \cos \theta = f(\theta) \cos \theta, \tag{10}$$
$$y = r \sin \theta = f(\theta) \sin \theta.$$

Looking at the extreme right side of equation set (10) we see that these equations can be regarded as parametric equations for the curve in rectangular coordinates, with θ as the parameter. Then from (10) we have

$$m = \frac{dy}{dx} = \frac{\dfrac{dy}{d\theta}}{\dfrac{dx}{d\theta}} = \frac{f(\theta) \cos \theta + f'(\theta) \sin \theta}{f'(\theta) \cos \theta - f(\theta) \sin \theta}. \tag{11}$$

But this is equivalent to (9).   Q.E.D.

Because formula (9) is a little complicated we prefer to have some geometric quantity that is given by a simpler formula. Such a quantity is the angle ψ shown in Fig. 11, and the formula for $\tan \psi$ is given in

THEOREM 4. *Let P be a point on the curve $r = f(\theta)$ and let ψ be the angle from the radial line OP extended, to the tangent line to the curve $r = f(\theta)$ at P (see Fig. 11). If $r \neq 0$ then*

$$\tan \psi = \frac{r}{\dfrac{dr}{d\theta}} \tag{12}$$

where the right side is computed at P.

PROOF. In the case shown in Fig. 11 it is clear that $\alpha = \theta + \psi$ or

$$\psi = \alpha - \theta. \tag{13}$$

Now by definition α and ψ must be in the intervals $0 \leq \alpha < \pi$ and $0 \leq \psi < \pi$, but θ itself is unrestricted. Hence in the general case (13) must be replaced by

$$\psi = \alpha - \theta + n\pi \tag{14}$$

where n is some suitably selected integer. But either (13) or (14) gives

$$\tan \psi = \frac{\tan \alpha - \tan \theta}{1 + \tan \alpha \tan \theta}. \tag{15}$$

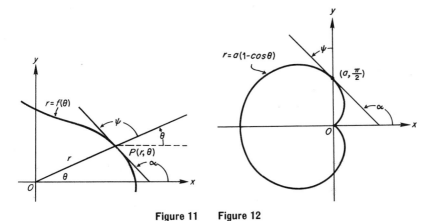

Figure 11   Figure 12

Now $\tan \alpha = m$, so using (11) and (15) yields

$$\tan \psi = \frac{\dfrac{f(\theta) \cos \theta + f'(\theta) \sin \theta}{f'(\theta) \cos \theta - f(\theta) \sin \theta} - \dfrac{\sin \theta}{\cos \theta}}{1 + \dfrac{f(\theta) \cos \theta + f'(\theta) \sin \theta}{f'(\theta) \cos \theta - f(\theta) \sin \theta} \cdot \dfrac{\sin \theta}{\cos \theta}}.$$

But after a little labor this simplifies to $\tan \psi = f(\theta)/f'(\theta)$ and this is equivalent to (12). Q.E.D.

EXAMPLE 1.   For the cardioid $r = a(1 - \cos \theta)$ find $\tan \alpha$ and $\tan \psi$ (a) in general, (b) at $P(a, \pi/2)$ (see Fig. 12).

SOLUTION.   (a) From equation (9) we have

$$\tan \alpha = m = \frac{a(1 - \cos \theta) \cos \theta + a \sin^2 \theta}{a \sin \theta \cos \theta - a(1 - \cos \theta) \sin \theta}$$

$$= \frac{\cos \theta + \sin^2 \theta - \cos^2 \theta}{2 \sin \theta \cos \theta - \sin \theta} = \frac{\cos \theta - \cos 2\theta}{\sin 2\theta - \sin \theta}$$

$$= \frac{2 \sin \dfrac{3\theta}{2} \sin \dfrac{\theta}{2}}{2 \cos \dfrac{3\theta}{2} \sin \dfrac{\theta}{2}} = \tan \frac{3\theta}{2}.$$

From equation (12)

$$\tan \psi = \frac{a(1 - \cos \theta)}{a \sin \theta} = \frac{2 \sin^2 \dfrac{\theta}{2}}{2 \sin \dfrac{\theta}{2} \cos \dfrac{\theta}{2}} = \tan \frac{\theta}{2}.$$

(b) At $\theta = \pi/2$, $\tan \alpha = \tan(3\pi/4) = -1$ and hence $\alpha = 3\pi/4$. Similarly $\tan \psi = \tan(\pi/4) = 1$ so $\psi = \pi/4$. These angles are shown in Fig. 12.

The same procedure used for proving Theorem 3 will give us a formula for ds, where s is the arc length on the curve.

THEOREM 5.   *If s denotes arc length on the curve $r = f(\theta)$ in polar coordinates then*

$$\boxed{ds^2 = dr^2 + r^2 d\theta^2.} \tag{16}$$

PROOF.   Again we regard θ as a parameter and the equation set (10) as parametric equations for the curve in rectangular coordinates. Then

$$ds^2 = dx^2 + dy^2 = \left(\frac{dx}{d\theta}\right)^2 d\theta^2 + \left(\frac{dy}{d\theta}\right)^2 d\theta^2$$

$$= [(f'(\theta) \cos \theta - f(\theta) \sin \theta)^2 + (f'(\theta) \sin \theta + f(\theta) \cos \theta)^2] d\theta^2$$

$$= [f'(\theta)^2 (\sin^2 \theta + \cos^2 \theta) + f(\theta)^2 (\sin^2 \theta + \cos^2 \theta)] d\theta^2$$

$$= \left(\frac{dr}{d\theta}\right)^2 d\theta^2 + r^2 d\theta^2 = dr^2 + r^2 d\theta^2. \qquad\qquad \text{Q.E.D.}$$

Once we have proved the formulas of Theorems 4 and 5, we may use any convenient device to assist in memorizing them. One such device is shown in Fig. 13. Here P and Q are neighboring points on the curve and

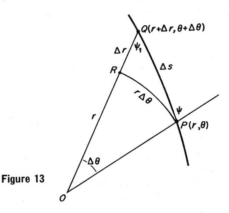

Figure 13

the point R is the intersection of the circle with center 0 and radius r, with the ray OQ. Since the angle at R is a right angle, the figure PQR is a curvilinear right triangle. Then (approximately)

$$(\Delta s)^2 \approx |RQ|^2 + |PR|^2 \approx (\Delta r)^2 + (r\Delta\theta)^2$$

and

$$\tan \psi \approx \tan \psi_1 \approx \frac{|PR|}{|RQ|} \approx \frac{r\Delta\theta}{\Delta r} = \frac{r}{\dfrac{\Delta r}{\Delta\theta}}.$$

These approximate equations readily suggest the limit equations (16) and (12) respectively.

EXAMPLE 2. Find the total length of the cardioid $r = a(1 - \cos \theta)$, (see Fig. 12).

SOLUTION. By Theorem 5, equation (16)

$$L = \int_0^{2\pi} ds = \int_0^{2\pi} \sqrt{r^2 + \left(\frac{dr}{d\theta}\right)^2} \, d\theta = \int_0^{2\pi} \sqrt{a^2(1 - \cos \theta)^2 + a^2 \sin^2 \theta} \, d\theta$$

$$= \int_0^{2\pi} a\sqrt{2 - 2\cos \theta} \, d\theta = \int_0^{2\pi} 2a \left| \sin \frac{\theta}{2} \right| d\theta,$$

since $1 - \cos \theta = 2 \sin^2(\theta/2)$. We are forced to use the absolute value signs in this last step because by definition $\dfrac{ds}{d\theta} \geq 0$, while $\sin(\theta/2)$ may be negative. Fortunately, however, for $0 \leq \theta \leq 2\pi$ it is true that $\sin(\theta/2) \geq 0$. Hence we can drop the absolute value signs and write

$$L = \int_0^{2\pi} 2a \sin \frac{\theta}{2}\, d\theta = -4a \cos \frac{\theta}{2} \Big|_0^{2\pi} = +4a - (-4a) = 8a.$$

For some problems it is advantageous to express the arc length as an integral on r. Starting from equation (16) it is easy to derive

$$L = \int_{r_1}^{r_2} \sqrt{1 + r^2 \left(\frac{d\theta}{dr}\right)^2}\, dr. \qquad (17)$$

EXERCISE 5

1. Find those points on the cardioid $r = a(1 - \sin \theta)$ where the tangent line is horizontal.

2. Find all the points on the parabola $r = a/(1 - \cos \theta)$ where the tangent line has slope 1.

3. Find α and ψ for the circle $r = a \sin \theta$.

4. Prove that $\tan \psi = \theta$ for the spiral of Archimedes $r = a\theta$.

5. Prove that for the *logarithmic spiral* $r = ae^{b\theta}$, ψ is a constant. For this reason the curve is also called the *equiangular spiral*.

*6. For the parabola $r = a/(1 - \cos \theta)$, prove that if $0 \leq \theta < \pi$, then $\tan \psi = -\tan(\theta/2)$ and consequently $\psi = \pi - \theta/2$. Show that this establishes the following optical property. If a ray of light starts from the focus of a parabolic reflector, it is reflected from the walls in a line parallel to the axis of the parabola.

7. If φ is the angle of intersection between the curves $r_1 = f_1(\theta)$ and $r_2 = f_2(\theta)$, measured from the first curve to the second curve, show that

$$\tan \varphi = \frac{\tan \psi_2 - \tan \psi_1}{1 + \tan \psi_2 \tan \psi_1}.$$

Deduce from this a condition that a pair of curves intersect orthogonally.

8. Use the condition found in problem 7 to show that the following pairs of curves intersect orthogonally.

    a. $r = a \sin \theta$, $\quad r = b \cos \theta$.
    b. $r = a/(1 - \cos \theta)$, $\quad r = b/(1 + \cos \theta)$.
    c. $r^2 = a^2/\sin 2\theta$, $\quad r^2 = b^2/\cos 2\theta$.
    d. $r = a(1 - \cos \theta)$, $\quad r = a(1 + \cos \theta)$, except at the origin.
    e. $r^2 = a^2 \sin 2\theta$, $\quad r^2 = b^2 \cos 2\theta$, except at the origin.
    f. $r = 9/(2 - \cos \theta)$, $\quad r = 3/\cos \theta$.

9. Sketch the two curves $r = a/\theta$, and $r = a\theta$, and show that these two

curves intersect infinitely often.   Prove that they intersect orthogonally at only
two of the points, and find those points.

   10.   For each of the following curves find the length of the indicated arc.

     a. $r = 2\theta^2,\ \ 0 \leq \theta \leq 5$.

     b. $r = ae^{b\theta},\ \ 0 \leq \theta \leq \pi$.

     c. $r = a\sin^3(\theta/3),\ \ 0 \leq \theta \leq 3\pi$.

     d. $r = a/\theta^3,\ \ 1 \leq \theta \leq 4$.

   11.   Use equation (17) to compute the length of the curve $r\theta = 1$ for $\frac{1}{2} \leq \theta \leq 1$.

   12.   Show that the part of the curve $r\theta = 1$, that lies inside the circle $r = 1$,
has infinite length.

   13.   An arc of the curve $r = f(\theta)$ that lies above the x-axis is rotated about the
x-axis.   Find a formula for the area of the surface generated.

   14.   The lemniscate $r^2 = a^2 \cos 2\theta$ is rotated about the x-axis.   Find the area
of the surface.   *Hint:* Use symmetry and integrate from 0 to $\pi/4$.

   ★15.   The cardioid $r = a(1 - \cos\theta)$ is rotated about the x-axis.   Find the area
of the surface.

   ★16.   The arc of the curve $r = e^{\theta}$ for $0 \leq \theta \leq \pi$ is rotated about the x-axis.
Find the area of the surface.

   17.   The lemniscate of problem 14 is rotated about the y-axis.   Find the area
of the surface.

   18.   The circle $r = a \cos\theta$ is rotated about the y-axis.   Find the area of the
surface.

   ★19.   Suppose the function $f(\theta)$ is positive and has period 2π.   Then the graph
of $r = f(\theta)$ is a *simple closed curve* that goes around the origin.   Such a curve is
said to be *convex* if the tangent line to the curve turns in a counterclockwise manner
as θ increases from 0 to 2π.   Prove that if the curve is convex then $2(r')^2 + r^2 \geq rr''$.

   ★20.   Use the criterion of problem 19 to prove that the limaçon $r = a + b\cos\theta$
is convex if $a \geq 2b$ and not otherwise.   Sketch the curves for the cases $a = 3b$,
$a = 2b$, $a = b/2$.

6.   Plane areas in polar coordinates

     THEOREM 6.   *Let $r = f(\theta)$ be a positive continuous function
for $\alpha \leq \theta \leq \beta$.   Let R be the region bounded by the curve $r = f(\theta)$
and the rays $\theta = \alpha$ and $\theta = \beta$ (see Fig. 14).   Then the area of R
is given by*

$$A = \int_{\alpha}^{\beta} \tfrac{1}{2}r^2\,d\theta. \tag{18}$$

PROOF.   We divide the interval $\alpha \leq \theta \leq \beta$ into n subintervals and let
$\theta_0, \theta_1, \cdots, \theta_n$ be the points of subdivision where $\alpha = \theta_0$ and $\beta = \theta_n$.   We
draw the rays $\theta = \theta_k$ for $k = 1, 2, 3, \cdots, n - 1$, and these rays divide the

region R into n parts as shown in Fig. 15 where $n = 5$.   At each point $P_k(r_k, \theta_k)$ we draw an arc of a circle $r = r_k$ extending from the ray $\theta = \theta_k$ to $\theta = \theta_{k+1}$.   Let us assume for simplicity that the function $r = f(\theta)$ is increasing in the interval $\alpha \le \theta \le \beta$, as shown in the two figures.   Then the

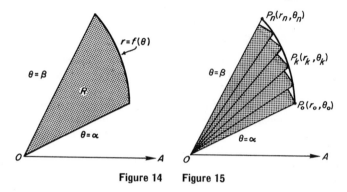

Figure 14   Figure 15

rays $\theta = \theta_k$, and the circular arcs $r = r_k$ taken together form the boundaries of a set of circular sectors, shown shaded in Fig. 15, and because $f(\theta)$ is increasing, these sectors are all contained in the region R.   Further the total area of the sectors forms a good approximation (from below) to the area of R and the error in this approximation can be made arbitrarily small if we take n, the number of subdivisions, sufficiently large.   Let A_k denote the area of the sector bounded by the two radial lines $\theta = \theta_{k-1}$ and $\theta = \theta_k$ and the arc of the circle $r = r_k$.   Then

$$A = \lim_{n \to \infty} \sum_{k=1}^{n} A_k. \qquad (19)$$

To find A_k we recall from Chapter 7 (equation (1)) that if γ is the radian measure of the sector angle and r is the radius then the area of the sector is $r^2\gamma/2$.   Now in our case the kth sector has radius r_k and angle $\gamma = \theta_k - \theta_{k-1} = \Delta\theta_k$, so $A_k = \frac{1}{2}r_k^2\Delta\theta_k$, and hence (19) becomes

$$A = \lim_{n \to \infty} \sum_{k=1}^{n} \tfrac{1}{2}r_k^2\Delta\theta_k. \qquad (20)$$

But by the definition of a definite integral the right side of (20) is the integral in (18).

If the function $r = f(\theta)$ is not increasing then the picture is only slightly different, but the conclusion is the same.

EXAMPLE 1.   Use polar coordinates to compute the area of the circle $r = a \cos \theta$.

SOLUTION.   The full circle is described as θ runs from $-\pi/2$ to $\pi/2$.   Hence

$$A = \int_{-\pi/2}^{\pi/2} \tfrac{1}{2}r^2 \, d\theta = \int_{-\pi/2}^{\pi/2} \tfrac{1}{2}a^2 \cos^2 \theta \, d\theta$$

$$= \frac{a^2}{2} \int_{-\pi/2}^{\pi/2} \frac{1 + \cos 2\theta}{2} \, d\theta = \frac{a^2}{4} \left(\theta + \frac{\sin 2\theta}{2} \right) \Bigg|_{-\pi/2}^{\pi/2}$$

$$= \frac{\pi a^2}{4}.$$

We expected this answer because a is the diameter of the circle $r = a \cos \theta$.

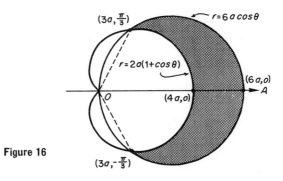

Figure 16

EXAMPLE 2.   Find the area of the region that lies outside the cardioid $r = 2a(1 + \cos \theta)$ and inside the circle $r = 6a \cos \theta$.

SOLUTION.   The region in question is shown shaded in Fig. 16.   The intersection points of these two curves were already determined in Example 3 of section 2, as the origin and the points $(3a, \pm\pi/3)$.   The area is obviously the difference between two areas, one bounded by the circle, and the other bounded by the cardioid.   Hence

$$A = \int_{-\pi/3}^{\pi/3} \tfrac{1}{2}(6a \cos \theta)^2 \, d\theta - \int_{-\pi/3}^{\pi/3} \tfrac{1}{2}[2a(1 + \cos \theta)]^2 \, d\theta$$

$$= a^2 \int_{-\pi/3}^{\pi/3} [18 \cos^2 \theta - 2(1 + 2 \cos \theta + \cos^2 \theta)] \, d\theta$$

$$= a^2 \int_{-\pi/3}^{\pi/3} [16 \frac{1 + \cos 2\theta}{2} - 2 - 4 \cos \theta] \, d\theta$$

$$= a^2(6\theta + 4 \sin 2\theta - 4 \sin \theta) \Bigg|_{-\pi/3}^{\pi/3} = 4\pi \, a^2.$$

EXERCISE 6

In problems 1 through 5 find the area of the region enclosed by the given curve.

1. $r = a \sin \theta$.
2. $r = 3 + 2 \cos \theta$.
3. $r = 3 + 2 \cos n \theta$.
4. $r = 1 + \sin^2 \theta$.

★**5.** $r = a + b \sin \theta + c \cos \theta,\ a > |b| + |c|$.

6.   Find the area of one petal of the rose $r = a \sin n\ \theta$.

7.   Find the total area enclosed by the lemniscate $r^2 = a^2 \cos 2\theta$.

8.   Find the area enclosed by the small loop of the limaçon $r = \sqrt{2} + 2 \cos \theta$.

In problems 9 through 11 find the area bounded by the given curve and the given rays.

9. $r = a \sec \theta,\ \theta = 0$, and $\theta = \pi/4$.

10. $r = a \tan \theta,\ \theta = 0$, and $\theta = \pi/4$.

11. $r = e^{\sin \theta} \sqrt{\cos \theta},\ \theta = 0$, and $\theta = \pi/2$.

In problems 12 through 15 calculate the area of the region that lies outside of the first curve and inside the second curve.

12. $r = a(1 - \cos \theta),\quad r = a$.

13. $r = a,\quad r = 2a \cos \theta$.

★**14.** $r = a,\quad r = 2a \sin n\theta,\quad n$ odd.

★**15.** $r^2 = 2a^2 \cos 2\theta,\quad r = a$.

★**16.**   Find the area of the region common to the two circles $r = a \cos \theta$, and $r = b \sin \theta$.

★★**17.**   Interpret geometrically as an area the following computation.

$$A = \tfrac{1}{2} \int_0^{4\pi} (e^\theta)^2\ d\theta = \frac{1}{4}\ (e^{8\pi} - 1).$$

13

INFINITE SERIES

1. Objective. An expression of the form

$$a_1 + a_2 + a_3 + \cdots + a_k + \cdots \tag{1}$$

is called an *infinite series*. The three dots at the end indicate that the terms go on indefinitely. In other words, for each positive integer k there is a term a_k and in (1) we are instructed to add together this infinite collection of terms. The sum in (1) may be written more briefly and more accurately as

$$\sum_{k=1}^{\infty} a_k \tag{2}$$

(read, the sum from $k = 1$ to infinity of a_k).

Now at first glance it may seem impossible to form such a sum, and certainly it is physically impossible to perform the operation of addition an infinite number of times (there isn't enough time). It is one of the real achievements of mathematics that a perfectly satisfactory meaning can be attached to the symbols in (1) and (2), a meaning which will allow us to work with such expressions just as though they involved only a finite number of terms. In fact in many cases we will be able to actually find the number that is the sum of the infinite series.

The theory of infinite series is both useful and beautiful, and the manipulations involved are rather simple, in spite of the fact that we are dealing with infinite sets of numbers. But the ideas involved are new to the student, and it is here that the difficulty lies.

Quite naturally our objective is to give an introduction to the theory of infinite series. At the beginning, however, we shall concentrate mostly on examples, and the mechanical procedures, and we shall frequently make use of theorems before proving them. The proofs will be given toward the end of the chapter. In this way the student will be in a better position to follow the proofs, because he then has some familiarity with the subject matter.

2. **Convergence and divergence of series.** Consider the specific series

$$\sum_{k=1}^{\infty} \frac{1}{2^k} = \frac{1}{2} + \frac{1}{4} + \frac{1}{8} + \cdots + \frac{1}{2^k} + \cdots. \tag{3}$$

We begin to add the terms, and we let s_n denote the sum of the first n terms. Then simple arithmetic gives

$$s_1 = \frac{1}{2} \qquad\qquad = \frac{1}{2}, \qquad s_5 = \frac{31}{32},$$

$$s_2 = \frac{1}{2} + \frac{1}{4} \qquad\qquad = \frac{3}{4}, \qquad s_6 = \frac{63}{64},$$

$$s_3 = \frac{1}{2} + \frac{1}{4} + \frac{1}{8} \qquad = \frac{7}{8}, \qquad s_7 = \frac{127}{128},$$

$$s_4 = \frac{1}{2} + \frac{1}{4} + \frac{1}{8} + \frac{1}{16} = \frac{15}{16}, \qquad s_8 = \frac{255}{256},$$

and so on. But why continue? It is perfectly obvious that the sum s_n is always less than 1, but gets closer and closer to 1 as we take more and more terms. This is clear because at each stage the next term to be added is just $1/2$ of the difference between 1 and the sum of all the preceding terms. Therefore it is reasonable to claim that 1 is the sum of the infinite series (3), and we have just found the sum of our first infinite series. All that remains is to give a *precise* definition of the sum of an infinite series, and see that the above work fits the definition.

For the present we assume that each term a_k of the infinite series is a number. Later on we will consider series in which each term is a function. Just as in our example, we let s_n denote the sum of the first n terms, thus for any infinite series (1)

$$s_n = \sum_{k=1}^{n} a_k = a_1 + a_2 + a_3 + \cdots + a_n. \tag{4}$$

These sums, s_n, are called the *partial sums* of the series.

DEFINITION 1. *The series (1) is said to converge if there is a number L such that*

$$L = \lim_{n \to \infty} s_n. \tag{5}$$

*The number L is called the sum of the infinite series. If there is
no such number then the series is said to diverge.*

We can state the definition of convergence in two other ways, both of
which are obviously equivalent to the above.

(I)   The series (1) converges to L (has the sum L) if

$$\lim_{n \to \infty} (L - s_n) = 0. \tag{6}$$

(II)   The series (1) converges to the sum L if for each $\epsilon > 0$, no matter
how small, there is an integer N, such that

$$|L - s_n| < \epsilon \tag{7}$$

whenever $n > N$.

EXAMPLE 1. Settle the divergence or convergence of the following series.

(a) $\displaystyle\sum_{k=1}^{\infty} \frac{1}{2^k}$, **(b)** $\displaystyle\sum_{k=1}^{\infty} 0 = 0 + 0 + 0 + \cdots$,

(c) $\displaystyle\sum_{k=1}^{\infty} 1 = 1 + 1 + 1 + \cdots$, **(d)** $\displaystyle\sum_{k=1}^{\infty} (-1)^{k+1} = 1 - 1 + 1 - \cdots$.

SOLUTION.   **(a)** On the basis of our arithmetic it appears that $s_n = 1 - \dfrac{1}{2^n}$.

We shall prove this in the next section. Assume that $s_n = 1 - \dfrac{1}{2^n}$. Then
obviously

$$\lim_{n \to \infty} 1 - \frac{1}{2^n} = 1$$

so the series (3) converges and its sum is 1.   If we prefer to look at the criterion
in equation (6) we would have

$$L - s_n = 1 - \left(1 - \frac{1}{2^n}\right) = \frac{1}{2^n}.$$

and this certainly tends to zero as $n \to \infty$.   The criterion in (7) merely asks
that we can make $1/2^n < \epsilon$ by selecting n sufficiently large, and this is obviously
so, for any given positive ϵ.

(b) Each partial sum s_n is zero because all the terms are zero.   But then
$\lim_{n \to \infty} s_n = 0$.   Consequently the series in (b) converges and the sum is zero.

(c)   If we add together n ones the sum is n.   Hence $s_n = n$ and $\lim_{n \to \infty} s_n = \infty$.
Consequently the series does not converge.   Therefore it diverges.

(d) If we take an even number of terms the sum is zero.   If we take an odd
number the sum is 1.   In symbols $s_{2n} = 0$ and $s_{2n-1} = 1$.   Hence there is no
number L to which the partial sums converge.   The series is divergent.

EXERCISE 1

In problems 1 through 14 write out the first few terms of the series.   Try to *guess* whether the series converges or diverges, and if the series converges try to guess an exact (or approximate) value for the sum.   Make no attempt at a proof. These will be given later.

1. $\sum_{k=1}^{\infty} \frac{1}{2^{k-1}}.$

2. $\sum_{k=1}^{\infty} \frac{1 + (-1)^k}{2}.$

3. $\sum_{k=1}^{\infty} \frac{1}{3^k}.$

4. $\sum_{k=1}^{\infty} \left(\frac{2}{3}\right)^k.$

5. $\sum_{k=1}^{\infty} \frac{1}{k}.$

6. $\sum_{k=1}^{\infty} \frac{1}{k^2}.$

7. $1 + \sum_{k=1}^{\infty} \frac{1}{k!}.$

8. $\sum_{k=1}^{\infty} \frac{3}{k(k + 1)}.$

9. $\sum_{k=1}^{\infty} \frac{1}{10^k}.$

10. $\sum_{k=1}^{\infty} \log \frac{1}{10^k}.$

11. $\sum_{k=1}^{\infty} \cos k\pi.$

12. $\sum_{k=1}^{\infty} \sin \frac{k\pi}{2}.$

13. $\sum_{k=1}^{\infty} \frac{(-1)^{k+1}}{k}.$

14. $\sum_{k=1}^{\infty} \frac{4(-1)^{k+1}}{(2k - 1)}.$

In problems 15 through 24 the first few terms of an infinite series are given. Try to find a general expression (a function of n) for the nth term.   In each such problem there are infinitely many functions that will do.   Try to find a very simple function.

15. $1 + \frac{1}{4} + \frac{1}{9} + \frac{1}{16} + \cdots.$

16. $\frac{1}{4} + \frac{1}{7} + \frac{1}{10} + \frac{1}{13} + \cdots.$

17. $\frac{1}{4} + \frac{1}{7} + \frac{1}{12} + \frac{1}{19} + \cdots.$

18. $\frac{1}{3} + \frac{1}{15} + \frac{1}{35} + \frac{1}{63} + \cdots.$

19. $\frac{3}{2} + \frac{5}{4} + \frac{7}{8} + \frac{9}{16} + \cdots.$

★20. $\frac{1}{3} + \frac{1}{3} + \frac{3}{11} + \frac{2}{9} + \frac{5}{27} + \cdots.$

★21. $36 + \frac{49}{4} + \frac{64}{27} + \frac{81}{256} + \cdots.$

★22. $\dfrac{3}{2} + 1 + \dfrac{5}{8} + \dfrac{3}{8} + \dfrac{7}{32} + \cdots$

★23. $3 + \dfrac{6}{5} + \dfrac{3}{5} + \dfrac{6}{17} + \dfrac{3}{13} + \cdots$

★★24. $\dfrac{1}{12} + \dfrac{1}{15} + \dfrac{1}{20} + \dfrac{4}{105} + \dfrac{5}{168} + \cdots$

3. **The geometric series.** The series (1) is called a *geometric series* if there is a fixed constant r such that $a_{k+1} = ra_k$ for each $k > 0$. In other words the ratio of each term to its predecessor is r. If we let a_1, the first term, be a, then clearly $a_2 = ar$, $a_3 = ar^2$, and in general $a_k = ar^{k-1}$. Notice that the power on r is one less than the subscript. This is a nuisance, but can easily be adjusted. Instead of writing

$$\sum_{k=1}^{\infty} ar^{k-1} = a + ar + ar^2 + \cdots + ar^{k-1} + \cdots \tag{8}$$

we will lower the index of the beginning term by 1, and write

$$\sum_{k=0}^{\infty} ar^{k} = a + ar + ar^2 + \cdots + ar^{k} + \cdots \tag{9}$$

which obviously gives the same series. The form (9) is more convenient, but in either series the nth term is ar^{n-1}.

THEOREM 1. *If $a \neq 0$ and $-1 < r < 1$, the geometric series (9) converges and the sum is given by*

$$\boxed{\sum_{k=0}^{\infty} ar^{k} = \frac{a}{1 - r}.} \tag{10}$$

If $a = 0$, the series converges to the sum 0 for all r. In all other cases the geometric series diverges.

This theorem is extremely important, and should be memorized. The proof is quite easy.

PROOF. If $a = 0$ the convergence is obvious since all terms are zero. If $a \neq 0$ and $r = 1$ the divergence is also obvious. Suppose now that $a \neq 0$ and $r \neq 1$. Let s_n be as usual the sum of the first n terms. Then

$$s_n = a + ar + ar^2 + \cdots + ar^{n-2} + ar^{n-1}. \tag{11}$$

Multiplying through by r we have

$$rs_n = \qquad ar + ar^2 + ar^3 + \cdots + \qquad ar^{n-1} + ar^n. \qquad (12)$$

We next subtract equation (12) from equation (11). Most of the terms drop out on the right side, and we find that

$$s_n - rs_n = a - ar^n.$$

Since $r \neq 1$, we can divide both sides by $1 - r$ (not zero) and we obtain

$$s_n = \frac{a(1 - r^n)}{1 - r}. \qquad (13)$$

Now take the limit in (13) as $n \to \infty$. If $|r| < 1$, the term $r^n \to 0$, and hence

$$\lim_{n \to \infty} s_n = \lim_{n \to \infty} \frac{a(1 - r^n)}{1 - r} = \frac{a}{1 - r}. \qquad (14)$$

This proves the convergence part of the theorem, and establishes formula (10). If $|r| > 1$ then $|r|^n \to \infty$ as $n \to \infty$. If r is negative r^n oscillates in sign, giving negative numbers when n is odd and positive numbers when n is even. But they grow in absolute value without bound as n grows, hence the quantity s_n cannot tend to a limit. We leave it to the student to prove that the series is also divergent if $r = -1$.

EXAMPLE 1. Find the sum of each of the following series.

(a) $\displaystyle\sum_{k=0}^{\infty} 15\left(\frac{2}{7}\right)^k,$

(b) $\displaystyle\sum_{k=0}^{\infty} \frac{3^k}{5^{k+2}},$

(c) $\displaystyle\sum_{k=2}^{\infty} \left(\frac{4}{7}\right)^k,$

(d) $\displaystyle\sum_{k=0}^{\infty} \left(\frac{-7}{11}\right)^k.$

SOLUTION. Each of the above is a geometric series with $-1 < r < 1$. Hence we can use formula (10).

(a) Here $a = 15$, $r = \frac{2}{7}$. Hence $L = \dfrac{15}{1 - \dfrac{2}{7}} = 15 \cdot \dfrac{7}{5} = 21.$

(b) If we factor 5^2 from the denominator we see that (b) then fits the standard pattern with $a = \dfrac{1}{5^2}$ and $r = \dfrac{3}{5}.$

Hence

$$L = \frac{1}{5^2} \frac{1}{1 - \dfrac{3}{5}} = \frac{1}{10}.$$

(c) Notice that here the sum starts with $k = 2$, so the first term is $(4/7)^2$. Since $r = 4/7$, we have

$$L = \left(\frac{4}{7}\right)^2 \frac{1}{1 - \frac{4}{7}} = \frac{16}{49} \cdot \frac{7}{3} = \frac{16}{21}.$$

(d) Here $a = 1$ and $r = -7/11$. Hence $L = \dfrac{1}{1 + \dfrac{7}{11}} = \dfrac{11}{18}.$

EXAMPLE 2. The decimal fraction .31555··· continues with infinitely many 5's as indicated by the dots. Find the equivalent rational fraction.

SOLUTION. The meaning of the decimal fraction is

$$.31555\cdots = \frac{31}{100} + 5\left(\frac{1}{1000} + \frac{1}{10000} + \frac{1}{100000} + \cdots\right)$$

$$= \frac{31}{100} + \frac{5}{1000} \sum_{k=0}^{\infty} \frac{1}{10^k}.$$

Hence

$$.31555\cdots = \frac{31}{100} + \frac{5}{1000} \cdot \frac{1}{1 - \frac{1}{10}} = \frac{31}{100} + \frac{5}{1000} \times \frac{10}{9}$$

$$= \frac{9 \cdot 31 + 5}{900} = \frac{279 + 5}{900} = \frac{284}{900} = \frac{71}{225}.$$

EXERCISE 2

1. In the problems of Exercise 1, locate those that are geometric series, and find their sums using formula (10).

In problems 2 through 11 state whether the geometric series is convergent or divergent. If the series is convergent find its sum.

2. $\displaystyle\sum_{k=0}^{\infty} \left(\frac{3}{4}\right)^k.$

3. $\displaystyle\sum_{k=0}^{\infty} \left(\frac{4}{5}\right)^k.$

4. $\displaystyle\sum_{k=0}^{\infty} \left(-\frac{5}{6}\right)^k.$

5. $\displaystyle\sum_{k=0}^{\infty} \left(-\frac{3}{8}\right)^k.$

6. $\displaystyle\sum_{k=0}^{\infty} \left(\frac{5}{7}\sqrt{2}\right)^k.$

7. $\displaystyle\sum_{k=0}^{\infty} \left(\frac{8}{5\sqrt{3}}\right)^k.$

8. $\displaystyle\sum_{k=1}^{\infty} 3\left(\frac{2}{9}\right)^k.$

9. $\displaystyle\sum_{k=3}^{\infty} \frac{5 \cdot 2^k}{3^{k+1}}.$

10. $\displaystyle\sum_{k=1}^{\infty} \frac{5^k}{100 \cdot 4^k}.$

11. $\displaystyle\sum_{k=1}^{\infty} \frac{1}{(4 - \sqrt{10})^k}.$

In problems 12 through 17 find the rational fraction that is equivalent to the given infinite repeating decimal fraction. The braces indicate the part that is repeated.

12. $.13\overline{33}\cdots$.

13. $.2\overline{777}\cdots$.

14. $.61\overline{11}\cdots$.

15. $.2727\overline{27}\cdots$.

16. $.8484\overline{84}\cdots$.

17. $.918918\overline{918}\cdots$.

*18. A ball is dropped from a height of 10 ft onto a concrete walk. Each time it bounces it rises to a height of $\frac{3}{4}h$, where h is the height attained after the previous bounce. Find the total distance that the ball travels before coming to a rest.

*19. If the ball of problem 18 is dropped from an initial height of H feet, and after each bounce rises to a height rh feet where r is a constant, prove that the total distance traveled by the ball is $s = H(1 + r)/(1 - r)$.

**20. A ball dropped from a height of h feet will reach the ground in $\sqrt{h}/4$ secs. The same length of time is required for a ball to bounce upward to a maximum height of h feet. Find a formula for the length of time required for the ball of problem 19 to come to a rest. Apply this formula to the ball of problem 18.

4.   Polynomials. It is customary to write a polynomial in the form

$$P(x) = a_0 + a_1x + a_2x^2 + a_3x^3 + \cdots + a_nx^n \qquad (15)$$

that is, in terms of powers of x. But we could also write the polynomial in powers of $x - a$, where a is some constant. In this case $P(x)$ would have the form

$$P(x) = b_0 + b_1(x - a) + b_2(x - a)^2 + \cdots + b_n(x - a)^n. \qquad (16)$$

We call the form (16) an *expansion* of $P(x)$ in terms of $x - a$, or a *development* of $P(x)$ in terms of $x - a$. We also refer to it as an *expansion* or *development* about the point a. The point a is called the *center* of the expansion or development.

EXAMPLE 1.   Expand the polynomial $P(x) = x^3 - x^2 + 3x + 11$ about the point $x = 2$.

SOLUTION.   We are to find the coefficients b_k so that

$$11 + 3x - x^2 + x^3 = b_0 + b_1(x - 2) + b_2(x - 2)^2 + b_3(x - 2)^3.$$

Expanding the terms on the right side we have

$$
\begin{aligned}
b_3(x - 2)^3 &= b_3x^3 - 6b_3x^2 + 12b_3x - 8b_3 \\
b_2(x - 2)^2 &= \qquad\qquad b_2x^2 - 4b_2x + 4b_2 \\
b_1(x - 2) &= \qquad\qquad\qquad\qquad b_1x - 2b_1 \\
b_0 &= \qquad\qquad\qquad\qquad\qquad\qquad b_0
\end{aligned}
$$

Therefore on adding we obtain

$$x^3 - x^2 + 3x + 11 = b_3x^3 + (b_2 - 6b_3)x^2 + (b_1 - 4b_2 + 12b_3)x + (b_0 - 2b_1 + 4b_2 - 8b_3).$$

Equating coefficients of like powers of x, gives

$$
\begin{aligned}
x^3: \quad & 1 = b_3 \\
x^2: \quad & -1 = b_2 - 6b_3 \\
x^1: \quad & 3 = b_1 - 4b_2 + 12b_3 \\
x^0: \quad & 11 = b_0 - 2b_1 + 4b_2 - 8b_3.
\end{aligned}
$$

Solving these four equations in the four unknowns, we find that $b_3 = 1$, $b_2 = 5$, $b_1 = 11$, $b_0 = 21$. Thus we have proved that for all x

$$11 + 3x - x^2 + x^3 = 21 + 11(x - 2) + 5(x - 2)^2 + (x - 2)^3. \tag{17}$$

This example suggests

THEOREM 2. *Any polynomial (15) has a unique expansion of the form (16) about any given point.*

We omit the detailed proof of this theorem because it is just an extension to the general situation of the method already illustrated in the example. In general one always obtains $n + 1$ linear equations in the unknowns b_0, b_1, b_2, $\cdots$, b_n and the knowns a, a_0, a_1, $\cdots$, a_n, and these equations can always be solved for the b_k uniquely.

Once this theorem is settled, there is an easier way to find the coefficients using the calculus. We first consider the polynomial (15) and we will see that the coefficients are determined by the value of the polynomial and its derivatives at the origin. First set $x = 0$ in (15). Then $P(0) = a_0 + a_1 \cdot 0 + \cdots + a_n \cdot 0 = a_0$. Next we compute the derivative of $P(x)$ obtaining

$$\frac{dP}{dx} = P'(x) = a_1 + 2a_2x + 3a_3x^2 + \cdots + na_nx^{n-1}. \tag{18}$$

Then setting $x = 0$ in (18) we find that $a_1 = P'(0)$. Differentiating (18) gives

$$\frac{d^2P}{dx^2} = P''(x) = 2a_2 + 6a_3x + \cdots + n(n - 1)a_nx^{n-2}$$

and hence on setting $x = 0$ we find that $2a_2 = P''(0)$ or $a_2 = P''(0)/2$. Clearly this process can be continued. If $k \leq n$, then the kth derivative is

$$P^{(k)}(x) = k!a_k + \text{terms in } x \text{ with positive powers}$$

and setting $x = 0$, gives $a_k = P^{(k)}(0)/k!$ This proves

THEOREM 3. *The coefficients in (15) are given by*[1]

---

[1] This formula also holds when $k = 0$ if we define $P^{(0)}(x)$ to be just the polynomial $P(x)$ and $0!$ to be 1. So we make these definitions. Later on the student will see that there are other reasons for setting $0! = 1$.

$$a_k = \frac{P^{(k)}(0)}{k!} \qquad k = 0, 1, 2, \cdots, n. \tag{19}$$

*A polynomial of nth degree is completely determined by its value and
the value of its first n derivatives at $x = 0$.*

But exactly the same proof will also give the expansion about any point.
We merely replace $x = 0$, by $x = a$ and have

THEOREM 4.   *The coefficients in (16) are given by*

$$b_k = \frac{P^{(k)}(a)}{k!} \qquad k = 0, 1, 2, \cdots, n. \tag{20}$$

*A polynomial of nth degree is completely determined by its value and
the value of its first n derivatives at a fixed point a.*

We leave the details of the proof of Theorem 4 to the student.   This
theorem allows us to shorten the work in solving example 1.   We have

$$
\begin{aligned}
P(x) &= x^3 - x^2 + 3x + 11 & P(2) &= 8 - 4 + 6 + 11 = 21 \\
P'(x) &= 3x^2 - 2x + 3 & P'(2) &= 12 - 4 + 3 = 11 \\
P''(x) &= 6x - 2 & P''(2) &= 12 - 2 = 10 \\
P'''(x) &= 6 & P'''(2) &= 6 = 6.
\end{aligned}
$$

Whence by (20) $b_0 = 21$, $b_1 = 11$, $b_2 = 10/2! = 5$, and $b_3 = 6/3! = 1$.
But these are just the coefficients in (17), only now we have obtained them
in a much simpler and quicker way.

EXERCISE 3

In problems 1 through 6 express the given polynomial as a polynomial in
$(x - a)$ where a has the given value.

1. $P(x) = 1 + x + x^2 + x^3,$ $a = 1.$
2. $P(x) = 9 - 6x^2 + x^4,$ $a = 3.$
3. $P(x) = 3 + 7x - 4x^2 - x^5,$ $a = -2.$
4. $P(x) = -15 + 13x + 7x^2,$ $a = -5.$
5. $P(x) = 1 - 4x - 6x^2 + 32x^3,$ $a = 1/2.$
6. $P(x) = 12x^2 + 8x^3,$ $a = -3/2.$

7. Find the expansion of $(x - 1)^6 + (x + 1)^6$ about the point $x = 0$.

8. Find the expansion of $(x - 1)^3 + 4(x - 1)^2 + 6(x - 1) + 4$ about the point $x = 0$.

9. Find a polynomial $P(x)$ such that $P(2) = 1$, $P'(2) = 5$, $P''(2) = -8\sqrt{3}$, and $P'''(2) = 48\pi$. Is there only one such polynomial?

★10. Prove the following theorem, which is a converse of Theorem 4. Given $x = a$, and a set of $n + 1$ numbers $c_0, c_1, c_2, \cdots, c_n$, there is a polynomial $P(x)$ such that $P^{(k)}(a) = c_k$, for $k = 0, 1, 2, \cdots, n$. If the polynomial is of nth degree there is exactly one such polynomial.

In other words prove that we can prescribe in advance, the value of a polynomial and its first n derivatives at a given point, if the polynomial has degree $\geq n$.

★11. Expand the polynomial $(2x + 1)^6$ about the point $x = -1$.

5. Power series. It is convenient to think of a power series as a polynomial of infinite degree. If the power series is an expansion about the origin it has the form

$$\sum_{k=0}^{\infty} a_k x^k = a_0 + a_1 x + a_2 x^2 + \cdots + a_k x^k + \cdots. \tag{21}$$

If the expansion is about the point $x = a$, it has the form

$$\sum_{k=0}^{\infty} a_k (x - a)^k = a_0 + a_1(x - a) + a_2(x - a)^2 + \cdots + a_k(x - a)^k \cdots. \tag{22}$$

A power series of the form (21) is also called a *Maclaurin series*. The form (22) is called a *Taylor series*. Clearly a Maclaurin series is just a Taylor series with $a = 0$.

Of course (21) and (22) have a meaning only for those values of x for which the series converge. The collection of x for which a given series of functions converges, is called the *convergence set* of the series. We will see in section 12 that for a power series the convergence set is an interval and that the center of the power series $x = a$, is the midpoint of the interval of convergence, as it should be.

We have already had one example of a power series, namely the geometric series. In (9) we replace a by A and r by x. Then Theorem 1 gives us

THEOREM 5. *The geometric series*

$$\sum_{k=0}^{\infty} A x^k = A + Ax + Ax^2 + \cdots + A x^k + \cdots \tag{23}$$

$$= A(1 + x + x^2 + \cdots + x^k + \cdots)$$

converges for all x in the interval $-1 < x < 1$ and has for its sum

$$\sum_{k=0}^{\infty} A x^k = \frac{A}{1 - x}. \tag{24}$$

A substitution in (24) replacing x by $x - a$ will give us an equivalent theorem for Taylor series.   Now for convergence we must have

$$- 1 < x - a < 1$$

or

$$a - 1 < x < a + 1.$$

In other words if x lies in an interval with center at a and length 2, the Taylor series

$$\sum_{k=0}^{\infty} A (x - a)^k = \frac{A}{1 + a - x} \tag{25}$$

converges to the sum indicated.

Let us now start with some function and try to find a power series expansion for the function.   Of course if our given function is a polynomial this is easy, and this case has already been discussed in the preceding section.   To be specific suppose that we want to develop the function e^x as a Maclaurin series.   We can always get a polynomial of nth degree that fits e^x "closely" at $x = 0$, i.e., we can find a polynomial whose value at $x = 0$, and whose first n derivatives at $x = 0$ are equal to the corresponding quantities for the function e^x.   If we then let the degree of the polynomial be infinite we will have a power series for which, at $x = 0$ the value and the values of all its derivatives equal the corresponding quantities for e^x.   Such a power series should be equal to e^x and in section 13 we will prove that this is the case.   To carry out the program we need the very plausible theorem that a power series can be differentiated term-by-term.

THEOREM 6.   *If the two power series*

$$f(x) = \sum_{k=0}^{\infty} a_k x^k = a_0 + a_1 x + a_2 x^2 + \cdots + a_k x^k + \cdots \tag{26}$$

and

$$\sum_{k=1}^{\infty} k a_k x^{k-1} = a_1 + 2a_2 x + 3a_3 x^2 + \cdots + k a_k x^{k-1} + \cdots \tag{27}$$

are both convergent[2] in $-r < x < r$, *then for each x in that interval the power series (27) converges to $f'(x)$.*

The proof of this theorem will be given in section 15.   Let us see how this theorem is used.   Putting $x = 0$ in (26) we have $f(0) = a_0$.

---

[2] It can be proved that the series (26) and (27) always have the same interval of convergence, so the hypotheses in Theorems 6, 7, and 8 could be weakened. The proof is a little difficult, and we omit it. The interested reader can find a proof in any book on Advanced Calculus.

Putting $x = 0$ in (27) gives $f'(0) = a_1$. We apply Theorem 6 to (27) obtaining

$$f''(x) = \sum_{k=2}^{\infty} k(k-1)a_k x^{k-2} = 2a_2 + 6a_3 x + 12a_4 x^2 + \cdots$$

and on setting $x = 0$, we find that $f''(0) = 2a_2$ or $a_2 = f''(0)/2$. Continuing in this way we can determine each of the coefficients a_k in (26). The general formula is given in

THEOREM 7. *If the series*

$$f(x) = \sum_{k=0}^{\infty} a_k x^k = a_0 + a_1 x + \cdots + a_k x^k + \cdots \tag{26}$$

and all of the series obtained by differentiating (26) converge in $-r < x < r$, (where $r > 0$) then

$$a_k = \frac{f^{(k)}(0)}{k!}, \qquad k = 0, 1, 2, \cdots. \tag{28}$$

Exactly the same type of proof gives a similar theorem for the Taylor series.

THEOREM 8. *If the series*

$$f(x) = \sum_{k=0}^{\infty} a_k(x-a)^k = a_0 + a_1(x-a) + a_2(x-a)^2 + \cdots$$

and all of the series obtained by differentiating it converge in $a - r < x < a + r$, (where $r > 0$) then

$$a_k = \frac{f^{(k)}(a)}{k!}, \qquad k = 0, 1, 2, \cdots. \tag{29}$$

EXAMPLE 1. Assuming that e^x has an expansion as a power series about the origin, find the power series.

SOLUTION. We are assuming that if the coefficients are properly chosen then

$$e^x = \sum_{k=0}^{\infty} a_k x^k$$

where the series and all of its derivatives are convergent for some suitable interval. Computing the successive derivatives for e^x we have

$$f(x) = e^x \qquad\qquad f(0) = e^0 = 1,$$
$$f'(x) = e^x \qquad\qquad f'(0) = e^0 = 1,$$
$$\vdots \qquad\qquad\qquad \vdots$$
$$f^{(k)}(x) = e^x \qquad\qquad f^{(k)}(0) = e^0 = 1,$$

etc. Hence by formula (28) we have $a_k = \dfrac{1}{k!}$ for $k = 0, 1, \cdots$. Thus the Maclaurin series for e^x is

$$e^x = \sum_{k=0}^{\infty} \frac{x^k}{k!} = 1 + x + \frac{x^2}{2!} + \frac{x^3}{3!} + \cdots + \frac{x^k}{k!} + \cdots. \qquad (30)$$

EXAMPLE 2. Assuming that $1/(2 - x)^2$ has a Maclaurin series, find it.

SOLUTION. We merely compute the various derivatives at $x = 0$, and use equation (28).

$$f(x) = \frac{1}{(2 - x)^2} \qquad\qquad f(0) = \frac{1}{4} \qquad\qquad a_0 = \frac{1}{4}$$

$$f'(x) = \frac{2 \cdot 1}{(2 - x)^3} \qquad\qquad f'(0) = \frac{2!}{2^3} \qquad\qquad a_1 = \frac{2}{2^3}$$

$$f''(x) = \frac{3 \cdot 2 \cdot 1}{(2 - x)^4} \qquad\qquad f''(0) = \frac{3!}{2^4} \qquad\qquad a_2 = \frac{3}{2^4}$$

etc. Here the pattern becomes evident after computing a few derivatives and it is easy to guess (and one can prove by mathematical induction) that

$$f^{(k)}(x) = \frac{(k + 1)!}{(2 - x)^{k+2}} \qquad f^{(k)}(0) = \frac{(k + 1)!}{2^{k+2}} \qquad a_k = \frac{k + 1}{2^{k+2}},$$

for $k = 0, 1, 2, \cdots$. Then

$$\frac{1}{(2 - x)^2} = \sum_{k=0}^{\infty} \frac{k + 1}{2^{k+2}} x^k = \sum_{k=0}^{\infty} \frac{k + 1}{4} \left(\frac{x}{2}\right)^k$$

$$= \frac{1}{4}\left[1 + 2\left(\frac{x}{2}\right) + 3\left(\frac{x}{2}\right)^2 + 4\left(\frac{x}{2}\right)^3 + \cdots\right].$$

We will see in section 11 that this series converges for x in the interval $-2 < x < 2$.

EXERCISE 4

In all of the problems in this list assume that the given functions have a Maclaurin or Taylor series. In each problem this assumption is correct, but in some cases the proof is difficult and is best postponed to the course in Advanced Calculus.

In problems 1 through 10 find the Maclaurin series for the given function. The series in problems 2, 3, 4, and 5 are so important they should be memorized.

1. e^{2x}.

2. $\sin x$.

3. $\cos x$.

4. $\ln(1 + x)$.

5. $\ln \dfrac{1}{1 - x}$.

6. $\dfrac{5}{1 - 4x}$.

7. $\dfrac{1}{(1 - 3x)^3}$.

★8. $\dfrac{1}{\sqrt{1 - x}}$.

★9. xe^x.

★10. $\sqrt{1 - x}$.

11. Use enough terms in equation (30) to prove that $e > 2.71$.

12. Recall that the calculus of trigonometric functions is based on radian measure, so that in the series for $\sin x$ the variable x is in radians. Use the first three nonzero terms of the Maclaurin series to obtain an approximate value for $\sin 2°$ ($2° = \pi/90$ radians). Give answer to four decimal places.

13. Power series can be added under suitable conditions. Use the power series found in problems 4 and 5 to obtain a power series for $\ln((1 + x)/(1 - x))$.

In problems 14 through 17 find a Taylor series for the given function about the given point.

14. e^x, $a = 2$.

15. $\dfrac{1}{x}$, $a = 3$.

★16. $\sin x$, $a = \dfrac{\pi}{6}$.

17. $\ln x$, $a = 3$.

In some cases it is not easy to find an explicit formula for the kth derivative. In problems 18 through 21 find the first three nonzero terms of the Maclaurin series for the given function.

18. $\dfrac{x}{(1 - x)^2}$.

19. $e^{x^2 - x}$.

20. $e^x \sin x$.

21. $\tan x$.

22. Use the Taylor series for $\sin x$ about $x = \pi/6$, to obtain an estimate for $\sin 31°$. Give answer to four decimal places.

23. The binomial series is frequently given without proof in algebra courses. This series for $(1 + x)^m$ is

$$(1 + x)^m = 1 + \frac{m}{1} x + \frac{m(m - 1)}{1 \cdot 2} x^2 + \frac{m(m - 1)(m - 2)}{1 \cdot 2 \cdot 3} x^3 + \cdots$$

$$+ \frac{m(m - 1)(m - 2) \cdots (m - n + 1)}{1 \cdot 2 \cdot 3 \cdots n} x^n + \cdots.$$

Prove that the binomial series is just the Maclaurin series for the function $(1 + x)^m$. Show that if m is an integer greater than or equal to zero, then the binomial series is just a polynomial. In all other cases the binomial series has infinitely many nonzero terms.

6. Operations with power series.

Under suitable conditions, the standard mathematical operations can be applied to infinite series. Roughly, we can say that the series involved must be convergent. In this section we consider some examples involving (1) substitution, (2) addition, (3) multiplication, (4) differentiation, and (5) integration.

EXAMPLE 1. Find the Maclaurin expansion for $\dfrac{1}{1 + x^3}$.

SOLUTION. If we attempt to find a general formula for the nth derivative of this function, we will soon give up in despair, because the derivatives of higher order are very complicated. But if we recall the geometric series, and use a new variable, we have

$$\frac{1}{1 - u} = \sum_{k=0}^{\infty} u^k = 1 + u + u^2 + \cdots + u^k + \cdots. \tag{31}$$

Now replace u by $-x^3$. This gives the desired Maclaurin series

$$\frac{1}{1 - (-x^3)} = \frac{1}{1 + x^3} = \sum_{k=0}^{\infty} (-1)^k x^{3k} = 1 - x^3 + x^6 - x^9 + \cdots + (-1)^k x^{3k} + \cdots. \tag{32}$$

Since (31) converges for $-1 < u < 1$, the series in (32) will converge for $-1 < -x^3 < 1$, that is for $-1 < x < 1$.

EXAMPLE 2. Find the series for $x^2 \cosh x$.

SOLUTION. Here the differentiations are not too bad, but we want another and shorter solution. We already have a series for e^x, namely

$$e^x = \sum_{k=0}^{\infty} \frac{x^k}{k!} = 1 + x + \frac{x^2}{2!} + \frac{x^3}{3!} + \cdots. \tag{30}$$

Hence on replacing x by $-x$ we find

$$e^{-x} = \sum_{k=0}^{\infty} \frac{(-1)^k x^k}{k!} = 1 - x + \frac{x^2}{2!} - \frac{x^3}{3!} + \cdots. \tag{33}$$

On adding (30) and (33), the odd powers of x drop out. Hence

$$\cosh x = \frac{e^x + e^{-x}}{2} = 1 + \frac{x^2}{2!} + \frac{x^4}{4!} + \cdots = \sum_{k=0}^{\infty} \frac{x^{2k}}{(2k)!}.$$

Finally multiplying both sides by x^2 we have

$$x^2 \cosh x = x^2 + \frac{x^4}{2!} + \frac{x^6}{4!} + \cdots = \sum_{k=0}^{\infty} \frac{x^{2k+2}}{(2k)!} = \sum_{k=1}^{\infty} \frac{x^{2k}}{(2k - 2)!}.$$

Either one of the two forms on the right side is acceptable.

EXAMPLE 3.   Find the Maclaurin series for $1/(1-x)^3$.   We begin with the known geometric series

$$\frac{1}{1-x} = \sum_{k=0}^{\infty} x^k = 1 + x + x^2 + \cdots + x^k + \cdots$$

and differentiate both sides, twice with respect to x.   Thus

$$\frac{1}{(1-x)^2} = \sum_{k=1}^{\infty} kx^{k-1} = 1 + 2x + 3x^2 + \cdots + kx^{k-1} + \cdots.$$

$$\frac{2}{(1-x)^3} = \sum_{k=2}^{\infty} k(k-1)x^{k-2} = 2 + 6x + 12x^2 + \cdots + k(k-1)x^{k-2} + \cdots.$$

Hence on dividing by 2

$$\frac{1}{(1-x)^3} = 1 + 3x + 6x^2 + \cdots = \sum_{k=2}^{\infty} \frac{k(k-1)}{2} x^{k-2} = \sum_{k=0}^{\infty} \frac{(k+2)(k+1)}{2} x^k.$$

EXAMPLE 4.   Find the definite integral $\int_0^1 e^{-x^2}\,dx$.

SOLUTION.   We cannot find an indefinite integral in terms of a finite number of combinations of the functions now at our disposal.   But with infinite series, this problem becomes trival.   Replace x by $-x^2$ in (30).   Hence

$$e^{-x^2} = \sum_{k=0}^{\infty} \frac{(-1)^k x^{2k}}{k!} = 1 - x^2 + \frac{x^4}{2!} - \frac{x^6}{3!} + \cdots \qquad (34)$$

Then

$$\int_0^1 e^{-x^2}\,dx = \sum_{k=0}^{\infty} \frac{(-1)^k x^{2k+1}}{k!(2k+1)} \bigg|_0^1 = x - \frac{x^3}{3} + \frac{x^5}{10} - \frac{x^7}{42} + \cdots \bigg|_0^1$$

$$\approx 1 - \frac{1}{3} + \frac{1}{10} - \frac{1}{42} + \frac{1}{216} \approx .747$$

to three decimal places.   Of course we still must prove that the term-by-term integration of the series (34) is valid.   The claim, that the answer is accurate to three decimal places, also requires a proof.   The first item is covered in section 15, and the second follows from the work on alternating series in section 10.

EXERCISE 5

All of the problems in this list can be worked using suitable operations (substitution, addition, multiplication, differentiation, and integration) on the series that we already know (e^x, $\sin x$, $\cos x$, and $(1-x)^{-1}$).

In problems 1 through 10 find the Maclaurin series for the given function.

1. $x \sinh x$.

2. $\sin x^2$.

3. $\dfrac{1}{(1-x)^4}$.

4. $\dfrac{1+x}{1-x}$.

5. $x \cos \sqrt{x}$.

6. $\ln(1 + x)$.

7. $\dfrac{1}{1 + x^2}$.

8. $\dfrac{x}{(1 - x)^2}$.

9. $\tan^{-1} x$.

10. $\dfrac{1 - 3x}{1 + 2x}$.

★11. Use partial fractions to decompose the function $\dfrac{10}{x^2 - x - 6}$ and then find a Maclaurin series for this function.

12. Find a series for π, by setting $x = 1$ in the series of problem 9.

In problems 13 through 16, use the first three nonzero terms of a power series to estimate the given integral. Give your answer to three decimal places.

13. $\displaystyle\int_0^1 \sin x^3 \, dx$.

14. $\displaystyle\int_0^{1/4} e^{x^2} \, dx$.

15. $\displaystyle\int_0^1 x^2 \cos \sqrt{x} \, dx$.

16. $\displaystyle\int_0^{1/2} \tan^{-1} x^4 \, dx$.

★★17. What function has the Maclaurin series

$$\sum_{k=1}^{\infty} k^2 x^k = x + 4x^2 + 9x^3 + 16x^4 + \cdots ?$$

★18. From problem 10 of Exercise 4 we know that

$$\sqrt{1 - x} = 1 - \frac{1}{2}x - \frac{1}{8}x^2 - \frac{1}{16}x^3 - \frac{5}{128}x^4 - \cdots .$$

Try to check this result by squaring the power series on the right. Go as far as showing that when this power series is squared the coefficients of x^2, x^3, and x^4 are all zero.

★★19. Find the first five nonzero terms of the Maclaurin expansion for the function $\dfrac{1}{1 + x + x^2}$.

20. Show that differentiating the Maclaurin series for $\sin x$, gives the Maclaurin series for $\cos x$. What series results when we differentiate once more?

21. Show that if you differentiate the series for e^x you obtain the very same series.

7. Sequences and series. Now that we have seen what can be done with power series, it is time to begin proving some of the theorems we have used.

In a rigorous study of infinite series it is very convenient to use sequences. Roughly speaking a sequence is just a collection of numbers, in which there is a first number, and a second number, and a third one, and so on. If we use subscripts to indicate the place of a number in the sequence, then the sequence would have the appearance

$$s_1, \; s_2, \; s_3, \; \cdots, \; s_n, \; \cdots \tag{35}$$

where s_1 is the first term of the sequence, s_2 is the second term, etc.   The student should observe that there are no $+$ signs in (35) but just commas. Thus in an infinite series we *add* the terms.   In a sequence we merely *examine* the members in turn to see how the general term s_n is behaving as $n \to \infty$.

> DEFINITION 2.   *A collection of numbers of the form (35) in which, to each positive integer n there corresponds a number s_n, is called an infinite sequence, or just a sequence.*
>
> DEFINITION 3.   *A sequence s_1, s_2, s_3, $\cdots$, s_n, $\cdots$ is said to converge to the limit L (or have the limit L) if*
>
> $$\lim_{n \to \infty} s_n = L.$$
>
> *Otherwise the sequence is said to diverge.*

We can state the definition of the convergence of a sequence in two other ways, both of which are obviously equivalent to the above.

(I) The sequence (35) converges to L if

$$\lim_{n \to \infty} (L - s_n) = 0$$

(II) The sequence (35) has the limit L if for each $\epsilon > 0$, there is an N such that

$$|L - s_n| < \epsilon$$

whenever $n > N$.

We already know quite a bit about the limit of $f(x)$ as $x \to a$.   The student should observe that we are now confronted with a situation that is very similar.   Here s_n is really just a function of n, where now the independent variable n just takes on positive integer values, and $n \to \infty$.   So our knowledge of functions and their limits carries over immediately to sequences and their limits.[3]

> EXAMPLE 1.   Settle the convergence or divergence of the following sequences: (a) $s_n = n^2$, (b) $s_n = 1/n^2$, (c) $s_n = \sqrt{2} + \sin(\pi/n)$, (d) $s_n = 1/p_n$ where p_n denotes the nth prime number,   (e) s_n denotes the nth digit after the decimal point in the decimal expression for e,   (f) $s_n = (n^3 + 1)/(n^2 + 100n)$.
>
> SOLUTION.   (a) The sequence is 1, 4, 9, 16, $\cdots$ and obviously has no limit. So the sequence diverges.

[3] The student who wants more details should consult Appendix 4.

(b) The sequence is 1, 1/4, 1/9, 1/16, $\cdots$ and obviously $\lim\limits_{n\to\infty} \dfrac{1}{n^2} = 0$. Hence the sequence converges and the limit is zero.

(c) As $n \to \infty$ we have $\pi/n \to 0$ and hence $\sin(\pi/n) \to 0$. Therefore $\lim\limits_{n\to\infty}$ $\sqrt{2} + \sin(\pi/n) = \sqrt{2}$. This sequence converges to $\sqrt{2}$.

(d) The sequence is 1/2, 1/3, 1/5, 1/7, 1/11, $\cdots$. This is an infinite sequence because there are infinitely many primes.[4] This sequence obviously converges to zero.

(e) Since $e = 2.7182818285 \cdots$ we have $s_1 = 7$, $s_2 = 1$, $s_3 = 8$, $\cdots$. Now e is an irrational number, and no general formula is known for its nth digit. But we do know that the sequence cannot converge, for if it did, then e would be a rational number. Hence this sequence is divergent.

(f) $s_n = \dfrac{n^3 + 1}{n^2 + 100n} = \dfrac{n + \dfrac{1}{n^2}}{1 + \dfrac{100}{n}} \to \infty$, as $n \to \infty$.

Hence this sequence is divergent.

DEFINITION 4. *A sequence (35) is said to be increasing[5] if*

$$s_1 \leqq s_2 \leqq s_3 \cdots \leqq s_n \leqq s_{n+1} \leqq \cdots, \tag{36}$$

that is, if each element is less than or equal to the following one. The sequence is said to be decreasing if

$$s_1 \geqq s_2 \geqq s_3 \cdots \geqq s_n \geqq s_{n+1} \geqq \cdots. \tag{37}$$

DEFINITION 5. *A sequence is bounded above if there is some number M that is greater than or equal to each term of the sequence, that is*

$$s_n \leqq M \tag{38}$$

for every positive integer n. A sequence is bounded below if there is a number m such that

$$m \leqq s_n \tag{39}$$

for every positive integer n.

The values for m and M in this definition are not unique.

---

[4] See any book on Number Theory.

[5] Some authors prefer to have the strict inequality $s_n < s_{n+1}$ (for all n) in (36), and reserve the word nondecreasing for what we have called increasing. There is no real gain to be had by making such a fine distinction. Our increasing sequences can be stationary, i.e., adjacent terms equal.

EXAMPLE 2. Which of the sequences in example 1 are bounded above, and which are bounded below?

SOLUTION. (a) is bounded below, set $m = 0$, but it is not bounded above. We could also take $m = 1/2$ or in fact any number less than or equal to one.

   (b) is bounded below and above. Take $m = 0$, $M = 1$.
   (c) is bounded below and above. Take $m = 0$, $M = 3$.
   (d) is bounded below and above. Take $m = 0$, $M = 1$.
   (e) is bounded below and above. Take $m = 0$, $M = 9$.
   (f) is bounded below but not above. Take $m = 0$.

As a starting point for our rigorous treatment of sequences and series we use

THEOREM 9. *An increasing sequence that is bounded above converges.*

A rigorous proof of this theorem is not difficult. But it does require a detailed examination of the definition of a number. This path leads us backward into a study of the foundations of mathematics. Instead we wish to go forward to see how mathematics grows both in its theoretical and practical applications. So instead of presenting a rigorous proof, we will give the following convincing argument. We imagine a directed line with an origin, and corresponding to each number s_n in the sequence we mark on the line a point P_n whose coordinate is s_n. The situation is illustrated in Fig. 1. The point P_M whose coordinate is the upper bound

Figure 1

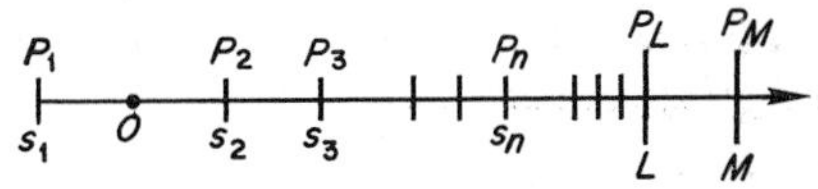

M will lie to the right of each P_n. Hence it acts as a physical barrier to the sequence of points, and beyond this barrier the points of the sequence cannot penetrate. On the other hand the sequence is increasing so each point is either to the right of its predecessor or perhaps coincides with it. Thus the points move steadily to the right toward P_M as n increases. Clearly either these points approach P_M in the limit, or they approach some other point P_L to the left of P_M. In either case the sequence has a limit L where $L \leq M$, and $\lim\limits_{n \to \infty} s_n = L$.

EXAMPLE 3. Is the sequence with $s_n = \dfrac{2n - 3}{5n - 4}$ increasing?

SOLUTION. We test the inequality $s_n \leq s_{n+1}$, i.e.,

$$\frac{2n - 3}{5n - 4} \leq \frac{2(n + 1) - 3}{5(n + 1) - 4} = \frac{2n - 1}{5n + 1}.$$

For $n \geq 1$, both denominators are positive so we obtain an equivalent inequality by multiplying both sides of (40) by their product. This gives

$$10n^2 - 13n - 3 \leq 10n^2 - 13n + 4$$

or

$$-3 \leq 4.$$

Since this last is true, retracing our steps we infer that (40) is true for $n \geq 1$, and in fact without the equality sign. Hence the given sequence is increasing.

Finally let us test that this sequence has the bound 2. The inequality $s_n < 2$ leads to

$$\frac{2n - 3}{5n - 4} < 2$$
$$2n - 3 < 10n - 8$$
$$5 < 8n.$$

But this last is obvious for $n \geq 1$. Since the steps are reversible we have proved that $s_n < 2$. Now we have an increasing sequence bounded above, so by Theorem 9 this sequence has a limit.

Of course we knew all along that this sequence has the limit $2/5$ because

$$\lim_{n \to \infty} s_n = \lim_{n \to \infty} \frac{2n - 3}{5n - 4} = \lim_{n \to \infty} \frac{2 - \dfrac{3}{n}}{5 - \dfrac{4}{n}} = \frac{2 - 0}{5 - 0} = \frac{2}{5}.$$

We now apply sequences to series. We recall that for any infinite series $\sum_{k=1}^{\infty} a_k$, we formed the partial sums, really the sequence of partial sums,

$$s_1 = a_1$$
$$s_2 = a_1 + a_2$$
$$s_3 = a_1 + a_2 + a_3$$
$$\vdots$$
$$s_n = a_1 + a_2 + a_3 + \cdots + a_n$$
$$\vdots$$

Then by definition the series converges if and only if the sequence of partial sums s_n converges. Now if $a_n \geq 0$ for all n, then obviously the sequence s_n is increasing. So Theorem 9 gives immediately the following very important theorem.

THEOREM 10. *If all the terms of the infinite series $\sum_{k=1}^{\infty} a_k$ are positive or zero, and if the partial sums are bounded above then the series converges.*

EXAMPLE 4. Show that the series

$$\sum_{k=1}^{\infty} \frac{k}{k+5} x^k \tag{41}$$

converges for each x such that $0 \leq x < 1$.

SOLUTION. We apply Theorem 10. Each term of this series is obviously nonnegative. Further since $k/(k+5) < 1$, the kth term is less than x^k. Thus

$$s_n = \sum_{k=1}^{n} \frac{k}{k+5} x^k \leq \sum_{k=1}^{n} x^k = \frac{1-x^{n+1}}{1-x} \leq \frac{1}{1-x}.$$

Therefore the partial sums are bounded by $1/(1-x) = M$. By Theorem 10, the infinite series converges.

We will learn in section 11 that this series also converges for $-1 < x \leq 0$, and consequently converges for x in the interval $-1 < x < 1$.

EXERCISE 6

In problems 1 through 13 the nth term of a sequence is given. In each case write out the first four terms of the sequence and state whether the sequence is convergent or divergent. If it is convergent give its limit.

1. $\dfrac{1}{\sqrt{n}}.$ **2.** $\dfrac{128}{2^n}.$ **3.** $\dfrac{1}{100} \log n.$

4. $2 + \dfrac{(-1)^n}{n}.$ **5.** $\dfrac{3n}{\sqrt{n+700}}.$ **6.** $\dfrac{5n^2 + 100}{n^3 + 1}.$

7. $\sqrt[5]{n}.$ **8.** $\dfrac{\sqrt{n+5}}{\sqrt{2n+3}}.$ **9.** $\left(50 + \dfrac{1}{\sqrt{n}}\right)^2.$

10. $\dfrac{3n}{n+2} - \dfrac{n+3}{2n}.$ **11.** $\dfrac{n^2}{2n+5} - \dfrac{n^2}{2n+1}.$ **12.** $\dfrac{\sqrt{n+1}}{\sqrt[3]{n+2}}.$

13. s_n is the nth digit in the decimal expansion of $131/150$.

14. If all of the terms of the sequence s_n are positive and $s_{n+1}/s_n \geq 1$ for each positive integer n, then the sequence is increasing. If the inequality is reversed then the sequence is decreasing. Prove this statement.

In problems 15 through 19 the nth term of a sequence is given. Use either the test of problem 14 or the test $s_{n+1} - s_n \gtrless 0$ to determine whether the given sequence is increasing or decreasing.

15. $\dfrac{n}{2^n}.$ **16.** $\dfrac{n!}{2^n}.$ **17.** $n^2 + (-1)^n n.$

18. $\dfrac{(n+1)!}{1 \cdot 3 \cdot 5 \cdots (2n+1)}.$ **19.** $\dfrac{2^{2n}(n!)^2}{(2n)!}.$

20. Prove that the series for e, $\sum_{k=0}^{\infty} \dfrac{1}{k!}$ is convergent.

Hint: If $k \geq 4$ then $k! > 2^k$. Prove this, and then apply Theorem 10.

In problems 20 through 23 prove that the given series converges for $0 \leq x < 1$.

21. $\sum_{k=1}^{\infty} \dfrac{x^k}{k}$.

22. $\sum_{k=1}^{\infty} \dfrac{5k+1}{k+3} x^k$.

★23. $\sum_{k=1}^{\infty} \dfrac{3^k x^k}{k!}$.

★24. $\sum_{k=1}^{\infty} \dfrac{\log^2 k}{k} x^k$.

8.   Some general theorems. In a definite integral the variable of integration is a dummy variable. Similarly in a sum, the index k is a dummy index, and any letter may be used in its place. Thus if $a_1, a_2, \cdots$ is a given sequence the five series

$$\sum_{k=1}^{\infty} a_k, \quad \sum_{n=1}^{\infty} a_n, \quad \sum_{j=1}^{\infty} a_j, \quad \sum_{m=1}^{\infty} a_m, \quad \sum_{\alpha=1}^{\infty} a_\alpha$$

are all equal. Up to now we have been using the index k consistently. Henceforth, we shall use any letter that seems suitable as a summation index. However the letter n is the most popular one for this task.

THEOREM 11. *Convergent series can be added. If the two convergent series*

$$S = \sum_{n=1}^{\infty} a_n \quad and \quad T = \sum_{n=1}^{\infty} b_n$$

have the sums indicated, then the series

$$\sum_{n=1}^{\infty} (a_n + b_n) = (a_1 + b_1) + (a_2 + b_2) + \cdots + (a_n + b_n) + \cdots$$

converges, and has the sum $S + T$.

PROOF. Let S_n and T_n denote the sum of the first n terms of the two given series. Then by hypothesis $S_n \to S$ and $T_n \to T$ as $n \to \infty$. But

$$\sum_{k=1}^{n} (a_k + b_k) = (a_1 + b_1) + (a_2 + b_2) + \cdots + (a_n + b_n)$$
$$= (a_1 + a_2 + \cdots + a_n) + (b_1 + b_2 + \cdots + b_n) = S_n + T_n.$$

Therefore

$$\lim_{n \to \infty} \sum_{k=1}^{n} (a_k + b_k) = \lim_{n \to \infty} (S_n + T_n) = \lim_{n \to \infty} S_n + \lim_{n \to \infty} T_n = S + T.$$

THEOREM 12. *A convergent series can be multiplied by a constant. Under the hypotheses of Theorem 11, the series*

$$\sum_{n=1}^{\infty} ca_n = ca_1 + ca_2 + \cdots + ca_n + \cdots$$

converges and has the sum cS.

PROOF. As before, let $S_n = a_1 + a_2 + \cdots + a_n$. Then

$$\sum_{k=1}^{n} ca_k = ca_1 + ca_2 + \cdots + ca_n = c(a_1 + a_2 + \cdots + a_n) = cS_n.$$

$$\lim_{n \to \infty} \sum_{k=1}^{n} ca_k = \lim_{n \to \infty} cS_n = c \lim_{n \to \infty} S_n = cS. \qquad \text{Q.E.D.}$$

THEOREM 13. *If the series $a_1 + a_2 + \cdots$ converges then $a_n \to 0$, as $n \to \infty$.*

PROOF. By definition $S_n \to S$ and $S_{n-1} \to S$ as $n \to \infty$. Hence

$$\lim_{n \to \infty} (S_n - S_{n-1}) = \lim_{n \to \infty} S_n - \lim_{n \to \infty} S_{n-1} = S - S = 0.$$

But $S_n - S_{n-1} = (a_1 + a_2 + \cdots + a_n) - (a_1 + a_2 + \cdots + a_{n-1}) = a_n$
Therefore $a_n \to 0$ as $n \to \infty$. Q.E.D.

If the series converges then $a_n \to 0$. But this necessary condition for convergence is not sufficient. In section 9 we will prove that the *harmonic* series

$$\sum_{n=1}^{\infty} \frac{1}{n} = 1 + \frac{1}{2} + \frac{1}{3} + \cdots + \frac{1}{n} + \cdots$$

is divergent, although its general term $\dfrac{1}{n} \to 0$.

THEOREM 14. THE COMPARISON TEST. *Suppose that for each positive integer n*

$$0 \le a_n \le b_n. \tag{42}$$

(a) *If $\sum b_n$ converges then $\sum a_n$ converges.*
(b) *If $\sum a_n$ diverges then $\sum b_n$ diverges.*

PROOF. Assume that the series $\sum_{n=1}^{\infty} b_n$ is convergent and let the sum be T. Then from (42) it follows that for each positive integer n, the partial sum

$$S_n = a_1 + a_2 + \cdots + a_n \le b_1 + b_2 + \cdots + b_n \le \sum_{n=1}^{\infty} b_n = T.$$

Hence the sequence of partial sums is bounded above by T.   By hypothesis $a_n \geqq 0$.   Hence by Theorem 10, the series converges.   This proves (a).

To prove (b), assume that the series $\sum a_n$ diverges.   There are only two possibilities for the series $\sum b_n$, namely, it can converge or diverge. If the series $\sum b_n$ converges then by part (a) of the theorem $\sum a_n$ converges.   But this contradicts the hypothesis that $\sum a_n$ diverges.   Therefore $\sum b_n$ cannot converge, and therefore must diverge.   Q.E.D.

It is appropriate to remark at this point that the early terms in a series have no effect on the convergence or divergence of the series, although it does affect the sum.   The first million or so terms can be quite "wild," but if the terms eventually "settle down and behave nicely" the series can still converge.   Stated more precisely, the condition $0 \leqq a_n \leqq b_n$ in Theorem 14, need not be satisfied for all n.   If $0 \leqq a_n \leqq b_n$ for all $n \geqq N$, where N is some suitably selected integer, then the conclusions of the theorem are still true.

9.   Some practical tests for convergence.   So far in our work we have had only one type of series that is convergent, namely the geometric series.   In order to use the comparison test of Theorem 14 we need a supply of convergent series and divergent series.   A very nice supply is provided by Theorem 16 and its corollary.   The next two theorems are the really useful ones for practical testing for convergence.

THEOREM 15.   THE RATIO TEST.   *Suppose that $a_n > 0$ for each n and that*

$$\lim_{n \to \infty} \frac{a_{n+1}}{a_n} = L. \tag{43}$$

(a)   *If $L < 1$ then the series $\sum_{n=1}^{\infty} a_n$ converges.*

(b)   *If $L > 1$ then this series diverges.*

(c)   *If $L = 1$, no conclusion can be drawn.*

PROOF.   **a.** Suppose first that $L < 1$.   We can select a number R such that $L < R < 1$, and then for all n sufficiently large we have from (43)

$$\frac{a_{n+1}}{a_n} < R. \tag{44}$$

Suppose that N is some integer such that for all $n \geqq N$ the inequality (44) holds.   We multiply both sides of (44) by the positive a_n and write the resulting inequality for each index $n \geqq N$.   This gives the first column of inequalities in (45).

$$a_{N+1} < Ra_N$$

$$a_{N+2} < Ra_{N+1} \longrightarrow a_{N+2} < R^2 a_N$$

$$a_{N+3} < Ra_{N+2} \longrightarrow a_{N+3} < R^3 a_N$$

$$a_{N+4} < Ra_{N+3} \longrightarrow a_{N+4} < R^4 a_N. \tag{45}$$

Now use the first inequality in the second as indicated in the diagram. This gives $a_{N+2} < Ra_{N+1} < R(Ra_N) = R^2 a_N$. Continuing in the manner indicated by the arrows, we obtain each of the inequalities in the second column of (45). In general, we find that for each $k \geq 0$,

$$a_{N+k} \leq R^k a_N. \tag{46}$$

Then

$$\sum_{k=0}^{\infty} a_{N+k} = a_N + a_{N+1} + a_{N+2} + \cdots + a_{N+k} + \cdots$$

$$< a_N + a_N R + a_N R^2 + \cdots + a_N R^k + \cdots = a_N \sum_{k=0}^{\infty} R^k = \frac{a_N}{1 - R} \tag{47}$$

since $R < 1$. In other words we have compared the given series, starting with the term a_N, with a geometric series that is known to be convergent. Hence the series on the left side of (47) is convergent by Theorem 14. Adding the finite number of terms $a_1 + a_2 + \cdots + a_{N-1}$ does not alter the convergence of the series.

b. Suppose that $L > 1$. This time we select R such that $L > R > 1$. Then there is some N such that for all $n \geq N$ we have

$$\frac{a_{n+1}}{a_n} > R \tag{48}$$

Notice that this is (44), with the inequality sign reversed. Then in (45) and (46) all of the inequality signs must be reversed. But $R > 1$ and $a_{N+k} \geq R^k a_N \geq a_N$, hence the general term cannot tend to zero. Then by Theorem 13, the series is divergent.

c. Consider the two series

$$\sum_{n=1}^{\infty} \frac{1}{n} = 1 + \frac{1}{2} + \frac{1}{3} + \cdots + \frac{1}{n} + \cdots, \tag{49}$$

and

$$\sum_{n=1}^{\infty} \frac{1}{n^2} = 1 + \frac{1}{4} + \frac{1}{9} + \cdots + \frac{1}{n^2} + \cdots. \tag{50}$$

The ratio test applied to (49) gives

$$\lim_{n \to \infty} \frac{a_{n+1}}{a_n} = \lim_{n \to \infty} \frac{1/(n+1)}{1/n} = \lim_{n \to \infty} \frac{n}{n+1} = 1.$$

When applied to the series (50), the ratio test yields

$$\lim_{n\to\infty}\frac{a_{n+1}}{a_n} = \lim_{n\to\infty}\frac{1/(n+1)^2}{1/n^2} = \lim_{n\to\infty}\frac{n^2}{n^2+2n+1} = 1.$$

We shall see as a corollary to the next theorem, that the series in (49) diverges, and the series in (50) converges.   Hence if $L = 1$, no conclusion can be drawn about the convergence of the series.

EXAMPLE 1.   Does the series $\sum_{n=1}^{\infty} n^2 \left(\frac{3}{4}\right)^n$ converge?

SOLUTION.   Applying the ratio test we find

$$\lim_{n\to\infty}\frac{(n+1)^2(\frac{3}{4})^{n+1}}{n^2(\frac{3}{4})^n} = \lim_{n\to\infty}\frac{(n+1)^2}{n^2}\frac{3}{4} = \lim_{n\to\infty}\left(1+\frac{2}{n}+\frac{1}{n^2}\right)\frac{3}{4}$$

$$= \frac{3}{4} < 1.$$

Hence by Theorem 15, the given series converges.

THEOREM 16.   THE CAUCHY INTEGRAL TEST.   *Suppose $f(x)$ has the following properties:*

(1) *$f(n) = a_n$ for each integer n,*
(2) *$f(x)$ is a decreasing function for $x \geq 1$,*
(3) *$f(x) > 0$, for $x \geq 1$.*

Then the series $\sum_{n=1}^{\infty} a_n$ and the integral $\int_1^{\infty} f(x)\,dx$ converge or diverge together.

When the integral converges, the sum can be estimated by

$$\int_1^{\infty} f(x)dx \leq \sum_{n=1}^{\infty} a_n \leq a_1 + \int_1^{\infty} f(x)dx. \tag{51}$$

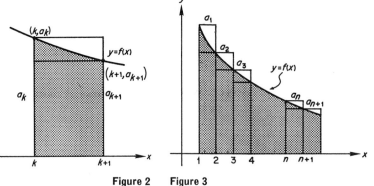

Figure 2   Figure 3

PROOF. Since the function is decreasing, the area under the curve $y = f(x)$ between $x = k$ and $x = k + 1$ lies between the areas of two rectangles of unit width and height $f(k) = a_k$ and $f(k + 1) = a_{k+1}$ (see Fig. 2). In symbols

$$a_k \geq \int_k^{k+1} f(x)dx \geq a_{k+1}. \tag{52}$$

Forming the sum of n such terms $k = 1, 2, 3, \cdots, n$ we have

$$a_1 + a_2 + \cdots + a_n \geq \int_1^{n+1} f(x)dx \geq a_2 + a_3 + \cdots + a_{n+1}. \tag{53}$$

This inequality is shown graphically in Fig. 3.

If the integral converges then by the right side of (53) the partial sums are bounded and hence by Theorem 10 the series converges. If the integral diverges it must tend to infinity because $f(x)$ is positive. Then the left side of (53) shows that the series is also divergent. Finally if the series converges, we can let $n \to \infty$ in (53). Then the left half of (53) gives the left half of (51). To obtain the right half of (51), just add a_1 to the middle and right side of (53) and then let $n \to \infty$.

COROLLARY. The p-series

$$\sum_{n=1}^{\infty} \frac{1}{n^p} = 1 + \frac{1}{2^p} + \frac{1}{3^p} + \cdots + \frac{1}{n^p} + \cdots \tag{54}$$

converges if $p > 1$, and diverges if $p \leq 1$.

PROOF. For $p > 0$, the function $f(x) = 1/x^p$ satisfies the three conditions of Theorem 16, so we only need to compute the integral. If $0 < p < 1$, then

$$\int_1^M f(x)dx = \int_1^M \frac{dx}{x^p} = \frac{x^{1-p}}{1 - p}\bigg|_1^M = \frac{M^{1-p} - 1}{1 - p} \tag{55}$$

and this quantity tends to infinity as $M \to \infty$. In this case the series diverges. The case $p = 1$ requires special treatment. In this case

$$\int_1^M f(x)dx = \int_1^M \frac{dx}{x} = \ln M$$

and since $\ln M \to \infty$ as $M \to \infty$, the series again diverges.
If $p > 1$ then

$$\int_1^M \frac{dx}{x^p} = \frac{1}{(1 - p)x^{p-1}}\bigg|_1^M = \frac{1}{p - 1}\left(1 - \frac{1}{M^{p-1}}\right)$$

This tends to $1/(p - 1)$ as $M \to \infty$. In this case the series converges. Furthermore by (51) we have the estimate

$$\frac{1}{p - 1} \leq \sum_{n=1}^{\infty} \frac{1}{n^p} \leq 1 + \frac{1}{p - 1}, \qquad p > 1.$$

We leave it for the student to consider the trivial case in which p is zero or negative.

As a special case when $p = 1$ the p-series gives the harmonic series (49) and hence the harmonic series diverges. When $p = 2$, we have the series (50) and hence that series converges.

EXAMPLE 2.   Does the series $\sum_{n=1}^{\infty} \dfrac{n}{(4 + n^2)^{3/4}}$ converge?

SOLUTION.   We apply the integral test (Theorem 16).

$$I_M = \int_1^M \frac{x\,dx}{(4 + x^2)^{3/4}} = \frac{1}{2} \cdot \frac{(4 + x^2)^{1/4}}{1/4} \Big|_1^M = 2\sqrt[4]{4 + M^2} - 2\sqrt[4]{5}.$$

Since $I_M \to \infty$ as $M \to \infty$, the given series diverges.

EXAMPLE 3.   Does the series $\sum_{n=1}^{\infty} \dfrac{1}{\sqrt{n^3 + 1}}$ converge?

SOLUTION.   The student should try the ratio test on this series. He will find that the limit of the ratio is 1. More powerful methods are needed. The integral test is more powerful, but in this case the integration of $1/\sqrt{x^3 + 1}$ is difficult. But the function is approximately $1/\sqrt{x^3}$, so this suggests the use of the comparison test (Theorem 14). Indeed $\sqrt{n^3 + 1} > \sqrt{n^3}$, and hence

$$\frac{1}{\sqrt{n^3 + 1}} < \frac{1}{\sqrt{n^3}} = \frac{1}{n^{3/2}}.$$

But on the right side we have the general term of the p-series with $p = 3/2$, and hence the series $\sum 1/n^{3/2}$ is convergent. Therefore the given series is convergent.

The comparison test is quite useful when used in conjunction with the p-series.

EXERCISE 7

In problems 1 through 15 determine whether the given series converges or diverges.

1. $\sum_{n=1}^{\infty} \dfrac{2^n}{n!}$.

2. $\sum_{n=1}^{\infty} \dfrac{n^3}{2^n}$.

3. $\sum_{n=1}^{\infty} \dfrac{n^2}{n^3 + 100}$.

4. $\sum_{n=1}^{\infty} \dfrac{n}{n^3 + 1}$.

5. $\sum_{n=0}^{\infty} \dfrac{\sqrt{n}}{n^2 - 3}$.

6. $\sum_{n=0}^{\infty} \dfrac{(n!)^2 2^n}{(2n)!}$.

7. $\displaystyle\sum_{n=1}^{\infty} \frac{1}{100\,n}$.

8. $\displaystyle\sum_{n=1}^{\infty} \frac{10^n}{n!}$.

9. $\displaystyle\sum_{n=3}^{\infty} \frac{1}{n \ln n}$.

10. $\displaystyle\sum_{n=2}^{\infty} \frac{2^n \sin^4 n}{3^n}$.

11. $\displaystyle\sum_{n=2}^{\infty} \frac{(n+2)!}{(n-1)!\,2^n}$.

12. $\displaystyle\sum_{n=1}^{\infty} \frac{n!}{n^n}$.

★13. $\displaystyle\sum_{n=2}^{\infty} \frac{1}{n \ln^2 n}$.

★14. $\displaystyle\sum_{n=1}^{\infty} \frac{\ln n}{n^2}$.

★15. $\displaystyle\sum_{n=1}^{\infty} \cot^{-1} n$.

★16. Prove the following generalization of the comparison test. Suppose that for each positive integer n, $a_n > 0$, and $b_n > 0$, and suppose that

$$\lim_{n \to \infty} \frac{a_n}{b_n} = L$$

where $L \neq 0$. Then the two series $\sum a_n$ and $\sum b_n$ diverge or converge together, i.e., if the first series converges, the second one does, and if the first series diverges, the second one does. *Hint:* For all sufficiently large values of n

$$\frac{1}{2} L\,b_n < a_n < 2L\,b_n.$$

★17. Use the theorem proved in problem 16 to settle the behavior of the series in problems 3, 4, 5, and 7.

18. Use the theorem proved in problem 16 to settle the behavior of the following series

a. $\displaystyle\sum_{n=1}^{\infty} \frac{n^2 + 2n - 9}{n^3 - 5n - 17}$

b. $\displaystyle\sum_{n=1}^{\infty} \frac{43n + 51}{n^3 + n^2 - 11}$

c. $\displaystyle\sum_{n=1}^{\infty} \frac{\ln(n+5)}{n\sqrt{7n - 3}}$

d. $\displaystyle\sum_{n=1}^{\infty} \frac{\sqrt{3n - 2}}{\sqrt{n}(n+1)\ln(n+2)}$.

19. Show that the ratio test cannot be applied directly to the series

$$\sum_{n=1}^{\infty} \frac{1 + (-1)^{n+1}}{2^n} = 1 + 0 + \frac{1}{4} + 0 + \frac{1}{16} + 0 + \cdots.$$

Prove that this series converges and has the sum 4/3.

20. Prove that $\dfrac{\pi}{4} < \displaystyle\sum_{k=1}^{\infty} \frac{1}{1 + k^2} < \frac{\pi}{4} + \frac{1}{2}$.

10. **Alternating series.** In section 9 all of the terms of the series were greater than or equal to zero. We now allow negative terms to appear in the series in a regular way.

DEFINITION 6. *A series of the form*

$$\sum_{n=1}^{\infty} (-1)^{n+1}a_n = a_1 - a_2 + a_3 - a_4 + a_5 - \cdots + (-1)^{n+1}a_n + \cdots \quad (56)$$

is called an alternating series if $a_n \geq 0$ for all n.

A simple and beautiful test for the convergence of an alternating series is given in

THEOREM 17.   *If the terms of an alternating series (56) satisfy the following conditions:*

(1)   *The terms a_n are decreasing, i.e., $a_1 \geqq a_2 \geqq a_3 \cdots \geqq a_n \geqq \cdots$,*

(2)   *The terms tend to zero, i.e., $\lim\limits_{n \to \infty} a_n = 0$,*

then the series converges.   Further if S is the sum of the series, and S_n is the sum of the first n terms then

$$S_{2n} \leqq S \leqq S_{2n+1}, \qquad n = 1, 2, 3, \cdots. \tag{57}$$

Before proving this theorem let us observe that the behavior of the partial sums is very similar to a swinging pendulum that is slowly coming to rest in a fixed position, equivalent to the sum of the series.   This is illustrated in Fig. 4.   It may be helpful to keep this figure in view while reading the proof.

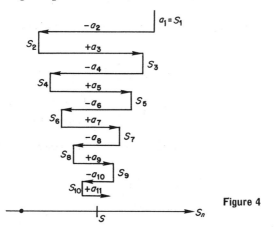

Figure 4

PROOF.   We first consider the partial sums with an even number of terms.   These terms can be paired thus:

$$S_{2n} = a_1 - a_2 + a_3 - a_4 + \cdots + a_{2n-1} - a_{2n} =$$
$$(a_1 - a_2) + (a_3 - a_4) + \cdots + (a_{2n-1} - a_{2n}).$$

Since the individual terms are decreasing, the pair in each parenthesis gives a positive or zero result.   More precisely

$$a_{2n-1} - a_{2n} \geqq 0$$

for every n.   In going from S_{2n} to S_{2n+2} we therefore add a quantity

$a_{2n+1} - a_{2n+2}$ that is either positive or zero. Hence the sequence of partial sums with even subscripts is increasing, or in symbols

$$S_2 \leqq S_4 \leqq S_6 \leqq \cdots \leqq S_{2n} \leqq S_{2n+2} \leqq \cdots. \tag{58}$$

For the partial sums with an odd number of terms, we may group the terms a little differently and write

$$S_{2n+1} = a_1 - a_2 + a_3 - \cdots - a_{2n} + a_{2n+1} =$$
$$a_1 - (a_2 - a_3) - (a_4 - a_5) - \cdots - (a_{2n} - a_{2n+1}).$$

Here again each grouped pair gives a positive or zero result, but now this result is to be *subtracted*. Hence the sequence of partial sums with odd subscripts is decreasing, or in symbols

$$S_1 \geqq S_3 \geqq S_5 \geqq \cdots \geqq S_{2n-1} \geqq S_{2n+1} \geqq \cdots. \tag{59}$$

In order to combine the inequalities in (58) and (59) we observe that

$$S_{2n+1} - S_{2n} = \sum_{k=1}^{2n+1} (-1)^{k+1} a_k - \sum_{k=1}^{2n} (-1)^{k+1} a_k = (-1)^{2n+1+1} a_{2n+1} = a_{2n+1} \tag{60}$$

But $a_{2n+1} \geqq 0$, so $S_{2n} \leqq S_{2n+1}$. Combining this with (58) and (59) we find that for each n

$$S_2 \leqq S_4 \leqq S_6 \leqq \cdots \leqq S_{2n} \leqq S_{2n+1} \leqq \cdots \leqq S_5 \leqq S_3 \leqq S_1. \tag{61}$$

Hence the sequence $S_2, S_4, \cdots$ is increasing and bounded above by S_1. So by Theorem 9 this sequence has a limit. Call it L. Similarly the sequence $S_1, S_3, \cdots$ is decreasing and bounded below so it has a limit which we call M. Now $a_n \to 0$ as $n \to \infty$ so using equation (60) we have

$$0 = \lim_{n \to \infty} a_{2n+1} = \lim_{n \to \infty} (S_{2n+1} - S_{2n}) = \lim_{n \to \infty} S_{2n+1} - \lim_{n \to \infty} S_{2n} = M - L$$

Hence $M = L$. Both sequences converge to the same limit. Therefore the series (56) converges and its sum S is the common limit. Since the one sequence is decreasing to S and the other is increasing to S this also proves the inequality (57). Q.E.D.

EXAMPLE 1. Investigate the convergence of the series

(a) $\displaystyle\sum_{n=1}^{\infty} \frac{(-1)^{n+1}}{n}$, (b) $\displaystyle\sum_{n=1}^{\infty} \frac{(-1)^{n+1} n}{100 + 10n}$, (c) $\displaystyle\sum_{n=0}^{\infty} \frac{\sin\left(\frac{\pi}{4} + \frac{n\pi}{2}\right)}{n+1}$.

SOLUTION. Written out the series (a) is

$$1 - \frac{1}{2} + \frac{1}{3} - \frac{1}{4} + \cdots + \frac{1}{2n-1} - \frac{1}{2n} \cdots. \tag{62}$$

The series is alternating and the general term $1/n$ decreases steadily to zero. Hence by Theorem 17, this series converges. Further using the first three or four terms, (57) gives for the sum S, the bounds $.5833\cdots < S < .8333\cdots$

(b) This series is alternating but the general term $n/(100 + 10n)$ tends to $1/10$ as $n \to \infty$. Hence by Theorem 13 this series diverges.

(c) Each term has the common factor $\sqrt{2}/2$. Putting this out front this series can be written

$$\frac{\sqrt{2}}{2}\left(1 + \frac{1}{2} - \frac{1}{3} - \frac{1}{4} + \frac{1}{5} + \frac{1}{6} - \frac{1}{7} - \frac{1}{8} + \cdots\right).$$

Now this series is not an alternating series, but if we pair the terms in an obvious way we get an alternating series, namely

$$\frac{\sqrt{2}}{2}\left(\frac{3}{2} - \frac{7}{12} + \frac{11}{30} - \frac{15}{56} + \cdots + \frac{(-1)^n(4n + 3)}{(2n + 1)(2n + 2)} + \cdots\right).$$

But this new series is alternating, and its terms satisfy the conditions of Theorem 17. Hence this series converges. Consequently the given series also converges, because its general term tends to zero.

*The general theory for grouping terms or rearranging terms in an infinite series is a little complicated and it is best to postpone this study until the Advanced Calculus course. A divergent series may become convergent when the terms are grouped. For example the series

$$\sum_{n=0}^{\infty} (-1)^n = 1 - 1 + 1 - 1 + 1 - 1\cdots$$

is divergent, but when the terms are paired we have

$$(1 - 1) + (1 - 1) + (1 - 1) + \cdots = 0 + 0 + 0 + \cdots$$

a convergent series. However if the general term of the original series tends to zero, and the new series obtained by grouping converges (where the number of terms in each group is less than some constant), then the original series also converges. This is the situation in example 1c.

When the terms of a series are rearranged (reordered) a convergent series can become divergent, or may remain convergent but have a different sum.

In the next section we discuss series that are absolutely convergent. It turns out that if a series is absolutely convergent, the above pathological behavior cannot occur. Thus if the terms are rearranged in an absolutely convergent series, the new series is convergent, and has the same sum as the original series.

EXERCISE 8

In problems 1 through 14 determine whether the given series converges or diverges.

1. $\displaystyle\sum_{n=1}^{\infty} \frac{(-1)^{n+1}}{\sqrt{n}}.$

2. $\displaystyle\sum_{n=3}^{\infty} \frac{(-1)^n}{\sqrt[3]{n^2}}.$

3. $\displaystyle\sum_{n=1}^{\infty} (-1)^n \log \frac{1}{n}.$

4. $\displaystyle\sum_{n=1}^{\infty} (-1)^n \sin n\pi.$

5. $\displaystyle\sum_{n=0}^{\infty} (-1)^n \sin \frac{\pi}{n+1}.$

6. $\displaystyle\sum_{n=2}^{\infty} \frac{(-1)^n \ln n}{n}.$

7. $\displaystyle\sum_{n=2}^{\infty} \frac{(-1)^n \sqrt[4]{n}}{\ln n}.$

8. $\displaystyle\sum_{n=2}^{\infty} \frac{(-1)^n 2^n}{n^{10}}.$

9. $\displaystyle\sum_{n=1}^{\infty} \frac{(-1)^n 3^n}{n!}.$

10. $\displaystyle\sum_{n=2}^{\infty} \frac{(-1)^n}{\log n}.$

11. $\displaystyle\sum_{n=1}^{\infty} (-1)^n \ln \sqrt[n]{n}.$

12. $\displaystyle\sum_{n=7}^{\infty} \frac{(-1)^n \sqrt[n]{n+100}}{n-5}.$

13. $\displaystyle\sum_{n=1}^{\infty} \frac{(-1)^n \cos n\pi}{n}.$

14. $\displaystyle\sum_{n=1}^{\infty} \frac{(-1)^n \ln^3 n^3}{n}.$

11. Absolute and conditional convergence. We have seen in section 9 that the harmonic series

$$1 + \frac{1}{2} + \frac{1}{3} + \frac{1}{4} + \cdots + \frac{1}{n} + \cdots \qquad (49)$$

diverges (by the Corollary to the Cauchy integral test). However if we alter this series by subtracting instead of adding the terms $1/2n$ we have the series

$$1 - \frac{1}{2} + \frac{1}{3} - \frac{1}{4} + \cdots + \frac{(-1)^{n+1}}{n} + \cdots. \qquad (62)$$

But this series converges (an alternating series whose general term tends to zero). Thus a series [such as (62)] may converge, but when each term is replaced by its absolute value the new series may diverge.

DEFINITION 7. *The series* $\displaystyle\sum_{n=1}^{\infty} a_n$ *is said to be absolutely convergent if the series formed by using the absolute values of the terms,*

$$\sum_{n=1}^{\infty} |a_n| = |a_1| + |a_2| + \cdots + |a_n| + \cdots, \qquad (63)$$

is convergent.

It can happen that a series is convergent and yet not be absolutely convergent. The prize example is the series (62). It is a convergent series, but when absolute values are taken (62) gives the divergent series (49). Such a series is said to be *conditionally convergent*.

DEFINITION 8. *If a series* $\displaystyle\sum_{n=1}^{\infty} a_n$ *is convergent, and if its series*

*of absolute values (63) diverges, then the series is said to be condi-
tionally convergent.*

A central result about absolutely convergent series is

THEOREM 18.   *An absolutely convergent series is convergent.*

PROOF.   This states that if (63) converges then so also does

$$\sum_{n=1}^{\infty} a_n = a_1 + a_2 + \cdots + a_n + \cdots. \tag{64}$$

Let p_n denote the positive and zero terms and let q_n denote the negative
terms in (64).   More precisely set

$$\begin{cases} p_n = a_n \\ q_n = 0 \end{cases} \text{if } a_n \geq 0, \qquad \begin{cases} p_n = 0 \\ q_n = -a_n > 0 \end{cases} \text{if } a_n < 0, \tag{65}$$

and consider the two new series

$$\sum_{n=1}^{\infty} p_n, \qquad \text{and} \qquad \sum_{n=1}^{\infty} q_n.$$

For example if our series is the series of (62) then by (65), the two new
series are

$$\sum_{n=1}^{\infty} p_n = 1 + 0 + \frac{1}{3} + 0 + \frac{1}{5} + \cdots + 0 + \frac{1}{2n+1} + 0 + \cdots,$$

and

$$\sum_{n=1}^{\infty} q_n = 0 + \frac{1}{2} + 0 + \frac{1}{4} + 0 + \cdots + \frac{1}{2n} + 0 + \frac{1}{2n+2} + \cdots.$$

From the definition of p_n and q_n in (65) it is clear that

$$p_n + q_n = |a_n| \qquad \text{and} \qquad p_n - q_n = a_n, \tag{66}$$

for $n = 1, 2, \cdots$.   Let A_n, S_n, P_n, and Q_n denote the sum of the first n
terms of the series $\sum |a_n|$, $\sum a_n$, $\sum p_n$, and $\sum q_n$ respectively.   Then from
(66) we have

$$P_n + Q_n = (p_1 + q_1) + (p_2 + q_2) + \cdots + (p_n + q_n) = $$
$$|a_1| + |a_2| + \cdots + |a_n| = A_n \tag{67}$$

and

$$P_n - Q_n = (p_1 - q_1) + (p_2 - q_2) + \cdots + (p_n - q_n) = $$
$$a_1 + a_2 + \cdots + a_n = S_n. \tag{68}$$

Since the given series is absolutely convergent the partial sums A_n form a
monotonic sequence that converges to a limit A.   By (67) we have

$P_n \leq A_n \leq A$, and $Q_n \leq A_n \leq A$ for $n = 1, 2, \cdots$. But the sequence of partial sums P_1, P_2, $\cdots$ is increasing and since it is bounded converges to a limit which we denote by P. Similarly the sequence Q_1, Q_2, $\cdots$ is increasing and bounded and so has a limit Q. Finally from (68)

$$\lim_{n \to \infty} S_n = \lim_{n \to \infty} (P_n - Q_n) = \lim_{n \to \infty} P_n - \lim_{n \to \infty} Q_n = P - Q.$$

Hence the given series converges and its sum is $P - Q$.   Q. E. D.

Notice that this theorem is completely reasonable, because it states that when a series is absolutely convergent, the sum of the series is $P - Q$ (the sum of its positive terms minus the sum of the absolute values of its negative terms).

This theorem is also a comfortable one. For it allows us to "throw away the negative signs" in a preliminary investigation, because whenever the new series is convergent, then the one with the "negative signs restored" is also convergent.

EXAMPLE 1. Find the convergence set for the series

$$\sum_{n=1}^{\infty} \frac{(-1)^{n+1}x^n}{n} = x - \frac{x^2}{2} + \frac{x^3}{3} - \frac{x^4}{4} + \cdots. \tag{69}$$

SOLUTION. We are to find all values of x for which this series converges. We first consider the absolute convergence, i.e., we consider

$$\sum_{n=1}^{\infty} \frac{|x|^n}{n} = |x| + \frac{|x|^2}{2} + \frac{|x|^3}{3} + \frac{|x|^4}{4} + \cdots.$$

Applying the ratio test we have

$$\lim_{n \to \infty} \frac{a_{n+1}}{a_n} = \lim_{n \to \infty} \frac{|x|^{n+1}}{n+1} \bigg/ \frac{|x|^n}{n} = \lim_{n \to \infty} \frac{|x|^{n+1}}{n+1} \cdot \frac{n}{|x|^n} = |x|.$$

Therefore if $-1 < x < 1$, the series converges absolutely and hence it converges. Suppose $|x| > 1$. Then by L'Hospital's rule

$$\lim_{n \to \infty} \frac{|x|^n}{n} = \lim_{n \to \infty} \frac{|x|^n \ln|x|}{1} = \infty.$$

So the general term does not tend to zero, and consequently the series diverges. We need to consider only the end points of the interval $-1 < x < 1$. When $x = 1$, the series (69) becomes the series (62) which we already know converges. When $x = -1$, the series (69) becomes the negative of the harmonic series (49) and hence diverges. Summarizing, the given series converges for x in the half open interval $-1 < x \leq 1$ and diverges for all other real values of x.

EXAMPLE 2. Find the convergence set for

$$\sum_{n=1}^{\infty} \frac{(-1)^n}{n^2} \left(\frac{x}{3x + 8} \right)^n. \tag{70}$$

SOLUTION.   To simplify matters replace the quantity $x/(3x + 8)$ by t, and consider the series $\sum(-1)^n t^n/n^2$. If we test the absolute convergence by the comparison test we find that for $|t| \leq 1$ we have term by term

$$\sum_{n=1}^{\infty} \frac{|t|^n}{n^2} \leq \sum_{n=1}^{\infty} \frac{1}{n^2},$$

and the series on the right is known to converge.   If $|t| > 1$, a computation similar to the one in the first example will show that the series diverges.   Hence the convergence set for the series (70) is the set x for which

$$-1 \leq t = \frac{x}{3x + 8} \leq 1$$

Solving for x in terms of t we find that $x = 8t/(1 - 3t)$.   When $t = 1$, $x = -4$ and when $t = -1$, $x = -2$.   We leave it to the student to show that the convergence set is *not* the interval $-4 \leq x \leq -2$.   Rather the series (70) converges if $x \geq -2$ or if $x \leq -4$, and diverges for all other x.   The set is shown shaded in Fig. 5.

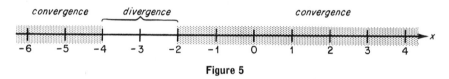

Figure 5

EXERCISE 9

In problems 1 through 14 find the convergence set for the given series.   Observe that in each of these problems the convergence set is an interval.   Be sure to test the series at the end points of the interval.

1. $\displaystyle\sum_{n=1}^{\infty} n x^n.$

2. $\displaystyle\sum_{n=1}^{\infty} \frac{2^n x^n}{n^2}.$

3. $\displaystyle\sum_{n=1}^{\infty} \frac{x^n}{n}.$

4. $\displaystyle\sum_{n=3}^{\infty} \frac{(-1)^n x^n}{n\, 5^n}.$

5. $\displaystyle\sum_{n=0}^{\infty} \frac{x^n}{n!}.$

6. $\displaystyle\sum_{n=0}^{\infty} \frac{(-1)^n x^{2n+1}}{(2n + 1)!}.$

7. $\displaystyle\sum_{n=0}^{\infty} n!\, x^n.$

8. $\displaystyle\sum_{n=1}^{\infty} \sqrt{n}(x - 3)^n.$

9. $\displaystyle\sum_{n=2}^{\infty} \frac{(x + 5)^n}{2^n \ln n}.$

10. $\displaystyle\sum_{n=2}^{\infty} \frac{2^n (x - 4)^n}{n \ln n}.$

11. $\displaystyle\sum_{n=1}^{\infty} \frac{(x - 2)^n}{3n + 1}.$

12. $\displaystyle\sum_{n=1}^{\infty} \frac{(2x + 11)^n}{3^n(2n - 1)}.$

13. $\displaystyle\sum_{n=1}^{\infty} \frac{(-1)^n(3x + 2)^n}{5^n\, n\sqrt{n}}.$

14. $\displaystyle\sum_{n=1}^{\infty} \frac{105\, x^n}{n(n + 3)}.$

In problems 15 through 26 find the convergence set for the given series.

15. $\displaystyle\sum_{n=1}^{\infty} \frac{n}{x^n}.$

16. $\displaystyle\sum_{n=1}^{\infty} \frac{1}{n\,x^n}.$

17. $\displaystyle\sum_{n=2}^{\infty} \frac{1}{n^2}\left(\frac{3x-18}{x-2}\right)^n.$

18. $\displaystyle\sum_{n=0}^{\infty} n\left(\frac{3x-15}{x+3}\right)^n.$

19. $\displaystyle\sum_{n=1}^{\infty} \frac{3^n}{n}\left(\frac{x-3}{x+13}\right)^n.$

20. $\displaystyle\sum_{n=0}^{\infty} \left(\frac{3x-17}{2x+5}\right)^n.$

21. $\displaystyle\sum_{n=2}^{\infty} \frac{\ln n}{n}\left(\frac{2x+3}{3x+2}\right)^n.$

22. $\displaystyle\sum_{n=0}^{\infty} \left(\frac{x+5}{x-3}\right)^n.$

★23. $\displaystyle\sum_{n=1}^{\infty} \frac{(x-n)^n}{n}.$

★24. $\displaystyle\sum_{n=1}^{\infty} \frac{x^{n!}}{n}.$

★25. $\displaystyle\sum_{n=1}^{\infty} \frac{(-1)^n}{n+x^2}.$

★26. $\displaystyle\sum_{n=1}^{\infty} \frac{1}{n^2}\sin n^3 x.$

★27. Suppose that in the series $\sum a_n x^n$ we have $\lim |a_{n+1}|/|a_n| = L$ as $n \to \infty$. Prove that the series converges for $|x| < 1/L$.

★28. Prove that if we differentiate term by term the series of problem 27, then the new series $\sum n a_n x^{n-1}$ also converges in the same interval $|x| < 1/L$.

★29. Find the convergence set for $\displaystyle\sum_{n=1}^{\infty} \frac{(x^2-5)^n}{4^n}$ and the sum of the series.

30. Prove that $\lim\limits_{n\to\infty} x^n/n! = 0$ for each fixed x no matter how large, by observing that the series of problem 5 converges for all x.

31. Find the convergence set for $\displaystyle\sum_{n=1}^{\infty} \frac{x^n}{n+x^{2n}}.$

★12. The radius of convergence of a power series. We observe that in problems 1 through 6 of Exercise 9 the convergence set in each case is an interval with center at the origin. The next theorem shows that this is always the case for a Maclaurin series.

THEOREM 19. *For each Maclaurin series*

$$\sum_{n=0}^{\infty} a_n x^n \tag{21}$$

there is a number $R \geq 0$ called the radius of convergence of the series such that if $-R < x < R$ the series converges, and if $|x| > R$ the series diverges.

We remark that we may have $R = 0$, and then the series converges only at $x = 0$. See problem 7 of Exercise 9. Or it may be that $R = \infty$, and the series converges for all x. See problems 5 and 6 of Exercise 9. Further the behavior of the series at $x = R$ and at $x = -R$ (the end points of the interval of convergence) follows no general pattern, as problems 1, 2, 3, and 4 of Exercise 9 clearly illustrate.

PROOF.   The series (21) always converges when $x = 0$. If it diverges for all other values of x, then $R = 0$.

We can suppose now that the series (21) converges not only at $x = 0$ but for some other value of x, let us call it x_0. Then $a_n x_0{}^n \to 0$ as $n \to \infty$. Let x_1 be any number such that $|x_1| < |x_0|$. We can write

$$\sum_{n=0}^{\infty} |a_n x_1{}^n| = \sum_{n=0}^{\infty} |a_n| \, |x_0|^n \, \frac{|x_1|^n}{|x_0|^n} = \sum_{n=0}^{\infty} A_n r^n, \tag{71}$$

where $A_n = |a_n| \, |x_0|^n$ and $r = |x_1| / |x_0| < 1$. Since $A_n \to 0$ as $n \to \infty$ these numbers have a bound M. Hence the series (71) is term by term less than the terms of the geometric series $\sum M r^n$ with $r < 1$. By Theorem 14, the series (71) converges. Thus (21) is absolutely convergent when $x = x_1$ and hence is convergent for $x = x_1$.

This proves that if the series converges for $x = x_0$, then it converges for all x in the interval $-|x_0| < x < |x_0|$. If the series diverges for all x outside this interval then $|x_0|$ is the value for R mentioned in the theorem. Otherwise we can find another x, say $x_0{}'$ outside of this interval for which (21) converges. Then the same argument shows that the series (21) converges for all x in the larger interval $-|x_0{}'| < x < |x_0{}'|$.

Now consider the collection of all numbers r with the property that the series (21) converges for x in the interval $-r < x < r$. If this set contains all positive numbers, then the series (21) converges for all x and the radius of convergence of the series is infinite ($R = \infty$). If this set does not contain all of the positive numbers, let R be the largest[6] number in the set. Then obviously R has just the properties ascribed to it in the theorem.

Q.E.D.

For Taylor series we have

THEOREM 20.   *For each Taylor series*

$$\sum_{k=0}^{\infty} a_k (x - a)^k \tag{22}$$

there is a number $R \geqq 0$, called the radius of convergence of the series such that if $a - R < x < a + R$ the series converges, and if x lies outside of this interval the series diverges.

In other words the interval of convergence now has its center at $x = a$, instead of at $x = 0$. To prove this theorem merely replace $x - a$ by t

---

[6] It is reasonably obvious that this set has a maximum. A proof of this fact would take us too far away from our main objective.

in (22) and obtain a Maclaurin series which by Theorem 19 converges for $-R < t < R$ and diverges outside this interval. Then (22) converges when $-R < x - a < R$, or what is the same thing when $a - R < x < a + R$. Q.E.D.

*13. **Taylor's Theorem with remainder.** We have now acquired a reasonable array of theorems about the convergence and divergence of series. It is time to learn something about the sum of the series. To be specific we know that the series

$$\sum_{n=0}^{\infty} \frac{x^n}{n!} = 1 + x + \frac{x^2}{2!} + \frac{x^3}{3!} + \cdots \tag{72}$$

converges for all x. From section 5 we suspect that the sum of this series is e^x. Can we prove it?

In general if we start with a function $f(x)$, we can find a polynomial that fits it closely by a process already described in section 5. Indeed the polynomial

$$P_n(x) = f(a) + f'(a)(x - a) + \frac{f''(a)}{2!}(x - a)^2 + \cdots + \frac{f^{(n)}(a)}{n!}(x - a)^n \tag{73}$$

has the property that it agrees with the function $f(x)$ and its first n derivatives at $x = a$. Let us define a new quantity $R_n(x)$, as the difference between $f(x)$ and $P_n(x)$, i.e.,

$$R_n(x) = f(x) - P_n(x). \tag{74}$$

Thus $R_n(x)$ measures just how close the polynomial $P_n(x)$ is to $f(x)$. $R_n(x)$ is called the *remainder*. From (73) and (74) we have

$$f(x) = f(a) + f'(a)(x-a) + \frac{f''(a)}{2!}(x-a)^2 + \cdots + \frac{f^{(n)}(a)}{n!}(x-a)^n + R_n(x). \tag{75}$$

In order to prove that the infinite series

$$\sum_{n=0}^{\infty} \frac{f^{(n)}(a)}{n!}(x - a)^n = f(a) + f'(a)(x - a) + \frac{f''(a)}{2!}(x - a)^2 + \cdots \tag{76}$$

converges to $f(x)$, it is sufficient to prove that $R_n(x) \to 0$ as $n \to \infty$. For this we need some information about $R_n(x)$. A nice formula for $R_n(x)$ is given in

THEOREM 21. *If $R_n(x)$ is the remainder, as defined by equations (74) or (75), then for $n = 0, 1, 2, \cdots$*

$$R_n(x) = \frac{1}{n!} \int_a^x f^{(n+1)}(t)(x-t)^n \, dt. \tag{77}$$

PROOF.   We use mathematical induction.   Clearly

$$\int_a^x f'(t)dt = f(t) \Big|_a^x = f(x) - f(a)$$

or on transposition

$$f(x) = f(a) + \int_a^x f'(t)dt.$$

But this is (75) and (77) in the special case that $n = 0$.

We next assume the theorem is true for index k.   Thus we assume that

$$f(x) = f(a) + f'(a)(x-a) + \cdots + \frac{f^{(k)}(a)}{k!}(x-a)^k + \frac{1}{k!} \int_a^x f^{(k+1)}(t)(x-t)^k dt. \tag{78}$$

We now integrate the last term in (78) using integration by parts.   Keeping in mind that t is the variable of integration and x is a constant we have

$$u = f^{(k+1)}(t), \qquad\qquad dv = (x-t)^k dt,$$

$$du = f^{(k+2)}(t)dt, \qquad\qquad v = \frac{-(x-t)^{k+1}}{k+1},$$

$$\int_a^x u \, dv = \int_a^x f^{(k+1)}(t)(x-t)^k \, dt = \frac{-f^{(k+1)}(t)(x-t)^{k+1}}{k+1} \Big|_{t=a}^{t=x}$$

$$+ \int_a^x \frac{f^{(k+2)}(t)(x-t)^{k+1} \, dt}{k+1},$$

or

$$\int_a^x f^{(k+1)}(t)(x-t)^k \, dt = \frac{f^{(k+1)}(a)}{k+1}(x-a)^{k+1} + \frac{1}{k+1} \int_a^x f^{(k+2)}(t)(x-t)^{k+1} \, dt. \tag{79}$$

Using (79) in (78) and observing that $k!(k+1) = (k+1)!$ we find that

$$f(x) = f(a) + f'(a)(x-a) + \cdots + \frac{f^{(k)}(a)}{k!}(x-a)^k + \frac{f^{(k+1)}(a)}{(k+1)!}(x-a)^{k+1} +$$

$$\frac{1}{(k+1)!} \int_a^x f^{(k+2)}(t)(x-t)^{k+1} \, dt.$$

But this is the statement of the theorem when the index n is $k+1$. Q.E.D.

COROLLARY. *Let M be the maximum of $|f^{(n+1)}(t)|$ for t in the interval between a and x.   Then*

$$|R_n(x)| \leq \frac{M}{(n+1)!}|x-a|^{n+1}. \tag{80}$$

PROOF. We observe that there are two cases to consider depending on whether $x > a$ or $x < a$. Suppose first that $x > a$. Then $x - t \geq 0$, and from (77) we have

$$|R_n(x)| = \left|\frac{1}{n!}\int_a^x f^{(n+1)}(t)(x-t)^n dt\right| \leq \frac{1}{n!}\int_a^x M(x-t)^n dt = \frac{-M}{n!}\frac{(x-t)^{n+1}}{n+1}\Big|_{t=a}^{t=x}$$

Hence

$$|R_n(x)| \leq \frac{M}{(n+1)!}(x-a)^{n+1} = \frac{M}{(n+1)!}|x-a|^{n+1}.$$

In case $x < a$ then $x - t \leq 0$ as t runs from a to x.   Then

$$|R_n(x)| = \left|\frac{1}{n!}\int_a^x f^{(n+1)}(t)(x-t)^n dt\right| \leq \frac{1}{n!}\int_x^a M(t-x)^n dt$$

$$\leq \frac{M}{n!}\frac{(t-x)^{n+1}}{n+1}\Big|_{t=x}^{t=a} = \frac{M}{(n+1)!}(a-x)^{n+1} = \frac{M}{(n+1)!}|x-a|^{n+1}.$$

Hence in either case we get (80).   Q.E.D.

EXAMPLE 1.   Prove that the series (72) converges to e^x.

SOLUTION.   We already know that when $a = 0$, the first $n + 1$ terms of the series (72) is the approximating polynomial (73) when $f(x) = e^x$. In other words we already have

$$e^x = 1 + x + \frac{x^2}{2!} + \frac{x^3}{3!} + \cdots + \frac{x^n}{n!} + R_n(x).$$

We apply formula (80) of the corollary. In this case $f^{(n+1)}(t) = e^t$. If $x > 0$ the maximum value of e^t for $0 \leq t \leq x$ is e^x. If $x < 0$, the maximum value of e^t for $x \leq t \leq 0$ is $e^0 = 1$. In the first case

$$|R_n(x)| \leq \frac{e^x}{(n+1)!}x^{n+1}. \tag{81}$$

But we already know that the series (72) converges, so by Theorem 13 the general term $x^{n+1}/(n+1)! \to 0$ as $n \to \infty$. Then from (81) we see that $|R_n(x)| \to 0$ as $n \to \infty$, and consequently the series (72) converges to e^x. If $x < 0$, then (81) is replaced by $|R_n(x)| \leq |x|^{n+1}/(n+1)!$ with the same conclusion. Hence for all values of x

$$e^x = 1 + x + \frac{x^2}{2!} + \frac{x^3}{3!} + \cdots + \frac{x^n}{n!} + \cdots. \tag{30}$$

EXAMPLE 2.   Compute $\sqrt{e}$ to three decimal places.

SOLUTION.   This means to compute $\sqrt{e} = e^{1/2}$ within .0005 at least.   Using the corollary, we are to find a value of n such that

$$|R_n(x)| \leq \frac{M}{(n+1)!}|x|^{n+1} \leq .0005$$

when $x = 1/2$.   Now M is the maximum of e^x in the interval $0 \leq x \leq 1/2$, so we take as a conservative estimate $e \leq 4$, and so $M = e^{1/2} \leq \sqrt{4} = 2$.   Then

$$|R_n(x)| \leq \frac{2}{(n+1)!}\left(\frac{1}{2}\right)^{n+1} = \frac{1}{2^n(n+1)!}.$$

For $n = 4$ the right side gives $1/1920 \approx .00052$ and this is not quite sufficient. For $n = 5$, the right side gives $1/23{,}040 \approx .000043$.   So we need only the first six terms of the series, for the desired accuracy.   We find that

$$\sqrt{e} \approx 1 + \frac{1}{2} + \frac{1}{2^2 2!} + \frac{1}{2^3 3!} + \frac{1}{2^4 4!} + \frac{1}{2^5 5!}$$

$$\approx 1.0000 + .5000 + .1250 + .0208 + .0026 + .0003$$

$$\approx 1.6487 \approx 1.649.$$

EXERCISE 10

In problems 1 through 5 prove that the given series converges to the indicated sum, for x in the given interval

1. $\sin x = \sum_{n=0}^{\infty} \frac{(-1)^n x^{2n+1}}{(2n+1)!}$,   all x.

2. $\cos x = \sum_{n=0}^{\infty} \frac{(-1)^n x^{2n}}{(2n)!}$,   all x.

★3. $\ln(1+x) = \sum_{n=1}^{\infty} \frac{(-1)^{n+1} x^n}{n}$, $0 \leq x \leq 1$.

★4. $\sqrt{1+x} = 1 + \sum_{n=1}^{\infty} \frac{(-1)^{n+1}(2n-2)! x^n}{2^{2n-1} n!(n-1)!}$, $0 \leq x \leq 1$.

5. $\sinh x = \sum_{n=0}^{\infty} \frac{x^{2n+1}}{(2n+1)!}$,   all x.

In problems 6 through 10 use a Maclaurin series for the given function to compute the indicated quantity to four decimal places.

6. Use $\sqrt{1+x}$ to find $\sqrt{1.1}$.
7. Use e^x to find $\sqrt[5]{e}$.
8. Use $\ln(1+x)$ to find $\ln(1.2)$.
9. Use $\sin x$ to find $\sin 3°$.
10. Use $\cos x$ to find $\cos 3°$.

11. Use $\sqrt{1+x}$ to find $\sqrt{27}$ to three decimal places.

Hint: $\sqrt{27} = 5\sqrt{1 + \frac{2}{25}}$.

12. Use $\sqrt[3]{1+x}$ to find $\sqrt[3]{100}$ to three decimal places.

13. Use the Taylor series for $\sin x$ about $a = \pi/6$ to compute $\sin 33°$ to three decimal places.

14. Find $\ln 1.2$ by using the series for $\ln \dfrac{1+x}{1-x}$ (Exercise 4, problem 13) with $x = 1/11$. Compare this computation with the one of problem 8.

*14. Uniformly convergent series. We recall that a series of functions

$$\sum_{k=1}^{\infty} u_k(x) \qquad (82)$$

converges for a certain value of x, if the remainder after n terms[7] can be made as small as we please, providing that we take n sufficiently large. We let $r_n(x)$ be the remainder, i.e., we set

$$r_n(x) = \sum_{k=n+1}^{\infty} u_k(x) = u_{n+1}(x) + u_{n+2}(x) + \cdots. \qquad (83)$$

Then the given series converges for $x = x_0$ if for each $\epsilon > 0$, there is a N, such that $|r_n(x_0)| < \epsilon$ for each $n > N$.

Suppose now that the series (82) converges for each x in some interval $I: a \leq x \leq b$. Given $\epsilon > 0$, there is always some N with the property just described, namely $|r_n(x_0)| < \epsilon$ for each $n > N$. But as x_0 runs through the interval I, the integer N may change from point to point, and it can happen that no single value of N will do for every x in I. If however there is a N that works uniformly for all x in I then the series is said to be *uniformly convergent* in I.

> DEFINITION 9. *A series of functions (82) is said to be uniformly convergent in a closed interval $I: a \leq x \leq b$ if the remainder $r_n(x)$ given by (83) has the following property.*
>
> *For each $\epsilon > 0$, there is an integer N (that may depend on the particular ϵ) such that $|r_n(x)| < \epsilon$ for each $n > N$, and for all x in I.*

For clarity we repeat that if the last phrase of the definition is deleted, then we have the definition of convergence. It is the phrase "for all x in I" that makes the convergence uniform.

EXAMPLE 1. Prove that the series $\sum\limits_{k=0}^{\infty} x^k(1-x)$ is *not* uniformly convergent in the interval $0 \leq x \leq 1$.

---

[7] In case the index k in equation (82) runs from $k = 0$ to ∞ then $r_n(x)$ is the remainder after the first $n + 1$ terms.

SOLUTION. We first find the sum of this series. Now

$$S(x) = (1 - x) + x(1 - x) + x^2(1 - x) + \cdots + x^n(1 - x) + \cdots$$
$$= (1 - x) + (x - x^2) + (x^2 - x^3) + \cdots + (x^n - x^{n+1}) + \cdots.$$

If we denote the sum of the first $n+1$ terms by $S_n(x)$ we have
$$S_n(x) = 1 - x + x - x^2 + x^2 - x^3 + \cdots + x^n - x^{n+1} = 1 - x^{n+1}.$$
Then

$$S(x) = \lim_{n \to \infty} S_n(x) = \lim_{n \to \infty} 1 - x^{n+1} = \begin{cases} 1, & \text{if } 0 \leq x < 1, \\ 0, & \text{if } \quad x = 1. \end{cases}$$

Hence the given series converges in the interval $0 \leq x \leq 1$. But the peculiar form of the sum should warn us that this particular series differs essentially from the ones previously studied. The remainder $r_n(x)$ after $n+1$ terms is just the difference

$$r_n(x) = S(x) - S_n(x) \tag{84}$$

and hence

$$r_n(x) = \begin{cases} 1 - (1 - x^{n+1}) = x^{n+1}, & \text{if } 0 \leq x < 1, \\ 0 - (1 - x^{n+1}) = x^{n+1} - 1 = 0, & \text{if } x = 1. \end{cases}$$

We could also arrive at this same result by writing

$$r_n(x) = \sum_{k=n+1}^{\infty} x^k(1 - x) = x^{n+1}(1 - x) + x^{n+2}(1 - x) + \cdots$$
$$= (x^{n+1} - x^{n+2}) + (x^{n+2} - x^{n+3}) + \cdots = \begin{cases} x^{n+1} & \text{if } 0 \leq x < 1. \\ 0 & \text{if } \quad x = 1. \end{cases}$$

Is the series uniformly convergent? Can we make $r_n(x) = x^{n+1}$ very small by taking n sufficiently large. The answer is *no* if x is allowed to run in the interval $0 \leq x < 1$. For no matter how large an n we take, once it is selected and held fixed, then

$$\lim_{x \to 1} r_n(x) = \lim_{x \to 1} x^{n+1} = 1$$

and hence $r_n(x)$ cannot be made less than ϵ throughout the interval $0 \leq x < 1$. (Take $\epsilon = 1/2$.)

Observe that in this example the given series is not a Taylor series. Roughly speaking a Taylor series is always uniformly convergent. More precisely we have

THEOREM 22. *A Taylor series* $\sum a_n(x - a)^n$ *is always uniformly convergent in any interval that lies together with its end points inside the interval of convergence of the series.*

PROOF. It is sufficient to consider the simpler case of a Maclaurin series. Suppose indeed that the series

$$\sum_{n=0}^{\infty} a_n x^n = a_0 + a_1 x + a_2 x^2 + \cdots \tag{21}$$

converges for all x in $-R < x < R$. Let $0 < b < R$. We will prove that this series is uniformly convergent for all x in $-b \leq x \leq b$. Let c be a real number lying between b and R then the series $\sum a_n c^n$ converges (by hypothesis) and consequently $a_n c^n \to 0$ as $n \to \infty$. Hence $|a_n c^n| < 1$ for all n sufficiently large (say all $n > N_1$). We consider $r_n(x)$. Here we can write that

$$|r_n(x)| = \left| \sum_{k=n+1}^{\infty} a_k x^k \right| \leq \sum_{k=n+1}^{\infty} |a_k x^k| = \sum_{k=n+1}^{\infty} |a_k c^k| \frac{|x^k|}{c^k} \leq \sum_{k=n+1}^{\infty} |a_k c^k| \frac{b^k}{c^k}$$

because by hypothesis $-b \leq x \leq b$. So if $n > N_1$

$$|r_n(x)| \leq \sum_{k=n+1}^{\infty} 1 \left(\frac{b}{c}\right)^k = \frac{(b/c)^{n+1}}{1 - b/c} = \frac{c}{c - b} \left(\frac{b}{c}\right)^{n+1}. \tag{85}$$

But $b < c$, so $b/c < 1$ and hence $(b/c)^{n+1} \to 0$ as $n \to \infty$. Therefore if we are given any $\epsilon > 0$, we can select N so large that for all $n > N$, the right side of (85) is less than ϵ. Then $|r_n(x)| < \epsilon$ for all x in $-b \leq x \leq b$. Q.E.D.

EXERCISE 11

In problems 1 through 4 prove that the given series is uniformly convergent in the indicated interval.

1. $\displaystyle \sum_{n=1}^{\infty} \frac{\sin nx}{n^2}$,   all x.

2. $\displaystyle \sum_{n=1}^{\infty} \frac{\cos n^2 x}{n^{3/2}}$,   all x.

3. $\displaystyle \sum_{n=1}^{\infty} n e^{nx}$, $x < -1$.

4. $\displaystyle \sum_{n=1}^{\infty} n \cos^n x$, $\dfrac{\pi}{3} \leq x \leq \dfrac{2\pi}{3}$

5. The above results are all special cases of the following general theorem, known as the Weierstrass M-test for uniform convergence.

Let $u_1(x) + u_2(x) + \cdots + u_n(x) + \cdots$ be a series of functions where each $u_n(x)$ is defined for some common interval I. If there is a convergent series of constants $M_1 + M_2 + M_3 + \cdots$ such that for each n, the functions satisfy the inequality $|u_n(x)| \leq M_n$ for all x in I, then the series $u_1(x) + u_2(x) + \cdots$ is uniformly convergent for x in I. Prove this theorem.

6. Prove that the series $\displaystyle \sum_{n=1}^{\infty} \frac{x}{[nx + 1][(n - 1)x + 1]}$ has the sum 0 if $x = 0$, and the sum 1 if $x > 0$.
Hint: Using partial fractions each term of the series can be written

$$\frac{x}{[nx + 1][(n - 1)x + 1]} = \frac{1}{(n - 1)x + 1} - \frac{1}{nx + 1}.$$

★7. Prove that the series of problem 6 is not uniformly convergent in $0 \leq x \leq 1$.

★15.   Properties of uniformly convergent series.   A uniformly convergent series can be integrated termwise within its interval of uniform convergence.   For simplicity we will consider Maclaurin series and prove

THEOREM 23.   *If*

$$f(x) = \sum_{k=0}^{\infty} a_k x^k = a_0 + a_1 x + a_2 x^2 + \cdots \tag{86}$$

where the series is uniformly convergent in $-R \leq x \leq R$ *then for any pair of numbers a and b in that interval*

$$\int_a^b f(x)dx = \sum_{k=0}^{\infty} \int_a^b a_k x^k \, dx = a_0(b-a) + \frac{a_1(b^2-a^2)}{2} + \frac{a_2(b^3-a^3)}{3} + \cdots. \tag{87}$$

PROOF.   The series (86) can always be broken into two pieces

$$f(x) = s_n(x) + r_n(x) \tag{88}$$

where as usual $s_n(x)$ is the sum of the first $n+1$ terms and $r_n(x)$ is the remainder.   The integral of a sum of a finite number of terms is the sum of the integrals of the individual terms, hence (88) gives

$$\int_a^b f(x)dx = \int_a^b s_n(x)dx + \int_a^b r_n(x)dx$$

$$= \sum_{k=0}^{n} \int_a^b a_k x^k \, dx + \int_a^b r_n(x)dx. \tag{89}$$

Now by the uniform convergence of the given series we can make the remainder arbitrarily small.   So if $\epsilon > 0$ is given we can find a N such that $|r_n(x)| < \epsilon/2R$ for all $n > N$ and all x in $-R \leq x \leq R$.   Then

$$\left| \int_a^b r_n(x)dx \right| < \left| \int_a^b \frac{\epsilon}{2R} \, dx \right| < \frac{\epsilon|b-a|}{2R} \leq \epsilon.$$

This, taken together with (89) proves that the series

$$\sum_{k=0}^{\infty} \int_a^b a_k x^k \, dx$$

converges to the integral on the left side of (89).   Q.E.D.

EXAMPLE 1.   Find an indefinite integral for $\int \sin x^2 \, dx$.

SOLUTION.   This indefinite integral does not lie in $\mathfrak{F}$, but we can find an infinite series for it.   We know that

$$\sin l^2 = \sum_{n=0}^{\infty} \frac{(-1)^n (l^2)^{2n+1}}{(2n+1)!}$$

where the series is uniformly convergent in $-R \leq t \leq R$, for any R. So, by Theorem 23, the function $F(x)$ defined by

$$F(x) = \int_0^x \sin t^2 \, dt$$

can be written as the infinite series

$$F(x) = \sum_{n=0}^{\infty} \int_0^x \frac{(-1)^n t^{4n+2}}{(2n+1)!} \, dt = \sum_{n=0}^{\infty} \frac{(-1)^n x^{4n+3}}{(4n+3)(2n+1)!}.$$

But (by Theorem 4 of Chapter 8, page 274) the derivative of $F(x)$ is just $\sin x^2$.
Q.E.D.

The corresponding theorem on differentiating a series term by term is a little more complicated. Roughly speaking the differentiated series must also be uniformly convergent. For example the series

$$F(x) = \sum_{n=1}^{\infty} \frac{\sin n^3 x}{n^2}$$

is uniformly convergent for all x, but the series obtained by termwise differentiation

$$\sum_{n=1}^{\infty} \frac{n^3 \cos n^3 x}{n^2} = \sum_{n=1}^{\infty} n \cos n^3 x$$

is not even convergent at $x = 0$, and hence cannot represent $F'(x)$.

THEOREM 24. *Let* $f(x)$ *be given by* (86) *and suppose that the series*

$$g(x) = \sum_{k=1}^{\infty} k a_k x^{k-1} \tag{90}$$

is uniformly convergent in $-R \leq x \leq R$. *Then* $f'(x) = g(x)$ *in that interval.*

PROOF. The function $g(x)$ satisfies the conditions of Theorem 23, so if $-R \leq x \leq R$, then the function defined by

$$F(x) = \int_0^x g(t) dt \tag{91}$$

has the power series

$$F(x) = \sum_{k=1}^{\infty} \int_0^x k a_k t^{k-1} \, dt = \sum_{k=1}^{\infty} a_k x^k. \tag{92}$$

Hence $F(x)$ and $f(x)$ differ by the constant a_0. From (91) $F'(x) = g(x)$. Therefore $f'(x) = F'(x) = g(x)$. Q.E.D.

EXAMPLE 2.   Prove that for $-1 < x < 1$

$$\frac{1}{(1-x)^2} = \sum_{k=1}^{\infty} kx^{k-1}. \tag{93}$$

SOLUTION.   The ratio test shows that the series on the right side is convergent in $-1 < x < 1$.   Hence by Theorem 22 it is uniformly convergent in the interval $-R \le x \le R$, for each $R < 1$.   We already know the sum of the geometric series, namely

$$\frac{1}{1-x} = \sum_{k=0}^{\infty} x^k.$$

Now apply Theorem 24, which states that the series $\sum kx^{k-1}$ converges to the derivative of $1/(1-x)$.   This gives (93) valid for $-R \le x \le R$.   But R is any number less than 1.   Q.E.D.

EXERCISE 12

In problems 1 through 8 prove that the given series has the indicated sum.

1. $\displaystyle\sum_{n=1}^{\infty} \frac{x^n}{n} = -\ln(1-x), \qquad -1 < x < 1.$

2. $\displaystyle\sum_{n=1}^{\infty} \frac{(-1)^{n+1}x^n}{n} = \ln(1+x), \qquad -1 < x < 1.$

3. $\displaystyle\sum_{n=1}^{\infty} \frac{x^{2n-1}}{2n-1} = \frac{1}{2}\ln\frac{1+x}{1-x}, \qquad -1 < x < 1.$

4. $\displaystyle\sum_{n=0}^{\infty} \frac{(-1)^n x^{2n+1}}{2n+1} = \tan^{-1} x, \qquad -1 < x < 1.$

★5. $\displaystyle\sum_{n=1}^{\infty} \frac{x^n}{n^2} = -\int_0^x \frac{\ln(1-t)}{t}\, dt, \qquad -1 < x < 1.$

6. $\displaystyle\sum_{n=0}^{\infty} \frac{(n+1)(n+2)}{2} x^n = \frac{1}{(1-x)^3}, \qquad -1 < x < 1.$

7. $\displaystyle\sum_{n=0}^{\infty} \frac{(n+1)(n+2)(n+3)}{6} x^n = \frac{1}{(1-x)^4}, \qquad -1 < x < 1.$

★8. $\displaystyle\sum_{n=1}^{\infty} nx^{2n-1} = \frac{x}{1-2x^2+x^4}, \qquad -1 < x < 1.$

9.   By differentiating the Maclaurin series for $1/(1-x)$ find the Maclaurin series for $1/(1-x)^k$ for any positive integer k.

10.   Define R_n by writing the series of problem 3 in the form

$$\ln\frac{1+x}{1-x} = 2\left(x + \frac{x^3}{3} + \cdots + \frac{x^{2n-1}}{2n-1}\right) + R_n.$$

Using a geometric series that is term by term greater than the terms of R_n prove that

$$|R_n| \leq \frac{2|x|^{2n+1}}{2n+1} \frac{1}{1-x^2}.$$

11. Find ln 2 to four decimal places by setting $x = 1/3$ in the series of problem 10.

12. Find ln 3/2 to four decimal places.

13. Find ln 3 using the results of problems 11 and 12.

14. Find ln(5/3) and use this to find ln 5.

★15. Prove that $\pi/4 = \tan^{-1}(1/2) + \tan^{-1}(1/3)$. Then combine this with the series of problem 4 (used twice) to compute π to four decimal places.

In problems 16 through 19 express the given definite integral as the sum of an infinite series of constants.

16. $\displaystyle\int_0^1 \cos x^2 \, dx.$ **17.** $\displaystyle\int_0^1 \frac{\sin x}{x} \, dx.$

18. $\displaystyle\int_0^{1/2} \frac{e^{-x} - 1}{x} \, dx.$ **★19.** $\displaystyle\int_0^1 \sqrt{1 - x^3} \, dx.$

★20. Explain why the function $y = x^{1/3}$ does not have a Maclaurin series representation.

16. **Some concluding remarks on infinite series.** Although it may seem to the student that we have learned quite a bit about infinite series, the truth is that we have just scratched the surface. The reader who desires further information may consult any book on Advanced Calculus, but for infinite series the best such text is the one by I. S. Sokolnikoff (McGraw Hill Book, 1939). The most complete single book on the topic is the one by Konrad Knopp, *Theory and Application of Infinite Series* (Blackie, London, 1951).

In closing this chapter, we remark that given two infinite series, we may form their product or their quotient under suitable conditions. The process is illustrated in the following examples.

EXAMPLE 1. Find the Maclaurin series for $1/(1 - x)^2$ by squaring the series for $1/(1 - x)$.

SOLUTION. The series for $1/(1 - x)$ is just the geometric series

$$\frac{1}{1 - x} = 1 + x + x^2 + \cdots + x^n + \cdots.$$

To square this series we multiply first by 1, then by x, then x^2, $\cdots$, and add the results.   The computation can be arranged as follows.

$$1 + \ x + \ x^2 + \ x^3 + \ x^4 + \ x^5 + \ x^6 + \ x^7 + \cdots$$
$$1 + \ x + \ x^2 + \ x^3 + \ x^4 + \ x^5 + \ x^6 + \ x^7 + \cdots$$

$$1 + \ x + \ x^2 + \ x^3 + \ x^4 + \ x^5 + \ x^6 + \ x^7 + \cdots$$
$$x + \ x^2 + \ x^3 + \ x^4 + \ x^5 + \ x^6 + \ x^7 + \cdots$$
$$x^2 + \ x^3 + \ x^4 + \ x^5 + \ x^6 + \ x^7 + \cdots$$
$$x^3 + \ x^4 + \ x^5 + \ x^6 + \ x^7 + \cdots$$
$$x^4 + \ x^5 + \ x^6 + \ x^7 + \cdots$$
$$x^5 + \ x^6 + \ x^7 + \cdots$$
$$x^6 + \ x^7 + \cdots$$
$$x^7 + \cdots$$
$$\ddots$$

$$1 + 2x + 3x^2 + 4x^3 + 5x^4 + 6x^5 + 7x^6 + 8x^7 + \cdots.$$

It is obvious that the general term is nx^{n-1} and hence

$$\frac{1}{(1-x)^2} = \sum_{n=1}^{\infty} nx^{n-1}$$

a result that we have already proved earlier (Example 2, section 15).

EXAMPLE 2.   Find a rule for forming the product of two Maclaurin series.

SOLUTION.   Let

$$f(x) = \sum_{n=0}^{\infty} a_n x^n \qquad g(x) = \sum_{n=0}^{\infty} b_n x^n$$

be the given series.   Let the product have the Maclaurin series

$$f(x)g(x) = \sum_{n=0}^{\infty} c_n x^n.$$

We are to find a rule that gives each c_n in terms of the coefficients a_k and b_k. A little reflection shows that each product of the form

$$a_j x^i b_k x^k = a_j b_k x^{j+k} \qquad j = 0, 1, 2, \cdots, \quad k = 0, 1, 2, \cdots,$$

enters exactly once in the series for $f(x)g(x)$.   We can group together those for which the exponent on x is the same.   Thus let $j + k = n$, then as j runs through the integers $0, 1, 2, \cdots, n$, the index k runs through the same set in the reverse order.   Hence c_n, the coefficient of x^n in $f(x)g(x)$, is just the sum of such terms and so

$$c_n = \sum_{j=0}^{n} a_j b_{n-j}.$$

Thus the desired rule is expressed by the formula

$$f(x)g(x) = \left(\sum_{n=0}^{\infty} a_n x^n \right) \left(\sum_{n=0}^{\infty} b_n x^n \right) = \sum_{n=0}^{\infty} \left(\sum_{j=0}^{n} a_j b_{n-j} \right) x^n. \qquad (94)$$

EXAMPLE 3. Find the Maclaurin series for tan x, by dividing the series for sin x by the series for cos x.

SOLUTION. We can arrange the work just as in the division of one polynomial by another, except that this time we write the two quantities with the exponents increasing. Now

$$\sin x = x - \frac{x^3}{6} + \frac{x^5}{120} - \cdots, \qquad \cos x = 1 - \frac{x^2}{2} + \frac{x^4}{24} - \cdots.$$

$$x + \frac{x^3}{3} + \frac{2x^5}{15} + \cdots$$

$$1 - \frac{x^2}{2} + \frac{x^4}{24} - \cdots \enspace\bigg|\enspace x - \frac{x^3}{6} + \frac{x^5}{120} - \cdots$$

$$x - \frac{x^3}{2} + \frac{x^5}{24} - \cdots$$

$$\frac{x^3}{3} - \frac{x^5}{30} + \cdots$$

$$\frac{x^3}{3} - \frac{x^5}{6} + \cdots$$

$$\frac{2x^5}{15} + \cdots$$

Hence

$$\tan x = x + \frac{x^3}{3} + \frac{2x^5}{15} + \cdots. \qquad (95)$$

It is practically impossible to obtain a general formula for the nth term. It can be proved that this series converges for $|x| < \pi/2$, but the proof is not easy.

There are two other methods for solving this type of problem. One such method is to write

$$\cos x = 1 - u \qquad \text{where } u = \frac{x^2}{2} - \frac{x^4}{24} + \frac{x^6}{720} - \cdots$$

and expand $1/\cos x = 1/(1 - u)$ as a geometric series. Thus

$$\frac{\sin x}{\cos x} = \left[x - \frac{x^3}{6} + \frac{x^5}{120} - \cdots \right]\left[1 + u + u^2 + u^3 + \cdots \right]$$

$$= \left[x - \frac{x^3}{6} + \frac{x^5}{120} - \cdots \right]\left[1 + \left(\frac{x^2}{2} - \frac{x^4}{24} + \frac{x^6}{720} - \cdots \right) + \left(\frac{x^2}{2} - \frac{x^4}{24} + \frac{x^6}{720} - \cdots \right)^2 + \left(\frac{x^2}{2} - \cdots \right)^3 + \cdots \right].$$

The reader can continue this computation and show that it also gives (95).

A third method is to write the quotient with unknown coefficients, multiply both sides by the denominator using (94), and then equate coefficients of like powers of x on both sides and solve for the unknown coefficients. In this example the computation runs as follows.

$$x - \frac{x^3}{6} + \frac{x^5}{120} - \cdots = \left(1 - \frac{x^2}{2} + \frac{x^4}{24} - \cdots\right)\left(a_0 + a_1 x + a_2 x^2 + \cdots\right)$$

$$= a_0 + a_1 x + \left(a_2 - \frac{a_0}{2}\right) x^2 + \left(a_3 - \frac{a_1}{2}\right) x^3 + \left(a_4 - \frac{a_2}{2} + \frac{a_0}{24}\right) x^4 + \cdots$$

Equating coefficients of like powers of x on both sides gives

$$0 = a_0$$
$$1 = a_1$$
$$0 = a_2 - \frac{a_0}{2}$$
$$-\frac{1}{6} = a_3 - \frac{a_1}{2}$$
$$0 = a_4 - \frac{a_2}{2} + \frac{a_0}{24}$$
$$\cdots$$

The reader should find the next equation in this infinite set, and show that on solving we again obtain (95).

EXERCISE 13

In problems 1 through 13 use the methods of this section to show that the given function has the Maclaurin series on the right, as far as the terms indicated.

1. $\ln^2 (1 - x) = x^2 + x^3 + \frac{11}{12} x^4 + \frac{5}{6} x^5 + \cdots.$

2. $\dfrac{\sin x}{1 - x} = x + x^2 + \frac{5}{6} x^3 + \frac{5}{6} x^4 + \frac{101}{120} x^5 + \cdots.$

3. $\dfrac{e^x}{2 + x} = \frac{1}{2} + \frac{1}{4} x + \frac{1}{8} x^2 + \frac{1}{48} x^3 + \frac{1}{96} x^4 + \cdots.$

4. $e^x \cos x = 1 + x - \frac{1}{3} x^3 - \frac{1}{6} x^4 - \frac{1}{30} x^5 + \cdots.$

5. $e^{x + x^2} = 1 + x + \frac{3}{2} x^2 + \frac{7}{6} x^3 + \frac{25}{24} x^4 + \cdots.$

6. $\dfrac{x}{\sin x} = 1 + \frac{1}{6} x^2 + \frac{7}{360} x^4 + \cdots.$

7. $\sec x = \dfrac{1}{\cos x} = 1 + \frac{1}{2} x^2 + \frac{5}{24} x^4 + \cdots.$

8. $\dfrac{1}{\displaystyle\sum_{n=0}^{\infty} x^n} = 1 - x.$

9. $\dfrac{\sin x}{\ln (1 + x)} = 1 + \dfrac{1}{2} x - \dfrac{1}{4} x^2 - \dfrac{1}{24} x^3 + \cdots.$

10. $\dfrac{x + x^2}{1 + x - x^2} = x + x^3 - x^4 + 2x^5 + \cdots.$

11. $e^{\sin x} = 1 + x + \dfrac{1}{2} x^2 - \dfrac{1}{8} x^4 + \cdots.$

12. $\ln \cos x = -\dfrac{1}{2} x^2 - \dfrac{1}{12} x^4 - \dfrac{1}{45} x^6 + \cdots.$

13. $\tanh x = x - \dfrac{1}{3} x^3 + \dfrac{2}{15} x^5 + \cdots.$

14. Prove that $\dfrac{1 + x}{1 + x + x^2} = 1 - x^2 + x^3 - x^5 + x^6 - x^8 + x^9 - \cdots.$

15. Prove that $\dfrac{1}{1 - x + x^2 - x^3} = 1 + x + x^4 + x^5 + x^8 + x^9 + x^{12} + x^{13} + \cdots.$

16. The Maclaurin series for $1/\sqrt{1 - x}$ is

$$\frac{1}{\sqrt{1 - x}} = 1 + \frac{1}{2} x + \frac{1 \cdot 3}{2^2 \cdot 2} x^2 + \frac{1 \cdot 3 \cdot 5}{2^3 \cdot 3!} x^3 + \frac{1 \cdot 3 \cdot 5 \cdot 7}{2^4 \cdot 4!} x^4 + \cdots.$$

Check this result by squaring the series and showing that the result is $1 + x + x^2 + x^3 + x^4 + \cdots$, as far as the first five terms are concerned.

*17. By squaring the series for $\sin x$ and $\cos x$, show that $\sin^2 x + \cos^2 x = 1$, at least as far as the first four terms are concerned.

**18. By multiplying the two series for e^x and e^y prove that $e^x e^y = e^{x+y}$.

EXERCISE 14

REVIEW PROBLEMS FOR CHAPTER 13.

In problems 1 through 10 test the given series for convergence or divergence.

1. $\displaystyle\sum_{n=1}^{\infty} \frac{1}{n^2 - \ln n}.$

2. $\displaystyle\sum_{n=1}^{\infty} \frac{(-1)^n}{2n - \sqrt{17n}}.$

3. $\displaystyle\sum_{n=1}^{\infty} \frac{4 \cdot 7 \cdot 10 \cdots (3n + 1)}{1 \cdot 5 \cdot 9 \cdots (4n - 3)}.$

4. $\displaystyle\sum_{n=1}^{\infty} \frac{1 \cdot 4 \cdot 7 \cdots (3n - 2)}{7 \cdot 9 \cdot 11 \cdots (2n + 5)}.$

5. $\displaystyle\sum_{n=2}^{\infty} \frac{1}{n \ln^p n}, \quad p > 1.$

6. $\displaystyle\sum_{n=1}^{\infty} \frac{3^n (n!)^2}{(2n)!}.$

7. $\displaystyle\sum_{n=1}^{\infty} \frac{(n!)^{5/2}}{(2n)!}.$

8. $\displaystyle\sum_{n=1}^{\infty} \frac{2^n n!}{4 \cdot 7 \cdot 10 \cdots (3n + 1)}.$

★9. $\displaystyle\sum_{n=1}^{\infty} \frac{(n+10)!}{n^n}$.

★10. $\displaystyle\sum_{n=1}^{\infty} \frac{1}{n\sqrt[n]{1+n}}$

★11. By finding an explicit expression for the sum of the first n terms settle the convergence or divergence of the series.

a. $\displaystyle\sum_{n=1}^{\infty} \ln\left(\frac{n}{n+1}\right)$,

b. $\displaystyle\sum_{n=2}^{\infty} \ln\left(1 - \frac{1}{n^2}\right)$.

12. Find the convergence set for

$$\sum_{n=1}^{\infty} x^{n^2} = x + x^4 + x^9 + x^{16} + \cdots.$$

13. By a suitable substitution in the series for $\ln[(1+x)/(1-x)]$ derive the series

$$\ln\left(1 + \frac{1}{M}\right) = \sum_{n=1}^{\infty} \frac{2}{(2n-1)} \left(\frac{1}{2M+1}\right)^{2n-1} =$$

$$2\left[\frac{1}{2M+1} + \frac{1}{3(2M+1)^3} + \frac{1}{5(2M+1)^5} + \cdots\right].$$

14. By integrating the series for $1/\sqrt{1-x^2}$ derive the series

$$\sin^{-1} x = x + \frac{1}{2}\frac{x^3}{3} + \frac{1\cdot 3}{2\cdot 4}\frac{x^5}{5} + \cdots + \frac{1\cdot 3\cdot 5\cdots(2n-1)}{2\cdot 4\cdot 6\cdots 2n}\frac{x^{2n+1}}{2n+1} + \cdots$$

$$= \sum_{n=0}^{\infty} \frac{(2n)!}{4^n(n!)^2}\frac{x^{2n+1}}{2n+1}.$$

15. Find the Maclaurin series for $\ln(a+x)$.
16. Expand $\ln x$ in a Taylor series about the point $x = 2$.
17. Prove that for $|x| > 1$

$$\frac{1}{1-x} = -\sum_{n=1}^{\infty} \frac{1}{x^n}.$$

18. Find the Maclaurin series for $\dfrac{c}{ax+b}$, where $b \neq 0$.

19. Use partial fractions to find a Maclaurin series for $7x/(6 - 5x + x^2)$.
20. Expand $2/(1-x)$ as a Taylor series about the point $x = 3$.
21. By multiplying the series

$$\frac{1}{(1-x)^2} = 1 + 2x + 3x^2 + \cdots + (n+1)x^n + \cdots$$

by the series for $1/(1-x)$ find the first five terms of the series for $1/(1-x)^3$.

★22. By integrating a suitable series prove that

$$(1+x)\ln(1+x) = x + \sum_{n=2}^{\infty} \frac{(-1)^n x^n}{n(n-1)}.$$

23. Find the convergence set for $\displaystyle\sum_{n=1}^{\infty} \frac{1}{n}\left(\frac{x-1}{x}\right)^n$.

★**24.**   By comparing areas show that $\ln n > \int_{n-1}^{n} \ln x \, dx$ for $n \geq 2$.   Use this to prove that $\ln(n!) > n \ln n - n + 1$ for $n \geq 2$.   Then show that for $n \geq 2$

$$\frac{n!}{n^n} > e \frac{1}{e^n}.$$

★★**25.**   Use the methods of problem 24 to prove that

$$\frac{n!}{n^n} < \frac{ne^2}{4} \frac{1}{e^n}, \qquad n \geq 3.$$

In problems 26 through 29 show that the given function has the Maclaurin series on the right, as far as the terms indicated

26. $(1 + x) \cos \sqrt{x} = 1 + \frac{1}{2} x - \frac{11}{24} x^2 + \frac{29}{720} x^3 + \cdots.$

27. $\dfrac{1}{1 + \sin x} = 1 - x + x^2 - \frac{5}{6} x^3 + \frac{2}{3} x^4 - \frac{61}{120} x^5 + \cdots.$

28. $\ln(1 + \sin x) = x - \frac{1}{2} x^2 + \frac{1}{6} x^3 - \frac{1}{12} x^4 + \frac{1}{24} x^5 + \cdots.$

29. $\dfrac{x}{e^x - 1} = 1 - \frac{1}{2} x + \frac{1}{12} x^2 - \frac{1}{720} x^4 + \cdots.$

In problems 30 through 33 estimate the given integral to the fourth decimal place.

30. $\displaystyle\int_{0}^{1/4} \sqrt{x} \sin x \, dx.$

31. $\displaystyle\int_{0}^{0.1} \ln (1 + \sin x) dx.$

32. $\displaystyle\int_{0}^{1/2} e^{-x^2} dx.$

33. $\displaystyle\int_{0}^{1} \cos x^3 \, dx.$

In problems 34 through 38 use infinite series to find the indicated limit.

34. $\displaystyle\lim_{x \to 0} \frac{1 - \sqrt{1 + x}}{x}.$

35. $\displaystyle\lim_{x \to 0} \frac{x^2 - \sinh x^2}{x^6}.$

36. $\displaystyle\lim_{x \to 0} \frac{x \sin x}{1 - \cos x}.$

★**37.** $\displaystyle\lim_{x \to 0} \frac{\sin^2 x - \sin x^2}{x^3 \sin x}.$

★**38.** $\displaystyle\lim_{x \to 0} \frac{xe^{-3x} + \sin 5x - 6 \ln (1 + x)}{x \sin x \ln (1 - x)}.$

39.   By rationalizing the denominator show that

$$\sum_{k=1}^{n} \frac{1}{\sqrt{k+1} + \sqrt{k}} = \sqrt{n+1} - 1.$$

Deduce from this that $\displaystyle\sum_{k=1}^{\infty} \frac{1}{\sqrt{k}}$ diverges.

14

VECTORS AND SOLID ANALYTIC GEOMETRY

1.   The rectangular coordinate system.   In order to locate points in three-dimensional space we must have some fixed reference frame. We obtain such a frame by selecting a fixed point O and selecting at O three mutually perpendicular lines as indicated in Fig. 1.   On each of these lines a positive direction is assigned, and these three lines are called the x-axis, y-axis, and z-axis.

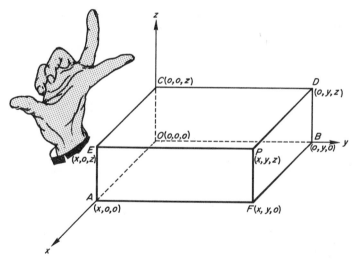

Figure 1

It is customary and convenient to have the x-axis and y-axis in a horizontal plane and the z-axis vertical.   Suppose that we place our right hand so that the thumb points in the positive direction of the x-axis and the index finger points in the positive direction of the y-axis.   If the middle finger points in the positive direction of the z-axis, then the coordinate

454

system is called *right-handed.* If the middle finger points in the negative direction along the z-axis, the coordinate system is called *left-handed.* The system shown in Fig. 1 is right-handed, and in this book we will always use a right-handed system.

The x-axis and y-axis together determine a horizontal plane called the xy-plane. Similarly the xz-plane is the vertical plane containing the x-axis and z-axis, and the yz-plane is the plane determined by the y-axis and z-axis.

If P is any point in space it has three coordinates with respect to this fixed frame of reference, and these coordinates are indicated by writing $P(x, y, z)$. These coordinates can be defined thus:

x is the directed distance of P from the yz-plane,

y is the directed distance of P from the xz-plane,

z is the directed distance of P from the xy-plane.

Referring to Fig. 1 these are the directed distances DP, EP, and FP respectively. These line segments form the edges of a box[1], with each face perpendicular to one of the coordinate axes. With the lettering of Fig. 1, A is the projection of P on the x-axis, B is the projection of P on the y-axis, and C is the projection of P on the z-axis. Clearly an alternate definition for the coordinates of P is:

x is the directed distance OA,

y is the directed distance OB,

z is the directed distance OC.

The points $P(5, 9, 2)$, $Q(-7, 4, 3)$, $R(-2, -8, 5)$ and $S(2, -5, -4)$ are shown in Fig. 2, along with their associated boxes. It is clear that if x is negative, the point (x, y, z) lies in back of the yz-plane. If y is negative the point lies to the left of the xz-plane, and if z is negative the point lies below the xy-plane. These three coordinate planes divide space into 8 separate pieces called *octants.* The octant in which all three coordinates are positive is called the *first octant.* The other octants could be named, but there is no real reason for doing so.

The preceding discussion suggests the obvious

THEOREM 1. *With a fixed set of coordinate axes, there is a one-to-one correspondence between the set of points in space and the set of all triples of real numbers (x, y, z). For each point P there is a uniquely determined set of three real numbers, the coordinates (x, y, z) of P. Conversely for each such set of three real numbers there is a uniquely determined point in space with this set for its coordinates.*

[1] This three dimensional figure with vertices O, A, F, B, C, E, P, and D is usually called a rectangular parallelopiped. We will use the shorter word "box" for such figures.

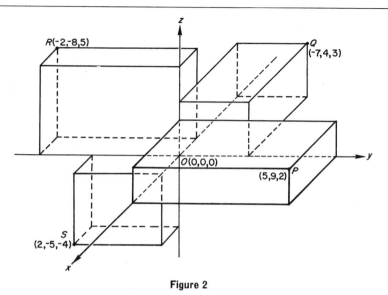

Figure 2

Many of the theorems from plane analytic geometry have a simple and obvious extension in solid analytic geometry and in fact their proofs can be relegated to the exercise list.

Just as in the plane, the graph of an equation in the three variables x, y, and z is the collection of all points whose coordinates satisfy the given equation. Such an equation can be written symbolically as $F(x, y, z) = 0$ where $F(x, y, z)$ denotes, as usual, some suitable function of three variables. We recall that in plane analytic geometry the graph of an equation $F(x, y) = 0$ usually turns out to be some curve. By contrast we will see that in three dimensional analytic geometry the graph of an equation $F(x, y, z) = 0$ is usually a surface. One way of describing a curve in three-dimensional space is as the intersection of two surfaces. Hence the points P whose coordinates satisfy simultaneously two given equations $F(x, y, z) = 0$ and $G(x, y, z) = 0$, usually form a curve.

We will prove in section 9 that the graph of $Ax + By + Cz + D = 0$ is always a plane if at least one of the coefficients A, B, C is not zero. Conversely each plane has an equation of this form.

EXAMPLE 1.   Sketch (a) the surface $2x + 3y = 6$, (b) the surface $5y + 2z = 10$, and (c) the curve of intersection of these two surfaces.

SOLUTION.   (a) In the xy-plane the graph of $2x + 3y = 6$ is a straight line with intercepts 3 and 2 on the x-axis and y-axis respectively. Hence the straight line through the points $A(3, 0, 0)$ and $B(0, 2, 0)$ is a part of the three-dimensional graph of $2x + 3y = 6$ (see Fig. 3). Since z does not enter explicitly in the equation $2x + 3y = 6$, we see that z can assume any value, and the point $P(x, y, z)$ will be a part of the graph as long as x and y are taken properly.   Thus P will lie directly above (or below, or on) the line AB.   Hence the graph of $2x + 3y = 6$ is the plane containing the line AB and perpendicular to the xy-plane.   A portion of this plane is shown in Fig. 3

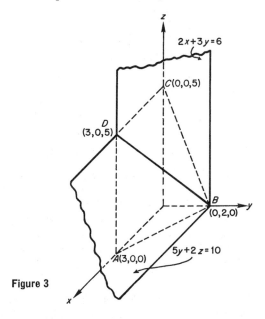

Figure 3

(b)   The graph of $5y + 2z = 10$ in the yz-plane is just the straight line through the points $B(0, 2, 0)$ and $C(0, 0, 5)$.   Since x may assume any value, the graph of $5y + 2z = 10$ in three-dimensional space is just the plane through the line BC and perpendicular to the yz-plane.   A portion of this plane is shown in Fig. 3.

(c)   The intersection of these two planes is a straight line.   Since $B(0, 2, 0)$ and $D(3, 0, 5)$ lie on both planes, the graph of the pair of equations $2x + 3y = 6$ and $5y + 2z = 10$ is the line through the points B and D.

DEFINITION 1.   *Let C be a plane curve and let a line L move along C in such a way that the line L is always perpendicular to the plane of C.   The surface generated by the moving line L is called a cylinder and the lines on the surface are called its elements.*

From the discussion in the solution of example 1, it is clear that whenever one variable is missing from the equation $F(x, y, z) = 0$, the graph is a cylinder.   For example the graph of $y^2 + z^2 - 16 = 0$ in the yz-plane is a circle about the origin.   Then in three-dimensional space the graph of this same equation is the cylinder generated by a line perpendicular to the yz-plane moving along this circle.   A portion of this cylinder is shown in Fig. 4.

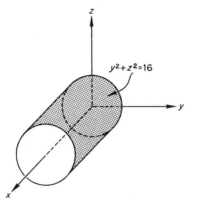

Figure 4

EXERCISE 1

1. Locate each of the following points, and sketch its associated box. Observe that there is one point in each octant. $P_1(1, 2, 3)$, $P_2(-1, 2, 3)$, $P_3(5, -8, 1)$, $P_4(-5, -8, 1)$, $P_5(3, 4, -9)$, $P_6(-7, 4, -3.5)$, $P_7(\pi, -\sqrt{15}, -1.5)$, $P_8(-1, -1, -1)$.

2. Sketch the planes (a) $z = 5$, (b) $x = 3$, and (c) $y = -6$. Observe that each of these planes is parallel to a coordinate plane.

3. Sketch the box bounded by the following six planes: $x = 2$, $x = 7$, $y = 3$, $y = 10$, $z = 4$, and $z = -3$. Find the coordinates for each of the eight vertices of this box.

In problems 4 through 7 sketch the given pair of planes, and their line of intersection. In each case find the coordinates of the points in which the line of intersection meets the xz-plane and the yz-plane.

4. $y + 6z = 6,$ $\qquad 6x + 5y = 30.$
5. $2x + 7y = 14,$ $\qquad x + z = 7.$
6. $x + y = 4,$ $\qquad y + 2z = 16.$
★7. $5x + z = 10,$ $\qquad 2y - z = 5.$

In problems 8 through 11 sketch that portion of the graph of the given equation that lies in the first octant.

8. $x^2 + y^2 = 4.$ $\qquad\qquad$ **9.** $4y = x^2.$
10. $y = 8 - z^2.$ $\qquad\qquad$ **11.** $9x^2 + 25y^2 = 225.$

12. Prove that r, the distance of the point $P(x, y, z)$ from the origin, is given by $r = \sqrt{x^2 + y^2 + z^2}$. *Hint:* In the box of Fig. 1 draw in the lines OF and OP and consider the right triangles OAF and OFP. First compute $|OF|$ and then $r = |OP|$.

13. Give an equation for the sphere of radius 5 and center at the origin.

14. Find the length of the diagonal of the box of problem 3.

2.   Vectors in three-dimensional space. Solid analytic geometry can be presented without the use of vectors. However when vectors are used the presentation can be simplified, and indeed to such an extent that we will be amply rewarded for the additional time and energy required to learn the necessary vector algebra.

Much of the material on vectors covered in Chapter 10 is valid for three-dimensional space and needs no detailed discussion. We ask the reader to quickly review the following items: (1) the definition of a vector, (2) the definition of addition of two vectors, (3) the definition of multiplication of a vector by a scalar, and (4) the properties of these two operations stated in Theorems 1, 2, 3, 4, 5 and the problems of Exercise 1 of Chapter 10. It is easy to see that in all of these items, there is no need to suppose that the vectors lie in a plane.

By contrast, when we compute, using the two unit vectors **i** and **j**, we are able to handle only those vectors that lie in the plane of **i** and **j**. In order to compute with vectors in three dimensional space it is convenient to introduce a third unit vector **k**. Accordingly we let **i**, **j**, and **k** be three mutually perpendicular unit vectors with **i** pointing in the positive direction along the x-axis, **j** pointing in the positive direction along the y-axis, and **k** pointing in the positive direction along the z-axis. These vectors are shown in Fig. 5. If $P(x, y, z)$ is any point then the position vector **R** = **OP** can always be written in the form

$$\mathbf{OP} = x\mathbf{i} + y\mathbf{j} + z\mathbf{k}. \tag{1}$$

For example, as indicated in Fig. 5, the vector from the origin to the point $(3, 7, 4)$ is **R** $= 3\mathbf{i} + 7\mathbf{j} + 4\mathbf{k}$.

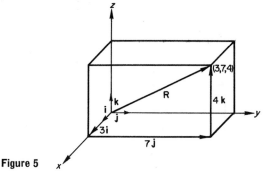

Figure 5

Since any vector may be shifted parallel to itself, we can always regard a vector as starting at the origin of the coordinate system, whenever it is convenient to do so. Thus any vector can be written in the form (1).

Given two vectors, **A** $= a_1\mathbf{i} + a_2\mathbf{j} + a_3\mathbf{k}$ and **B** $= b_1\mathbf{i} + b_2\mathbf{j} + b_3\mathbf{k}$, their sum is found by adding the corresponding components, thus

$$\mathbf{A} + \mathbf{B} = (a_1 + b_1)\mathbf{i} + (a_2 + b_2)\mathbf{j} + (a_3 + b_3)\mathbf{k}. \tag{2}$$

This is just the generalization of Theorem 6 of Chapter 10, to three dimensional space. The proof is similar to the proof for plane vectors, and hence we omit it.

In the same way, it is easy to see that if c is any number, then

$$c\mathbf{A} = ca_1\mathbf{i} + ca_2\mathbf{j} + ca_3\mathbf{k}. \qquad (3)$$

By the Pythagorean Theorem (see problem 12 of the preceding exercise) the length of the vector $\mathbf{R} = x\mathbf{i} + y\mathbf{j} + z\mathbf{k}$ is given by

$$R = |\mathbf{R}| = \sqrt{x^2 + y^2 + z^2}. \qquad (4)$$

The vector $\mathbf{R}$ is completely determined whenever we specify its three components x, y, and z along the three axes. But we could also specify the vector by giving its length and the angle that it makes with each of the coordinate axes. These angles are called the *direction angles* of the vector and are denoted by α, β, and γ. Thus as indicated in Fig. 6:

α is the angle between the vector and the positive x-axis.
β is the angle between the vector and the positive y-axis.
γ is the angle between the vector and the positive z-axis.

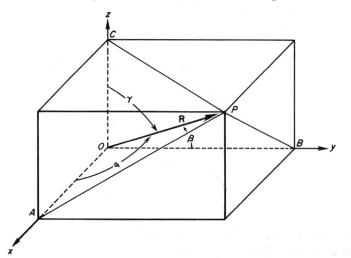

Figure 6

By definition each of these angles lies between 0 and π. Actually we are more interested in the cosines of these angles, and if P is in the first octant, it is obvious from the right triangles shown in Fig. 6 that

$$\cos \alpha = \frac{x}{\sqrt{x^2 + y^2 + z^2}}, \qquad \text{right triangle } OAP,$$

$$\cos \beta = \frac{y}{\sqrt{x^2 + y^2 + z^2}}, \qquad \text{right triangle } OBP, \qquad (5)$$

$$\cos \gamma = \frac{z}{\sqrt{x^2 + y^2 + z^2}}, \qquad \text{right triangle } OCP.$$

Of course if P is not in the first octant some of the numbers $\cos \alpha$, $\cos \beta$, $\cos \gamma$, may be negative. For example if P lies to the left of the xz-plane then β is a second quadrant angle and $\cos \beta$ is negative. But in this case y is also negative. A little reflection will show that the formulas (5) hold for any position of the point P.

The numbers $\{\cos \alpha, \cos \beta, \cos \gamma\}$ are called the *direction cosines* of the vector **R**. Obviously these specify the direction of R. However these direction cosines cannot be assigned arbitrarily, because they must satisfy the condition

$$\boxed{\cos^2 \alpha + \cos^2 \beta + \cos^2 \gamma = 1.} \qquad (6)$$

To prove this we have from the equation set (5)

$$\cos^2 \alpha + \cos^2 \beta + \cos^2 \gamma = \frac{x^2}{x^2 + y^2 + z^2} + \frac{y^2}{x^2 + y^2 + z^2} + \frac{z^2}{x^2 + y^2 + z^2}$$

$$= \frac{x^2 + y^2 + z^2}{x^2 + y^2 + z^2} = 1.$$

If m is any positive constant, the set of numbers

$$\{m \cos \alpha, \, m \cos \beta, \, m \cos \gamma\}$$

also serves to specify the direction of R. Such a set is called a set of *direction numbers* for the vector R. Conversely, given a set of direction numbers we can always find the direction cosines for the vector, as illustrated in the next example.

Finally we remark that if we know the length of the vector and its direction cosines, then the vector is completely specified, and combining equation (4) with equation set (5) we have

$$\mathbf{R} = |\mathbf{R}| \, (\cos \alpha \mathbf{i} + \cos \beta \mathbf{j} + \cos \gamma \mathbf{k}). \qquad (7)$$

EXAMPLE 1. A certain vector has length 21 and direction numbers $\{2, -3, 6\}$. Find the direction cosines and the components of this vector.

SOLUTION.   The direction cosines are proportional to 2, -3, 6.   We let m be the constant of proportionality and hence $\cos \alpha = 2m$, $\cos \beta = -3m$, and $\cos \gamma = 6m$.   From equation (6)

$$1 = \cos^2 \alpha + \cos^2 \beta + \cos^2 \gamma = (2m)^2 + (-3m)^2 + (6m)^2$$
$$= (4 + 9 + 36)m^2 = 49m^2.$$

Hence $m^2 = 1/49$, and $m = 1/7$.   Consequently $\cos \alpha = 2/7$, $\cos \beta = -3/7$, and $\cos \gamma = 6/7$.   Using this, and the fact that $|\mathbf{R}| = 21$, in equation (7) yields

$$R = 21 \left(\frac{2}{7}\, \mathbf{i} - \frac{3}{7}\, \mathbf{j} + \frac{6}{7}\, \mathbf{k} \right) = 6\mathbf{i} - 9\mathbf{j} + 18\mathbf{k}.$$

EXAMPLE 2.   Find the direction cosines of the vector from $A(4, 8, -3)$ to $B(-1, 6, 2)$.

SOLUTION.   We recall from Theorem 9 of Chapter 10 that for any two points A and B

$$\mathbf{AB} = \mathbf{OB} - \mathbf{OA}.$$

Hence

$$\mathbf{AB} = -\mathbf{i} + 6\mathbf{j} + 2\mathbf{k} - (4\mathbf{i} + 8\mathbf{j} - 3\mathbf{k}) = -5\mathbf{i} - 2\mathbf{j} + 5\mathbf{k}.$$

It follows that $|\mathbf{AB}| = \sqrt{5^2 + 2^2 + 5^2} = \sqrt{54} = 3\sqrt{6}$, and then from equation set (5), that $\cos \alpha = -5/3\sqrt{6}$, $\cos \beta = -2/3\sqrt{6}$, and $\cos \gamma = 5/3\sqrt{6}$.

This example suggests

THEOREM 2.   *The length of the vector from* $A(a_1, a_2, a_3)$ *to to* $B(b_1, b_2, b_3)$ *is given by*

$$|\mathbf{AB}| = \sqrt{(b_1 - a_1)^2 + (b_2 - a_2)^2 + (b_3 - a_3)^2} \qquad (8)$$

and the direction cosines are

$$\cos \alpha = \frac{b_1 - a_1}{|\mathbf{AB}|}, \quad \cos \beta = \frac{b_2 - a_2}{|\mathbf{AB}|}, \quad \cos \gamma = \frac{b_3 - a_3}{|\mathbf{AB}|}. \qquad (9)$$

PROOF.   Just as in the example

$$\mathbf{AB} = \mathbf{OB} - \mathbf{OA} = b_1\mathbf{i} + b_2\mathbf{j} + b_3\mathbf{k} - (a_1\mathbf{i} + a_2\mathbf{j} + a_3\mathbf{k})$$
$$\mathbf{AB} = (b_1 - a_1)\mathbf{i} + (b_2 - a_2)\mathbf{j} + (b_3 - a_3)\mathbf{k}. \qquad (10)$$

Then (8) follows by applying equation (4) to (10), and (9) follows from equation (5) in the same way.

COROLLARY. *The distance between the points $A(a_1, a_2, a_3)$ and $B(b_1, b_2, b_3)$ is given by equation (8).*

EXERCISE 2

1. Make a three-dimensional sketch showing each of the following vectors with its initial point at the origin. $A = i + 2j + 3k$, $B = 4i - 3j - k$, $C = -5i - 3j + 5k$, $D = -7i + j - 15k$, $E = 4i - 7k$.

2. Using the vectors of problem 1, compute each of the following vectors

    a. $A + B$,   b. $2A - C$,   c. $C + D + E$,   d. $3A - 2B + C - 2D + E$.

3. With the vectors of problem 1, show that $4A + 2B + C + D = 0$.

4. Find the direction cosines for the vectors $F = 2i + j - 2k$, $G = 6i - 3j + 2k$, $H = i + j + k$, and $I = -5i + 6j + 8k$.

5. In each of the following find the length of the vector from the first point to the second point.

    a. $(3, 2, -2)$, $(7, 4, 2)$.   b. $(5, -1, -6)$, $(-3, -5, 2)$.

    c. $(-3, 11, -4)$, $(4, 10, -9)$.   d. $(-1, 9, 11)$, $(-13, 22, 16)$.

★6. Equation (6) is the generalization to three-dimensional space of an important formula from plane trigonometry. What is that formula?

★7. Prove that two vectors $A = a_1 i + a_2 j + a_3 k$ and $B = b_1 i + b_2 j + b_3 k$ are equal if and only if $a_1 = b_1$, $a_2 = b_2$, and $a_3 = b_3$.

★8. Given $A = -i + 3j + k$, $B = 8i + 2j - 4k$, $C = i + 2j - k$, and $D = -i + j + 3k$, find scalars m, n, and p such that

$$mA + nB + pC = D.$$

9. Prove that the points $A(2, -1, 6)$, $B(3, 2, 8)$, and $C(8, 7, -9)$ form the vertices of a right triangle.

10. Find an equation for the sphere with center $P_0(2, -3, 6)$ and radius 7. *Hint: P* is on the sphere if and only if the vector P_0P has length 7.

11. Find a simple equation for the set of all points that are equidistant from the points $A(1, 3, 5)$ and $B(2, -3, -4)$. Naturally these points form a plane.

12. Repeat problem 11 for the pairs of points (a) $(0, 0, 1)$, $(1, 1, 0)$ and (b) $(0, 0, 0)$ $(2a, 2b, 2c)$.

★13. Let a, b, and c be any three real numbers. Prove that $P_1(a, b, c)$, $P_2(b, c, a)$, $P_3(c, a, b)$ either all coincide or form the vertices of an equilateral triangle.

14. Find an equation for the sphere with center at (a, b, c) and radius r.

15. Find the center and radius for each of the following spheres

    a. $x^2 + y^2 + z^2 + 4x - 6z = 0$,

    b. $x^2 + y^2 + z^2 + 12x - 6y + 4z = 0$,

    c. $x^2 + y^2 + z^2 - 10x + 6y + 8z + 14 = 0$,

    d. $3x^2 + 3y^2 + 3z^2 - x - 5y - 4z = 2$.

16. A point P moves in three-dimensional space so that its distance from the point $A(0, 2, 0)$ is always twice its distance from the point $B(0, 5, 0)$. Prove that P always lies on a sphere. Find the center and radius of that sphere.

17. Find the distance of the point $P(s, t, u)$ from

    a. the x-axis,

    b. the y-axis,

    c. the z-axis,

    d. the plane $x = 2$,

    e. the line of intersection of the planes $y = -3$, $z = 5$.

3.   Equations of lines in space. A straight line l in three-dimensional space is completely determined if we are given two points on the line, or if we are given one point on the line together with the direction of the line. The direction of the line is specified by giving a vector parallel to the line. Suppose that the two points $P_0(x_0, y_0, z_0)$ and $P_1(x_1, y_1, z_1)$ are on the line l. Then the vector

$$\mathbf{P_0P_1} = \mathbf{OP_1} - \mathbf{OP_0} = (x_1 - x_0)\mathbf{i} + (y_1 - y_0)\mathbf{j} + (z_1 - z_0)\mathbf{k}$$

that joins the two points on the line is obviously parallel to the given line, and specifies the direction of the line.

To obtain a vector equation for the line we observe that we can reach any point P on the line by proceeding first from O to P_0 and then travelling along the line a suitable multiple t of the vector $\mathbf{P_0P_1}$ to P, as illustrated in Fig. 7. Thus if $\mathbf{R}$ is the position vector of the point P on the line, then

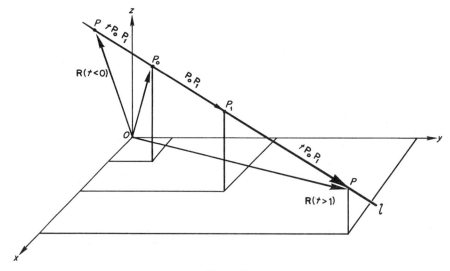

Figure 7

there is a scalar t such that

$$\mathbf{R} = \mathbf{OP}_0 + t\mathbf{P}_0\mathbf{P}_1. \tag{11}$$

Conversely for each real number t, the vector $\mathbf{R}$ of equation (11) is the position vector of a point on the line through P_0 and P_1. Thus we have proved that (11) is a vector equation for the line through P_0 and P_1.

Observe that if $0 \leq t \leq 1$, then P is on the line segment joining P_0 and P_1. If $t > 1$ the points are in the order P_0, P_1, P on the line. Finally if $t < 0$, the points are in the order P, P_0, P_1 on the line.

If we put $\mathbf{R} = x\mathbf{i} + y\mathbf{j} + z\mathbf{k}$, equation (11) can be written as

$$x\mathbf{i} + y\mathbf{j} + z\mathbf{k} = x_0\mathbf{i} + y_0\mathbf{j} + z_0\mathbf{k} + t(x_1 - x_0)\mathbf{i} \tag{12}$$
$$+ t(y_1 - y_0)\mathbf{j} + t(z_1 - z_0)\mathbf{k}.$$

Equating corresponding components on both sides of (12) leads to

$$\begin{aligned} x &= x_0 + t(x_1 - x_0), \\ y &= y_0 + t(y_1 - y_0), \\ z &= z_0 + t(z_1 - z_0). \end{aligned} \tag{13}$$

This set of equations forms a set of parametric equations for the line. For brevity we set $x_1 - x_0 = a$, $y_1 - y_0 = b$, and $z_1 - z_0 = c$. Then the vector $a\mathbf{i} + b\mathbf{j} + c\mathbf{k}$ is a vector parallel to the line and the set of numbers $\{a, b, c\}$ is a set of direction numbers for the line. The set (13) is equivalent to

$$x = x_0 + at, \qquad y = y_0 + bt, \qquad z = z_0 + ct. \tag{14}$$

Finally since the set (14) is a set of simultaneous equations in t, we may eliminate t and arrive at

$$\frac{x - x_0}{a} = \frac{y - y_0}{b} = \frac{z - z_0}{c} \tag{15}$$

as long as a, b, and c are all different from zero.

To summarize, each of the equations (11), (13), (14), and (15) is an equation of a straight line in space, and the vector $a\mathbf{i} + b\mathbf{j} + c\mathbf{k}$ is parallel to the straight line. We observe that (15) can be thought of as a pair of equations

$$\frac{x - x_0}{a} = \frac{y - y_0}{b} \quad \text{and} \quad \frac{y - y_0}{b} = \frac{z - z_0}{c}. \tag{16}$$

The first equation in (16) is the equation of a plane perpendicular to the xy-plane. The second is the equation of a plane perpendicular to the yz-plane. The straight line in question is then the intersection of these two planes. This is illustrated in Example 2 below.

EXAMPLE 1. Find an equation for the line through the points $(7, -3, 5)$ and $(-2, 8, 1)$. Where does this line pierce the xy-plane?

SOLUTION. Let the two points be P_0 and P_1 respectively. Then $\mathbf{P_0P_1} = -9\mathbf{i} + 11\mathbf{j} - 4\mathbf{k}$, and the vector equation is

$$\mathbf{R} = 7\mathbf{i} - 3\mathbf{j} + 5\mathbf{k} + t(-9\mathbf{i} + 11\mathbf{j} - 4\mathbf{k}). \tag{11e}$$

The set of parametric equations, obtained from (13) or (14) is

$$x = 7 - 9t, \quad y = -3 + 11t, \quad z = 5 - 4t. \tag{14e}$$

Eliminating t from this set, we find

$$\frac{x - 7}{-9} = \frac{y + 3}{11} = \frac{z - 5}{-4}. \tag{15e}$$

The numbers $\{-9, 11, -4\}$ form a set of direction numbers for this line.

This line meets the xy-plane when $z = 0$. Using this in the last equation of set (14e) gives $t = 5/4$. Then from the other equations of this set we have

$$x = 7 - 9 \cdot \frac{5}{4} = -\frac{17}{4} \quad \text{and} \quad y = -3 + 11 \cdot \frac{5}{4} = \frac{43}{4}.$$

Hence the pierce point is $\left(-\frac{17}{4}, \frac{43}{4}, 0\right)$.

EXAMPLE 2. Find an equation for the line of intersection of the two planes $2x + 3y = 6$ and $5y + 2z = 10$.

SOLUTION. We first need to find one point on the line, i.e., a point that simultaneously lies on both planes. We can find such a point by selecting at random, a value for one of the coordinates. Suppose we set $y = 0$ (a very simple choice), then the equation $2x + 3y = 6$ gives $x = 3$, and the equation $5y + 2z = 10$ gives $z = 5$. Clearly the point $(3, 0, 5)$ is on both planes. Using this as our point (x_0, y_0, z_0), we transform the equation $2x + 3y = 6$ into the form $2(x - 3) = -3(y - 0)$ or

$$\frac{x - 3}{-3} = \frac{y - 0}{2},$$

and this has the form of the first equation in (16). Similarly $5y + 2z = 10$ becomes $5(y - 0) = -2(z - 5)$ or

$$\frac{y - 0}{2} = \frac{z - 5}{-5}.$$

Combining these two equations gives the set

$$\frac{x - 3}{-3} = \frac{y - 0}{2} = \frac{z - 5}{-5},$$

a set of equations for the line of intersection of the two given planes. The numbers $\{-3, 2, -5\}$ form a set of direction numbers for the line. Using these numbers in (14) we have

$$x = 3 - 3t, \qquad y = 0 + 2t = 2t, \qquad z = 5 - 5t,$$

a set of parametric equations for the straight line. In vector form these would appear as

$$\mathbf{R} = 3\mathbf{i} + 5\mathbf{k} + t(-3\mathbf{i} + 2\mathbf{j} - 5\mathbf{k}).$$

A portion of the two planes and their line of intersection is shown in Fig. 3.

EXAMPLE 3. Find a formula for the coordinates of the midpoint of the line segment joining the points P_0 and P_1.

SOLUTION. Referring to Fig. 7, it is clear that the position vector of the midpoint is

$$\mathbf{R} = \mathbf{OP_0} + \tfrac{1}{2}\mathbf{P_0P_1}.$$

Setting $t = 1/2$ in equations (12) or (13) yields

$$x = x_0 + \tfrac{1}{2}(x_1 - x_0), \qquad y = y_0 + \tfrac{1}{2}(y_1 - y_0), \qquad z = z_0 + \tfrac{1}{2}(z_1 - z_0)$$

or

$$x = \frac{x_0 + x_1}{2}, \qquad y = \frac{y_0 + y_1}{2}, \qquad z = \frac{z_0 + z_1}{2}. \qquad (17)$$

EXERCISE 3

In problems 1 through 4 find equations for the line joining the two given points.

1. $(1, 2, 3)$, $(4, 6, -9)$.   2. $(0, -5, 8)$, $(1, 6, 2)$.
3. $(2, 1, -3)$, $(5, -4, 7)$.   4. $(-2, 6, 8)$, $(2, 6, -8)$.

5. Where does the line of problem 1 meet the yz-plane?
6. Where does the line of problem 2 meet the plane $y = -16$?
7. Is there a point on the line of problem 3 at which all of the coordinates are equal?

*8. Find all points on the line of problem 3 in which two of the coordinates are equal.

In problems 9 through 12 find a vector equation for the line of intersection of the two given planes.

9. $2x + 7y = 14$, $\quad x + z = 7$.
10. $5x + z = 10$, $\quad 2y - z = 5$.
11. $3x - 4y = 9$, $\quad 4y - 5z = 20$.
*12. $x + 7y - z = 7$, $\quad 2x + 21y - 4z = 14$.

In problems 13 through 16 the points P_0, P_1, and P_2 are collinear, and occur in that order on the line.

13. Find the coordinates of P_2 if $|P_0P_2| = 2|P_0P_1|$, and P_0 and P_1 are $(1, 2, 3)$ and $(4, 6, -9)$ respectively.
14. Find the coordinates of P_2 if $2|P_0P_1| = 3|P_1P_2|$ and P_0 and P_1 are $(-2, 7, 4)$ and $(7, -2, 1)$ respectively.
*15. Find the coordinates of P_0 if $|P_0P_1| = 10|P_1P_2|$ and P_1 and P_2 are $(2, 1, 3)$ and $(-3, 2, -1)$ respectively.
*16. Find the coordinates of P_1 if $4|P_0P_1| = |P_1P_2|$ and P_0 and P_2 are $(4, 6, 7)$ and $(9, -14, 2)$ respectively.

*17. Prove that the two sets of equations

$$\frac{x-1}{3} = \frac{y-2}{4} = \frac{z-3}{-12} \quad \text{and} \quad \frac{x+5}{-6} = \frac{y+6}{-8} = \frac{z-27}{24}$$

are equations for the same straight line.

18. Find the equation of the line through the origin that makes the same angle with each of the three coordinate axes.

19. Find the coordinates of the point P in which the line

$$\frac{x-2}{3} = \frac{y-3}{4} = \frac{z+4}{2}$$

intersects the plane $4x + 5y + 6z = 87$.

*20. Prove that the line

$$\frac{x-1}{9} = \frac{y-6}{-4} = \frac{z-3}{-6}$$

lies in the plane $2x - 3y + 5z = -1$.

21. Find the point of intersection of the line through P and Q with the given plane in each of the following cases.

a. $P(-1, 5, 1)$, $\quad Q(-2, 8, -1)$, $\quad 2x - 3y + z = 10$,
b. $P(-1, 0, 9)$, $\quad Q(-3, 1, 14)$, $\quad 3x + 2y - z = 6$,
c. $P(0, 0, 0)$, $\quad Q(A, B, C)$, $\quad Ax + By + Cz = D$.

4. **The scalar product of two vectors.** We want to formulate a definition for the product of two vectors. It turns out that there are two different ways of doing this, both of which give interesting and useful results. Rather than select one of these definitions in preference to the other, we keep both using the "dot" in the first case and the "cross" in the second, in order to distinguish between the two. The scalar product (or dot product) **A·B** of the two vectors **A** and **B** is a number. The vector product (or cross product) **A × B** is a vector. We will define **A × B**, and obtain some of its properties in section 5.

Given any pair of vectors **A** and **B**, we can always make a parallel shift of both vectors so that both have the origin as their common initial point. If θ denotes an angle between these two vectors, we can always select θ so that $0 \leq \theta \leq \pi$. We call this angle the angle between the two vectors, and whenever it is necessary to name the particular vectors we can write θ_{AB}, using the vectors as subscripts. For example with this convention the direction angles α, β, and γ of a vector **R** would be

$$\alpha = \theta_{Ri}, \quad \beta = \theta_{Rj}, \quad \text{and} \quad \gamma = \theta_{Rk}.$$

DEFINITION 2. *The scalar product of two vectors is the product of their lengths and the cosine of the angle between them. In symbols*

$$\mathbf{A \cdot B} = |\mathbf{A}||\mathbf{B}| \cos \theta. \tag{18}$$

Some consequences of this definition are immediate. Clearly the dot product is *commutative* (**A·B** = **B·A**) because an interchange in the order of multiplication does not change either the lengths of the vectors or the angle between them.

Let us pass a plane perpendicular to **B** through the initial point of **B**. If **A** and **B** lie on the same side of this plane, then $\cos \theta > 0$ and **A·B** > 0. If **A** and **B** lie on opposite sides of this plane, then $\pi/2 < \theta < \pi$, $\cos \theta < 0$, and **A·B** < 0.

If the vectors **A** and **B** are perpendicular then **A·B** = 0, because $\cos \theta = 0$. Conversely if **A·B** = 0, then either **A** = 0 or **B** = 0, or the two vectors are perpendicular. If the two vectors are parallel and in the same direction, $\cos \theta = 1$ and **A·B** is just the product of their lengths. In particular, **A·A** = $|\mathbf{A}|^2$ and for this reason is frequently written **A²**. The various dot products that can be formed with the basic unit vectors **i**, **j**, and **k** give a pretty array,

$$\begin{array}{lll}
\mathbf{i \cdot i} = 1 & \mathbf{i \cdot j} = 0 & \mathbf{i \cdot k} = 0 \\
\mathbf{j \cdot i} = 0 & \mathbf{j \cdot j} = 1 & \mathbf{j \cdot k} = 0 \\
\mathbf{k \cdot i} = 0 & \mathbf{k \cdot j} = 0 & \mathbf{k \cdot k} = 1.
\end{array} \tag{19}$$

Suppose that we are given the two vectors $\mathbf{A} = a_1\mathbf{i} + a_2\mathbf{j} + a_3\mathbf{k}$ and

$B = b_1\mathbf{i} + b_2\mathbf{j} + b_3\mathbf{k}$, is there a formula expressing $\mathbf{A}\cdot\mathbf{B}$ in terms of their components? If we knew that the ordinary rules of algebra were valid for the dot product we could expand the right side of

$$\mathbf{A}\cdot\mathbf{B} = (a_1\mathbf{i} + a_2\mathbf{j} + a_3\mathbf{k})\cdot(b_1\mathbf{i} + b_2\mathbf{j} + b_3\mathbf{k}) \tag{20}$$

obtaining 9 terms. Using (19) we see that 6 of these terms vanish and the other three simplify so that we obtain

THEOREM 3. *For any two vectors* $\mathbf{A}$ *and* $\mathbf{B}$

$$\mathbf{A}\cdot\mathbf{B} = (a_1\mathbf{i} + a_2\mathbf{j} + a_3\mathbf{k})\cdot(b_1\mathbf{i} + b_2\mathbf{j} + b_3\mathbf{k}) = a_1b_1 + a_2b_2 + a_3b_3.$$

$$\tag{21}$$

We have not proved this theorem yet, because we have not justified the expansion of the right side of (20). This expansion can be justified in a direct way (see problems 7, 8, 9, and 10 of Exercise 4), but for simplicity we select an alternate method of proof.

PROOF OF THEOREM 3. As shown in Fig. 8 we place the given vectors $\mathbf{A}$ and $\mathbf{B}$ with their initial point at the origin. Let $A(a_1, a_2, a_3)$ and

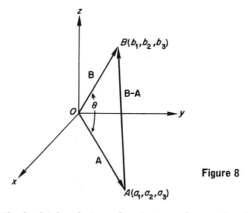

Figure 8

$B(b_1, b_2, b_3)$ be their end points, and consider the triangle OAB. We apply the law of cosines to this triangle to determine the length of the side opposite the angle θ. This gives

$$|\mathbf{B} - \mathbf{A}|^2 = |\mathbf{A}|^2 + |\mathbf{B}|^2 - 2|\mathbf{A}||\mathbf{B}|\cos\theta,$$

or

$$|\mathbf{A}||\mathbf{B}|\cos\theta = \tfrac{1}{2}\{|\mathbf{A}|^2 + |\mathbf{B}|^2 - |\mathbf{B} - \mathbf{A}|^2\}. \tag{22}$$

Using formulas (4) and (8) for the length of a vector in the right side of (22) we find

$$|\mathbf{A}||\mathbf{B}|\cos\theta =$$

$$\tfrac{1}{2}\{a_1{}^2 + a_2{}^2 + a_3{}^2 + b_1{}^2 + b_2{}^2 + b_3{}^2 - (b_1 - a_1)^2 - (b_2 - a_2)^2 - (b_3 - a_3)^2\}$$

$$= a_1 b_1 + a_2 b_2 + a_3 b_3. \hspace{4cm} \text{Q.E.D.}$$

EXAMPLE 1. For the points $A(1, 1, 2)$, $B(3, 4, 1)$, $C(-1, 4, 8)$, and $D(-6, 5, 1)$, prove that the line through A and B is perpendicular to the line through C and D.

SOLUTION. The vectors **AB** and **CD** specify the directions of the two lines. The lines are perpendicular if the vectors are. Now

$$\mathbf{AB} = \mathbf{OB} - \mathbf{OA} = 3\mathbf{i} + 4\mathbf{j} + \mathbf{k} - (\mathbf{i} + \mathbf{j} + 2\mathbf{k}) = 2\mathbf{i} + 3\mathbf{j} - \mathbf{k},$$
$$\mathbf{CD} = \mathbf{OD} - \mathbf{OC} = -6\mathbf{i} + 5\mathbf{j} + \mathbf{k} - (-\mathbf{i} + 4\mathbf{j} + 8\mathbf{k}) = -5\mathbf{i} + \mathbf{j} - 7\mathbf{k}.$$

By Theorem 3 the dot product is

$$\mathbf{AB}\cdot\mathbf{CD} = (2\mathbf{i} + 3\mathbf{j} - \mathbf{k}) \cdot (-5\mathbf{i} + \mathbf{j} - 7\mathbf{k}) = 2(-5) + 3 \cdot 1 + (-1)(-7)$$
$$= -10 + 3 + 7 = 0.$$

Since the dot product is zero the two vectors are perpendicular. Observe that we never proved that the two lines intersect, and in fact they do not. This step was omitted because the concept of an angle between two lines is independent of whether the lines intersect or not.

EXAMPLE 2. Find the angle between the two vectors $\mathbf{A} = \mathbf{i} - 2\mathbf{j} + 3\mathbf{k}$ and $\mathbf{B} = 5\mathbf{i} + 8\mathbf{j} + 6\mathbf{k}$.

SOLUTION. From the definition of the scalar product

$$|\mathbf{A}||\mathbf{B}|\cos\theta = \mathbf{A}\cdot\mathbf{B} = (\mathbf{i} - 2\mathbf{j} + 3\mathbf{k})\cdot(5\mathbf{i} + 8\mathbf{j} + 6\mathbf{k}) = 5 - 16 + 18 = 7.$$

Therefore, on dividing by $|\mathbf{A}||\mathbf{B}|$ and using formula (4) we have

$$\cos\theta = \frac{7}{|\mathbf{A}||\mathbf{B}|} = \frac{7}{\sqrt{5^2 + 8^2 + 6^2}\,\sqrt{1^2 + 2^2 + 3^2}} = \frac{7}{\sqrt{125}\,\sqrt{14}} = \frac{\sqrt{7}}{5\sqrt{10}}.$$

$$\theta = \cos^{-1}\left(\frac{\sqrt{7}}{5\sqrt{10}}\right) \approx \cos^{-1}.1673 \approx 80°22'.$$

THEOREM 4. *The scalar product is distributive, that is*

$$\mathbf{A}\cdot(\mathbf{B} + \mathbf{C}) = \mathbf{A}\cdot\mathbf{B} + \mathbf{A}\cdot\mathbf{C}. \hspace{3cm} (23)$$

PROOF. Let $\mathbf{A} = a_1\mathbf{i} + a_2\mathbf{j} + a_3\mathbf{k}$, $\mathbf{B} = b_1\mathbf{i} + b_2\mathbf{j} + b_3\mathbf{k}$, and $\mathbf{C} = c_1\mathbf{i} + c_2\mathbf{j} + c_3\mathbf{k}$. By Theorem 3 the left side of (23) is

$$\mathbf{A}\cdot(\mathbf{B} + \mathbf{C}) = (a_1\mathbf{i} + a_2\mathbf{j} + a_3\mathbf{k})\cdot[(b_1 + c_1)\mathbf{i} + (b_2 + c_2)\mathbf{j} + (b_3 + c_3)\mathbf{k}]$$

$$= a_1(b_1 + c_1) + a_2(b_2 + c_2) + a_3(b_3 + c_3)$$
$$= (a_1b_1 + a_2b_2 + a_3b_3) + (a_1c_1 + a_2c_2 + a_3c_3).$$

But this last is just $\mathbf{A} \cdot \mathbf{B} + \mathbf{A} \cdot \mathbf{C}$.   Q.E.D.

THEOREM 5.   *For any two vectors $\mathbf{A}$ and $\mathbf{B}$ and any number c*

$$c(\mathbf{A} \cdot \mathbf{B}) = (c\mathbf{A}) \cdot \mathbf{B} = \mathbf{A} \cdot (c\mathbf{B}). \tag{24}$$

Following the pattern of the proof of Theorem 4, this theorem is easily proved using equations (3) and (21).   We leave the details for the student.

EXERCISE 4

1. Compute the following scalar products

    a. $(3\mathbf{i} + 2\mathbf{j} - 4\mathbf{k}) \cdot (3\mathbf{i} - 2\mathbf{j} + 7\mathbf{k})$,   **b.** $(-\mathbf{i} + 6\mathbf{j} + 5\mathbf{k}) \cdot (10\mathbf{i} + 3\mathbf{j} - \mathbf{k})$,
    c. $(2\mathbf{i} + 5\mathbf{j} + 6\mathbf{k}) \cdot (6\mathbf{i} + 6\mathbf{j} - 7\mathbf{k})$,   **d.** $(7\mathbf{i} + 8\mathbf{j} + 9\mathbf{k}) \cdot (5\mathbf{i} - 9\mathbf{j} + 4\mathbf{k})$.

2. For each pair of vectors given in problem 1, find $\cos \theta$, where θ is the angle between the vectors.

3. Find z so that the vectors $\mathbf{i} + 2\mathbf{j} + 3\mathbf{k}$ and $4\mathbf{i} + 5\mathbf{j} + z\mathbf{k}$ are perpendicular.

4. A triangle has vertices at $A(1, 0, 0)$, $B(0, 2, 0)$, and $C(0, 0, 3)$.   Find $\cos \theta$ for each angle of the triangle.

5. Repeat problem 4, for the points $D(1, 1, 1)$, $E(-1, -1, 1)$, and $F(1, -1, -1)$.

6. Repeat problem 4 for the points $G(3, 1, -5)$, $H(-5, 3, 1)$, and $J(1, -5, 3)$. Compare your result with that obtained in Exercise 2 problem 13.

7. Let $\mathbf{PQ}$ be a vector and let l be a directed line segment whose direction is given by the vector $\mathbf{L}$.   Let P' and Q' be the projections of the points P and Q on the line l (see Fig. 9).   Then the vector $\mathbf{P'Q'}$ is called the *vector projection* of $\mathbf{PQ}$ on l (or on $\mathbf{L}$).   By the *scalar projection* of $\mathbf{PQ}$ on l we mean the signed length of the vector $\mathbf{P'Q'}$, i.e., $|\mathbf{P'Q'}|$ if the direction of $\mathbf{P'Q'}$ coincides with that of $\mathbf{L}$, and $-|\mathbf{P'Q'}|$ if $\mathbf{P'Q'}$ is opposed to $\mathbf{L}$.   We denote this scalar by $\mathrm{proj_L}\ \mathbf{PQ}$.   Prove that the scalar product $\mathbf{A} \cdot \mathbf{B}$ is given by

$$\mathbf{A} \cdot \mathbf{B} = |\mathbf{A}|\,\mathrm{proj_A}\mathbf{B}.$$

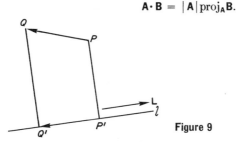

Figure 9

*8. Give a second proof of the distributive law of scalar multiplication (Theorem 4), by filling in the details in the following outline.

Projection is distributive, $\text{proj}_A(B + C) = \text{proj}_A B + \text{proj}_A C.$
Therefore $|A|\,\text{proj}_A(B + C) = |A|\,\text{proj}_A B + |A|\,\text{proj}_A C.$
Hence $A \cdot (B + C) = A \cdot B + A \cdot C.$

*9.   Prove Theorem 5, working directly with the definition of $A \cdot B$ (do not use Theorem 3). *Hint:* Consider various cases according as c is positive, negative, or zero.

*10.   Use the results of problems 8 and 9 to give a new proof of Theorem 3. *Hint:* We can now expand the right side of (20) using the rules of ordinary algebra.

11.   Use the dot product to derive formulas (8) and (9) of Theorem 2.

*12.   Use the dot product to prove that an angle inscribed in a semicircle is a right angle.   *Hint:* From Fig. 10

$$(B - A) \cdot (B + A) = B \cdot B - A \cdot A = |B|^2 - |A|^2 = 0.$$

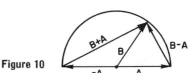

Figure 10

*13.   For any pair of sets of real numbers

$$\left(\sum_{\alpha=1}^{n} a_\alpha b_\alpha \right)^2 \leq \left(\sum_{\alpha=1}^{n} a_\alpha^2 \right)\left(\sum_{\alpha=1}^{n} b_\alpha^2 \right).$$

This is Cauchy's inequality, and although the proof for any integer n is not difficult, it would lead us too far astray.   Use the dot product to prove this inequality when $n = 3$.   When does the equality sign occur?

14.   Find the cosine of the angle between the diagonal of a cube and the diagonal of one of its faces.

15.   A right pyramid has a square base 2 ft on each side and a height of 3 ft. Find the cosine of the angle of intersection of two adjacent edges that meet at the vertex.

16.   Suppose that A and B are vectors of unit length.   Prove that $A + B$ is a vector that bisects the angle between A and B.

17.   Use the results of problem 16 to find a vector that bisects the angle between $3i + 2j + 6k$ and $9i + 6j + 2k$.

5.   The vector product of two vectors.

DEFINITION 3.   *The vector product* $A \times B$ *of two vectors* A *and* B *is a vector of length* $|A||B| \sin \theta$, *perpendicular to the plane of* A *and* B *and such that* A, B, *and* $A \times B$ *form a righthanded set. In symbols*

$$\boxed{A \times B = |A||B| \sin \theta \, e,}\tag{25}$$

where **e** *is a unit vector perpendicular to the plane of* **A** *and* **B** *and such that* **A**, **B**, *and* **e** *form a righthanded set.*

Observe that if **A** and **B** are parallel they do not determine a plane, and hence the vector **e** is not defined. But in this case $\sin \theta = 0 (\theta = 0$, or $\pi)$ so by (25) **A** $\times$ **B** $= 0$ and the determination of **e** is not necessary.

We can also describe **e** as a unit vector that points in the direction of advance of a righthand screw when turned through the angle θ from **A** to **B**.

Just as in the case of the dot product, the various cross products formed from the unit vectors **i**, **j**, and **k** give a pretty array. The student is asked to check each of the entries in equation set (26).

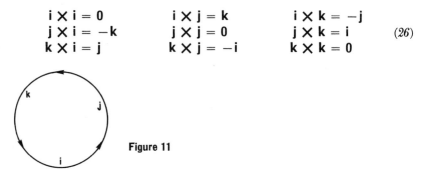

$$\begin{array}{lll}
\mathbf{i} \times \mathbf{i} = 0 & \mathbf{i} \times \mathbf{j} = \mathbf{k} & \mathbf{i} \times \mathbf{k} = -\mathbf{j} \\
\mathbf{j} \times \mathbf{i} = -\mathbf{k} & \mathbf{j} \times \mathbf{j} = 0 & \mathbf{j} \times \mathbf{k} = \mathbf{i} \\
\mathbf{k} \times \mathbf{i} = \mathbf{j} & \mathbf{k} \times \mathbf{j} = -\mathbf{i} & \mathbf{k} \times \mathbf{k} = 0
\end{array} \qquad (26)$$

Figure 11

Figure 11 shows a mnemonic device for placing the signs in (26). If in forming a cross product of two of the unit vectors, we proceed counterclockwise around the circle of Fig. 11, then the result is the third unit vector with a plus sign. If the direction is clockwise, then the cross product is the third unit vector with a minus sign.

Four theorems that are basic for the cross product now present themselves.

> **THEOREM 6.** *Let* **A** *and* **B** *be nonzero vectors. Then* **A** *and* **B** *are parallel if and only if* **A** $\times$ **B** $= 0$.

PROOF. This is obvious from equation (25) because if $|\mathbf{A}| \neq 0$ and $|\mathbf{B}| \neq 0$ then **A** $\times$ **B** $= 0$ if and only if $\sin \theta = 0$, so that $\theta = 0$ or π.

> **THEOREM 7.** *For any two vectors*

$$\boxed{\mathbf{A} \times \mathbf{B} = -(\mathbf{B} \times \mathbf{A}).} \qquad (27)$$

In other words a reversal of the order of multiplication introduces a negative sign. To prove this observe that in (25) all of the scalar factors $|\mathbf{A}|$, $|\mathbf{B}|$, and $\sin \theta$ are unaffected by the change in the order of the vectors $\mathbf{A}$ and $\mathbf{B}$ in the product. Further $\mathbf{e}$ is perpendicular to the plane of $\mathbf{A}$ and $\mathbf{B}$ in both of the products $\mathbf{A} \times \mathbf{B}$ and $\mathbf{B} \times \mathbf{A}$. But in the first case $\mathbf{e}$ points on one side of the plane, and in the second case it points in the opposite direction. Q.E.D.

THEOREM 8. *For any scalar c and any pair of vectors* $\mathbf{A}$ *and* $\mathbf{B}$

$$c(\mathbf{A} \times \mathbf{B}) = (c\mathbf{A}) \times \mathbf{B} = \mathbf{A} \times (c\mathbf{B}). \qquad (28)$$

PROOF. If $c = 0$, all of the products in (28) are the zero vector. If $c > 0$, then (28) is obvious. If $c < 0$ then $c(\mathbf{A} \times \mathbf{B})$ is a vector that is parallel to $\mathbf{A} \times \mathbf{B}$ but points in the opposite direction. On the other hand $c\mathbf{A}$ is parallel to $\mathbf{A}$ but also points in the opposite direction so $(c\mathbf{A}) \times \mathbf{B}$ has the opposite direction from that of $\mathbf{A} \times \mathbf{B}$ (see Fig. 12). Since the lengths of $c(\mathbf{A} \times \mathbf{B})$ and $(c\mathbf{A}) \times \mathbf{B}$ are equal, the vectors are equal. A similar argument shows that $c(\mathbf{A} \times \mathbf{B}) = \mathbf{A} \times (c\mathbf{B})$.

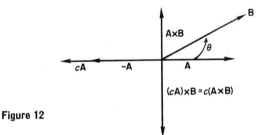

Figure 12

THEOREM 9. THE DISTRIBUTIVE LAW. *For any three vectors*

$$\mathbf{A} \times (\mathbf{B} + \mathbf{C}) = \mathbf{A} \times \mathbf{B} + \mathbf{A} \times \mathbf{C}. \qquad (29)$$

This is the hard nut to crack. Up to the present no really simple proof is known, and it is doubtful if there is one. We will give a reasonably simple proof in section 7, using some material developed in section 6. In the meantime let us see how this theorem is used.

Theorems 8 and 9 allow us to expand the cross product

$$\mathbf{A} \times \mathbf{B} = (a_1\mathbf{i} + a_2\mathbf{j} + a_3\mathbf{k}) \times (b_1\mathbf{i} + b_2\mathbf{j} + b_3\mathbf{k})$$

using the usual rules of algebra, except that Theorem 7 warns us that we must not change the order of the factors. Expansion gives

$$\mathbf{A} \times \mathbf{B} = a_1b_1\mathbf{i} \times \mathbf{i} + a_1b_2\mathbf{i} \times \mathbf{j} + a_1b_3\mathbf{i} \times \mathbf{k} +$$
$$a_2b_1\mathbf{j} \times \mathbf{i} + a_2b_2\mathbf{j} \times \mathbf{j} + a_2b_3\mathbf{j} \times \mathbf{k} +$$
$$a_3b_1\mathbf{k} \times \mathbf{i} + a_3b_2\mathbf{k} \times \mathbf{j} + a_3b_3\mathbf{k} \times \mathbf{k}.$$

Using (26) the terms on the main diagonal vanish and the others can be grouped in pairs giving

$$\mathbf{A} \times \mathbf{B} = (a_2b_3 - a_3b_2)\mathbf{i} + (a_3b_1 - a_1b_3)\mathbf{j} + (a_1b_2 - a_2b_1)\,\mathbf{k}. \qquad (30)$$

Equation (30) is not exactly easy to memorize, but fortunately we do not need to memorize it. If we are familiar with the expansions of third order determinants, and not afraid to use vectors as elements of a determinant, then it is easy to see that the expansion of the determinant

$$\begin{vmatrix} \mathbf{i} & \mathbf{j} & \mathbf{k} \\ a_1 & a_2 & a_3 \\ b_1 & b_2 & b_3 \end{vmatrix}$$

gives the right side of (30). Therefore (when Theorem 9 has been proved) we have

THEOREM 10. *If* $\mathbf{A} = a_1\mathbf{i} + a_2\mathbf{j} + a_3\mathbf{k}$ *and* $\mathbf{B} = b_1\mathbf{i} + b_2\mathbf{j} + b_3\mathbf{k}$ *then*

$$\mathbf{A} \times \mathbf{B} = \begin{vmatrix} \mathbf{i} & \mathbf{j} & \mathbf{k} \\ a_1 & a_2 & a_3 \\ b_1 & b_2 & b_3 \end{vmatrix} \qquad (31)$$

EXAMPLE 1. Find the cross product $\mathbf{A} \times \mathbf{B}$ where $\mathbf{A} = \mathbf{i} + 2\mathbf{j} - 3\mathbf{k}$ and $\mathbf{B} = 4\mathbf{i} - 5\mathbf{j} - 6\mathbf{k}$. Find $\sin \theta$ for these two vectors.

SOLUTION. By Theorem 10

$$\mathbf{A} \times \mathbf{B} = \begin{vmatrix} \mathbf{i} & \mathbf{j} & \mathbf{k} \\ 1 & 2 & -3 \\ 4 & -5 & -6 \end{vmatrix} = (-12 - 15)\mathbf{i} + (-12 + 6)\mathbf{j} + (-5 - 8)\mathbf{k}$$

$$= -27\mathbf{i} - 6\mathbf{j} - 13\mathbf{k}.$$

From the definition of the cross product, equation (25),

$$\sin \theta = \frac{|\mathbf{A} \times \mathbf{B}|}{|\mathbf{A}||\mathbf{B}|} = \frac{\sqrt{27^2 + 6^2 + 13^2}}{\sqrt{1^2 + 2^2 + 3^2}\,\sqrt{4^2 + 5^2 + 6^2}} = \frac{\sqrt{934}}{\sqrt{14}\,\sqrt{77}} = \frac{\sqrt{467}}{7\sqrt{11}}.$$

We can check this result by computing $\cos \theta$ from the dot product. Indeed

$$\cos \theta = \frac{\mathbf{A} \cdot \mathbf{B}}{|\mathbf{A}||\mathbf{B}|} = \frac{4 - 10 + 18}{\sqrt{14} \sqrt{77}} = \frac{12}{7\sqrt{2} \sqrt{11}} = \frac{6\sqrt{2}}{7\sqrt{11}}.$$

Hence

$$\sin^2 \theta + \cos^2 \theta = \frac{467}{49 \cdot 11} + \frac{72}{49 \cdot 11} = \frac{539}{539} = 1.$$

Observe that if $0 < \theta < \pi$, then $\sin \theta > 0$. Hence if we wish to determine whether θ is a first or second quadrant angle for two given vectors, the computation of $\sin \theta$ by the cross product is useless. For this purpose we should examine $\mathbf{A} \cdot \mathbf{B}$. Clearly if $0 \leqq \theta < \pi/2$, then $\mathbf{A} \cdot \mathbf{B} > 0$, and if $\pi/2 < \theta \leqq \pi$, then $\mathbf{A} \cdot \mathbf{B} < 0$.

EXERCISE 5

1. In problem 1 of Exercise 4, replace the dot by a cross and compute the cross products.

2. Use the cross product to find $\sin \theta$, where θ is the angle between the two vectors, for each pair given in problem 1 of Exercise 4. Check your answers by showing that they satisfy $\sin^2 \theta + \cos^2 \theta = 1$.

★3. Prove Theorems 6, 7, 8 and 9, using only the determinant expression given in Theorem 10 for $\mathbf{A} \times \mathbf{B}$. In other words, as an alternate approach we might take equation (31) as our *definition* of $\mathbf{A} \times \mathbf{B}$. Then we would want to prove the earlier theorems, using only the properties of determinants. Observe that with this definition, it becomes difficult to prove that $\mathbf{A} \times \mathbf{B} = |\mathbf{A}||\mathbf{B}|\sin \theta \, \mathbf{e}$.

4. Find a vector of unit length that is perpendicular to both $\mathbf{i} + \mathbf{j}$ and $\mathbf{j} + \mathbf{k}$.

5. Prove that $|\mathbf{B} \times \mathbf{C}|$ is the area of the parallelogram that has $\mathbf{B}$ and $\mathbf{C}$ as coterminal sides.

6. Use the cross product to find the area of the triangle OP_1P_2 in each of the following cases:

a. $P_1(5, 1, 0)$, $\quad P_2(2, 3, 0)$; $\qquad$ b. $P_1(4, 2, 0)$, $\quad P_2(-3, 7, 0)$;

c. $P_1(1, 2, 3)$, $\quad P_2(4, 5, 6)$; $\qquad$ d. $P_1(2, -1, 4)$, $\quad P_2(-3, 5, -7)$.

★7. Prove that the area of the plane triangle with vertices at $A(a_1, a_2)$, $B(b_1, b_2)$, and $C(c_1, c_2)$ is $|D|/2$ where

$$D = \begin{vmatrix} a_1 & a_2 & 1 \\ b_1 & b_2 & 1 \\ c_1 & c_2 & 1 \end{vmatrix}$$

Show that D is positive if the points A, B, and C are in counterclockwise order, and D is negative if A, B, and C are in clockwise order. When is $D = 0$?

8. Find a vector that is perpendicular to the plane through the points P_1, P_2, and P_3 for each of the following sets of points

a. $P_1(1, 3, 5)$, $\quad P_2(2, -1, 3)$, $\quad P_3(-3, 2, -6)$;

b. $P_1(2, 4, 6)$, $\quad P_2(-3, 1, -5)$, $\quad P_3(2, -6, 1)$.

6.   The triple scalar product of three vectors.   Given three vectors
A, B, and **C** we can form products with dots and crosses in a number
of ways thus: **A·B·C,   A × B × C,   A·B × C,** and **A × B·C.**

The first way is meaningless because **A·B** is a number, and hence
requires forming the dot product of the number **A·B** with a vector **C** and
this is impossible.

The second is somewhat complicated, and will not be considered further
in this book.   However it has the peculiar property that in general

$$(A \times B) \times C \neq A \times (B \times C).$$

It turns out that **A·B × C** and **A × B·C** are equal, and since this
product is a number it is called the *triple scalar product* of the three vectors.
Further it has a lovely geometric meaning which is presented in

> THEOREM 11.   *Let* **A, B,** *and* **C** *be a righthanded set of vectors
> (not coplanar).   Then* **A·B × C** *is the volume of the parallelo-
> piped that has* **A, B,** *and* **C** *as coterminal edges (see Fig. 13).*

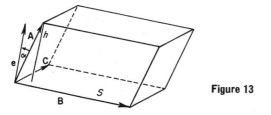

Figure 13

PROOF.   Let S denote the area of the parallelogram that has coterminal
edges **B** and **C,** and let h denote the height of the parallelopiped when this
parallelogram is regarded as the base.   Then from elementary geometry
$V = Sh$, where V denotes the volume of the parallelopiped.   From prob-
lem 5 of Exercise 5, $S = |B \times C|$.   Further **B × C** is a vector perpen-
dicular to the plane of **B** and **C** and lies on the same side with **A,** because
A, B, and **C** form a righthanded set.   Thus **B × C** $= S$**e** where **e** is the
unit vector shown in Fig. 13.   Further $A·e = |A||e| \cos \alpha = |A| \cos \alpha = h$.
Consequently

$$A·B \times C = A·(Se) = SA·e = Sh = V. \qquad \text{Q.E.D.}$$

It is obvious that if **A, B, C** form a lefthanded set then **A·B × C** $=
- V$, for in this case **B × C** points in the "wrong" direction and **A·B × C**
is negative.   Of course if **A, B, C** are coplanar, then the "box" is flat and
$V = 0$.

As a corollary to this theorem we have

> THEOREM 12.   *For any three vectors* **A, B, C**

$$\mathbf{A \cdot B \times C = B \cdot C \times A = C \cdot A \times B} \qquad (32)$$

and

$$\mathbf{A \cdot B \times C = A \times B \cdot C.} \qquad (33)$$

PROOF. Suppose first that **A, B, C** form a righthanded set. Then all three terms in (32) give the volume of the same parallelopiped, the first with **B, C** regarded as forming the base, the second with **C, A** regarded as forming the base, and the third with **A, B** regarded as forming the base. Hence they are all equal. We leave it for the student to supply the argument when **A, B, C** are coplaner or form a lefthanded set.

Since the dot product is commutative $\mathbf{C \cdot A \times B = A \times B \cdot C}$, and so the extreme terms in (32) give (33). Q.E.D.

Equation (32) states that any cyclic permutation of the letters **A, B, C** does not change the value of the triple scalar product.

Equation (33) states that we may put the dot and cross wherever we wish, as long as there is one multiplication symbol between each pair of vectors.

7. **The distributive law for the vector product.** We now prove Theorem 9. Let the vector **D** be defined by

$$\mathbf{D = A \times (B + C) - A \times B - A \times C} \qquad (34)$$

and let **V** be any vector. Dotting both sides of (34) with **V** gives

$$\begin{aligned}\mathbf{V \cdot D} &= \mathbf{V \cdot [A \times (B + C) - A \times B - A \times C]} \qquad (35)\\ &= \mathbf{V \cdot A \times (B + C) - V \cdot A \times B - V \cdot A \times C}\end{aligned}$$

by the distributive law for the dot product (Theorem 4). By Theorem 12 we can interchange the dot and cross. Then (35) gives

$$\mathbf{V \cdot D = V \times A \cdot (B + C) - V \times A \cdot B - V \times A \cdot C.} \qquad (36)$$

Using again the distributive law for the dot product, on the first term of (36) we find that

$$\mathbf{V \cdot D = V \times A \cdot B + V \times A \cdot C - V \times A \cdot B - V \times A \cdot C = 0.}$$

Thus for any vector **V** we have $\mathbf{V \cdot D} = 0$. In particular if we select for **V** the vector **D**, we find that $\mathbf{D \cdot D} = |\mathbf{D}|^2 = 0$. This is possible only if

D itself is the zero vector.   Consequently from (34)

$$\mathbf{A} \times (\mathbf{B} + \mathbf{C}) = \mathbf{A} \times \mathbf{B} + \mathbf{A} \times \mathbf{C}.$$

This completes the proof of Theorem 9.   Further Theorem 10 is now established.   The proof presented is due to Morgan Ward of the University of California at Los Angeles.

8.   **Computations with vector products.**   The dot and cross products are quite useful in solving problems in three-dimensional geometry.

EXAMPLE 1.   Find the distance from the point $A(1, 2, 3)$ to the line through the points $B(-1, 2, 1)$ and $C(4, 3, 2)$.

SOLUTION.   We pass a plane through the three points.   From the plane diagram shown in Fig. 14, it is clear that the distance s is given by

$$s = |\mathbf{BA}| \sin \theta.$$

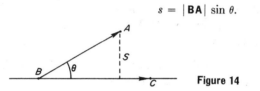

Figure 14

But $\mathbf{BA} \times \mathbf{BC} = |\mathbf{BA}||\mathbf{BC}| \sin \theta$ **e**.   Hence we can find s by taking the length of this vector, and dividing by the length of **BC**.   Thus

$$s = \frac{|\mathbf{BA} \times \mathbf{BC}|}{|\mathbf{BC}|}. \tag{37}$$

Carrying out these computations we have $\mathbf{BA} = 2\mathbf{i} + 0\mathbf{j} + 2\mathbf{k}$, $\mathbf{BC} = 5\mathbf{i} + \mathbf{j} + \mathbf{k}$,

$$\mathbf{BA} \times \mathbf{BC} = \begin{vmatrix} \mathbf{i} & \mathbf{j} & \mathbf{k} \\ 2 & 0 & 2 \\ 5 & 1 & 1 \end{vmatrix} = -2\mathbf{i} + 8\mathbf{j} + 2\mathbf{k},$$

$$s = \frac{|-2\mathbf{i} + 8\mathbf{j} + 2\mathbf{k}|}{|5\mathbf{i} + \mathbf{j} + \mathbf{k}|} = \frac{2\sqrt{1 + 16 + 1}}{\sqrt{25 + 1 + 1}} = \frac{2\sqrt{18}}{3\sqrt{3}} = \frac{2}{3}\sqrt{6}.$$

EXAMPLE 2.   Find the distance from the point $P(2, 2, 9)$ to the plane through the three points $A(2, 1, 3)$, $B(3, 3, 5)$, and $C(1, 3, 6)$.

SOLUTION.   As indicated in Fig. 15, the vectors **AB** and **AC** lie in the plane $\mathcal{P}$ through the three given points.   Hence $\mathbf{AB} \times \mathbf{AC}$ gives the direction of the unit vector **e** perpendicular to $\mathcal{P}$.   Thus

$$\mathbf{e} = \frac{\mathbf{AB} \times \mathbf{AC}}{|\mathbf{AB} \times \mathbf{AC}|}$$

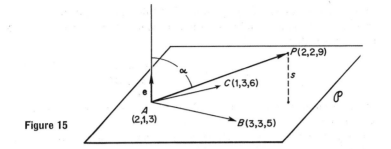

Figure 15

Then the distance s from P to the plane $\mathcal{P}$ is

$$s = |\mathbf{AP}|\cos \alpha = \mathbf{AP} \cdot \mathbf{e} = \frac{\mathbf{AP} \cdot \mathbf{AB} \times \mathbf{AC}}{|\mathbf{AB} \times \mathbf{AC}|}. \tag{38}$$

Carrying out the computations for the specific points given we have $\mathbf{AB} = \mathbf{i} + 2\mathbf{j} + 2\mathbf{k}$, $\mathbf{AC} = -\mathbf{i} + 2\mathbf{j} + 3\mathbf{k}$, $\mathbf{AP} = \mathbf{j} + 6\mathbf{k}$,

$$\mathbf{AB} \times \mathbf{AC} = \begin{vmatrix} \mathbf{i} & \mathbf{j} & \mathbf{k} \\ 1 & 2 & 2 \\ -1 & 2 & 3 \end{vmatrix} = 2\mathbf{i} - 5\mathbf{j} + 4\mathbf{k}$$

$$s = \frac{(\mathbf{j} + 6\mathbf{k}) \cdot (2\mathbf{i} - 5\mathbf{j} + 4\mathbf{k})}{|2\mathbf{i} - 5\mathbf{j} + 4\mathbf{k}|} = \frac{-5 + 24}{\sqrt{4 + 25 + 16}} = \frac{19}{3\sqrt{5}}.$$

EXAMPLE 3. Find the distance between the two lines l_1 and l_2 where l_1 goes through the points $A(1, -2, 1)$ and $B(4, 5, 6)$ and l_2 goes through $C(-3, -2, 1)$ and $D(1, 1, 4)$.

SOLUTION. We first observe that if $\mathbf{N} = \mathbf{AB} \times \mathbf{CD}$ then $\mathbf{N}$ is a vector that is simultaneously perpendicular to the two lines l_1 and l_2. Hence there is a pair of parallel planes $\mathcal{P}_1$ and $\mathcal{P}_2$ containing the lines l_1 and l_2 respectively,

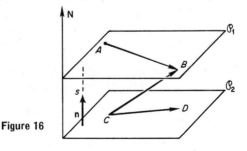

Figure 16

namely two planes each perpendicular to the vector $\mathbf{N}$. These planes are shown in Fig. 16. If we take any two points, one in each plane, and project the line segment joining them onto the common perpendicular, we obtain s, the distance between the two planes. But this is also the distance between the two lines. Thus if B and C are the two points chosen, and $\mathbf{n} = \mathbf{N}/|\mathbf{N}|$ is a unit normal, then

$$s = |\mathbf{CB} \cdot \mathbf{n}| = \left| \mathbf{CB} \cdot \frac{\mathbf{AB} \times \mathbf{CD}}{|\mathbf{AB} \times \mathbf{CD}|} \right|. \tag{39}$$

In this formula we could replace $\mathbf{CB}$ by $\mathbf{CA}$, or $\mathbf{DA}$, or $\mathbf{DB}$, and still obtain the same result.

Carrying out the computations for the specific points given we find that $\mathbf{AB} = 3\mathbf{i} + 7\mathbf{j} + 5\mathbf{k}$, $\mathbf{CD} = 4\mathbf{i} + 3\mathbf{j} + 3\mathbf{k}$, and

$$\mathbf{N} = \mathbf{AB} \times \mathbf{CD} = \begin{vmatrix} \mathbf{i} & \mathbf{j} & \mathbf{k} \\ 3 & 7 & 5 \\ 4 & 3 & 3 \end{vmatrix} = 6\mathbf{i} + 11\mathbf{j} - 19\mathbf{k}.$$

To obtain a unit normal we must divide by $|\mathbf{N}| = \sqrt{518}$. Finally $\mathbf{CB} = 7\mathbf{i} + 7\mathbf{j} + 5\mathbf{k}$ so

$$s = \frac{(7\mathbf{i} + 7\mathbf{j} + 5\mathbf{k}) \cdot (6\mathbf{i} + 11\mathbf{j} - 19\mathbf{k})}{\sqrt{518}} = \frac{42 + 77 - 95}{\sqrt{518}} = \frac{24}{\sqrt{518}}.$$

As a check we can use AD in place of CB. This gives

$$s = \left| \frac{(0\mathbf{i} + 3\mathbf{j} + 3\mathbf{k}) \cdot (6\mathbf{i} + 11\mathbf{j} - 19\mathbf{k})}{\sqrt{518}} \right| = \left| \frac{-24}{\sqrt{518}} \right| = \frac{24}{\sqrt{518}}.$$

EXERCISE 6

1. Find the distance from the point A to the line through the points B and C for each of the following sets of points.

   a. $A(1, 1, 7)$, $B(2, -1, 4)$, $C(3, 1, 6)$,
   b. $A(1, 2, 2)$, $B(-1, 3, 5)$, $C(1, 6, 11)$,
   c. $A(3, 3, 4)$, $B(0, 0, 0)$, $C(6, 6, 7)$,
   d. $A(2, 6, 5)$, $B(3, 1, 11)$, $C(5, -9, 23)$.

2. Find the distance from the point P to the plane through the points A, B, and C for each of the following sets of points.

   a. $P(0, 0, 1)$, $A(-1, -2, -3)$, $B(0, 5, 1)$, $C(-2, 1, 0)$,
   b. $P(2, 1, 7)$, $A(3, -1, 6)$, $B(1, 5, 5)$, $C(4, -6, 4)$,
   c. $P(3, 12, 17)$, $A(2, -1, 5)$, $B(4, -2, 2)$, $C(1, 4, 11)$,
   d. $P(0, 0, -1)$, $A(-1, -1, 0)$, $B(0, -2, 0)$, $C(0, 0, 1)$.

3. Let $\mathbf{A} = a_1\mathbf{i} + a_2\mathbf{j} + a_3\mathbf{k}$, $\mathbf{B} = b_1\mathbf{i} + b_2\mathbf{j} + b_3\mathbf{k}$ and $\mathbf{C} = c_1\mathbf{i} + c_2\mathbf{j} + c_3\mathbf{k}$. Prove that

$$\mathbf{A \cdot B \times C} = \begin{vmatrix} a_1 & a_2 & a_3 \\ b_1 & b_2 & b_3 \\ c_1 & c_2 & c_3 \end{vmatrix}$$

Hint: Use Theorem 10.

★**4.** Using the result of problem 3, interpret equation (32) of Theorem 12, as a theorem on determinants.

5. Find the volume of the parallelopipeds if one vertex is at the origin and three of the edges are the vectors **A**, **B**, and **C** for each of the following sets.

a. $\mathbf{A} = \mathbf{i} + \mathbf{j}$, $\mathbf{B} = -2\mathbf{i} + 3\mathbf{j}$, $\mathbf{C} = \mathbf{i} + \mathbf{j} + \mathbf{k}$,
b. $\mathbf{A} = \mathbf{i} - \mathbf{j} - \mathbf{k}$, $\mathbf{B} = \mathbf{i} + 3\mathbf{j} + \mathbf{k}$, $\mathbf{C} = 2\mathbf{i} + 3\mathbf{j} + 5\mathbf{k}$,
c. $\mathbf{A} = 2\mathbf{i} + \mathbf{j} + \mathbf{k}$, $\mathbf{B} = -\mathbf{i} + 4\mathbf{j} + 2\mathbf{k}$, $\mathbf{C} = 7\mathbf{i} - 10\mathbf{j} - 4\mathbf{k}$,
d. $\mathbf{A} = 2\mathbf{i} - \mathbf{j} + \mathbf{k}$, $\mathbf{B} = \mathbf{i} + 2\mathbf{j} + 3\mathbf{k}$, $\mathbf{C} = \mathbf{i} + \mathbf{j} - 2\mathbf{k}$.

6. Find the distance between the line through the points A and B and the line through the points C and D, for each of the following sets of points.

a. $A(1, 0, 0)$, $B(0, 1, 1)$, $C(-1, 0, 0)$, $D(0, -1, 1)$,
b. $A(1, 1, 0)$, $B(-2, 3, 1)$, $C(1, -1, 3)$, $D(0, 0, 0)$,
c. $A(-2, 3, -1)$, $B(2, 4, 4)$, $C(1, 2, 1)$, $D(-1, 5, 2)$,
d. $A(-2, 3, -1)$, $B(2, 4, 4)$, $C(-1, 0, 3)$, $D(-3, 3, 4)$.

7. Find the distance between the two lines

$$\frac{x-1}{2} = \frac{y-2}{3} = \frac{z+1}{-1}$$

and

$$\frac{x+1}{3} = \frac{y-1}{2} = \frac{z-2}{1}.$$

8. Find the distance of the origin from each of the lines in problem 7.

9. Under what circumstances may formula (39) of Example 3 fail?

10. If A, B, and C are three noncollinear points and **A**, **B**, and **C** are their position vectors prove that $\mathbf{A \times B + B \times C + C \times A}$ is a vector perpendicular to the plane of the triangle ABC.

11. Let A, B, C, and D be the vertices of a proper tetrahedron (the points are not coplanar). On each face of the tetrahedron erect a vector normal to the face, pointing outward from the tetrahedron, and having length equal to the area of the face. Prove that the sum of these four vectors is zero.

9. Equations of planes. Let $\mathcal{P}$ be the plane through the three points P_0, P_1, and P_2 where P_0 has the coordinates (x_0, y_0, z_0). For simplicity let $\mathbf{P_0P_1} = a_1\mathbf{i} + a_2\mathbf{j} + a_3\mathbf{k}$ and $\mathbf{P_0P_2} = b_1\mathbf{i} + b_2\mathbf{j} + b_3\mathbf{k}$. To find an equation for this plane we first observe that the vector

$$\mathbf{N} = \mathbf{P_0P_1 \times P_0P_2} \tag{40}$$

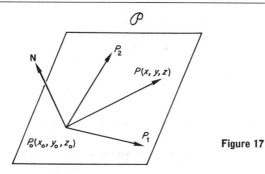

Figure 17

is normal to the plane (see Fig. 17). Then the point $P(x, y, z)$ is on the plane if and only if $\mathbf{P_0P}$ is perpendicular to $\mathbf{N}$ (or is zero). Hence P is on the plane if and only if

$$\mathbf{P_0P \cdot N} = 0 \tag{41}$$

and this is a vector equation of the plane $\mathcal{P}$. To turn this into a scalar equation, that is, an equation in the usual form, we use the result of problem 3 of Exercise 6. Since $\mathbf{P_0P} = (x - x_0)\mathbf{i} + (y - y_0)\mathbf{j} + (z - z_0)\mathbf{k}$, equations (40) and (41) give

$$\begin{vmatrix} x - x_0 & y - y_0 & z - z_0 \\ a_1 & a_2 & a_3 \\ b_1 & b_2 & b_3 \end{vmatrix} = 0. \tag{42}$$

On expanding this determinant we see that the plane has an equation of the form

$$Ax + By + Cz = D. \tag{43}$$

Of course this equation is not unique because we can always multiply through by any nonzero constant. Nevertheless we shall refer to (43) occasionally as *the* equation of the plane.

THEOREM 12. *Any plane has an equation of the form (43). Conversely, if the numbers A, B, and C are not all zero, equation (43) is the equation of some plane. Finally the vector $\mathbf{N} = A\mathbf{i} + B\mathbf{j} + C\mathbf{k}$ is always perpendicular to the plane (43).*

We have already proved the first part of this theorem. To prove the converse suppose that we are given an equation of the form (43). If not all the coefficients are zero we can always find one point $P_0(x_0, y_0, z_0)$ whose coordinates satisfy (43), i.e.,

$$Ax_0 + By_0 + Cz_0 = D. \tag{44}$$

Suppose that $P(x, y, z)$ is any point whose coordinates satisfy equation (43). Subtracting equation (44) from equation (43) gives

$$A(x - x_0) + B(y - y_0) + C(z - z_0) = 0$$

or

$$[A\mathbf{i} + B\mathbf{j} + C\mathbf{k}] \cdot [(x - x_0)\mathbf{i} + (y - y_0)\mathbf{j} + (z - z_0)\mathbf{k}] = 0$$

or in vector form

$$\mathbf{N} \cdot \mathbf{P_0 P} = 0. \tag{45}$$

This shows that $\mathbf{P_0 P}$ is either the zero vector or is perpendicular to the vector $\mathbf{N}$. Hence every point P whose coordinates satisfy (43) lies in the plane through P_0 perpendicular to $\mathbf{N}$. Further each such point satisfies (45) and hence (43). Consequently (43) is the equation of that plane.

Q.E.D.

EXAMPLE 1. Find the equation of the plane through $P_0(1, 2, 2)$, $P_1(2, -1, 1)$, and $P_2(-1, 3, 0)$.

SOLUTION. $\mathbf{P_0 P_1} = \mathbf{i} - 3\mathbf{j} - \mathbf{k}$, $\mathbf{P_0 P_2} = -2\mathbf{i} + \mathbf{j} - 2\mathbf{k}$. Then (42) gives

$$\begin{vmatrix} x - 1 & y - 2 & z - 2 \\ 1 & -3 & -1 \\ -2 & 1 & -2 \end{vmatrix} = 0$$

$$7(x - 1) + 4(y - 2) - 5(z - 2) = 0$$
$$7x + 4y - 5z = 5. \tag{43e}$$

The vector $7\mathbf{i} + 4\mathbf{j} - 5\mathbf{k}$ is normal to this plane. The student should check that each of the given points satisfies equation (43e).

EXAMPLE 2. Find the equation of a line through the point $(3, -1, 2)$ that is perpendicular to the plane $x - 2y + 7z = 28$.

SOLUTION. The vector $\mathbf{i} - 2\mathbf{j} + 7\mathbf{k}$ is perpendicular to the given plane, and hence gives the direction of the line. Therefore from equation (15), we have

$$\frac{x - 3}{1} = \frac{y + 1}{-2} = \frac{z - 2}{7}$$

as the equation of the line. In parametric form we have

$$x = 3 + t, \quad y = -1 - 2t, \quad z = 2 + 7t.$$

EXAMPLE 3. Prove that if $P(x, y, z)$ is any point and d is the distance of that point from the plane $Ax + By + Cz = D$, then

$$d = \frac{|Ax + By + Cz - D|}{\sqrt{A^2 + B^2 + C^2}}.$$ (46)

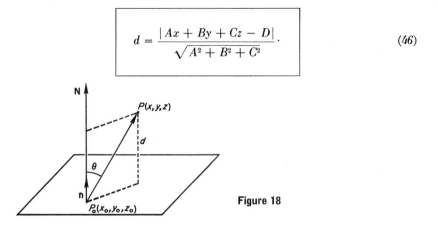

Figure 18

SOLUTION. If **n** is a unit normal to the plane, then it is obvious from Fig. 18 that

$$d = |\mathbf{P_0P}|\cos\theta = \mathbf{P_0P \cdot n}$$

if $\mathbf{P_0P}$ and **n** lie on the same side of the plane. If the plane separates these vectors then $|\mathbf{P_0P}|\cos\theta$ is negative. But in any case $|\mathbf{P_0P}|\cos\theta = \mathbf{n \cdot P_0P}$ and $d = |\mathbf{n \cdot P_0P}|$. Since $\mathbf{N} = A\mathbf{i} + B\mathbf{j} + C\mathbf{k}$ is normal to the plane we have

$$d = \left| \frac{[A\mathbf{i} + B\mathbf{j} + C\mathbf{k}] \cdot [(x - x_0)\mathbf{i} + (y - y_0)\mathbf{j} + (z - z_0)\mathbf{k}]}{\sqrt{A^2 + B^2 + C^2}} \right|,$$

$$d = \frac{|A(x-x_0)+B(y-y_0)+C(z-z_0)|}{\sqrt{A^2 + B^2 + C^2}} = \frac{|Ax+By+Cz-Ax_0-By_0-Cz_0|}{\sqrt{A^2 + B^2 + C^2}}.$$ (47)

But $P_0(x_0, y_0, z_0)$ lies in the plane so that $Ax_0 + By_0 + Cz_0 = D$. Using this in (47) gives (46).

EXERCISE 7

1. Find the equation of the plane through P_0, P_1, and P_2 for each of the following sets of points.

a.	$P_0(2, 1, 6)$,	$P_1(5, -2, 0)$,	$P_2(4, -5, -2)$,
b.	$P_0(1, 2, 17)$,	$P_1(-1, -2, 3)$,	$P_2(-4, 2, 2)$,
c.	$P_0(2, -2, 2)$,	$P_1(1, -8, 6)$,	$P_2(4, 3, -1)$,
d.	$P_0(a, 0, 0)$,	$P_1(0, b, 0)$,	$P_2(0, 0, c)$,
e.	$P_0(a, b, 0)$,	$P_1(0, b, c)$,	$P_2(a, 0, c)$.

2. Find the equation of the plane through $(2, -3, 5)$ parallel to the plane $3x + 5y - 7z = 11$.

3. Find the distance from the origin to each of the planes in problem 1.

4. Find the distance of the point $(1, -2, 3)$ from each of the first three planes in problem 1.

5. Prove that the planes $Ax + By + Cz = D_1$ and $Ax + By + Cz = D_2$ are parallel.

6. Prove that the distance between the two planes of problem 5 is $|D_1 - D_2|/\sqrt{A^2 + B^2 + C^2}$.

7. Find the distance between the two planes $2x - 3y - 6z = 5$ and $4x - 6y - 12z = -18$.

8. Find the equation of the line through $P(-9, 4, 3)$ perpendicular to the plane $2x + 6y + 9z = 0$. Find the point Q where this line intersects the plane.

9. For the points of problem 8, find the distance $|PQ|$ in two ways (a) directly from the coordinates and (b) by the method of example 3.

10. Find an equation for the straight line through $(3, -1, 6)$ and parallel to both of the planes $x - 2y + z = 2$ and $2x + y - 3z = 5$.

11. Find an equation for the line of intersection for each of the following pairs of planes

    a. $3x + 4y - z = 10,$ $2x + y + z = 0,$
    b. $x + 5y + 3z = 14,$ $x + y - 2z = 4,$
    c. $2x + 3y + 5z = 21,$ $3x - 2y + z = 12.$

12. Find an equation for the plane through A and perpendicular to the line through B and C for each of the following sets of points

    a. $A(0, 0, 0),$ $B(1, 2, 3),$ $C(3, 2, 1),$
    b. $A(1, 5, 9),$ $B(2, 3, -4),$ $C(5, 1, -1),$
    c. $A(-3, -7, 11),$ $B(7, 5, 3),$ $C(8, -4, 2).$

13. Prove that if $P(x, y)$ is any point in the plane and d is the distance of P from the line $ax + by = c$ then

$$d = \frac{|ax + by - c|}{\sqrt{a^2 + b^2}}.$$

14. Let L be the line of intersection of two planes $\mathcal{P}_1$ and $\mathcal{P}_2$. Let P be a point on L and let l_1 and l_2 be lines in $\mathcal{P}_1$ and $\mathcal{P}_2$ respectively each perpendicular to L at P. Then θ, the least positive angle between l_1 and l_2, is called the angle between

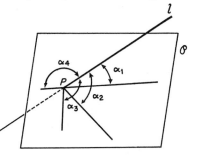

Figure 19 (For Problem 15)

the two planes.   Show that $\cos \theta$ can be found by considering the vectors normal to the planes.   Use your result to compute $\cos \theta$ for each pair of planes in problem 11.

15.   Let the line l intersect the plane $\mathcal{P}$ at a point P.   If the line l is not normal to the plane, then different lines in $\mathcal{P}$ through P may make different angles with l. (See Fig. 19.)   By definition the angle θ between l and $\mathcal{P}$ is the smallest of these various angles.   Find $\sin \theta$ for the angle between the line and the plane in each of the following:

a. $\dfrac{x-5}{2} = \dfrac{y+17}{-3} = \dfrac{z-\ln 15}{6},$ $x + 2y + 2z = e^2,$

b. $\dfrac{x+\sqrt{2}}{6} = \dfrac{y+\sqrt{3}}{7} = \dfrac{z+\sqrt{5}}{-6},$ $2x - 4y + 4z = \sqrt{11},$

c. $\dfrac{x}{5} = \dfrac{y}{6} = \dfrac{z}{2},$ $20x - 11y - 17z = 1,$

d. $x - 1 = y - 2 = z - 3,$ $5x + 5y + 5z = 1.$

16.   A unit cube lies in the first octant with three edges along the coordinate axes.   Find the equation of a plane that intersects the surface of this cube in a regular hexagon.

10.   Differentiation of vectors.

Just as we can have vector functions where the vector $\mathbf{R}(t)$ lies in the xy-plane, so we can also consider vector functions in three-dimensional space.   In this case $\mathbf{R} = \mathbf{R}(t)$ denotes a vector function, in which to every real value of t (perhaps t is restricted to some interval) there corresponds a three dimensional vector $\mathbf{R}$. Such a function arises quite naturally if we consider some particle moving in space along a curve, and $\mathbf{R}$ is the vector from the origin to this particle. Then the symbol t would denote the time at which the particle had a given location and $\mathbf{R}(t)$ would be the position vector of the particle at that time. Of course it is not necessary to regard t as representing time, nor $\mathbf{R}(t)$ as a position vector, but in most cases it is convenient to make these interpretations.

Most of the material in section 4 of Chapter 10 is valid in three-dimensional space, and the student would do well to review that section at this time.   The following three-dimensional generalizations will then appear to be obvious.

The vector function $\mathbf{R}(t)$ can always be written in terms of its components as

$$\mathbf{R}(t) = f(t)\mathbf{i} + g(t)\mathbf{j} + h(t)\mathbf{k}. \tag{48}$$

If (x, y, z) denotes the coordinates of P, the end point of the position vector $\mathbf{R}$, then (48) represents three scalar equations,

$$x = f(t), \qquad y = g(t), \qquad z = h(t), \tag{49}$$

the parametric equations of the curve described by P. If the scalar functions in (49) are differentiable then so is the vector function $R(t)$ and indeed

$$\mathbf{R}'(t) = \frac{d\mathbf{R}(t)}{dt} = \frac{df}{dt}\mathbf{i} + \frac{dg}{dt}\mathbf{j} + \frac{dh}{dt}\mathbf{k}. \tag{50}$$

This is frequently abbreviated by writing

$$\frac{d\mathbf{R}}{dt} = \frac{dx}{dt}\mathbf{i} + \frac{dy}{dt}\mathbf{j} + \frac{dz}{dt}\mathbf{k}. \tag{51}$$

For example if

$$\mathbf{R} = \sin t \cos t\mathbf{i} + \cos^2 t\mathbf{j} + \sin t\mathbf{k} \tag{52}$$

then

$$\frac{d\mathbf{R}}{dt} = (\cos^2 t - \sin^2 t)\mathbf{i} - 2\sin t \cos t\mathbf{j} + \cos t\mathbf{k}.$$

The curve defined by the position vector in (52) lies on the surface of a sphere of radius 1, because for this vector

$$\begin{aligned}|\mathbf{R}|^2 = x^2 + y^2 + z^2 &= (\sin t \cos t)^2 + (\cos^2 t)^2 + \sin^2 t \\ &= \cos^2 t\,(\sin^2 t + \cos^2 t) + \sin^2 t \\ &= \cos^2 t + \sin^2 t = 1.\end{aligned}$$

If in (50), $\mathbf{R}'(t) \neq \mathbf{0}$ then $\mathbf{R}'(t)$ is a vector tangent to the curve. In fact $\mathbf{R}'(t)$ is just the velocity of the moving particle and $|\mathbf{R}'(t)|$ is its speed. Similarly the acceleration of the particle is just $\mathbf{R}''(t)$. For example if a particle moves so that (52) is the position vector, then

$$\mathbf{V}(t) = (\cos^2 t - \sin^2 t)\mathbf{i} - 2\sin t \cos t\mathbf{j} + \cos t\mathbf{k} = \cos 2t\mathbf{i} - \sin 2t\mathbf{j} + \cos t\mathbf{k},$$
$$\mathbf{A}(t) = -2\sin 2t\mathbf{i} - 2\cos 2t\mathbf{j} - \sin t\mathbf{k},$$

give the velocity and acceleration respectively for the particle.

Whenever $\mathbf{R}'(t)$ is not zero, we can obtain a unit tangent vector $\mathbf{T}$, by dividing by $|\mathbf{R}'(t)|$. Thus

$$\mathbf{T} = \frac{\dfrac{dx}{dt}\mathbf{i} + \dfrac{dy}{dt}\mathbf{j} + \dfrac{dz}{dt}\mathbf{k}}{\sqrt{\left(\dfrac{dx}{dt}\right)^2 + \left(\dfrac{dy}{dt}\right)^2 + \left(\dfrac{dz}{dt}\right)^2}} \tag{53}$$

and if α, β, γ denote the directions angles for $\mathbf{T}$, then

$$\cos\alpha = \frac{\dfrac{dx}{dt}}{\sqrt{\left(\dfrac{dx}{dt}\right)^2 + \left(\dfrac{dy}{dt}\right)^2 + \left(\dfrac{dz}{dt}\right)^2}},$$

$$\cos \beta = \frac{\dfrac{dy}{dt}}{\sqrt{\left(\dfrac{dx}{dt}\right)^2 + \left(\dfrac{dy}{dt}\right)^2 + \left(\dfrac{dz}{dt}\right)^2}},$$

$$\cos \gamma = \frac{\dfrac{dz}{dt}}{\sqrt{\left(\dfrac{dx}{dt}\right)^2 + \left(\dfrac{dy}{dt}\right)^2 + \left(\dfrac{dz}{dt}\right)^2}}.$$

EXAMPLE 1.   For the curve defined by (52), show that the tangent vector is always perpendicular to the position vector.

SOLUTION.   Since neither $\mathbf{R}$ nor $\mathbf{V}$ is zero it suffices to show that $\mathbf{R} \cdot \mathbf{V} = 0$. Clearly

$$
\begin{aligned}
\mathbf{R} \cdot \mathbf{V} &= [\sin t \cos t\mathbf{i} + \cos^2 t\mathbf{j} + \sin t\mathbf{k}] \cdot [(\cos^2 t - \sin^2 t)\mathbf{i} - 2 \sin t \cos t\mathbf{j} + \cos t\mathbf{k}] \\
&= \sin t \cos^3 t - \sin^3 t \cos t - 2 \sin t \cos^3 t + \sin t \cos t \\
&= \sin t \cos t\,(-\sin^2 t - \cos^2 t) + \sin t \cos t = 0. \qquad\qquad \text{Q.E.D.}
\end{aligned}
$$

The basic formulas for the differentiation of vector functions are covered in

THEOREM 13.   *If $\mathbf{U}(t)$ and $\mathbf{V}(t)$ are differentiable vector functions and $f(t)$ is a differentiable scalar function then,*

$$\frac{d}{dt}(\mathbf{U} + \mathbf{V}) = \frac{d\mathbf{U}}{dt} + \frac{d\mathbf{V}}{dt}, \tag{54}$$

$$\frac{d}{dt}f\mathbf{V} = f\frac{d\mathbf{V}}{dt} + \frac{df}{dt}\mathbf{V}, \tag{55}$$

$$\frac{d}{dt}\mathbf{U} \cdot \mathbf{V} = \mathbf{U} \cdot \frac{d\mathbf{V}}{dt} + \frac{d\mathbf{U}}{dt} \cdot \mathbf{V}, \tag{56}$$

and

$$\frac{d}{dt}\mathbf{U} \times \mathbf{V} = \mathbf{U} \times \frac{d\mathbf{V}}{dt} + \frac{d\mathbf{U}}{dt} \times \mathbf{V}. \tag{57}$$

The proof of (54) is sufficiently simple, so we omit it.   The other three formulas all have the form of products, although the type of multiplication is different in each case.   Since the method of proof is exactly the same in each case we will give the proof only for (57).

Let $\mathbf{W} = \mathbf{U} \times \mathbf{V}$ and suppose that for a certain increment Δt, in the variable t, the vector functions $\mathbf{U}$, $\mathbf{V}$, and $\mathbf{W}$ change by amounts $\Delta\mathbf{U}$, $\Delta\mathbf{V}$, and $\Delta\mathbf{W}$ respectively.   Then from the definition of $\Delta\mathbf{W}$ we have

$$\mathbf{W} + \Delta\mathbf{W} = (\mathbf{U} + \Delta\mathbf{U}) \times (\mathbf{V} + \Delta\mathbf{V})$$
$$= \mathbf{U} \times \mathbf{V} + \mathbf{U} \times \Delta\mathbf{V} + \Delta\mathbf{U} \times \mathbf{V} + \Delta\mathbf{U} \times \Delta\mathbf{V}.$$

Subtracting $\mathbf{W} = \mathbf{U} \times \mathbf{V}$ from both sides and then dividing by Δt yields

$$\frac{\Delta\mathbf{W}}{\Delta t} = \mathbf{U} \times \frac{\Delta\mathbf{V}}{\Delta t} + \frac{\Delta\mathbf{U}}{\Delta t} \times \mathbf{V} + \frac{\Delta\mathbf{U}}{\Delta t} \times \Delta\mathbf{V}. \tag{58}$$

If we let $\Delta t \rightarrow 0$ then $\Delta\mathbf{V} \rightarrow 0$, and the last term in (58) vanishes.   The other three terms obviously give (57).

To obtain the proof of (56) just replace the crosses by dots in the above proof.   To obtain (55) just suppress the crosses.   Q.E.D.

Because the dot product of two vectors is commutative we could reverse the order of the factors in the last term of (56) and write

$$\frac{d}{dt}\mathbf{U} \cdot \mathbf{V} = \mathbf{U} \cdot \frac{d\mathbf{V}}{dt} + \mathbf{V} \cdot \frac{d\mathbf{U}}{dt}.$$

But in (57) such a reversal will lead to an error, unless a minus sign were also introduced.   In deference to (57) it is customary to preserve the order of the factors in (55) and (56).

EXAMPLE 2.   Let $f(t) = t^2$, $\mathbf{U}(t) = t\mathbf{i} + t^2\mathbf{j} + 2t\mathbf{k}$, $\mathbf{V}(t) = (1 + t^2)\mathbf{i} + (2 - t)\mathbf{j} + 3\mathbf{k}$.   With these functions compute the derivative with respect to t of $f\mathbf{V}$, $\mathbf{U} \cdot \mathbf{V}$, and $\mathbf{U} \times \mathbf{V}$.

SOLUTION.   Direct computation for $f\mathbf{V}$ gives

$$\frac{d}{dt}f\mathbf{V} = \frac{d}{dt}[(t^2 + t^4)\mathbf{i} + (2t^2 - t^3)\mathbf{j} + 3t^2\mathbf{k}]$$
$$= (2t + 4t^3)\mathbf{i} + (4t - 3t^2)\mathbf{j} + 6t\mathbf{k}.$$

If we use the right side of (55) for the same computation we find

$$f\frac{d\mathbf{V}}{dt} + \frac{df}{dt}\mathbf{V} = t^2[2t\mathbf{i} - \mathbf{j} + 0\mathbf{k}] + 2t[(1 + t^2)\mathbf{i} + (2 - t)\mathbf{j} + 3\mathbf{k}]$$
$$= (2t^3 + 2t + 2t^3)\mathbf{i} + (-t^2 + 4t - 2t^2)\mathbf{j} + 6t\mathbf{k},$$

and this agrees with the result obtained from the first computation, just as the theorem tells us it should.

Similarly direct computation gives

$$\frac{d}{dt} \mathbf{U} \cdot \mathbf{V} = \frac{d}{dt} [t + t^3 + 2t^2 - t^3 + 6t] = \frac{d}{dt} [7t + 2t^2] = 7 + 4t.$$

If we use the right side of (56) for the same computation we find

$$\mathbf{U} \cdot \frac{d\mathbf{V}}{dt} + \frac{d\mathbf{U}}{dt} \cdot \mathbf{V} = [t\mathbf{i} + t^2\mathbf{j} + 2t\mathbf{k}] \cdot [2t\mathbf{i} - \mathbf{j} + 0\mathbf{k}]$$
$$+ [\mathbf{i} + 2t\mathbf{j} + 2\mathbf{k}] \cdot [(1 + t^2)\mathbf{i} + (2 - t)\mathbf{j} + 3\mathbf{k}]$$
$$= 2t^2 - t^2 + 0 + 1 + t^2 + 4t - 2t^2 + 6 = 7 + 4t.$$

We leave it for the student to compute $\frac{d}{dt} \mathbf{U} \times \mathbf{V}$ in two different ways and show that both ways give

$$(10t - 4)\mathbf{i} + (6t^2 - 1)\mathbf{j} + (2 - 4t - 4t^3)\mathbf{k}.$$

EXAMPLE 3. Prove that if the length of the vector function $\mathbf{R}(t)$ is a constant, then $\mathbf{R}$ and $d\mathbf{R}/dt$ are perpendicular whenever neither of the vectors is zero.

SOLUTION. By hypothesis

$$\mathbf{R} \cdot \mathbf{R} = |\mathbf{R}|^2 = \text{constant}.$$

Then differentiating with respect to t, and using (56)

$$\mathbf{R} \cdot \frac{d\mathbf{R}}{dt} + \frac{d\mathbf{R}}{dt} \cdot \mathbf{R} = 0$$

Consequently $2\mathbf{R} \cdot \frac{d\mathbf{R}}{dt} = 0$ and the two vectors are perpendicular.

EXERCISE 8

In problems 1 through 6, $\mathbf{R}$ is the position vector for a moving particle, and t denotes time. Find the velocity and acceleration.

1. $\mathbf{R} = a \sin 5t\mathbf{i} + a \cos 5t\mathbf{j} + 3t\mathbf{k}.$
2. $\mathbf{R} = a \sin t\mathbf{i} + a \cos t\mathbf{j} + 2 \sin 2t\mathbf{k}.$
3. $\mathbf{R} = (1 + 3t)\mathbf{i} + (2 - 5t)\mathbf{j} + (7 - t)\mathbf{k}.$
4. $\mathbf{R} = t\mathbf{i} + t^2\mathbf{j} + t^3\mathbf{k}.$
5. $\mathbf{R} = (t^2 - 1)\mathbf{i} + (t^3 - 3t^2)\mathbf{j} + 5t\mathbf{k}.$
6. $\mathbf{R} = (1 - te^{-t})\mathbf{i} + (t^{-1} + 5)\mathbf{j} + t^{-1}\ln t\mathbf{k}.$

7. For the motion of problem 1 prove (a) that $\mathbf{A}$ and $\mathbf{V}$ have constant length, (b) $\mathbf{A}$ and $\mathbf{V}$ are perpendicular, and (c) $\mathbf{A}$ is always parallel to the xy-plane.

★8. In problem 3 the particle moves on a line and the acceleration vector is zero. Prove that whenever the acceleration vector is constantly zero, then the motion is along a line.

9. For the motion of problem 4, show that if $t \neq 0$ no two of the vectors **R**, **V**, and **A** are ever perpendicular.

10. For the motion of problem 5, find where the particle is when the velocity vector is parallel to the xz-plane.

11. As $t \to \infty$, for the motion of problem 6, what is the limiting position of the particle? What is the limiting velocity and acceleration vector?

★★12. Suppose that for some motion, the particle tends to a limiting position as $t \to \infty$. Is it necessary for either the velocity vector or the acceleration vector to approach zero?

★13. Suppose that for a certain motion we always have $\mathbf{R} \cdot \mathbf{V} = 0$. Prove that the particle must at all times lie on the surface of some sphere.

★14. At a certain instant one airplane is 1 mile directly above another airplane. Both are flying level, the first going due north at 120 mi/hr and the second going due west at twice the speed. Find the rate at which the distance between them is changing 2 minutes later.

★15. If in problem 14 one airplane is 2 miles above the other, and they are traveling as before but with speeds of 100 mi/hr and 110 mi/hr respectively, find the rate at which they are separating 6 minutes later.

11. Space curves. Any curve in space can be described by giving parametric equations

$$x = f(t), \qquad y = g(t), \qquad z = h(t) \tag{59}$$

for the coordinates (x, y, z) of a point P on the curve. The same curve is described by writing the equation for the position vector to the point on the curve

$$\mathbf{R} = \mathbf{R}(t) = f(t)\mathbf{i} + g(t)\mathbf{j} + h(t)\mathbf{k}. \tag{60}$$

A number of results follow immediately from this vector equation for the curve. The proofs are completely similar to those given in the case of a plane curve in Chapter 10, so it will be sufficient to state the facts.

If $\mathbf{R}'(t)$ is not zero, it is a vector tangent to the curve, and pointing in the direction of increase of t on the curve. If the arc length s is taken as the parameter then

$$\frac{d\mathbf{R}}{ds} = \mathbf{T}$$

a unit vector. Using the chain rule for differentiation we have

$$\frac{d\mathbf{R}}{dt} = \frac{d\mathbf{R}}{ds}\frac{ds}{dt} = \mathbf{T}\frac{ds}{dt}.$$

Taking the dot product of each side with itself we have

$$\frac{d\mathbf{R}}{dt} \cdot \frac{d\mathbf{R}}{dt} = \mathbf{T}\cdot\mathbf{T}\left(\frac{ds}{dt}\right)^2 = \left(\frac{ds}{dt}\right)^2 \tag{61}$$

since **T** is a unit vector. Consequently, using (60) and (61) we obtain

$$\left(\frac{ds}{dt}\right)^2 = \left(\frac{dx}{dt}\right)^2 + \left(\frac{dy}{dt}\right)^2 + \left(\frac{dz}{dt}\right)^2 = f'(t)^2 + g'(t)^2 + h'(t)^2,$$

and if s and t increase together

$$\frac{ds}{dt} = \sqrt{f'(t)^2 + g'(t)^2 + h'(t)^2}. \qquad (62)$$

If the position vector **R** describes a plane curve, then (Theorem 17, Chapter 10)

$$\frac{d\mathbf{T}}{ds} = \kappa\mathbf{N} \qquad (63)$$

where κ is the curvature, and **N** is a unit vector perpendicular to **T**. For space curves we take (63) as the definition of κ, and **N**. In this definition we require that $\kappa \geqq 0$, and that **N** be a unit vector. Then (63) yields the following formula for the curvature of a space curve,

$$\kappa = \sqrt{\frac{d\mathbf{T}}{ds} \cdot \frac{d\mathbf{T}}{ds}}. \qquad (64)$$

Since **T** is a unit vector, $\mathbf{T}\cdot\mathbf{T} = 1$, and on differentiating with respect to s we have

$$0 = \mathbf{T} \cdot \frac{d\mathbf{T}}{ds} + \frac{d\mathbf{T}}{ds} \cdot \mathbf{T} = 2\mathbf{T} \cdot \frac{d\mathbf{T}}{ds} = 2\kappa\mathbf{T}\cdot\mathbf{N}.$$

Consequently if $\kappa \neq 0$ then **T** and **N** are mutually perpendicular.

Once **T** and **N** have been found, it is convenient to define a third unit vector **B** that is perpendicular to both **T** and **N**, by the equation

$$\mathbf{B} = \mathbf{T} \times \mathbf{N}.$$

The vector **N** is called the *principal normal* to the curve, and the vector **B** is called the *binormal* to the curve. These three unit vectors are extremely useful in the differential geometry of space curves.

EXAMPLE 1. Find κ, **T**, **N**, and **B** for the *circular helix*

$$\mathbf{R} = a \cos t\mathbf{i} + a \sin t\mathbf{j} + bt\mathbf{k}, \qquad (65)$$

where a and b are positive constants.

SOLUTION. The projection of this curve on the xy-plane is obtained by setting the z-component equal to zero. This gives $\mathbf{R} = a \cos t\mathbf{i} + a \sin t\mathbf{j}$, so the projection of this space curve is a circle with center at the origin and radius *a.* Since $z = bt$ is steadily increasing with t, it is easy to see that this curve has the appearance indicated in Fig. 20.

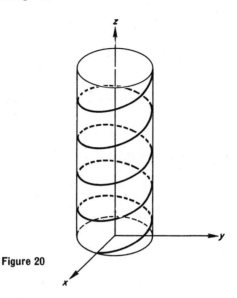

Figure 20

Differentiating **R**(t) we find that

$$\mathbf{R'}(t) = \frac{d\mathbf{R}}{dt} = -a \sin t\mathbf{i} + a \cos t\mathbf{j} + b\mathbf{k}$$

is a tangent vector. To obtain a unit tangent vector we divied by $|R'(t)| = \sqrt{a^2 + b^2}$. Consequently

$$\mathbf{T} = \frac{1}{\sqrt{a^2 + b^2}} [-a \sin t\mathbf{i} + a \cos t\mathbf{j} + b\mathbf{k}].$$

If we decide to measure arc length along this curve from the point $(a, 0, 0)$ corresponding to $t = 0$, we have

$$s = \int_0^t \frac{ds}{dt} \, dt = \int_0^t \sqrt{(-a \sin t)^2 + (a \cos t)^2 + b^2} \, dt = \int_0^t \sqrt{a^2 + b^2} \, dt$$

$$s = t\sqrt{a^2 + b^2}.$$

In this case it is a simple matter to introduce the arc length s as a parameter in the curve. Indeed, using $t = s/\sqrt{a^2 + b^2}$ in (65) gives

$$\mathbf{R} = a \cos \frac{s}{\sqrt{a^2 + b^2}} \mathbf{i} + a \sin \frac{s}{\sqrt{a^2 + b^2}} \mathbf{j} + \frac{bs}{\sqrt{a^2 + b^2}} \mathbf{k},$$

the parametric equations for the circular helix with the arc length s as parameter.

To find κ we use (63).   Thus

$$\kappa\mathbf{N} = \frac{d\mathbf{T}}{ds} = \frac{d\mathbf{T}}{dt}\frac{dt}{ds} = \frac{1}{\sqrt{a^2+b^2}}[-a\cos t\mathbf{i} - a\sin t\mathbf{j}]\frac{dt}{ds}$$

$$= \frac{-a}{\sqrt{a^2+b^2}}[\cos t\mathbf{i} + \sin t\mathbf{j}]\frac{1}{\sqrt{a^2+b^2}} = \frac{a}{a^2+b^2}[-\cos t\mathbf{i} - \sin t\mathbf{j}].$$

Since $-\cos t\mathbf{i} - \sin t\mathbf{j}$ is a unit vector it is clear that

$$\kappa = \frac{a}{a^2+b^2}, \qquad \mathbf{N} = -\cos t\mathbf{i} - \sin t\mathbf{j}.$$

Finally $\mathbf{B} = \mathbf{T} \times \mathbf{N}$, so

$$\mathbf{B} = \frac{1}{\sqrt{a^2+b^2}}\begin{vmatrix} \mathbf{i} & \mathbf{j} & \mathbf{k} \\ -a\sin t & a\cos t & b \\ -\cos t & -\sin t & 0 \end{vmatrix} = \frac{1}{\sqrt{a^2+b^2}}[b\sin t\mathbf{i} - b\cos t\mathbf{j} + a\mathbf{k}].$$

As a check, we observe that $\mathbf{B}\cdot\mathbf{T} = 0$, $\mathbf{B}\cdot\mathbf{N} = 0$, and $\mathbf{N}\cdot\mathbf{T} = 0$.

EXAMPLE 2.   Find a formula for κ in terms of $\mathbf{R}(t)$ and its derivatives.

SOLUTION.   Using the chain rule for differentiation we have

$$\frac{d\mathbf{R}}{dt} = \frac{d\mathbf{R}}{ds}\frac{ds}{dt} = \mathbf{T}\frac{ds}{dt}, \tag{66}$$

$$\frac{d^2\mathbf{R}}{dt^2} = \mathbf{T}\frac{d^2s}{dt^2} + \frac{d\mathbf{T}}{dt}\frac{ds}{dt} = \mathbf{T}\frac{d^2s}{dt^2} + \left(\frac{d\mathbf{T}}{ds}\frac{ds}{dt}\right)\frac{ds}{dt}$$

$$\frac{d^2\mathbf{R}}{dt^2} = \frac{d^2s}{dt^2}\mathbf{T} + \left(\frac{ds}{dt}\right)^2\kappa\mathbf{N}. \tag{67}$$

[Compare this equation with equation (68) of Chapter 10, obtained there for plane curves.]   Taking the cross product of the vectors in equation (67) with those in (66), and noting that $\mathbf{T} \times \mathbf{T} = \mathbf{0}$, we have

$$\frac{d\mathbf{R}}{dt} \times \frac{d^2\mathbf{R}}{dt^2} = \mathbf{T}\frac{ds}{dt} \times \left[\frac{d^2s}{dt^2}\mathbf{T} + \left(\frac{ds}{dt}\right)^2\kappa\mathbf{N}\right] = \kappa\left(\frac{ds}{dt}\right)^3\mathbf{B}. \tag{68}$$

But $\mathbf{B}$ is a unit vector, so taking lengths in (68) yields

$$\kappa\left(\frac{ds}{dt}\right)^3 = \left|\frac{d\mathbf{R}}{dt} \times \frac{d^2\mathbf{R}}{dt^2}\right|$$

or

$$\kappa = \frac{|\mathbf{R}'(t) \times \mathbf{R}''(t)|}{|\mathbf{R}'(t)|^3}.$$

We leave it to the reader to apply this formula to the curve of Example 1, and show that $\kappa = a/(a^2 + b^2)$ for that curve.

EXERCISE 9

In problems 1 through 5 find an equation for the line tangent to the given curve at the given point, and an equation for the plane normal to the given curve at that point.

1. $R = 6ti + 3t^2j + t^3k$, $P(0, 0, 0)$.
2. $R = \sqrt{2}ti + e^tj + e^{-t}k$, $P(0, 1, 1)$.
3. $R = t \sin ti + t \cos tj + \sqrt{3}\, tk$, $P(0, 0, 0)$.
4. $R = \sin 3ti + \cos 3tj + 2t^{3/2}k$, $P(0, 1, 0)$.
5. $R = ti + tj + \frac{2}{3}t^{3/2}k$, $P(9, 9, 18)$.

6. For each of the curves of problems 1 through 5 find the arc length as a function of t presuming that $s = 0$ when $t = 0$, and that they increase together.

In problems 7 through 9 find the curvature for the given curve. Use the formula from example 2.

7. $R = e^ti + \sqrt{2}tj + e^{-t}k$.
8. $R = 6ti + 3\sqrt{2}\, t^2j + 2t^3k$.
*9. $R = 3at^2i + a(3t + t^3)j + a(3t - t^3)k$.

10. Find $\cos \theta$ for the angle of intersection of the two curves $R_1 = (1 + t^4)i + 2 \cos \pi tj + t^3k$ and $R_2 = (t + t^2)i + (t - 3t^2)j + te^{t-1}k$ at the point $(2, -2, 1)$.

11. Find $\cos \theta$ for the angle of intersection of the curve $R_3 = \frac{1}{4}t^3i + (6 - t^3)j + (t^2 - 3)k$ and the curve R_1 of problem 10 at the point $(2, -2, 1)$.

12. Show that for the straight line, $d\mathbf{T}/ds = \mathbf{0}$. Consequently for the straight line the vectors $\mathbf{N}$ and $\mathbf{B}$ are not defined.

In problems 13 through 15 find the principal normal vector $\mathbf{N}$, and check that $\mathbf{N} \cdot \mathbf{T} = 0$ in each case.

13. The conical helix $R = e^ti + e^t \cos tj + e^t \sin tk$.
14. $R = 4 \sin ti + (2t - \sin 2t)j + \cos 2tk$.
15. The curve of problem 1.

16. Prove that for a curve

$$\frac{dx}{ds} = \cos \alpha, \qquad \frac{dy}{ds} = \cos \beta, \qquad \frac{dz}{ds} = \cos \gamma$$

where α, β, γ are the direction angles of the unit tangent vector.

12. Surfaces.

The locus of all points $P(x, y, z)$ whose coordinates satisfy an equation

$$F(x, y, z) = 0 \qquad\qquad (69)$$

usually constitutes a surface, and will always do so for any function $F(x, y, z)$ that is of practical importance. For example,

$$Ax + By + Cz - D = 0$$

represents a plane, if not all of the coefficients A, B, and C are zero.   The equation

$$(x - a)^2 + (y - b)^2 + (z - c)^2 - r^2 = 0$$

is the equation of a sphere of radius r and center (a, b, c).

In some cases (69) can be explicitly solved for z, and we may write

$$z = f(x, y) \qquad (70)$$

as the equation for a surface.   Thus to each point (x, y) in the base plane (or in some suitable region of the plane) there corresponds a point on the surface, z units directly above (or below if $z < 0$).   The situation is illustrated in Fig. 21, where (x, y) is supposedly restricted to lie in a rectangle.

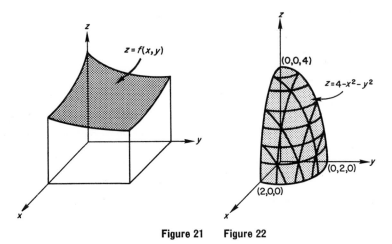

Figure 21   Figure 22

As a specific illustration of (70), consider the surface

$$z = 4 - x^2 - y^2. \qquad (71)$$

We will prove in the discussion of Example 1 below that this surface can be obtained by rotating the parabola $z = 4 - y^2$ (lying in the yz-plane) about the z-axis.   The surface is called a *paraboloid of revolution*.   That portion of the surface that lies in the first octant is shown in Fig. 22.

Just as the vector function $\mathbf{R}(t)$, of a single variable, describes a curve, so we may expect a vector function $\mathbf{R}(u, v)$, of two variables, to describe a surface.   Thus in (70) we could set $x = u$, $y = v$, and $z = f(x, y) = f(u, v)$, and then the position vector $\mathbf{R} = x\mathbf{i} + y\mathbf{j} + z\mathbf{k}$ to a point on the surface would take the form

$$\mathbf{R}(u, v) = u\mathbf{i} + v\mathbf{j} + f(u, v)\mathbf{k}, \qquad (72)$$

a vector equation for the surface (70).

More generally any three functions of two variables

$$x = f(u, v), \qquad y = g(u, v), \qquad z = h(u, v) \tag{73}$$

give *parametric equations* for a surface, and the vector function

$$\mathbf{R} = f(u, v)\mathbf{i} + g(u, v)\mathbf{j} + h(u, v)\mathbf{k} \tag{74}$$

describes the same surface.

There are always infinitely many ways in which a given surface can be described by a vector equation. Although perhaps not obvious, the four vector equations

$$\mathbf{R} = u\mathbf{i} + v\mathbf{j} + (4 - u^2 - v^2)\mathbf{k},$$
$$\mathbf{R} = (u - 2)\mathbf{i} + (v - 1)\mathbf{j} + (4u + 2v - u^2 - v^2 - 1)\mathbf{k},$$
$$\mathbf{R} = u \cos v\mathbf{i} + u \sin v\mathbf{j} + (4 - u^2)\mathbf{k},$$
$$\mathbf{R} = u^2 \cos 3v\mathbf{i} + u^2 \sin 3v\mathbf{j} + (4 - u^4)\mathbf{k},$$

all describe the paraboloid of revolution (71).

We will postpone the study of the vector representation of a surface until Chapter 16, and for the present devote our attention to the graph of $F(x, y, z) = 0$. Here it is best to proceed by examples, and then at the end to summarize with some general principles on sketching a surface from its equation.

EXAMPLE 1. Sketch the surface $z = 4 - x^2 - y^2$.

SOLUTION. A portion of this surface is already shown in Fig. 22, but how did we arrive at this sketch?

If we want to find the curve of intersection of the surface with some plane parallel to one of the coordinate planes, we merely regard the appropriate variable as a constant. Now the plane parallel to the xy-plane and 1 unit above it is just the collection of points on which $z = 1$, i.e., it has the equation $z = 1$. Setting $z = 1$ in $z = 4 - x^2 - y^2$ gives the equation in x and y for the points on the curve of intersection. In this case we find $1 = 4 - x^2 - y^2$ or $x^2 + y^2 = 3$. Hence the curve of intersection is a circle, with center on the z-axis and radius $\sqrt{3}$. If we write the equation of the surface in the form $x^2 + y^2 = 4 - z$ we see that if z_0 is any fixed number with $z_0 < 4$, then the intersection of the plane $z = z_0$ with the surface is a circle with center on the z-axis and radius $\sqrt{4 - z_0}$. If $z_0 = 4$, the intersection is the point $(0, 0, 4)$, and if $z_0 > 4$, the intersection is empty (the plane and the surface do not meet). Since each section of the surface obtained by cutting with a plane perpendicular to the z-axis is a circle (or a point, or empty) with center on the z-axis, the surface itself can be generated by rotating a suitable curve around the z-axis. To find this suitable curve we take the intersection of the surface with the yz-plane, by setting $x = 0$ in the equation of the surface. We find $z = 4 - y^2$, the equation of a parabola.

It is of interest to find the intersection of this surface with other planes, for example, a plane parallel to the yz-plane. This is done by setting $x = x_0$, a constant. We obtain $z = (4 - x_0^2) - y^2$, or $z = A - y^2$ the equation of a parabola. Similarly planes parallel to the xz-plane also intersect this surface in a parabola. Portions of these parabolas are shown in Fig. 22.

EXAMPLE 2.   Sketch the *ellipsoid* $\dfrac{x^2}{a^2} + \dfrac{y^2}{b^2} + \dfrac{z^2}{c^2} = 1$.

SOLUTION. A portion of this surface is shown in Fig. 23. Obviously the complete surface is symmetrical with respect to each of the coordinate planes, and consequently it is symmetrical with respect to each coordinate axis, and with respect to the origin. The full surface resembles an egg except that the egg has only one axis of symmetry. Solving for x, gives

$$x = \pm a\sqrt{1 - \frac{y^2}{b^2} - \frac{z^2}{c^2}}$$

and hence for points on the surface with real coordinates we must have $-a \leq x \leq a$. Similarly $-b \leq y \leq b$ and $-c \leq z \leq c$ and therefore the surface must lie inside the box bounded by the six planes $x = \pm a$, $y = \pm b$, $z = \pm c$. The intersection of this surface with a plane $z = z_0$, $|z_0| < c$ is the curve

$$\frac{x^2}{a^2} + \frac{y^2}{b^2} = 1 - \frac{z_0^2}{c^2}.$$

This is a circle if $a = b$ and an ellipse if $a \neq b$. Consequently if $a \neq b$, $b \neq c$, and $a \neq c$, this surface is *not* a surface of revolution.

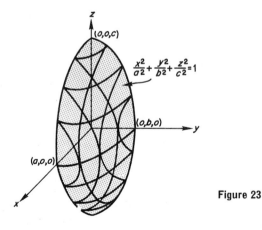

Figure 23

EXAMPLE 3.   Sketch the surface $\dfrac{x^2}{a^2} + \dfrac{y^2}{b^2} - \dfrac{z^2}{c^2} = 1$.

SOLUTION. A portion of this surface is shown in Fig. 24. It is called a *hyperboloid of one sheet*. We leave it to the student to establish the following properties. It is symmetric with respect to each of the coordinate planes, and also with respect to each of the coordinate axes. Planes parallel to the xy-plane intersect this surface in an ellipse (if $a \neq b$). Planes parallel to the xz-plane or yz-plane intersect it in a hyperbola, or two straight lines.

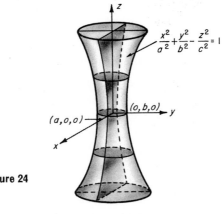

$$\frac{x^2}{a^2}+\frac{y^2}{b^2}-\frac{z^2}{c^2}=1$$

(o,b,o)

(a,o,o)

Figure 24

EXAMPLE 4. Sketch the surface $\dfrac{z}{c} = \dfrac{y^2}{a^2} - \dfrac{x^2}{b^2}$

SOLUTION. This surface is called the *hyperbolic paraboloid* and a portion is shown in Fig. 25. For obvious reasons, it is also called a *saddle surface*, and the origin in this case is called a *saddle point*. This surface is of great importance in further theoretical studies, and the student should convince himself

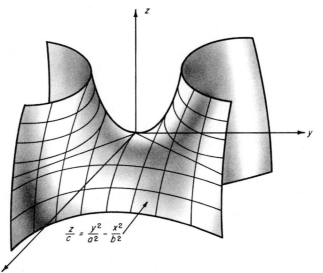

$$\frac{z}{c} = \frac{y^2}{a^2} - \frac{x^2}{b^2}$$

Figure 25

that the graph of this equation does indeed have the form indicated in the picture. We leave it for the student to examine the symmetry, and to prove (a) every plane parallel to the xy-plane intersects this surface in a hyperbola, except in one case where the hyperbola degenerates into two straight lines. Each plane parallel to the xz-plane or yz-plane intersects this surface in a parabola, but in the first case the parabola opens downward, while in the second case it opens upward.

The following statements (really theorems) are useful in sketching surfaces or finding their equations. We leave the proofs to the student.

1. If $f(x, y, -z) = f(x, y, z)$ then the surface $f(x, y, z) = 0$ is symmetrical with respect to the xy-plane.

2. If z is missing in $f(x, y, z) = 0$, then the surface is a cylinder perpendicular to the xy-plane.

3. If $f(x, y) = 0$ is the equation of a curve in the xy-plane, then $f(x, \pm \sqrt{y^2 + z^2}) = 0$ is an equation for the surface generated by rotating this curve about the x-axis.

4. If $f(x, y, z) = 0$ and $g(x, y, z) = 0$ are the equations of two surfaces, and algebraic elimination of the variable z yields $F(x, y) = 0$, then this latter is an equation for the projection on the xy-plane of the curve of intersection of the two surfaces.

5. If $f(x, y, z)$ is a quadratic in x, y, and z, then the intersection of any plane with the surface $f(x, y, z) = 0$ projects onto the xy-plane (or xz-plane, or zy-plane) giving a conic section, or a circle, or one or two straight lines, or a point, or no points.

6. A curve $x = f(t), y = g(t), z = h(t)$ lies on the surface $F(x, y, z) = 0$, if the substitution gives $F(f(t), g(t), h(t)) = 0$ for every value of t.

EXAMPLE 5. The straight line $y = 2z$ is rotated about the z-axis. Find an equation for the cone generated, and prove that each of the straight lines $R(t) = 2ati + 2btj + \sqrt{a^2 + b^2}\, t\mathbf{k}$ lies on the surface.

SOLUTION. By (3), with a suitable change of letters, an equation for the cone is $2z = \pm \sqrt{y^2 + x^2}$ or $4z^2 - x^2 - y^2 = 0$. Substituting $x = 2at$, $y = 2bt$ and $z = \sqrt{a^2 + b^2}\, t$ in this equation yields

$$4(a^2 + b^2)t^2 - 4a^2t^2 - 4b^2t^2 = 0.$$

But this is true for any t, so the lines $R(t)$ lie on the surface.

EXERCISE 10

1. Give a condition on the function $f(x, y, z)$ so that the surface $f(x, y, z) = 0$ is (a) symmetric with respect to the xz-plane, (b) symmetric with respect to the yz-plane, (c) symmetric with respect to the x-axis, (d) symmetric with respect to the z-axis, (e) symmetric with respect to the plane $x = y$.

2. Without computing any points what can you say about the surface $x \sin z + zx^5 = 7$?

3. Find the values of x_0 such that the plane $x = x_0$ intersects the hyperboloid of one sheet of Example 3, in two straight lines.

4. For what value of z_0 does the plane $z = z_0$ intersect the saddle surface of Example 4, in two straight lines?

In problems 5 through 12 sketch enough of the given surface to indicate clearly what the surface looks like.

5. $z + 9 - y^2 = 0$.   **6.** $4x^2 + z^2 - 24x + 32 = 0$.

7. $x^2 - y^3 = 0$.   **8.** $4z - x^2 - y^2 = 0$.

9. $4z^2 - x^2 - y^2 = 0$.   **10.** $\dfrac{z}{c^2} - \dfrac{x^2}{a^2} - \dfrac{y^2}{b^2} = 0$.

11. $y - x^2 - z^2 = 0$.   **12.** $x^2 - 2y^2 + z^2 - 1 = 0$.

13. The ellipse $\dfrac{z^2}{a^2} + \dfrac{y^2}{b^2} = 1$ is rotated about the z-axis. Find a formula for the surface generated. If $a > b$, the surface is called a *prolate ellipsoid*. If $a < b$ the surface is called an *oblate ellipsoid*. Sketch the surface in both cases.

14. The surface $\dfrac{z^2}{c^2} - \dfrac{x^2}{a^2} - \dfrac{y^2}{b^2} = 1$ is called a hyperboloid of two sheets. Sketch this surface, and explain the "two sheets."

In problems 15 through 21 find an equation for the projection onto the xy-plane of the curve of intersection of the two given surfaces. In each case sketch the surfaces.

15. $z = x^2 + y^2$, $z = 4y$.

16. $z = 8 - x^2 - y^2$, $z = 2x$.

17. $x^2 + z^2 = 4$, $y^2 + z^2 = 4$.

18. $x^2 + z^2 = 9$, $y^2 + z^2 = 4$.

19. $z = y^2 + 4x^2$, $z = 4xy$.

20. $z = y^2 + 4x^2$, $z = Axy$, $A > 4$.

21. $x^2 + y^2 + z^2 = 4A^2$, $x + y + z = 2A$.

22. Show that the curve $\mathbf{R} = a \cos t\mathbf{i} + a \sin t\mathbf{j} + a \cos t\mathbf{k}$ lies on both of the cylinders $x^2 + y^2 = a^2$ and $y^2 + z^2 = a^2$.

23. Prove that for any pair of numbers a and b the straight line $\mathbf{R} = (t + a)\mathbf{i} + (t + b)\mathbf{j} + [2(b - a)t + b^2 - a^2]\mathbf{k}$ lies on the saddle surface $z = y^2 - x^2$. Show further that through each point on this surface there passes at least one such line. This shows that the surface can be made up of straight lines.

24. Show that the curve $\mathbf{R} = e^t \cos 3t\mathbf{i} + e^t \sin 3t\mathbf{j} + (4 - e^{2t})\mathbf{k}$ lies on the surface $z = 4 - x^2 - y^2$.

★25. Find a condition on a, b, and c so that the curve $\mathbf{R} = at^4\mathbf{i} + bt^3\mathbf{j} + ct^6\mathbf{k}$ lies on the surface $z^2 = x^3 + 2y^4$. Prove that through each point on the surface there is at least one curve from this family. Is there a point on the surface through which every curve of the family runs?

26. Consider the circle $(x - A)^2 + z^2 = a^2$ (with $A > a > 0$) lying in the *xz*-plane. If this circle is rotated about the *z*-axis it generates a surface called the *torus*, or *anchor ring* (an idealized doughnut). Find an equation for this surface.

13. The cylindrical coordinate system.

In addition to the rectangular coordinate system, there are two other coordinate systems that are useful in solving problems in three-dimensional space. These are, the spherical coordinate system that we will study in the next section, and the cylindrical coordinate system that we consider now.

The cylindrical coordinate system is obtained by putting a *z*-axis "on top" of a polar coordinate system. Thus, as indicated in Fig. 26, if O is

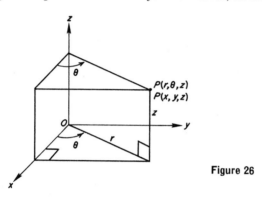

Figure 26

the pole of a plane polar coordinate system, a *z*-axis is erected at O perpendicular to that plane. Then the coordinates (r, θ, z) for a point in space, describe its location. We will always consider such a coordinate system as superimposed on a rectangular coordinate system in such a way that the two origins and the two *z*-axes coincide, and the positive *x*-axis falls on the polar line. Then the coordinates in the two different systems, for a given point are related by the equation set

$$
\begin{aligned}
x &= r \cos \theta \\
y &= r \sin \theta \\
z &= z.
\end{aligned}
\qquad (75)
$$

EXAMPLE 1. Describe each of the surfaces: (a) $\theta = \pi/3$, (b) $r = 5$, (c) $z + r = 7$, and (d) $r(2 \sin \theta + 3 \cos \theta) + 4z = 0$.

SOLUTION. (a) The collection of all points $P(r, \theta, z)$ for which $\theta = \pi/3$ fills a plane that contains the *z* axis and that intersects the *xy*-plane in a line that makes an angle $\pi/3$ with the polar line. At first glance it might seem that we get only a half plane, but we recall that *r* may be negative, and those values for *r* give the points in back of the *yz*-plane.

(b) The surface $r = 5$ is just a right circular cylinder of radius 5, with the z-axis as a center line.

(c) For the surface $z + r = 7$, think of its intersection with the yz-plane ($\theta = \pi/2$). Then $r = y$ and we have just the straight line $z + y = 7$. But the original equation does not contain θ, hence the surface is just the cone obtained by rotating the line $z + y = 7$ about the z-axis.

(d) Using the equation set (75), the equation $r(2 \sin \theta + 3 \cos \theta) + 4z = 0$ is transformed into $2y + 3x + 4z = 0$. So the surface is just a plane through the origin with the normal vector $3\mathbf{i} + 2\mathbf{j} + 4\mathbf{k}$.

EXAMPLE 2. Find an equation for the saddle surface $z = x^2 - y^2$ in cylindrical coordinates.

SOLUTION. From equation set (75) $x = r \cos \theta$, $y = r \sin \theta$, hence $z = x^2 - y^2 = r^2 \cos^2 \theta - r^2 \sin^2 \theta$, and consequently $z = r^2 \cos 2\theta$.

EXERCISE 11

In problems 1 through 6 change from the given cylindrical coordinates of a point, to the set of rectangular coordinates for the same point.

1. $(3, \pi/2, 5)$. **2.** $(-3, \pi/2, -5)$. **3.** $(4, -4\pi/3, 1)$.
4. $(-1, 25\pi, 6)$. **5.** $(6, 7\pi/4, 19)$. **6.** $(4, 2, 1)$.

In problems 7 through 12 change from the given rectangular coordinates of a point to a suitable set of cylindrical coordinates for the same point.

7. $(1, 1, 1)$. **8.** $(2, -2, -2)$. **9.** $(-3\sqrt{3}, 3, 6)$.
10. $(-4, 4 - 7)$. **11.** $(-8, -8\sqrt{3}, \pi)$. **12.** $(10, 0, -10)$.

In problems 13 through 16 translate the given equation into an equation in cylindrical coordinates.

13. $x^2 + y^2 + z^2 = 16$. **14.** $z = x^3 - 3xy^2$.
15. $z^2(x^2 - y^2) = 2xy$. **16.** $Ax + By + Cz = D$.

In problems 17 through 20 translate the given equation into an equation in rectangular coordinates.

17. $r = 4 \cos \theta$. **18.** $r^3 = z^2 \sin^3 \theta$.
19. $r^3 = 2z \sin 2\theta$. **20.** $r^2 \cos 2\theta = z^3$.
21. Sketch a portion of the surfaces

a. $z = \sin \theta$, **b.** $z = \tan \theta$, **c.** $z = r$, **d.** $z = \theta$,

where the equations are given in cylindrical coordinates.

14. **The spherical coordinate system.** In Fig. 27 we show a spherical coordinate system superimposed on a rectangular coordinate system. The spherical coordinates of a point P are (ρ, φ, θ). Here ρ is the distance of the point P from O, the common origin in both systems. Hence by

agreement $\rho \geq 0$.   The angle φ is the angle from the positive z-axis to the
radial line OP.   Here it is convenient to restrict φ to the interval $0 \leq \varphi \leq \pi$.
Finally θ plays the same role in spherical coordinates that it does in cylin-

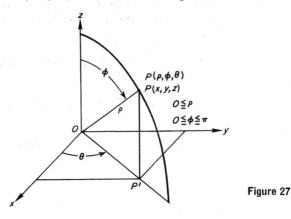

Figure 27

drical coordinates, namely θ is the angle from the positive x-axis to the
projection OP' of the ray OP on the xy-plane. Clearly $OP' = \rho \sin \varphi$ and
is just r of the polar coordinate system (or cylindrical coordinate system).
Consequently $x = r \cos \theta = \rho \sin \varphi \cos \theta$. Similarly $y = r \sin \theta = \rho \sin \varphi \sin \theta$.   Therefore

$$
\begin{aligned}
x &= \rho \sin \varphi \cos \theta, \\
y &= \rho \sin \varphi \sin \theta, \\
z &= \rho \cos \varphi,
\end{aligned}
\tag{76}
$$

are the equations of transformation from the spherical coordinate system
to the rectangular coordinate system.

EXAMPLE 1.   Describe each of the surfaces (a) $\rho = 5$, (b) $\varphi = 2\pi/3$, (c)
$\theta = \pi/2$, (d) $\rho = 2 \sin \varphi$.

SOLUTION. **(a)**   The collection of all points 5 units distant from the
origin, forms a sphere of radius 5 with center at the origin.
    (b)   The graph of $\varphi = 2\pi/3$ is one-half of the cone with the z-axis as an
axis of the cone and with angle $\pi/3$ between the axis and any one of its elements.
The graph is only one-half of this cone, because only points on or below the
xy-plane can be on this surface.
    (c)   The graph of $\theta = \pi/2$ is that half of the yz-plane that lies to the right
of the z-axis.
    (d)   The equation $\rho = 2 \sin \varphi$ is independent of θ, so we have a surface of
revolution with the z-axis as the axis of revolution.   In the yz-plane the equa-

tion $\rho = 2 \sin \varphi$ gives a circle of unit radius as indicated in Fig. 28. Whence the full surface is the one obtained by rotating this circle about the z-axis. This surface is a degenerate torus in which the hole has radius zero.

EXAMPLE 2. Find an equation in rectangular coordinates for the surface $\rho = 2 \sin \varphi$ shown in Fig. 28.

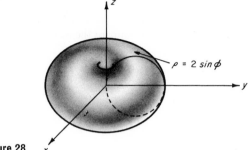

Figure 28

SOLUTION. From $\rho = 2 \sin \varphi$ we have $\rho^2 = 2\rho \sin \varphi$ and on squaring $\rho^4 = 4\rho^2 \sin^2 \varphi = 4\rho^2(1 - \cos^2 \varphi) = 4\rho^2 - 4\rho^2 \cos^2 \varphi$. Since $\rho^2 = x^2 + y^2 + z^2$ we have

$$(x^2 + y^2 + z^2)^2 = 4(x^2 + y^2 + z^2) - 4z^2$$

or

$$(x^2 + y^2 + z^2)^2 = 4(x^2 + y^2). \qquad (77)$$

EXERCISE 12

In problems 1 through 6 change from the given spherical coordinates of a point to the set of rectangular coordinates for the same point.

1. $(8, \pi/6, \pi/4)$.   2. $(4, \pi/2, \pi/3)$.   3. $(16, \pi/6, 5\pi/4)$.
4. $(7, 0, 7\pi/13)$.   5. $(\pi, \pi, 4)$.   6. $(0, 5, 9)$.

In problems 7 through 10, the equation of a surface is given in rectangular coordinates. Translate the equation into an equation in spherical coordinates and describe or sketch the surface.

7. $x^2 + y^2 + z^2 - 8z = 0$.   8. $z = 10 - x^2 - y^2$.
9. $(x^2 + y^2 + z^2)^3 = (x^2 + y^2)^2$.   ★10. $(x^2 + y^2)\sqrt{x^2 + y^2 + z^2} = x^2$.

11. Deduce the equation set $\sin \varphi = \sqrt{x^2 + y^2}/\sqrt{x^2 + y^2 + z^2}$, $\sin \theta = y/\sqrt{x^2 + y^2}$, $\cos \varphi = z/\sqrt{x^2 + y^2 + z^2}$, $\cos \theta = x/\sqrt{x^2 + y^2}$. These equations can be helpful in transforming from spherical coordinates to rectangular coordinates.

In problems 12 through 15 the equation of a surface is given in spherical coordinates. Translate the equation into an equation in rectangular coordinates, and describe the surface.

12. $\rho \cos \varphi = -7.$ **13.** $\rho = 2 \cos \varphi + 4 \sin \varphi \cos \theta.$
14. $\rho \sin \varphi = 10.$ **15.** $\rho = 2 \tan \theta.$

16. Obtain equations for transforming from spherical coordinates to cylindrical coordinates.

17. For the torus of problem 26, Exercise 10, find an equation (a) in cylindrical coordinates, (b) in spherical coordinates.

18. Transform each of the following equations for a sphere of radius A into spherical coordinates and compare the results for simplicity,

    a. $(x - A)^2 + y^2 + z^2 = A^2,$
    b. $x^2 + y^2 + (z - A)^2 = A^2.$

15

SOME APPLICATIONS TO PHYSICS

1.   The moment of a system of weighted particles. In many physical
problems where the bodies under consideration are small in comparison with the distances between them it is convenient to think of all of
the material of each body as concentrated at a single point, presumably the
center of that body.   The best example of this, is the system of planets
revolving about the sun.   Here the diameter of the earth is roughly 8,000
miles, while its distance from the sun is 92,000,000 miles so that indeed the
earth is but a small particle in the solar system.

Henceforth the term *system of weighted*[1] *particles* or *system of weighted
points* means a collection of weights, each one regarded as being concentrated at a certain point in space.

We are interested in finding the turning effect of such a collection of
weighted particles about an axis.   For simplicity we shall assume first that
all of the particles lie in a plane, and in fact we will regard the plane as
horizontal and use it as our xy-plane (see Fig. 1).

Simple observations of two children on a seesaw indicate that the seesaw will balance when $m_1d_1 = m_2d_2$, where naturally m_1 and m_2 are the
weights of the two children, and d_1 and d_2 are their respective distances
from the fulcrum which is located between the children.   This suggests
that we regard the product ml as the turning effect of the weight m placed
at directed distance l from an axis, assigning a positive sign to l for those
particles on one side of the axis (fulcrum) and a negative sign to l for those
particles on the other side.   Then the condition for balance is that $m_1l_1 +
m_2l_2 = 0$, that is, the total turning effect or total moment of the system is
zero.   Abstracting the essentials, from the above discussion we are led to

---

[1]Weight and mass are not the same.   For a discussion of the difference *see* Resnick
and Halliday *Physics Part I* New York: John Wiley and Sons Inc., 1960, pp 70-79,
265-268.   In a uniform gravitational field, weight is proportional to mass, and hence
we may use the weight as a measure of the mass.

DEFINITION 1. *Let P_1, P_2, $\cdots$, P_n be a system of n points (or particles) in the plane with weights m_1, m_2, $\cdots$, m_n respectively. Let the line L in the plane be taken as an axis and let l_1, l_2, $\cdots$, l_n be the directed distances from the line L of the points P_1, P_2, $\cdots$, P_n respectively. Then the moment of this system of weighted points (or particles) about the axis L is denoted by M_L and is given by*

$$M_L = \sum_{k=1}^{n} m_k l_k = m_1 l_1 + m_2 l_2 + \cdots + m_n l_n. \tag{1}$$

For the most part we are interested in M_x and M_y, the moments about the x and y-axis respectively. In these two cases the positive direction for measuring directed distances is the usual one and hence the positive moments have the rotational effect indicated by the arrows in Fig. 1.

If each point P_k has coordinates (x_k, y_k) then from equation (1) it is easy to see that

$$M_x = \sum_{k=1}^{n} m_k y_k = m_1 y_1 + m_2 y_2 + \cdots + m_n y_n, \tag{2}$$

and

$$M_y = \sum_{k=1}^{n} m_k x_k = m_1 x_1 + m_2 x_2 + \cdots + m_n x_n. \tag{3}$$

The reader should note carefully the interchange of x and y in formulas (2) and (3). Thus to compute M_x we use y_k and to compute M_y we use x_k.

EXAMPLE 1. Suppose that for the system shown in Fig. 1 the weights are $m_1 = 2$, $m_2 = 1$, $m_3 = 4$, and $m_4 = 7$ at the points P_1, P_2, P_3, and P_4 respectively. Compute M_x, M_y, M_{L_1}, and M_{L_2} where L_1 is the line $x = 2$, and L_2 is the line $y = 2$.

SOLUTION.   From equations (2) and (3)

$M_x = 2 \times (-1) + 1 \times 1 + 4 \times 2 + 7 \times 3 = -2 + 1 + 8 + 21 = 28.$
$M_y = 2 \times 1 + 1 \times (-1) + 4 \times 1 + 7 \times 2 = 2 - 1 + 4 + 14 = 19.$

A similar computation for the axes L_1 and L_2 gives

$M_{L_1} = 2 \times (-1) + 1 \times (-3) + 4 \times (-1) + 7 \times 0 = -2 - 3 - 4 = -9.$
$M_{L_2} = 2 \times (-3) + 1 \times (-1) + 4 \times 0 + 7 \times 1 \quad = -6 - 1 + 7 = 0.$

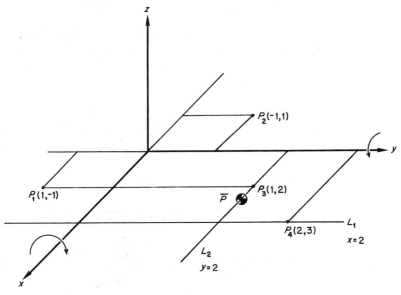

Figure 1

If the weights are measured in pounds and the distance in feet then the moment is in pounds-feet. Notice that M_{L_1} is negative. This is to be expected since all of the points are on the axis L_1 or behind it so the turning effect is negative. Finally observe that $M_{L_2} = 0$, so the given weighted system is in balance with respect to this axis.

> **DEFINITION 2.** *The point $\bar{P}(\bar{x}, \bar{y})$ is called the center of gravity of a system of weighted points (or particles) if, when all of the weight of the system is concentrated at $\bar{P}$, then this new system has the same moment as the original system of weighted points with respect to any axis.*

We will not prove that there is always such a center of gravity because the proof is a little complicated. However, assuming there is such a point, we can obtain simple formulas for its coordinates. If m denotes the total weight of the system,

$$m = m_1 + m_2 + \cdots + m_n, \tag{4}$$

then it is clear that for the moment of the new system to equal the moment of the original system about the two coordinate axes we must have

$$m\bar{x} = M_y = m_1x_1 + m_2x_2 + \cdots + m_nx_n \tag{5}$$

and

$$m\bar{y} = M_x = m_1y_1 + m_2y_2 + \cdots + m_ny_n. \tag{6}$$

Consequently, division by m gives

THEOREM 1.   If $\bar{P}(\bar{x}, \bar{y})$ is the center of gravity of a system of weighted points $P_k(x_k, y_k)$ with weights $m_k(k = 1, 2, \cdots, n)$ then

$$\bar{x} = \frac{m_1 x_1 + m_2 x_2 + \cdots + m_n x_n}{m} = \frac{\sum\limits_{k=1}^{n} m_k x_k}{\sum\limits_{k=1}^{n} m_k}, \qquad (7)$$

and

$$\bar{y} = \frac{m_1 y_1 + m_2 y_2 + \cdots + m_n y_n}{m} = \frac{\sum\limits_{k=1}^{n} m_k y_k}{\sum\limits_{k=1}^{n} m_k}. \qquad (8)$$

EXAMPLE 2.   Find the center of gravity of the system of example 1.

SOLUTION.   Since $m = 2 + 1 + 4 + 7 = 14$, then $\bar{x} = M_y/m = 19/14$ and $\bar{y} = M_x/m = 28/14 = 2$.

As a check we compute the moment about the axis L_1 of the system in which the total weight 14 is concentrated at $(\bar{x}, \bar{y})$. This point is $2 - 19/14$ units behind L_1 and hence $M_{L_1} = -14(2 - 19/14) = -28 + 19 = -9$, the same moment that we found before.

Clearly the moment about any axis through $\bar{P}$ must be zero, so $\bar{P}$ represents a point of balance for the original system of weighted points.

EXERCISE 1

In problems 1 through 5 a system of weighted points is given.   In each case find M_x, M_y, $\bar{P}$ and the moment about the line $y = 3$.   For each problem make a plane diagram showing the points and the center of gravity.

   1. $P_1(2, 3)$, $m_1 = 7$; $P_2(5, 3)$, $m_2 = 14$.
   2. $P_1(6, -2)$, $m_1 = 10$; $P_2(-2, 6)$, $m_2 = 10$.
   3. $P_1(7, 1)$, $m_1 = 5$; $P_2(3, 5)$, $m_2 = 5$; $P_3(-2, -4)$, $m_3 = 2$.
   4. $P_1(1, 5)$, $m_1 = 2$; $P_2(3, 6)$, $m_2 = 1$; $P_3(4, 2)$, $m_3 = 1$;
$P_4(2, -2)$, $m_4 = 2$; $P_5(-7, 3)$, $m_5 = 4$.
   5. $P_1(0, 2)$, $m_1 = 2$; $P_2(1, 7)$, $m_2 = 5$; $P_3(8, 4)$, $m_3 = 2$;
$P_4(7, -1)$, $m_4 = 5$; $P_5(4, 3)$, $m_5 = 6$.
   6. What weight should be placed at $(4, -7)$ in addition to the weights in problem 1, so that the new system will have its center of gravity at $(4, 0)$?

★7.   Suppose that each particle of a given system of weighted particles is moved parallel to the x-axis h units to the right.   Prove that the center of gravity of the new system of weighted particles is h units to the right of the center of gravity of the original system.

Observe that in your proof h could be negative (particles moved to the left). Also observe that the same type of proof will give a similar result for a translation of the particles parallel to the y-axis.   Thus you have proved that for a translation of a system of weighted particles, the center of gravity undergoes the same translation.

★★8.   Suppose that each particle of a given system of weighted particles is rotated about the origin through an angle α.   Prove that the center of gravity of this new system of weighted particles can be obtained by rotating the center of gravity of the original system about the origin through an angle α.   (See Chapter 6, Exercise 7, problem 17.)

Observe that in problems 8 and 9 we could just as easily regard the points as fixed, and the axes as being translated or rotated.   Thus you have proved that the center of gravity of a system of weighted particles is independent of the selection of the axes used to compute it.   For this reason we may be content to compute M_x and M_y.   In practical work we can select our axes in a convenient way.   Thus in the design of ships or airplanes, one axis is taken along the longitudinal center line, and the other is taken perpendicular to this line at the front end of the ship or airplane.

★9.   Prove that if P_1 and P_2 are two given points then positive weights can be assigned at these two points in such a way that the center of gravity of the system will be at any preassigned point in the interior of the line segment joining P_1 and P_2. *Hint:* By problems 7 and 8 you may assume that P_1 is at the origin and P_2 is on the x-axis.

★10.   Generalize the statements of problem 9 to the case of three given points P_1, P_2, and P_3.

★11.   (A paradox).   Consider the set of infinitely many weighted points on the positive part of the x-axis distributed as follows.   Weight $m_1 = 1$ located at $x_1 = 1/2$; $m_2 = 1/2$ at $x_2 = 1/3$; $m_3 = 1/3$ at $x_3 = 1/4$; $\cdots$.   In general for each positive integer n, there is a mass of weight $1/n$ located at $x_n = 1/(n+1)$.   Show that this system has no center of gravity, i.e., there is no axis parallel to the y-axis about which the moment of the system is zero.   *Hint:* For this system

$$M_y = \sum_{n=1}^{\infty} \frac{1}{n(n+1)} = 1.$$

12.   A particle of weight $1/2^k$ is placed on the x-axis at $x = 1/2^k$ for $k = 0, 1, 2, \cdots$.   Find $\bar{x}$ for this system.

13.   Suppose that a system consisting of a finite number of weighted points is symmetric with respect to the y-axis.   This means that if $P_k(x_k, y_k)$ with weight m_k is in the system, then there is a second point with the same weight, but coordinates $(-x_k, y_k)$ that is also in the system.   Prove that such a system, symmetric with respect to the y-axis, has its center of gravity on the y-axis.

★14.   Consider the system consisting of weights $m_n = 1/n^2$ placed at $(\pm n, 0)$ for $n = 1, 2, 3 \cdots$.   This system has infinitely many points and is symmetric with respect to the y-axis.   Prove that the total weight of the system is finite, but that the system does not have a uniquely determined center of gravity.   This explains the need for the hypothesis of finitely many points in problem 13.

2.   Systems of weighted particles in space.   Naturally our problem is to find the center of gravity of a system of weighted particles when they do not lie in a plane.   Our first impulse would be to compute M_x and M_y as before and also M_z, the moment about the z-axis.

To see that this is incorrect consider the system of three weighted points pictured in Fig. 2, where unit weights are placed at $P_1(1, 1, 0)$ and $P_3(1, 5, 0)$, and a weight of two units is placed at $P_2(1, 3, 4)$.

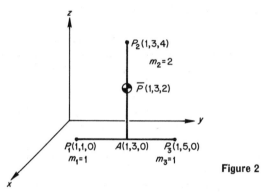

Figure 2

Purely on intuitive grounds we could replace the two unit weights at P_1 and P_3 by a weight of two units at $A(1, 3, 0)$ and then obviously $\bar{P}$ should lie at $(1, 3, 2)$, the midpoint of the segment P_2A.   But the computations of $\bar{P}$ via M_x and M_y give a different location.   Indeed using the distances of the points from the axes we have

$$M_x = 1 \times 1 + 2\sqrt{3^2 + 4^2} + 1 \times 5 = 1 + 10 + 5 = 16,$$

$$M_y = 1 \times 1 + 2\sqrt{1^2 + 4^2} + 1 \times 1 = 1 + 2\sqrt{17} + 1 \approx 10.246,$$

and since $m = 1 + 2 + 1 = 4$,

$$\bar{x} = \frac{M_y}{4} \approx \frac{10.246}{4} = 2.5615, \quad \bar{y} = \frac{M_x}{4} = \frac{16}{4} = 4. \tag{9}$$

These answers are obviously *wrong*.

To find the correct procedure we observe that the force of gravity acting upon the weight at P_2 acts along the line P_2A, and its turning effect about the x-axis is really the weight multiplied by the distance of the line of action of the force from the x-axis.   This distance is not $\sqrt{3^2 + 4^2} = 5$, but is just 3, the y coordinate of P_2. We observe that this is the distance of P_2 from the xz-plane, and for convenience we regard this product as a moment about the xz-plane, and denote it by M_{xz}.

DEFINITION 3. *The moments about the coordinate planes of a system of weighted points are denoted by M_{yz}, M_{xz}, and M_{xy} and are given by*

$$M_{yz} = \sum_{k=1}^{n} m_k x_k = m_1 x_1 + m_2 x_2 + \cdots + m_n x_n, \qquad (10)$$

$$M_{xz} = \sum_{k=1}^{n} m_k y_k = m_1 y_1 + m_2 y_2 + \cdots + m_n y_n \qquad (11)$$

$$M_{xy} = \sum_{k=1}^{n} m_k z_k = m_1 z_1 + m_2 z_2 + \cdots + m_n z_n. \qquad (12)$$

DEFINITION 4. *The coordinates of $\bar{P}(\bar{x}, \bar{y}, \bar{z})$, the center of gravity of a system of weighted points in three dimensional space, is given by*

$$\bar{x} = \frac{M_{yz}}{m}, \qquad \bar{y} = \frac{M_{xz}}{m}, \qquad \bar{z} = \frac{M_{xy}}{m}. \qquad (13a,b,c)$$

It may seem unreasonable to speak about the moment of our system about the xy-plane, because gravity acts perpendicular to this plane. But keep in mind that the system of points together with the y and z coordinate axes could be rotated 90° about the x-axis and then the xy-plane would be a vertical plane, with the force of gravity acting parallel to it.

EXAMPLE 1. Find the center of gravity of the system of weighted points shown in Fig. 2.

SOLUTION. By Definitions 3 and 4,

$$M_{yz} = 1 \times 1 + 2 \times 1 + 1 \times 1 = 1 + 2 + 1 = 4, \qquad \bar{x} = \frac{4}{4} = 1,$$

$$M_{xz} = 1 \times 1 + 2 \times 3 + 1 \times 5 = 1 + 6 + 5 = 12, \qquad \bar{y} = \frac{12}{4} = 3,$$

$$M_{xy} = 1 \times 0 + 2 \times 4 + 1 \times 0 = 0 + 8 + 0 = 8, \qquad \bar{z} = \frac{8}{4} = 2.$$

Thus we find that $\bar{P}$ is at $(1, 3, 2)$, where it should be, as we knew all along.

EXERCISE 2

In problems 1 through 5 a system of weighted points is given. In each case find $\bar{P}$, the center of gravity. Make a sketch of the given system.

1. $m = 1$ for each of the points $(0, 0, 0)$, $(2, 0, 0)$, $(0, 2, 0)$, $(2, 2, 0)$, and $(1, 1, 5)$.

2. $m = 1$ at $(3a, 0, 0)$, $(0, 3b, 0)$, and $(0, 0, 3c)$.

3. $m = 1$ at $(0, 0, 0)$, $(4a, 0, 0)$, $(0, 4b, 0)$, and $(0, 0, 4c)$.

4. $m = 1$ at $(1, 0, 0)$, $m = 2$ at $(2, 1, 1)$, $m = 3$ at $(0, 1, 1)$, $m = 4$ at $(0, 1, -1)$, $m = 5$ at $(2, 1, -1)$, $m = 6$ at $(1, 3, 1)$.

5. $m = 2$ at $(-1, 0, 5)$, $m = 1$ at $(0, 1, 4)$, $m = 1$ at $(2, 3, 2)$, $m = 2$ at $(3, 4, 1)$.

*6. Prove that if all of the points of a weighted system lie in a fixed plane $Ax + By + Cz = D$, then the center of gravity also lies in that plane.

*7. Prove that if all of the points of a weighted system lie on a straight line then the center of gravity also lies on that straight line.

*8. Suppose that in a given weighted system each weight is multiplied by the same positive constant c to form a new weighted system. Prove that the center of gravity of the new system coincides with the center of gravity of the original system.

3.   Density. Roughly speaking the density of a material is its weight per unit volume. For example if a steel beam weighs 976 lbs and has a volume of 2 cu ft, then it is customary to say that its density is $976/2 = 488$ lbs per cubic foot. This is assuming that the steel beam is uniform or homogeneous. If the beam has air pockets, or has a variable composition, the density of one end of the beam may differ from the density at the other end. In such a case we say that the density is variable and that the beam has an *average density* of 488 lbs per cubic foot.

In some cases we are interested in flat sheets of material, where the thickness of the sheet is the same throughout. Under such circumstances it is natural to divide the weight by the area, and to speak of the surface density (or area density). For instance a certain sheet of copper approximately .2 in. thick is 3 ft wide and 4 ft long and weighs 96 lbs. Then its surface density is $96/3 \times 4 = 8$ lbs per square foot. Here again this represents the density only if the material is homogeneous. Otherwise the sheet has an *average surface density* of 8 lbs per square foot.

In the case of a wire of uniform thickness we would divide the weight by the length of the wire. For example a certain aluminum wire is 10 ft long and weighs .024 lbs. Then the *average linear density* of this wire is .024/10 × 12 = .0002 lbs per inch.

When the material is not homogeneous we define the density at a point as the limiting value of the average density. We use δ (Greek letter delta) for this quantity, and whenever it is necessary to distinguish between linear, surface, and solid density we use δ_1, δ_2, and δ_3 respectively.

> DEFINITION[2] 4. *Let $P_0(x_0, y_0, z_0)$ be a fixed point inside a solid body and let C be a cube of side r with P_0 as center. Let m(r) denote the weight of the material inside the cube C, and let $V(r) = r^3$ be the volume of C. Then $\delta_3(x_0, y_0, z_0)$, the density of the solid at P_0, is given by*

$$\delta_3(x_0, y_0, z_0) = \lim_{r \to 0} \frac{m(r)}{V(r)}. \tag{13}$$

For the surface density (13) is replaced by

$$\delta_2(x_0, y_0) = \lim_{r \to 0} \frac{m(r)}{A(r)}, \tag{14}$$

where the sheet of material is now considered as lying in the *xy*-plane, and $A(r) = r^2$ denotes the area of a square of side *r* and center at (x_0, y_0).

For linear density, we take a segment of the arc of length *s* with P_0 as center, and then by definition

$$\delta_1(x_0, y_0) = \lim_{s \to 0} \frac{m(s)}{s}, \tag{15}$$

where $m(s)$ denotes the weight of the segment.

---

[2] There are some logical difficulties with this definition. We naturally think of the cube *C* as having its faces parallel to the coordinate planes. But if we select our cubes so that this is not true, will we get the same number as a limit in (13)? Again suppose we use spheres, or ellipsoids, or some other closed surface and m(r) and V(r) denote the weight and volume enclosed by the surface, will we still obtain the same limit in (13)? At this stage, it is much simpler to just ignore such questions.

Another block that may occur to the reader at this point lies in the atomic theory of matter. If P_0 happens to be at some point not occupied by an elementary particle (electron, proton, neutron, etc.) then the limit in (13) is zero. For other locations, we need to have a knowledge of the internal composition of these elementary particles in order to evaluate the limit in (13). Actually this causes no practical difficulty because in the applications the solids will be extremely large compared to the dimensions of the atoms. On the other hand we can regard the work of this chapter as purely mathematical in which we assume that matter is continously distributed (not discrete as in the atomic theory) and our results are completely independent of the true nature of the physical world.

Although these limiting ratios are not derivatives in the usual sense it is convenient to use derivative notation and write

$$\delta_1 = \frac{dm}{ds}, \qquad \delta_2 = \frac{dm}{dA}, \qquad \delta_3 = \frac{dm}{dV}. \qquad (16a,b,c)$$

Equation set (16) suggests the approximate relations

$$\Delta m \approx \delta_1 \Delta s, \qquad \Delta m \approx \delta_2 \Delta A, \qquad \Delta m \approx \delta_3 \Delta V, \qquad (17a,b,c)$$

when the quantities Δs, ΔA, and ΔV are small, and these last are easily justified on the basis of the definitions (13), (14), and (15).

EXAMPLE 1.   A piece of wire bent in the shape of the parabola $y = x^2$, runs from the point $(1, 1)$ to the point $(2, 4)$.   The density is variable and when the wire is placed in the position described above, $\delta_1 = .003x$ lbs/ft.   If x and y are in feet, find the total weight of the wire.

SOLUTION.   We divide the wire up into n pieces, as indicated in Fig. 3. From equation (17a) a good approximation to Δm_k, the weight of the kth piece is

$$\Delta m_k \approx \delta_1(x_k)\Delta s_k \approx .003x_k\Delta s_k$$

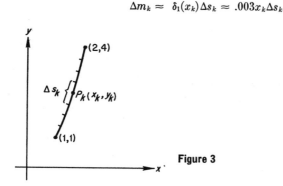

Figure 3

and hence for the total weight m,

$$m = \sum_{k=1}^{n} \Delta m_k \approx \sum_{k=1}^{n} .003x_k\Delta s_k.$$

In the limit as the number of subdivisions n tends to infinity

$$m = \int_1^2 .003x\,ds = \int_1^2 .003x\sqrt{1 + (2x)^2}\,dx = \frac{.003}{8}\frac{(1 + 4x^2)^{3/2}}{3/2}\Big|_1^2$$

$$= \frac{.001}{4}[(\sqrt{17})^3 - (\sqrt{5})^3] \approx .0147 \text{ lbs.}$$

EXERCISE 3

1.   Aluminum has a density of 168 lbs/ft³.   Find the surface density of a homogeneous sheet .05 in. thick.

2. Copper has a density of 540 lbs/ft³. Find the surface density of a homogeneous sheet .03 in. thick.

3. Find the linear density of a homogeneous copper wire if the area of the cross section is .012 in².

4. Find the linear density of a homogeneous aluminum wire if the cross section area is .006 in².

5. Find the surface density in lbs/in.² of a sheet of copper .01 in. thick.

6. A homogeneous piece of copper wire 6 ft. long and of constant cross section weighs .09 lbs. Find the cross section area.

7. A certain piece of wire is placed on the x-axis from $x = 1$ to $x = 4$ (units in ft) and in this position has a variable density of x lbs/ft. Find the weight of the wire.

8. Find the weight of the wire if the density in problem 7 is $\sqrt{x}$ lbs/ft.

★9. A piece of wire of variable density is placed on the x-axis and in this position has the property that for each $a > 0$ the weight of the wire lying between $x = -a$ and $x = a$ is a^n. Show that if $n > 1$ the linear density of the wire at $x = 0$ is 0, and if $n < 1$ the linear density at $x = 0$ is infinite.

★★10. Assuming that the weight of the wire in problem 9 is distributed symmetrically with respect to $x = 0$, find the linear density at $x = 3$.

★11. A rectangular plate 2 ft wide and 5 ft high has a variable surface density of $(3 + y)$ lbs/ft² where y is the distance from the base. Find the weight of this plate.

★12. A sphere of radius 2 ft has density $\dfrac{1}{r + 4}$ lbs/ft³ where r is the distance from the origin. Find the weight of this sphere. *Hint:* Consider the solid as built of spherical shells so that $dV = 4\pi r^2 dr$.

★13. Suppose that the solid of problem 12 has density $1/r$ lbs/ft³, so that at the center the density is infinite. Is the weight of the sphere finite?

★14. Find the weight of a wire bent in the form of the catenary $y = \cosh x$, $-a \leq x \leq a$, $\delta_1 = y$ lbs/ft, and y and x are in feet.

4. The centroid of a plane region.

EXAMPLE 1. A sheet of metal has the form of the region in the first quadrant enclosed by the axes and the curve $y = 4 - x^2$, as shown in Fig. 4. If the sheet is homogeneous and has surface[3] density δ find the center of gravity.

SOLUTION. We first compute the total weight of the sheet. Dividing the sheet into vertical strips by lines parallel to the y-axis, each strip has weight

$$m_k = \delta \, A_k \approx \delta \, y_k \Delta x_k.$$

Hence $m \approx \sum\limits_{k=1}^{n} \delta y_k \Delta x_k$ and taking the limit as $n \to \infty$

$$m = \int_0^2 \delta y \, dx = \delta \int_0^2 y \, dx = \delta \int_0^2 (4 - x^2) \, dx = \delta\left(4x - \frac{x^3}{3}\right)\Big|_0^2 = \frac{16\delta}{3}.$$

[3] From here on it will always be obvious whether the density is linear, surface, or volume and hence we can drop the subscript and use δ without decorations.

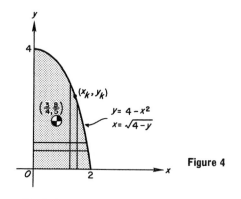

Figure 4

To find $\bar{x}$ we must compute M_y. Each particle in the kth vertical strip is approximately at distance x_k from the y-axis, and this approximation becomes better as $\Delta x_k \to 0$. Hence the moment of each strip about the y-axis is approximately $x_k m_k = x_k \delta A_k \approx x_k y_k \Delta x_k$; and on summing

$$M_y \approx \sum_{k=1}^{n} \delta x_k y_k \Delta x_k.$$

Then on taking the limit as $n \to \infty$, we have

$$M_y = \int_0^2 \delta xy \, dx = \delta \int_0^2 xy \, dx = \delta \int_0^2 x(4 - x^2) \, dx$$

$$= \delta \left(2x^2 - \frac{x^4}{4} \right) \Bigg|_0^2 = \delta(8 - 4) = 4\delta.$$

Then

$$\bar{x} = \frac{M_y}{m} = \frac{4\delta}{\dfrac{16\delta}{3}} = \frac{3}{4}.$$

To find M_x we divide the sheet into horizontal strips by lines parallel to the x-axis. The reasoning is similar, except that now the roles played by x and y are interchanged. We find that

$$M_x = \int_0^4 y \, dm = \int_0^4 y \delta dA = \int_0^4 y \delta x \, dy = \delta \int_0^4 y\sqrt{4 - y} \, dy.$$

To evaluate this integral make the substitution $u = 4 - y$, $y = 4 - u$. Then

$$M_x = \delta \int_4^0 (4 - u)\sqrt{u}(-du) = \delta \int_0^4 (4\sqrt{u} - u\sqrt{u}) \, du$$

$$= \delta \left(\frac{8}{3} u^{3/2} - \frac{2}{5} u^{5/2} \right) \Bigg|_0^4 = \delta \left(\frac{64}{3} - \frac{64}{5} \right) = \frac{128\delta}{15}.$$

Finally

$$\bar{y} = \frac{M_x}{m} = \frac{\dfrac{128\delta}{15}}{\dfrac{16\delta}{3}} = \frac{128}{15} \times \frac{3}{16} = \frac{8}{5}.$$

Then the center of gravity is at $(3/4, 8/5)$. Notice that this point lies inside the shaded region of Fig. 4, as our intuition tells us it must.

We observe that in finding M_x the integration was a little difficult. In some cases the actual work may be quite involved. Therefore it pays to have an alternate method. We now compute M_x using vertical strips. In this case each strip is approximately a rectangle, but some of the particles are near the x-axis while others are far away. The key idea is that the center of gravity of a rectangle is its geometric center. Hence for the near-rectangle the center of gravity is very close to the point $(x_k, y_k/2)$. The moment of the kth strip about the x-axis is approximately $m_k y_k/2$. Summing over all such strips and taking the limit as $n \to \infty$ gives

$$M_x = \int_0^2 \frac{y}{2}\, dm = \int_0^2 \frac{y}{2}\, \delta dA = \delta \int_0^2 \frac{y}{2}\, y\, dx = \frac{\delta}{2} \int_0^2 (4 - x^2)^2 dx$$

$$= \frac{\delta}{2} \int_0^2 (16 - 8x^2 + x^4) dx = \frac{\delta}{2} \left(16x - \frac{8}{3} x^3 + \frac{1}{5} x^5 \right) \Big|_0^2$$

$$= \frac{\delta}{2} \left(32 - \frac{64}{3} + \frac{32}{5} \right) = \frac{128\delta}{15}.$$

Similarly we can compute M_y using horizontal strips. This is left for the student.

We now abstract from this example the essential features. We observe that the center of gravity $(3/4, 8/5)$ did not depend on δ, but only on the shape of the metal sheet. Indeed whenever a solid is homogeneous the center of gravity is independent of the density of the solid. Hence as a matter of convenience we may take $\delta = 1$. When this is done, we drop the term "metal sheet," and instead refer to a "region." The center of gravity is then called the *centroid* of the region. This is stated precisely in

DEFINITION 5. *Let R be a plane region, lying in the rectangle $a \le x \le b$, $c \le y \le d$ (see Fig. 5). Let the line $x = x_0$ intersect this region in a segment of length $h(x_0)$ for each x_0 in $a \le x_0 \le b$, and let the line $y = y_0$ intersect this region in a line segment of length $l(y_0)$ for each y_0 in $c \le y_0 \le d$. Then M_x and M_y, the moments of R about the x and y axis respectively, are given by*

$$M_x = \int_c^d yl(y)dy, \qquad M_y = \int_a^b xh(x)dx. \qquad (18a,b)$$

The coordinates $(\bar{x}, \bar{y})$ of the centroid $\bar{P}$ of the region are given by

$$\bar{x} = \frac{M_y}{A}, \qquad \bar{y} = \frac{M_x}{A}, \tag{19a,b}$$

where A is the area of the region R.

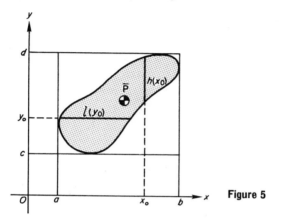

Figure 5

EXAMPLE 2.   Find the centroid of the shaded region of Fig. 4.

SOLUTION.   We have already solved this problem in Example 1.   Just repeat all of the computations, omitting the factor δ.   The centroid is $(3/4, 8/5)$.

EXAMPLE 3.   Find the centroid of the region bounded above by the line $y = 1$ and bounded below by the curve $y = x^2/4$.

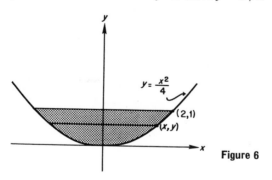

Figure 6

SOLUTION.   The region is shown shaded in Fig. 6.   It is immediately obvious that the region is symmetric with respect to the y-axis, and hence

(see problem 21 in the next exercise list) the centroid lies on the y-axis.   Therefore $\bar{x} = 0$.   Whenever such a symmetry presents itself, we can and should
use it to shorten the labor of locating the centroid.

To find $\bar{y}$ we need M_x.   Using horizontal strips as indicated in the figure we
see that $l(y) = 2x$ where x is the coordinate of the appropriate point on the
curve.   Since $x = 2\sqrt{y}$, (18a) gives

$$M_x = \int_0^1 yl(y)dy = \int_0^1 y2(2\sqrt{y})dy = 4 \times \frac{2}{5}y^{5/2}\Big|_0^1 = \frac{8}{5}.$$

To find the area, we can just drop the first y in the above computation:

$$A = \int_0^1 l(y)dy = \int_0^1 2(2\sqrt{y})dy = 4 \times \frac{2}{3}y^{3/2}\Big|_0^1 = \frac{8}{3}.$$

Then $\bar{y} = M_x/A = \dfrac{8}{5} \times \dfrac{3}{8} = \dfrac{3}{5}.$ The centroid is at $\left(0, \dfrac{3}{5}\right).$

EXAMPLE 4.   Find the centroid of the region bounded by the parabola
$y = 4x - x^2$ and the line $y = x$.

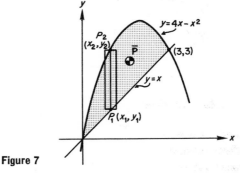

Figure 7

SOLUTION.   The region is shown shaded in Fig. 7.   For the area we have
as usual

$$A = \int_0^3 (y_2 - y_1)dx = \int_0^3 (4x - x^2 - x)dx = \frac{3x^2}{2} - \frac{x^3}{3}\Big|_0^3 = \frac{27}{2} - 9 = \frac{9}{2}.$$

Since the length of each vertical strip is given by $h(x) = y_2 - y_1 = 4x - x^2 - x = 3x - x^2$, equation (18b) gives

$$M_y = \int_0^3 xh(x)dx = \int_0^3 (3x^2 - x^3)dx = x^3 - \frac{x^4}{4}\Big|_0^3 = \frac{27}{4}.$$

Hence $\bar{x} = M_y/A = \dfrac{27}{4} \times \dfrac{2}{9} = \dfrac{3}{2}.$ It is not easy to find M_x using formula
(18a) because the expression for $l(y)$, the length of the horizontal segments,
involves difficulties.   The reader should convince himself that this is so, by

trying to use (18a). To avoid these difficulties, we stay with the vertical strips and observe that the midpoint of the line segment P_1P_2 has y-coordinate $(y_1 + y_2)/2$. Then the vertical strip of width Δx_k will have a moment about the x-axis approximately equal to

$$\frac{y_1 + y_2}{2}\Delta A_k = \frac{y_1 + y_2}{2}(y_2 - y_1)\Delta x_k.$$

Taking a sum of such strips, and then the limit as $n \to \infty$ in the usual way, we have the general formula

$$M_x = \int_a^b \frac{y_1 + y_2}{2}(y_2 - y_1)dx. \tag{20}$$

In our specific case, equation (20) yields

$$M_x = \int_0^3 \left(\frac{5x - x^2}{2}\right)(3x - x^2)dx = \frac{1}{2}\int_0^3 (15x^2 - 8x^3 + x^4)dx$$

$$= \frac{1}{2}\left(5x^3 - 2x^4 + \frac{1}{5}x^5\right)\Big|_0^3 = \frac{x^3}{2}\left(5 - 2x + \frac{1}{5}x^2\right)\Big|_0^3 = \frac{54}{5}.$$

Hence $\bar{y} = M_x/A = \frac{54}{5} \times \frac{2}{9} = \frac{12}{5}$. The student should prove that the centroid $(3/2, 12/5)$ lies inside the region.

EXERCISE 4

In these problems a and b are positive constants.

1. Prove by integration that the rectangle bounded by the coordinate axes and the lines x $= a$ and y $= b$ has its centroid at $(a/2, b/2)$, the geometric center of the rectangle.

In problems 2 through 15 find the centroid of the region bounded by the given curves.

2. $y = 3 - x$, $y = 0$, and $x = 0$ (a triangle).
3. $bx + ay = ab$, $y = 0$, and $x = 0$ (a triangle).
4. $y = 8 - x$, $y = 0$, $y = 6$, and $x = 0$ (a trapezoid).
5. $y = x^2$, $x = 2$, and $y = 0$.
6. $y = \sqrt[3]{x}$, $x = 8$, and $y = 0$.
7. $y = \sqrt{x}$, $x = 1$, $x = 4$, and $y = 0$.
8. $y = 2 + x^2$, $x = -1$, $x = 1$, and $y = 0$.
9. $y = x - x^4$, and $y = 0$.
10. $y = x^3$, and $y = 4x$ $(x \geq 0)$.
★11. $x = y^2 - 2y$, and $x = 6y - y^2$.
12. $y = \sqrt{a^2 - x^2}$, and $y = 0$ (semicircle).
13. $y = \sin x$, and $y = 0$ $(0 \leq x \leq \pi)$.

14. $y = e^x$, $y = 0$, $x = 0$, and $x = 2$.

★15. $y = e^x$, $y = 0$ $(-\infty < x \leqq 2)$.

★16. The region below the curve $y = 1/x$, above the x-axis and to the right of the line $x = 1$ has infinite extent. Prove that the area and M_y are infinite, but M_x is finite. Find M_x.

★17. The region below the curve $y = 1/x^2$, above the x-axis and to the right of the line $x = 1$ has infinite extent. Prove that the area and M_x are finite; but M_y is infinite. Hence we can compute $\bar{y}$, but $\bar{x} = \infty$. Find $\bar{y}$.

★18. In problem 17 replace $y = 1/x^2$ by the curve $y = 1/x^3$ and find the centroid of the region. Notice that $\bar{y}$ for this region is *greater* than $\bar{y}$ for the region of problem 17.

★19. A rectangular sheet of metal 4 ft by 6 ft is placed in the first quadrant of a rectangular coordinate system in such a way that one corner is at the origin, and another corner is at the point $(4, 6)$. In this position the surface density is $(3 + x)$ lbs/ft². Find M_x, M_y, and the center of gravity.

★20. The sheet of problem 19 is cut along the diagonal from $(4, 0)$ to $(0, 6)$ and the upper part is rejected. Find the center of gravity of the remaining piece.

★21. Prove that if a region is bounded and symmetric with respect to the y-axis, then the centroid is on the y-axis.

5.   The moment of inertia of a plane region. In section 1 we defined the moment of a particle about an axis as ml where m is the weight of the particle and l is its distance from the axis. There is nothing to prevent us from considering other types of moments in which we use different powers on l. We call ml^2 the second moment, ml^3 the third moment, etc. All of these quantities are mathematically of interest, but we will consider only the second moment ml^2, because it is this one that is important in dynamics and in the mechanics of materials. Because of the importance of the second moment, it is given a special name "moment of inertia," and a special symbol I. Just as in the case of the first moment, whenever the body is homogeneous, δ is a constant, and it is convenient to assume that $\delta = 1$. For the present we consider just the moment of inertia of a flat sheet of material, and from a mathematical point of view this amounts to a plane region with surface density $\delta = 1$.

DEFINITION 6. *With the notation and the conditions of Definition 5 (as illustrated in Fig. 5), the moment of inertia of the region R about the x-axis and y-axis is given by*

$$I_x = \int_c^d y^2 l(y)\,dy, \qquad I_y = \int_a^b x^2 h(x)\,dx. \qquad (21a,b)$$

It is natural to seek some ideal point such that if all of the material were concentrated at that point it would give the same second moment. For the first moment, this ideal point is the center of gravity. For the moment of inertia, there is no such point, because the location of such a point is found to change as the axis changes. However if we fix the axis we can define a distance k such that $mk^2 = I$, and k is called the *radius of gyration*.

In the simple case of a plane region of area A (with $\delta = 1$) we have by definition that the two radii of gyration with respect to the x and y axes are

$$k_x = \sqrt{\frac{I_x}{A}}, \qquad k_y = \sqrt{\frac{I_y}{A}}. \tag{22a,b}$$

EXAMPLE 1. Find the moment of inertia of a rectangle about one of its edges. Find the radius of gyration with respect to that edge.

SOLUTION. We place the rectangle in a coordinate system as indicated in Fig. 8, and compute I_x and k_x. We divide the rectangle into horizontal strips,

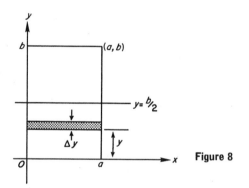

Figure 8

each strip having all its points approximately y units from the x-axis. Forming a sum and taking the limit in the usual way (or appealing to Definition 6) we find

$$I_x = \int_0^b y^2 l(y)dy = \int_0^b y^2\, a\, dy = \frac{ay^3}{3}\Big|_0^b = \frac{ab^3}{3}, \tag{23}$$

$$k_x = \sqrt{\frac{I_x}{A}} = \sqrt{\frac{ab^3}{3ab}} = \frac{b}{\sqrt{3}}.$$

By interchanging the role of x and y it is easy to see that

$$I_y = \frac{ba^3}{3}, \qquad k_y = \frac{a}{\sqrt{3}}. \tag{24}$$

EXAMPLE 2. Find I for the rectangle of Fig. 8 with respect to the axis $y = b/2$.

SOLUTION. Since this line runs through the centroid, one might guess at the answer zero, but this is wrong. Why?

We divide the rectangle into two pieces by the axis, and now each piece has dimensions a and $b/2$. Then applying (23) to each piece and adding we have

$$I_{y=b/2} = \frac{1}{3} a \left(\frac{b}{2}\right)^3 + \frac{1}{3} a \left(\frac{b}{2}\right)^3 = \frac{1}{12} ab^3.$$

SECOND SOLUTION. Each horizontal line has distance $| y - b/2 |$ from the axis. Hence formula (21a) gives

$$I_{y=b/2} = \int_0^b \left(y - \frac{b}{2}\right)^2 l(y) dy = a \int_0^b \left(y - \frac{b}{2}\right)^2 dy$$

$$= \frac{a}{3} \left(y - \frac{b}{2}\right)^3 \Big|_0^b = \frac{a}{3}\left(\frac{b}{2}\right)^3 - \frac{a}{3}\left(-\frac{b}{2}\right)^3 = \frac{ab^3}{12}.$$

EXAMPLE 3. Find I_x and I_y for the region shaded in Fig. 4 (Example 1 of section 4).

SOLUTION. Using vertical strips, equation (21b) gives

$$I_y = \int_0^2 x^2 y \, dx = \int_0^2 x^2(4 - x^2)dx = \frac{4x^3}{3} - \frac{x^5}{5}\Big|_0^2 = 2^5 \left(\frac{1}{3} - \frac{1}{5}\right) = \frac{64}{15}.$$

Using horizontal strips, equation (21a) gives

$$I_x = \int_0^4 y^2 x \, dy = \int_0^4 y^2 \sqrt{4 - y} \, dy. \tag{25}$$

Using the substitution $4 - y = u$, this integral can be evaluated. Our purpose is to show that we can also find I_x using vertical strips. Each such strip is approximately a rectangle of width Δx and height y, so formula (23), derived in Example 1, gives $y^3 \Delta x/3$ as an approximation to ΔI_x for that strip. Summing and taking a limit in the usual way yields

$$I_x = \int_0^2 \frac{y^3}{3} \, dx = \frac{1}{3} \int_0^2 (4 - x^2)^3 dx = \frac{1}{3} \int_0^2 (64 - 48x^2 + 12x^4 - x^6)dx$$

$$= \frac{1}{3} \left(64x - 16x^3 + \frac{12x^5}{5} - \frac{x^7}{7}\right)\Big|_0^2 = \frac{2^7}{3} \left(1 - 1 + \frac{3}{5} - \frac{1}{7}\right) = \frac{2^{11}}{3 \cdot 5 \cdot 7}.$$

The student should complete the computation of (25) and show that he obtains the same answer. He should also compute I_y using horizontal strips.

EXERCISE 5

1. Find I_x for the rectangle with vertices at $(0, b_1)$, $(0, b_2)$, (a, b_1) and (a, b_2) where $a > 0$, and $b_2 > b_1 > 0$. Is the restriction $b_1 > 0$ necessary?

As problems 2 through 9 find I_x and I_y for the regions described in problems 2 through 9 of Exercise 4 of this chapter.

*10.   Find I_x and I_y for the region under the curve $y = \sin x$ and above the x-axis for $0 \leq x \leq \pi$.

*11.   Find I_x and I_y for the region under the curve $y = e^x$ and above the x-axis for $0 \leq x \leq 2$.

**12.   Consider the region of infinite extent below the curve $y = 1/x^p$, above the x-axis and to the right of the line $x = 1$.   Find all values of p such that M_x is infinite and I_x is finite.   Find I_x in terms of p.

*13.   For the region of problem 12, find all values of p for which I_y is finite.

*14.   Find I_x for the region bounded by the curve $y = x^2$ and the straight line $y = 4$.   Hint: Use the results of problem 1.

6.   Three-dimensional regions.

We have already seen that in computing the moments for a three-dimensional set of weighted points it is the directed distance from a *plane* that is of interest.   Hence for a solid body we have by definition

$$M_{yz} = \int x\,dm, \qquad M_{xz} = \int y\,dm, \qquad M_{xy} = \int z\,dm, \qquad (26a,b,c)$$

where the integration is taken over the figure under consideration, and M denotes the moment with respect to the plane indicated by the subscripts.

By contrast the applications to be made in dynamics of the moment of inertia dictate that these be computed with respect to an axis.   Hence by definition, the moments of inertia with respect to the coordinate axes are

$$I_x = \int (y^2 + z^2)\,dm, \qquad I_y = \int (x^2 + z^2)\,dm, \qquad I_z = \int (x^2 + y^2)\,dm. \qquad (27a,b,c)$$

If δ denotes the density then we can substitute $dm = \delta dV$ in (26) and (27).   For simplicity we assume that our body is homogeneous and $\delta = 1$.   Then (26) and (27) give the moments, and moments of inertia of a three-dimensional region and we have

$$M_{yz} = \int x\,dV, \qquad M_{xz} = \int y\,dV, \qquad M_{xy} = \int z\,dV, \qquad (28a,b,c)$$

and

$$I_x = \int (y^2 + z^2)\,dV, \qquad I_y = \int (x^2 + z^2)\,dV, \qquad I_z = \int (x^2 + y^2)\,dV. \qquad (29a,b,c)$$

At present we can carry through the detailed computations only for certain simple cases, such as figures of revolution.   After we have mastered the technique of multiple integration, covered in Chapter 17, we will be able to make our definitions of M and I more precise, and we will be able to compute these quantities for a much greater selection of regions.

EXAMPLE 1. A cone of height H and radius of base R is placed with its vertex at the origin, and axis on the positive y-axis. Find M_{xz} for this cone. Find the centroid of the cone.

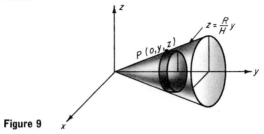

Figure 9

SOLUTION. As indicated in Fig. 9 the cone is cut into elementary disks by planes perpendicular to the y-axis. Each such disk has volume $dV = \pi r^2 h = \pi z^2 dy$. All of the points of such a disk are roughly the same distance y from the xz-plane. Then (28b) gives

$$M_{xz} = \int y\,dV = \int_0^H y\pi z^2\,dy = \int_0^H \pi y\left(\frac{R}{H}y\right)^2 dy$$

$$= \frac{\pi R^2}{H^2} \int_0^H y^3\,dy = \frac{\pi R^2}{H^2}\frac{H^4}{4} = \frac{\pi R^2 H^2}{4}.$$

We can locate the centroid in the usual way. By symmetry $\bar{x} = \bar{z} = 0$. Since the volume of the cone is $\pi R^2 H/3$, we have

$$\bar{y} = \frac{M_{xz}}{V} = \frac{\pi R^2 H^2}{4} \cdot \frac{3}{\pi R^2 H} = \frac{3}{4} H.$$

EXAMPLE 2. Compute the moment of inertia of a solid right circular cylinder with respect to its axis, if the radius of the cylinder is R and its height is H.

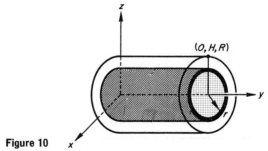

Figure 10

SOLUTION. We place the cylinder as indicated in Fig. 10 and this time we consider the cylinder as built up of hollow cylindrical shells. The surface area of each shell of radius r is $2\pi rH$. Therefore $dV = 2\pi rHdr$. Since all of the points in any one shell are roughly the same distance r from the axis, formula (29b) gives

$$I_y = \int (x^2 + z^2)dV = \int_0^R r^2 2\pi rHdr = 2\pi H\int_0^R r^3dr = \frac{\pi R^4 H}{2}. \qquad (30)$$

EXAMPLE 3. The region in the xz-plane bounded by the curve $z = 4 - x^2$ and the x-axis, is rotated about the z-axis. For the figure generated, find I_z by two different methods.

SOLUTION. **SHELL METHOD.** The portion of the figure that lies in the first octant is shown in Fig. 11.

We consider the solid as built up from cylindrical shells with axes coinciding with the z-axis. One-quarter of such a shell is indicated in the figure. The full shell has surface area $2\pi rh = 2\pi rz$. Consequently $dV = 2\pi rzdr$. Since all points on the shell have the same distance $r = \sqrt{x^2 + y^2}$ from the z-axis, formula (29c) gives

$$I_z = \int (x^2 + y^2)dV = \int_0^2 r^2 2\pi rzdr = 2\pi \int_0^2 r^3(4 - r^2)dr.$$

$$= 2\pi \int_0^2 (4r^3 - r^5)dr = 2\pi \left(r^4 - \frac{r^6}{6} \right)\Big|_0^2 = \frac{32}{3}\pi.$$

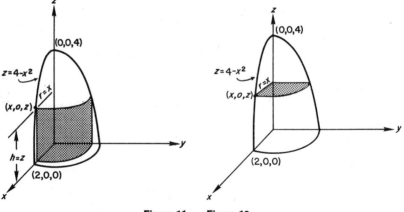

Figure 11   Figure 12

DISK METHOD. We consider the solid as built up from disks, obtained by slicing with planes perpendicular to the z-axis. One-quarter of a typical disk is shown in Fig. 12. Now each such disk can be regarded as a solid cylinder of the type considered in Example 2, except that the height H of the disk is now dz and the radius R is $x = \sqrt{4 - z}$.

Hence by the formula (30) obtained in Example 2, the moment of inertia of each such elementary disk is $\frac{1}{2}\pi R^4 H = \frac{1}{2}\pi(4 - z)^2 dz$. Consequently for the whole solid

$$I_z = \int_0^4 \frac{1}{2}\pi(4 - z)^2 dz = -\frac{\pi}{2}\frac{(4 - z)^3}{3}\bigg|_0^4 = \frac{64\pi}{6} = \frac{32\pi}{3}.$$

EXERCISE 6

In problems 1 through 6 the region in the yz-plane bounded by the given curves is revolved about the z-axis. Find the centroid of the figure generated.

1. $z = \sqrt{R^2 - y^2}$ and $z = 0$ (a hemisphere).
2. $z = y^2$ and $z = 1$.
3. $z = 8 - y^3$, $z = 0$, and $y = 0$.
★4. $z = y^2$, $z = 0$, and $y = 1$.
★5. $z = \sqrt{y}$, $z = 0$, and $y = 4$.
★★6. $z = \sin y$, $z = 0$, and $y = \pi/2$.

7. Find I_z for the solids of revolution described in each of problems 1 through 6.
8. Consider the region of infinite extent below the curve $y = 1/x^n$, above the x-axis, and to the right of the line $x = 1$. This region is rotated about the x-axis to form a solid of infinite extent. For what values of n is I_x finite for this solid? Find I_x in those cases.
9. For the solid of problem 8, find those values of n for which M_{yz} is finite. Find M_{yz} in those cases.

★7. **Curves and surfaces.** The definitions of moment and moment of inertia given in equations (26) and (27) can be applied also to curves and surfaces. In the first case $dm = \delta ds$ where δ is the linear density, and ds is the differential of arc length. For surfaces $dm = \delta dS$ where now δ is the surface density and dS is the differential of surface area. Here a curve is the mathematical idealization of a bent wire, and a surface is the mathematical idealization of a curved sheet of metal. In most applications the wire or the sheet are homogeneous and δ is a constant. We can then take $\delta = 1$ for simplicity.

EXAMPLE 1. Find the centroid of a semicircular arc of radius R.

SOLUTION. We consider the semicircle placed in an xy-plane as shown in Fig. 13. By symmetry $\bar{x} = 0$. To find $\bar{y}$ we need M_x. Now

$$M_x = \int_{-R}^R y\,ds = 2\int_0^R y\sqrt{1 + \left(\frac{dy}{dx}\right)^2}\,dx$$

$$= 2\int_0^R \sqrt{R^2 - x^2}\sqrt{1 + \frac{x^2}{R^2 - x^2}}\,dx$$

$$= 2\int_0^R \sqrt{R^2 - x^2 + x^2}\,dx = 2Rx\bigg|_0^R = 2R^2.$$

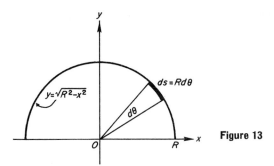

Figure 13

Sometimes it is convenient to use polar coordinates to shorten the labor. In this case we have $ds = Rd\theta$ and $y = R \sin \theta$. Then

$$M_x = \int y\,ds = \int_0^\pi R \sin \theta \; Rd\theta = R^2 \int_0^\pi \sin \theta \; d\theta = -R^2 \cos \theta \Big|_0^\pi = 2R^2.$$

Since the semicircle has length πR, we have $\bar{y} = M_x/L = 2R^2/\pi R = 2R/\pi$.

EXAMPLE 2.   Find the centroid of a hemisphere of radius R.

SOLUTION.   We can consider the hemisphere as generated by rotating the semicircle of Fig. 13 about the y-axis.   Then by symmetry $\bar{x} = \bar{z} = 0$.

$$M_{xz} = \int y\,dS = \int y2\pi \; x\,ds = \int_0^{\pi/2} (R \sin \theta)2\pi(R \cos \theta)\,Rd\theta$$

$$= \pi R^3 \int_0^{\pi/2} 2 \sin \theta \cos \theta \; d\theta = \pi R^3 \sin^2 \theta \Big|_0^{\pi/2} = \pi R^3.$$

Since the surface area is $2\pi R^2$, we have $\bar{y} = \dfrac{\pi R^3}{2\pi R^2} = \dfrac{R}{2}.$

EXERCISE 7

1.   Find the centroid of the quarter circle $y = \sqrt{R^2 - x^2}$, $0 \le x \le R$.

2.   Find the centroid of the portion of the spherical surface $x^2 + y^2 + z^2 = R^2$ that lies in the first octant.

3.   Find I_x for the curve of problem 1.

4.   Find I_x for the surface of problem 2.

5.   The segment of the straight line $Bx + Ay = AB$ ($A > 0, B > 0$) that lies in the first quadrant is rotated about the x-axis.   Find the centroid of the surface generated (right circular cone).

6.   Find I_x for the surface of problem 5.

7.   Find the centroid of that portion of the hypocycloid $x = A \cos^3 t$, $y = A \sin^3 t$ that lies in the first quadrant.

★8.   The curve of problem 7 is rotated about the x-axis.   Find $\bar{x}$ for the surface generated.

9.   Find the centroid for the arch of the cycloid $x = A(t - \sin t)$, $y = A(1 - \cos t)$ for which $0 \le t \le 2\pi$.

10. Find $\bar{y}$ for the portion of the catenary $y = \cosh x$ between $x = -a$ and $x = a$.

★11. The curve of problem 10 is rotated about the y-axis. Find $\bar{y}$ for the surface generated.

12. A wire has the form of the quarter circle $x^2 + y^2 = R^2$ lying in the first quadrant, and in that position has density $\delta = R + x$. Find the center of gravity of the wire.

★8. Two Theorems of Pappus. Let A denote the area of a plane region R, and let V be the volume of the figure generated when the region is rotated about an axis in the plane of the region, that does not intersect the region. A convenient method of computing V is given by

THEOREM 2. *Under the conditions described*

$$V = AL \qquad (31)$$

where L is the perimeter of the circle described by the centroid of R.

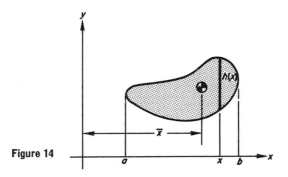

Figure 14

PROOF. We may take our region in the first quadrant and suppose that it is rotated about the y-axis (see Fig. 14). Clearly

$$V = \int_a^b 2\pi x h(x)\,dx$$

$$= 2\pi \int_a^b x h(x)\,dx$$

$$= 2\pi M_y$$

by formula (18b) of Definition 5. But $M_y = \bar{x}A$, and so $V = 2\pi \bar{x}A$. But $2\pi \bar{x} = L$, the distance traveled by the centroid during the rotation. Hence $V = AL$. Q.E.D.

EXAMPLE 1. Find the volume of the torus generated when the region bounded by the circle $(x - R)^2 + y^2 = r^2$ $(R > r > 0)$ is rotated about the y-axis (see Fig. 15).

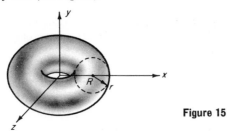

Figure 15

SOLUTION. The centroid is obviously at $(R, 0)$ and the area is πr^2. Hence by (31)

$$V = \pi r^2 (2\pi R) = 2\pi^2 r^2 R.$$

THEOREM 3. *Let s denote the length of a plane curve, and let S be the area of the surface generated when the curve is rotated about an axis in the plane of the curve, that does not intersect the curve. Then*

$$\boxed{S = sL} \qquad\qquad (32)$$

where L is the perimeter of the circle described by the centroid of the curve.

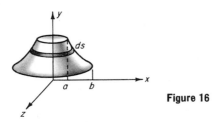

Figure 16

PROOF. We may suppose that our curve lies to the right of the y-axis, and that it is rotated about the y-axis (see Fig. 16). Then the surface area is given by

$$S = \int_a^b 2\pi x \, ds$$

$$= 2\pi \int_a^b x \, ds$$

$$= 2\pi M_y.$$

But $M_y = \bar{x}s$ and $2\pi\bar{x} = L$.   Consequently $S = 2\pi\bar{x}s = sL$.   Q.E.D.

EXAMPLE 2.   Find the surface of the torus of example 1.

SOLUTION.   Here $s = 2\pi r$ and $L = 2\pi R$.   Consequently

$$S = sL = (2\pi r)(2\pi R) = 4\pi^2 Rr.$$

EXERCISE 8

1. A ring shaped solid is generated by rotating a rectangle A units wide and B units high, around a vertical axis R units from the nearest side of the rectangle. Find the volume and the surface area of this figure.

2. The region above the parabola $y = x^2$ and below the line $y = 4$ is rotated about the line $x = -R$, $(R > 2)$.   Find the area of the given region, and use this to find the volume of the solid generated.

3. The triangular region bounded by the coordinate axes and the line $Bx + Hy = BH$ $(B > 0, H > 0)$ is rotated about the line $x = -R$, $(R > 0)$. Find the volume and the surface area of the solid generated.

4. The region of problem 3 is rotated about the line $x = R$ $(R > H)$.   Find the volume and the surface area of the solid generated.

5. Assuming as known the area of a circle and the volume of a sphere, use Theorem 2 to locate the centroid of the semicircular region bounded by the y-axis, and the circle $x^2 + y^2 = r^2$, and lying to the right of the y-axis.

6. Assuming as known that the surface area of a sphere is $4\pi r^2$, use Theorem 3 to find the centroid of the semicircular arc $x^2 + y^2 = r^2$, $x \geq 0$.

7. The semicircular region of problem 5 is rotated about the line $x = -R$ $(R > 0)$.   Find the volume of the solid generated.

8. The semicircular region of problem 5 is rotated about the line $x = R$ $(R > r)$.   Find the volume of the solid generated.

9. Should the sum of the volumes obtained in problems 7 and 8 give the volume of the torus obtained in Example 1?

*9.   Fluid pressure. We have already discussed fluid pressure in section 3 of Chapter 5.   Our objective here is to show how the total force on a submerged vertical plate can be computed if the area and the centroid of the plate are known.

THEOREM 4.   *Suppose that a plate of area A is submerged vertically in a liquid of density w, and that the centroid of the plate has a distance $\bar{y}$ from the surface of the liquid.   Then the total force F exerted by the liquid on one side of the plate is given by*

$$F = w\bar{y}A. \tag{33}$$

Naturally if the plate is completely surrounded by the liquid there is

an equal but oppositely directed force on the other side of the plate so that
the sum of the lateral forces is zero.

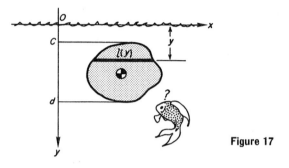

Figure 17

PROOF.   For simplicity we set the x-axis at the surface of the liquid, and
take the positive direction on the y-axis *downward* (see Fig. 17).   Then
the total force on the plate is given by

$$F = \int_c^d P\,dA = \int_c^d wy\,dA = w \int_c^d yl(y)\,dy = wM_x.$$

But $M_x = A\bar{y}$, hence $F = wA\bar{y}$.   Q.E.D.

In practical applications, the engineer has available a handbook listing
various shapes of plates together with their areas and centroids.   The computation in (33) is then extremely simple.

EXAMPLE 1.   A gate for a dam has the form of the region bounded by the
parabola $y = x^2$ and the line $y = 4$ (units in ft) and the top of the gate is
10 ft below the surface of the water.   Find the force of the water on the gate.

SOLUTION.   A suitable handbook (or computations) gives $A = 32/3$ sq. ft,
and locates the centroid at $(0, 12/5)$.   Hence the distance of the centroid from
the surface of the water is $(10 + 4 - 12/5)$ ft.   Consequently (33) gives

$$F = 62.5 \times \frac{58}{5} \times \frac{32}{3} \approx 7{,}730 \text{ lbs.}$$

EXERCISE 9

1.   Find the force on one face of a tank if it is full of water, and the face is a
rectangle 4 ft wide and 6 ft high.

2.   Find the force in problem 1 if the face is an inverted triangle 8 ft wide at
the top and 6 ft high.

3.   A tank car is full of crude oil of density 50 lbs/ft^3.   Find the force on one
end if the tank is a cylinder of radius 3 ft.

4.   A gate for a dam has the form of an inverted isosceles triangle.   The base
is 6 ft and the altitude 10 ft, and the base is 10 ft below the surface of the water.
Find the force of the water on the gate.

5. A gate for a dam has the form of an ellipse and its major axis is horizontal and 10 ft below the surface of the water. Find the force of the water on the gate if the area of the gate is 8 ft².

*10. The parallel axis theorem. If we know the moment of inertia about an axis *g* through the center of gravity of a body then it is a simple matter to find the moment of inertia of the body about any other axis *p*, that is parallel to *g*. If I_g and I_p denote the moments about the axes *g* and *p* respectively, then I_p is given by the formula

$$I_p = I_g + Ms^2 \qquad\qquad (34)$$

where *M* is the weight of the body, and *s* is the distance between the two axes.

In order to prove (34) in this general situation we must use multiple integration, and this is covered in Chapter 17. For the present we will be content with proving (34) when the body is a homogeneous sheet of material of unit density. In this special case we have

THEOREM 5. The Parallel Axis Theorem. *Let R be a plane region, let I_g be the moment of inertia of R about an axis g through the centroid, and let I_p be the moment of inertia about an axis p that is parallel to g.   Then*

$$\boxed{I_p = I_g + As^2} \qquad\qquad (35)$$

where A is the area of the given region and s is the distance between the two axes.

PROOF. As illustrated in Fig. 18 we put the origin of the coordinate system at the center of gravity and we rotate the region (or the axes) so

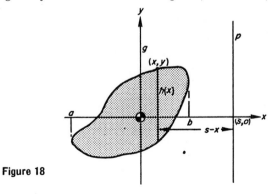

Figure 18

that the y-axis coincides with g.   Then the axis p will be parallel to the
y-axis, and meet the x-axis at the point $(s, 0)$.   We divide the region into
vertical strips, and let $h(x)$ be the height.   Then by definition

$$I_p = \int_a^b (s - x)^2 dA = \int_a^b (s - x)^2 h(x) dx$$

$$= \int_a^b s^2 h(x) dx + \int_a^b (-2sx)h(x) dx + \int_a^b x^2 h(x) dx$$

$$= s^2 \int_a^b h(x) dx - 2s \int_a^b xh(x) dx + \int_a^b x^2 h(x) dx.$$

The first integral is $s^2 A$.   The second integral is the moment of R about
the y-axis, and this is zero because by hypothesis the y-axis passes through
the centroid of R.   Finally the third integral is I_y (or I_g) by definition.
Hence $I_p = s^2 A + I_g$.   Q.E.D.

EXAMPLE.   Find the moment of inertia of a rectangle about one of its sides.

SOLUTION.   Let A and B be the lengths of the sides of the rectangle, and
suppose that the axis p coincides with a side of length A, (see Fig. 8).   By
Example 2 of section 5, $I_g = AB^3/12$.   Hence by (35)

$$I_p = \frac{AB^3}{12} + (AB)\left(\frac{B}{2}\right)^2 = AB^3\left(\frac{1}{12} + \frac{1}{4}\right) = \frac{AB^3}{3}.$$

Observe that this is consistent with the result of Example 1 of section 5.

EXERCISE 10

In problems 1 through 4 a region and an axis are given.   Use results already
obtained in Exercises 4 and 5 to find the moment of inertia of the given region
about the given axis.
   1.   The triangle bounded by the coordinate axes and the line $y = 3 - x$.
The axis is the line $y = 1$.
   2.   The region of problem 1.   The axis is the line $y = -5$.
   3.   The region bounded by $y = x^2$, $x = 2$, and $y = 0$.   (a) The axis is the
line $x = 3/2$ (b) The axis is the line $x = 4$.
   4.   The region bounded by $y = \sqrt[3]{x}$, $x = 8$, and $y = 0$.   The axis is the line
$y = 4/5$.
   5.   Find the moment of inertia of the region shown in Fig. 19 about its vertical
axis of symmetry.
   ★6.   For the region of Fig. 19 find I_g for the axis g indicated in the figure.
The moment of inertia for a region of the type shown is very important in the
strength of materials.
   7.   Given a fixed region, what can you say about the axis, for which I is a
minimum?

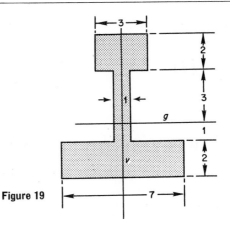

Figure 19

In problems 8 through 10 assume that the general form of the parallel axis theorem (equation (34)) has been proved. A sketch of the proof is given in problem 21 of Exercise 7, Chapter 17.

8. Find the moment of inertia of a solid homogeneous cylinder of unit density, radius R, and height H with respect to an axis lying on the surface.

9. Find the moment of inertia of a solid homogeneous sphere of unit density and radius R, with respect to an axis tangent to the sphere.

★10. A homogeneous sphere of radius 5 and total weight M has a moment of inertia of $26M$ with respect to a certain axis. How far is this axis from the center of the sphere?

16

PARTIAL DIFFERENTIATION

1. Functions of several variables. We have already met functions of several variables in our study of solid analytic geometry. The equation $z = y^2 - x^2$ is the equation for the saddle surface. At the same time it sets forth z as a function of the two variables x and y. To denote an arbitrary function of two variables we can write $z = f(x, y)$. The notation extends in an obvious way for example $w = f(x, y, z, t, r, u)$ means that w is some function of the six variables set forth in the parentheses. As examples we mention:

$$V = lwh, \tag{1}$$

$$A = P(1 + r)^n, \tag{2}$$

$$y = \frac{W}{6EI} (x^3 - 3l^2x + 2l^3). \tag{3}$$

Equation (1) obviously gives the volume of a box as a function of the three variables l, w, and h. Equation (2) gives the amount of money after n interest periods when P dollars are invested at r rate of interest. Here A is also a function of three variables P, r, and n. Equation (3) gives the deflection y in a cantilever beam at a point x distance from the fixed end. Here l is the total length of a beam, W is the weight or load applied at the free end of the beam, I is the moment of inertia of the cross section of the beam, and E is the modulus of elasticity for the material of the beam. In this example y is a function of *five* independent variables W, E, I, x, and l.

The concept of continuity of a function of several variables is a natural extension of the concept for one variable. Roughly it means that if we make a small change in the independent variables, then the change in the function is also small, and that we can make this latter change to be as small as we please, if we restrict the changes in the independent variables to be sufficiently small.   When there are only two independent variables, we can write $z = f(x, y)$ and interpret the function geometrically as a surface.   Then if $f(x, y)$ is a continuous function of two variables, this means that the surface has no vertical cliffs or breaks.   A precise definition of continuity is given in

> **DEFINITION 1.**   *The function $z = f(x, y)$ is continuous at the point (a, b) if for each $\epsilon > 0$, there is a $\delta > 0$ such that if*
>
> $$|x - a| < \delta \qquad and \qquad |y - b| < \delta \tag{4}$$
>
> *then*
>
> $$|f(x, y) - f(a, b)| < \epsilon. \tag{5}$$

The equation set (4) restricts the point (x, y) to lie inside a certain small square of side 2δ and center at (a, b), and equation (5) states that the function does not differ much from $f(a, b)$ in that square.   For most practical purposes it is not necessary to use this $\epsilon - \delta$ definition.

In order to locate points of discontinuity the following set of working rules will cover the great majority of cases.

A.   If z is a rational function, $z = \dfrac{N(x, y)}{D(x, y)}$, where N and D are polynomials, then z is continuous wherever the denominator is not zero.

B.   If $z = \ln f(x, y)$ and $f(x, y)$ is continuous, then z is continuous wherever $f(x, y) > 0$.

C.   If $z = \tan f(x, y)$ and $f(x, y)$ is continuous then z is continuous wherever $f(x, y) \neq \pi/2 + n\pi$.

We leave it to the reader to add rules for $z = \sec f(x, y)$, $z = \cot f(x, y)$, etc.

For example each one of the functions (1), (2), and (3) is continuous. Of course in using (1) and (2) all of the variables are positive, and in fact n is always an integer.   The function given in equation (3), can be regarded as discontinuous (actually undefined) when either E or I are zero, but this can happen only if there is no beam.   Thus (3) is continuous in the natural domain of definition of the function.

Just as in the case of a function of one variable, the derivative gives the rate of change of the function.   But now that we have many independent variables a difficulty arises in deciding what increment to give each of the independent variables.   Actually this complicated situation will be easy to handle, if we first consider the simple case in which we let just *one* of the independent variables change while keeping all of the others constant.   When we do this we obtain the "*partial derivative.*"

If $z = f(x, y)$, the partial derivative is symbolized by writing[1]

$$\frac{\partial z}{\partial x} \quad \text{or} \quad \frac{\partial f}{\partial x}$$

and is read "the partial of z with respect to x" or "the partial of f with respect to x."

DEFINITION 2.   *If $z = f(x, y)$ then*

$$\frac{\partial f}{\partial x} = \lim_{\Delta x \to 0} \frac{f(x + \Delta x, y) - f(x, y)}{\Delta x} = \lim_{\Delta x \to 0} \frac{\Delta z}{\Delta x}, \tag{6}$$

and

$$\frac{\partial f}{\partial y} = \lim_{\Delta y \to 0} \frac{f(x, y + \Delta y) - f(x, y)}{\Delta y} = \lim_{\Delta y \to 0} \frac{\Delta z}{\Delta y}, \tag{7}$$

whenever the limits exist.

Naturally these concepts extend to functions of more than two variables. All of the formulas for differentiation that we have learned so far are still valid for functions of several variables.   The only difficulty is keeping in mind which variables are held constant during the differentiation.

EXAMPLE 1.   Find $\partial y/\partial I$, $\partial y/\partial x$, and $\partial y/\partial l$ for the function (3).

SOLUTION.   We use the standard differentiation formulas.

$$\frac{\partial y}{\partial I} = -\frac{W}{6EI^2}(x^3 - 3l^2x + 2l^3),$$

$$\frac{\partial y}{\partial x} = \frac{W}{6EI}(3x^2 - 3l^2) = \frac{W(x^2 - l^2)}{2EI},$$

$$\frac{\partial y}{\partial l} = \frac{W}{6EI}(-6lx + 6l^2) = \frac{Wl(l - x)}{EI}.$$

Higher order partial derivatives are defined just as in the case of one variable. For example,

$$\frac{\partial^2 z}{\partial x^2} = \frac{\partial}{\partial x}\left(\frac{\partial z}{\partial x}\right), \qquad \frac{\partial^2 z}{\partial y \partial x} = \frac{\partial}{\partial y}\left(\frac{\partial z}{\partial x}\right)$$

$$\frac{\partial^2 z}{\partial x \partial y} = \frac{\partial}{\partial x}\left(\frac{\partial z}{\partial y}\right), \qquad \frac{\partial^4 z}{\partial y^4} = \frac{\partial}{\partial y}\left(\frac{\partial^3 z}{\partial y^3}\right)$$

where in each equation the quantity on the left is defined by the expression on the right.

[1] The symbol ∂ is frequently called a "roundback d."   It is the script d from the Russian alphabet.

EXAMPLE 2. Find each of the four partial derivatives listed above for the function $z = xy^3 + x \sin xy$.

SOLUTION. We must first find $\dfrac{\partial z}{\partial x}$ and $\dfrac{\partial z}{\partial y}$.

$$\frac{\partial z}{\partial x} = y^3 + \sin xy + x(\cos xy)y = y^3 + \sin xy + xy \cos xy \qquad (8)$$

$$\frac{\partial z}{\partial y} = 3xy^2 + x(\cos xy)x = 3xy^2 + x^2 \cos xy. \qquad (9)$$

Using (8) we find

$$\frac{\partial^2 z}{\partial x^2} = \frac{\partial}{\partial x}(y^3 + \sin xy + xy \cos xy)$$

$$= (\cos xy)y + y \cos xy + xy(-\sin xy)y = 2y \cos xy - xy^2 \sin xy.$$

$$\frac{\partial^2 z}{\partial y \partial x} = \frac{\partial}{\partial y}(y^3 + \sin xy + xy \cos xy)$$

$$= 3y^2 + (\cos xy)x + x \cos xy + xy(-\sin xy)x$$

$$\frac{\partial^2 z}{\partial y \partial x} = 3y^2 + 2x \cos xy - x^2 y \sin xy. \qquad (10)$$

Using (9) we find

$$\frac{\partial^2 z}{\partial x \partial y} = \frac{\partial}{\partial x}(3xy^2 + x^2 \cos xy) = 3y^2 + 2x \cos xy - x^2 y \sin xy. \qquad (11)$$

To find $\dfrac{\partial^4 z}{\partial y^4}$, we have from (9)

$$\frac{\partial^2 z}{\partial y^2} = \frac{\partial}{\partial y}(3xy^2 + x^2 \cos xy) = 6xy - x^3 \sin xy.$$

$$\frac{\partial^3 z}{\partial y^3} = \frac{\partial}{\partial y}(6xy - x^3 \sin xy) = 6x - x^4 \cos xy.$$

$$\frac{\partial^4 z}{\partial y^4} = \frac{\partial}{\partial y}(6x - x^4 \cos xy) = x^5 \sin xy.$$

Observe that from (10) and (11)

$$\frac{\partial^2 z}{\partial y \partial x} = \frac{\partial^2 z}{\partial x \partial y} \qquad (12)$$

for the particular function $z = xy^3 + x \sin xy$, and hence the order in which the partial derivatives are taken seems to be unimportant. Actually equation (12) is not true for every function of two variables, but in order to find a function for which (12) is false, one must work very hard (see the problems of Exercise 10). In all practical cases equation (12) is true. We will make this statement precise in Theorem 13 of section 12.

EXERCISE 1

In problems 1 through 10 find the first partial derivative of the given function with respect to each of the independent variables. In each of problems 1 through 8 compute the two mixed partial derivatives of second order and show that for each of the given functions the two mixed partials are equal (see equation (12)).

1. $z = x^2y - xy^3$.
2. $z = e^{xy} \sin(x + 2y)$.

3. $z = x \sec 2y \tan 3x$.
4. $z = \ln(x \cot y^2)$.

5. $v = \sin^{-1} \dfrac{y}{\sqrt{x^2 + y^2}}$.
6. $w = \tan^{-1} \dfrac{y - x}{y + x}$.

7. $x = r \cos \theta$.
8. $u = (s^{1/2} + t^{1/2})^{1/2}$.

9. $w = (x^2 + y^2 + z^2)\ln\sqrt{x^2 + y^2 + z^2}$.

10. $Z = \dfrac{x}{y^2} + \dfrac{y^2}{z^3} + \dfrac{z^3}{t^4} + \dfrac{t^4}{x}$.

11. Prove that if $z = Cx^n y^m$ then equation (12) is satisfied. Then observe that (12) is satisfied whenever z is a sum of such terms. This proves that (12) is satisfied whenever z is a polynomial in the two variables.

12. If $u = xz^2 + yx^2 + zy^2$ show that

$$\frac{\partial u}{\partial x} + \frac{\partial u}{\partial y} + \frac{\partial u}{\partial z} = (x + y + z)^2.$$

13. If $u = A \cos m(x + at) + B \sin n(x - at)$ prove that

$$\frac{\partial^2 u}{\partial t^2} = a^2 \frac{\partial^2 u}{\partial x^2}$$

for all values of the constants A, B, m, n, and a.

14. If $z = x \sin (x/y) + ye^{y/x}$ prove that

$$x \frac{\partial z}{\partial x} + y \frac{\partial z}{\partial y} = z.$$

15. Prove that $u = e^x \sin y + \ln(x^2 + y^2) + x^3 - 3xy^2$ satisfies *Laplace's equation*, $\partial^2 u/\partial x^2 + \partial^2 u/\partial y^2 = 0$. A function that satisfies Laplace's equation is called a *harmonic function*.

16. Prove that each of the following functions satisfies Laplace's equation.

a. $u = \tan^{-1} \dfrac{y}{x}$,
b. $u = x^4 - 6x^2y^2 + y^4$,

★c. $u = \dfrac{x + y}{x^2 + y^2}$,
★d. $u = e^{x^2 - y^2} \sin 2xy$.

★17. Begin the proof that the function $z = x + 2y$ is continuous at the point $(1, 3)$ by finding a suitable δ, when $\epsilon = 1/10$. Observe that δ is not unique.

★18. Complete the proof stated in problem 17 by finding a suitable δ, for any positive ϵ. Observe that δ depends on ϵ, and that δ approaches zero as ϵ approaches zero.

★19. Repeat problem 17 for the function $z = xy$ at $(2, 1)$ with $\epsilon = 1/10$.

★20. Find $\dfrac{\partial^8 z}{\partial y^5 \partial x^3}$ if $z = x^2 y^9 + 2x^5 y^3 - 9x^7 y + y^2 e^x \sin^3 x$.

2. Alternate notations for partial derivatives.

Suppose that we are to find $\partial z / \partial x$ at the point $(1, 2)$ when $z = x^2 y + xy^3$. Naturally we compute

$$\frac{\partial z}{\partial x} = 2xy + y^3$$

and on putting $x = 1$ and $y = 2$ we obtain $4 + 8 = 12$. What we really want is a symbol to indicate this process. One reasonable suggestion is to write

$$\left. \frac{\partial z}{\partial x} \right|_{\substack{x=1 \\ y=2}} \tag{13}$$

where the bar indicates that we are to evaluate the quantity using the indicated values. Such a symbol is indeed frequently used, but it is somewhat awkward. A perfectly satisfactory alternate is to use subscripts to denote partial differentiation. Thus by the meaning of the symbols we have

$$f_x(x, y) = \frac{\partial f}{\partial x}, \quad z_x = \frac{\partial z}{\partial x}, \quad f_y(x, y) = \frac{\partial f}{\partial y}, \quad z_y = \frac{\partial z}{\partial y}.$$

Using the subscript for partial differentiation our problem would be stated. If $f(x, y) = x^2 y + xy^3$ find

$$f_x(1, 2). \tag{14}$$

It is obvious that for this purpose the notation (14) is superior to (13).

In some situations, we want to differentiate and then introduce new variables in place of x and y, for example we may want to replace x by $x + y$, and y by $x - y$. Then the notation $f_x(x + y, x - y)$ would be ambiguous. A good alternate is to use f_1 to denote differentiation with respect to the first variable (whatever the name may be), f_2 for the second variable and so on. As illustrations of the various possibilities we have

$$f_1(x, y) = f_x(x, y) = \frac{\partial f}{\partial x},$$

$$f_2(x, y) = f_y(x, y) = \frac{\partial f}{\partial y},$$

$$f_{12}(x, y) = f_{xy}(x, y) = \frac{\partial}{\partial y}\left(\frac{\partial f}{\partial x}\right),$$

$$f_{21}(x, y) = f_{yx}(x, y) = \frac{\partial}{\partial x}\left(\frac{\partial f}{\partial y}\right),$$

$$f_{123}(x, y, z) = f_{xyz}(x, y, z) = \frac{\partial}{\partial z}\left(\frac{\partial}{\partial y}\left(\frac{\partial f}{\partial x}\right)\right).$$

Observe that with the subscript notation, f_{xy} means that we differentiate f first with respect to x and then with respect to y.

EXAMPLE 1.   If $f(x, y) = 3xy(x^2 - 1) + xy^3 + 2\tan 4x$, find $f_2(1, 2), f_2(a, b)$, $f_2(\cos\theta, \sin\theta)$, and $\frac{\partial}{\partial y}f(x + y, x - y)$.

SOLUTION. $f_2(x, y) = 3x^3 - 3x + 3xy^2$.   Therefore

$$
\begin{aligned}
f_2(1, 2) &= 3 - 3 + 12 = 12, \\
f_2(a, b) &= 3a^3 - 3a + 3ab^2 = 3a(a^2 + b^2 - 1), \\
f_2(\cos\theta, \sin\theta) &= 3\cos^3\theta - 3\cos\theta + 3\cos\theta\sin^2\theta \\
&= 3\cos\theta(\cos^2\theta + \sin^2\theta - 1) = 0.
\end{aligned}
$$

The notation $\frac{\partial}{\partial y}f(x + y, x - y)$ is a little ambiguous but standard practice is to interpret this as $f_2(x + y, x - y)$; namely, differentiation followed by substitution.   Thus in our example we have

$$\frac{\partial}{\partial y}f(x + y, x - y) = f_2(x + y, x - y)$$

$$
\begin{aligned}
&= 3x^3 - 3x + 3xy^2 \Big|_{\substack{x \to x + y \\ y \to x - y}} \\
&= 3(x + y)^3 - 3(x + y) + 3(x + y)(x - y)^2 \\
&= 3(x + y)(2x^2 + 2y^2 - 1).
\end{aligned}
$$

Suppose that we want to express the instructions "first substitute and then differentiate."   The clearest method is to introduce a new symbol for the new function obtained on substitution.   Thus we might write: Let $F(x, y) = f(x + y, x - y)$ and compute $F_2(x, y)$.   In our example this would give

$$
\begin{aligned}
F(x, y) &= 3(x + y)(x - y)\{(x + y)^2 - 1\} + (x + y)(x - y)^3 + 2\tan 4(x + y) \\
&= (x^2 - y^2)(4x^2 + 4xy + 4y^2 - 1) + 2\tan 4(x + y). \\
F_2(x, y) &= 4x^3 - 12xy^2 - 16y^3 + 2y + 8\sec^2 4(x + y).
\end{aligned}
$$

Notice that $F_2(x, y)$ and $f_2(x + y, x - y)$ are quite different, just as we expected they would be.

EXERCISE 2

For the functions in problems 1, 2, 3, and 4 compute $f_1(1, -2)$ and $f_2(2, 3)$.

1. $f(x, y) = x^2y + y^2$ **2.** $f(x, y) = x^2y^3\sin\pi xy$

3. $f(x, y) = \dfrac{x + y^2}{x - y^2}$ **4.** $f(x, y) = \sqrt{8 + \dfrac{x}{y}}.$

5. For each of the functions of problems 1 through 4 let $F(x, y) = f(y^2, x)$ and compute $F_1(x, y)$.

3. Tangent planes and normal lines to a surface. Let $z = f(x, y)$ be a given function, and let S be the surface represented by this function. Suppose that we hold x constant by setting $x = x_0$. Then we are selecting those points on the surface for which $x = x_0$. But geometrically those points are just the points of intersection of the plane $x = x_0$ with S. These points form the curve CPD in Fig. 1. On this curve z changes with y

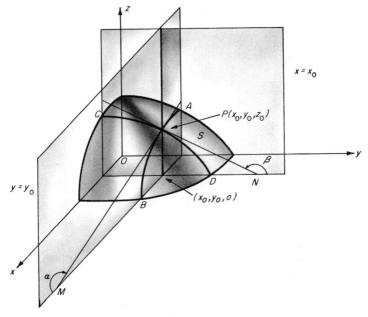

Figure 1

while x remains constant. Since dz/dy is just the slope of a line tangent to the curve CPD when z is a function of y alone, we conclude that at the point P

$$\frac{\partial z}{\partial y} = \text{slope of the line } PN = \tan \beta \qquad (15)$$

where β is the angle indicated in the figure. Similarly the plane $y = y_0$ cuts the surface in a curve APB and on that curve y is a constant, so that at P

$$\frac{\partial z}{\partial x} = \text{slope of the line } PM = \tan \alpha \qquad (16)$$

The above work suggests that the plane containing the lines PM and PN, is the tangent plane to the surface S at the point P. But we must first define a tangent plane.

> DEFINITION 3. *Let T be a plane through a point P on the surface $z = f(x, y)$, and let Q be any other point on the surface. If, as Q approaches P, the angle between the line segment PQ and the plane T tends to zero, then T is called the tangent plane to the surface S at P (see Fig. 2).*

Of course a surface need not have a tangent plane. The simplest example is the half-cone $z = a\sqrt{x^2 + y^2}$ shown in Fig. 3. Here it is clear that there is no tangent plane at the origin.

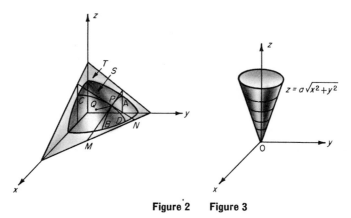

Figure 2   **Figure 3**

If the surface has a tangent plane, then it is obvious from Fig. 2 that the plane must contain the lines PM and PN, and this fact will provide us with a very easy way to obtain an equation for the tangent plane. Indeed if $z = f(x, y)$ is the equation of the surface, and $P(x_0, y_0, z_0)$ is the point under consideration, then $f_x(x_0, y_0)$ is the rate of change of z as x changes along the line PM. A unit change in x produces a change of $f_x(x_0, y_0)$ in z, and y does not change along the line PM. Consequently the vector

$$\mathbf{V} = \mathbf{i} + 0\mathbf{j} + f_x(x_0, y_0)\mathbf{k}$$

is parallel to the line PM. Similarly the vector

$$\mathbf{U} = 0\mathbf{i} + \mathbf{j} + f_y(x_0, y_0)\mathbf{k}$$

is parallel to the line PN. Then the cross product of $\mathbf{U}$ and $\mathbf{V}$ determines a vector $\mathbf{N}$ that is normal to the tangent plane, and is called a *normal to the surface S at P*. This gives

$$\mathbf{N} = \mathbf{U} \times \mathbf{V} = \begin{vmatrix} \mathbf{i} & \mathbf{j} & \mathbf{k} \\ 0 & 1 & f_y(x_0, y_0) \\ 1 & 0 & f_x(x_0, y_0) \end{vmatrix}$$

or

$$\mathbf{N} = f_x(x_0, y_0)\mathbf{i} + f_y(x_0, y_0)\mathbf{j} - \mathbf{k}. \qquad (17)$$

If $R(x, y, z)$ is any point on the tangent plane then the line PR is perpendicular to $\mathbf{N}$, consequently $\mathbf{PR} \cdot \mathbf{N} = 0$,

$$0 = [(x - x_0)\mathbf{i} + (y - y_0)\mathbf{j} + (z - z_0)\mathbf{k}] \cdot [f_x(x_0, y_0)\mathbf{i} + f_y(x_0, y_0)\mathbf{j} - \mathbf{k}]$$
$$0 = f_x(x_0, y_0)(x - x_0) + f_y(x_0, y_0)(y - y_0) - (z - z_0)$$

or

$$z - z_0 = f_x(x_0, y_0)(x - x_0) + f_y(x_0, y_0)(y - y_0). \qquad (18)$$

We have proved

THEOREM 1.   *If the surface $z = f(x, y)$ has a tangent plane at $P(x_0, y_0, z_0)$ then (18) is an equation of the tangent plane, and (17) gives a vector $\mathbf{N}$ that is normal to the surface at P.*

We know that there are surfaces that do not have a tangent plane at certain points. For the present we will assume that each surface has a tangent plane at the point under consideration. Later on, in Theorem 5, we will prove that at any point where the two partial derivatives are continuous, the surface has a tangent plane.

EXAMPLE 1.   Find a normal vector and the tangent plane to the saddle surface $z = y^2 - x^2$ at the point $P(1, -2, 3)$. Where does the normal line to this surface at P meet the xy-plane? Find the intercepts of the tangent plane on the three axes. Make a sketch showing all of the quantities.

SOLUTION.   The point $P(1, -2, 3)$ is on the surface since $z = (-2)^2 - (1)^2 = 4 - 1 = 3$. At $P, f_x = -2x = -2$ and $f_y = 2y = -4$. A suitable normal vector is $\mathbf{N} = -2\mathbf{i} - 4\mathbf{j} - \mathbf{k}$ or $\mathbf{N}_1 = 2\mathbf{i} + 4\mathbf{j} + \mathbf{k}$. From (18) an equation of the tangent plane is

$$z - 3 = -2(x - 1) - 4(y + 2),$$

or

$$2x + 4y + z + 3 = 0.$$

The intercepts of this plane on the three axes are $-3/2$, $-3/4$, and -3. The equation of the normal line is

$$\frac{x-1}{2} = \frac{y+2}{4} = \frac{z-3}{1}.$$

The line meets the xy-plane when $z = 0$. Then these equations give $x = -5$ and $y = -14$, so the point of intersection is $(-5, -14, 0)$. We leave the sketch for the student.

EXAMPLE 2. Find the angle between the line $\mathbf{R} = (2 - t)\mathbf{i} + t\mathbf{j} + 2t\mathbf{k}$ and the normal to the surface $z = x^2 + y^2$ at the points of intersection of the line and the surface.

SOLUTION. The line has parametric equations $x = 2 - t$, $y = t$, $z = 2t$. To find the points of intersection we substitute these in $z = x^2 + y^2$, the equation of the surface and obtain

$$2t = (2 - t)^2 + t^2$$
$$0 = 2t^2 - 6t + 4 = 2(t - 1)(t - 2).$$

Hence $t = 1$ or $t = 2$ and the points are $P_1(1, 1, 2)$ and $P_2(0, 2, 4)$. In general a normal vector to the surface is $f_1\mathbf{i} + f_2\mathbf{j} - \mathbf{k}$. In our case this gives $2x\mathbf{i} + 2y\mathbf{j} - \mathbf{k}$, and at the points in question $\mathbf{N}_1 = 2\mathbf{i} + 2\mathbf{j} - \mathbf{k}$ and $\mathbf{N}_2 = 4\mathbf{j} - \mathbf{k}$. A vector parallel to the given line is $\mathbf{R}'(t) = -\mathbf{i} + \mathbf{j} + 2\mathbf{k}$. The dot product gives:

$$\text{At } P_1, \quad \cos\theta = \frac{\mathbf{N}_1 \cdot \mathbf{R}'(t)}{|\mathbf{N}_1||\mathbf{R}'(t)|} = \frac{-2 + 2 - 2}{\sqrt{9}\sqrt{6}} = \frac{-2}{3\sqrt{6}}$$

$$\text{At } P_2, \quad \cos\theta = \frac{\mathbf{N}_2 \cdot \mathbf{R}'(t)}{|\mathbf{N}_2||\mathbf{R}'(t)|} = \frac{4 - 2}{\sqrt{17}\sqrt{6}} = \frac{2}{\sqrt{17}\sqrt{6}}.$$

The student should make a sketch, showing the surface, the line through the two points, the normals, and the angle θ at each point.

EXERCISE 3

In problems 1 through 6 find an equation for the tangent plane and the normal line at the indicated point on the given surface.

1. $z = 10 - x^2 - y^2$, $P(1, 2, 5)$.
2. $z = 2x^2 - 3y^2$, $P(3, 2, 6)$.
3. $z = 6/xy$, $P(1, 2, 3)$.
4. $z = e^x \sin \pi y$, $P(2, 1, 0)$.
5. $z = x + y + 2 \ln xy$, $P(1, 1, 2)$.
6. $x^2 + y^2 + z^2 = 121$, $P(6, 7, 6)$.

7. Find the angle between the line $\mathbf{R} = (-2 + 4t)\mathbf{i} + (5 + t)\mathbf{j} + (12 - 3t)\mathbf{k}$ and the normal to the sphere $x^2 + y^2 + z^2 = 121$ at the points of intersection of the line and the sphere.

*8. Prove that at any point P_0 on the sphere $x^2 + y^2 + z^2 = r^2$ the tangent plane is $x_0x + y_0y + z_0z = r^2$, and the normal line is $\mathbf{R} = t(x_0\mathbf{i} + y_0\mathbf{j} + z_0\mathbf{k})$. Deduce from this, that each line normal to the surface of a sphere passes through the center of the sphere.

*9. Show that at each point P_0 of the cone $z^2 = A(x^2 + y^2)$, other than at the vertex, the tangent plane has the equation $z_0z = A(x_0x + y_0y)$. Hence each such tangent plane passes through the vertex of the cone. Show that $\mathbf{R} = x_0(1 + At)\mathbf{i} + y_0(1 + At)\mathbf{j} + z_0(1 - t)\mathbf{k}$ is an equation for the line normal to the cone at P_0.

*10. Suppose that on the cone of problem 9, we take all points of fixed height H above the xy-plane and erect normals to the cone at these points. Prove that the set of points in which these normals intersect the xy-plane forms a circle. Find the radius of the circle.

**11. Find the equation of the curve of intersection with the xy-plane of the normals to the surface $z = ax^2 + by^2$ when all of the normals are erected at the same height $z = H$ on the surface.

*4.   **Descriptive properties of point sets.** We let the symbol[2] $\mathcal{S}$ represent some set of points $P(x, y)$ in the xy-plane. By this we mean that we have some property, or character, or method, by which we can tell whether a given point is in the set $\mathcal{S}$ or not. For example let the set $\mathcal{S}$ consist of all points in which both coordinates are even integers. Then $(4, -6)$ and $(0, 100)$ are in $\mathcal{S}$, while $(1, 2)$, $(\pi, 8)$, $(.4, 4)$, and $(6, 2\sqrt{2})$ are not in $\mathcal{S}$.

The set $\mathcal{S}_1$, of all points for which

$$(x - x_0)^2 + (y - y_0)^2 < r^2, \qquad r > 0, \qquad (19)$$

is called a *neighborhood* of the point $P_0(x_0, y_0)$. The points of a neighborhood are just those points inside a circle of radius $r > 0$ with center at P_0. The set of points $\mathcal{S}_2$ for which

$$(x - x_0)^2 + (y - y_0)^2 = r^2, \qquad r > 0, \qquad (20)$$

form the *boundary* of the neighborhood $\mathcal{S}_1$. These are just the points on the circumference of the circle.

A neighborhood in the plane is the two-dimensional analogue of the open interval $a < x < b$ on the x-axis. A set of points $\mathcal{S}$ in the plane is called *open* if every point of $\mathcal{S}$ has a neighborhood, all points of which are also in $\mathcal{S}$. For example the set of points $\mathcal{S}_3$, for which $a < x < b$ and $c < y < d$, is an open set, and in fact an open rectangle. By contrast the set $\mathcal{S}_4$ of points for which

$$(x - x_0)^2 + (y - y_0)^2 \leqq r^2, \qquad r > 0, \qquad (21)$$

is not open, because the point $(x_0 + r, y_0)$ is in the set, but it has no neighborhood that is entirely in $\mathcal{S}_4$.

---

[2] In general we will use script letters to denote sets.

A point that has a neighborhood that lies entirely in the set $\mathcal{S}$ is called an *interior* point of $\mathcal{S}$.   A point P is called a *boundary point* of $\mathcal{S}$ if P is not an interior point of $\mathcal{S}$, but every neighborhood of P has at least one point in common with $\mathcal{S}$.   Notice that a boundary point may be in the set, but it does not have to be in the set.   It is easy to see that a set is open if and only if all of its points are interior points.   The simplest example of an open set is the open circle $\mathcal{S}_1$, described by (19).

We obtain the *closure* of a set $\mathcal{S}$ if we add to $\mathcal{S}$ all of its boundary points. The set is called *closed* if all of its boundary points are already in $\mathcal{S}$.

For example the boundary of the set $\mathcal{S}_1$, described by (19) is just the set $\mathcal{S}_2$ described by (20).   If we "add" the sets $\mathcal{S}_1$ and $\mathcal{S}_2$ we obtain the set $\mathcal{S}_4$ described by (21).   Thus $\mathcal{S}_4$ is an example of a closed set.   It is the closure of the set $\mathcal{S}_1$.

A precise definition of a connected set is rather complicated.   For our purposes the following simplified definition will be satisfactory.   A set is said to be *connected* if given any two points in the set it is possible to join the two points with a curve, such that all points of the curve are in the set. A set is called a *region* if it is both open and connected.   To illustrate these terms, the sets $\mathcal{S}_1$, $\mathcal{S}_2$, $\mathcal{S}_3$, and $\mathcal{S}_4$ are all connected.   But $\mathcal{S}_2$ and $\mathcal{S}_4$ are not open so they are not regions.   The sets $\mathcal{S}_1$ and $\mathcal{S}_3$ are regions.   The set $\mathcal{S}_5$ of points (x, y) for which $y < 1/2$ and simultaneously $y > \sin x$ forms an open set, that is not connected.   The student should sketch this set and explain why it is not connected.

Sometimes it is convenient to add to a region all of its boundary points. The resulting set is called a *closed region*.   For example the set $\mathcal{S}_4$ is a closed region.

The above items are "descriptive properties" of sets of points.   We have merely touched here on a vast domain of mathematics that has been thoroughly explored and highly developed in recent times.   It is an extremely fascinating subject, and the end of research in this direction is not yet in sight.   But we have given enough terminology for our present purposes[3].

EXERCISE 4

In problems 1 through 15 a set of points is described by imposing one or more conditions on the coordinates (x, y) of the point in order that it be in the set.   In each case make a sketch of the point set and determine whether the set is open, closed, or neither.

1. $x > 4$.	**2.** $y \leq -5$.
3. $x^2 + y^2 < 1$.	**4.** $x^2 + y^2 > 0$.
5. $y \geq x + 5$.	**6.** $y < -2x + 3$.

[3] The student who wishes to learn more about the properties of point sets, should consult *The Topology of Plane Point Sets*, by M. H. A. Newman (Cambridge University Press, London, 1951).

7. $1 < x \leq 4, 2 < y \leq 7.$ **8.** $x + y < 1, x > -3,$ and $y > x - 2.$

9. $1 \leq (x - 2)^2 + (y - 3)^2 \leq 4.$ **10.** $2x + 3y \leq 6, 3y + 4x \geq 0, 3y \geq 2x - 18.$

11. x is a rational number, y is arbitrary.

12. $y > \sin x, y < x^2.$

13. $\dfrac{x^2}{a^2} - \dfrac{y^2}{b^2} > 1.$ **14.** $x + y$ is a rational number.

15. $x + y$ is an irrational number.

16. Among the sets defined in problems 1 through 15, find those that are *not* connected.

*17. How would you define a neighborhood of a point in three dimensional space?

**18. Three-dimensional Euclidean space can be regarded algebraically (not geometrically) as the collection of all sets (x_1, x_2, x_3) of three real numbers where the distance between (x_1, x_2, x_3) and (y_1, y_2, y_3) is $\left(\sum\limits_{k=1}^{3} (y_k - x_k)^2 \right)^{1/2}$. We can define n-dimensional Euclidean space as the collection of all sets $(x_1, x_2, x_3, \cdots, x_n)$ of n real numbers. What would you expect to be the definition of the distance between $(x_1, x_2, x_3, \cdots, x_n)$ and $(y_1, y_2, y_3, \cdots, y_n)$?

5.   The increment of a function of two variables. We recall that if $z = f(x)$ is a differentiable function of a single independent variable, then

$$\Delta z = \frac{df}{dx} \Delta x + \epsilon \Delta x \tag{22}$$

where $\epsilon \to 0$, as $\Delta x \to 0$. In fact this is merely a restatement of the definition of a derivative. For if we divide both sides of (22) by Δx and take the limit we have

$$\lim_{\Delta x \to 0} \frac{\Delta z}{\Delta x} = \lim_{\Delta x \to 0} \left(\frac{df}{dx} + \epsilon \right) \tag{23}$$

and since at a given point $\dfrac{df}{dx}$ is a constant, it is clear from (23) that $\epsilon \to 0$ as $\Delta x \to 0$.

Similarly if $z = f(y)$ is a differentiable function of y, (perhaps a different function, but we use the same letter f) then

$$\Delta z = \frac{df}{dy} \Delta y + \epsilon \Delta y \tag{24}$$

where $\epsilon \to 0$ as $\Delta y \to 0$.

What is the analogue of (22) and (24) when $z = f(x, y)$ is a function of two variables? Can we just add the two expressions on the right side of (22) and (24) using partial derivatives? The affirmative answer is contained in

THEOREM 2.   *Let* $z = f(x, y)$ *and suppose that the partial derivatives* $f_x(x, y)$ *and* $f_y(x, y)$ *are continuous in a neighborhood of* (x_0, y_0).   *Set*

$$\Delta z = f(x_0 + \Delta x, y_0 + \Delta y) - f(x_0, y_0). \tag{25}$$

Then

$$\Delta z = f_x(x_0, y_0)\Delta x + f_y(x_0, y_0)\Delta y + \epsilon_1 \Delta x + \epsilon_2 \Delta y \tag{26}$$

where $\epsilon_1 \rightarrow 0$ *and* $\epsilon_2 \rightarrow 0$ *as both* $\Delta x \rightarrow 0$ *and* $\Delta y \rightarrow 0$.

DISCUSSION.   The similarity between (26) and (22) or (24) becomes obvious if we write (26) in the form

$$\Delta z = \frac{\partial f}{\partial x} \Delta x + \frac{\partial f}{\partial y} \Delta y + \epsilon_1 \Delta x + \epsilon_2 \Delta y. \tag{27}$$

From equation (25), Δz is the change in the function as the point $P(x, y)$ moves from (x_0, y_0) to a neighboring point $(x_0 + \Delta x, y_0 + \Delta y)$ as indicated in Fig. 4.   The theorem asserts that this change can be approximated by

$$\Delta z \approx f_x(x_0, y_0)\Delta x + f_y(x_0, y_0)\Delta y \tag{28}$$

because the terms $\epsilon_1 \Delta x + \epsilon_2 \Delta y$ will tend to zero much more rapidly than $f_x \Delta x + f_y \Delta y$ if at least one of the two partial derivatives is not zero.

If we compare (28) with the equation for a tangent plane developed in section 3,

$$z - z_0 = f_x(x_0, y_0)(x - x_0) + f_y(x_0, y_0)(y - y_0) \tag{18}$$

and identify Δx with $x - x_0$ and Δy with $y - y_0$, it is clear that Δz is approximated by $z - z_0$ where here z is the corresponding point on the tangent plane (see Fig. 4).   Using $(\Delta z)_T$ to denote the change of z on the tangent plane, and reserving Δz for the change in z on the surface, equation (26) states that

$$\Delta z = (\Delta z)_T + \epsilon_1 \Delta x + \epsilon_2 \Delta y.$$

PROOF OF THEOREM 2.   On the right side of (25) we subtract the quantity $f(x_0 + \Delta x, y_0)$ and then add the same quantity, so that the equal sign is not disturbed.   Thus we can write

$$\Delta z = [f(x_0 + \Delta x, y_0 + \Delta y) - f(x_0 + \Delta x, y_0)] + [f(x_0 + \Delta x, y_0) - f(x_0, y_0)]$$
$$\Delta z = \qquad\qquad \Delta_1 \qquad\qquad + \qquad\qquad \Delta_2 \tag{29}$$

Observe that in Δ_1 the first variable x is held constant at $x_0 + \Delta x$, and so Δ_1 represents a change due to the change in the second variable only. Similarly in Δ_2, y is held constant at y_0, and only x is changing.   Thus the introduction of the terms $\pm f(x_0 + \Delta x, y_0)$ allows us to decompose Δz into

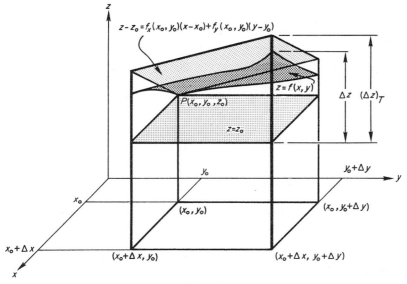

Figure 4

the sum of two increments, in each of which only one variable actually undergoes a change.

We can apply (22) to the computation of Δ_2, since only x is changing. This gives

$$\Delta_2 = f_x(x_0, y_0)\Delta x + \epsilon_1 \Delta x \tag{30}$$

where $\epsilon_1 \to 0$ as $\Delta x \to 0$.

Similarly we can apply (24) to the computation of Δ_1 except that now the derivative is computed at $(x_0 + \Delta x, y_0)$. Hence

$$\Delta_1 = f_y(x_0 + \Delta x, y_0)\Delta y + \epsilon_3 \Delta y \tag{31}$$

where $\epsilon_3 \to 0$ as $\Delta y \to 0$. Next we can replace $f_y(x_0 + \Delta x, y_0)$ by $f_y(x_0, y_0) + \epsilon_4$ in (31), and since by hypothesis $f_y(x, y)$ is continuous in a neighborhood of (x_0, y_0), we know that $\epsilon_4 \to 0$ as $\Delta x \to 0$. Using this (31) becomes

$$\Delta_1 = f_y(x_0, y_0)\Delta y + \epsilon_4 \Delta y + \epsilon_3 \Delta y. \tag{32}$$

Finally we set $\epsilon_4 + \epsilon_3 = \epsilon_2$ in (32) and using the result, together with (30) in (29) we obtain (26) with $\epsilon_1 \to 0$ and $\epsilon_2 \to 0$ as both $\Delta x \to 0$ and $\Delta y \to 0$.

Q.E.D.

With considerably more writing, but no new ideas, this proof can be extended to the case where $f(x, y, \cdots, s, t, u)$ is a function of any finite

number of variables.   There is no need to burden ourselves with the
details.   For three variables the result is stated in

> THEOREM 3.   *Let $w = f(x, y, z)$ and suppose that the partial*
> *derivatives $f_x(x, y, z), f_y(x, y, z)$ and $f_z(x, y, z)$ are continuous in a*
> *neighborhood of (x_0, y_0, z_0).   Set*
>
> $$\Delta w = f(x_0 + \Delta x, y_0 + \Delta y, z_0 + \Delta z) - f(x_0, y_0, z_0). \qquad (33)$$
>
> *Then*
>
> $$\Delta w = f_x(x_0, y_0, z_0)\Delta x + f_y(x_0, y_0, z_0)\Delta y + f_z(x_0, y_0, z_0)\Delta z \qquad (34)$$
> $$+ \ \epsilon_1\Delta x + \epsilon_2\Delta y + \epsilon_3\Delta z$$
>
> *where $\epsilon_1 \to 0$, $\epsilon_2 \to 0$, and $\epsilon_3 \to 0$ as Δx, Δy, and $\Delta z \to 0$.*

EXAMPLE 1.   Illustrate Theorem 2 by finding an explicit expression for
each of the quantities mentioned in that theorem, for the particular function
$z = y^2 - x^2$ at the point $x_0 = 1$, $y_0 = -2$.

SOLUTION.   For this function and any point (x_0, y_0) equation (25) becomes

$$\begin{aligned}
\Delta z &= (y_0 + \Delta y)^2 - (x_0 + \Delta x)^2 - (y_0{}^2 - x_0{}^2) \\
&= y_0{}^2 + 2y_0\Delta y + (\Delta y)^2 - x_0{}^2 - 2x_0\Delta x - (\Delta x)^2 - y_0{}^2 + x_0{}^2 \\
&= -2x_0\Delta x + 2y_0\Delta y - (\Delta x)^2 + (\Delta y)^2.
\end{aligned}$$

At the particular point $(1, -2)$

$$\Delta z = -2\Delta x - 4\Delta y - (\Delta x)(\Delta x) + (\Delta y)(\Delta y). \qquad (35)$$

Comparing (35) with (26) we see that $f_x(1, -2)$ should be -2 and $f_y(1, -2)$
should be -4, and this is indeed the case for the function $z = y^2 - x^2$.   Further
$\epsilon_1 = -\Delta x$ and $\epsilon_2 = +\Delta y$, so that obviously $\epsilon_1 \to 0$ and $\epsilon_2 \to 0$ as $\Delta x \to 0$ and
$\Delta y \to 0$.   Comparing (35) and (28) we have $\Delta z \approx -2\Delta x - 4\Delta y$ and the error
in the approximation is $-(\Delta x)^2 + (\Delta y)^2$ which certainly tends to zero more
rapidly than $-2\Delta x - 4\Delta y$.

Finally at $(1, -2)$ we have $z_0 = 4 - 1 = 3$, and the approximation $\Delta z_T =$
$-2\Delta x - 4\Delta y$ can be written

$$z - 3 = -2(x - 1) - 4(y + 2).$$

But this is just the equation for the tangent plane that we found when we
solved Example 1 of section 3.

EXAMPLE 2.   In a certain survey the two sides of a triangle were measured
and found to be 160 ft and 300 ft respectively with an error at most of $\pm.5$ ft.
The included angle was found to be 60° with an error of at most 5 minutes.
The third side is computed from this data.   Find an approximate value for
the maximum error in the third side, and for the percentage error.

SOLUTION.   This amounts to finding the change in c, where

$$c^2 = a^2 + b^2 - 2ab \cos C \qquad (36)$$

when a, b, and C change as indicated. With the given measurements

$$c^2 = (160)^2 + (300)^2 - 2(160)(300)\tfrac{1}{2} = 67,600 = (260)^2,$$

so the computed value of $c = 260$. By Theorem 3

$$\Delta c \approx \frac{\partial c}{\partial a} \Delta a + \frac{\partial c}{\partial b} \Delta b + \frac{\partial c}{\partial C} \Delta C. \tag{37}$$

Differentiating (36) implicitly gives

$$2c \frac{\partial c}{\partial a} = 2a - 2b \cos C, \quad 2c \frac{\partial c}{\partial b} = 2b - 2a \cos C, \quad 2c \frac{\partial c}{\partial C} = 2ab \sin C.$$

Using these expressions for the partial derivatives in (37) together with $a = 160$, $b = 300$, $C = 60°$ we find

$$\Delta c \approx \frac{160 - 150}{260} \Delta a + \frac{300 - 80}{260} \Delta b + \frac{160 \times 300\sqrt{3}/2}{260} \Delta C. \tag{38}$$

We want to maximize this approximate value for Δc, under the conditions $-1/2 \leq \Delta a \leq 1/2$, $-1/2 \leq \Delta b \leq 1/2$, and (converting 5 minutes to radian measure) $-5\pi/10,800 \leq \Delta C \leq 5\pi/10,800$. Let $(\Delta c)_{\max}$ denote the maximum error. To maximize the right hand side of (38) we must give Δa, Δb, and ΔC their maximum values. We then find

$$(\Delta c)_{\max} \approx \frac{5 + 110 + 60.5}{260} \approx .675 \text{ ft.}$$

A close approximation for the maximum percentage error is

$$\frac{(\Delta c)_{\max}}{c} \times 100 \approx \frac{.675}{260} \times 100 \approx .26\%.$$

EXERCISE 5

In problems 1 through 4 find an explicit expression for

$$\Delta z - (\Delta z)_T = \Delta z - \left\{ \frac{\partial f}{\partial x} \Delta x + \frac{\partial f}{\partial y} \Delta y \right\}.$$

Observe that each term in your answer has at least one of the factors $(\Delta x)^2$, $(\Delta x)(\Delta y)$, or $(\Delta y)^2$.

1. $z = 2x^2 + 3y^2$
2. $z = x^3 + xy^2 - y^3$
*3. $z = x/y$
4. $z = 3x^2y^2 + 5x - 7y$.

5. In a certain survey the two sides of a triangle were measured and found to be 160 and 210 ft with an error of at most .1 ft. The included angle was measured to be 60° with an error of at most 1 minute. The third side is computed from this data. Find an approximate value for the maximum error in the third side, and for the percentage error.

6. Repeat problem 5 if the sides were measured 550 ft, 160 ft and the angle was measured to be 60°, and each measurement was accurate within 1%.

7. The legs of a right triangle were measured and found to be 120 ft and 160 ft with an error of at most 1 ft. Find an approximation for the maximum error when the area and the hypotenuse are computed from this data.

8. A certain tin can is supposed to be 10 in. high and have a base radius of 2 in. If each of these measurements may be in error by as much as .1 in. find an approximate value for the maximum error when the volume is computed from these dimensions.

9. Find an approximate value for the change in z, on the surface $z = 2x^2 - 3y^2$ when x changes from 4 to 4.3 and y changes from 5 to 4.8.

10. Repeat problem 9 for the surface $z = 2x^2 + 3y^2$.

11. The electrical resistance of a certain wire can be computed from the formula $V = IR$ where V is the voltage drop across the ends of the wire, I is the current flowing through the wire and R is the resistance of the wire. If V and I are measured with an error of at most 1%, find an approximate value for the maximum percentage error in the computed value of R.

12. The focal length f of a lens is given by

$$\frac{1}{f} = \frac{1}{p} + \frac{1}{q}$$

where p and q are the distance of the lense from the object and image respectively. For a certain lense p and q are each 20 cm with a possible error of at most .5 cm. Find an approximate value for the maximum error made when f is computed with this data.

13. The period of a pendulum is given by $P = 2\pi\sqrt{l/g}$ where l is the length of the pendulum and g is the acceleration due to gravity. But if P and l are measured accurately, this equation can be used to compute g. Suppose that in a certain pendulum $l = 5.1$ ft with an error of at most .1 ft and $P = 2.5$ secs with an error of at most .05 secs. Find an approximate value for the maximum error in the computed value of g.

14. The eccentricity of the ellipse $b^2x^2 + a^2y^2 = a^2b^2$ is given by $e = \sqrt{a^2 - b^2}/a$. In a certain ellipse a and b were measured and found to be 25 and 24 respectively with an accuracy of $\pm.2$. Find an approximate value for the maximum error when e is computed with this data.

★15. Let $f(x, y) = \dfrac{2xy}{x^2 + y^2}$ when $x^2 + y^2 > 0$, and let $f(0, 0) = 0$. Letting the point $P(x, y)$ approach the origin, first along the x-axis, then along the y-axis, and then along the line $y = x$, prove that $f(x, y)$ approaches the limits 0, 0, and 1 respectively. Hence conclude that $f(x, y)$ is not continuous at the origin.

★16. The formula for differentiating a quotient is not valid when the denominator is zero. In such a case we must return to the definition of a derivative. Use definition 2, page 542 to show that for the function of problem 15, we have $f_1(0, 0) = 0$ and $f_2(0, 0) = 0$.

★★17. If we apply Theorem 2 to the function of problem 15 we find that at the origin

$$\Delta z = \epsilon_1 \Delta x + \epsilon_2 \Delta y.$$

But $f(0, 0) = 0$, and so $\Delta z = f(\Delta x, \Delta y) = \dfrac{2(\Delta x)(\Delta y)}{(\Delta x)^2 + (\Delta y)^2}$ and consequently

$$\frac{2(\Delta x)(\Delta y)}{(\Delta x)^2 + (\Delta y)^2} = \epsilon_1 \Delta x + \epsilon_2 \Delta y.$$

But when $\Delta x = \Delta y$ the left side is 1, and the right side is supposed to tend to zero. Consequently Theorem 2 appears to be false. Actually one of the conditions of Theorem 2 is not satisfied. What condition is that?

6.   **The chain rule.** Suppose that $z = f(x, y)$ and that x and y are each in turn functions of a third variable t, that is $x = x(t)$ and $y = y(t)$. Then z is a function of t and it is reasonable to ask for a formula for $\dfrac{dz}{dt}$.

Let Δt be a change in t and Δx and Δy be the changes induced in x and y respectively by this change in t. If the conditions of Theorem 2 are satisfied then we can write for Δz

$$\Delta z = \frac{\partial z}{\partial x} \Delta x + \frac{\partial z}{\partial y} \Delta y + \epsilon_1 \Delta x + \epsilon_2 \Delta y.$$

Dividing by Δt gives

$$\frac{\Delta z}{\Delta t} = \frac{\partial z}{\partial x}\frac{\Delta x}{\Delta t} + \frac{\partial z}{\partial y}\frac{\Delta y}{\Delta t} + \epsilon_1 \frac{\Delta x}{\Delta t} + \epsilon_2 \frac{\Delta y}{\Delta t}. \tag{39}$$

If we take the limit as $\Delta t \to 0$ and recall that $\epsilon_1 \to 0$ and $\epsilon_2 \to 0$ we obtain the desired formula

$$\boxed{\frac{dz}{dt} = \frac{\partial z}{\partial x}\frac{dx}{dt} + \frac{\partial z}{\partial y}\frac{dy}{dt}.} \tag{40}$$

We have proved

THEOREM 4.   *If $x(t)$ and $y(t)$ are differentiable functions of t and if the partial derivatives $f_1(x, y)$ and $f_2(x, y)$ are continuous in a neighborhood of the point $(x(t), y(t))$ then the function*

$$z = f(x(t), y(t))$$

is differentiable, and its derivative is given by (40).

This Theorem is a natural generalization of the chain rule (Theorem 15, Chapter 2 page 72).

EXAMPLE 1.   If $z = 2x^2 + 3xy - 4y^2$ where $x = \cos t$ and $y = \sin t$, find dz/dt.

SOLUTION.   By (40) we have

$$\frac{dz}{dt} = (4x + 3y)(-\sin t) + (3x - 8y)\cos t.$$

We can use $x = \cos t$, $y = \sin t$, to express everything in terms of t,

$$\frac{dz}{dt} = (4 \cos t + 3 \sin t)(-\sin t) + (3 \cos t - 8 \sin t)\cos t$$

$$= 3 \cos^2 t - 12 \sin t \cos t - 3 \sin^2 t = 3 \cos 2t - 6 \sin 2t.$$

We could also first substitute and then differentiate, thus

$$\frac{dz}{dt} = \frac{d}{dt} (2 \cos^2 t + 3 \cos t \sin t - 4 \sin^2 t)$$

$$= 4 \cos t(-\sin t) + 3 \cos^2 t - 3 \sin^2 t - 8 \sin t \cos t$$

$$= 3 \cos 2t - 6 \sin 2t.$$

Theorem 4 and its associated formula generalize in an obvious way to any number of variables.   For example if $w = f(x, y, z)$ and x, y, and z are each functions of t, then

$$\frac{dw}{dt} = \frac{\partial w}{\partial x}\frac{dx}{dt} + \frac{\partial w}{\partial y}\frac{dy}{dt} + \frac{\partial w}{\partial z}\frac{dz}{dt}. \tag{41}$$

Suppose that x, y, and z are each functions of two variables, for instance $x = x(t, u)$, $y = y(t, u)$, and $z = z(t, u)$.   Then the partial derivatives are given by

$$\frac{\partial w}{\partial t} = \frac{\partial w}{\partial x}\frac{\partial x}{\partial t} + \frac{\partial w}{\partial y}\frac{\partial y}{\partial t} + \frac{\partial w}{\partial z}\frac{\partial z}{\partial t} \tag{42}$$

and

$$\frac{\partial w}{\partial u} = \frac{\partial w}{\partial x}\frac{\partial x}{\partial u} + \frac{\partial w}{\partial y}\frac{\partial y}{\partial u} + \frac{\partial w}{\partial z}\frac{\partial z}{\partial u}. \tag{43}$$

Using the subscript notation for partial derivatives, these two formulas would be written

$$w_t = w_x x_t + w_y y_t + w_z z_t,$$
$$w_u = w_x x_u + w_y y_u + w_z z_u.$$

We can also consider the much simpler case in which $w = f(u)$, a single variable, where u in turn depends on several variables.   This is illustrated in

EXAMPLE 2.   Prove that if f is any differentiable function, then $z = f(x^3 - y^2)$ is a solution of the partial differential equation.

$$2y \frac{\partial z}{\partial x} + 3x^2 \frac{\partial z}{\partial y} = 0.$$

SOLUTION.   The notation $z = f(x^3 - y^2)$ means that $z = f(u)$ where $u = x^3 - y^2$.   In this case, the chain rule gives

$$\frac{\partial z}{\partial x} = \frac{\partial f}{\partial u} \frac{\partial u}{\partial x} = \frac{df}{du} \frac{\partial u}{\partial x} = f'(x^3 - y^2)3x^2 \qquad \bigg|\; 2y$$

$$\frac{\partial z}{\partial y} = \frac{\partial f}{\partial u} \frac{\partial u}{\partial y} = \frac{df}{du} \frac{\partial u}{\partial y} = f'(x^3 - y^2)(-2y). \qquad \bigg|\; 3x^2$$

Multiplying these equations by $2y$ and $3x^2$ respectively (as indicated schematically) and adding, obviously gives zero.

To illustrate the meaning of this result let us select for $f(u)$ the function

$$f(u) = \tan e^u + \ln[u^2 + u^4] + \sinh[\tan^{-1}u].$$

Then our work shows that

$$f(x^3 - y^2) = \tan e^{x^3-y^2} + \ln[(x^3 - y^2)^2 + (x^3 - y^2)^4] + \sinh[\tan^{-1}(x^3 - y^2)]$$

is a solution of the given partial differential equation.

7.   **The total differential.** If we multiply (40) formally by dt we
obtain the expression

$$dz = \frac{\partial z}{\partial x}\, dx + \frac{\partial z}{\partial y}\, dy \tag{44}$$

and this is taken as the definition of the *differential of the function* $z = f(x, y)$.
If x and y are independent variables then $dx = \Delta x$, any change in x; and
$dy = \Delta y$, any change in y.   The corresponding dz is not equal to Δz, the
change in z, but as stated in Theorem 2, represents a close approximation
to Δz.   The individual products on the right side of (44) are sometimes
called *partial differentials*, and then their sum deserves the title *total differential*.

This definition of the total differential naturally extends to any number
of variables.   For example if $w = f(x, y, z)$ then by definition the differential dw is given by

$$dw = \frac{\partial w}{\partial x}\, dx + \frac{\partial w}{\partial y}\, dy + \frac{\partial w}{\partial z}\, dz. \tag{45}$$

If x, y, and z are each functions of t, then we merely divide both sides of
(45) by dt to obtain the correct formula (41).

Suppose that $w = f(x, y, z)$ where now x, y, and z are *not independent
variables* but are each functions of the two variables t and u.   Then w is a
function of t and u and we can write

$$w = f(x(t, u), y(t, u), z(t, u)) = F(t, u). \tag{46}$$

Then by definition of dw we have from (46)

$$dw = \frac{\partial F}{\partial t} dt + \frac{\partial F}{\partial u} du. \tag{47}$$

In order that our definition of dw be meaningful, it is necessary to prove that (45) and (47) are consistent. We do this by deriving (47) from (45). Indeed if x, y, and z are each functions of t and u we have by definition that

$$dx = \frac{\partial x}{\partial t} dt + \frac{\partial x}{\partial u} du$$

$$dy = \frac{\partial y}{\partial t} dt + \frac{\partial y}{\partial u} du \tag{48}$$

$$dz = \frac{\partial z}{\partial t} dt + \frac{\partial z}{\partial u} du.$$

Using (48) in (45) and then regrouping terms we can write

$$dw = \frac{\partial w}{\partial x}\left(\frac{\partial x}{\partial t} dt + \frac{\partial x}{\partial u} du\right) + \frac{\partial w}{\partial y}\left(\frac{\partial y}{\partial t} dt + \frac{\partial y}{\partial u} du\right) + \frac{\partial w}{\partial z}\left(\frac{\partial z}{\partial t} dt + \frac{\partial z}{\partial u} du\right)$$

$$= \left(\frac{\partial w}{\partial x}\frac{\partial x}{\partial t} + \frac{\partial w}{\partial y}\frac{\partial y}{\partial t} + \frac{\partial w}{\partial z}\frac{\partial z}{\partial t}\right) dt + \left(\frac{\partial w}{\partial x}\frac{\partial x}{\partial u} + \frac{\partial w}{\partial y}\frac{\partial y}{\partial u} + \frac{\partial w}{\partial z}\frac{\partial z}{\partial u}\right) du.$$

Using (42) and (43), this last expression gives

$$dw = \frac{\partial w}{\partial t} dt + \frac{\partial w}{\partial u} du$$

and this is (47).

More generally let $w = f(x, y, z, \cdots, u)$ be a function of n variables, and let each of these n variables be functions of k independent variables, $x = x(p, q, r, \cdots, t), \cdots, u = u(p, q, r, \cdots, t)$. The same type of proof will show that

$$dw = \frac{\partial w}{\partial x} dx + \frac{\partial w}{\partial y} dy + \frac{\partial w}{\partial z} dz + \cdots + \frac{\partial w}{\partial u} du$$

whether the variables x, y, z, $\cdots$, u are independent or not. We have given the proof in detail for the case $n = 3$, $k = 2$.

EXERCISE 6

In problems 1 through 5 find dw/dt in two ways (a) by using the chain rule and then expressing everything in terms of t, and (b) first expressing w as a function of t alone and then differentiating.

1. $w = e^{x^2+y^2}$, $x = \sin t$, $y = \cos t$.

2. $w = \tan^{-1}xyz$, $x = t^2$, $y = t^3$, $z = 1/t^4$.

3. $w = xy + yz + zx$, $x = e^t$, $y = 2t^3$, $z = e^{-t}$.

4. $w = \dfrac{2xy}{x^2 + y^2}$, $x = 2t$, $y = t^2$.

5. $w = \ln(x^2 + 3xy^2 + 4y^4)$, $x = 2t^2$, $y = 3t$.

In problems 6 and 7 find $\partial w/\partial t$ and $\partial w/\partial u$ in two ways.

6. $w = x \ln(x^2 + y^2)$, $x = t + u$, $y = t - u$.

7. $w = e^{x+2y}\sin(2x - y)$, $x = t^2 + 2u^2$, $y = 2t^2 - u^2$.

8. The area of a rectangle is given by $A = xy$ where x is the base and y is the altitude. Let r be the length of a diagonal and θ the angle it makes with the base. Compute A_r and A_θ in two ways.

9. The volume of a right circular cone is given by $V = \frac{1}{3}\pi r^2 h$. Compute in two ways V_θ and V_l, where θ is the angle between the axis and an element of the surface of the cone, and l is the slant height. Here the notation V_θ means that l is regarded as constant, and V_l means that θ is regarded as constant.

10. With the notation of problem 9 prove that $lV_l = 3hV_h$, and that $V_\theta = hV_r - rV_h$.

★11. With θ and r as in problem 9 prove that the volume is given by $V = \frac{1}{3}\pi h^3\tan^2\theta$. Then $V_h = \pi h^2\tan^2\theta$ and $V_\theta = \frac{2}{3}\pi h^3\tan\theta \sec^2\theta$. Prove that these expressions for V_h and V_θ are in general not equal to those obtained in problem 10 and explain why.

12. Given $z = f(x, y)$ where $x = a + ht$ and $y = b + kt$, show that

$$\frac{dz}{dt} = hf_x(a + ht, b + kt) + kf_y(a + ht, b + kt),$$

and if $f_{xy} = f_{yx}$ show that

$$\frac{d^2z}{dt^2} = h^2f_{xx}(a + ht, b + kt) + 2hkf_{xy}(a + ht, b + kt) + k^2f_{yy}(a + ht, b + kt).$$

13. Prove that if f is any differentiable function then $z = xf(y/x)$ is a solution of the partial differential equation

$$x\frac{\partial z}{\partial x} + y\frac{\partial z}{\partial y} = z.$$

14. Prove that if f is any differentiable function, then $z = f(x^2 - y^2)$ is a solution of the partial differential equation

$$x\frac{\partial z}{\partial y} + y\frac{\partial z}{\partial x} = 0.$$

15. Prove that $z = x^2 + xf(xy)$ is a solution of

$$x\frac{\partial z}{\partial x} - y\frac{\partial z}{\partial y} = x^2 + z.$$

16. Prove that $z = F(x - ay)$ is a solution of

$$a \frac{\partial z}{\partial x} + \frac{\partial z}{\partial y} = 0, \quad a \neq 0.$$

★17. Find all solutions of the partial differential equation of problem 16, by filling in the details in the following outline. Introducing the new variables $t = x + ay$, $u = x - ay$, the solution z has the form

$$z = f(x, y) = f\left(\frac{t + u}{2}, \frac{t - u}{2a}\right) = F(t, u)$$

and the given differential equation transforms into the equation $aF_t = 0$. But then F must be a function of u alone. Consequently any solution of the given equation must have the form $z = F(x - ay)$.

18. If $u = f(x, y)$ and $x = r \cos \theta$, $y = r \sin \theta$ (transformation equations from polar coordinates to rectangular coordinates) prove that

$$\left(\frac{\partial u}{\partial x}\right)^2 + \left(\frac{\partial u}{\partial y}\right)^2 = \left(\frac{\partial u}{\partial r}\right)^2 + \frac{1}{r^2}\left(\frac{\partial u}{\partial \theta}\right)^2.$$

★19. With the notation of problem 18 prove that

$$\frac{\partial^2 u}{\partial x^2} + \frac{\partial^2 u}{\partial y^2} = \frac{\partial^2 u}{\partial r^2} + \frac{1}{r}\frac{\partial u}{\partial r} + \frac{1}{r^2}\frac{\partial^2 u}{\partial \theta^2}$$

20. Use the result in problem 19 to show that each of the functions $u_1 = r^n \cos n\theta$ and $u_2 = r^n \sin n\theta$ satisfies Laplace's equation

$$\frac{\partial^2 u}{\partial x^2} + \frac{\partial^2 u}{\partial y^2} = 0.$$

21. Prove that if $z = f(u, v)$ where $u = x + ay$ and $v = x - ay$, then

$$\left(\frac{\partial z}{\partial u}\right)^2 - \left(\frac{\partial z}{\partial v}\right)^2 = \frac{1}{a}\frac{\partial z}{\partial x}\frac{\partial z}{\partial y}.$$

22. Prove that if $F(x, y) = f(x + ay) + g(x - ay)$ then

$$a^2 \frac{\partial^2 F}{\partial x^2} - \frac{\partial^2 F}{\partial y^2} = 0.$$

★23. The mean value theorem for functions of two variables. Prove that if $F(x, y)$ has continuous first partial derivatives in a neighborhood of the point (x_0, y_0) and if h and k are sufficiently small, then there is some interior point $(x_0 + \xi, y_0 + \eta)$, (η is the Greek letter eta) in the rectangle bounded by the lines $x = x_0$, $x = x_0 + h$, $y = y_0$, $y = y_0 + k$, such that

$$F(x_0 + h, y_0 + k) = F(x_0, y_0) + hF_1(x_0 + \xi, y_0 + \eta) + kF_2(x_0 + \xi, y_0 + \eta).$$

Hint: Apply the Mean Value Theorem (Theorem 6, Chapter 3) to the function of a single variable t, $F(x_0 + ht, y_0 + kt)$.

*24. If $w = f(x, y)$ and $x = x(t, u)$, $y = y(t, u)$ prove that

$$\frac{\partial^2 w}{\partial t^2} = \frac{\partial f}{\partial x}\frac{\partial^2 x}{\partial t^2} + \frac{\partial f}{\partial y}\frac{\partial^2 y}{\partial t^2} + \frac{\partial^2 f}{\partial x^2}\left(\frac{\partial x}{\partial t}\right)^2 + \left(\frac{\partial^2 f}{\partial x \partial y} + \frac{\partial^2 f}{\partial y \partial x}\right)\frac{\partial x}{\partial t}\frac{\partial y}{\partial t} + \frac{\partial^2 f}{\partial y^2}\left(\frac{\partial y}{\partial t}\right)^2$$

and that

$$\frac{\partial^2 w}{\partial u \partial t} = \frac{\partial f}{\partial x}\frac{\partial^2 x}{\partial u \partial t} + \frac{\partial f}{\partial y}\frac{\partial^2 y}{\partial u \partial t} + \frac{\partial^2 f}{\partial x^2}\frac{\partial x}{\partial u}\frac{\partial x}{\partial t} + \frac{\partial^2 f}{\partial y \partial x}\frac{\partial y}{\partial u}\frac{\partial x}{\partial t} + \frac{\partial^2 f}{\partial x \partial y}\frac{\partial x}{\partial u}\frac{\partial y}{\partial t} + \frac{\partial^2 f}{\partial y^2}\frac{\partial y}{\partial u}\frac{\partial y}{\partial t}.$$

*8.   The tangent plane.   We are now in a position to prove that under very mild conditions a surface always has a tangent plane.   This is the content of

THEOREM 5.   *Let* $z = f(x, y)$ *be an equation for a surface* $\mathcal{S}$ *and suppose that* $f_x(x, y)$ *and* $f_y(x, y)$ *are continuous in a neighborhood of* (x_0, y_0). *Then the surface* $\mathcal{S}$ *has a tangent plane at* $P_0(x_0, y_0, z_0)$ *and equation (18) is an equation for this plane.*

PROOF.   We will prove that the vector $\mathbf{N} = f_x\mathbf{i} + f_y\mathbf{j} - \mathbf{k}$ is a normal vector to $\mathcal{S}$ at P_0.   Let P be a second point on the surface $\mathcal{S}$, and consider the vector $\Delta\mathbf{R} = \mathbf{P_0P}$ (see Fig. 5).   Let θ denote the angle between the two

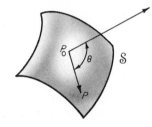

Figure 5

vectors $\mathbf{N}$ and $\Delta\mathbf{R} = \Delta x\mathbf{i} + \Delta y\mathbf{j} + \Delta z\mathbf{k}$.   Then the dot product gives

$$\cos\theta = \frac{[f_x\mathbf{i} + f_y\mathbf{j} - \mathbf{k}] \cdot [\Delta x\mathbf{i} + \Delta y\mathbf{j} + \Delta z\mathbf{k}]}{\sqrt{f_x^2 + f_y^2 + 1}\sqrt{(\Delta x)^2 + (\Delta y)^2 + (\Delta z)^2}},$$

$$\cos\theta = \frac{f_x\Delta x + f_y\Delta y - \Delta z}{\sqrt{f_x^2 + f_y^2 + 1}\sqrt{(\Delta x)^2 + (\Delta y)^2 + (\Delta z)^2}}. \tag{49}$$

The conditions of Theorem 2 are satisfied so that at P_0

$$\Delta z = f_x\Delta x + f_y\Delta y + \epsilon_1\Delta x + \epsilon_2\Delta y$$

where $\epsilon_1 \to 0$ and $\epsilon_2 \to 0$ as Δx and $\Delta y \to 0$.   Using this expression in the numerator in (49) we find

$$\cos\theta = \frac{-\epsilon_1\Delta x - \epsilon_2\Delta y}{\sqrt{f_x^2 + f_y^2 + 1}\sqrt{(\Delta x)^2 + (\Delta y)^2 + (\Delta z)^2}}.$$

Now $\sqrt{f_x^2 + f_y^2 + 1}\,\sqrt{(\Delta x)^2 + (\Delta y)^2 + (\Delta z)^2} \geqq \sqrt{(\Delta x)^2 + (\Delta y)^2}$,

consequently

$$|\cos\theta| \leqq \frac{|-\epsilon_1\Delta x - \epsilon_2\Delta y|}{\sqrt{(\Delta x)^2 + (\Delta y)^2}} \leqq \frac{|\epsilon_1\Delta x|}{\sqrt{(\Delta x)^2 + (\Delta y)^2}} + \frac{|\epsilon_2\Delta y|}{\sqrt{(\Delta x)^2 + (\Delta y)^2}}$$

$$|\cos\theta| \leqq |\epsilon_1| + |\epsilon_2|.$$

As P approaches P_0, Δx and $\Delta y \to 0$, so that ϵ_1 and ϵ_2 also approach zero. Thus $\cos\theta \to 0$ and $\theta \to \pi/2$. This proves that $\mathbf{N}$ is a normal vector to $\mathcal{S}$ at P_0. Consequently the plane (18), which is a plane perpendicular to $\mathbf{N}$ at P_0, is the tangent plane to $\mathcal{S}$ at P_0.

9.   The directional derivative.   Let $w = f(x, y)$, and let $\mathcal{C}$ be a curve in the xy-plane that has a tangent at the point P_0 on $\mathcal{C}$. We want to develop a formula for the rate of change of the function $f(x, y)$ along the curve $\mathcal{C}$. For this purpose, we use s, the arc length of the curve, and define the *directional derivative of $f(x, y)$ along the curve $\mathcal{C}$* to be the rate of change of $f(x, y)$ with respect to s along $\mathcal{C}$. In symbols

$$\frac{df}{ds} = \lim_{\Delta s \to 0} \frac{\Delta f}{\Delta s} \tag{50}$$

where P approaches P_0 on the curve $\mathcal{C}$, and Δs is the length of the arc P_0P. We observe that the notation for the directional derivative is defective because the curve itself does not appear in (50), although the value of df/ds depends upon the curve. In other words, if $f(x, y)$ is a fixed function, two different curves through P_0 may well give rise to two different values for df/ds.

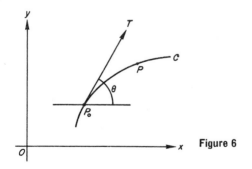

Figure 6

To obtain a formula for computing the directional derivative along the curve $\mathcal{C}$, we use the arc length as a parameter, and suppose that the curve has the equations $x = x(s)$, $y = y(s)$. If the partial derivatives of $f(x, y)$ are continuous in a neighborhood of P_0, then the chain rule (Theorem 4) is applicable, since along $\mathcal{C}$, $f = f(x(s), y(s))$ is now a function of s alone. Hence

$$\frac{df}{ds} = \frac{\partial f}{\partial x}\frac{dx}{ds} + \frac{\partial f}{\partial y}\frac{dy}{ds}. \tag{51}$$

If the tangent vector to the curve $\mathcal{C}$ at P_0 makes an angle θ with the positive x-axis (see Fig. 6) then $dx/ds = \cos\theta$, $dy/ds = \sin\theta$ (see equations (59) Chapter 10) and (51) becomes

$$\frac{df}{ds} = \frac{\partial f}{\partial x}\cos\theta + \frac{\partial f}{\partial y}\sin\theta. \tag{52}$$

It is clear from (52) that if two curves through P_0 have the same direction (θ is the same) then the directional derivative of f on the two curves is the same. Thus the directional derivative does not depend on the curve, but only on the direction of the curve at P_0.

EXAMPLE 1. Find the directional derivative of $f = x + 2xy - 3y^2$ in the direction of the vector $3\mathbf{i} + 4\mathbf{j}$ at the point $(1, 2)$.

SOLUTION. For this function (52) gives

$$\frac{df}{ds} = (1 + 2y)\cos\theta + (2x - 6y)\sin\theta.$$

Using $\cos\theta = 3/5$, $\sin\theta = 4/5$, $x = 1$, and $y = 2$, we find

$$\frac{df}{ds} = (1 + 4)\frac{3}{5} + (2 - 12)\frac{4}{5} = 3 - 8 = -5.$$

EXAMPLE 2. Find the directional derivative of the function of example 1 at $(1, 2)$ along each of the curves $\mathcal{C}_1$: $x = 1 + 3t + t^3$, $y = 2 + 4t + t^4$, and $\mathcal{C}_2$: $x = 1 + 6t + \sin^3 t + \tan t^5$, $y = 2 + 8t + t^2 e^t \sinh^3 t$.

SOLUTION. Each curve passes through the point $(1, 2)$, as is easily checked by setting $t = 0$. When $t = 0$ we have:

$$\text{For } \mathcal{C}_1: \quad \frac{dx}{dt} = 3, \quad \frac{dy}{dt} = 4,$$

$$\text{For } \mathcal{C}_2: \quad \frac{dx}{dt} = 6, \quad \frac{dy}{dt} = 8.$$

Hence for both curves the unit tangent vector is $(3\mathbf{i} + 4\mathbf{j})/5$, the same as in example 1. Hence along both curves, the directional derivative of $f(x, y) = x + 2xy - 3y^2$ at $(1, 2)$ is -5, and the computation is identical with that performed in example 1.

The concept of a directional derivative, and the proof of formula (52) generalize immediately to functions of three variables. Stated precisely we have

THEOREM 6.   *If f_x, f_y, and f_z are continuous in a neighborhood of P_0, and $\mathbf{u} = \cos\alpha\mathbf{i} + \cos\beta\mathbf{j} + \cos\gamma\mathbf{k}$ is a unit vector, then the directional derivative of $f(x, y, z)$ in the direction of the vector $\mathbf{u}$ is given by*

$$\frac{df}{ds} = \frac{\partial f}{\partial x}\cos\alpha + \frac{\partial f}{\partial y}\cos\beta + \frac{\partial f}{\partial z}\cos\gamma. \tag{53}$$

EXAMPLE 2.   Find the directional derivative of $f = ze^x\cos\pi y$ at the point $(0, -1, 2)$ in the direction of the vector $\mathbf{U} = -\mathbf{i} + 2\mathbf{j} + 2\mathbf{k}$.

SOLUTION.   Formula (53) gives

$$\frac{df}{ds} = ze^x\cos\pi y\cos\alpha - \pi ze^x\sin\pi y\cos\beta + e^x\cos\pi y\cos\gamma.$$

To obtain a unit vector we write

$$\mathbf{u} = \frac{\mathbf{U}}{|\mathbf{U}|} = \frac{-\mathbf{i} + 2\mathbf{j} + 2\mathbf{k}}{\sqrt{1 + 4 + 4}} = -\frac{1}{3}\mathbf{i} + \frac{2}{3}\mathbf{j} + \frac{2}{3}\mathbf{k}.$$

For the point $(0, -1, 2)$, and the direction $\mathbf{u}$, we find

$$\frac{df}{ds} = \frac{-2e^0\cos(-\pi)}{3} - \frac{2\pi 2e^0\sin(-\pi)}{3} + \frac{2e^0\cos(-\pi)}{3}$$

$$= \frac{2 - 0 - 2}{3} = 0.$$

EXERCISE 7

1.   As a special case of equation (52) show that $f_x(x, y)$ is just the directional derivative in the direction of the positive x-axis, and $f_y(x, y)$ is the directional derivative in the direction of the positive y-axis. How would you interpret $-f_x(x, y)$ and $-f_y(x, y)$?

2.   We can use the notation $\left(\dfrac{df}{ds}\right)_\theta$ to denote the directional derivative in equation (52), where the subscript θ gives the direction. With this notation prove that for any function $f(x, y)$

$$\left(\frac{df}{ds}\right)_\theta = -\left(\frac{df}{ds}\right)_{\theta+\pi}$$

and

$$\left(\frac{df}{ds}\right)_\theta^2 + \left(\frac{df}{ds}\right)_{\theta+\pi/2}^2 = f_x^2 + f_y^2.$$

Consequently in two perpendicular directions, the sum of the squares of the directional derivatives is a constant at a given point.

3. Deduce from the results of problem 2, that if either $f_x \neq 0$ or $f_y \neq 0$, at P_0, there is always a curve leading from P_0 along which $f(x, y)$ is increasing, and a second curve along which $f(x, y)$ is decreasing.

4. Use the result of problem 3 to prove that if $P_0(x_0, y_0, z_0)$ is a high point or a low point on the surface $z = f(x, y)$, then at P_0, $f_x = 0$ and $f_y = 0$.

5. Prove that the surface $z = x^2 + 4xy + 4y^2 + 7y - 13$ has neither a high point nor a low point.

10. The gradient. The symmetric form of equation (53) suggests immediately that it can be regarded as the dot product of two vectors. Indeed we can write

$$\frac{df}{ds} = \frac{\partial f}{\partial x} \cos \alpha + \frac{\partial f}{\partial y} \cos \beta + \frac{\partial f}{\partial z} \cos \gamma \tag{53}$$

in the form

$$\frac{df}{ds} = \left(\frac{\partial f}{\partial x} \mathbf{i} + \frac{\partial f}{\partial y} \mathbf{j} + \frac{\partial f}{\partial z} \mathbf{k}\right) \cdot (\cos \alpha \mathbf{i} + \cos \beta \mathbf{j} + \cos \gamma \mathbf{k}). \tag{54}$$

This representation as a dot product is so important that the first vector is given a special symbol and name.

DEFINITION 4. *The gradient of $f(x, y, z)$ written **grad** f or ∇f (read, del f) is by definition the vector*

$$\mathbf{grad}\, f = \nabla f = f_x \mathbf{i} + f_y \mathbf{j} + f_z \mathbf{k}. \tag{55}$$

Returning to equation (54) we recall that $\mathbf{u} = \cos \alpha \mathbf{i} + \cos \beta \mathbf{j} + \cos \gamma \mathbf{k}$ is a unit vector that specifies the direction for the directional derivative. Consequently (54) can be written in the compact form

$$\frac{df}{ds} = (\nabla f) \cdot \mathbf{u} = |\nabla f| \cos \varphi \tag{56}$$

where φ is the angle between the two vectors ∇f and $\mathbf{u}$. But (56) is more than a short hand notation. We can derive very valuable information from it and with great ease. If $f_x = f_y = f_z = 0$, then $\nabla f = 0$ and the directional derivative is zero in all directions. In all other cases $|\nabla f| > 0$. It follows from (56) that the directional derivative ranges between $-|\nabla f|$ and $|\nabla f|$, and attains these two extreme values at $\varphi = \pi$ and $\varphi = 0$

respectively. Consequently the maximum value of the directional derivative is attained by selecting for **u** the direction of the vector ∇f, and the minimum is attained by selecting the opposite direction. We summarize in

THEOREM 7. *If $\nabla f \neq 0$, then it points in the direction in which $f(x, y, z)$ has its maximum directional derivative and this maximum is just $|\nabla f|$. Further if **u** is any unit vector, then in the direction of* **u**

$$\frac{df}{ds} = (\nabla f) \cdot \mathbf{u}. \qquad (57)$$

EXAMPLE 1. Find the direction at the point $(2, -1, 5)$ in which the function $f(x, y, z) = x^2 y (z - 4)^3$ has its maximum directional derivative, and find this maximum.

SOLUTION. By definition, equation (55),

$$\nabla f = \nabla[x^2 y (z - 4)^3] = 2xy(z - 4)^3 \mathbf{i} + x^2(z - 4)^3 \mathbf{j} + 3x^2 y (z - 4)^2 \mathbf{k}.$$

At the point $(2, -1, 5)$, $\nabla f = -4\mathbf{i} + 4\mathbf{j} - 12\mathbf{k}$. The maximum for df/ds occurs in the direction of this vector. Further by Theorem 7

$$\max \frac{df}{ds} = |\nabla f| = |-4\mathbf{i} + 4\mathbf{j} - 12\mathbf{k}| = 4\sqrt{1 + 1 + 9} = 4\sqrt{11}.$$

EXERCISE 8

1. The material of Definition 4 and Theorem 7 is also valid if $f(x, y)$ is just a function of two variables. In this plane case, write the analogue of: (a) equation (54), (b) Definition 4, and (c) Theorem 7.

In problems 2 through 7 find the directional derivative of the given function at the given point, in the given direction.

2. e^{x+y}, $(0, 0)$, $\mathbf{i} + \mathbf{j}$.

3. $e^{x^2+y^3}$, $(0, 0)$, any direction.

4. $\sin \pi x \cos \pi y^2$, $(1, 2)$, $\mathbf{i} - 2\mathbf{j}$.

5. $xy^2 z^3$, $(-3, 2, 1)$, $6\mathbf{i} - 2\mathbf{j} + 3\mathbf{k}$.

6. $xy^2 + y^2 z^3 + z^3 x$, $(4, -2, -1)$, $\mathbf{i} + 3\mathbf{j} + 2\mathbf{k}$.

7. $x \sin \pi yz + zy \tan \pi x$, $(1, 2, 3)$, $2\mathbf{i} + 6\mathbf{j} - 9\mathbf{k}$.

8. Find the locus of those points for which the gradient of $f = xy + \cos x + zy^2$ is parallel to the yz-plane.

9. Is there any point at which the gradient of $f = x^3 + y^2 - 5z$ makes the same angle with each of the three coordinate axes?

10. Find the locus of points for which the gradient of $f = x^2 + xy - z^2 + 4y - 3z$ makes the same angle with each of the three coordinate axes.

11. Repeat problem 10 for $f = xy^2z^3$. Observe that points in the xy-plane or xz-plane are exceptional.

★12. Repeat problem 10 for $f = 2x \cos \pi y + 3yz$.

13. Find the locus of those points in the xy-plane for which the length of the vector $\nabla(x^2 + xy - y^2)$ is a constant.

★14. At each point in 3-dimensional space a line is drawn with the direction of $\nabla(x^3 + y^2 - 5z)$. Find those points for which the line passes through the origin.

15. Prove that the gradient of $F = e^{ax+by+cz}$ is always parallel to the gradient of $f = ax + by + cz$ and hence always points in the direction of the constant vector $a\mathbf{i} + b\mathbf{j} + c\mathbf{k}$.

16. A generalization of problem 15. If $F(x, y, z) = G(u)$ where $u = f(x, y, z)$ prove that ∇F and ∇f are parallel vectors at each point where neither one of the vectors is zero.

17. If u and v are functions of x, y, and z, and if a and b are constants prove that

$$\nabla(au + bv) = a\nabla u + b\nabla v,$$
$$\nabla uv = u\nabla v + v\nabla u,$$
$$\nabla u^n = nu^{n-1}\nabla u.$$

18. Suppose that $\nabla f = 0$ for all values of x, y, and z in a certain region $\mathcal{R}$. What can you say about f in $\mathcal{R}$?

19. Suppose that $\nabla f = a\mathbf{i} + b\mathbf{j} + c\mathbf{k}$ throughout $\mathcal{R}$. What can you say about f in $\mathcal{R}$?

11.   Implicit functions. Suppose that x and y are related by an equation

$$F(x, y) = c \tag{58}$$

where c is some constant, and that this determines y as some function of x. Writing $y = f(x)$ for this function, then (58) gives

$$F(x, f(x)) = c. \tag{59}$$

We now differentiate $F(x, f(x))$ with respect to x. On the one hand, by (59) the result is zero, and on the other hand using the chain rule (Theorem 4, with t replaced by x) we obtain

$$\frac{\partial F}{\partial x}\frac{dx}{dx} + \frac{\partial F}{\partial y}\frac{dy}{dx} = 0. \tag{60}$$

Solving (60) for dy/dx will complete the proof of

THEOREM 8. *Suppose that $F(x, y)$ has continuous first partial derivatives and that $F_y(x, y) \neq 0$. Let $y = f(x)$ denote the function defined implicitly by (58). Then*

$$\frac{dy}{dx} = -\frac{\dfrac{\partial F}{\partial x}}{\dfrac{\partial F}{\partial y}} = \frac{-F_1(x,\,y)}{F_2(x,\,y)}. \tag{61}$$

It is instructive to examine this situation geometrically. The collection of points in the xy-plane on which $F(x,\,y) = c$, forms a curve, called a *level curve* of the function $F(x,\,y)$. As c varies we obtain a collection of level curves which together fill out the domain of definition of $F(x,\,y)$, usually the entire plane (see Fig. 7).

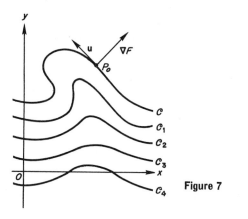

Figure 7

Let us fix our attention on one of these curves and suppose that it has the parametric equations $x = x(s)$ and $y = y(s)$ where for convenience we have selected s, the arc length, as our parameter. Then $F(x,\,y) = F(x(s),\,y(s))$, becomes a function of s and the chain rule applied to (58) gives

$$\frac{\partial F}{\partial x}\frac{dx}{ds} + \frac{\partial F}{\partial y}\frac{dy}{ds} = 0. \tag{62}$$

This can be written in the vector form as

$$0 = \left[\frac{\partial F}{\partial x}\mathbf{i} + \frac{\partial F}{\partial y}\mathbf{j}\right] \cdot \left[\frac{dx}{ds}\mathbf{i} + \frac{dy}{ds}\mathbf{j}\right] = (\boldsymbol{\nabla}F)\cdot\mathbf{u} \tag{63}$$

where $\mathbf{u} = \dfrac{dx}{ds}\mathbf{i} + \dfrac{dy}{ds}\mathbf{j}$. By Theorem 16 (Equation (58)) of Chapter 10,

$\mathbf{u}$ is a tangent vector to the level curve $\mathcal{C}$ of the function $F(x,\,y) = c$. Then if $\boldsymbol{\nabla}F \neq 0$, (63) assures us that $\boldsymbol{\nabla}F$ is perpendicular to $\mathbf{u}$ and hence is normal to $\mathcal{C}$. We have proved

THEOREM 9. *If F_x and F_y are continuous in a neighborhood of $P_0(x_0, y_0)$ and if ∇F is not zero at P_0, then it is normal to the level curve (58) through P_0.*

Further we remark that from equation (62) we have for this curve

$$\frac{dy}{dx} = \frac{\dfrac{dy}{ds}}{\dfrac{dx}{ds}} = -\frac{F_1(x_0, y_0)}{F_2(x_0, y_0)} \tag{64}$$

as long as the denominators are not zero. Thus we obtain again formula (61) of Theorem 8.

EXAMPLE 1. Sketch those level curves for the function $F(x, y) = y - x^2/4$ that pass through the points $(2, 1)$, $(2, 4)$, and $(-3, -1)$. At each of these points compute and sketch the vector ∇F, and a unit vector $\mathbf{u}$ tangent to the level curve.

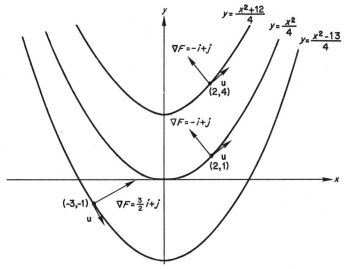

Figure 8

SOLUTION. Each of the level curves $y - x^2/4 = c$ is a parabola $y = x^2/4 + c$. For the curve through $(2, 1)$ we have $c = y - x^2/4 = 1 - 4/4 = 0$. For the other two points the values of c are $4 - 1 = 3$ and $-1 - 9/4 = -13/4$ respectively. The three level curves are shown in Fig. 8.

In general $\nabla F = -\dfrac{x}{2}\mathbf{i} + \mathbf{j}$, and at the three points in question we have $-\mathbf{i} + \mathbf{j}$, $-\mathbf{i} + \mathbf{j}$, and $\frac{3}{2}\mathbf{i} + \mathbf{j}$ respectively for ∇F. Given any nonzero vector $\mathbf{v} = a\mathbf{i} + b\mathbf{j}$, it is easy to see from the dot product that the vector $\mathbf{u} = b\mathbf{i} - a\mathbf{j}$ is perpendicular to $\mathbf{v}$. Hence unit vectors tangent to the level curves at the given points are easily seen to be $(i + j)/\sqrt{2}$, and $(2i - 3j)/\sqrt{13}$ respectively.   These six vectors are shown in Fig. 8.

The above considerations generalize immediately to three-dimensional space.   Suppose indeed that the equation

$$F(x, y, z) = c \tag{65}$$

defines z as a function of the remaining variables x and y and we can write $z = f(x, y)$.   For example the equation of a sphere is

$$x^2 + y^2 + z^2 = c, \tag{66}$$

and on solving we find that either

$$z = \sqrt{c - x^2 - y^2} \quad \text{or} \quad z = -\sqrt{c - x^2 - y^2}. \tag{67}$$

The first of these two equations gives the upper half of the surface of the sphere, and the second gives the lower half.   In this case (66) defines z as a double-valued function of x and y, but each branch is the equation of a surface.

The collection of all points (x, y, z) that satisfy equation (65) is called a *level surface* of the function $F(x, y, z)$.   As c varies we obtain a collection of level surfaces which together fill out the domain of definition of $F(x, y, z)$, usually the whole of three-dimensional space.

By analogy with the plane case we expect that at any point P_0, the vector ∇F is normal to the level surface $F(x, y, z) = c$ through P_0.   To

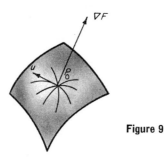

Figure 9

prove this, let us take any curve that lies on the surface, passes through P_0, and has a tangent at P_0 (see Fig. 9).   We use the arc length as a parameter for this curve, so that it has the parametric equations

$$x = x(s), \qquad y = y(s), \qquad z = z(s).$$

Since the curve lies on the level surface (65) we have

$$F(x(s), y(s), z(s)) = c. \tag{68}$$

The chain rule applied to (68) gives

$$\frac{\partial F}{\partial x}\frac{dx}{ds} + \frac{\partial F}{\partial y}\frac{dy}{ds} + \frac{\partial F}{\partial z}\frac{dz}{ds} = 0. \tag{69}$$

This can be put in the vector form

$$0 = \left[\frac{\partial F}{\partial x}\mathbf{i} + \frac{\partial F}{\partial y}\mathbf{j} + \frac{\partial F}{\partial z}\mathbf{k}\right] \cdot \left[\frac{dx}{ds}\mathbf{i} + \frac{dy}{ds}\mathbf{j} + \frac{dz}{ds}\mathbf{k}\right] = (\nabla F)\cdot\mathbf{u} \tag{70}$$

where $\mathbf{u} = \dfrac{dx}{ds}\mathbf{i} + \dfrac{dy}{ds}\mathbf{j} + \dfrac{dz}{ds}\mathbf{k}$, and is a unit vector tangent to the curve

(see section 11 of Chapter 14).   Thus if ∇F is not zero it is perpendicular to $\mathbf{u}$, and hence normal to the curve.   But this is true for any such curve through P_0, and hence ∇F is normal to the surface.   We have proved

> Theorem 10.   *If F_x, F_y, and F_z are continuous in a neighborhood of $P_0(x_0, y_0, z_0)$, and if ∇F is not zero at P_0, then it is normal to the level surface $F(x, y, z) = c$ through P_0.*

From this we deduce immediately an equation for the tangent plane.

> THEOREM 11.   *Under the conditions of Theorem 10*
>
> $$(x - x_0)F_x(x_0, y_0, z_0) + (y - y_0)F_y(x_0, y_0, z_0) + (z - z_0)F_z(x_0, y_0, z_0) = 0 \tag{71}$$
>
> *is an equation for the plane tangent to the level surface $F(x, y, z) = c$, through P_0.*

PROOF.   The point $P(x, y, z)$ is on the tangent plane if and only if the vector $\mathbf{P_0P}$ is perpendicular to ∇F.   Clearly this is the case if and only if $\mathbf{P_0P} \cdot \nabla F = 0$.   But when this orthogonality condition is written in component form it gives (71).   Q.E.D.

We leave it for the student to prove

> THEOREM 12.   *Under the conditions of Theorem 10 the straight line normal to the surface $F(x, y, z) = c$ at P_0 has the equation*
>
> $$\frac{x - x_0}{F_x(x_0, y_0, z_0)} = \frac{y - y_0}{F_y(x_0, y_0, z_0)} = \frac{z - z_0}{F_z(x_0, y_0, z_0)}, \tag{72}$$
>
> *provided that the denominators are all different from zero.*

EXAMPLE 2.   Find an equation for the tangent plane and normal line to the level surface of the function $F = xy^2z^3$ at the point $P_0(3, -2, 1)$.

SOLUTION.   For any point we have

$$\nabla F = y^2z^3\mathbf{i} + 2xyz^3\mathbf{j} + 3xy^2z^2\mathbf{k}$$

and at the given point $(3, -2, 1)$,

$$\nabla F = (-2)^2 \times 1^3 \mathbf{i} + 2 \times 3 \times (-2) \times 1^3 \mathbf{j} + 3 \times 3 \times (-2)^2 \times 1^2 \mathbf{k}$$
$$= 4\mathbf{i} - 12\mathbf{j} + 36\mathbf{k}.$$

Setting $\mathbf{P_0P} \cdot \nabla F = 0$, where $\mathbf{P_0P} = (x - 3)\mathbf{i} + (y + 2)\mathbf{j} + (z - 1)\mathbf{k}$, we have

$$4(x - 3) - 12(y + 2) + 36(z - 1) = 0.$$

On simplifying, the equation of the tangent plane is $x - 3y + 9z = 18$. Similarly for the normal line at P_0

$$\frac{x - 3}{1} = \frac{y + 2}{-3} = \frac{z - 1}{9}.$$

EXERCISE 9

In problems 1 through 8 sketch the level curves for the given function through the given points. At each of these points compute and sketch ∇F and a unit vector $\mathbf{u}$ tangent to the level curve.

1. $F(x, y) = 2x + 5y$, $(1, 1), (4, 7), (-2, -3)$.
2. $F(x, y) = x^2 - y$, $(1, 3), (-1, -5)$.
3. $F(x, y) = x^2 + y^2$, $(3, -4), (-5, 12)$.
4. $F(x, y) = 4x^2 + y^2$, $(1, 4), (0, -3)$.
5. $F(x, y) = y + 4x - x^3$, $(1, -3), (0, 5)$.
★6. $F(x, y) = \cos(x + y)$, $(0, 0), (\pi, 0)$.
★7. $F(x, y) = y^2 - \sin x$, $(\pi, 0), (\pi, -2)$.
★8. $F(x, y) = x^2 - y^2$, $(0, 0), (4, 0)$.

In problems 9 through 12 find an equation for the plane tangent to the given surface at the given point.

9. $x^2 + y^2 + z^2 = 30$, $(2, 1, -5)$.
10. $x^3 + y^3 + z^3 = 6xyz$, $(1, 2, 3)$.
11. $x \sin \pi y + z e^{x^2} = e - y \tan \pi z$, $(1, 1, 1)$.
12. $\ln(x + y) + x \cos z + \tan^{-1}(y + z) = 1$, $(1, 0, 0)$.

13. Prove that the plane tangent to the quadric surface $ax^2 + by^2 + cz^2 = r^2$ at (x_0, y_0, z_0) has the equation $ax_0x + by_0y + cz_0z = r^2$.

14. Prove that the parametric equations for a line normal to the surface $F(x, y, z) = c$ at P_0 are

$$x = x_0 + tF_x, \qquad y = y_0 + tF_y, \qquad z = z_0 + tF_z$$

where F_x, F_y, and F_z are computed at P_0. From this, prove Theorem 12.

In problems 15 and 16 find an equation for the line normal to the given surface at the given point.

15. $xy^3 + yz^3 + zx^3 = 5$, $(1, 2, -1)$.
16. $\dfrac{x}{yz} + \dfrac{4z}{xy} = xz - 2$, $(2, 1, -1)$.

17. If the equation $F(x, y, z) = c$ defines z as a function of x and y, show that

$$\frac{\partial z}{\partial x} = -\frac{\dfrac{\partial F}{\partial x}}{\dfrac{\partial F}{\partial z}}, \quad \text{and} \quad \frac{\partial z}{\partial y} = -\frac{\dfrac{\partial F}{\partial y}}{\dfrac{\partial F}{\partial z}}.$$

18. Show that equation (18) of Theorem 1 can be obtained as a special case of equation (71) of Theorem 11.

19. If two surfaces $F(x, y, z) = c_1$ and $G(x, y, z) = c_2$ intersect in a curve, the tangent to the curve at a point P_0 must lie in each of the planes tangent to the surface at P_0. Prove that therefore the tangent line must be parallel to $\nabla F \times \nabla G$.

20. Use the result of problem 19 to find an equation for the tangent line to the curve of intersection of the two surfaces $x^2 + 2y^2 = 3z^2$ and $x + 3y + 4z = 8$ at the point $(1, 1, 1)$.

21. Repeat problem 20 for the two surfaces $y = 1 + \sin \pi xz$, $z = 2 + \cos \pi xy$ at $(2, 1, 3)$.

★22. Suppose that under the conditions of problem 19, the curve of intersection has an equation of the form $y = f(x)$, $z = g(x)$. Prove that

$$\frac{dy}{dx} = \frac{F_3 G_1 - F_1 G_3}{F_2 G_3 - F_3 G_2}, \qquad \frac{dz}{dx} = \frac{F_1 G_2 - G_1 F_2}{F_2 G_3 - F_3 G_2},$$

provided of course that $F_2 G_3 - F_3 G_2 \neq 0$.

23. Apply the results of problem (22) to find $f'(x)$ and $g'(x)$ for the curve formed by the intersection of the plane $Ax + By + Cz = D$, $D \neq 0$, with the cone $z^2 = x^2 + y^2$. Explain the restriction $D \neq 0$.

24. Repeat problem 23 for the curve of intersection of the two surfaces $x^2 + y^2 + z^2 = 14$, and $x^3 + y^3 + z^3 + 3xyz = 54$.

25. Prove that the surfaces in problem (24) actually intersect in more than just one point, by showing that $(1, 2, 3)$ is on both surfaces and that ∇F is not parallel to ∇G at that point.

★26. Show that the two surfaces $x^2 + y^2 + z^2 = 18$, and $72x^2 + 13y^2 + 13z^2 - 10yz = 144$, meet in just two points $P_1(0, 3, 3)$ and $P_2(0, -3, -3)$. *Hint:* Consider the rotation of axis $x = X$, $\sqrt{2}y = Y + Z$, and $\sqrt{2}z = Y - Z$. Show that for these surfaces at P_1, the computations of problem (22) yield the indeterminate forms $0/0$. Prove that at P_1, these two surfaces have the same tangent plane by showing that $\nabla G = 8\nabla F$.

★27. Prove that if at a common point P on the surfaces $F = c$, $G = c$, the tangent planes coincide, then at P, $\nabla F = k\nabla G$ and as a result the computations of problem (22) will always yield indeterminate forms $0/0$.

★28. Show that at every point common to the two surfaces $z = x^2 + y^2$ and $z = x^2 + 2y^2$ the two tangent planes coincide. Prove that on the curve of intersection of these two surfaces $dz/dx = 2x$ and $dz/dy = 0$. Make a sketch of these two surfaces.

*12.   The equality of the mixed partial derivatives. We have seen that each function considered in section 1 satisfies the equation

$$\frac{\partial^2 f}{\partial x \partial y} = \frac{\partial^2 f}{\partial y \partial x},$$ (73)

or in subscript notation, $f_{21}(x, y) = f_{12}(x, y)$. A set of conditions sufficient to insure (73) is given in

THEOREM 13.   *If f_1, f_2, f_{12}, and f_{21} are all continuous functions in a neighborhood of a point $P(a, b)$, then $f_{21}(a, b) = f_{12}(a, b)$.*

PROOF. We use the method of contradiction. In this method we assume to the contrary that $f_{21}(a, b) \neq f_{12}(a, b)$, and after a sequence of steps, each logically correct, we will arrive at an impossible conclusion. Since, as we shall see, the only possible error is in our initial assumption, we will be forced to conclude that $f_{21}(a, b) = f_{12}(a, b)$.

To supply the details in this argument let us assume first that $f_{21}(a, b) <$ $f_{12}(a, b)$. The case in which the inequality sign is reversed will be con-

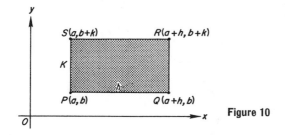

Figure 10

sidered later. Since the mixed partials are continuous we can find a little rectangle $PQRS$ (see Fig. 10), and a number M such that inside and on the boundary of the rectangle

$$f_{21}(x, y) < M < f_{12}(x, y).$$ (74)

We introduce the notation

$$\int F(x, y) \partial x$$ (75)

to mean that the integral is computed with x as the variable of integration while y is held constant. For example

$$\int_\alpha^\beta \frac{\partial F(x, y)}{\partial x} \partial x = F(x, y) \Big|_{x=\alpha}^{x=\beta} = F(\beta, y) - F(\alpha, y).$$ (76)

Using the left side of (74) and recalling that $f_{21} = \dfrac{\partial^2 f}{\partial x \partial y}$

we have

$$Mh > \int_a^{a+h} f_{21}(x, y)\partial x = f_2(x, y)\Big|_a^{a+h} = f_2(a + h, y) - f_2(a, y) \quad (77)$$

for every y in the interval $b \leq y \leq b + k$. Integrating again, (77) yields

$$Mhk > \int_b^{b+k} [f_2(a + h, y) - f_2(a, y)]\partial y = f(a + h, y) - f(a, y)\Big|_b^{b+k}$$

$$Mhk > f(a + h, b + k) - f(a, b + k) - f(a + h, b) + f(a, b). \quad (78)$$

Using an obvious abbreviation we can write (78) as

$$Mhk > f(R) - f(S) - f(Q) + f(P). \quad (79)$$

We now use the right side of (74) and this time we integrate first with respect to y and then with respect to x. The first integration gives

$$Mk < \int_b^{b+k} f_{12}(x, y)\partial y = f_1(x, y)\Big|_b^{b+k} = f_1(x, b + k) - f_1(x, b) \quad (80)$$

for each x in the interval $a \leq x \leq a + h$. Integrating again, (80) yields

$$Mkh < \int_a^{a+h} [f_1(x, b + k) - f_1(x, b)]\partial x = f(x, b + k) - f(x, b)\Big|_a^{a+h}$$

$$Mkh < f(a + h, b + k) - f(a + h, b) - f(a, b + k) + f(a, b). \quad (81)$$

Using the same abbreviation as before we can write (81) as

$$Mhk < f(R) - f(Q) - f(S) + f(P). \quad (82)$$

Combining (79) and (82) we arrive at

$$f(R) - f(S) - f(Q) + f(P) < Mhk < f(R) - f(S) - f(Q) + f(P). \quad (83)$$

This is impossible because (83) states that the two extreme numbers, which are obviously the same, are not equal. Consequently the initial assumption that $f_{21}(a, b) < f_{12}(a, b)$ must be false.

If we now assume that $f_{21}(a, b) > f_{12}(a, b)$ then in the above work all of the inequality signs must be reversed. But we still arrive at the same ridiculous conclusion (83). Consequently the assumption $f_{21}(a, b) > f_{12}(a, b)$ must also be false. Therefore $f_{21}(a, b) = f_{12}(a, b)$.   Q.E.D.

We will see in the next set of problems an example of a function for which $f_{21} \neq f_{12}$ at the origin. Naturally this example function does not satisfy all of the conditions of Theorem 13.

EXERCISE 10

1. The function $f(x, y) = xy\dfrac{x^2 - y^2}{x^2 + y^2}$ is defined for every pair (x, y) for which

the denominator is not zero. We complete the definition of this function when $x = y = 0$ by setting $f(0, 0) = 0$. At the origin, where the denominator vanishes, the rule for differentiating a quotient can not be applied, but at all other points the rule is valid. Prove that if $x^2 + y^2 > 0$, then

$$f_1(x, y) = y \frac{x^2 - y^2}{x^2 + y^2} + xy \frac{4xy^2}{(x^2 + y^2)^2},$$

and

$$f_2(x, y) = x \frac{x^2 - y^2}{x^2 + y^2} - xy \frac{4x^2y}{(x^2 + y^2)^2}.$$

$\star$**2.** When $x = y = 0$ in problem 1 above, we must return to the definition to obtain the partial derivatives. For the function of problem 1, prove that

$$f_1(0, 0) = \lim_{\Delta x \to 0} \frac{f(\Delta x, 0) - f(0, 0)}{\Delta x} = 0,$$

and

$$f_2(0, 0) = \lim_{\Delta y \to 0} \frac{f(0, \Delta y) - f(0, 0)}{\Delta y} = 0.$$

$\star$**3.** Using the results of problems 1 and 2 prove that

$$f_{12}(0, 0) = \lim_{\Delta y \to 0} \frac{f_1(0, \Delta y) - f_1(0, 0)}{\Delta y} = \lim_{\Delta y \to 0} \frac{-\Delta y}{\Delta y} = -1,$$

$$f_{21}(0, 0) = \lim_{\Delta x \to 0} \frac{f_2(\Delta x, 0) - f_2(0, 0)}{\Delta x} = \lim_{\Delta x \to 0} \frac{\Delta x}{\Delta x} = +1.$$

Observe that $f_{12}(0, 0) \neq f_{21}(0, 0)$, so the function defined in problem 1 is an example of a function for which the two mixed partial derivatives are not equal.

13.   Maxima and minima of functions of several variables. Suppose

that $z = f(x, y)$ is a continuous function for some closed region in the xy-plane, that is for some region plus its boundary points. We want to find the maximum and minimum values for z as the point (x, y) varies over the closed region. It is convenient to think of $z = f(x, y)$ as the equation of some surface, and then the maximum value of z corresponds to the highest point on the surface and the minimum value of z corresponds to the lowest point on the surface. The situation is illustrated in Fig. 11, where $f(x, y)$ is supposed to be defined over a certain closed rectangular region with two sides on the axes. It is clear from the picture that for this particular function the maximum occurs at the point (a, b) in the interior of the region, while the minimum occurs at $(c, 0)$ on the boundary. To obtain some necessary conditions for a relative maximum at an interior point, let us pass the plane $x = a$ through this surface and let $\mathcal{C}_1$ be the intersection curve. If z_M is the maximum value of z on the surface it is also the maximum value of z on the curve $\mathcal{C}_1$. On this curve x is constant and y is the variable, hence from our work on plane curves it is obvious that at a maximum point we must have

$$\frac{\partial f}{\partial y} = 0 \quad \text{and} \quad \frac{\partial^2 f}{\partial y^2} \leqq 0. \tag{84}$$

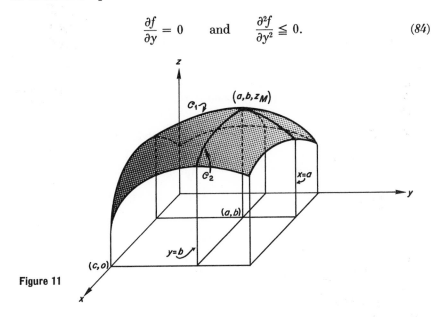

Figure 11

Similar considerations about $\mathcal{C}_2$, the intersection curve of the surface with the plane $y = b$, show that at a maximum point we must also have

$$\frac{\partial f}{\partial x} = 0 \quad \text{and} \quad \frac{\partial^2 f}{\partial x^2} \leqq 0. \tag{85}$$

Thus (84) and (85) must be simultaneously satisfied for a maximum point. Unfortunately these necessary conditions are not sufficient, as we shall see in section 14.

To find a minimum point for $f(x, y)$ we may repeat the above considerations with a different surface in mind, or we may apply the results already obtained to the function $z = -f(x, y)$. In either case we will find that for $f(x, y)$ to have a minimum value at (a, b) it is necessary that at (a, b)

$$\frac{\partial f}{\partial x} = 0, \quad \frac{\partial f}{\partial y} = 0, \quad \frac{\partial^2 f}{\partial x^2} \geqq 0, \quad \text{and} \quad \frac{\partial^2 f}{\partial y^2} \geqq 0. \tag{86}$$

In looking for extreme values for z, the first step is to solve simultaneously the pair of equations

$$\frac{\partial f}{\partial x} = 0, \quad \frac{\partial f}{\partial y} = 0. \tag{87}$$

Each point at which (87) is satisfied is called a *critical point*. If the maximum or minimum value of z occurs at an interior point, these equations must be satisfied and the point must be a critical point. If it occurs on the boundary of the region under consideration then the situation is more complicated. Thus for the function pictured in Fig. 11, the minimum of z occurs at $(c, 0)$ but neither partial derivative is zero at that point.

EXAMPLE 1.   Find the extreme values for the function $z = x^2 + xy + y^2 - 6x + 2$ inside the closed region $\mathfrak{R}$ bounded by a circle of radius 6 and center at the origin.

SOLUTION.   We first find all critical points. Solving

$$\frac{\partial f}{\partial x} = 2x + y - 6 = 0, \qquad \frac{\partial f}{\partial y} = x + 2y = 0$$

simultaneously yields $x = 4$, $y = -2$. At the point $(4, -2)$ we find $z = -10$,

$$\frac{\partial^2 f}{\partial x^2} = 2 > 0, \qquad \frac{\partial^2 f}{\partial y^2} = 2 > 0,$$

and consequently $z = -10$ appears to be a minimum value for z.

We next investigate the behavior of the function on the boundary of our region, namely on the circle $x^2 + y^2 = 36$. Using $x = 6 \cos \theta$, $y = 6 \sin \theta$, as a parametric set of equations for the boundary, we see that for points on the boundary

$$z = (6 \cos \theta)^2 + (6 \cos \theta)(6 \sin \theta) + (6 \sin \theta)^2 - 36 \cos \theta + 2$$
$$= 38 + 36 \sin \theta \cos \theta - 36 \cos \theta = 38 + 36(\sin \theta \cos \theta - \cos \theta).$$

Then

$$\frac{dz}{d\theta} = 36(\cos^2 \theta - \sin^2 \theta + \sin \theta) = 36(1 - 2 \sin^2 \theta + \sin \theta)$$
$$= 36(1 - \sin \theta)(1 + 2 \sin \theta).$$

Hence the relative extreme values of z on the boundary must be among the points $\sin \theta = 1$, $\theta = \pi/2$, or $\sin \theta = -1/2$, $\theta = 7\pi/6$ or $11\pi/6$. For these values of θ we find $z = 38$, $38 + 27\sqrt{3}$, and $38 - 27\sqrt{3}$ respectively. Consequently it appears that $38 + 27\sqrt{3}$ is the maximum value of z, and -10 is the minimum value of z in the given closed region.

A rigorous proof that this conclusion is correct, is long and tedious, but not difficult. A basic step is the proof of

THEOREM 14.   *If $f(x, y)$ is a continuous function in a closed region $\mathfrak{R}$ then it has a maximum value at some point of $\mathfrak{R}$, and a minimum value at some (other) point of $\mathfrak{R}$.*

Our intuition tells us that this theorem must be true, and indeed it is. In order to avoid long and unimportant digressions we omit the proof.

We apply Theorem 14 to our example as follows. The first computation proved that $z = -10$ is the only possible contender for the title of an extreme value for interior points of $\mathcal{R}$. The second computation yields $z = 38$, $38 + 27\sqrt{3}$, and $38 - 27\sqrt{3}$ as the only possible contenders on the boundary of $\mathcal{R}$. But by Theorem 14, there is a largest and smallest value for z. From these contenders it is easy to select $38 + 27\sqrt{3}$ as the largest and -10 as the smallest.

EXAMPLE 2. Find three positive numbers whose product is as large as possible, and such that the first plus twice the second plus three times the third is 54.

SOLUTION. Restated in symbols, we are to maximize $Q = xyz$ subject to the side conditions that $x + 2y + 3z = 54$, $x > 0$, $y > 0$, and $z > 0$. Using $x = 54 - 2y - 3z$ in Q we find that we are maximizing

$$Q = yz(54 - 2y - 3z)$$

where the point (y, z) must lie in a certain triangular region in the yz-plane. We leave it for the student to determine this region. Searching for the critical points for the function Q, we set

$$Q_y = z(54 - 2y - 3z) - 2yz = 0,$$
$$Q_z = y(54 - 2y - 3z) - 3yz = 0.$$

Solving this pair of equations simultaneously for *positive* y and z, we find that $y = 9$, $z = 6$, and consequently $x = 54 - 2 \times 9 - 3 \times 6 = 18$. Thus it appears that the maximum for the product is $Q = 18 \times 9 \times 6 = 972$. We leave it for the student to show that at the point $y = 9$, $z = 6$,

$$Q_{yy} < 0, \qquad Q_{zz} < 0,$$

and that on the boundary of our triangular region, $Q = 0$.

★14. A sufficient condition for a relative extremum. Our object is to sort out from among the critical points those that are relative maximum or minimum points and those that are not. If $P_0(a, b)$ is a critical point of $f(x, y)$, then $f_x(a, b) = f_y(a, b) = 0$, and consequently the tangent plane to the surface $z = f(x, y)$ at P_0 is horizontal. If near P_0 the surface lies above or on the tangent plane, then P_0 is a *relative minimum*

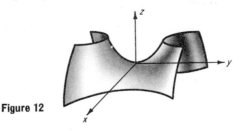

Figure 12

point. If the surface lies below or on the tangent plane, then P_0 is a *relative maximum point.* If the surface lies partly above and partly below, then P_0 is called a *saddle point.* The simplest example of a saddle point is the origin on the surface $z = y^2 - x^2$, shown in Fig. 12. Here it is clear that at $(0, 0)$

$$\frac{\partial z}{\partial x} = -2x = 0, \qquad \frac{\partial z}{\partial y} = 2y = 0.$$

In this case it is easy to spot the origin as a saddle point by looking at the second derivatives. Indeed at $(0, 0)$

$$\frac{\partial^2 z}{\partial x^2} = -2 < 0, \qquad \frac{\partial^2 z}{\partial y^2} = 2 > 0 \tag{88}$$

so that along the x-axis, z has a local maximum, while along the y-axis z has a local minimum.

But even if both second partial derivatives have the same sign, the point may still be a saddle point. Consider for example the surface

$$z = x^2 + y^2 - 4xy. \tag{89}$$

It is easy to see that at $(0, 0)$ this function gives

$$\frac{\partial z}{\partial x} = 2x - 4y = 0, \qquad \frac{\partial z}{\partial y} = 2y - 4x = 0, \qquad \frac{\partial^2 z}{\partial x^2} = 2 > 0, \qquad \frac{\partial^2 z}{\partial y^2} = 2 > 0$$

and hence the conditions (86) are satisfied. Along the x and y axes we do have $z \geq 0$, so that at first glance $z = 0$ seems to be a relative minimum value for z. But if we consider points along the line $y = x$, then we find that

$$z = x^2 + x^2 - 4x^2 = -2x^2 < 0, \qquad \text{when } x \neq 0.$$

Consequently $z = 0$ is not the smallest value for z in a neighborhood of the origin. Hence for the surface defined by (89), the origin is a saddle point.

We now consider the general situation. Suppose that $z = f(x, y)$ has a critical point at $P_0(a, b)$ so that $f_x = f_y = 0$ there. Let us proceed along some line through the point P_0. Let $x = a + ht$, $y = b + kt$ be parametric equations for this line, where h and k are two constants that fix the direction of the line. Then on this line z becomes a function of t alone and we can write

$$z = F(t) = f(a + ht, b + kt).$$

By the chain rule

$$\frac{dz}{dt} = F'(t) = hf_x(a + ht, b + kt) + kf_y(a + ht, b + kt), \tag{90}$$

and

$$\frac{d^2z}{dt^2} = F''(t) = h^2f_{xx}(a + ht, b + kt) + 2hkf_{xy}(a + ht, b + kt) + \qquad (91)$$
$$k^2f_{yy}(a + ht, b + kt).$$

For brevity we introduce constants A, B, and C defined by

$$A = f_{xx}(a, b), \quad B = f_{xy}(a, b), \quad C = f_{yy}(a, b). \qquad (92)$$

Then at $t = 0$, equations (90) and (91) yield $F'(0) = 0$ and

$$F''(0) = Ah^2 + 2Bhk + Ck^2. \qquad (93)$$

If we know the sign of $F''(0)$ then we know the behavior of z along the line $x = a + ht$, $y = b + kt$ at P_0. For example if we know that $F''(0) > 0$ for all choices of h and k (not both zero) then obviously $F(a, b)$ is a relative minimum.

CASE 1.   Suppose $A \neq 0$.   Then (93) can be put in the form

$$F''(0) = \frac{1}{A}[(Ah + Bk)^2 + (AC - B^2)k^2]. \qquad (94)$$

Now for any h, k, we have $(Ah + Bk)^2 \geq 0$, but there are always particular values of h and k for which $(Ah + Bk)^2 = 0$. Passing to the second term in (94) we see that if $AC - B^2 > 0$, then the quantity in square brackets is always positive so $F''(0)$ has the sign of A. On the other hand if $AC - B^2 < 0$ then by a suitable selection of h and k we can make $F''(0)$ negative, and with another choice of h and k we can make $F''(0)$ positive. We have given a portion of the proof of

THEOREM 15.   *Let $P_0(a, b)$ be a critical point of $z = f(x, y)$, and assume $AC - B^2 \neq 0$, where A, B, C are defined by (92).*

1.   *If $AC - B^2 < 0$, then P_0 is a saddle point.*
2.   *If $AC - B^2 > 0$, and $A > 0$, then P_0 is a relative minimum point.*
3.   *If $AC - B^2 > 0$, and $A < 0$, then P_0 is a relative maximum point.*

If $AC - B^2 = 0$, then the nature of the point requires further and more elaborate investigation. But in practical cases, Theorem 15 will supply the needed information.

The proof of Theorem 15 has been given for the case $A \neq 0$. Suppose that $A = 0$. Then $AC - B^2 = -B^2$, and since by hypothesis $AC - B^2 \neq 0$, we have $B \neq 0$. In this case (93) simplifies to

$$F''(0) = 2Bhk + Ck^2 = k(2Bh + Ck), \quad B \neq 0. \qquad (95)$$

We can now select $k = 1$, and then take $|h|$ large enough so that in (95)

$F''(0)$ has the sign of $2Bh$. But taking h first positive, and then negative, we find two different directions, such that for one line, $F''(0) > 0$, and for the other line $F''(0) < 0$. Then P_0 is a saddle point. But this is item 1 of Theorem 15.

Q.E.D.

EXAMPLE 1. Use Theorem 15 to determine the nature of the critical point for $z = x^2 + y^2 - 4xy$.

SOLUTION. Solving

$$f_x = 2x - 4y = 0, \quad \text{and} \quad f_y = 2y - 4x = 0$$

simultaneously, gives $(0, 0)$ as the only critical point. Now $A = f_{xx} = 2$, $B = f_{xy} = -4$, $C = f_{yy} = 2$, consequently $AC - B^2 = 4 - 16 < 0$. So $(0, 0)$ is a saddle point.

EXERCISE 11

In problems 1 through 6 find the maximum and minimum values for the given function in the given closed region.

1. $z = 8x^2 + 4y^2 + 4y + 5$, $\qquad x^2 + y^2 \leq 1$.

2. $z = 8x^2 - 24xy + y^2$, $\qquad x^2 + y^2 \leq 25$. *Hint:* If $\tan 2\theta = -24/7$, then $\tan \theta = 4/3$ or $-3/4$.

3. $z = 8x^2 - 24xy + y^2$, $\qquad x^2 + y^2 \leq r^2$, r fixed.

4. $z = 6x^2 + y^3 + 6y^2$, $\qquad x^2 + y^2 \leq 25$.

★5. $z = x^3 - 6xy + y^3$, $\qquad -8 \leq x \leq 8$, $-8 \leq y \leq 8$.

★6. $z = \dfrac{2x + 2y + 1}{x^2 + y^2 + 1}$, $\qquad x^2 + y^2 \leq 4$.

7. Show that on the circle $x^2 + y^2 = r^2$ the maximum and minimum values of z for the function of problem 6 both tend to zero as $r \to \infty$.

8. Find the maximum value of $\sin x + \sin y + \sin(x + y)$.

9. Find the maximum value of xyz when x, y, z are positive numbers such that $x + 3y + 4z = 108$.

10. Find the point on the surface $xyz = 25$ in the first octant that makes $Q = 3x + 5y + 9z$ a minimum.

11. Find the box of maximum volume that has three faces in the coordinate planes and one vertex in the plane $ax + by + cz = d$, where a, b, c, and d are positive constants. Observe that problem 9 is a special case of this problem.

12. Show that the cube is the largest box that can be placed inside a sphere.

13. Find the volume of the largest box that can be inscribed in the ellipsoid

$$\frac{x^2}{a^2} + \frac{y^2}{b^2} + \frac{z^2}{c^2} = 1.$$

14. Use the methods of this section to find the distance from the origin to the given planes

a. $x - y + z = 7$, $\qquad\qquad$ **b.** $3x + 2y - z + 10 = 0$.

15. Use the methods of this section to find the distance between the two given lines.

a.
$$\begin{cases} x = 1 - t \\ y = t \\ z = t \end{cases} \quad \begin{cases} x = -1 + u \\ y = -u \\ z = u \end{cases}$$

b.
$$\begin{cases} x = -2 + 4t \\ y = 3 + t \\ z = -1 + 5t \end{cases} \quad \begin{cases} x = -1 - 2t \\ y = 3t \\ z = 3 + t \end{cases}$$

c.
$$\begin{cases} x = 2 + 4t \\ y = 4 + t \\ z = 4 + 5t \end{cases} \quad \begin{cases} x = 5 + 2t \\ y = -4 - 3t \\ z = -1 - t \end{cases}$$

★d.
$$\begin{cases} x = 12 + 3t \\ y = 13 + t \\ z = 15 + 8t \end{cases} \quad \begin{cases} x = 20 + 6t \\ y = -10 - 3t \\ z = -10 - 4t. \end{cases}$$

16. Find the point (x, y, z) in the first octant for which $x + 2y + 3z = 24$, and $f = xyz^2$ is a maximum.

17. Find the point (x, y, z) in the first octant for which $2x + y + 5z = 40$, and $f = xy^3z^2$ is a maximum.

18. Find the maximum and minimum values of the function $Q = x^4 + y^4 + z^4$ for points on the surface of the sphere $x^2 + y^2 + z^2 = R^2$.

19. Find the points on the surface $x^2y^2z^3 = 972$ that are closest to the origin. Prove that at each such point the line normal to the surface passes through the origin.

20. What are the dimensions of a box that has a volume of 125 in.³, and has the least possible surface area?

21. A cage for a snake is to be built in the shape of a box with one glass face, the remaining five sides of wood, and should have a volume of 12 ft³. If the glass costs twice as much per square ft as the wood, what are the dimensions of the cage that will minimize the total cost for materials?

The methods of finding extreme values for a function $F(x, y)$ can be extended to functions of three or more independent variables. This is illustrated in problems 22 through 26.

22. Find the maximum value of $F = xyze^{-(2x+3y+5z)}$ for points (x, y, z) in the first octant.

23. Assuming that the function

$$F = 2x^2 + 6y^2 + 45z^2 - 4xy + 6yz + 12xz - 6y + 14$$

has a minimum, find it. Prove that this function has no maximum value.

★**24.** Show that the function

$$G = x^2 + 10y^2 - 27z^2 - 8xy + 6yz - 12xz - 6y + 14$$

has the same critical point as the function F of problem 23. Prove that G has neither a maximum nor a minimum value.

★**25.** Let $P_k(x_k, y_k)$, $k = 1, 2, \cdots, n$ be n fixed points in the plane, let $P(x, y)$ be a variable point, and let s_k be the distance from P to P_k. Prove that

$$F = s_1^2 + s_2^2 + \cdots + s_n^2$$

is a minimum when P is at the center of gravity of the system of weighted points obtained by placing the same weight at each of the points P_k.

★★26. Let a_1, a_2, $\cdots$, a_n be n fixed positive constants.   Find the maximum and minimum values of

$$F = \sum_{k=1}^{n} a_k x_k = a_1 x_1 + a_2 x_2 + \cdots + a_n x_n,$$

where x_1, x_2, $\cdots$, x_n is any set of numbers such that $x_1{}^2 + x_2{}^2 + \cdots + x_n{}^2 = 1$.

★27. Theorem 15 makes no assertion if $AC - B^2 = 0$. Prove that if $F = x^4 + y^2$, and $G = x^4 - y^2$, then both F and G have a critical point at $(0, 0)$, and that for both F and G we have $AC - B^2 = 0$.   Prove further that F has a minimum point at $(0, 0)$ while G has a saddle point at $(0, 0)$.   Hence it is impossible to give a simple extension of Theorem 15 that will cover the case $AC - B^2 = 0$.

17

MULTIPLE INTEGRALS

1.   Regions described by inequalities.   One simple and convenient way
to describe a region in the plane, is to give an inequality or a system
of inequalities which the coordinates of P must satisfy in order that P be-
long to the region.   Of course if the region is extremely complicated, then
we may expect the system of inequalities to be correspondingly complicated.   However in most practical cases the inequalities will be rather
elementary.   For example the inequality $x^2 + y^2 < 16$ describes the region
bounded by the circle of radius 4, with center at the origin.   The inequality
$x^2 + y^2 \leq 16$ describes the closed region obtained by adding the boundary
points to the region $x^2 + y^2 < 16$.   Similarly the pair of inequalities
$a < x < b, c < y < d$ describes a rectangular region, and the pair $a \leq x \leq b$,
$c \leq y \leq d$ describes the corresponding closed region.

Sometimes the same region can be described by two different sets of
inequalities which at first glance appear to have no connection.   This is
illustrated in

EXAMPLE 1.   Sketch the region described by the inequalities

$$0 < x < 4, \qquad 0 < y < \sqrt{x}. \tag{1}$$

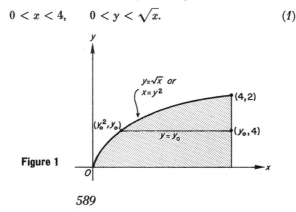

Figure 1

589

Give a second set of inequalities that describe the same region.

SOLUTION. We notice that the upper limit on y depends on x. Consequently we sketch the two curves $y = 0$ and $y = \sqrt{x}$, and observe that (1) states that a point in the region must lie above the curve $y = 0$, and below the curve $y = \sqrt{x}$. Further the point must lie between the vertical lines $x = 0$, and $x = 4$. This gives the shaded region shown in Fig. 1.

An alternate set of inequalities is obtained by allowing $y = y_0$ to be any number in the interval $0 < y < 2$, and then finding restrictions on x. A glance at Fig. 1, shows that we must have $y_0^2 < x < 4$. Consequently the set

$$0 < y < 2, \qquad y^2 < x < 4 \qquad\qquad (2)$$

describes the same region that (1) does.

EXAMPLE 2. Repeat the instructions of example 1 for the region defined by

$$0 < x < 3, \qquad 0 < y < 3 + 2x - x^2. \qquad\qquad (3)$$

SOLUTION. A sketch of the curve $y = .3 + 2x - x^2$ shows that the inequalities (3) describe the shaded region of Fig. 2.

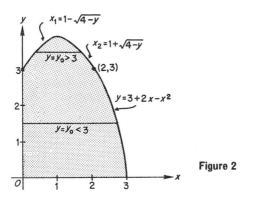

Figure 2

To obtain a set of inequalities in which the bounds on x are given as functions of y, we solve the equation $y = 3 + 2x - x^2$ for x obtaining

$$x = 1 \pm \sqrt{4 - y}.$$

Here the plus sign gives x for the right branch of the parabola, and the minus sign gives x for the left branch of the parabola. Then if y is given, the bounds on x depend on whether $y \leq 3$, or $y \geq 3$. The two cases yield,

$$0 < y \leq 3, \qquad 0 < x < 1 + \sqrt{4 - y}, \qquad\qquad (4)$$

$$3 \leq y < 4, \qquad 1 - \sqrt{4 - y} < x < 1 + \sqrt{4 - y}. \qquad\qquad (5)$$

From the figure it is clear that if the coordinates of $P(x, y)$ satisfy (3), they satisfy either (4) or (5). Conversely if they satisfy either (4) or (5), then they satisfy (3). Hence (3) and the system (4) and (5) describe the same region.

EXERCISE 1

In problems 1 through 14 sketch the region determined by the given inequalities. In each case give an alternate set of inequalities that describes the same region.

1. $0 < x < 2$, $0 < y < 4 - x^2$.
2. $-2 < x < 2$, $0 < y < 4 - x^2$.
3. $0 < x < 4$, $0 < y < e^x - 1$.
4. $\pi/6 < x < \pi/2$, $1/2 < y < \sin x$.
5. $3 < x < 5$, $4 < 4y < x^2 - 6x + 13$.
6. $0 < x < \ln 5$, $2/5 < y < 2e^{-x}$.
7. $-1 < x < 1$, $-3 < y < x^4$.
8. $0 < x < 2$, $1 + x^3/8 < y < 1 + x - x^2/4$.
9. $16x^2 + 9y^2 < 144$.
10. $4y > x^2$.
★11. $2x + 8 > 4y > x^2$.
★12. $x^2 + y^2 < 25$, $x^2 + y^2 < 20x - 35$.
★13. $x^4 < y < 20 - x^2$.
★14. $x^4 < y < 12 + x^2$.

★15. Let $\mathcal{R}$ be the closed region between the two concentric circles of radius 1 and 2 with center at the origin. In other words $\mathcal{R}$ consists of the points (x, y) for which $1 \leq x^2 + y^2 \leq 4$. Show that $\mathcal{R}$ cannot be described by a pair of inequalities of the form $a \leq x \leq b$, $y_1(x) \leq y \leq y_2(x)$, nor by a pair of inequalities of the form $c \leq y \leq d$, $x_1(y) \leq x \leq x_2(y)$. Show that $\mathcal{R}$ can be broken into four pieces (closed subregions) such that each piece can be described by inequalities of the given form. These pieces may have some boundary points in common, but no two pieces may have common interior points.

2. Iterated integrals. The expression

$$I = \int_a^b \int_{y_1(x)}^{y_2(x)} f(x, y) dy \, dx \tag{6}$$

is called an *iterated integral* or a *repeated integral*. By definition the symbol on the right side of (6) means that we are to integrate first with respect to y, obtaining the function

$$g(x) = \int_{y_1(x)}^{y_2(x)} f(x, y) dy, \tag{7}$$

where x is held constant, during the integration, and then follow by integrating $g(x)$ obtaining

$$I = \int_a^b g(x) dx. \tag{8}$$

So by definition the computation of I in (6) is done in the two steps indicated by equations (7) and (8).   Alternate forms for writing (6) are

$$\int_a^b \left[\int_{y_1(x)}^{y_2(x)} f(x,\,y)dy \right] dx \quad \text{and} \quad \int_a^b dx \int_{y_1(x)}^{y_2(x)} f(x,\,y)dy.$$

Naturally the functions $y_1(x)$ and $y_2(x)$ are functions of x that in some cases may be constant.

If in the iterated integral, we wish to integrate first with respect to x and then with respect to y, we would write

$$J = \int_c^d \int_{x_1(y)}^{x_2(y)} f(x,\,y)dx\,dy \tag{9}$$

with suitable changes in (7) and (8).   In the next section we will see that these iterated integrals have a very nice interpretation as the volume of a certain solid.

EXAMPLE 1.   Compute the two iterated integrals

$$I = \int_0^2 \int_0^{4-x^2} (4 - x^2 - y)dy\,dx, \qquad J = \int_0^4 \int_0^{\sqrt{4-y}} (4 - x^2 - y)dx\,dy.$$

SOLUTION.   To compute I we have for the first integral

$$g(x) = \int_0^{4-x^2} (4 - x^2 - y)dy = \left((4 - x^2)y - \frac{y^2}{2} \right)\Big|_0^{4-x^2} = \frac{(4 - x^2)^2}{2}.$$

$$I = \int_0^2 g(x)dx = \int_0^2 \left(8 - 4x^2 + \frac{x^4}{2} \right)dx = \left(8x - \frac{4}{3}x^3 + \frac{x^5}{10} \right)\Big|_0^2 = \frac{128}{15}.$$

Similarly for J

$$\int_0^{\sqrt{4-y}} (4 - x^2 - y)dx = \left(4x - \frac{x^3}{3} - yx \right)\Big|_0^{\sqrt{4-y}}$$

$$= 4\sqrt{4-y} - \frac{(4 - y)\sqrt{4 - y}}{3} - y\sqrt{4-y} = \frac{2}{3}(4-y)\sqrt{4-y}.$$

$$J = \int_0^4 \frac{2}{3}(4 - y)^{3/2}dy = -\frac{2}{3} \times \frac{2}{5}(4 - y)^{5/2}\Big|_0^4 = \frac{128}{15}.$$

The fact that $I = 128/15 = J$ is not an accident, and we will see why in the next section.

3.   **Volumes as iterated integrals.**   Suppose that $z = f(x,\,y)$ is a continuous nonnegative function for $(x,\,y)$ in some closed region $\Re$ in the xy-plane, and we want to compute the volume of the solid bounded above by the surface $z = f(x,\,y)$, below by the xy-plane, and on the sides

by the cylinder generated by erecting at each point on the boundary of $\mathcal{R}$, a line parallel to the z-axis. Such a solid is shown in Fig. 3. Henceforth, for brevity we shall speak of such a solid, as the solid under the surface $z = f(x, y)$ and above the closed region $\mathcal{R}$ in the xy-plane. As indicated in the figure, $\mathcal{R}$ is determined by a set of inequalities

$$a \leq x \leq b, \qquad y_1(x) \leq y \leq y_2(x).$$

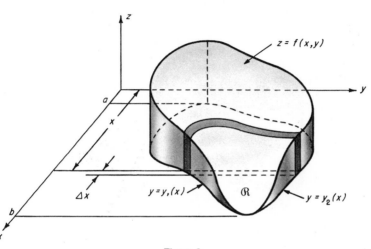

Figure 3

To compute the volume V of such a cylindrical shaped solid, we first pass a plane perpendicular to the x-axis through this solid. Then the area of the face of the solid cut by this plane is just

$$A(x) = \int_{y_1(x)}^{y_2(x)} f(x, y)dy \tag{10}$$

for each fixed x in the interval $a \leq x \leq b$. If we use two such planes at distance Δx apart, then the volume ΔV of the slab cut out from our solid is given approximately by

$$\Delta V \approx A(x)\Delta x = \int_{y_1(x)}^{y_2(x)} f(x, y)dy \, \Delta x. \tag{11}$$

Forming a sum of n such terms and taking the limit as $\Delta x \to 0$, and $n \to \infty$, in the usual way, it is easy to see that the volume is given by the iterated integral

$$V = \int_a^b \int_{y_1(x)}^{y_2(x)} f(x, y)dy \, dx. \tag{12}$$

In a similar way we can first cut our solid with planes perpendicular to the y-axis. If $\mathcal{R}$ is also specified by a set of inequalities of the form $c \leqq y \leqq d$, $x_1(y) \leqq x \leqq x_2(y)$, then the volume is also given by the iterated integral

$$V = \int_c^d \int_{x_1(y)}^{x_2(y)} f(x, y)dx \, dy. \tag{13}$$

Now the two volumes given by (12) and (13) must be equal, so the two types of iterated integrals (6) and (9) will give the same answer, provided the limits chosen determine the same closed region $\mathcal{R}$.

EXAMPLE 1.   Find the volume of the solid under the surface $z = 4 - x^2 - y$, and in the first octant.

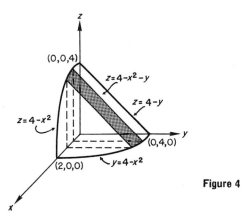

Figure 4

SOLUTION.   This solid is shown in Fig. 4. If we set $z = 0$, it becomes clear that the bottom of our solid is the region bounded by the x-axis, the y-axis, and the curve $y = 4 - x^2$ (with $x \geq 0$). Thus our solid is above the closed region $\mathcal{R}$, where $\mathcal{R}$ is described by the inequalities $0 \leqq x \leqq 2$, $0 \leqq y \leqq 4 - x^2$. Hence by equation (12)

$$V = \int_0^2 \int_0^{4-x^2} (4 - x^2 - y)dy \, dx.$$

The base $\mathcal{R}$ is also described by the inequalities $0 \leqq y \leqq 4$, $0 \leqq x \leqq \sqrt{4 - y}$. Hence by (13)

$$V = \int_0^4 \int_0^{\sqrt{4-y}} (4 - x^2 - y)dx \, dy.$$

But these are just the integrals evaluated in the example of the preceding section. Hence $V = 128/15$, and we see now why the two integrals in that example gave the same number.

EXERCISE 2

In problems 1 through 9 sketch the solid under the given surface and above the given closed region in the xy-plane. Compute the volume of the solid. In problems 1, 2, 3, 4, and 5 check your work by computing the volume in two different ways.

1. $z = 5 - x - 2y$, $0 \leq x \leq 1$, $0 \leq y \leq 2$.
2. $z = 5 - x - 2y$, $0 \leq x \leq 1$, $0 \leq y \leq 2(1 - x)$.
3. $z = y$, $0 \leq x \leq 2$, $0 \leq y \leq 4 - x^2$.
4. $z = 3 + x$. $-2 \leq x \leq 2$, $0 \leq y \leq 4 - x^2$.
5. $z = 4 - 4x^2 - y^2$, $0 \leq x \leq 1$, $0 \leq y \leq 2 - 2x$.
6. $z = e^y - x$, $0 \leq x \leq e^y - 1$, $0 \leq y \leq 4$.
7. $z = 6$, $\pi/6 \leq x \leq \pi/2$, $1/2 \leq y \leq \sin x$.
8. $z = 1 - x^2$, $0 \leq y \leq 1$, $0 \leq x \leq y$.
9. $z = \sin(x + y)$, $0 \leq y \leq \pi$, $0 \leq x \leq \pi - y$.

10. Find the volume of the solid bounded by the four planes $x = 0$, $y = 0$, $z = 0$, and $\dfrac{x}{a} + \dfrac{y}{b} + \dfrac{z}{c} = 1$, where a, b, and c are positive.

11. Find the volume of the solid bounded by the planes $x = 0$, $x = 2$, $y = 0$, $y = 1$, $z = 0$, and the surface $z = \dfrac{16}{(x + 2)^2(y + 1)^2}$.

★12. The solid in the first octant bounded by the three coordinate planes and the surface $z = \dfrac{16}{(x + 2)^2(y + 1)^2}$ has infinite extent, but finite volume. Find the volume.

★13. Find the volume of the solid bounded by the planes $x = 0$, $y = 0$, $z = 0$, $x + y = 1$, and the surface of problem 12.

14. Find the volume of the solid bounded by the cylinders $y = x^2$, $y = x^3$, and the planes $z = 0$, and $z = 1 + 3x + 2y$.

15. Find the volume of the solid bounded by the surfaces $y = e^x$, $y = z$, $z = 0$, $x = 0$, and $x = 2$.

16. Find the volume of the solid lying in the first octant and bounded by the coordinate planes, and the cylinders $x^2 + z^2 = 16$ and $x^2 + y^2 = 16$.

17. The surfaces $z = 1 + y^2$, $3x + 2y = 12$, and $x = 2$ divide the first octant into a number of pieces, two of which are finite. Find the volume of the piece that contains the point $(1, 2, 3)$.

4.   **Double integrals.** We recall that the integral of $f(x)$ is defined as a limit of a certain sum. Our object now is to give an analogous definition when our function $f(x, y)$ depends on two independent variables.

We suppose that $f(x, y)$ is defined and continuous for all points in a certain closed region $\mathfrak{R}$ in the xy-plane. As indicated in Fig. 5 we partition $\mathfrak{R}$ by a network of lines, using a finite number of lines each of which is parallel either to the x-axis or to the y-axis. Call this partition p. Some of the rectangles formed by the lines will lie partly or wholly outside of $\mathfrak{R}$.

Henceforth we consider only those rectangles in the partition that lie entirely in $\Re$. These are shown shaded in Fig. 5. We number these rectangles (in any order) from 1 to n. Let[1] ΔA_α be the area of the αth rec-

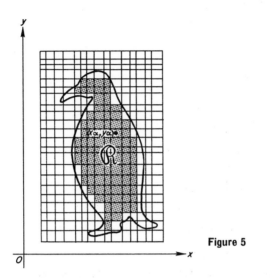

Figure 5

tangle, let d_α be the length of its diagonal, and let D be the maximum of the lengths d_α $(\alpha = 1, 2, \cdots, n)$, i.e., the largest diagonal. We select a point (x_α, y_α) in each rectangle and form the sum

$$I_p = \sum_{\alpha=1}^{n} f(x_\alpha, y_\alpha)\Delta A_\alpha. \tag{14}$$

Naturally the number I_p depends on the way in which $\Re$ is partitioned. For example a shift in one of the lines may leave n, the number of rectangles, unchanged but alter the sum. For this reason it is more accurate to write I_p in (14), rather than I_n. Further I_p depends on the particular selection of the points (x_α, y_α).

We now make our partition of $\Re$ finer by adding more lines, and we take the limit of I_p as the number of lines becomes infinite. In this process we always insist that D, the maximum of the lengths of the diagonals of the rectangles, tends to zero. It can be proved that if $f(x, y)$ is continuous in $\Re$ then I_p tends to a limit called the double integral of $f(x, y)$ over $\Re$ and denoted by the symbol

$$\iint\limits_{\Re} f(x, y)dA. \tag{15}$$

---

[1] We use α as an index here, rather than the conventional i, j, or k, because we want to reserve these letters for use later on as indices on x, y, and z respectively.

DEFINITION 1.   *The double integral of $f(x, y)$ over $\mathcal{R}$ is defined by*

$$\iint\limits_{\mathcal{R}} f(x, y)dA = \lim_{\substack{n \to \infty \\ D \to 0}} \sum_{\alpha=1}^{n} f(x_\alpha, y_\alpha)\Delta A_\alpha \tag{16}$$

whenever the limit on the right side exists.

Since the area of a rectangle can be written as $\Delta A = \Delta x \Delta y$ this suggests that $dA = dx\, dy$, and that

$$\iint\limits_{\mathcal{R}} f(x, y)dx\, dy \tag{17}$$

is a good alternate notation for the double integral (16).   In this form the double integral looks like an iterated integral, and in fact we will see, in Theorem 2 below, that when $f(x, y)$ is continuous in a closed region then the double integral in (16) is always equal to a suitably chosen iterated integral.   Because of this equality, students sometimes regard the double integral and the iterated integral as being the same.   But they are quite different in concept, and in order to emphasize the difference, the notation (15) is frequently used, rather than the notation (17).

We will now show that if $f(x, y) \geq 0$ in a closed region $\mathcal{R}$ and is continuous, then the double integral (16) is just the volume of the solid under the surface $z = f(x, y)$ and above $\mathcal{R}$.   To this end let M_α and m_α be the maximum and minimum values respectively of $f(x, y)$ in the αth rectangle. Then for each $\alpha = 1, 2, \cdots, n$.

$$m_\alpha \Delta A_\alpha \leq f(x_\alpha, y_\alpha)\Delta A_\alpha \leq M_\alpha \Delta A_\alpha. \tag{18}$$

Now $m_\alpha \Delta A_\alpha$ is just the volume of the prism with height m_α and the αth rectangle as base (see Fig. 6).   Similarly $M_\alpha \Delta A_\alpha$ is the volume of a prism

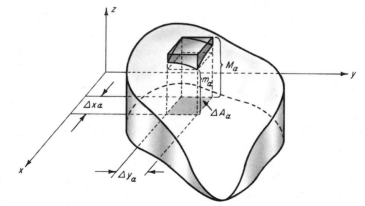

Figure 6

with the same base, and height M_α.   If ΔV_α represents the volume under
the surface $z = f(x, y)$ and above the αth rectangle, as indicated in Fig. 6,
then the inequality (18) provides a lower and upper bound for ΔV_α.   If
we sum a collection of such inequalities, one for each rectangle, we obtain

$$\sum_{\alpha=1}^{n} m_\alpha \Delta A_\alpha \leqq V_p \leqq \sum_{\alpha=1}^{n} M_\alpha \Delta A_\alpha, \tag{19}$$

where V_p is the volume of the solid under the surface and above those
rectangles of the partition that lie entirely in $\Re$.   But as $n \to \infty$ and $D \to 0$,
these rectangles fill out the interior of $\Re$ and consequently $V_p \to V$, the
volume of the solid under the surface $z = f(x, y)$ and above $\Re$.

At the same time, because of the continuity of $f(x, y)$ in $\Re$, we can
make $M_\alpha - m_\alpha < \epsilon$ for each α by taking the partition so that D is very
small.

Therefore

$$\lim_{n \to \infty} \sum_{\alpha=1}^{n} (M_\alpha - m_\alpha) \Delta A_\alpha = 0. \tag{20}$$

Using (20) it is easy to see that each of the sums in (19) also approaches the
same limit V as $n \to \infty$.   Finally from (18) it is clear that

$$\sum_{\alpha=1}^{n} m_\alpha \Delta A_\alpha \leqq \sum_{\alpha=1}^{n} f(x_\alpha, y_\alpha) \Delta A_\alpha \leqq \sum_{\alpha=1}^{n} M_\alpha \Delta A_\alpha,$$

and consequently the middle sum approaches the limit V.   But this is
just the double integral over $\Re$.

THEOREM 1.   *If $f(x, y) \geq 0$ and is continuous in a closed
region $\Re$, then the double integral (16) is the volume of the solid
under the surface $z = f(x, y)$ and over $\Re$.*

Actually we have given only an outline of the proof of this theorem.
But the numerous details that should be supplied in order to complete the
proof, add very little to the main idea, and so we omit them.

It is now clear that a double integral, and a suitably chosen iterated
integral give the volume of the same solid, and hence are equal, provided
only that $f(x, y) \geqq 0$.

If $f(x, y) \leqq 0$, in $\Re$ then it is clear that the double integral gives the
negative of the volume of the solid that lies *above* the surface $z = f(x, y)$
and *below* the closed region $\Re$.   But it is clear that the iterated integral
also gives the negative of this volume, so once again the double integral
is equal to the iterated integral.   Finally suppose that $f(x, y)$ changes sign
in the closed region $\Re$.   Let $\Re_2$ be the set of points at which $f(x, y) \geqq 0$,
and let $\Re_1$ be the remaining points of $\Re$, namely the points at which

$f(x, y) < 0$.   Let V_2 be the volume of the solid under the surface $z = f(x, y)$ and over $\mathcal{R}_2$, and let V_1 be the volume of the solid above that surface and below $\mathcal{R}_1$ (see Fig. 7).   Then it is clear from the proof of Theorem 1 that

$$\iint_{\mathcal{R}} f(x, y)dA = V_2 - V_1.$$

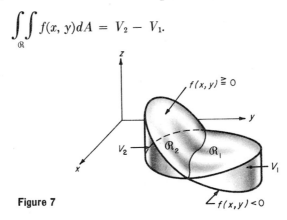

Figure 7

Further a reconsideration of the material of section 3 shows that the iterated integral also gives $V_2 - V_1$.   Thus we have

THEOREM 2.   *Suppose that the closed region $\mathcal{R}$ is described by the inequalities $a \leq x \leq b$, $y_1(x) \leq y \leq y_2(x)$, and is also described by the inequalities $x_1(y) \leq x \leq x_2(y)$, $c \leq y \leq d$.   If $f(x, y)$ is continuous in $\mathcal{R}$ then*

$$\iint_{\mathcal{R}} f(x, y)dA = \int_a^b \int_{y_1(x)}^{y_2(x)} f(x, y)dy\, dx = \int_c^d \int_{x_1(y)}^{x_2(y)} f(x, y)dx\, dy. \quad (21)$$

The direct evaluation of the limit of the sum, in the definition of the double integral, may be quite troublesome.   But this can now be avoided because by Theorem 2, the double integral is equal to a certain iterated integral, and as we have seen these are frequently easy to compute.

There are closed regions that do not satisfy the conditions of this theorem, for example the closed region $1 \leq x^2 + y^2 \leq 4$ (see problem 15, Exercise 1).   However this is no real loss because in any natural problem $\mathcal{R}$ can be broken up into a finite number of pieces in such a way that the hypotheses of Theorem 2 are satisfied in each piece.   Then the double integral in (21) is evaluated by adding the values obtained for the double integral over each piece.

EXAMPLE 1.   Find $I = \iint_{\mathcal{R}} (y^2 - x^2)dA$ where $\mathcal{R}$ is the closed rectangle

$0 \leq x \leq 3$, $0 \leq y \leq 3$.

SOLUTION.   If we recall the shape of the saddle surface $z = y^2 - x^2$ (Fig. 12 of Chapter 16), we suspect that this double integral is zero, because "the surface lies as much above the plane, as it does below the plane." By Theorem 2, I is equal to an appropriate iterated integral.   Thus

$$I = \int_0^3 \int_0^3 (y^2 - x^2) dy\, dx = \int_0^3 \left(\frac{y^3}{3} - x^2 y\right)\Big|_0^3 dx$$

$$= \int_0^3 (9 - 3x^2) dx = (9x - x^3)\Big|_0^3 = 27 - 27 = 0,$$

as predicted.

EXAMPLE 2.   Find the volume of the solid bounded by the surface $z = y^2 - x^2$ and the planes $z = 0$, $x = 0$, $x = 3$, $y = 0$, and $y = 3$.

SOLUTION.   The plane $z = 0$ divides this solid into two pieces of volumes V_1 and V_2 respectively.   By the result of Example 1, we see that $V_1 = V_2$. Hence we can compute V_2 and double the result.   Now $z = y^2 - x^2 \geq 0$ in our closed rectangle, if and only if $0 \leq x \leq y$.   Hence

$$V_2 = \int_0^3 \int_0^y (y^2 - x^2) dx\, dy = \int_0^3 \left(y^2 x - \frac{x^3}{3}\right)\Big|_0^y dy$$

$$= \int_0^3 \left(y^3 - \frac{y^3}{3}\right) dy = \frac{2}{3}\frac{y^4}{4}\Big|_0^3 = \frac{27}{2}.$$

Therefore $V = V_1 + V_2 = 2V_2 = 27$.

EXERCISE 3

Below are a number of statements about multiple integrals.   One of the statements is false, and the rest are theorems that can be proved easily from the definition.   In all statements the functions are continuous in the closed regions involved. Find the false statement and prove that it is false.

1.   If c is a constant $\iint_{\mathcal{R}} cf(x, y) dA = c \iint_{\mathcal{R}} f(x, y) dA$.

2. $\iint_{\mathcal{R}} [f(x, y) + g(x, y)] dA = \iint_{\mathcal{R}} f(x, y) dA + \iint_{\mathcal{R}} g(x, y) dA$.

3.   If $f(x, y) \geq g(x, y)$ in $\mathcal{R}$ then

$$\iint_{\mathcal{R}} f(x, y) dA \geq \iint_{\mathcal{R}} g(x, y) dA.$$

4.   If $\mathcal{R}_1$ and $\mathcal{R}_2$ are closed regions with some boundary points in common, but no interior points in common, and if $\mathcal{R}_3$ is the closed region obtained by taking the union of $\mathcal{R}_1$ and $\mathcal{R}_2$ (putting them together) then

$$\iint_{\mathcal{R}_1} f(x, y) dA + \iint_{\mathcal{R}_2} f(x, y) dA = \iint_{\mathcal{R}_3} f(x, y) dA.$$

5. If $f(x, y) \geq 0$ in $\Re_2$ and if $\Re_1$ is contained in $\Re_2$ then

$$\iint_{\Re_1} f(x, y)dA \leq \iint_{\Re_2} f(x, y)dA.$$

6. If $\Re$ is the rectangle $a \leq x \leq b, c \leq y \leq d$ then

$$\iint_{\Re} f(x)g(y)dA = \left(\int_a^b f(x)dx\right)\left(\int_c^d g(y)dy\right).$$

7. $$\iint_{\Re} f(x)g(y)dA = \left(\iint_{\Re} f(x)dA\right)\left(\iint_{\Re} g(y)dA\right).$$

5. **Applications of the double integral.** We have already seen that the double integral

$$\iint_{\Re} f(x, y)dA \tag{15}$$

gives the volume of a certain solid if $f(x, y) \geq 0$. But (15) has many other useful interpretations that arise by making special selections of the function $f(x, y)$.

If $f(x, y) = 1$, then (15) gives the area of the closed region $\Re$. This is obvious because then (15) is the limit of the sum

$$\sum_{\alpha=1}^n \Delta A_\alpha = \sum_{\alpha=1}^n \Delta x_\alpha \, \Delta y_\alpha$$

where the sum includes those rectangles that lie entirely in $\Re$ (see Fig. 8).

If $f(x, y) = \delta(x, y)$, the surface density of a sheet of material having the form of the closed region $\Re$, then (15) gives the weight of the material. This is clear because each term in the sum

$$\sum_{\alpha=1}^n \delta(x_\alpha, y_\alpha)\Delta x_\alpha \, \Delta y_\alpha$$

gives a close approximation to the weight of the material in the αth rectangle.

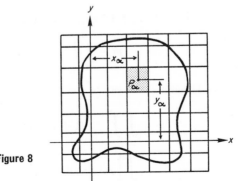

Figure 8

In the same way, an inspection of Fig. 8 immediately suggests the following formulas:

$$M_x = \iint_{\mathcal{R}} y\delta(x, y)dA, \qquad M_y = \iint_{\mathcal{R}} x\delta(x, y)dA,$$

$$I_x = \iint_{\mathcal{R}} y^2\delta(x, y)dA, \qquad I_y = \iint_{\mathcal{R}} x^2\delta(x, y)dA.$$

Finally if we set $f(x, y) = r^2\delta(x, y)$, where $r^2 = x^2 + y^2$ is the distance of the point (x, y) from the origin, then we obtain the *polar moment of inertia* (by definition). Using J to denote this new quantity we have

$$J = \iint_{\mathcal{R}} (x^2 + y^2)\delta(x, y)dx\, dy.$$

In all of these formulas we may set $\delta = 1$ and obtain the moments, and moments of inertia of the closed region $\mathcal{R}$.

EXAMPLE 1.   A triangular sheet of metal is placed as shown in Fig. 9. with its vertices at the points $(0, 0)$, $(1, 0)$, and $(0, 2)$ (dimensions in ft) and in this position has surface density $\delta = (1 + x + y)$ lbs/ft². Find its center of gravity and I_x.

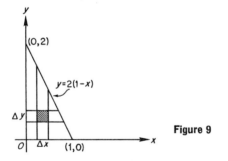

Figure 9

SOLUTION.   To find the weight, we have

$$m = \iint_{\mathcal{R}} (1 + x + y)dA$$

and by Theorem 2 this can be computed as an iterated integral.

$$m = \int_0^1 \int_0^{2(1-x)} (1 + x + y)dy\, dx$$

$$= \int_0^1 \left[y(1 + x) + \frac{y^2}{2} \right] \Big|_0^{2(1-x)} dx$$

$$= \int_0^1 [2(1 - x^2) + 2(1 - x)^2]dx$$

$$= 4\int_0^1 (1 - x)dx = 4\left(x - \frac{x^2}{2}\right)\Big|_0^1 = 2 \text{ lbs.}$$

Similarly an iterated integral for M_x gives

$$M_x = \int_0^1 \int_0^{2(1-x)} y(1 + x + y)dy\, dx = \int_0^1 \left[(1 + x)\frac{y^2}{2} + \frac{y^3}{3}\right]\Big|_0^{2(1-x)} dx$$

$$= \int_0^1 \left[2(1 + x)(1 - x)^2 + \frac{8}{3}(1 - x)^3\right] dx = \int_0^1 \left(\frac{14}{3} - 10x + 6x^2 - \frac{2}{3}x^3\right) dx$$

$$= \left(\frac{14}{3}x - 5x^2 + 2x^3 - \frac{1}{6}x^4\right)\Big|_0^1 = \frac{14}{3} - 5 + 2 - \frac{1}{6} = \frac{3}{2} \text{ lbs-ft.}$$

Therefore $\bar{y} = M_x/m = 3/4$ ft. A similar computation gives $M_y = 2/3$ and hence $\bar{x} = M_y/m = 1/2$ ft. The center of gravity is at $(1/2, 3/4)$.

$$I_x = \int_0^1 \int_0^{2(1-x)} y^2(1 + x + y)dy\, dx$$

$$= \int_0^1 \left[(1 + x)\frac{y^3}{3} + \frac{y^4}{4}\right]\Big|_0^{2(1-x)} dx = \int_0^1 8(1 - x)^3 \left[\frac{1 + x}{3} + \frac{1 - x}{2}\right] dx$$

$$= \int_0^1 8(1 - x)^3 \frac{5 - x}{6} dx = \int_0^1 \left[\frac{16}{3}(1 - x)^3 + \frac{4}{3}(1 - x)^4\right] dx$$

$$= \left(-\frac{4}{3}(1 - x)^4 - \frac{4}{15}(1 - x)^5\right)\Big|_0^1 = \frac{4}{3} + \frac{4}{15} = \frac{8}{5} \text{ lbs-ft}^2.$$

We leave it to the reader to reverse the order of integration and show that

$$I_x = \int_0^2 \int_0^{1-y/2} y^2(1 + x + y)dx\, dy = \frac{8}{5} \text{ lbs-ft}^2.$$

Up to this point we have been careful to distinguish between a region (an open connected set) and the closed region obtained by adding all of its boundary points. However, it is intuitively clear (although the proof is involved) that such physical quantities as area, weight, moment of inertia, etc., will be the same, whether computed for a region, or for the closed region obtained by adjoining its boundary points, as long as the boundary consists of a finite number of smooth curves. Hence, whenever it is convenient to do so, we may drop the requirement that $\Re$ be closed.

EXERCISE 4

In problems 1 through 4 use double integrals to find the area enclosed by the given curves.

1. $y = x$, $y = 4x - x^2$.
2. $xy = 4$, $x + y = 5$.
3. $x = y^2$, $x = 4 + 2y - y^2$.
4. $x + y = 8$, $xy - x^2 = 6$.

In problems 5 through 7, a metal sheet has the shape of the closed region bounded by the given lines, and has the given density. In each case find the center of gravity, I_x and I_y.

5. $x = 1$, $x = 2$, $y = 0$, $y = 3$, $\delta = x + y$.
6. $2x + y = 2$, $y = 2$, $x = 1$, $\delta = 2x + 4y$.
7. $x = 0$, $y = 0$, $x + y = 1$, $\delta = 2xy$.

★8. Prove that $J = I_x + I_y$ and use this to compute J for the metal sheets of problems 5, 6, and 7.

9. Find the centroid of the region in the first quadrant bounded by the curves $y = x^3$ and $y = 2x^2$. Prove that the centroid is a point of the region.

10. Find I_x and I_y for the region of problem 9.

★11. Find the moment of inertia inertia about the line $y = x$ for the region of problem 9. *Hint:* Recall the formula for the distance from a point to a line.

12. Find the centroid of the region in the first quadrant bounded by the curve $y = \sin x$ and the line $y = 2x/\pi$. Show that the centroid lies in the given region.

★13. Find $\bar{y}$ for the region bounded by the two curves $y = x^4$ and $y = (Ax^2 + 1)/(A + 1)$ for $A > 0$.

★14. Prove that if $A > 2$ then the centroid for the region of problem 13 does *not* lie in the region. Why is this possible?

6.   Area of a surface.

Our objective is to find a formula for the area of that part of the surface $z = f(x, y)$ that lies over a given closed region $\mathcal{R}$ in the xy-plane. To obtain such a formula we first take the simplest case in which the surface is a plane $z = ax + by$ and $\mathcal{R}$ is a rectangle of sides Δx and Δy (see Fig. 10). Let γ denote the angle between the

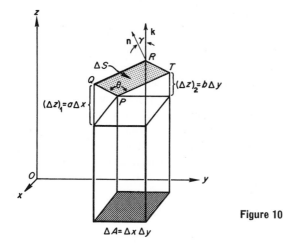

Figure 10

vector **n** normal to the plane and the z-axis, and let ΔS be the area of that part of the plane that lies over the rectangle. Since γ is also the angle between the given plane and the xy-plane, we might conjecture, by projection, that

$$\Delta A = \Delta S \cos \gamma. \tag{22}$$

Then on division by $\cos \gamma$, we have the desired result.

THEOREM 3. *With the meanings of the symbols as shown in Fig. 10.*

$$\boxed{\Delta S = \sec \gamma \ \Delta x \ \Delta y.} \tag{23}$$

Equation (22) and consequently (23) have been obtained purely by intuition. To give a proof, we first observe that the area of the parallelogram $PQRT$ is just $|\mathbf{PQ}||\mathbf{PT}| \sin \theta$ and hence is the length of the cross product **V**, where

$$\mathbf{V} = \mathbf{PQ} \times \mathbf{PT}.$$

But

$$\mathbf{PQ} = \Delta x\mathbf{i} + (\Delta z)_1\mathbf{k} = \Delta x\mathbf{i} + a\Delta x\mathbf{k},$$

and

$$\mathbf{PT} = \Delta y\mathbf{j} + (\Delta z)_2\mathbf{k} = \Delta y\mathbf{j} + b\Delta y\mathbf{k}.$$

Then an easy computation shows that

$$\mathbf{V} = (-a\mathbf{i} - b\mathbf{j} + \mathbf{k})\Delta x \ \Delta y$$

and consequently

$$\Delta S = |\mathbf{V}| = \sqrt{a^2 + b^2 + 1} \ \Delta x \ \Delta y. \tag{24}$$

But the vector **V** is also normal to the plane $z = ax + by$ and so it is easy to find $\sec \gamma$. Indeed

$$\cos \gamma = \frac{\mathbf{V} \cdot \mathbf{k}}{|\mathbf{V}|} = \frac{\Delta x \ \Delta y}{\sqrt{a^2 + b^2 + 1} \ \Delta x \ \Delta y} = \frac{1}{\sqrt{a^2 + b^2 + 1}},$$

or $\sec \gamma = \sqrt{a^2 + b^2 + 1}$. Using this in (24) gives (23).   Q.E.D.

We are now prepared to find the area for a curved surface. We first partition $\Re$ by lines parallel to the x and y-axes, in the usual way, and number the rectangles that lie in $\Re$. Let (x_α, y_α) be a point in the αth rectangle and at the corresponding point P_α on the surface pass a plane tangent to the surface $z = f(x, y)$ (see Fig. 11). Let ΔS_α be the area of that part of the tangent plane that lies over the αth rectangle. Then ΔS_α represents a good approximation to the area of the surface that lies over the αth rectangle, and we expect that the sum

$$\sum_{\alpha=1}^{n} \Delta S_\alpha$$

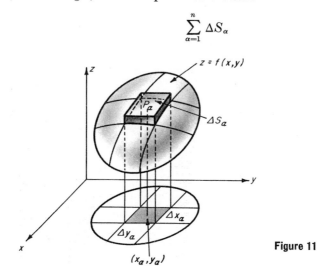

Figure 11

will be a good approximation for the area under consideration, and that this approximation will improve as we refine our partition of $\mathcal{R}$. This suggests

DEFINITION 2. *If S denotes the area of the surface over the region $\mathcal{R}$, then*

$$S = \lim_{n \to \infty} \sum_{\alpha=1}^{n} \Delta S_\alpha. \tag{25}$$

By Theorem 3 we can replace ΔS_α by $\sec \gamma_\alpha \, \Delta x_\alpha \, \Delta y_\alpha$ in (25). To obtain $\sec \gamma_\alpha$ we recall that the vector

$$\mathbf{N} = -f_x(x_\alpha, y_\alpha)\mathbf{i} - f_y(x_\alpha, y_\alpha)\mathbf{j} + \mathbf{k}$$

is normal to the surface $z = f(x, y)$ at P_α and consequently

$$\sec \gamma_\alpha = \sqrt{f_x^2(x_\alpha, y_\alpha) + f_y^2(x_\alpha, y_\alpha) + 1}.$$

Using this and $\Delta S_\alpha = \sec \gamma_\alpha \, \Delta x_\alpha \, \Delta y_\alpha$ in (25) gives

$$S = \lim_{n \to \infty} \sum_{\alpha=1}^{n} \sqrt{f_x^2(x_\alpha, y_\alpha) + f_y^2(x_\alpha, y_\alpha) + 1} \, \Delta x_\alpha \, \Delta y_\alpha.$$

Then by the definition of a double integral we have

THEOREM 4. *If S is the area of the part of the surface* $z = f(x, y)$ *that lies over the closed region* $\mathcal{R}$ *and if* f_x *and* f_y *are continuous in* $\mathcal{R}$ *then*

$$S = \iint\limits_{\mathcal{R}} \sqrt{1 + f_x^2 + f_y^2}\, dA. \tag{26}$$

If the surface is given by an equation of the form $x = f(y, z)$ or $y = f(x, z)$ then certain obvious changes must be made in (26).

If the surface is given by an equation $F(x, y, z) = c$, then the vector

$$\mathbf{V} = F_x\mathbf{i} + F_y\mathbf{j} + F_z\mathbf{k}$$

is normal to the surface. In this case

$$\sec \gamma = \frac{\sqrt{F_x^2 + F_y^2 + F_z^2}}{|F_z|},$$

and (26) is replaced by

$$S = \iint\limits_{\mathcal{R}} \frac{\sqrt{F_x^2 + F_y^2 + F_z^2}}{|F_z|}\, dA.$$

EXAMPLE 1. Find the area of the surface $z = \frac{2}{3}(x^{3/2} + y^{3/2})$ over the square $0 \le x \le 3$, $0 \le y \le 3$.

SOLUTION. Here $f_x = x^{1/2}$, $f_y = y^{1/2}$ and (26) gives

$$S = \int_0^3 \int_0^3 \sqrt{1 + x + y}\, dy\, dx = \int_0^3 \frac{2}{3}(1 + x + y)^{3/2}\Big|_0^3 dx$$

$$= \frac{2}{3}\int_0^3 [(x + 4)^{3/2} - (x + 1)^{3/2}]\, dx = \frac{2}{3}\frac{2}{5}[(x + 4)^{5/2} - (x + 1)^{5/2}]\Big|_0^3$$

$$= \frac{4}{15}[7^{5/2} - 32 - 32 + 1] = \frac{4}{15}[7^{5/2} - 63] \approx 16.36.$$

Observe that $S > 9$, the area of the square base, as it should be.

EXERCISE 5

In problems 1 through 8 find the area of that portion of the given surface that lies over the given closed region.

1. $z = a + bx + cy$, $\quad 0 \le y \le x^2$, $0 \le x \le 3$.
2. $z = x + \frac{2}{3}y^{3/2}$, $\quad 1 \le x \le 4$, $2 \le y \le 7$.

3. $z = x^2 + \sqrt{3}y,$ $0 \leq y \leq 2x,$ $0 \leq x \leq 2\sqrt{2}.$

4. $z = e^{-y} + \sqrt{7}x,$ $0 \leq x \leq e^{-2y},$ $0 \leq y \leq 3.$

5. $z = \sqrt{x^2 + y^2},$ $0 \leq x \leq 2,$ $0 \leq y \leq 5.$

6. $z = \sqrt{a^2 - y^2},$ $0 \leq x \leq 2y,$ $0 \leq y \leq a.$

★7. $z = -\ln y,$ $0 \leq x \leq y^2,$ $0 \leq y \leq 1.$

★8. $z = 1/y,$ $0 \leq x \leq y,$ $0 \leq y \leq 1.$

9. Prove that the points $A(0, 0, 1)$, $B(2, 0, 4)$, and $C(5, 6, 2)$ form the vertices of a right triangle. Find the area of this triangle, (a) by elementary means, and (b) by double integration.

10. Find the area of the cylinder $x^2 + z^2 = a^2$ lying in the first octant and between the planes $y = x$ and $y = 3x.$

11. Find the area of that part of the cylinder $y^2 + z^2 = a^2$ that lies inside the cylinder $x^2 + y^2 = a^2.$

12. Prove that if $\Re$ is any closed region in the xy-plane, then the area of the portion of the cone $z = a\sqrt{x^2 + y^2}$ that lies above $\Re$ is $\sqrt{1 + a^2}\, A$ where A is the area of $\Re$.

13. Consider that portion of the cylinder $y^2 + z^2 = 1$ that lies in the first octant and above the unit square $0 \leq x \leq 1,\ 0 \leq y \leq 1.$ A rough sketch seems to indicate that the plane $y = x$ bisects this surface into two congruent parts. Prove that the parts are not congruent by finding the area of each part.

★14. We have previously used the formula

$$2\pi \int_a^b y \sqrt{1 + \left(\frac{dy}{dx}\right)^2}\, dx$$

for the area of the surface of revolution obtained when the curve $y = f(x)$ is rotated about the x-axis. Prove that our new definition is consistent, by deriving this formula from (26). *Hint:* The surface of revolution has the equation $y^2 + z^2 = f^2(x).$

15. Prove that if $\Re$ is any closed region in the xy-plane then the area of the portion of the paraboloid $z = ax^2 + by^2$ that lies above $\Re$ is equal to the area of the portion of the saddle surface $z = ax^2 - by^2$ that lies above (or below) $\Re$.

16. Prove that the statement of problem 15 is also true for each of the following pairs of surfaces

    a. $z = x^2 + y^2,$ $z = 2xy,$

    b. $z = \ln(x^2 + y^2),$ $z = 2\tan^{-1}(y/x),$

    c. $z = e^x(x \cos y - y \sin y),$ $z = e^x(y \cos y + x \sin y).$

7.   **Polar coordinates.** In certain problems, the evaluation of a given double integral becomes simpler if polar coordinates are used. Now x and y are replaced by $r \cos \theta$ and $r \sin \theta$ respectively and $f(x, y)$ becomes $f(r \cos \theta, r \sin \theta) = F(r, \theta)$, a function of r and θ. Instead of using a network of horizontal and vertical lines, the region $\Re$ is partitioned by a finite number of circles with center at the origin, and a finite number of radial lines, as indicated in Fig. 12. This partition divides $\mathcal{R}$ into a finite number of cells, and a typical one is shown in Fig. 13. We call such a cell a *polar rectangle*. To find an expression for ΔA, the area of a polar rectangle, let r_s and r_l be the radii of the smaller and larger circles respectively, with a similar meaning for θ_s and θ_l.

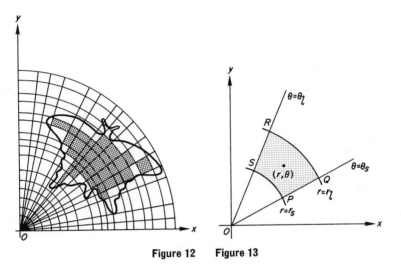

Figure 12   Figure 13

Then referring to the lettering of Fig. 13, the area of the sector SOP is $\frac{1}{2}r_s{}^2(\theta_l - \theta_s)$, the area of the sector ROQ is $\frac{1}{2}r_l{}^2(\theta_l - \theta_s)$, and consequently

$$\Delta A = \tfrac{1}{2}r_l{}^2(\theta_l - \theta_s) - \tfrac{1}{2}r_s{}^2(\theta_l - \theta_s) = \tfrac{1}{2}(r_l{}^2 - r_s{}^2)(\theta_l - \theta_s)$$

$$\Delta A = \frac{r_l + r_s}{2}(r_l - r_s)(\theta_l - \theta_s) = r\,\Delta r\,\Delta\theta. \qquad (27)$$

Here $r = \frac{1}{2}(r_l + r_s)$ and represents the radius of a circle that is midway between the smaller and larger circles forming the boundary of the polar rectangle.

We next examine the sum

$$\sum_{\alpha=1}^{n} F(r_\alpha, \theta_\alpha)\Delta A_\alpha \qquad (28)$$

where the sum is taken over all of the polar rectangles that lie completely in $\mathcal{R}$. We select the point $(r_\alpha, \theta_\alpha)$ so that it lies inside each polar rectangle, and for convenience so that it lies on the circle midway between the larger and smaller circles of the boundary.   Then using (27) we can write the sum (28) as

$$\sum_{\alpha=1}^{n} F(r_\alpha, \theta_\alpha) r_\alpha \, \Delta r_\alpha \, \Delta \theta_\alpha \tag{29}$$

and on taking the limit, the double integral in polar coordinates becomes

$$\iint_{\Re} F(r, \theta) r \, dr \, d\theta. \tag{30}$$

Just as before, various physical interpretations can be assigned to (30) in accordance with the selection of the function $F(r, \theta)$.   If $z = F(r, \theta)$ is the equation of a surface in cylindrical coordinates, then (30) gives the volume of the solid under the surface and over $\Re$.   If $F(r, \theta) = 1$, then (30) gives the area of $\Re$, etc.

It is convenient to refer to the expression $r \, dr \, d\theta$ as the *differential element of area* in polar coordinates.   This expression is easy to recall if we observe that in Fig. 13 the arc PS has length $r_s \Delta \theta$ and the segment PQ has length Δr, so that the polar rectangle has area (approximately) equal to their product $r_s \Delta r \, \Delta \theta$.

EXAMPLE 1.   For the solid bounded by the xy-plane, the cylinder $x^2 + y^2 = a^2$ and the paraboloid $z = b(x^2 + y^2)$ with $b > 0$, find (a) the volume, (b) its centroid, (c) I_z, and (d) the area of its upper surface.

SOLUTION.   Since $x^2 + y^2 = r^2$, the equation for the paraboloid in cylindrical coordinates is $z = br^2$.   For the volume we have

$$V = \iint_{\Re} z \, dx dy = \iint_{\Re} z \, r \, dr \, d\theta = \int_0^{2\pi} \int_0^a br^2 r \, dr \, d\theta$$

$$= \int_0^{2\pi} b \frac{r^4}{4} \Big|_0^a d\theta = \frac{ba^4}{4} \int_0^{2\pi} d\theta = \frac{\pi ba^4}{2}.$$

By symmetry the centroid is on the z-axis, so $\bar{x} = \bar{y} = 0$.   To find $\bar{z}$, we must compute M_{xy}.   The partition of the plane region $\Re$, shown in Fig. 12, simultaneously divides the solid into elements with cylindrical sides.   A typical element is shown in Fig. 14.   If the sides of the polar rectangle are sufficiently small then $zr\Delta r\Delta\theta$ represents a good approximation to the volume of the element, and $z/2$ is a good approximation for the z-coordinate of its centroid.   Hence the sum

$$\sum_{\alpha=1}^{n} \frac{z_\alpha}{2} z_\alpha r_\alpha \, \Delta r_\alpha \, \Delta \theta_\alpha$$

gives a good approximation to M_{xy}.   Taking the limit as $n \to \infty$, we can write

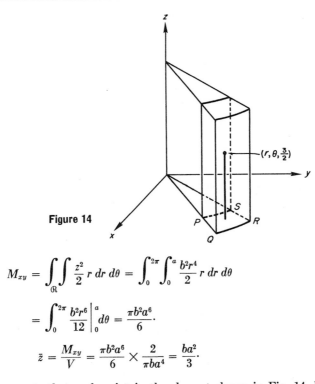

Figure 14

$$M_{xy} = \int\!\!\int_{\mathcal{R}} \frac{z^2}{2} r \, dr \, d\theta = \int_0^{2\pi}\!\!\int_0^a \frac{b^2 r^4}{2} r \, dr \, d\theta$$

$$= \int_0^{2\pi} \frac{b^2 r^6}{12}\Big|_0^a d\theta = \frac{\pi b^2 a^6}{6}.$$

Then
$$\bar{z} = \frac{M_{xy}}{V} = \frac{\pi b^2 a^6}{6} \times \frac{2}{\pi b a^4} = \frac{ba^2}{3}.$$

To find I_z we note that each point in the element shown in Fig. 14, has roughly the same distance r from the z-axis. Then forming a sum and taking the limit as $n \to \infty$ we have

$$I_z = \int\!\!\int_{\mathcal{R}} r^2 dV = \int\!\!\int_{\mathcal{R}} r^2 z dA = \int\!\!\int_{\mathcal{R}} r^2 z \, r \, dr \, d\theta$$

$$= \int_0^{2\pi}\!\!\int_0^a b r^5 dr \, d\theta = \int_0^{2\pi} \frac{b r^6}{6}\Big|_0^a d\theta = \frac{\pi b a^6}{3}.$$

For the surface area we have

$$S = \int\!\!\int_{\mathcal{R}} \sqrt{1 + f_x^2 + f_y^2}\, dx \, dy = \int\!\!\int_{\mathcal{R}} \sqrt{1 + 4b^2(x^2 + y^2)}\, dx \, dy$$

$$= \int_0^{2\pi}\!\!\int_0^a \sqrt{1 + 4b^2 r^2}\, r \, dr \, d\theta = \frac{1}{8b^2} \int_0^{2\pi} \frac{2}{3}(1 + 4b^2 r^2)^{3/2}\Big|_0^a d\theta$$

$$= \frac{\pi}{6b^2}\left[(1 + 4b^2 a^2)^{3/2} - 1\right].$$

EXAMPLE 2. Use double integration to find the area enclosed by the circle $r = a \cos \theta$.

SOLUTION.   The circle is described once as θ runs from $-\pi/2$ to $\pi/2$.   Thus

$$A = \int_{-\pi/2}^{\pi/2} \int_0^{a\cos\theta} r\,dr\,d\theta = \int_{-\pi/2}^{\pi/2} \frac{r^2}{2}\Big|_0^{a\cos\theta} d\theta$$

$$= \frac{a^2}{2} \int_{-\pi/2}^{\pi/2} \cos^2\theta\,d\theta = \frac{a^2}{4} \int_{-\pi/2}^{\pi/2} (1 + \cos 2\theta)d\theta$$

$$= \frac{a^2}{4}\left(\theta + \frac{1}{2}\sin 2\theta\right)\Big|_{-\pi/2}^{\pi/2} = \frac{\pi a^2}{4}.$$

EXERCISE 6

In problems 1 through 6 use double integrals to find the area of the region enclosed by the given curve or curves.

1. $r^2 = a^2 \cos 2\theta$, $\theta = 0$, and $\theta = \pi/6$.
2.   One loop of the curve $r = 6 \cos 3\theta$.
3. $r = 3 + \sin 4\theta$.
4. $r = \tan\theta$, $\theta = 0$, and $\theta = \pi/4$.
5.   Outside the circle $r = 3a$ and inside the cardioid $r = 2a(1 + \cos\theta)$.
★6. $\theta = r$, $\theta = 2r$, $r = \pi/4$, $r = \pi/2$, $(\theta \geq 0)$.

In problems 7 through 10 a solid is bounded by the given surfaces.   Find the indicated quantity.   Here S denotes the area of the upper surface.

7. $z = 4 - x^2 - y^2$, $z = 0$.   Find V, I_z, and S.
8. $z = a + x$, $z = 0$, $x^2 + y^2 = a^2$.   Find V, $\bar{x}$, $\bar{z}$, and I_z.
9. $z = 0$, $z = r$ $(r \geq 0)$, $r = a + b \cos\theta$, $a > |b|$.   Find V.
10. $z = 0$, $z = 1/r$ $(r > 0)$, $r = a \sec\theta$, $r = b \sec\theta$ $(b > a > 0)$, $\theta = 0$, $\theta = \pi/4$.   Find V, M_{yz}, M_{zx}, and M_{xy}.

11.   Find the volume of the solid in the first octant bounded by the planes $z = 0$, $z = y$, and the cylinder $r = \sin 2\theta$.
12.   Find the volume of that portion of the sphere $x^2 + y^2 + z^2 = a^2$ that is also inside the cylinder $x^2 + y^2 = ax$.
13.   Find the area of the top surface of the solid of problem 12.
★14.   Show that the volume of the solid bounded by $z = 0$, $z = 1/r$, and the cylinder $(x - 2)^2 + y^2 = 1$, is given by the elliptic integral

$$V = 4 \int_0^{\pi/6} \sqrt{4 \cos^2\theta - 3}\,d\theta.$$

15.   A sheet of material has the shape of a plane region $\Re$ and has surface density δ.   Give the specific function $F(r, \theta)$ to be used in equation (30) to compute M_x, M_y, I_x, I_y, and J.
16.   For the circular region bounded by $r = a$ find I_x and I_y by first finding J and dividing by 2.

In problems 17 through 21 find the centroid of the region described.

17.   The half circle $0 < r < a$, $-\pi/2 < \theta < \pi/2$.

18. $0 < r < \sqrt[3]{\theta}, 0 < \theta < \pi.$

19. Inside the cardioid $r = a(1 + \cos \theta)$.

20. Inside the circle $r = 2a \cos \theta$ and outside the circle $r = \sqrt{2}a$.

★21. The smaller of the two regions bounded by the circle $r = a$ and the straight-line $r = b \sec \theta, 0 < b < a$.

22. Obtain the answer to problem 17, by putting $b = 0$ in the answer to problem 21.

23. Find $\bar{x}$ for a sheet of material having the shape of the region bounded by the curve $r = a + b \cos \theta$, $(0 < b < a)$ with $0 \leq \theta \leq \pi$, and the x-axis, where the material has the surface density $\delta = \sin \theta$.

★24. Find $\bar{x}$ for the material of problem 23 if $\delta = r \sin \theta$.

25. Find I_x and I_y for the region enclosed by the circle $r = \sin \theta$.

26. Check your answers to problem 25 by finding J for that circle in two different ways.

27. Find I_x and I_y for the semicircle $0 < r < a$, $0 < \theta < \pi$, if the surface density is $\delta = \sin \theta$. As in problem 26 check your answer by finding J.

★28. We call the region on the surface of a sphere between two circles of latitude and two circles of longitude a *spherical rectangle*. Suppose that in cylindrical coordinates the sphere has the equation $z^2 + r^2 = \rho^2$. Then the spherical rectangle can be described by the inequalities $\rho \sin \varphi_0 < r < \rho \sin(\varphi_0 + \Delta \varphi)$ and $\theta_0 < \theta < \theta_0 + \Delta \theta$, (here φ_0 has the meaning that is standard in spherical coordinates). Prove that the area of this spherical rectangle is $S = \rho^2[\cos \varphi_0 - \cos (\varphi_0 + \Delta \varphi)]\Delta \theta$. Prove further that if $\sin \varphi_0 \neq 0$, then

$$\lim_{\substack{\Delta \theta \to 0 \\ \Delta \varphi \to 0}} \frac{S}{\rho^2 \sin \varphi_0 \Delta \theta \Delta \varphi} = 1.$$

Hence the denominator furnishes a good approximation to S.

★29. The region in the first octant bounded by the coordinate planes and the surface $z = e^{-(x^2 + y^2)}$ has infinite extent but finite volume. Find the volume.

★30. It can be proved that under suitable conditions

$$\int_0^a f(x)dx \int_0^b g(y)dy = \int\int_{\Re} f(x)g(y)dA$$

where $\Re$ is the rectangle $0 \leq x \leq a$, $0 \leq y \leq b$. Use this result, together with the result of problem (29) to prove that

$$\int_0^\infty e^{-x^2} dx = \frac{\sqrt{\pi}}{2}.$$

This is curious, because if the upper limit a in $\int_0^a e^{-x^2} dx$ is not infinity or zero, the integral cannot be evaluated by elementary means.

8. **Triple integrals.** The double integral was obtained by dividing a plane region into little rectangles and taking the limit of a certain sum.   A triple integral is the natural extension of this concept to three dimensional regions.

We let $\mathcal{R}$ denote some closed region in three dimensional space and we partition this region by a finite number of planes parallel to the coordinate planes.   These planes form a finite number of boxes, some of which lie entirely in $\mathcal{R}$, some lie partly in $\mathcal{R}$, and some lie outside of $\mathcal{R}$.   Henceforth we consider only those boxes that lie entirely in $\mathcal{R}$, and we number these boxes from 1 to n.   A typical box is shown in Fig. 15.   We let $\Delta V_\alpha = \Delta x_i \Delta y_j \Delta z_k$ be the volume of the box, we select a point $P_\alpha(x_\alpha, y_\alpha, z_\alpha)$ in or on the boundary of the αth box, and for a given function $f(x, y, z)$ we set

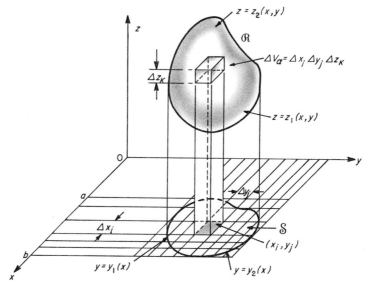

Figure 15

$f(P_\alpha) = f(x_\alpha, y_\alpha, z_\alpha)$ for brevity.   Just as in the case of a double integral we form the sum

$$I_p = \sum_{\alpha=1}^{n} f(P_\alpha)\Delta V_\alpha \qquad (31)$$

where the value of I_p depends on the partitioning planes and on the choice of the points P_α.   But if the boxes are all small and if $f(x, y, z)$ is continuous then I_p is close to a certain limit number.   To state this result precisely we introduce the letter d_α for the length of the diagonal of the αth box and the letter D for the maximum of the lengths $d_\alpha(\alpha = 1, 2, \cdots, n)$.   Then we agree that in taking the limit of I_p as the number of partitioning planes tends to infinity, we shall always have $D \to 0$.   It can be proved that if $f(x, y, z)$ is a continuous function in the closed region $\mathcal{R}$, then I_p tends to a limit called the triple integral of $f(x, y, z)$ over $\mathcal{R}$, and denoted by the symbol

$$\iiint\limits_{\mathcal{R}} f(x, y, z) dV.$$

DEFINITION 3. *The triple integral of $f(x, y, z)$ over $\mathcal{R}$ is defined by*

$$\iiint\limits_{\mathcal{R}} f(x, y, z) dV = \lim_{\substack{n \to \infty \\ D \to 0}} \sum_{\alpha=1}^{n} f(P_\alpha) \Delta V_\alpha \qquad (32)$$

whenever the limit on the right side exists.

We will see presently that the actual computation of such limits is an easy matter, by changing the triple integral into a suitably selected iterated integral. But first we examine the physical interpretation of (32).

If in (32) we set $f(x, y, z) = 1$ for all points in $\mathcal{R}$, then the triple integral gives V, the volume of $\mathcal{R}$. For the sum in (31) is then $\sum \Delta V_\alpha$ and gives the volume of a collection of boxes all contained in $\mathcal{R}$. As $n \to \infty$ and $D \to 0$, each interior point of $\mathcal{R}$ is in some box, so in the limit as $n \to \infty$, we have $I_p \to V$.

Suppose next that $\mathcal{R}$ is the closed region occupied by some solid of variable density $\delta(x, y, z)$ and we select $f(x, y, z)$ to be the density $\delta(x, y, z)$. Then $f(P_\alpha)\Delta V_\alpha = \delta(P_\alpha)\Delta V_\alpha$ is a good approximation to m_α, the weight of the αth box. In the limit as $n \to \infty$, and $D \to 0$, the sum I_p approaches the weight of the body, i.e.,

$$m = \iiint\limits_{\mathcal{R}} \delta(x, y, z) dV. \qquad (33)$$

Similar considerations lead to formulas for M_{yz}, M_{zx}, and M_{xy}, the moments with respect to the various coordinate planes; and to formulas for I_z, I_x, and I_y, the moments of inertia about the various axes. These formulas are:

$$M_{yz} = \iiint\limits_{\mathcal{R}} x\delta\, dV, \quad M_{zx} = \iiint\limits_{\mathcal{R}} y\delta\, dV, \quad M_{xy} = \iiint\limits_{\mathcal{R}} z\delta\, dV, \quad (34)$$

$$I_z = \iiint\limits_{\mathcal{R}} (x^2 + y^2)\delta\, dV, \quad I_x = \iiint\limits_{\mathcal{R}} (y^2 + z^2)\delta\, dV,$$

$$(35)$$

$$I_y = \iiint\limits_{\mathcal{R}} (z^2 + x^2)\delta\, dV.$$

As usual, when we speak of the moment, or moment of inertia of a closed region (instead of a solid) we mean the above quantities computed with $\delta = 1$.

The proof that a triple integral can be evaluated by computing an appropriate iterated integral follows the pattern outlined in the case of a double integral, and so we omit it. The main practical difficulty lies in selecting the correct iterated integral, and we now discuss this problem.

Suppose that the three dimensional closed region is projected on the xy-plane as indicated in Fig. 15, and let $\mathcal{S}$ be the shadow of $\mathcal{R}$ on the xy-plane, i.e., $\mathcal{S}$ is the collection of all points that are the projection of some point in $\mathcal{R}$. Any partition of $\mathcal{R}$ by planes, simultaneously effects a partitioning of the closed region $\mathcal{S}$ by lines parallel to the x and y-axes. We select a representative rectangle from this partition of $\mathcal{S}$ and with this rectangle fixed we consider at first all of the boxes in $\mathcal{R}$ that lie directly above it. We select $x_\alpha = x_i$ and $y_\alpha = y_j$ to be the same for each of these boxes while $z_\alpha = z_k$ naturally varies, from box to box in the vertical stack. In the sum (31) we first take only those terms that correspond to boxes in this vertical stack. These terms can be written as

$$\sum_{k=1}^{m(i,j)} f(x_i, y_j, z_k)\Delta V = \sum_{k=1}^{m(i,j)} f(x_i, y_j, z_k)\Delta x_i\, \Delta y_j\, \Delta z_k \qquad (36)$$

where in this sum x_i, y_j, Δx_i, Δy_j are constant, and only the subscript k is changing in the summation. Here $m(i, j)$ denotes the number of terms in the sum and is just the number of boxes in the partition that lie above the fixed rectangle selected in $\mathcal{S}$. This number depends on the rectangle selected and hence may change as we move from one rectangle to the next in $\mathcal{S}$. This accounts for the notation $m(i, j)$ for the upper limit in the sum (36). We next vary y_j while holding x_i constant. By this we mean that with x_i fixed we consider all of the rectangles in $\mathcal{S}$ that lie on the line $x = x_i$. These rectangles are shown shaded in Fig. 16. For each such rectangle we form a sum of the type (36) and then add all of these sums obtaining the *double sum*.

$$\sum_{j=1}^{m(i)} \sum_{k=1}^{m(i,j)} f(x_i, y_j, z_k)\Delta x_i\, \Delta y_j\, \Delta z_k = \sum_{j=1}^{m(i)} \left[\sum_{k=1}^{m(i,j)} f(x_i, y_j, z_k)\Delta z_k \right] \Delta y_j\, \Delta x_i. \qquad (37)$$

Here $m(i)$ denotes the number of rectangles in $\mathcal{S}$ and on the line $x = x_i$. The brackets on the right side indicate that the inner sum, the sum on k, is taken first with i and j constant, and then a sum of such sums is taken with i constant. The sum in (37) includes all of the boxes in $\mathcal{R}$ that lie over the shaded rectangle of Fig. 16. These boxes together form a slice that is shown shaded in Fig. 16. All of the terms in (37) are terms in the sum (31), but (37) does not necessarily exhaust (31). To obtain all of the terms in (31) we now let x_i change so as to include all of the rectangles in

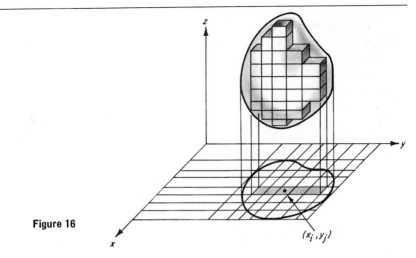

Figure 16

(x_i, y_j)

the shadow $\mathcal{S}$.   Then adding sets of expressions of the form (37) we obtain the *triple sum*

$$\sum_{i=1}^{m} \sum_{j=1}^{m(i)} \sum_{k=1}^{m(i,j)} f(x_i, y_j, z_k)\Delta x_i, \ \Delta y_j \ \Delta z_k =$$

$$\sum_{i=1}^{m} \left[\sum_{j=1}^{m(i)} \left[\sum_{k=1}^{m(i,j)} f(x_i, y_j, z_k)\Delta z_k \right] \Delta y_j \right] \Delta x_i. \quad (38)$$

Now each term in the sum

$$I_p = \sum_{\alpha=1}^{n} f(P_\alpha)\Delta V_\alpha \qquad (31)$$

is present exactly once in (38) and conversely, so that (38) is merely a rearrangement of the order of addition of the terms in (31).   Consequently both (31) and (38) have the same limit as $n \to \infty$ and $D \to 0$.

Let us examine the right side of (38).   As $n \to \infty$ and $D \to 0$, the inner sum

$$\sum_{k=1}^{m(i,j)} f(x_i, y_j, z_k)\Delta z_k \to \int f(x_i, y_j, z)dz,$$

where we defer until later the determination of the limits of integration. Then the second sum tends to an integral of this integral, namely

$$\sum_{j=1}^{m(i)} \left[\sum_{k=1}^{m(i,j)} f(x_i, y_j, z_k)\Delta z_k \right] \Delta y_j \to \int \left[\int f(x_i, y, z)dz \right] dy$$

and finally the triple integral is given by the threefold iterated integral

$$\iiint_{\mathcal{R}} f(x, y, z)dV = \int \left[\int \left[\int f(x, y, z)dz \right] dy \right] dx. \quad (39)$$

It has not been our purpose to prove (39) but merely to describe how it arises so that we can determine the proper limits for the iterated integral on the right. However the details can be supplied that will make the above outline into a rigorous proof.

In order to place limits on the iterated integral on the right side of (39) let us consider the region shown in Fig. 15. We suppose that the equations for the upper and lower boundary surfaces are $z = z_2(x, y)$ and $z = z_1(x, y)$ respectively. Further we suppose that the projection of $\mathcal{R}$ on the xy-plane is bounded by two curves $y = y_2(x)$ and $y = y_1(x)$ as x varies from a to b. Under these circumstances, the iterated integral in (39) would be written

$$\int_a^b \int_{y_1(x)}^{y_2(x)} \int_{z_1(x,y)}^{z_2(x,y)} f(x, y, z) dz\, dy\, dx. \qquad (40)$$

The integral from $z_1(x, y)$ to $z_2(x, y)$ corresponds to the summation over the boxes in a vertical stack (see equation (36)) and is performed with x and y fixed. The integral from $y_1(x)$ to $y_2(x)$ corresponds to the summation over the rectangles on a fixed line parallel to the y-axis in the xy-plane (see equation (37)) and is performed with x fixed. Finally the integral from a to b corresponds to a summation over all of the rectangles in $\mathcal{S}$.

It should be clear that $\mathcal{R}$ could also be projected into the xz-plane or into the yz-plane. Further in each case the computation of the resulting double integral over the shadow region can be done in two different ways. Hence there is a total of *six* different ways of writing the right side of (39), one way for each of the six permutations of the symbols dx, dy, and dz. With each of these six different ways, the limits of integration must be selected accordingly. This is illustrated in

EXAMPLE 1.   Compute the triple integral of $f(x, y, z) = 2x + 4y$ over the region in the first octant bounded by the coordinate planes and the plane

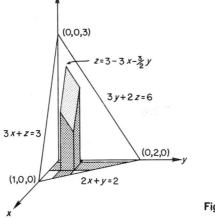

Figure 17

$6x + 3y + 2z = 6$. Set up each of the six different iterated integrals that give this triple integral.

SOLUTION. The region is shown in Fig. 17, together with the equations of the boundary lines. For this region (40) becomes

$$I = \int_0^1 \int_0^{2-2x} \int_0^{3-3x-3y/2} (2x + 4y)dz\, dy\, dx.$$

$$I = \int_0^1 \int_0^{2-2x} (2x + 4y)z \Big|_0^{3-3x-3y/2} dy\, dx$$

$$= \int_0^1 \int_0^{2-2x} (2x + 4y)\left(3 - 3x - \frac{3}{2}y\right)dy\, dx$$

$$= \int_0^1 \int_0^{2(1-x)} (6x + 12y - 6x^2 - 15xy - 6y^2)dy\, dx$$

$$= \int_0^1 [12x(1 - x) + 24(1 - x)^2 - 12x^2(1 - x) - 30x(1 - x)^2 - 16(1 - x)^3]dx$$

$$= \int_0^1 (8 - 18x + 12x^2 - 2x^3)dx = 8x - 9x^2 + 4x^3 - \frac{x^4}{2}\Big|_0^1 = 5/2.$$

Other iterated integrals that give this same triple integral are

$$\int_0^2 \int_0^{1-y/2} \int_0^{3-3x-3y/2} (2x + 4y)dz\, dx\, dy,$$

$$\int_0^1 \int_0^{3-3x} \int_0^{2-2x-2z/3} (2x + 4y)dy\, dz\, dx,$$

$$\int_0^3 \int_0^{1-z/3} \int_0^{2-2x-2y/3} (2x + 4y)dy\, dx\, dz,$$

$$\int_0^3 \int_0^{2-2z/3} \int_0^{1-y/2-z/3} (2x + 4y)dx\, dy\, dz$$

$$\int_0^2 \int_0^{3-3y/2} \int_0^{1-y/2-z/3} (2x + 4y)dx\, dz\, dy.$$

EXERCISE 7

1. Evaluate the triple integral of $f = 24xy^2z^3$ over the box $0 \leq x \leq a$, $0 \leq y \leq b$, $0 \leq z \leq c$.

2. Evaluate the triple integral of $f = 24xy^2z^3$ over the region bounded by the planes $x = 0$, $x = 1$, $y = 0$, $z = y$, and $z = 2$.

3. Check the answer to example 1 of this section by evaluating at least two of the other five iterated integrals given at the end of the example.

In problems 4 through 9, use triple integration to find the volume of the region bounded by the given surfaces.

4. $x = 0$, $y = 0$, $z = 0$ and $6x + 4y + 3z = 12$.

5. $z = 6\sqrt{y}$, $z = \sqrt{y}$, $y = x$, $y = 4$, and $x = 0$.

6. $y = 0$, $x = 4$, $z = y$, and $z = x - y$.

★7. $z = x^2 + 2y^2$, and $z = 16 - x^2 - 2y^2$.

★8. $z = x^2 + y^2$, and $z = 2y$.

★9. $y = x^2 + 2x$, and $y = 4 - z^2 + 2x$.

In problems 10 through 15 find the weight of the solid bounded by the given surfaces, and having the given density.

10. $x = 0$, $x = 1$, $y = 0$, $y = 1$, $z = 0$, $z = 1$, $\delta = ky$.

11. $x = 0$, $x = a$, $y = 0$, $y = b$, $z = 0$, $z = c$, $\delta = ky$.

12.   The solid of problem 11, $\delta = 1 + 24kxy^2z^3$.

13. $z = x^2 + y^2$, $z = 4$, $x = 0$, $y = 0$, first octant, $\delta = 4ky$.

14. $z = xy$, $x = 1$, $y = x$, $z = 0$, $\delta = 1 + 2z$.

15. $z = e^{x+y}$, $z = 4$, $x = 0$, $y = 0$, $\delta = 1/z$.

16.   Obtain the answer to problem 12 from the solution to problem 1.

17.   Find the center of gravity for the solid of: (a) problem 10, (b) problem 11, (c) problem 12, and (d) problem 14.   In (d) prove that the center of gravity lies inside the solid.

18.   Find I_x and I_y, for the solid of (a) problem 10, (b) problem 11, (c) problem 12, and (d) problem 14.

19.   Find the centroid of the tetrahedron bounded by the coordinate planes and the plane $bcx + acy + abz = abc$, where a, b and c are positive.

20.   Find I_x for the region of problem 19.

★★21.   Prove the general form of the parallel axis theorem, equation (34) of Chapter 15.   *Hint:* Let g and p be the axis through the center of gravity and the parallel axis respectively.   Select the origin of the coordinate system at the center of gravity of the solid, let the y-axis coincide with g, and then rotate the xz-plane so that the x-axis intersects the line p at the point $(s, 0, 0)$.   Then

$$I_p = \iiint\limits_{\mathfrak{R}} [(s - x)^2 + z^2]\delta\, dx\, dy\, dz$$

$$= \iiint\limits_{\mathfrak{R}} (x^2 + z^2)\delta\, dx\, dy\, dz - 2s \iiint\limits_{\mathfrak{R}} x\delta\, dx\, dy\, dz + s^2 \iiint\limits_{\mathfrak{R}} \delta\, dx\, dy\, dz$$

$$= I_y - 2sM_{yz} + s^2M = I_g - 0 + Ms^2.$$

9.   **Cylindrical coordinates.**   In many cases the triple integral over a region $\mathfrak{R}$ can be evaluated more easily if cylindrical coordinates are used in place of rectangular coordinates.   As usual the region is partitioned into parts, but this time the partitioning is done by cylinders with the z-axis for an axis, together with horizontal planes and planes containing the z-axis.   These surfaces form a number of cylindrical boxes, and a typical one is shown in Fig. 18.

We have already seen in section 7 that in polar coordinates the differential element of area is $dA = r \, dr \, d\theta$. Consequently it follows that in cylindrical coordinates the differential of volume is $dV = r \, dr \, d\theta \, dz$. Then

$$\iiint_{\mathcal{R}} f(x, y, z)dV = \iiint_{\mathcal{R}} f(r \cos \theta, r \sin \theta, z)r \, dr \, d\theta \, dz. \qquad (41)$$

As usual, $f = 1$ gives the volume of $\mathcal{R}$, $f = r^2$ gives I_z for $\mathcal{R}$, and so on.

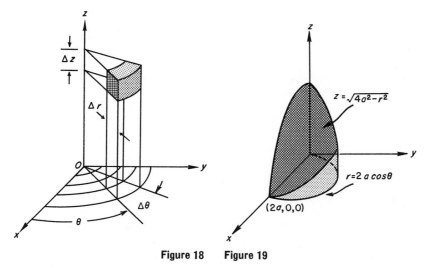

Figure 18   Figure 19

EXAMPLE 1.   For the region inside both the sphere $x^2 + y^2 + z^2 = 4a^2$, and the cylinder $(x - a)^2 + y^2 = a^2$ find (a) the volume and (b) I_z.

SOLUTION.   The portion of the region in the first octant is shown in Fig. 19. In cylindrical coordinates the equation of the sphere is $r^2 + z^2 = 4a^2$, and the equation of the cylinder is $r = 2a \cos \theta$. Using the symmetry, (41) gives

$$V = 4 \int_0^{\pi/2} \int_0^{2a \cos \theta} \int_0^{\sqrt{4a^2-r^2}} r \, dz \, dr \, d\theta$$

$$= 4 \int_0^{\pi/2} \int_0^{2a \cos \theta} (4a^2 - r^2)^{1/2} r \, dr \, d\theta$$

$$= -2 \int_0^{\pi/2} \frac{2}{3} (4a^2 - r^2)^{3/2} \Big|_0^{2a \cos \theta} d\theta$$

$$= \frac{4}{3} \int_0^{\pi/2} [8a^3 - (4a^2 - 4a^2 \cos^2 \theta)^{3/2}] \, d\theta$$

$$= \frac{32a^3}{3} \int_0^{\pi/2} (1 - \sin^3 \theta)d\theta = \frac{16a^3}{9} (3\pi - 4).$$

Similarly for I_z we have

$$I_z = 4 \int_0^{\pi/2} \int_0^{2a \cos \theta} \int_0^{\sqrt{4a^2-r^2}} r^2 r \, dz \, dr \, d\theta$$

$$= 4 \int_0^{\pi/2} \int_0^{2a \cos \theta} (4a^2 - r^2)^{1/2}(r^2 - 4a^2 + 4a^2)r \, dr \, d\theta$$

$$= 4 \int_0^{\pi/2} \int_0^{2a \cos \theta} [4a^2(4a^2 - r^2)^{1/2} - (4a^2 - r^2)^{3/2}] \, r \, dr \, d\theta$$

$$= -2 \int_0^{\pi/2} \left[\frac{8}{3} a^2(4a^2 - r^2)^{3/2} - \frac{2}{5} (4a^2 - r^2)^{5/2} \right] \Bigg|_0^{2a \cos \theta} d\theta$$

$$= \frac{128 \, a^5}{15} \int_0^{\pi/2} (2 + 3 \sin^5 \theta - 5 \sin^3 \theta) d\theta$$

$$= \frac{128 \, a^5}{15} \int_0^{\pi/2} (11 \cos^2 \theta + 3 \cos^4 \theta) \sin \theta \, d\theta = \frac{2^{13} a^5}{225}.$$

EXERCISE 8

1. Write the expression to be used for f in the right side of equation (41) when computing (a) M_{xy}, (b) M_{yz}, (c) I_x, and (d) I_y, assuming unit density.

2. Find the volume of the region bounded above by the sphere $z^2 + r^2 = \rho_0^2$ and below by the cone $z = r \cot \varphi_0$. Use this result to find the volume of a hemisphere.

3. Consider the portion of the region of problem 2 that lies between the half planes $\theta = \theta_0$ and $\theta = \theta_0 + \Delta\theta (r \geq 0)$. Prove that the volume is given by

$$V = \frac{\rho_0^3}{3} (1 - \cos \varphi_0) \Delta\theta.$$

This result will be used in the next section on spherical coordinates.

4. Find the centroid of the region bounded by the cone $z = m\sqrt{x^2 + y^2}$ and the plane $z = H$, where $m > 0$, and $H > 0$.

5. Find the volume of the region inside the sphere $r^2 + z^2 = 8$ and above the paraboloid $2z = r^2$.

6. Find $\bar{z}$ for the region of problem 5.

7. Find the volume of the region below the plane $z = y$, and above the paraboloid $z = r^2$.

8. Find the centroid of the region of problem 7.

9. A right circular cylinder has base radius R and height H. Find the moment of inertia about a generator (a line lying in its lateral surface). Find the moment of inertia about a diameter of the base.

10. A right circular cone has base radius R and height H. Find the moment of inertia about its axis, and about a diameter of the base.

★11. Find the volume of the region in the first octant above the surface $z = (x - y)^2$, below the surface $z = 4 - 2xy$ and between the planes $y = 0$ and $y = x$.

*12. A solid has the form of the region of problem 11. If the density is proportional to the distance from the xz-plane, find the weight, $\bar{x}$, and $\bar{y}$.

**13. Find the volume of the region bounded by the planes $z = H + my$, and $z = 0$ and the cylinder $r = a + b \sin \theta$. Here $a > b > 0, m > 0$, and $H > m(a - b)$.

*14. Find the volume and the centroid of the region in the first octant bounded by the coordinate planes, the cylinder $r = R$ and the surface $z = e^{-r}$.

*15. As $R \to \infty$, the region of problem 14 becomes infinite in extent, but this infinite region has a centroid. Find it.

10. Spherical coordinates. For triple integrals in spherical coordinates, the region is partitioned by the surfaces $\rho = \rho_i$, $\varphi = \varphi_j$, and $\theta = \theta_k$. The surfaces $\rho = \rho_i$ are a set of spheres with center at the origin, the surfaces $\varphi = \varphi_j$ are a set of cones with vertex at the origin, and the surfaces $\theta = \theta_k$ are a set of half-planes, each one containing the z-axis. These surfaces form a number of cells, that we will call *spherical boxes*, and a typical spherical box is shown in Fig. 20. Our purpose is to find an expression for the volume of such a spherical box, and to deduce from it the proper form for dV when spherical coordinates are used.

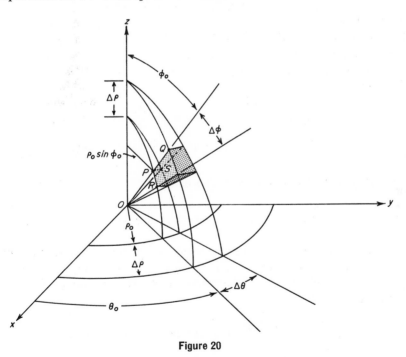

Figure 20

Let us proceed first on the basis of our intuition. The three coordinate arcs PQ, PR, and PS that meet at $P(\rho_0, \varphi_0, \theta_0)$ are mutually perpendicular (see Fig. 20). We therefore expect that ΔV, the volume of the spherical box, will be approximately the product of the lengths of the three arcs meeting at P. These lengths are $\Delta\rho$, $\rho_0\,\Delta\varphi$, and $\rho_0 \sin\varphi_0\,\Delta\theta$, respectively, and consequently

$$\Delta V \approx \rho_0^2 \sin\varphi_0\,\Delta\rho\,\Delta\varphi\,\Delta\theta. \tag{42}$$

If this approximation is close enough then

$$dV = \rho^2 \sin\varphi\,d\rho\,d\varphi\,d\theta, \tag{43}$$

and to evaluate a triple integral in spherical coordinates we would use

$$\iiint\limits_{\mathfrak{R}} f(x,\,y,\,z)dV =$$

$$\iiint\limits_{\mathfrak{R}} f(\rho\sin\varphi\cos\theta,\,\rho\sin\varphi\sin\theta,\,\rho\cos\varphi)\,\rho^2\sin\varphi\,d\rho\,d\varphi\,d\theta. \tag{44}$$

To prove that the approximation for ΔV given in (42) is sufficiently close, we will obtain a precise expression for ΔV using the formula $V = \rho_0{}^3(1 - \cos\varphi_0)\Delta\theta/3$ obtained in problem 3 of Exercise 8. First let V_1 denote the volume of the region inside the sphere $\rho = \rho_0$, between the half-planes $\theta = \theta_0$ and $\theta = \theta_0 + \Delta\theta$, and between the cones $\varphi = \varphi_0$ and $\varphi = \varphi_0 + \Delta\varphi$. This region is shaped like a pyramid, with its vertex at 0 and one corner of its spherical base at P (Fig. 20). But then V_1 is just the difference

$$V_1 = \frac{\rho_0^3}{3}\left[1 - \cos(\varphi_0 + \Delta\varphi)\right]\Delta\theta - \frac{\rho_0^3}{3}\left[1 - \cos\varphi_0\right]\Delta\theta$$

$$= \frac{\rho_0^3}{3}\left[\cos\varphi_0 - \cos(\varphi_0 + \Delta\varphi)\right]\Delta\theta.$$

By the Mean Value Theorem (with φ as the variable) we can write

$$V_1 = \frac{\rho_0^3}{3}\sin\varphi^*\,\Delta\varphi\,\Delta\theta, \qquad \varphi_0 < \varphi^* < \varphi_0 + \Delta\varphi. \tag{45}$$

Finally the spherical box is just the region of the above described pyramid that lies inside a sphere of radius $\rho_0 + \Delta\rho$ and outside a sphere of radius ρ_0, and hence its volume is just the difference of two expressions of the form (45). This gives

$$\Delta V = \frac{(\rho_0 + \Delta\rho)^3}{3}\sin\varphi^*\,\Delta\varphi\,\Delta\theta - \frac{\rho_0^3}{3}\sin\varphi^*\,\Delta\varphi\,\Delta\theta \tag{46}$$

where φ^* is the same in both terms. Using the Mean Value Theorem again (this time with ρ as the variable) (46) gives

$$\Delta V = (\rho^*)^2 \sin\varphi^*\Delta\rho\,\Delta\varphi\,\Delta\theta, \qquad \rho_0 < \rho^* < \rho_0 + \Delta\rho. \tag{47}$$

But this is (42) computed at $(\rho^*, \varphi^*, \theta_0)$ instead of at $(\rho_0, \varphi_0, \theta_0)$. Since the point $(\rho^*, \varphi^*, \theta_0)$ lies in the closed spherical box it follows that the approximation (42) is sufficiently close, and this proves (44).

EXAMPLE 1. Find the weight of a sphere of radius R if the density at each point is inversely proportional to its distance from the center of the sphere.

SOLUTION. Naturally we place the sphere in a spherical coordinate system, with its center at the origin. Then $\delta = k/\rho$ and (44) gives for the weight m,

$$m = \iiint \frac{k}{\rho}\, dV = \int_0^{2\pi}\int_0^\pi\int_0^R \frac{k}{\rho}\, \rho^2 \sin \varphi \, d\rho \, d\varphi \, d\theta$$

$$= \int_0^{2\pi}\int_0^\pi k\frac{R^2}{2} \sin \varphi \, d\varphi \, d\theta = \int_0^{2\pi} k\frac{R^2}{2}\, 2 \, d\theta$$

$$= 2k\pi R^2.$$

This result is interesting, because the weight is finite, although at the center of the sphere the density is infinite.

EXERCISE 9

1. Prove that the volume of the spherical box of Fig. 20 is given by the formula

$$\Delta V = 2\left(\rho_0{}^2 + \rho_0\Delta\rho + \frac{(\Delta\rho)^2}{3}\right) \sin\left(\varphi_0 + \frac{\Delta\varphi}{2}\right) \sin \frac{\Delta\varphi}{2}\, \Delta\rho\Delta\theta.$$

2. Use the result of problem 1 to prove that if $\rho_0 \sin \varphi_0 \neq 0$, then

$$\lim_{\substack{\Delta\rho\to 0\\ \Delta\varphi\to 0\\ \Delta\theta\to 0}} \frac{\Delta V}{\rho_0^2 \sin \varphi_0\Delta\rho\Delta\varphi\Delta\theta} = 1.$$

This permits an alternate approach to the proof of (44).

3. Assuming unit density, write the expression to be used for f in the right side of (44) when computing (a) M_{xy}, (b) M_{xz}, (c) I_x, (d) I_y, and (e) I_z.

4. Use triple integration to find (a) the volume of a sphere and (b) I_z, where the sphere has radius R and center at the origin.

5. Find the centroid of the hemispherical shell $A \leq \rho \leq B$, $0 \leq \varphi \leq \pi/2$.

6. For the hemispherical shell of problem 5, find I_x and I_z.

7. For the region inside the sphere $\rho = R$ and above the cone $\varphi = \gamma$ (a constant), find the volume, the centroid, I_z and I_y.

★8. As $\gamma \to 0$, the closed region of problem 7 tends to the straight line segment $0 \leq z \leq R$. The centroid of this line segment has $\bar{z} = R/2$. But for the $\bar{z}$ of the region of problem 7 we have $\lim_{\gamma\to 0} \bar{z} = 3R/4 \neq R/2$. Explain this apparent inconsistency.

9. Find the volume of the torus $\rho = A \sin \varphi$.

10. Find the volume of the region bounded by the surface $\rho = A(\sin \varphi)^{1/3}$.

11. Find $\bar{z}$ for the region between two spheres of radii A and $B(A < B)$ that are tangent to the xy-plane at the origin.

12. Discuss the limit of $\bar{z}$ in problem 11 as A approaches zero, and as A approaches B.

★13. Find the volume of the region inside of both of the spheres $\rho = B \cos \varphi$ and $\rho = A, (A < B)$. Check your answer by considering the special case $A = B$.

★14. Find the volume of the region bounded by the surface $\rho = A \sin \varphi \sin \theta$, with $0 \leqq \theta \leqq \pi$.

15. A hemispherical solid is bounded above by the sphere $\rho = R$ and below by the xy-plane, and has density $\delta = k/\rho^n$. For what values of n is the weight finite? Find the weight when it is finite.

16. For the solid of problem 15 find M_{xy} when it is finite. Find $\bar{z}$. For what values of n is M_{xy} finite and m infinite?

17. For the solid of problem 15, find I_z when it is finite.

18. Suppose that in problems 15, 16, and 17 the solid is a sphere tangent to the xy-plane at the origin. Without doing any computation, state whether m, M_{xy}, and I_z are finite for exactly the same values of n, as found in those problems.

★19. Consider a solid sphere of radius R with density $\delta = c/\rho^n$ when the sphere is placed with its center at the origin of a spherical coordinate system. Prove that if $3 \leqq n \leqq 5$, then the moment of inertia about any axis through the center of gravity is finite, but for any other axis the moment of inertia is infinite. *Hint:* Use the parallel axis theorem.

★11.   Gravitational attraction.

According to Newton's Law of Universal Gravitation, any two particles attract each other with a force that acts along the line joining them. The magnitude of the force is given by the formula

$$F = \gamma \frac{Mm}{r^2} \tag{48}$$

where M and m are the masses of the two particles, r is the distance between them, and γ is a constant that depends on the units used. In the C.G.S. system experimental determinations give $\gamma \approx 6.675 \times 10^{-8}$ cm³/gram sec², but we will have no need for the value of the constant γ in this book.

Equation (48) can be put into the vector form

$$\mathbf{F} = \gamma \frac{Mm}{r^2} \mathbf{e} \tag{49}$$

merely by introducing a unit vector $\mathbf{e}$ that has the proper direction. Equation (49) is convenient for theoretical discussions, but in practical work we decompose the vectors into components, and obtain from (49) three scalar equations which we use for computation.

The *gravitational attraction* of a certain body B at a point P, is the attractive force that the body would exert on a particle of *unit* mass placed at P. If the body B is small compared to its distance from P, we can regard all of the mass of B as being concentrated at a point. Then $m = 1$, and (49) gives

$$\mathbf{F} \approx \gamma \frac{M}{r^2} \mathbf{e} \tag{50}$$

for the gravitational attraction. If the body is large in comparison with its distance from P, then (50) is not a good approximation. We must then resort to integration. Dividing the body up into pieces of small diameter, forming a sum, and taking the limit in the usual way we arrive at the vector integral

$$\mathbf{F} = \gamma \iiint\limits_{B} \frac{\delta}{r^2} \mathbf{e} \, dV \tag{51}$$

for the gravitational attraction due to B. Here δ is the density of the body, and it together with r and $\mathbf{e}$ may vary during the integration. By contrast γ has been placed in front of the integral sign because according to Newton's law (and in conformity with all experimental evidence) it is a universal constant. Again we observe that for computation, equation (51) yields three scalar equations by taking components.

We mention in passing that the laws for electrical attraction, and magnetic attraction have the same form as (49), but with slightly different meanings attached to the symbols. Hence a careful study of gravitational attraction, automatically gives useful information about the other two phenomena.

EXAMPLE 1. Find the gravitational force exerted by a homogeneous solid sphere at a point Q outside of the sphere.

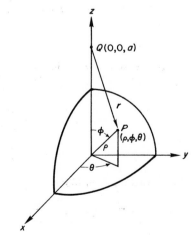

Figure 21

SOLUTION.   We place the sphere so that its center is at the origin of a rectangular coordinate system.   By the symmetry of the sphere we may assume that Q is on the z-axis at $(0, 0, a)$ where $a > R$ the radius of the sphere.   If we write $\mathbf{F} = F_1\mathbf{i} + F_2\mathbf{j} + F_3\mathbf{k}$ for the force of attraction, then by the symmetry of the sphere it follows that $F_1 = F_2 = 0$, and it only remains to compute F_3.

We now introduce a spherical coordinate system along with the rectangular coordinate system in the usual manner, as indicated in Fig. 21.   Then

$$|\mathbf{QP}|^2 = r^2 = a^2 + \rho^2 - 2a\rho \cos \varphi$$

and the component of the vector $\mathbf{QP}$ on the z-axis is $-(a - \rho \cos \varphi)$.

For the integrand in equation (51) we have

$$\frac{\delta}{r^2}\, \mathbf{e} = \frac{\delta}{r^2}\, \frac{\mathbf{QP}}{|\mathbf{QP}|} = \frac{\delta \mathbf{QP}}{r^3}$$

and for the z-component of this vector we have

$$\frac{-\delta(a - \rho \cos \varphi)}{(a^2 + \rho^2 - 2a \rho \cos \varphi)^{3/2}}.$$

Using spherical coordinates for the integration, (51) yields

$$F_3 = \gamma\delta \int_0^{2\pi} \int_0^{\pi} \int_0^R \frac{\rho \cos \varphi - a}{(a^2 + \rho^2 - 2a \rho \cos \varphi)^{3/2}} \rho^2 \sin \varphi \, d\rho \, d\varphi \, d\theta. \qquad (52)$$

Since the integrand is independent of θ we carry out this integration first, and obtain

$$F_3 = 2\pi\gamma\delta \int_0^R \int_0^{\pi} \frac{(\rho \cos \varphi - a)\rho^2 \sin \varphi}{(a^2 + \rho^2 - 2a\rho \cos \varphi)^{3/2}} \, d\varphi \, d\rho. \qquad (53)$$

To carry out the integration on φ, we make the substitutions

$$u^2 = a^2 + \rho^2 - 2a\rho \cos \varphi > 0,$$
$$2u \, du = 2a\rho \sin \varphi d\varphi,$$
$$\rho \cos \varphi = \frac{a^2 + \rho^2 - u^2}{2a}.$$

Then

$$\int_0^{\pi} \frac{(\rho \cos \varphi - a)\rho^2 \sin \varphi d\varphi}{(a^2 + \rho^2 - 2a\rho \cos \varphi)^{3/2}} = \int_{a-\rho}^{a+\rho} \frac{\left(\dfrac{a^2 + \rho^2 - u^2}{2a} - a\right)\rho \dfrac{u}{a}}{u^3} du$$

$$= \frac{-\rho}{2a^2} \int_{a-\rho}^{a+\rho} \frac{u^2 + a^2 - \rho^2}{u^2} \, du$$

$$= \frac{-\rho}{2a^2}\left(u - \frac{a^2 - \rho^2}{u}\right)\Bigg|_{a-\rho}^{a+\rho} = \frac{-2\rho^2}{a^2}.$$

Using this result in (53) we have

$$F_3 = 2\pi\gamma\delta \int_0^R \frac{-2\rho^2}{a^2} \, d\rho = -\frac{\gamma}{a^2} \frac{4}{3} \pi R^3 \delta = -\gamma \frac{M}{a^2}, \qquad (54)$$

where M is the mass of the sphere. We see from (54) that the gravitational attraction due to a homogeneous sphere at a point outside the sphere is the same as the attraction that would result if all of the mass were concentrated at the center of the sphere.

EXERCISE 10

1. Why is F_3 negative in equation (54)?

In problems 2, 3, and 5 express the answer in terms of the mass of the given body.

2. A homogeneous wire of length $2a$ is placed on the x-axis with its midpoint at the origin. Find the gravitational attraction at $(b, 0)$ where $b > a$.

3. For the wire of problem 2, find the attraction at $(0, b)$ where $b > 0$.

4. Find the attraction if the wire has infinite length in both directions, but all other conditions in problem 3 are the same.

5. A homogeneous circular disk of radius R is placed on the xy-plane with its center at the origin. Find the attraction at the point $(0, 0, a)$, $a > 0$.

★6. Let $\mathfrak{R}$ be the region between two concentric spheres of radii R_1 and R_2 respectively $(R_1 < R_2)$ and suppose that this region is filled with a homogeneous material. Prove that the gravitational attraction at any point inside the smaller sphere is zero. *Hint:* We may set up the integral just as in the example problem of this section, except that the point $Q(0, 0, a)$ is now inside the smaller circle and hence $a < R_1$. The integrand is exactly the same, and the same substitution $u^2 = a^2 + \rho^2 - 2a\rho \cos \varphi$ permits the same evaluation. The only difference is that now as φ runs from 0 to π, the new variable u runs from $\rho - a$ to $\rho + a$ (previously it ran from $a - \rho$ to $a + \rho$).

★7. Find the gravitational attraction at the vertex of a homogeneous right circular cone of base radius R and height H. *Hint:* Place the cone with its vertex at the origin and its axis on the z-axis. Then use spherical coordinates.

★8. Find the gravitational attraction for the cone of problem 7 if the density is $k\rho$, k a constant.

★9. Repeat problem 8 if $\delta = k\rho^n$, $n > 1$.

18

DIFFERENTIAL EQUATIONS

1. **Introduction.** A differential equation is any equation of the form

$$f\left(x, y, \frac{dy}{dx}, \frac{d^2y}{dx^2}, \cdots, \frac{d^ny}{dx^n}\right) = 0. \tag{1}$$

Examples of differential equations are:

$$(1 + x)\frac{d^2y}{dx^2} + x^2y^3\frac{dy}{dx} - y \sin xy^2 = 0, \tag{2}$$

$$e^x\left(\frac{d^3y}{dx^3}\right)^2 - y^4x^2 \cot^2 x + 1 = 0, \tag{3}$$

$$y\left(\frac{d^4y}{dx^4}\right)^3 + \sin x\left(\frac{dy}{dx}\right)^5 + 13yxe^{xy} = 0. \tag{4}$$

The *order* of a differential equation is the order of the highest order derivative that occurs in the equation. Thus equations (2), (3), and (4) are second, third, and fourth order differential equations respectively. If equation (1) is a polynomial in the derivatives, then the *degree* of the equation is the greatest exponent appearing on the derivative of highest order. Thus, equation (2) is of first degree, equation (3) is of second degree, and equation (4) is of third degree despite the exponent 5 that occurs in the second term.

The first objective is to find a solution to a given differential equation; that is, to find a function $y = F(x)$ which when used in (1) reduces (1) to an identity at least for all x in some interval. We will see that most[1] of

---

[1] We cannot solve every differential equation. For example the differential equation $\left(\frac{dy}{dx}\right)^2 + y^2 + x^2 = 0$ has no solution in the set of all real-valued functions of a real variable.

the time an nth order differential equation has not one solution, but a family of solutions depending upon n parameters or constants. We indicate such a solution by writing $y = F(x, C_1, C_2, \cdots, C_n)$ and if the constants are independent we call such a function the *general solution* of the differential equation. If specific values are assigned to the parameters C_i, then we obtain a *particular solution* of the given differential equation. A particular solution is also called an *integral curve*.

It is not easy to give a precise definition of the term "independent constants," so we will omit this and rely on our common sense. For example the function $y = mx + b_1 + b_2$ appears to have three constants m, b_1, and b_2. But clearly b_1 and b_2 are not independent, because we can set $b_1 + b_2 = b$ and obtain $y = mx + b$ which gives exactly the same collection of straight lines as the original function. Consequently $y = mx + b_1 + b_2$ has at most two independent constants.

It is not always possible to find a solution for a given differential equation. The equations (2), (3), and (4) are particularly nasty and for these the best that we can do is to find approximate solutions. The subject is a difficult one and many mathematicians are actively engaged in research in this field.

On the other hand if we consider differential equations that are reasonably simple, then we can find the general solution as we shall soon see.

2.   Families of curves.   Instead of integrating a differential equation, let us begin with the simpler problem of finding a differential equation that is satisfied by a given family of curves. The method is best explained by examples.

EXAMPLE 1.   Find the differential equation that is satisfied by the family of all circles with center at the origin.

SOLUTION.   The family is given by

$$x^2 + y^2 = r^2 \tag{5}$$

where r, the radius, is a constant (parameter) that assumes different values for different curves of the family. Notice that if we are given a fixed point P (other than the origin) there is exactly one curve of the family that passes through P. Differentiating (5) with respect to x yields $2x + 2y\dfrac{dy}{dx} = 0$, or

$$x + y\frac{dy}{dx} = 0. \tag{6}$$

Thus (6) is a differential equation for the given family of circles. Obviously it is not the only differential equation satisfied by the family (5). For example we could differentiate (6) obtaining

$$1 + \left(\frac{dy}{dx}\right)^2 + y\frac{d^2y}{dx^2} = 0, \tag{7}$$

or combine (6) and (7) to obtain

$$y^3\frac{d^2y}{dx^2} + x^2 + y^2 = 0. \tag{8}$$

However (6) appears to be simpler than (7) or (8). We will usually fasten on some simple equation of lowest order and refer to it as *the* differential equation of the family.

We have asked that a solution of (6) have the form $y = F(x, C)$ and equation (5) does not have this form. But (5) is easily broken up into two parts, $y = \sqrt{r^2 - x^2}$ and $y = -\sqrt{r^2 - x^2}$, each of which has the required form. If we had started with a different family defined by an implicit function, it might be very difficult to solve for y as an explicit function of x.

At the points $(\pm r, 0)$ the tangent to the curve is vertical and hence dy/dx does not exist at these points. Consequently (6) is not satisfied by (5) at these points. These exceptional cases require careful consideration in any rigorous treatment of differential equations. However in an introduction to the subject it is usually a good idea to ignore the exceptional points at which the differential equation or the solution breaks down.

EXAMPLE 2. Find the differential equation for the two-parameter family of curves

$$y = a \sin x + b \cos x. \tag{9}$$

SOLUTION. Since this family has two independent constants a and b, we expect the differential equation to be of second order.

Differentiating equation (9) twice gives

$$\frac{d^2y}{dx^2} = -a \sin x - b \cos x. \tag{10}$$

When we add equations (9) and (10) both constants disappear simultaneously. Hence

$$\frac{d^2y}{dx^2} + y = 0 \tag{11}$$

is a very simple differential equation satisfied by (9).

Given a specific point $P_0(x_0, y_0)$ we can select the constants a and b in infinitely many ways such that

$$y_0 = a \sin x_0 + b \cos x_0.$$

In other words through each fixed point P_0 of the plane, there are infinitely many curves of the family (9) that pass through P_0. However if we also specify y_0', the slope of the curve at P_0, then there is exactly one member of the family. This follows from the fact that the equation set

$$y_0 = a \sin x_0 + b \cos x_0$$
$$y_0' = a \cos x_0 - b \sin x_0 \tag{12}$$

has exactly one solution for the unknowns a and b in terms of the given numbers x_0, y_0, y_0'. The proof of this fact is left for the student.

EXAMPLE 3. Find the differential equation of the family of ellipses, each of which has its foci at $(-1, 0)$ and $(1, 0)$.

SOLUTION. We recall that if $a > b > 0$, the ellipse $\dfrac{x^2}{a^2} + \dfrac{y^2}{b^2} = 1$ has its foci at $(-c, 0)$ and $(c, 0)$, where $c = \sqrt{a^2 - b^2}$. For our family $c = 1$, hence $b^2 = a^2 - 1$, and our family has the equation

$$\frac{x^2}{a^2} + \frac{y^2}{a^2 - 1} = 1, \qquad a > 1. \tag{13}$$

If we eliminate the constant a, between (13) and its differential

$$\frac{2x\,dx}{a^2} + \frac{2y\,dy}{a^2 - 1} = 0$$

we will obtain

$$xy\left(\frac{dy}{dx}\right)^2 + (x^2 - y^2 - 1)\frac{dy}{dx} - xy = 0. \tag{14}$$

Notice that in the computation, the condition $a > 1$ is never used. It turns out that without this restriction the family (13) also contains the family of all hyperbolas with foci at $(-1, 0)$ and $(1, 0)$. The resulting differential equation (14) is of first order, but second degree. Through each point of the plane not on the x-axis or y-axis, there passes two curves of the family, one hyperbola and one ellipse.

In each of our examples, the equation can be put in differential form, by multiplying by a suitable power of dx. Equations (6), and (14) give

$$x\,dx + y\,dy = 0 \tag{6d}$$

$$xy(dy)^2 + (x^2 - y^2 - 1)dx\,dy - xy(dx)^2 = 0. \tag{14d}$$

For equation (11) we can set $y' = \dfrac{dy}{dx}$. Then $\dfrac{d^2y}{dx^2} = \dfrac{dy'}{dx}$, and (11) gives

$$dy' + y\,dx = 0. \tag{11d}$$

EXERCISE 1

In problems 1 through 10 find a simple differential equation satisfied by the given family of curves, by eliminating the constants.

1. $y = cx.$	**2.** $y = a(x - 1)^2.$
3. $Ax^2 + y^2 = 5.$	**4.** $x^2 + y^2 = 2hx.$
5. $x^3 + y^3 = axy.$	**6.** $y = x^2 + b \sin x.$
7. $y = c_1 e^x + c_2 e^{-x}.$	**★8.** $y = ae^{2x} + be^{-3x}.$
★9. $(x^2 + a)y = 1 + bx.$	**★10.** $y = Ae^x + B \cos x.$

In problems 11 through 20 a family of curves is described by some geometrical property.   In each case find a simple differential equation satisfied by each member of the family.

11.   The family of all straight lines with slope 2.

12.   The family of all circles with center on the y-axis and passing through the origin.

13.   The family of all circles with center on the line $y = x$ and passing through the origin.

14.   The family of all circles with center on the y-axis and passing through the point $(0, 1)$.

15.   The family of all parabolas with focus at the origin and axis parallel to the y-axis.

16.   The family of all ellipses with center at the origin and two vertices at $(-1, 0)$ and $(1, 0)$.   Observe that the family of such hyperbolas will give the same differential equation.

17.   The family of all straight lines in which the sum of the intercepts on the x and y-axis is 10.

18.   The family of all circles that pass through the two points $(-1, 0)$ and $(1, 0)$.

19.   The family of all parabolas for which the x-axis is an axis of symmetry.

★20.   The family of all circles that pass through the origin.

★21.   Prove that the family of confocal conics defined by equation (13) has the property that each point of the plane not on the x-axis or y-axis lies on exactly two curves of the family.

★22.   Find the differential equation for the family of all straight lines that are tangent to the parabola $y = x^2$.   Show that the parabola itself is also a solution of this differential equation.

3.   Variables separable.   A first order differential equation of first degree can always be put in the form

$$M(x, y)dx + N(x, y)dy = 0 \qquad (15)$$

where M and N are suitable functions.   Occasionally it is possible to find a function $D(x, y)$ such that when (15) is divided by $D(x, y)$ we obtain

$$f(x)dx + g(y)dy = 0 \qquad (16)$$

i.e., the new coefficients are functions of just one variable as indicated. When this occurs we say that the *variables are separable* in (15).   Whenever the variables are separable, we can integrate (16) directly and obtain

$$\int f(x)dx + \int g(y)dy = C$$

as a general solution of (15).

EXAMPLE 1. Solve the differential equation

$$(y^2 - 1)dx - 2(2y + xy)dy = 0. \tag{17}$$

SOLUTION. It is obvious that if we divide by $D = (2 + x)(y^2 - 1)$ we obtain

$$\frac{dx}{x + 2} - \frac{2y\, dy}{y^2 - 1} = 0. \tag{18}$$

This has the form (16), and consequently the variables in (17) are separable. Direct integration of (18) yields

$$\ln|x + 2| - \ln|y^2 - 1| = \ln|C|, \tag{19}$$

where the constant we have added, has been put in this peculiar form for convenience. Equation (19) yields

$$\ln \frac{|x + 2|}{|y^2 - 1|} = \ln|C|$$

$$x + 2 = C(y^2 - 1). \tag{20}$$

Observe that in going from (19) to (20) the absolute value signs have been dropped. There are a number of ways of justifying this step. Perhaps the simplest way is to observe that if $x + 2$, C, and $y^2 - 1$ are all positive then (19) does give (20). But if (20) satisfies the differential equation (17) under these restrictions, the same formal operations used to check that (20) is a solution, show that it solves the same differential equation without any restrictions. All that is required is that x, y, and C be such that (20) determines y as a differentiable function of x. Thus solving (20) for y we find

$$y = \pm\sqrt{\frac{x + 2}{C} + 1}$$

and this is a solution of the given differential equation as long as the quantity under the radical is positive.

We should also note that when we divided (17) by $D = (2 + x)(y^2 - 1)$ we tacitly assumed that $D \neq 0$. But $D = 0$ when $x = -2$ or $y = \pm 1$, and an inspection of the differential equation shows that these straight lines are also solutions.

Hence the solution of (17) consists of the three straight lines just mentioned and the family of parabolas (20).

EXAMPLE 2. Find the orthogonal trajectories for the family of parabolas

$$y = Ax^2. \tag{21}$$

SOLUTION. If $\mathfrak{F}_1$ and $\mathfrak{F}_2$ are two families of curves, each one is called a family of *orthogonal trajectories* of the other, if whenever two curves, one from each family meet, they are orthogonal at the point of intersection. If $\left(\dfrac{dy}{dx}\right)_1$ and $\left(\dfrac{dy}{dx}\right)_2$ denote the slopes of the curves $\mathcal{C}_1$ and $\mathcal{C}_2$ respectively, then at a common point (x, y) we must have

$$\left(\frac{dy}{dx}\right)_1 = -\frac{1}{\left(\dfrac{dy}{dx}\right)_2} \tag{22}$$

for orthogonality.

Eliminating the constant A in (21) we find that for each curve of that family

$$\left(\frac{dy}{dx}\right)_1 = \frac{2y}{x}.$$

Then for the family of orthogonal trajectories (22) gives

$$\left(\frac{dy}{dx}\right)_2 = -\frac{x}{2y}$$

or

$$2y\,dy + x\,dx = 0$$

or

$$x^2 + 2y^2 = a^2. \tag{23}$$

This is a family of ellipses. The student should sketch a few members from each of the families (21) and (23).

EXERCISE 2

In problems 1 through 6 solve the given differential equation

1. $y\,dx + (3x + xy)dy = 0.$
2. $\cos\theta\,dr - 4r\sin\theta\,d\theta = 0.$
3. $e^{x-3y^2}\,dx + y\,dy = 0.$
4. $(3y - xy)dx - (x^2 + 3x)dy = 0.$
5. $(1 + y^2)dx + (1 + x^2)dy = 0.$
6. $y\ln x\,dx + \dfrac{y-1}{x}\,dy = 0.$

In problems 7 through 12 find a family of orthogonal trajectories for the given family of curves. In each case try to sketch a few curves from each family.

7. $x^2 + y^2 = r^2.$
8. $x^2 - 2y^2 = a^2.$
9. $xy^3 = C.$
10. $ax^2 + y^3 = 1.$
11. $y = ce^{-x^2}.$
12. $y = A\ln x^2.$

★13. Prove that the family of parabolas $y^2 = 4C(x + C)$ is a self-orthogonal family of parabolas. Observe that each curve of the family has the same focus and the same axis.

★**14.** Prove that the family of confocal conics

$$\frac{x^2}{C^2} + \frac{y^2}{C^2 - 1} = 1$$

forms a self-orthogonal family of curves.

In problems 15 through 20 a certain family of curves is described by giving a property for each curve of the family. In each case find an equation for the family. Then find all curves of the family that go through the given point P_0.

15. At each point P of the curve, the tangent is perpendicular to the line OP. $P_0(3, 4)$.

16. The tangent at each point P on the curve and the line OP form the sides of an isosceles triangle, with a portion of the x-axis as the base. $P_0(1, 3)$.

17. Let the normal to the curve at P intersect the x-axis at Q. The line segment PQ has constant length L, the same for each point on the curve, and for each curve of the family. $P_0(2L, 0)$.

18. The projection of the segment PQ (of problem 17) on the x-axis has the same length A for each point P on the curve, and for each curve of the family. $P_0(4, 1)$.

★**19.** Each curve of the family passes through the origin. Consider the arc of the curve that joins the origin to a point P on the curve. The region below this arc and above the x-axis is rotated about the x-axis giving a solid of volume V_1. The region to the left of this arc and to the right of the y-axis is rotated about the y-axis giving a solid of volume V_2. For each point on the curve $V_1 = V_2$. $P_0(1, 1)$.

★**20.** Under the conditions of problem 19 suppose that for each point on the curve $V_1 = KV_2$, where K is a fixed positive constant. $P_0(2, 2)$.

★★**21.** Frequently in mathematics it is difficult to give a definition that is both simple and accurate. Show that the definition of orthogonal trajectories given in the text is defective by proving that each of the two families $\mathcal{F}_1: y = m^2 x$ and $\mathcal{F}_2: xy + 2 = \cos \theta_0$ is an orthogonal trajectory of the other. *Hint:* No curve from $\mathcal{F}_1$ meets any curve from $\mathcal{F}_2$. Consequently the condition (22) is automatically satisfied because there are no intersection points.

4. Homogeneous equations.

DEFINITION 1. *A function $f(x, y)$ is said to be homogeneous of degree n if*

$$f(tx, ty) = t^n f(x, y) \tag{24}$$

for all $t > 0$.

For example $f(x, y) = x^3 + 7x^2y - \dfrac{11x^4}{y}$ is homogeneous of degree 3 because

$$f(tx,\ ty) = (tx)^3 + 7(tx)^2(ty) - \frac{11(tx)^4}{ty}$$

$$= t^3\left(x^3 + 7x^2y - \frac{11x^4}{y}\right) = t^3 f(x,\ y).$$

The condition $t > 0$ in the definition, may at first glance seem unnecessary. But the function $f(x, y) = \sqrt{x^2 + y^2}$ ought to be regarded as homogeneous. A formal computation gives

$$f(tx,\ ty) = \sqrt{(tx)^2 + (ty)^2} = t\sqrt{x^2 + y^2} = tf(x,\ y). \qquad (25)$$

But actually if t is negative, the first two terms in (25) are positive and the last two are negative, and the middle equal sign is false. To avoid this difficulty we require that $t > 0$ in (24). The student should check each of the functions below to see that it has the property stated.

$$x^5 + \pi x^4 y - x^2 y^3 e^5, \qquad \text{homogeneous, } n = 5.$$

$$\frac{x}{y} + \frac{2y}{3x} + \sin\frac{x}{y} + \ln y - \ln x, \qquad \text{homogeneous, } n = 0.$$

$$(x^4 + 4x^2 y + y^2)x^2, \qquad \text{not homogeneous.}$$

$$\frac{x + y}{\sqrt[3]{x^{12} + y^{12}}} + \frac{x^2}{y^5} e^{x/y} \qquad \text{homogeneous, } n = -3.$$

This idea of homogeneity is very useful in differential equations, because if M and N are both homogeneous functions of the same degree, the equation $M\,dx + N\,dy = 0$ is easy to solve. The method is given in

THEOREM 1.   *If in the differential equation*

$$M(x,\ y)dx + N(x,\ y)dy = 0, \qquad (26)$$

M and N are both homogeneous functions of the same degree, then the substitution $y = vx$ will transform the differential equation into one in v and x in which the variables are separable.

PROOF.   Using $y = vx$, and $dy = v\,dx + x\,dv$, equation (26) becomes

$$M(x,\ vx)dx + N(x,\ vx)(v\,dx + x\,dv) = 0. \qquad (27)$$

We use the hypothesis of homogeneity of M and N, but now x plays the role of t in (24). Consequently we see that $M(x, vx) = x^n M(1, v)$, and $N(x, vx) = x^n N(1, v)$, and (27) yields

$$x^n M(1,\ v)dx + x^n N(1,\ v)(v\,dx + x\,dv) = 0$$

$$x^n[M(1,\ v) + vN(1,\ v)]dx + x^n N(1,\ v)x\,dv = 0.$$

If $x^{n+1}[M(1, v) + vN(1, v)] \neq 0$ we may divide by it and obtain

$$\frac{dx}{x} + \frac{N(1, v)dv}{M(1, v) + vN(1, v)} = 0, \qquad (28)$$

in which the variables have already been separated. Q.E.D.

EXAMPLE 1. Solve the differential equation

$$(y^2 - 2xy + 4x^2)dx + 2x^2dy = 0. \qquad (29)$$

SOLUTION. Obviously the variables are not separable, but both M and N are homogeneous of second degree. We could make the substitution $y = vx$ directly in (29), but for illustrative purposes we choose to use (28). From $M(x, y) = y^2 - 2xy + 4x^2$ we have $M(1, v) = v^2 - 2v + 4$. Similarly since $N(x, y) = 2x^2$ we have $N(1, v) = 2$. Then (28) gives

$$0 = \frac{dx}{x} + \frac{2\,dv}{v^2 - 2v + 4 + 2v} = \frac{dx}{x} + \frac{2\,dv}{v^2 + 4}$$

$$0 = \ln|x| + \ln|C| + \tan^{-1}\left(\frac{v}{2}\right)$$

$$v = 2\tan(-\ln|Cx|).$$

But $v = y/x$ and hence $y = 2x\tan(-\ln|Cx|)$. The student should start with this solution and derive the differential equation (29).

EXERCISE 3

In problems 1 through 6 solve the given differential equation.

1. $(x^3 + y^3)dx + xy^2dy = 0$.
2. $(9x - y)dx + (x - y)dy = 0$.
3. $\left(y + x\tan\dfrac{y - x}{x}\right)dx - x\,dy = 0$.
4. $3(x - y)e^{y/x}\,dx + x(1 + 3e^{y/x})dy = 0$.
5. $(\sqrt{x^2 - y^2} - 2y)dx + 2x\,dy = 0$.
6. $\left(3y - x\cos\dfrac{y}{x}\right)dx - 3x\,dy = 0$.
7. Find a family of orthogonal trajectories for the curves $y^5 = C(x + y)$.
8. Find a family of orthogonal trajectories for the curves $3x^2y + y^3 = C$.
9. From each point P in the first quadrant lines perpendicular to the x and y-axis are drawn, forming with these axes a rectangle. Find the family of curves such that at each point P in the first quadrant, the slope of the curve at P is one fourth the square of the perimeter of the rectangle divided by the area of the rectangle at P.
★10. It can be proved that if $M\,dx + N\,dy = 0$ is homogeneous it can be written in the form

$$\frac{dy}{dx} = f\left(\frac{y}{x}\right)$$

Prove that if polar coordinates are introduced, this equation can put in the form

$$\sin \theta \frac{dr}{d\theta} + r \cos \theta = f(\tan \theta) \left(\cos \theta \frac{dr}{d\theta} - r \sin \theta \right) \text{in which the variables are separable.}$$

Consequently the integral curves have the form

$$r = Ce^{F(\theta)}$$

for a suitable $F(\theta)$.

   *11.   It is sometimes asserted, on the basis of the results of problem 10 (or on other considerations), that if $\mathfrak{C}_1$ and $\mathfrak{C}_2$ are any two curves that are solutions for the same homogeneous differential equation, then $\mathfrak{C}_1$ and $\mathfrak{C}_2$ are similar.   Prove that this assertion is false by proving that $y = 1/x$ and $y = 0$ are both solutions of $y\,dx + x\,dy = 0$.

   12.   Prove that through each point in the plane except the origin there passes exactly one integral curve for the differential equation of problem 1.   Is the same assertion true for the differential equation of problem 5?

5.   **Exact equations.**   If we begin with an equation $f(x, y) = C$ and take its differential we obtain the differential equation

$$\frac{\partial f}{\partial x} dx + \frac{\partial f}{\partial y} dy = 0. \tag{30}$$

This suggests

   DEFINITION 2.   *A differential equation*

$$M(x, y)dx + N(x, y)dy = 0 \tag{26}$$

   is said to be exact if there is a function $f(x, y)$ such that

$$df = M\,dx + N\,dy.$$

   If there is such a function, then on comparing (26) and (30) it is obvious that

$$\frac{\partial f}{\partial x} = M \quad \text{and} \quad \frac{\partial f}{\partial y} = N, \tag{31a, b}$$

and the integration of the differential equation is simple, namely the solution is $f(x, y) = C$.

   For example, a mere inspection of the equation $3x^2y^2\,dx + 2x^3y\,dy = 0$ shows that the left side is the differential of x^3y^2 and hence the solution is $x^3y^2 = C$.

   The big task is to learn to recognize an exact differential equation when it is more complicated.   This problem is solved by

   THEOREM 2.   *A necessary and sufficient condition that equation (26) be exact, is that*

$$\boxed{\frac{\partial M}{\partial y} = \frac{\partial N}{\partial x}} \tag{32}$$

where these partial derivatives are continuous in the region under consideration.

PROOF. **Necessity.** We are to prove that if the equation is exact then (32) holds. By hypothesis there is an $f(x, y)$ such that (31) is valid. Differentiating (31a) with respect to y and (31b) with respect to x we find

$$\frac{\partial^2 f}{\partial y\, \partial x} = \frac{\partial M}{\partial y}, \qquad \frac{\partial^2 f}{\partial x\, \partial y} = \frac{\partial N}{\partial x}.$$

Since the partial derivatives M_y and N_x are continuous it follows that

$$\frac{\partial^2 f}{\partial y\, \partial x} = \frac{\partial^2 f}{\partial x\, \partial y}$$

and this gives (32).

PROOF. **Sufficiency.** We are to prove that if (32) holds then the equation is exact. We attempt to find a function $f(x, y)$ for which (26) is the differential. Let us set

$$f(x, y) = \int_a^x M(x, y)\partial x + \Phi(y). \tag{33}$$

Here the notation ∂x means that in the integration y is to be held constant. In adding the usual constant of integration, we may add any function that depends on y alone and this is denoted by $\Phi(y)$. As a result the function defined by (33) satisfies (31a). To obtain (31b) we must select $\Phi(y)$ appropriately. From (33) we find that[2]

$$\frac{\partial f}{\partial y} = \frac{\partial}{\partial y}\left[\int_a^x M(x, y)\partial x + \Phi(y)\right] = \int_a^x \frac{\partial M(x, y)}{\partial y}\partial x + \Phi'(y)$$

and using (32) this gives

$$\frac{\partial f}{\partial y} = \int_a^x \frac{\partial N(x, y)}{\partial x}\partial x + \Phi'(y) = N(x, y) - N(a, y) + \Phi'(y).$$

We can make $\partial f/\partial y = N(x, y)$ if $-N(a, y) + \Phi'(y) = 0$. But this is easy, we just integrate this last equation to find $\Phi((y)$. Then (33) is the desired function and (26) is exact. Q.E.D.

[2] To compute $\partial f/\partial y$ we must differentiate the integral (33) with respect to a variable, that is not the variable of integration. The proof that this can be done under the given conditions, is best postponed to the Advanced Calculus course.

EXAMPLE 1. Solve the differential equation

$$(3x^2 + 2xy^2 + 4y)dx + (2x^2y + 4x + 5y^4)dy = 0.$$

SOLUTION. Inspection shows that the variables are not separable, nor is the equation homogeneous. To test if the equation is exact we compute

$$\frac{\partial M}{\partial y} = \frac{\partial}{\partial y}(3x^2 + 2xy^2 + 4y) = 4xy + 4$$

and

$$\frac{\partial N}{\partial x} = \frac{\partial}{\partial x}(2x^2y + 4x + 5y^4) = 4xy + 4.$$

Since these are equal the equation is exact. To solve we follow the method of proof of the theorem. We set

$$f(x, y) = \int M\partial x = \int (3x^2 + 2xy^2 + 4y)\partial x = x^3 + x^2y^2 + 4xy + \Phi(y).$$

$$\frac{\partial f}{\partial y} = 2x^2y + 4x + \Phi'(y) = N = 2x^2y + 4x + 5y^4.$$

Therefore $\Phi'(y) = 5y^4$, $\Phi(y) = y^5$ and

$$f(x, y) = x^3 + x^2y^2 + 4xy + y^5 = C$$

is a general solution.

EXERCISE 4

In problems 1 through 6 prove that the given differential equation is exact and solve.

1. $(6x^2 + 5y^2)dx + 10xy\, dy = 0.$
2. $(3x^2y^2 + 2xy^4)dx + (2x^3y + 4x^2y^3 + 1)dy = 0.$
3. $(2r \sin \theta + \cos \theta)dr - (r \sin \theta - r^2 \cos \theta)d\theta = 0.$
4. $ye^{x/y}\, dx + (2ye^{x/y} - xe^{x/y})dy = 0.$
5. $\dfrac{2x}{y^3}\, dx + \dfrac{2y - 3x^2}{y^4}\, dy = 0.$
6. $(2x \sin xy^2 + x^2y^2 \cos xy^2)dx + (2x^3y \cos xy^2 - 2y \sin y^2)dy = 0.$

7. Show that the differential equation $(ax - by)dx - (ay + bx)dy = 0$ is exact and find an equation for $\mathcal{F}_1$ its family of integral curves. Then show that the differential equation for $\mathcal{F}_2$, the family of orthogonal trajectories of $\mathcal{F}_1$, is also exact, and find an equation for $\mathcal{F}_2$.

8. Repeat problem 7 for the differential equation $(x^2 - y^2)dx - 2xy\, dy = 0.$

9. (Continuation of problems 7 and 8). Let $\mathcal{F}_1$ be a family of integral curves for the differential equation $M\, dx + N\, dy = 0$, and let $\mathcal{F}_2$ be the family of orthogonal trajectories of $\mathcal{F}_1$. Prove that if the differential equations for the two families are both exact then

$$\frac{\partial^2 M}{\partial x^2} + \frac{\partial^2 M}{\partial y^2} = 0 \quad \text{and} \quad \frac{\partial^2 N}{\partial x^2} + \frac{\partial^2 N}{\partial y^2} = 0.$$

★10. If the equation $M\,dx + N\,dy = 0$ is not exact, there may be a factor $\mu(x, y)$ such that $\mu M\,dx + \mu N\,dy = 0$ is exact. If so μ is called an *integrating factor*. Prove that μ is an integrating factor if and only if

$$\mu\left(\frac{\partial M}{\partial y} - \frac{\partial N}{\partial x}\right) = \frac{\partial \mu}{\partial x} N - \frac{\partial \mu}{\partial y} M.$$

In problems 11 through 14 prove that the given function is an integrating factor, using the criterion of problem 10, and then solve the given differential equation.

★11. $(2x^3 y - y^3)dx + (xy^2 - x^4)dy = 0$, $\mu = 1/x^2 y^2$.
★12. $(xy + x + 1)dx + (x - 1)dy = 0$, $\mu = e^x$.
★13. $(2x - 3y + x^2 + y^2)dx + (2y + 3x)dy = 0$, $\mu = 1/(x^2 + y^2)$.
.★14. $y(x + y^3)dx + x(y^3 - x)dy = 0$, $\mu = 1/y^3$.

★15. Find an integrating factor and solve

    a. $y(1 + x^2 y)dx - x\,dy = 0$,
    b. $2x^2 y\,dx + (x^3 + 2xy)dy = 0$.

Notice that it may be more difficult to solve $\mu(M_y - N_x) = \mu_x N - \mu_y M$ for μ, than it is to solve the given differential equation by inspection.

6.   Linear equations, first order.

DEFINITION 3. *A first order differential equation is said to be linear if it can be put in the form*

$$\frac{dy}{dx} + p(x)y = q(x) \tag{34}$$

where p and q are functions of x alone.

From a theoretical point of view a first order linear differential equation can always be solved. Set

$$\mu = e^{\int p(x)\,dx} \tag{35}$$

and observe that

$$\frac{d\mu}{dx} = e^{\int p(x)\,dx} p(x) = p(x)\mu. \tag{36}$$

If we multiply both sides of (34) by μ we have

$$\mu\frac{dy}{dx} + \mu p(x)y = \mu q(x)$$

and using (36) this can be written in the form

$$\frac{d}{dx}(\mu y) = \mu q(x).$$

Since $\mu q(x)$ is a function of x alone this gives

$$\mu y = \int \mu q(x)dx + C, \tag{37}$$

a general solution of (34). Dividing both sides of (37) by μ and using (35), the solution can be put in the form

$$y = e^{-\int p(x)\,dx}\left[\int q(x)e^{\int p(x)\,dx}dx + C\right]. \tag{38}$$

It is much better to memorize the procedure, rather than the final formula (38).

EXAMPLE 1.   Solve the differential equation

$$\frac{dy}{dx} + \frac{3}{x}y = \frac{4}{x^2} + 10x, \qquad x > 0. \tag{39}$$

SOLUTION.   Equation (39) has the form (34) with $p(x) = 3/x$. Set

$$\mu(x) = e^{\int p(x)\,dx} = e^{\int \frac{3dx}{x}} = e^{3\ln x} = x^3.$$

Multiplying both sides of (39) by $\mu = x^3$ we have

$$x^3\frac{dy}{dx} + 3x^2y = 4x + 10x^4$$

$$\frac{d}{dx}(x^3y) = 4x + 10x^4$$

$$x^3y = \int (4x + 10x^4)dx = 2x^2 + 2x^5 + C,$$

$$y = \frac{2}{x} + 2x^2 + \frac{C}{x^3}.$$

EXERCISE 5

In problems 1 through 8 solve the given differential equation

1. $\dfrac{dy}{dx} + y = e^{2x}$.   2. $x\dfrac{dy}{dx} + 3y = 6x^3$.

3. $\dfrac{dy}{dx} + \dfrac{y}{x} = \sin x$.   4. $\dfrac{dy}{dx} + y = x + 5$.

5. $(xy + x + x^3)dx - (1 + x^2)dy = 0$.
6. $(3xy + 3y + 4)dx + (x + 1)^2\,dy = 0$.
7. $2\cos x(y - 3\sin x)dx + \sin x\,dy = 0$.
8. $(3xy - 4y - 3x)dx + (x^2 - 3x + 2)dy = 0$.

9. A differential equation of the form

$$\frac{dy}{dx} + p(x)y = q(x)y^n$$

is called a *Bernoulli equation*. If $n = 0$, it is a linear equation. Prove that if $n \neq 0$ the substitution $v = 1/y^{n-1}$ transforms it into an equation that is linear in v and x. Consequently a Bernoulli equation can be solved.

Use the method outlined in problem 9 to solve the Bernoulli equations given in problems 10 through 13.

10. $\dfrac{dy}{dx} - \dfrac{2}{x} y = y^4 x.$

11. $x \dfrac{dy}{dx} - 2y = 12x^3 \sqrt{y}.$

12. $y(1 + xy \sin x)dx - x\, dy = 0.$

13. $x^4 y^5\, dy + (x^3 y^6 + x^3 - 1)dx = 0.$

7. Second order linear homogeneous equations. An equation of the form

$$p_0(x) \frac{d^n y}{dx^n} + p_1(x) \frac{d^{n-1}y}{dx^{n-1}} + \cdots + p_{n-1}(x) \frac{dy}{dx} + p_n(x)y = q(x) \qquad (40)$$

is called a *linear equation*. If $q(x) = 0$ then the equation is said to be *homogeneous*.[3] Otherwise we call (40) a *nonhomogeneous linear equation*. In the particular case that all the coefficients $p_k(x)$ are constants, equation (40) is rather easy to solve, and the next three sections are devoted to this special case. The equation

$$\frac{d^n y}{dx^n} + a_1 \frac{d^{n-1}y}{dx^{n-1}} + \cdots + a_{n-1} \frac{dy}{dx} + a_n y = q(x) \qquad (41)$$

is called a *nonhomogeneous linear equation with constant coefficients*. If we set $q(x) = 0$ in (41) we obtain the *reduced equation* of (41), namely

$$\frac{d^n y}{dx^n} + a_1 \frac{d^{n-1}y}{dx^{n-1}} + \cdots + a_{n-1} \frac{dy}{dx} + a_n y = 0. \qquad (42)$$

To simplify matters we will first consider the second order homogeneous equations with constant coefficients

$$\frac{d^2 y}{dx^2} + a_1 \frac{dy}{dx} + a_2 y = 0. \qquad (43)$$

Let us try the function $y = e^{mx}$ to see if it is a solution of (43). Since $y' = me^{mx}$ and $y'' = m^2 e^{mx}$, substitution in (43) gives

$$\frac{d^2 y}{dx^2} + a_1 \frac{dy}{dx} + a_2 y = m^2 e^{mx} + a_1 m e^{mx} + a_2 e^{mx}$$
$$= e^{mx}(m^2 + a_1 m + a_2).$$

But we can always find a root r of the equation

$$m^2 + a_1 m + a_2 = 0. \qquad (44)$$

---

[3] Observe that the word "homogeneous" as used in this section does not have the same meaning that it had when used in section 4.

We have proved that if r is a root of (44) then $y = e^{rx}$ is a solution of (43). If (44) has two distinct roots r_1 and r_2, then $y = e^{r_1x}$ and $y = e^{r_2x}$ are two solutions. Because equation (44) is so helpful in finding solutions to (43), we call equation (44) the *auxiliary equation* of the differential equation (43).

To obtain the general solution of (43) we combine our particular solutions $y = e^{r_1x}$ and $y = e^{r_2x}$, in the form

$$y = C_1e^{r_1x} + C_2e^{r_2x} \tag{45}$$

where C_1 and C_2 are any pair of arbitrary constants. To prove that (45) is a solution of (43) we differentiate (45) twice and substitute in (43). We find

$$\frac{d^2y}{dx^2} + a_1\frac{dy}{dx} + a_2y$$

$$= C_1r_1^2e^{r_1x} + C_2r_2^2e^{r_2x} + a_1(C_1r_1e^{r_1x} + C_2r_2e^{r_2x}) + a_2(C_1e^{r_1x} + C_2e^{r_2x})$$

$$= C_1e^{r_1x}(r_1^2 + a_1r_1 + a_2) + C_2e^{r_2x}(r_2^2 + a_1r_2 + a_2)$$

$$= 0 + 0 = 0,$$

because r_1 and r_2 are roots of (44). We have proved

THEOREM 3. *If r_1 and r_2 are distinct roots of (44) then (45) is the general solution of (43).*

EXAMPLE 1. Solve the differential equation

$$y'' + 4y' - 77y = 0.$$

SOLUTION. The auxiliary equation is $m^2 + 4m - 77 = 0$, or on factoring $(m - 7)(m + 11) = 0$. The roots are $r_1 = 7$, $r_2 = -11$, hence

$$y = C_1e^{7x} + C_2e^{-11x}$$

is the general solution.

If the auxiliary equation (44) has a repeated root r, then (45) has the form

$$y = C_1e^{rx} + C_2e^{rx} = (C_1 + C_2)e^{rx} = Ce^{rx}$$

and the constants are not independent. But in this case $y = xe^{rx}$ is also a solution of (43) as we will now prove. Substituting $y' = e^{rx} + rxe^{rx}$ and $y'' = 2re^{rx} + r^2xe^{rx}$ in (43) gives

$$\frac{d^2y}{dx^2} + a_1\frac{dy}{dx} + a_2y$$

$$= 2re^{rx} + r^2xe^{rx} + a_1(e^{rx} + rxe^{rx}) + a_2xe^{rx}$$

$$= e^{rx}(a_1 + 2r) + xe^{rx}(r^2 + a_1r + a_2).$$

The second term vanishes because r is a root of (44). If r is a multiple root, then $m^2 + a_1 m + a_2 = (m - r)^2 = m^2 - 2rm + r^2$, so $a_1 = -2r$ and hence the first term also vanishes.

Since e^{rx} and xe^{rx} are solutions of (43) we expect the following to be true,

THEOREM 4. *If r is a repeated root of (44) then*

$$y = C_1 e^{rx} + C_2 x e^{rx} \tag{46}$$

is the general solution of (43).

We leave it to the reader to prove that (46) is a solution of (43).

It may happen that the roots of the auxiliary equation are complex numbers. However if the coefficients a_1 and a_2 are real then the complex roots occur in conjugate pairs. Suppose that these roots are $r_1 = \alpha + \beta i$ and $r_2 = \alpha - \beta i$, where α and β are real numbers, and as usual $i = \sqrt{-1}$. In accordance with Theorem 3 we expect that in this case

$$y = C_1 e^{(\alpha + i\beta)x} + C_2 e^{(\alpha - i\beta)x} \tag{47}$$

is the general solution of our differential equation. But as yet the exponential function has no meaning for complex exponents.

To attach a meaning to (47) let us proceed (as Euler did) to define the exponential function for complex exponents by using power series. Then for any complex z we have by definition

$$e^z = 1 + z + \frac{z^2}{2!} + \frac{z^3}{3!} + \cdots + \frac{z^n}{n!} + \cdots \tag{48}$$

In particular if we replace z by iz in (48) we have

$$e^{iz} = 1 + iz + \frac{(iz)^2}{2!} + \frac{(iz)^3}{3!} + \cdots + \frac{(iz)^n}{n!} + \cdots \tag{49}$$

Using the fact that $i^2 = -1$, $i^3 = -i$, $i^4 = 1$, etc. (49) splits into two series

$$e^{iz} = 1 - \frac{z^2}{2!} + \frac{z^4}{4!} - \frac{z^6}{6!} + \cdots + \frac{(-1)^n z^{2n}}{(2n)!} + \cdots$$
$$+ i\left(z - \frac{z^3}{3!} + \frac{z^5}{5!} - \cdots + \frac{(-1)^n z^{2n+1}}{(2n+1)!} + \cdots \right). \tag{50}$$

But if we use infinite series to extend the definitions of $\sin x$ and $\cos x$ to complex numbers, then (50) gives

$$\boxed{e^{iz} = \cos z + i \sin z.} \tag{51}$$

This is Euler's formula, and it is very important both in pure and applied mathematics.

Returning now to the problem at hand, (47) can be written as

$$y = C_1 e^{\alpha x} e^{i\beta x} + C_2 e^{\alpha x} e^{-i\beta x}.$$

If we apply (51), first with $z = \beta x$ and then with $z = -\beta x$ we have

$$y = e^{\alpha x}[C_1\{\cos \beta x + i \sin \beta x\} + C_2\{\cos (-\beta x) + i \sin (-\beta x)\}]$$

or

$$y = e^{\alpha x}[C_1 \cos \beta x + C_2 \cos \beta x + i(C_1 \sin \beta x - C_2 \sin \beta x)]. \quad (52)$$

Now in (52) select $C_1 = C_2 = 1/2$. This gives one real solution namely, $y = e^{\alpha x} \cos \beta x$.

Next in (52) select $C_1 = 1/2i$, and $C_2 = -1/2i$. This gives another real solution $y = e^{\alpha x} \sin \beta x$.

Putting these two real solutions together we expect the general solution as stated in

THEOREM 5. *If the auxiliary equation (44) has the roots $\alpha + \beta i$ and $\alpha - \beta i$, then*

$$y = C_1 e^{\alpha x} \cos \beta x + C_2 e^{\alpha x} \sin \beta x \qquad (53)$$

is the general solution of (43).

We have not proved this theorem, because our presentation has gaps. Perhaps the reader may enjoy searching for the gaps. But we have been led to (53) by a thoroughly reasonable process. It is a simple matter to prove the theorem by substituting the function defined by (53) in the differential equation. Incidentally none of the gaps are serious, but it would require considerable time to discuss and fill them. Direct substitution is quicker.

EXAMPLE 2. Solve the differential equation

$$y'' + 10y' + 29y = 0.$$

SOLUTION. The roots of the auxiliary equation $m^2 + 10m + 29 = 0$ are

$$r = \frac{-10 \pm \sqrt{100 - 116}}{2} = {}^{\prime}-5 \pm 2i.$$

Here $\alpha = -5$, $\beta = 2$, so by Theorem 5

$$y = C_1 e^{-5x} \cos 2x + C_2 e^{-5x} \sin 2x$$

is the general solution.

EXERCISE 6

In problems 1 through 12 solve the given differential equation

1. $y'' - 4y' + 3y = 0.$ **2.** $y'' - 12y' - 13y = 0.$

3. $y'' + 16y' = 0.$ **4.** $y'' + 8y' + 16y = 0.$

5. $y'' + 16y = 0.$ **6.** $y'' + 8y' + 17y = 0.$

7. $y'' + 2y' + 17y = 0.$ **8.** $y'' - \pi y' = 0.$

9. $\dfrac{d^2s}{dt^2} - 2\dfrac{ds}{dt} + 5s = 0.$ **10.** $\dfrac{d^2r}{d\theta^2} + 22\dfrac{dr}{d\theta} + 57r = 0.$

11. $\dfrac{d^2x}{dt^2} - 6\dfrac{dx}{dt} + 9x = 0.$ **12.** $\dfrac{d^2u}{dv^2} + 2u = 0.$

13. Find a solution of $y'' - 3y' + 2y = 0$, for which $y(0) = 4$ and $y'(0) = -3$.

14. Find a solution of $y'' - (r_1 + r_2)y' + r_1 r_2 y = 0$ for which $y(0) = A$ and $y'(0) = B$, assuming that $r_1 \neq r_2$. Use the formula that you obtain to check your answer to problem 13.

15. Find a solution of $4y'' + y = 0$ for which $y(0) = 0$ and $y(\pi) = e$.

★16. Obtain a solution of $y''' - 7y'' + 10y' = 0$ from the solution of $y'' - 7y' + 10y = 0$.

★★17. Obtain a solution of $y^{IV} + 4y''' + 4y'' =: 0$ from the solution of $y'' + 4y' + 4y = 0$.

★18. Prove Theorem 4, by direct substitution.

★19. Prove Theorem 5, by direct substitution.

★20. Prove that if $y = u(x)$ is a solution of $p_0(x)y'' + p_1(x)y' + p_2(x)y = 0$, then for any constant C, $y = Cu(x)$ is also a solution of the same differential equation. We call this property the *homogeneity* of the solutions.

★21. Prove that if $y = u(x)$ and $y = v(x)$ are solutions of $p_0(x)y'' + p_1(x)y' + p_2(x)y = 0$ then $y = u(x) + v(x)$ is a solution of the same differential equation. We call this property the *additivity* of the solutions.

★22. How would you combine the results of problems 20 and 21?

★23. Are the results of the three preceding problems valid for equation (40), the linear equation of nth order?

★24. Starting with Euler's formula, equation (51), prove the following

a. $e^{i\pi} + 1 = 0,$ **b.** $1 = e \cos i + ei \sin i,$

c. $\cos z = \dfrac{e^{iz} + e^{-iz}}{2},$ **d.** $\sin z = \dfrac{e^{iz} - e^{-iz}}{2i}.$

8. **Second order linear nonhomogeneous equations.** The solution of the nonhomogeneous equation

$$p_0(x)\frac{d^2y}{dx^2} + p_1(x)\frac{dy}{dx} + p_2(x)y = q(x) \qquad (54)$$

is related to the solution of the reduced equation

$$p_0(x)\frac{d^2y}{dx^2} + p_1(x)\frac{dy}{dx} + p_2(x)y = 0 \qquad (55)$$

as stated in the following theorem.

THEOREM 6. *If $y = u(x)$ is a solution of (55), and $y = v(x)$ is a solution of (54), then $y = u(x) + v(x)$ is a solution of (54).*

The proof is similar in character to the proofs of Theorems 3, 4, and 5, and so we leave it for the student. Notice that if $u(x)$ is the general solution of (55) then it contains two independent constants. Consequently so also does $y = u(x) + v(x)$, and then this latter is the general solution of (54).

EXAMPLE 1. Find the general solution of

$$y'' + 4y' - 5y = 19 - 5x. \tag{56}$$

SOLUTION. We first solve the reduced equation $y'' + 4y' - 5y = 0$. Since $m^2 + 4m - 5 = (m + 5)(m - 1)$, the general solution of the reduced equation is $u(x) = C_1e^x + C_2e^{-5x}$.

We next try to find any particular solution of the given equation. Based on the form of (56) we make a "scientific guess" that there is some solution that is a polynomial in x. A little thought will show that since $q(x)$ is a first degree polynomial, the solution $v(x)$ will also be a first degree polynomial. But it is instructive to watch what happens if we guess that $v(x)$ is a second degree polynomial. Let

$$y = v(x) = ax^2 + bx + c$$

where the coefficients a, b, and c are to be determined so that $v(x)$ is a solution of (56). On differentiating and substituting in the left side of (56) we have

$$2a + 4(2ax + b) - 5(ax^2 + bx + c) = 19 - 5x$$

or

$$-5ax^2 + (8a - 5b)x + (2a + 4b - 5c) = 19 - 5x.$$

This last, will be an identity, if and only if the coefficients of like powers of x are the same on both sides. Equating coefficients gives:

For x^2: $-5a = 0$
For x: $8a - 5b = -5$
For 1: $2a + 4b - 5c = 19.$

Solving this set, we obtain $a = 0$, $b = 1$, $c = -3$. Then $v(x) = x - 3$ is a particular solution of (56) and is a first degree polynomial as predicted. By Theorem 6, we merely add u and v to obtain

$$y = C_1e^x + C_2e^{-5x} + x - 3,$$

the general solution of (56).

The "scientific guess" will work only if $q(x)$ is reasonably decent. Further the method requires modification if $q(x)$, or some part of $q(x)$ is already a solution of the reduced equation. This will be illustrated in the exercise list. In guessing, the following table may be helpful.

Form of $q(x)$	Guess for $v(x)$
A polynomial of nth degree	$a_0x^n + a_1x^{n-1} + \cdots + a_n$
e^{kx}	ae^{kx}
$\sin kx$ or $\cos kx$	$a \sin kx + b \cos kx$
$x^n e^{kx}$	$(a_0x^n + a_1x^{n-1} + \cdots + a_n)e^{kx}$
$e^{kx} \sin cx$ or $e^{kx} \cos cx$	$e^{kx}(a \sin cx + b \cos cx)$.

If $q(x)$ is a sum of terms from the table then the guess for $v(x)$ is a sum of the corresponding terms from the table.

In general the method of undetermined coefficients will work if $q(x)$ has the property that all of its derivatives are linear combinations of only a finite number of different functions. Naturally the functions listed in the table have this property. Functions such as $\cot x$, $1/x$, and $\sin^{-1} x$ do not have this property.

EXAMPLE 2.   Find the general solution of

$$y'' + 6y' + 8y = 4 \cos 2x + 3xe^x. \tag{57}$$

SOLUTION.   The general solution of the reduced equation is $u(x) = C_1e^{-2x} + C_2e^{-4x}$. To find a particular solution of (56) we use the method of undetermined coefficients. Following the table we assume a solution of the form

$$y = v(x) = a \cos 2x + b \sin 2x + (cx + d)e^x. \tag{58}$$

Then

$$y' = v'(x) = 2b \cos 2x - 2a \sin 2x + (cx + c + d)e^x,$$

and

$$y'' = v''(x) = -4a \cos 2x - 4b \sin 2x + (cx + 2c + d)e^x.$$

In order to substitute in equation (57) we multiply these three equations by 8, 6, and 1 respectively, and add the results. This gives

$$(4a + 12b)\cos 2x + (4b - 12a)\sin 2x + (15cx + 8c + 15d)e^x = 4 \cos 2x + 3xe^x.$$

Equating coefficients of corresponding terms gives

For $\cos 2x$:	$4a + 12b = 4$	For xe^x:	$15c = 3$
For $\sin 2x$:	$-12a + 4b = 0$	For e^x:	$8c + 15d = 0$.

Solving this set we find $a = 1/10$, $b = 3/10$, $c = 1/5$, $d = -8/75$. Then from (58) we have

$$y = C_1e^{-2x} + C_2e^{-4x} + \frac{1}{10} (\cos 2x + 3 \sin 2x) + \left(\frac{x}{5} - \frac{8}{75}\right)e^x$$

for the general solution of (57).

EXERCISE 7

In problems 1 through 16 find the general solution of the given differential equation.

1. $y'' - 3y' = 8e^{2x}$.

2. $y'' + y = x^2$.

3. $y'' + 4y = \sin 3x + 2x$.

4. $y'' - 2y' + 15y = 36e^{-x} + 45x^2$.

5. $y'' - 4y' + 5y = 5x^3 - 7x^2$.

*6. $y'' + 4y = x \sin x$.

7. $y'' - 2y' + 4y = xe^{-x}$.

8. $y'' + 2y' + y = 5x + \pi e^{-2x}$.

9. $y'' - 4y' + 3y = 6e^x$.

   Hint: Try $y = axe^x$.

10. $y'' - y' = 3x^2$.

   Try $y = ax^3 + bx^2 + cx$.

11. $y'' - 7y' + 12y = e^{3x} + e^{4x}$.

   Try $y = axe^{3x} + bxe^{4x}$.

12. $y'' - 2y' + y = 8e^x$.

   Try $y = ax^2e^x$.

13. $y'' + 4y = \cos 2x$.

   Try $y = ax \cos 2x + bx \sin 2x$.

14. $y'' + y' - 12y = 14e^{3x} + 6x$.

15. $3y'' - 10y' = 10x^3 - 24x^2 - 11x - 4$.

16. $y'' + 6y' + 9y = 10e^{-3x} + 90$.

17. Prove Theorem 6.

In problems 18 through 21 find the particular solution of the given differential equation that satisfies the given boundary conditions.

18. $y'' = x^2$, $y(0) = y'(0) = 0$.

19. $y'' - 5y' + 6y = 8e^x$, $y(0) = 3$, $y'(0) = -1$.

20. $y'' - 5y' + 6y = 8e^x$, $y(0) = y'(0) = 0$.

21. $y'' - 4y = 16e^{2x}$, $y(0) = 0$, $y'(0) = 4$.

9.   Higher order linear equations. The theory of linear differential equations of order greater than two, parallels the theory of second order linear differential equations. The labor involved is somewhat greater.

To solve the reduced equation

$$\frac{d^n y}{dx^n} + a_1 \frac{d^{n-1}y}{dx^{n-1}} + \cdots + a_{n-1} \frac{dy}{dx} + a_n y = 0 \tag{59}$$

where the coefficients are all constants, we try $y = e^{mx}$. Substitution shows that this is a solution if and only if $m = r$, a root of the auxiliary equation

$$m^n + a_1 m^{n-1} + \cdots + a_{n-1}m + a_n = 0. \tag{60}$$

If the roots of (60) are $r_1, r_2, \cdots, r_n$, then it is easy to prove that

$$y = C_1 e^{r_1 x} + C_2 e^{r_2 x} + \cdots + C_n e^{r_n x} \tag{61}$$

is a solution of (59). This gives

THEOREM 7. *If the roots of (60) are real and distinct, then (61) is the general solution of (59).*

Suppose that some of the roots of (60) are complex. If the coefficients in (60) are real, then these roots occur in conjugate pairs $\alpha + \beta i,\ \alpha - \beta i$, and for each such pair the corresponding terms in (61) may be replaced by $e^{\alpha x}(C_1 \cos \beta x + C_2 \sin \beta x)$.

A root r may be a repeated root of order k. This means that the polynomial (60) has the factorization

$$(m - r)^k Q(m)$$

where r is not a root of $Q(m)$. If r is a k-fold root, then the k terms in (61) corresponding to that root are replaced by

$$(C_1 + C_2 x + C_3 x^2 + \cdots + C_k x^{k-1})e^{rx}.$$

The proof of this rule is somewhat involved so we omit it. The student can easily check it directly if k is small, for example if $k = 3$ or 4.

The same rule applies to repeated complex roots. For example if $\alpha + i\beta$ and $\alpha - i\beta$ are each double roots of (60) then

$$y = e^{\alpha x}(C_1 \cos \beta x + C_2 \sin \beta x + C_3 x \cos \beta x + C_4 x \sin \beta x)$$

is a solution of (59). It is clear that whatever the nature of the n roots of (60), these rules will give us a solution with n independent constants, and hence the general solution.

To solve the nonhomogeneous equation

$$\frac{d^n y}{dx^n} + a_1 \frac{d^{n-1} y}{dx^{n-1}} + \cdots + a_{n-1} \frac{dy}{dx} + a_n y = q(x) \tag{62}$$

we follow the method already used in the second order case. We first find the general solution of the reduced equation (59), and then add to it any particular solution of (62). The simplest way to find this particular solution is the method of undetermined coefficients, and this method will always work whenever $q(x)$ is a polynomial in x, $\cos ax$, $\sin bx$, and e^{cx}. Of course, the labor involved increases as the order of the differential equation, or the complexity of $q(x)$ increases.

EXAMPLE 1. Find the general solution of

$$y^{(7)} - 3y^{(6)} + 5y^{(5)} - 7y^{(4)} + 7y''' - 5y'' + 3y' - y = e^{-x} + 2x, \tag{63}$$

where $y^{(n)}$ denotes the nth derivative.

Inspection of the auxiliary equation

$$m^7 - 3m^6 + 5m^5 - 7m^4 + 7m^3 - 5m^2 + 3m - 1 = 0 \tag{64}$$

shows that $m = 1$ is a root. We divide by $m - 1$ and examine the quotient. Continuing in this manner we will eventually find that (64) is equivalent to

$(m - 1)^3(m^2 + 1)^2 = 0$ so that $r = 1$ is a triple root and $r = \pm i$ are each double roots. Then

$$u(x) = (C_1 + C_2 x + C_3 x^2)e^x + (C_4 + C_5 x)\cos x + (C_6 + C_7 x)\sin x \qquad (65)$$

is the general solution of (63) with the right side replaced by zero. To find a particular solution of (63) we set $v(x) = ae^{-x} + bx + c$. Then substitution in (63) yields

$$-32ae^{-x} + 3b - (bx + c) = e^{-x} + 2x.$$

Consequently $a = -1/32$, $b = -2$, and $c = -6$. Then

$$v(x) = -\frac{1}{32}e^{-x} - 2x - 6,$$

and the general solution of (63) is $y = u(x) + v(x)$.

EXERCISE 8

In problems 1 through 12 find the general solution.

1. $y^{(4)} - y = 0$.
2. $y^{(4)} + 16y = 0$.
3. $8y''' - 12y'' + 6y' - y = 0$.
4. $y^{(4)} - y'' - 12y = 0$.
5. $y''' + 4y' = 10e^x$.
6. $y''' + 9y' = 2 \sin 2x$.
7. $y''' + 6y'' + 11y' + 6y = 180e^{2x}$.
8. $y^{(4)} - 4y''' + 12y'' + 4y' - 13y = 26x^2 + 23x - 8$.
9. $y^{(4)} + 2y'' + y = 2x + 4e^x + 8e^{-x}$.
10. $y''' - 5y'' = 15x + 10e^{4x}$.
11. $y''' - y'' - 12y' = 3 + 7e^{4x}$.
★★12. $y''' + 3y'' + 3y' + y = 2e^{-x} + 3x^2e^{-x}$.

13. Find the solution of $y''' + 3y'' + 2y' = 0$ that satisfies the boundary conditions $y(0) = y'(0) = 0$, $y''(0) = 1$.
14. Find the family of solutions of $y''' + 8y = 0$ for which $y(0) = y'(0) = 0$.

10.   Series solutions.

If we select a differential equation at random, there is no reason to suppose that the solution can be expressed in terms of a finite number of combinations of the elementary functions. We need to have at hand a larger supply of functions, and the collection of all convergent power series provides such an enlarged supply of functions.

To illustrate the use of infinite series, let us suppose at first that we know nothing about the exponential and logarithmic functions, and we are faced with the differential equation

$$\frac{dy}{dx} = y. \qquad (66)$$

The standard procedure will lead to $\displaystyle\int \frac{dy}{y}$ and because we are assuming that we do not have the logarithmic function available, we will not obtain a solution. Instead we assume there is a solution in the form of a Maclaurin series

$$y = \sum_{n=0}^{\infty} a_n x^n = a_0 + a_1 x + a_2 x^2 + \cdots + a_n x^n + \cdots \qquad (67)$$

where the unknown coefficients a_n are to be determined so that (67) is a solution of (66). Differentiating (67) gives

$$\frac{dy}{dx} = \sum_{n=1}^{\infty} n a_n x^{n-1} = a_1 + 2 a_2 x + 3 a_3 x^2 + \cdots + n a_n x^{n-1} + \cdots. \qquad (68)$$

Using (68) and (67) in (66), we have

$$a_1 + 2 a_2 x + 3 a_3 x^2 + \cdots + n a_n x^{n-1} + \cdots = a_0 + a_1 x + a_2 x^2 + \cdots + a_n x^n + \cdots.$$

Combining terms we have

$$0 = a_1 - a_0 + (2 a_2 - a_1) x + (3 a_3 - a_2) x^2 + \cdots + (n a_n - a_{n-1}) x^{n-1} + \cdots. \qquad (69)$$

Now this power series will certainly be zero for all x if each coefficient is zero. In other words (67) is a solution of (66) if $a_1 - a_0 = 0$, $2 a_2 - a_1 = 0$, $3 a_3 - a_2 = 0$, etc. We expect one arbitrary constant in our solution, so we select a_0 to be C, where C is the arbitrary constant. Then

$$\begin{array}{llll} a_1 - a_0 = 0 & \text{yields} & a_1 = a_0 = C, \\ 2 a_2 - a_1 = 0 & \text{yields} & a_2 = \tfrac{1}{2} a_1 = \tfrac{1}{2} C, \\ 3 a_3 - a_2 = 0 & \text{yields} & a_3 = \tfrac{1}{3} a_2 = \tfrac{1}{6} C, \\ 4 a_4 - a_3 = 0 & \text{yields} & a_4 = \tfrac{1}{4} a_3 = \tfrac{1}{24} C. \end{array}$$

An inspection of these formulas suggests that in general $a_n = C/n!$, and this is easy to prove by mathematical induction using the condition $n a_n - a_{n-1} = 0$. Consequently (67) gives

$$y = C \sum_{n=0}^{\infty} \frac{1}{n!} x^n = C \left(1 + x + \frac{x^2}{2!} + \frac{x^3}{3!} + \frac{x^4}{4!} + \cdots \right) \qquad (70)$$

as the general solution of (66). Of course we recognize this power series as the series for e^x. Hence the solution is $y = C e^x$.

When we set the coefficients in (69) equal to zero we obtained the equation $n a_n - a_{n-1} = 0$ or $n a_n = a_{n-1}$. Such an equation is called a *recursion formula*. A recursion formula permits us to compute further coefficients, from the ones already obtained.

EXAMPLE 1. Find the general solution of

$$(1 + x^3) \frac{dy}{dx} = 3 x^2 y.$$

SOLUTION. Using (67) and (68) in the given differential equation, we have

$$(1 + x^3) \sum_{n=1}^{\infty} n a_n x^{n-1} = 3x^2 \sum_{n=0}^{\infty} a_n x^n,$$

or

$$\sum_{n=1}^{\infty} n a_n x^{n-1} + \sum_{n=1}^{\infty} n a_n x^{n+2} - \sum_{n=0}^{\infty} 3 a_n x^{n+2} = 0.$$

Next we alter the summation index so that the power on x is the same in each sum. To do this we replace n by $n + 3$ in the first sum, and start the new sum at $n = -2$. We have

$$\sum_{n=-2}^{\infty} (n + 3) a_{n+3} x^{n+2} + \sum_{n=1}^{\infty} n a_n x^{n+2} - \sum_{n=0}^{\infty} 3 a_n x^{n+2} = 0.$$

Setting the coefficient of x^{n+2} equal to zero for $n = -2, -1, 0, 1, \cdots$ yields the following set of equations.

$n = -2,$	$1a_1 = 0,$	$n = 1,$	$4a_4 + a_1 \ - 3a_1 = 0,$
$n = -1,$	$2a_2 = 0,$	$n = 2,$	$5a_5 + 2a_2 - 3a_2 = 0,$
$n = 0,$	$3a_3 - 3a_0 = 0,$	$n = 3,$	$6a_6 + 3a_3 - 3a_3 = 0,$

and for $n > 3$, $(n + 3)a_{n+3} + (n - 3)a_n = 0$. It is easy to see from this set of equations that $a_n = 0$ for all n, except $n = 0$ and $n = 3$. Here $3a_3 - 3a_0 = 0$ implies that $a_3 = a_0$. Setting $a_0 = C$ we have $y = C(1 + x^3)$ for the general solution of the given differential equation.

The method is actually more useful when applied to second order differential equations.

EXAMPLE 2. Find the general solution of

$$y'' = x^2 y. \tag{71}$$

SOLUTION. As usual we assume that a solution is given by a Maclaurin series of the form (67). Then

$$y'' = \sum_{n=2}^{\infty} n(n - 1) a_n x^{n-2}. \tag{72}$$

Using (67) and (72) in (71) we have

$$\sum_{n=2}^{\infty} n(n - 1) a_n x^{n-2} = \sum_{n=0}^{\infty} a_n x^{n+2}.$$

Replacing n by $n + 4$ in the first sum we obtain

$$\sum_{n=-2}^{\infty} (n + 4)(n + 3) a_{n+4} x^{n+2} = \sum_{n=0}^{\infty} a_n x^{n+2}. \tag{73}$$

Using $n = -2$, and -1 in (73) we see that $a_2 = 0$ and $a_3 = 0$. For $n \geq 0$ we have the recursion formula

$$(n + 4)(n + 3) a_{n+4} = a_n. \tag{74}$$

We expect the general solution to contain two arbitrary constants, so we set $a_0 = A$ and $a_1 = B$, where A and B are the arbitrary constants. Then from (74) we easily find

$$a_4 = \frac{1}{3\cdot4} a_0 = \frac{1}{3\cdot4} A, \qquad\qquad a_5 = \frac{1}{4\cdot5} a_1 = \frac{1}{4\cdot5} B,$$

$$a_8 = \frac{1}{7\cdot8} a_4 = \frac{1}{3\cdot4\cdot7\cdot8} A, \qquad\qquad a_9 = \frac{1}{8\cdot9} a_5 = \frac{1}{4\cdot5\cdot8\cdot9} B,$$

$$a_{12} = \frac{1}{11\cdot12} a_8 = \frac{1}{3\cdot4\cdot7\cdot8\cdot11\cdot12} A, \qquad a_{13} = \frac{1}{12\cdot13} a_9 = \frac{1}{4\cdot5\cdot8\cdot9\cdot12\cdot13} B,$$

$$\cdots \qquad\qquad\qquad\qquad \cdots$$

and the remaining coefficients are all zero, i.e., $a_{4n+2} = 0$ and $a_{4n+3} = 0$. Hence the general solution is

$$y = A \left(1 + \frac{x^4}{3\cdot4} + \frac{x^8}{3\cdot4\cdot7\cdot8} + \frac{x^{12}}{3\cdot4\cdot7\cdot8\cdot11\cdot12} + \cdots \right)$$

$$+ B \left(x + \frac{x^5}{4\cdot5} + \frac{x^9}{4\cdot5\cdot8\cdot9} + \frac{x^{13}}{4\cdot5\cdot8\cdot9\cdot12\cdot13} + \cdots \right). \tag{75}$$

Neither of the two infinite series that occur in (75) is recognizable as an elementary function, nor as a simple combination of elementary functions. It is reasonable to suppose that these series define new functions. Certainly it is clear from the complicated nature of the solution that in this case the use of power series gives a solution much quicker than any of our previous methods.

Naturally, we have a solution only for those x for which the given power series converges. A modified form of the ratio test will show that both series in this example converge for all x.

In some cases it is very difficult to obtain the coefficient of the general term, and then we are content to obtain the first few terms of the Maclaurin series. This is illustrated in

EXAMPLE 3. Find the first four nonzero terms in the Maclaurin series for the solution of

$$\frac{dy}{dx} = y^2 + x \tag{76}$$

for which $y(0) = 0$.

SOLUTION. The condition $y(0) = 0$ implies that $a_0 = 0$ in the Maclaurin series. So we set

$$y = a_1 x + a_2 x^2 + a_3 x^3 + \cdots = \sum_{n=1}^{\infty} a_n x^n. \tag{77}$$

If b_n is the coefficient of x^n in the series for y^2 we see that

$$b_2 = a_1{}^2, \qquad b_3 = a_1a_2 + a_2a_1, \qquad b_4 = a_1a_3 + a_2{}^2 + a_3a_1, \qquad (78)$$

and in general

$$b_n = a_1a_{n-1} + a_2a_{n-2} + a_3a_{n-3} + \cdots + a_{n-1}a_1 = \sum_{k=1}^{n-1} a_k a_{n-k}. \qquad (79)$$

If we use (77) and its derivative in (76) and equate coefficients of like powers of x on both sides, we obtain a set of infinitely many equations of which the first eight are

$$
\begin{array}{ll}
a_1 = 0, & 5a_5 = a_1a_3 + a_2{}^2 + a_3a_1, \\
2a_2 = 1, & 6a_6 = a_1a_4 + a_2a_3 + a_3a_2 + a_4a_1, \\
3a_3 = a_1{}^2, & 7a_7 = 2(a_1a_5 + a_2a_4) + a_3{}^2, \\
4a_4 = a_1a_2 + a_2a_1, & 8a_8 = 2(a_1a_6 + a_2a_5 + a_3a_4).
\end{array}
\qquad (80)
$$

In general for $n \geq 3$, we have $na_n = b_{n-1}$. Solving the set (80) we find that $a_2 = 1/2$, $a_5 = 1/20$, $a_8 = 1/160$, while $a_n = 0$ for $n = 1, 3, 4, 6$, and 7. But this gives only the first three nonzero terms. We must add the next three equations to the set (80). When this is done we find that $a_9 = a_{10} = 0$ $a_{11} = 7/8800$. Hence the solution to (76) with $y(0) = 0$ is

$$y = \frac{1}{2} x^2 + \frac{1}{20} x^5 + \frac{1}{160} x^8 + \frac{7}{8800} x^{11} + \cdots.$$

We might conjecture that this infinite series converges for all x, but we have not proved this. At this stage all that we know for sure, is that the series converges at $x = 0$. Methods for finding intervals of convergence for series solutions, are given in most differential equations books.

EXERCISE 9

In problems 1 through 6 find the solution of the given differential equation (a) in the form of a Maclaurin series using the method of undetermined coefficients, and (b) by methods learned earlier, and show that the two solutions are the same.

1. $x \dfrac{dy}{dx} = 2y.$

2. $\dfrac{dy}{dx} = 2xy.$

3. $\dfrac{dy}{dx} = 6x + 2xy.$

4. $\dfrac{dy}{dx} = 2x + 2y - 1.$

5. $(3x + 2x^2) \dfrac{dy}{dx} = 6y(1 + x).$

6. $\dfrac{dy}{dx} = y + e^x.$

In problems 7 through 14 find the solution of the given differential equation for which $y(0) = A$ and $y'(0) = B$.

7. $y'' = xy.$

8. $(1 - x^2)y'' + 2y = 0.$

9. $y'' - x^2y' - 2xy = 0.$

10. $y'' - xy' - y = 0.$

11. $(1 + x^2)y'' + 3xy' + y = 0.$

12. $y'' = 2xy' + 3y.$

13. $(1 + x^2)y'' + 4xy' + 2y = 0.$

14. $y'' = x^4y' + 4x^3y.$

15. Find a Maclaurin series solution of

$$y'' - y = -\frac{1}{x}y'$$

for which $y(0) = A$ and $y'(0) = 0$.

16. Find a Maclaurin series solution of

$$y'' - y = \frac{2}{x}y'$$

for which $y(0) = A$ and $y'''(0) = B$.

17. In problems 15 and 16, why is it impossible to find a Maclaurin series solution for which $y'(0) = B \neq 0$?

18. Prove that the equation $x^2y'' + y = 0$ has no Maclaurin series solution, other than the trivial solution $y \equiv 0(y = 0$ for all x).

19. Find a Maclaurin series that is a solution of $x^2y'' + y = x^3$.

In problems 20 through 25 find the first four nonzero terms in the Maclaurin series solution of the given equation, satisfying the given initial conditions.

20. $y'' + xy = e^x$, $\qquad\qquad y(0) = 1, y'(0) = 0$.

21. $y'' + xy = 1 + x + \dfrac{x^2}{2} + \dfrac{x^3}{6}$, $\qquad y(0) = 1, y'(0) = 0$.

22. $y'' + x^2y = \sin x$, $\qquad\qquad y(0) = 0, y'(0) = 1$.

23. $y'' = y^2 + 1 + x$, $\qquad\qquad y(0) = 0, y'(0) = 2$.

24. $y'' = xyy'$, $\qquad\qquad\qquad y(0) = 1, y'(0) = 3$.

25. $y''' = y^3$, $\qquad\qquad\qquad y(0) = y'(0) = y''(0) = 0$.

11. Applications. Although differential equations can be studied independently of any applications, the subject arose from the need to solve physical problems. Even today, growth in the theory of differential equations is stimulated by fresh and important problems that present themselves quite naturally in various branches of science and engineering. Let us examine a few of the simplest physical problems that can be solved by differential equations.

EXAMPLE 1. **Growth and Decay.** In a certain culture of bacteria, the rate of increase is proportional to the number present (as long as the food supply is sufficient). If the number doubles in 3 hours, how many are there after 9 hours? If there are 4×10^4 bacteria at the end of 6 hours, how many were present at the beginning?

SOLUTION. Despite the fact that bacteria come in units and are not continuously divisible, there are so many present that we may assume that the growth process is continuous. If N represents the number of bacteria present at time t, then by the conditions stated we have

$$\frac{dN}{dt} = k N \qquad\qquad (81)$$

where k is the constant of proportionality. Integrating, we find that $N = Ce^{kt}$. To determine C we suppose that initially (at $t = 0$) the number of bacteria is N_0. Then using $t = 0$ in $N = Ce^{kt}$ gives $N_0 = Ce^0 = C$. Hence $N = N_0e^{kt}$. To find k we use the fact that the population doubles in 3 hours. Then

$$2N_0 = N_0e^{k3}$$

whence $k = \frac{1}{3}\ln 2$, and consequently

$$N = N_0e^{(t \ln 2)/3} \tag{82}$$

is the equation that gives the population at time t. Finally setting $t = 9$ in (82) we find $N = N_0e^{3 \ln 2} = N_0e^{\ln 8} = 8N_0$. Hence after 9 hours the population will be 8 times the initial population (if the food supply holds out).

To determine N_0, we set $t = 6$ and $N = 4 \times 10^4$ in (82). This gives $4 \times 10^4 = N_0e^{2 \ln 2} = N_0e^{\ln 4} = N_04$. Consequently $N_0 = 10^4$.

EXAMPLE 2. **Mixing.** Brine containing 2 pounds of salt per gallon runs into a tank initially filled with 100 gallons of water containing 25 lbs of salt. If the brine enters at 5 gallons per minute, the concentration is kept uniform by stirring, and the mixture flows out at the same rate, find the amount of salt in the tank after 10 minutes, and after 100 minutes.

SOLUTION. Let Q denote the lbs of salt in the tank at t minutes after the process begins. The fundamental equation is:

Rate of increase in Q = Rate of input − Rate of exit.

Here: Rate of input = 2×5 lbs per minute,

$$\text{Rate of exit} = \frac{Q}{100} \times 5 \text{ lbs. per minute.}$$

Hence the differential equation for Q is

$$\frac{dQ}{dt} = 2 \times 5 - \frac{Q}{100} \times 5 = \frac{200 - Q}{20}.$$

The general solution is $Q = 200 - Ce^{-t/20}$. At $t = 0$, $Q = 25$ (the amount of salt in the tank at the start). This gives $C = 175$, and hence $Q = 200 - 175e^{-t/20}$. Putting $t = 10$ we find that $Q = 93.9$ i.e., after 10 minutes the tank contains 93.9 lbs of salt. Similarly after 100 minutes the tank contains 198.8 lbs of salt.

Observe that from the equation $Q = 200 - 175e^{-t/20}$, we see that Q increases with t (as it should) and that $\lim_{t \to \infty} Q = 200$. Is this reasonable?

EXAMPLE 3. **Mechanics.** A particle starting from rest falls in a resisting medium. Assuming that the resistance is proportional to the square of the velocity, find the distance it falls in t secs.

SOLUTION. Newton's fundamental law for moving bodies is the vector equation

$$\boxed{\mathbf{F} = M\mathbf{A}} \tag{83}$$

where **F** is the vector sum of all of the forces acting on a body of mass M, and **A** is the vector acceleration of the body.

Properly speaking, equation (83) contains a proportionality factor k which can be taken as 1 if the units are selected properly. To achieve this we suppose that a body of weight W lbs is falling under the influence of gravity in a vacuum. Under these circumstances the acceleration is 32 ft/sec^2 (denoted by g). If the force is measured in pounds then equation (83) gives $W = Mg$. Therefore the mass of the body must be $M = W/g$, and when the mass is measured in this manner, the unit of mass is called the *slug*.

For the problem as given only the vertical component of **F** is different from zero, so it is sufficient to consider the scalar equation obtained from (83) by taking that component. Since the resisting force is k^2v^2, (83) gives

$$W - k^2v^2 = \frac{W}{g}\frac{d^2x}{dt^2}$$

where W is the weight of the falling body, v is its velocity, and x is the distance it falls in t secs. Dividing by W/g we can write this as

$$\frac{dv}{dt} = g - \frac{k^2g}{W}v^2 = g - c^2v^2.$$

Integration gives

$$t + C_1 = \int \frac{dv}{g - c^2v^2} = \frac{1}{2c\sqrt{g}} \ln \frac{\sqrt{g} + cv}{\sqrt{g} - cv}. \tag{84}$$

Since $v = 0$ when $t = 0$, we see that $C_1 = 0$. If we solve (84) for v (with $C_1 = 0$) we find

$$v = \frac{\sqrt{g}}{c} \frac{e^{2c\sqrt{g}\,t} - 1}{e^{2c\sqrt{g}\,t} + 1} = \frac{\sqrt{g}}{c} \tanh c\sqrt{g}t. \tag{85}$$

Replacing v by dx/dt in (85), and integrating gives

$$x + C_2 = \frac{1}{c^2} \ln \cosh c\sqrt{g}t.$$

Since $x = 0$ when $t = 0$, we find that $C_2 = 0$. Hence

$$x = \frac{1}{c^2} \ln \cosh c\sqrt{g}t, \tag{86}$$

is the desired formula.

EXERCISE 10

GROWTH AND DECAY

1. The population of the United States was approximately 131,000,000 in 1940, and 179,000,000 in 1960. Assuming that the rate of increase is proportional to the population, in what year will the population be 250,000,000? When will it reach 300,000,000?

2. The decay of all radioactive elements follows the same general law, that the rate of decay is proportional to the amount of the element present. The constant of proportionality is different for different elements, and is customarily given by giving the half-life of the element. This is the length of time required for half of the radioactive material to disintegrate. If the half-life of radium is 1590 years, what percent of a given quantity of radium will be lost in 100 years?

3. Estimate the half-life of Cesium 137 if 11% disintegrates in a period of five years.

4. Age of the earth's crust. Uranium has a half-life of 4.5×10^9 years. The decomposition sequence is very complicated, producing a very large number of intermediate radioactive products, but the final product is an isotope of lead with an atomic weight of 206, and called uranium lead. Assuming for simplicity that the change from uranium to lead is direct, prove that $u = u_0 e^{-kt}$, $l = u_0(1 - e^{-kt})$, where u and l denote the number of uranium and uranium lead atoms present at time t.

We can measure the ratio $r = l/u$ in a rock and if we assume that all of the uranium lead came from decomposition of the uranium, originally present, we can obtain a lower bound for the age of the rock, and consequently a lower bound for the age of the earth's crust. Prove that this lower bound is given by

$$t = \frac{1}{k} \ln (1 + r) = \frac{1}{k}\left(r - \frac{r^2}{2} + \frac{r^3}{3} \cdots \right) \approx \frac{r}{k}.$$

In a certain rock, a chemical determination, gave $l/u = .054$. Using this data show that the rock is about 350 million years old.

5. In 1626 Peter Minuit paid the Indians 24 dollars for land in New York City. Assuming that in 1956 this same land is worth 4.8×10^{10} dollars (48 billion dollars) find the rate of interest continuously compounded, at which the same investment would have given the same increase in capital.

MIXING

6. Brine containing 2 pounds of salt per gallon runs into a tank initially filled with 160 gallons of fresh water (no salt). If the brine enters at 4 gallons per minute, the concentration is kept uniform by stirring, and the mixture flows out at the same rate, when will the tank contain 80 pounds of salt? When will the tank contain 160 pounds of salt?

7. Suppose that the tank of problem 6 initially contained 80 lbs of salt dissolved in the water. If all other conditions are the same, when will the tank contain 160 pounds of salt? When will it contain 240 pounds of salt?

8. Fresh water runs into a tank at the rate of 2 gallons per minute. The tank initially contained 50 pounds of salt dissolved in 100 gallons of water. The concentration is kept uniform by stirring, and the mixture flows out at the rate of 1 gallon per minute. Assuming the tank has a sufficient capacity, when will the tank contain 5 pounds of salt? How many gallons of water will be in the tank at that time?

9. A tank contains 100 gallons of saturated brine (3 pounds of salt per gallon). A salt solution containing 3/4 pounds of salt per gallon flows in at the rate of 4 gallons per minute and the uniform mixture flows out at 3 gallons per minute. Find the minimum concentration of the salt in the tank, and the time required to reach that minimum.

10. A room 150 ft by 50 ft by 20 ft receives fresh air at the rate of 5000 cubic ft per minute. If the fresh air contains .04% carbon dioxide, and the air in the room initially contained .3% carbon dioxide, find the percentage of carbon dioxide after one hour. What is the percentage after two hours?

MECHANICS

11. Solve the problem of example 3, if the resistance is proportional to the first power of the velocity.

12. Show that as $c \to 0$, the solution to problem 11 approaches $x = gt^2/2$.

13. Repeat problem 12 for the formula obtained in Example 3.

14. A roller coaster enters on a descent at 5 ft/sec. If the descent makes an angle $\theta = \sin^{-1} .7$ with the horizontal and if frictional resistance is .2 of the weight of the car, find the velocity after the car has travelled 42 ft along this descent.

15. Two weights W_1 and W_2 ($W_2 > W_1$) are attached by a cable which passes over a pulley. Assuming that the pulley is weightless and frictionless, and that the tension in the cable is the same throughout, find the acceleration with which the heavier weight descends. What is the tension in the cable?

16. Near the earth's surface the attraction due to gravity is practically constant, but according to Newton's law the force of attraction exerted by the earth on a given body is k/x^2 where x is the distance of the body from the center of the earth. Show that if a rocket is shot upward from the earth's surface with initial velocity v_0, and if air resistance is neglected then $v^2 = v^2{}_0 - 2Rg + 2R^2g/x$, where $R = 3960$ miles, is the radius of the earth. *Hint:* Observe that

$$\frac{d^2x}{dt^2} = \frac{dv}{dt} = \frac{dv}{dx}\frac{dx}{dt} = v\frac{dv}{dt}.$$

17. **Escape Velocity.** For the rocket of problem 16 find the least value of v_0 necessary to keep it going indefinitely (of course neglecting the attractive forces due to celestial bodies other than the earth). This is called the escape velocity for the earth.

18. Using Newton's law (problem 16) and Boyles law, $\delta = kp$, where δ is the density of a gas under pressure p, prove that at a point x miles from the center of the earth $(x > R)$ the pressure of the air is given by $p = p_0 e^{kR\left(\frac{R}{x}-1\right)}$, where p_0 is the pressure at the earth's surface.

19. Neglecting the changes in temperature, find the atmospheric pressure 5 miles above sea level. At sea level air has a density of .08 lb/cu. ft, and a pressure of 14.7 lbs/sq. in. or 2117 lbs/sq. ft.

20. A spring of natural length L, has its upper end fastened to a rigid support. When a weight W is supported by the spring, the equilibrium length of the spring is $L + s$, where $W = ks$, and k is the spring constant. The spring is then pulled down C units below its equilibrium position and released. Find the equation for x, its displacement from equilibrium, in terms of t.

21. If the spring of problem 20 requires a 4 lb weight to extend it 1/2 in., what is the period of its vibration when a 12 lb weight is suspended by the spring?

22. A chain 4 ft long starts with 1 ft hanging over the edge of a smooth table (more than 4 ft high). Find the time required for the chain to slide off.

ELECTRICITY

23. A simple electrical circuit shown in Fig. 1, consists of a generator which produces an electromotive force of E volts, a resistance of R ohms, a coil of inductance of L henries, and a condenser of capacitance C farads. The current I, measured in amperes, satisfies the differential equation

$$L \frac{d^2 I}{dt^2} + R \frac{dI}{dt} + \frac{1}{C} I = \frac{dE}{dt}.$$

Find I if E is constant, $R = 0$, and $LC = 1/\omega^2$ is constant.

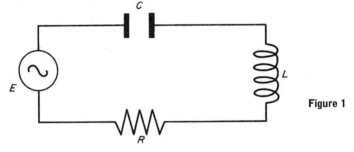

Figure 1

24. Find I for the circuit of problem 23 if $R = 0$, $LC = 1/\omega^2$, and $E = E_0 \sin \alpha t$ where $\alpha \neq \omega$.

25. Find I for the circuit of problem 23, if $R = 300$, $L = 10$, $C = 5 \times 10^{-4}$, and $E = 110 \sin 10t$.

26. When the condenser is removed from the circuit of Fig. 1, the term I/C is dropped from the differential equation. Find I in this case if $E = E_0 \sin \omega t$ and $I = I' = 0$ when $t = 0$.

MISCELLANEOUS

27. Assuming that a spherical drop of water evaporates at a rate proportional to its surface area, find the radius as a function of time.

28. A cylindrical tank has a leak in the bottom, and water flows out at a rate proportional to the pressure at the bottom. If the tank loses 2% of its water in 24 hours, when will it be half empty?

29. Suppose that the food supply available will support a maximum number M

of bacteria, and that the rate of growth of the bacteria is proportional to the difference between the maximum number and the number present. Find an expression for the number of bacteria as a function of time.

30. According to Newton's law the rate at which a body cools is proportional to the difference between the temperature of the body and that of the surrounding medium. If a certain steel bar has a temperature of 1230° C and cools to 1030° C in 10 minutes, when the surrounding temperature is 30° C, how long will it take for the bar to cool to 80° C?

31. If the water in a tank runs out through a small hole in the bottom, then the rate of flow is proportional to the square root of the height of the water in the tank. Prove that if the tank is a cylinder with its axis vertical, then the time required for three fourths of the water to run out is equal to the time required for the remaining fourth of the water to run out.

32. Suppose that in problem 31, the tank is a right circular cone with the vertex down and its axis vertical. If the level of the water falls to one half of its initial level in 31 minutes, how long does it take for the tank to empty?

33. A country has in circulation 3 billion dollars of paper currency. Each day about 10 million dollars comes into the banks and the same amount is paid out. The government decides to issue new currency, and whenever the old style currency comes into the bank it is destroyed and replaced by the new currency. How long will it take for the currency in circulation to become 95% new?

1

APPENDIX

INEQUALITIES[1]

1.   The elementary theorems.   If c is a positive number we write

$$0 < c, \qquad \text{(read zero is less than } c\text{)}$$

or with the same meaning,

$$c > 0, \qquad \text{(read } c \text{ is greater than zero.)}$$

If c is a negative number we write

$$c < 0, \qquad \text{(read } c \text{ is less than zero)}$$

or if we wish

$$0 > c, \qquad \text{(read zero is greater than } c\text{)}.$$

EXAMPLES. $0 < 3$, $-5 < 0$, $1/10 > 0$, $0 > -.000001$.   The comparison of any two numbers is then made to depend on the above basic inequalities.

DEFINITION 1.   *The number a is said to be less than b, in symbols*

$$a < b, \tag{1}$$

if and only if the difference $b - a$ is positive, i.e., if and only if

$$0 < b - a. \tag{2}$$

If $a < b$ (a is less than b) we also write $b > a$ (b is greater than a).   For example $86 < 99$ because $99 - 86 = 13$, a positive number.   For the same reason $99 > 86$.   Again $-19 < -6$ because $-6 - (-19) = -6 + 19 = 13$, a positive number.

It is convenient to have at hand a compound symbol $\leqq$.   Thus the symbols $a \leqq b$ (read a is less than or equal to b) means that either a is less than b, or a is equal to b.

---

[1] The material in this appendix and in the next is taken from the author's book *The Pleasures of Mathematics* (The Macmillan Company, 1965) with the permission of the publisher.

Using the simplest laws of arithmetic we can prove a number of basic theorems on inequalities.

THEOREM 1. *If $a < b$ and c is any positive number, then $ca < cb$.*

In other words, an inequality remains valid when multiplied on both sides by the same positive number.

PROOF. Since $a < b$, then $b - a$ is a positive number. Since the product of two positive numbers is again positive we have $c(b - a) > 0$. But then

$$0 < c(b - a) = cb - ca$$

and by definition 1 this gives

$$ca < cb \qquad \text{Q.E.D.}$$

We leave to the student the proof of

THEOREM 2. *If $a < b$ and c is any negative number, then $ca > cb$.*

In other words when an inequality is multiplied on both sides by the same negative number, the inequality sign is reversed.

THEOREM 3. *If $a < b$ and $b < c$, then $a < c$.*

PROOF. By hypothesis $b - a$ and $c - b$ are positive numbers. Then the sum $(b - a) + (c - b)$ is a positive number. But this sum is $c - a$. Since $0 < c - a$, we have by Definition 1 that $a < c$.   Q.E.D.

By a similar type of argument the student can prove

THEOREM 4. *If $a < c$ and $b < d$, then $a + b < c + d$.*

In other words two inequalities can be added termwise to give a valid inequality. Of course the inequality sign must be in the same direction, in all three of the inequalities.

THEOREM 5. *If $a < b$ and c is any number, then $a + c < b + c$.*

An inequality remains valid when the same number is added to both sides. We leave the proof for the student. Note that c can be a negative number, so that this theorem includes subtraction.

THEOREM 6. *If $0 < a < b$, then*

$$\frac{1}{a} > \frac{1}{b} > 0.$$

Thus reciprocation reverses the inequality sign, when both members are positive.

PROOF. Multiply both sides of $a < b$ by the positive number $1/ab$ and use Theorem 1.

THEOREM 7.   *If $0 < a < b$ and $0 < c < d$ then*

$$ac < bd.$$

Thus multiplication of the corresponding terms of an inequality preserves the inequality. Of course all terms should be positive, and the inequality sign must be in the same direction, in all three inequalities.

PROOF. Using Theorem 1 the inequality $a < b$ yields $ac < bc$. Similarly $c < d$ yields $bc < bd$. Since $ac < bc$ and $bc < bd$, Theorem 3 gives $ac < bd$.   Q.E.D.

THEOREM 8.   *If $0 < a < b$ and n is any positive integer then*

$$a^n < b^n.$$

PROOF. Apply Theorem 7, $n-1$ times with $c = a$, and $d = b$.

THEOREM 9.   *If $0 < a < b$ and n is any positive integer then*

$$\sqrt[n]{a} < \sqrt[n]{b}.$$

Here if n is even, the symbol $\sqrt[n]{}$ means the positive n^{th} root.

PROOF.   The proof is a little complicated because it uses the method of contradiction. We contend that for any positive numbers $\sqrt[n]{a}$ and $\sqrt[n]{b}$ there are only three possibilities, namely:

(A) $\sqrt[n]{a} < \sqrt[n]{b}$,   **(B)** $\sqrt[n]{a} = \sqrt[n]{b}$,   **(C)** $\sqrt[n]{a} > \sqrt[n]{b}$.

In each of the latter two cases we take the nth power of both sides. In case **(B)** we find obviously that $a = b$. But this is impossible because by hypothesis $a < b$. In case **(C)** we apply Theorem 8 to $\sqrt[n]{b} < \sqrt[n]{a}$ and find that $b < a$. Again this is contrary to the hypothesis that $a < b$. Since each of the cases **(B)** and **(C)** leads to a contradiction the only case that can occur is **(A)**.   Q.E.D.

There is one other important tool in proving inequalities, namely the innocent remark that the square of any number is either positive or zero, i.e., $c^2 \geqq 0$ for any[2] number c.

---

[2]The student may have heard that $i = \sqrt{-1}$ and hence $i^2 = -1 < 0$. In this book we consider only real numbers, except for a brief section in the chapter on differential equations.

EXAMPLE 1. Prove that for any two numbers

$$2ab \leq a^2 + b^2 \tag{3}$$

and that the equality sign occurs if and only if $a = b$.

SOLUTION. By our remark above

$$(a - b)^2 \geq 0 \tag{4}$$

and equality in (4) occurs if and only if $a = b$. Expanding (4) we have

$$a^2 - 2ab + b^2 \geq 0,$$

or

$$0 \leq a^2 - 2ab + b^2.$$

Then by Theorem 5 (adding $2ab$ to both sides)

$$2ab \leq a^2 + b^2.$$

Since the equality sign occurs in (4) if and only if $a = b$, it also occurs in (3) under the same conditions.

EXAMPLE 2. Prove that if a, b, c, and d are any set of positive numbers,

$$ab + cd \leq \sqrt{a^2 + c^2} \sqrt{b^2 + d^2}. \tag{5}$$

It is not easy to see the proper starting place for this problem, so instead we work backwards. That is, we start with the inequality (5) and see if we can deduce one that we know to be valid. This operation is called the *analysis* of the problem.

Analysis. If (5) is true we can square both sides and obtain

$$a^2b^2 + 2abcd + c^2d^2 \leq (a^2 + c^2)(b^2 + d^2), \tag{6}$$

or

$$a^2b^2 + 2abcd + c^2d^2 \leq a^2b^2 + c^2b^2 + a^2d^2 + c^2d^2, \tag{7}$$

or on transposing (Theorem 5)

$$0 \leq c^2b^2 - 2abcd + a^2d^2, \tag{8}$$

or

$$0 \leq (cb - ad)^2. \tag{9}$$

But we know that this last inequality is always valid. Hence if we can reverse our steps we can prove the given inequality is also valid.

SOLUTION. We begin with the known inequality (9) and on expanding we find that (8) is also valid. Then adding $a^2b^2 + 2abcd + c^2d^2$ to both sides of (8) we obtain (7). Factoring the right side of (7) gives (6). Finally taking the positive square root of both sides of (6) gives (5).   Q.E.D.

It is customary to do the analysis on scratch paper, and then write the solution in the proper order, i.e., in the reverse order of the analysis. The student should write out in detail the correct solution of this example, following the outline just given.

Some inequalities are valid only for certain values of the variable involved.

EXAMPLE 3.   For what values of x is

$$x^2 - x - 30 > 0? \tag{10}$$

SOLUTION.   Factoring this expression we have

$$x^2 - x - 30 = (x - 6)(x + 5). \tag{11}$$

This is certainly positive if both factors are positive. This happens only if $x > 6$. The product is also positive if both factors are negative. This happens only for $x < -5$. If $-5 < x$ and $x < 6$ the first factor is negative and the second factor is positive so that the product is negative.

Whence we conclude that the inequality (10) is valid if either $x < -5$ or if $x > 6$, and that these are the only values of x for which (10) is valid.

EXAMPLE 4.   Without using tables, prove that

$$\sqrt{2} + \sqrt{6} < \sqrt{3} + \sqrt{5}. \tag{12}$$

SOLUTION.   We give the analysis. Squaring both sides of (12) yields

$$2 + 2\sqrt{2}\,\sqrt{6} + 6 < 3 + 2\sqrt{3}\,\sqrt{5} + 5 \tag{13}$$

or on subtracting 8 from both sides and dividing by 2,

$$\sqrt{12} < \sqrt{15}. \tag{14}$$

But since $12 < 15$, the inequality (14) is obviously valid (Theorem 9). To prove the inequality (12) we start with the remark that $12 < 15$ and reverse the above steps.

EXERCISE 1

In problems 1 through 12 prove the given inequality under the assumption that all of the variables involved are positive. Determine the conditions under which the equality sign occurs.

1. $a + \dfrac{1}{a} \geqq 2.$

2. $\dfrac{a}{5b} + \dfrac{5b}{4a} \geqq 1.$

3. $\sqrt{\dfrac{c}{d}} + \sqrt{\dfrac{d}{c}} \geqq 2.$

4. $(c + d)^2 \geqq 4cd.$

5. $\dfrac{a + b}{2} \geqq \sqrt{ab} \geqq \dfrac{2ab}{a + b}.$

6. $(a + 5b)(a + 2b) \geqq 9b(a + b).$

7. $x^2 + 4y^2 \geqq 4xy.$

8. $x^2 + y^2 + z^2 \geqq xy + yz + zx.$

9. $\dfrac{c^2}{d^2} + \dfrac{d^2}{c^2} + 6 \geqq \dfrac{4c}{d} + \dfrac{4d}{c}.$

10. $\dfrac{a + 3b}{3b} \geqq \dfrac{4a}{a + 3b}.$

11. $cd(c + d) \leqq c^3 + d^3.$ **12.** $4ABCD \leqq (AB + CD)(AC + BD).$

13. Which of the above inequalities are still meaningful and valid if the variables are permitted to assume negative values also?

In problems 14 through 17 determine which quantity is the larger without using tables.

14. $\sqrt{19} + \sqrt{21},\quad \sqrt{17} + \sqrt{23}.$

15. $\sqrt{11} - \sqrt{8},\quad \sqrt{17} - \sqrt{15}.$

16. $\sqrt{17} + 4\sqrt{5},\quad 5\sqrt{7}.$

17. $2\sqrt{2},\quad \sqrt[3]{23}.$

18. Prove that if $1 < k < n$, then

$$\sqrt{n - k} + \sqrt{n + k} < \sqrt{n - 1} + \sqrt{n + 1}.$$

19. Prove that the inequality of example 2 (equation (5)) is valid even if some or all of the variables are negative.

In problems 20 through 25 find the values of x for which the given inequality is valid.

20. $10x - 15 < 7(x - 3).$ **21.** $2x - 19 < 11(x - 2).$

22. $x(x - 1) > 0.$ **23.** $(x - 8)(x - 1) < 0.$

24. $x^2 - 8x + 24 < 9.$ **25.** $4x^2 - 13x + 4 < 1.$

26. Prove that if $a < b$, then $a < \dfrac{a + b}{2} < b.$

27. By definition the absolute value of x, written $|x|$, is x when x is positive or zero, and is $-x$ if x is negative.

Prove that for any two numbers x and y

$$|x + y| \leqq |x| + |y|,$$

$$|x - y| \geqq |x| - |y|.$$

28. Find the values of x for which the following inequalities are satisfied:

a. $\dfrac{1}{x - 2} > 100,$ **b.** $\dfrac{1}{|x - 2|} > 100,$

c. $\dfrac{1}{(x - 5)^4} > 625,$ **d.** $\dfrac{1}{x^2 - x - 90} > 4.$

2

APPENDIX

MATHEMATICAL INDUCTION

1.   An example. Let us try to add together the first n odd positive integers, where n is any integer.   By direct computation we find that:

if $n = 1$	$1 = 1$	$= 1^2$,
if $n = 2$	$1 + 3 = 4$	$= 2^2$,
if $n = 3$	$1 + 3 + 5 = 9$	$= 3^2$,
if $n = 4$	$1 + 3 + 5 + 7 = 16$	$= 4^2$,
if $n = 5$	$1 + 3 + 5 + 7 + 9 = 25$	$= 5^2$,
if $n = 6$	$1 + 3 + 5 + 7 + 9 + 11 = 36$	$= 6^2$.

An examination of these cases leads us to believe that the sum is always the square of the number of terms in the sum.   To express this symbolically we should observe that if n is the number of terms, it seems as though $2n - 1$ is the last term in the sum.   To check this we notice that:

if $n = 1$	$2n - 1 = 2 - 1 = 1$,
if $n = 2$	$2n - 1 = 4 - 1 = 3$,
if $n = 3$	$2n - 1 = 6 - 1 = 5$,
if $n = 4$	$2n - 1 = 8 - 1 = 7$,

and so on.   Thus we can express our assertion for general n by the equation.

$$1 + 3 + 5 + 7 + \cdots + (2n - 1) = n^2. \qquad (1)$$

because the nth odd integer is $2n - 1$.

2.   A digression. Equation (1) has a set of three dots ($\cdots$) which may be strange to the reader.   The meaning of these three dots is quite simple.   They mean that the terms of the sum continue in the manner indicated by the first few written, until the last term, $2n - 1$, is reached and then the series stops.   Why do we use the three dots?   Simply because it is shorter.   Thus if $2n - 1 = 99$ in equation (1) we would waste considerable time in writing all of the terms.   If $2n - 1 = 9,999,999$ in equation (1) it would take about 58 days to write all of the terms of the sum, writing at the rate of one number per second, and not stopping to eat or sleep. But our assertion is that the equation (1) is valid for any n. It would be impossible to express this idea properly if we did not have some notation like the three dots.

3. **Some counterexamples.** We have already seen by direct calculation that equation (1) holds when $2n - 1$ has any one of the values 1, 3, 5, 7, 9, and 11. Does this mean that equation (1) is valid for any positive odd integer $2n - 1$? Can we settle this by continuing our numerical work? We might try the case when $2n - 1 = 23$, so that $n = 12$. Direct computation shows that:

$$1 + 3 + 5 + 7 + 9 + 11 + 13 + 15 + 17 + 19 + 21 + 23 = 144 = 12^2,$$

so that again our formula (1) seems to hold. One might be tempted to say that since the terminal odd number 23 was selected at random this proves that (1) is valid for every possible choice of the terminal number. Actually, no matter how many cases we check, we can never prove that (1) is always valid, because there are infinitely many cases, and no amount of pure computation can settle them all. What is needed is some *logical* argument that will prove that (1) is always valid. Before we give the details of this logical argument, we will give some examples of assertions which can be checked experimentally for small values of n, but which after careful investigation turned out to be *false* for certain other values of n.

Let us first examine the numbers A of the form

$$A = 2^{2^n} + 1. \tag{2}$$

We find by direct computation that:

$$
\begin{array}{lll}
\text{if } n = 0 & A = 2^1 + 1 = 3, \\
\text{if } n = 1 & A = 2^2 + 1 = 5, \\
\text{if } n = 2 & A = 2^4 + 1 = 17, \\
\text{if } n = 3 & A = 2^8 + 1 = 257, \\
\text{if } n = 4 & A = 2^{16} + 1 = 65{,}537.
\end{array}
$$

Each of these values for A is a prime, i.e., an integer (whole number) which has no divisor other than itself and one (with the quotient also an integer). Can we assert on the bases of these five examples, that A is always prime for every positive integer n? Of course not. We might conjecture (guess) that this is true but we should not make a positive assertion, unless we can supply a proof valid for all n. In fact Fermat (1601–65) the great French mathematician did conjecture exactly that, but about a hundred years later Euler (1707–83) the great Swiss mathematician showed that for

$n = 5$, $A = 2^{2^5} + 1 = 4{,}294{,}967{,}297 = 641 \times 6{,}700{,}417$ and hence A is not a prime for $n = 5$.

Next consider the inequality

$$2^n < n^{10} + 2. \tag{3}$$

If we put in values for n we find that:

if $n = 1$ we have $2 < 1 + 2 = 3$,
if $n = 2$ we have $4 < 1024 + 2 = 1026$,
if $n = 3$ we have $8 < 59{,}051$,
if $n = 4$ we have $16 < 1{,}048{,}578$.

It certainly looks as though the inequality (3) is valid for every positive integer n.   If we try a large value of n, say $n = 20$, then the inequality (3) asserts that

$$126{,}976 < 10{,}240{,}000{,}000{,}002$$

which is certainly true.   But even this computation does not prove that (3) is always valid, and in fact such an assertion is *false*.   For if we set $n = 59$ we find that (approximately)

$$2^{59} = 5.764 \times 10^{17} \quad \text{and} \quad 59^{10} + 2 = 5.111 \times 10^{17}.$$

In fact it is not hard to prove that for every $n \geq 59$ *the inequality (3) is false.*

We give one more example, which although trivial, still illustrates our central point.   We make the assertion that

"Every positive integer n is less than 1,000,001."

This is obviously false, and yet if we begin by setting first $n = 1$, then $n = 2$, then $n = 3, \cdots$, it is clear that for the first million cases that we check, the assertion is true.   The falsity is not revealed until we set $n = 1{,}000{,}001$.   Although this example may seem artificial, it is not difficult to give quite natural examples of the same phenomenon, although such examples would necessarily be more complicated.

We can not conclude that an assertion involving an integer n is true for all positive values of the integer n, merely by checking specific values of n, no matter how many we check.

4.   The general principle.   Let us use the symbol $P(n)$ (read "P of n") to denote some proposition which depends on n.   For example $P(n)$ might denote the proposition that

$$1 + 3 + 5 + 7 + \cdots + (2n - 1) = n^2 \tag{1}$$

Suppose that $P(n)$ is not always true, i.e., suppose there is some positive integer n for which the proposition is false.   Then obviously there is some smallest positive integer with the same property, i.e., if we denote this smallest positive integer by $k + 1$, then there is an integer k such that $P(k)$ is true and $P(k + 1)$ is false. If we want to prove that this *cannot occur* then we must prove that: whenever the proposition is true for the integer k then it is also true for the integer $k + 1$. If we have proved this, then it cannot happen that $P(k)$ is true and at the same time $P(k + 1)$ is false.

Finally among the set of all positive integers k, 1 is the smallest. The proposition might be meaningless for $k = 0$, and hence this exceptional case would not be covered by the preceding argument. Thus to prove that $P(n)$ is true for all positive integers, we must also prove it when $n = 1$.

Thus the proof that $P(n)$ is valid for all positive integers can be given in two steps, and these two steps together form the

Principle of mathematical induction. *If for a given assertion $P(n)$ we can prove that:*

1°. *The assertion is true for $n = 1$,*
2°. *If it is true for index $n = k$, then it is also true for index $n = k + 1$,*

then the assertion is true for every positive integer n.

We have already proved this principle in our preceding discussion. We now illustrate the use of this principle by proving the assertion embodied in equation (1).

1°. We have already seen that equation (1) is true when $n = 1$.
2°. We now assume that $P(n)$ is true for the index $n = k$, i.e., we assume that indeed

$$1 + 3 + 5 + \cdots + (2k - 1) = k^2. \tag{4}$$

To obtain the sum of the first $k + 1$ odd integers we merely add the next odd one, $2k + 1$, to both sides of (4). This gives

$$\begin{aligned}1 + 3 + 5 + \cdots + (2k - 1) + (2k + 1) &= k^2 + 2k + 1 \\ &= (k + 1)^2.\end{aligned}$$

But this equation is precisely equation (1) when the index n is $k + 1$, and hence we have shown that if the assertion is true for index k it is also true for index $k + 1$.

By the principle of mathematical induction this completes the proof that equation (1) is valid for every positive integer n.

5. Further examples. We next prove that for every positive integer n

$$\frac{1}{1 \cdot 2} + \frac{1}{2 \cdot 3} + \frac{1}{3 \cdot 4} + \cdots + \frac{1}{n(n + 1)} = \frac{n}{n + 1}. \tag{5}$$

1°.   For $n = 1$ the assertion of equation (5) is that

$$\frac{1}{1 \cdot 2} = \frac{1}{1 + 1}$$

and this is certainly the case.

2°.   We assume that (5) is valid for index k.   Thus we assume that

$$\frac{1}{1 \cdot 2} + \frac{1}{2 \cdot 3} + \frac{1}{3 \cdot 4} + \cdots + \frac{1}{k(k + 1)} = \frac{k}{k + 1}. \tag{6}$$

To obtain the left side of equation (5) for the index $n = k + 1$, we must add $1/(k + 1)(k + 2)$ to the left side of equation (6).   This gives

$$\frac{1}{1 \cdot 2} + \frac{1}{2 \cdot 3} + \frac{1}{3 \cdot 4} + \cdots \tag{7}$$

$$+ \frac{1}{k(k + 1)} + \frac{1}{(k + 1)(k + 2)} = \frac{k}{k + 1} + \frac{1}{(k + 1)(k + 2)}$$

$$= \frac{k(k + 2) + 1}{(k + 1)(k + 2)}$$

$$= \frac{k^2 + 2k + 1}{(k + 1)(k + 2)} = \frac{(k + 1)^2}{(k + 1)(k + 2)}$$

$$= \frac{k + 1}{(k + 1) + 1}.$$

But this is just equation (5) when the index n is $k + 1$.   Hence by the principle of mathematical induction (5) is valid for every positive integer n.

An assertion $P(n)$ may be false or meaningless for certain small values of n.   In this case the assertion would necessarily be modified to state only what is actually true.   Then the principle of mathematical induction would also be altered to meet the situation.   Thus in step 1 of the process we would not set $n = 1$, but we would use instead the smallest integer for which the assertion is true.   For example, let us investigate the inequality

$$2^n > 2n + 1. \tag{8}$$

For $n = 1$ this states that $2 > 3$ and this is false.

For $n = 2$ this states that $4 > 5$ and this is also false.

But for $n = 3$, the inequality asserts that $8 > 7$ and this is true.

Now assume that (8) is valid for the index $n = k$ where $k > 2$.   Since $2^k > 2$ we may add these terms to the assumed inequality $2^k > 2k + 1$ without disturbing the inequality.   We find that

$$2^k + 2^k > 2k + 1 + 2$$
$$2 \cdot 2^k > 2(k + 1) + 1$$
$$2^{k+1} > 2(k + 1) + 1.$$

But this is just the inequality (8) when the index n is $k + 1$. Hence, using the principle of mathematical induction we have proved that *the inequality (8) is valid for every integer $n \geq 3$.*

EXERCISE 1

In problems 1 through 14 prove that the assertion is true for all positive integers n.

1. The nth positive even integer is $2n$.

2. The nth positive odd integer is $2n - 1$.

3. $1 + 2 + 3 + 4 + \cdots + n = \dfrac{n(n + 1)}{2}$.

4. $1^2 + 2^2 + 3^2 + 4^2 + \cdots + n^2 = \dfrac{n(n + 1)(2n + 1)}{6}$.

5. $1 \cdot 2 + 2 \cdot 3 + 3 \cdot 4 + \cdots + n(n + 1) = \dfrac{n(n + 1)(n + 2)}{3}$.

6. $1^2 + 3^2 + 5^2 + \cdots + (2n - 1)^2 = \dfrac{n(2n - 1)(2n + 1)}{3}$.

7. $1^3 + 2^3 + 3^3 + \cdots + n^3 = \dfrac{n^2(n + 1)^2}{4}$.

8. $\dfrac{1}{1 \cdot 3} + \dfrac{1}{3 \cdot 5} + \dfrac{1}{5 \cdot 7} + \cdots + \dfrac{1}{(2n - 1)(2n + 1)} = \dfrac{n}{2n + 1}$.

9. $\dfrac{1}{1 \cdot 4} + \dfrac{1}{4 \cdot 7} + \dfrac{1}{7 \cdot 10} + \cdots + \dfrac{1}{(3n - 2)(3n + 1)} = \dfrac{n}{3n + 1}$.

10. $1 + x + x^2 + \cdots + x^n = \dfrac{x^{n+1} - 1}{x - 1}$, if $x \neq 1$.

11. $\dfrac{1}{x(x+1)} + \dfrac{1}{(x+1)(x+2)} + \cdots + \dfrac{1}{(x+n-1)(x+n)} = \dfrac{n}{x(x+n)}$, if $x > 0$.

★12. $\dfrac{1}{n} + \dfrac{1}{n + 1} + \dfrac{1}{n + 2} + \cdots + \dfrac{1}{2n - 1} = 1 - \dfrac{1}{2} + \dfrac{1}{3} - \dfrac{1}{4} + \cdots + \dfrac{1}{2n - 1}$.

★13. $1^3 + 2^3 + 3^3 + \cdots + n^3 = (1 + 2 + 3 + \cdots + n)^2$.

14. $1 \cdot 3 + 3 \cdot 5 + 5 \cdot 7 + \cdots + (2n - 1)(2n + 1) = \dfrac{n(4n^2 + 6n - 1)}{3}$.

15. For which positive integers n is $2^n > n^2$?

16. For which positive integers n is $2^n > n^3$?

17. Prove that if $x > -1$ and n is an integer greater than 1, then $(1 + x)^n > 1 + nx$.

18. Prove that for $n \geq 2$

$$\dfrac{1}{n + 1} + \dfrac{1}{n + 2} + \dfrac{1}{n + 3} + \cdots + \dfrac{1}{2n} > \dfrac{13}{24}.$$

19. Prove that $1 + 5 + 9 + \cdots + 4n - 3 = n(2n - 1)$.

20. Prove that $3 \cdot 4 + 4 \cdot 7 + 5 \cdot 10 + \cdots + (n + 2)(3n + 1) = n(n + 2)(n + 3)$.

21. Prove the formula for the sum of the terms of an arithmetical progression

$$a + (a + d) + (a + 2d) + \cdots + (a + (n - 1)d) = n\left(a + \frac{(n - 1)d}{2}\right).$$

Apply this formula to obtain the formulas of problems 3 and 19.

22. Prove that $2 \cdot 2 + 3 \cdot 2^2 + 4 \cdot 2^3 + \cdots + (n + 1)2^n = n2^{n+1}$.

23. Prove that $x + y$ divides $x^{2n-1} + y^{2n-1}$ for each positive integer n.

★24. Prove that if $x \neq \pm 1$, then

$$\frac{1}{1 + x} + \frac{2}{1 + x^2} + \frac{4}{1 + x^4} + \cdots + \frac{2^n}{1 + x^{2^n}} = \frac{1}{x - 1} + \frac{2^{n+1}}{1 - x^{2^{n+1}}}.$$

3

APPENDIX

LIMITS AND CONTINUOUS FUNCTIONS

In this appendix we give the proofs of theorems 1 through 5 of chapter 2. We then use these theorems to prove a number of related theorems on continuous functions.

THEOREM 1. *If*

$$\lim_{x \to a} f(x) = L \qquad and \qquad \lim_{x \to a} g(x) = M \tag{1}$$

then

$$\lim_{x \to a} (f(x) + g(x)) = L + M. \tag{2}$$

PROOF. By the definition of a limit we are to prove that for each $\epsilon > 0$, there is a $\delta > 0$ such that if $0 < |x - a| < \delta$, then

$$|f(x) + g(x) - (L + M)| < \epsilon.$$

This is the meaning of equation (2). By hypothesis $\lim_{x \to a} f(x) = L$. Hence there is a $\delta_1 > 0$ such that

$$|f(x) - L| < \frac{\epsilon}{2}, \qquad \text{if } 0 < |x - a| < \delta_1. \tag{3}$$

Similarly, by hypothesis $\lim_{x \to a} g(x) = M$, hence there is a $\delta_2 > 0$ such that

$$|g(x) - M| < \frac{\epsilon}{2}, \qquad \text{if } 0 < |x - a| < \delta_2. \tag{4}$$

Now let δ be the minimum of the two numbers δ_1 and δ_2. If $0 < |x - a| < \delta$, then both (3) and (4) are satisfied simultaneously. Consequently we can write

$$|f(x) + g(x) - (L + M)| = |f(x) - L + g(x) - M|$$
$$\leq |f(x) - L| + |g(x) - M| < \frac{\epsilon}{2} + \frac{\epsilon}{2} = \epsilon,$$

if $0 < |x - a| < \delta$.   But this is the meaning of equation (2).   Q.E.D.

THEOREM 2.   *If* $\lim\limits_{x \to a} f(x) = L$ *and c is any constant then*

$$\lim_{x \to a} cf(x) = cL.$$

PROOF.   This theorem is a special case of Theorem 3 (below) when $g(x)$ is just the constant c for all x.   Consequently Theorem 2 is established as soon as we prove Theorem 3.

THEOREM 3.   *If*

$$\lim_{x \to a} f(x) = L \qquad \text{and} \qquad \lim_{x \to a} g(x) = M \tag{1}$$

then

$$\lim_{x \to a} f(x)\, g(x) = LM. \tag{5}$$

PROOF.   We use the algebraic identity

$$f(x)\, g(x) - LM = [f(x) - L]g(x) + [g(x) - M]L. \tag{6}$$

On taking the absolute value of both sides we have

$$|f(x)\, g(x) - LM| \le |f(x) - L\|g(x)| + |g(x) - M\|L|. \tag{7}$$

If $\epsilon > 0$ is given, our objective is to make each of the two terms on the right side of (7) less than $\epsilon/2$, when x is suitably restricted.   First suppose that $L \ne 0$ and $M \ne 0$.   Then there is a $\delta_1 > 0$, such that

$$|g(x)| < 2|M|, \qquad \text{if } 0 < |x - a| < \delta_1. \tag{8}$$

By the hypothesis that $\lim\limits_{x \to a} f(x) = L$, there is a $\delta_2 > 0$ such that

$$|f(x) - L| < \frac{\epsilon}{4|M|}, \qquad \text{if } 0 < |x - a| < \delta_2. \tag{9}$$

Finally by the hypothesis that $\lim\limits_{x \to a} g(x) = M$, there is a $\delta_3 > 0$ such that

$$|g(x) - M| < \frac{\epsilon}{2|L|}, \qquad \text{if } 0 < |x - a| < \delta_3 \tag{10}$$

Now let δ be the minimum of the three numbers δ_1, δ_2, and δ_3.   Then if $0 < |x - a| < \delta$, all three of the inequalities (8), (9), and (10) are simultaneously satisfied.   Therefore for such x the right side of (7) gives

$$|f(x) - L\|g(x)| + |g(x) - M\|L| < \frac{\epsilon}{4|M|}\, 2|M| + \frac{\epsilon}{2|L|}\, |L| = \frac{\epsilon}{2} + \frac{\epsilon}{2} = \epsilon. \tag{11}$$

Hence from (7) and (11) we have

$$|f(x)\, g(x) - LM| < \epsilon, \qquad \text{if } 0 < |x - a| < \delta. \tag{12}$$

But this is the meaning of equation (5). This proves Theorem 3 if $L \neq 0$ and $M \neq 0$. If $L = 0$ and $M \neq 0$, the second term on the right side of (7) may be dropped since it is zero. The inequality (10) is not needed and the rest of the proof is just as before. If $M = 0$, then in (8) and (9) we replace $|M|$ by 1. Consequently the first term on the right side of (7) gives

$$|f(x) - L||g(x)| < \frac{\epsilon}{4} 2 = \frac{\epsilon}{2}, \qquad \text{if } 0 < |x - a| < \delta.$$

The second term $|g(x) - M||L|$ is handled just as before in the two cases $L \neq 0$, and $L = 0$. Thus in all cases we obtain (12). Q.E.D.

THEOREM 4. *If*

$$\lim_{x \to a} f(x) = L \qquad and \qquad \lim_{x \to a} g(x) = M \tag{1}$$

and if $M \neq 0$, then

$$\lim_{x \to a} \frac{f(x)}{g(x)} = \frac{L}{M}. \tag{13}$$

PROOF. We use the algebraic identity

$$\frac{f(x)}{g(x)} - \frac{L}{M} = \frac{[f(x) - L]M + L[M - g(x)]}{Mg(x)}. \tag{14}$$

On taking the absolute value of both sides we have

$$\left| \frac{f(x)}{g(x)} - \frac{L}{M} \right| \leqq \frac{|f(x) - L||M| + |L||M - g(x)|}{|M||g(x)|}. \tag{15}$$

If $\epsilon > 0$ is given, our objective is to make the right side of (15) less than ϵ. By hypothesis $M \neq 0$, hence there is a δ_1 such that

$$\tfrac{1}{2}|M| < |g(x)| < 2|M|, \qquad \text{if } 0 < |x - a| < \delta_1. \tag{16}$$

Further by the hypothesis on $f(x)$ there is a $\delta_2 > 0$ such that

$$|f(x) - L| < \frac{M^2 \epsilon}{2(|L| + |M|)}, \qquad \text{if } 0 < |x - a| < \delta_2. \tag{17}$$

Finally by the hypothesis on $g(x)$ there is a $\delta_3 > 0$, such that

$$|g(x) - M| < \frac{M^2 \epsilon}{2(|L| + |M|)}, \qquad \text{if } 0 < |x - a| < \delta_3. \tag{18}$$

Now let δ be the minimum of the three numbers δ_1, δ_2, and δ_3. Then if $0 < |x - a| < \delta$ all three of the inequalities (16), (17), and (18) are simultaneously satisfied.   Therefore for such x the right side of (15) gives

$$\frac{|f(x) - L\|M| + |L\|M - g(x)|}{|M\|g(x)|} < \frac{\frac{M^2\epsilon|M|}{2(|L|+|M|)} + \frac{|L|M^2\epsilon}{2(|L|+|M|)}}{\frac{1}{2}M^2} \qquad (19)$$

$$< \frac{M^2\epsilon(|M|+|L|)}{2(|L|+|M|)} \cdot \frac{2}{M^2} = \epsilon.$$

Hence from (15) and (19) we have

$$\left|\frac{f(x)}{g(x)} - \frac{L}{M}\right| < \epsilon, \qquad \text{if } 0 < |x - a| < \delta. \qquad (20)$$

But this is the meaning of (13).   Q.E.D.

THEOREM 5. $\lim_{x\to a} x = a.$

PROOF.   We are to prove that if $\epsilon > 0$ is given, then there is a $\delta > 0$ such that

$$|x - a| < \epsilon, \qquad \text{if } 0 < |x - a| < \delta. \qquad (21)$$

To do this we merely select δ to be ϵ and then (21) is obviously true, because it then states that $|x - a| < \epsilon$ if $0 < |x - a| < \epsilon$.   Q.E.D.

Now let us recall the definition of a continuous function given in Chapter 2 (page 52).

DEFINITION 2.   *A function $y = f(x)$ is said to be continuous at $x = a$ if*

(A) $y = f(x)$ is defined at $x = a$,
(B) $\lim_{x\to a} f(x)$ is a real number,
(C) $\lim_{x\to a} f(x) = f(a).$

As we mentioned in Chapter 2, only **C** is really necessary, because the symbol $f(a)$ already implies that the function $f(x)$ is defined at $x = a$, and the form of writing **C** already implies that there is a limit.

Now the definition of limit applied to **C** states that **C** is satisfied if and only if for each given $\epsilon > 0$, there is a $\delta > 0$ such that

$$|f(x) - f(a)| < \epsilon, \qquad \text{if } 0 < |x - a| < \delta. \qquad (22)$$

The effect of the condition $0 < |x - a|$ is to prevent x from assuming the value $x = a$.   But here no harm is done if $x = a$ because $f(x)$ is defined at $x = a$. Further when $x = a$, the first part of (22) becomes $|f(a) - f(a)| = 0$, and this is certainly less than ϵ. Consequently in defining a continuous function, we can drop the zero in the last part of (22). This gives the following alternate definition of a continuous function in terms of ϵ—δ.

> DEFINITION 2★. *A function $f(x)$ is said to be continuous at $x = a$, if for each given $\epsilon > 0$ there is a $\delta > 0$ such that*
>
> $$|f(x) - f(a)| < \epsilon, \qquad \text{if } |x - a| < \delta. \tag{23}$$

The reader should note carefully the very slight difference between (22) and (23). We have proved that if $f(x)$ satisfies the conditions of Definition 2, it satisfies the conditions of Definition 2★. We leave it to the student to prove conversely that if $f(x)$ satisfies the conditions of Definition 2★ then it satisfies the conditions of Definition 2. Consequently the two definitions are equivalent.

> THEOREM 1★. *If $f(x)$ and $g(x)$ are two functions each continuous at $x = a$, then their sum $f(x) + g(x)$ is continuous at $x = a$.*

PROOF. Using Definition 2★ for a continuous function, the proof has exactly the same structure as the proof of Theorem 1 on limits. In that theorem and proof replace L by $f(a)$, replace M by $g(a)$, and whenever the condition $0 < |x - a| < \delta$ (or δ_1, or δ_2) occurs just drop the symbols "$0 <$". These changes will give Theorem 1★ and its proof. It is a good exercise for the student to carry out this program, writing out the proof in full detail.

The same replacements and deletions in Theorems 3, 4, and 5 will give Theorems 3★, 4★, and 5★ together with their proofs. Theorem 2★ is a corollary of Theorem 3★. We recommend that the student write out the proofs.

> THEOREM 2★. *If $f(x)$ is continuous at $x = a$ and c is any constant, then $cf(x)$ is continuous at $x = a$.*

> THEOREM 3★. *If $f(x)$ and $g(x)$ are continuous at $x = a$, then their product $f(x)\,g(x)$ is continuous at $x = a$.*

> THEOREM 4★. *If $f(x)$ and $g(x)$ are continuous at $x = a$, and if $g(a) \neq 0$, then their quotient $f(x)/g(x)$ is continuous at $x = a$.*

> THEOREM 5★. *The function $f(x) = x$ is continuous for all values of x.*

> THEOREM 6★. *The function $f(x) = c$, the constant function, is continuous for all values of x.*

This theorem is trivial, and the proof is simple.   In fact equation (23) demands that $|c - c| < \epsilon$ and this is always true no matter what δ we select.

We now apply these theorems to prove

THEOREM 7★.   *Any polynomial*

$$P(x) = a_0 x^n + a_1 x^{n-1} + a_2 x^{n-2} + \cdots + a_{n-1} x + a_n \qquad (24)$$

is a continuous function for all values of x.

PROOF.   By Theorems 5★ and 3★ the product $x \cdot x = x^2$ is continuous for all values of x.   By Theorem 3★ applied to x and x^2, their product x^3 is again continuous.   Proceeding stepwise (or using mathematical induction) it is clear that x^k is a continuous function for each positive integer k. Then by Theorem 2★ the function cx^k is continuous for any constant c. Finally by a repeated application of Theorem 1★ (or by mathematical induction) the sum (24) is continuous for all values of x.   Q.E.D.

THEOREM 8★.   *If $f(x) = N(x)/D(x)$ where $N(x)$ and $D(x)$ are polynomials then $f(x)$ is continuous for any value of x for which $D(x) \neq 0$.*

PROOF.   By Theorem 7★ $N(x)$ and $D(x)$ are continuous and by Theorem 4★ their quotient is continuous whenever $D(x) \neq 0$.

Finally of a slightly different nature we have

THEOREM 9★.   *If $f(x)$ is differentiable at $x = a$, then it is continuous at $x = a$.*

PROOF.   The assumption that $f(x)$ is differentiable means that

$$\lim_{x \to a} \frac{f(x) - f(a)}{x - a} = f'(a). \qquad (25)$$

Equation (25) can be written in the form

$$\frac{f(x) - f(a)}{x - a} = f'(a) + \epsilon(x) \qquad (26)$$

where $\epsilon(x)$ is small and $\epsilon(x) \to 0$ as $x \to a$.   Solving (26) for $f(x)$ we have

$$f(x) = f(a) + (x - a)(f'(a) + \epsilon(x)). \qquad (27)$$

From (27) it is obvious that $f(x) \to f(a)$ as $x \to a$.

4

APPENDIX

THEOREMS ON SEQUENCES

The following theorems on sequences are fundamental in the theory of infinite series.   Both the statements and the proofs are similar to those given in Appendix 3 on limits.

> DEFINITION.   *A sequence $S_1, S_2, S_3, \cdots, S_n, \cdots$ is said to converge to a limit S if for each $\epsilon > 0$ there is an N such that*
>
> $$|S_n - S| < \epsilon, \qquad \text{if } n > N, \tag{1}$$
>
> *and we write $\lim_{n \to \infty} S_n = S$.   We also write $S_n \to S$ as $n \to \infty$.*

> THEOREM 1.   *If $S_1, S_2, \cdots, S_n, \cdots$ and $T_1, T_2, \cdots, T_n, \cdots$ are two infinite sequences and if*
>
> $$\lim_{n \to \infty} S_n = S, \qquad and \qquad \lim_{n \to \infty} T_n = T, \tag{2}$$
>
> *then*
>
> $$\lim_{n \to \infty} (S_n + T_n) = S + T. \tag{3}$$

PROOF.   Let $\epsilon > 0$ be given.   Since $S_n \to S$ as $n \to \infty$ there is an N_1 such that

$$|S_n - S| < \frac{\epsilon}{2}, \qquad \text{if } n > N_1. \tag{4}$$

Similarly since $T_n \to T$ as $n \to \infty$ there is an N_2 such that

$$|T_n - T| < \frac{\epsilon}{2}, \qquad \text{if } n > N_2. \tag{5}$$

Now let N be the maximum of the two numbers N_1 and N_2.   If $n > N$

then both (4) and (5) are satisfied simultaneously. Consequently if $n > N$, then

$$|S_n + T_n - (S + T)| = |S_n - S + T_n - T|$$
$$\leqq |S_n - S| + |T_n - T|$$
$$< \frac{\epsilon}{2} + \frac{\epsilon}{2} = \epsilon$$

But this is the meaning of equation (3).   Q.E.D.

THEOREM 2.   *If $S_n \to S$ as $n \to \infty$ and c is any constant, then $cS_n \to cS$ as $n \to \infty$.*

PROOF.   This theorem is a special case of Theorem 3 (below) when the elements of the sequence, $T_1, T_2, \cdots, T_n, \cdots$ are all equal to the constant c.   In this case it is obvious that the sequence $T_1, T_2, \cdots$ converges and the limit T is c.

THEOREM 3.   *If $S_n \to S$ as $n \to \infty$ and if $T_n \to T$ as $n \to \infty$, then*

$$\lim_{n \to \infty} S_n T_n = ST. \tag{6}$$

PROOF.   We use the algebraic identity

$$S_n T_n - ST = (S_n - S)T_n + (T_n - T)S. \tag{7}$$

On taking absolute values of both sides we have

$$|S_n T_n - ST| \leqq |S_n - S||T_n| + |T_n - T||S|. \tag{8}$$

Let $\epsilon > 0$ be given and suppose that $S \neq 0$ and $T \neq 0$.   Then there is an N_1 such that

$$|T_n| < 2|T|, \qquad \text{if } n > N_1. \tag{9}$$

By the hypothesis that $S_n \to S$ as $n \to \infty$, there is an N_2 such that

$$|S_n - S| < \frac{\epsilon}{4|T|}, \qquad \text{if } n > N_2. \tag{10}$$

Finally by the hypothesis that $T_n \to T$ as $n \to \infty$, there is an N_3 such that

$$|T_n - T| < \frac{\epsilon}{2|S|}, \qquad \text{if } n > N_3. \tag{11}$$

Now let N be the maximum of the three numbers N_1, N_2, and N_3.   If $n > N$, then all three of the inequalities (9), (10), and (11) are simultaneously satisfied. Therefore for $n > N$, the right side of (8) gives

$$|S_n - S||T_n| + |T_n - T||S| < \frac{\epsilon}{4|T|} 2|T| + \frac{\epsilon}{2|S|} |S|$$

$$< \frac{\epsilon}{2} + \frac{\epsilon}{2} = \epsilon. \tag{12}$$

Hence from (8) and (12) we have

$$|S_n T_n - ST| < \epsilon, \qquad \text{if } n > N. \tag{13}$$

This is the meaning of (6), and the proof is complete in the case that $S \neq 0$ and $T \neq 0$. The proof in the exceptional cases is simple and parallels that given for Theorem 3 in Appendix 3 and so we omit it.

THEOREM 4. *If* $S_n \to S$ *as* $n \to \infty$ *and* $T_n \to T$ *as* $n \to \infty$, *and if* $T \neq 0$, *then*

$$\lim_{n \to \infty} \frac{S_n}{T_n} = \frac{S}{T} \tag{14}$$

PROOF. Just as in the proofs of Theorems 1, 2, and 3, this proof also follows the pattern of the proof of the corresponding theorem on limits of functions given in Appendix 3, so we omit the details. The interested student may write out the proof, starting with the one given in Appendix 3 and making the following replacements as indicated by the arrows: $f(x) \to S_n$, $g(x) \to T_n$, $L \to S$, $M \to T$, $0 < |x - a| < \delta \to n > N$, etc.

5

APPENDIX

DETERMINANTS

1.   Pairs of linear equations in two unknowns.   The problem of solving systems of several linear equations in several variables occurs so often in mathematics that it is worthwhile to have a systematic method for handling such problems.   We begin by considering in detail the solution of the particular pair of equations in two unknowns,

$$2x + 3y = 12 \tag{1}$$

$$4x - 5y = 2. \tag{2}$$

If we multiply equation (1) by 2 and then subtract equation (2) we obtain

$$
\begin{aligned}
2(2x + 3y) = 2 \cdot 12 \ &\rightarrow\quad 4x + 6y \ = \ 24 \\
-1(4x - 5y) = -1 \cdot 2 \ &\rightarrow\quad \underline{-4x + 5y \ = \ -2} \\
&\qquad\ 0 + 11y = \quad 22, \ \rightarrow\ y = 2.
\end{aligned}
$$

Using $y = 2$ in either (1) or (2) gives $x = 3$.   We have proved that if our system has a solution it is $x = 3$, $y = 2$.   It is a simple matter to put these numbers in (1) and (2) and show that they do indeed form a solution.

EXERCISE 1

In problems 1 through 8 solve the given pair of linear equations for the two unknowns.   Check your work by substituting the solutions in the given equations.

1. $2x - y = 4$
$5x + 2y = 37.$

2. $3x + 2y = 29$
$5x - 6y = 11.$

3. $3x - 2y = -7$
$5x - y = 7.$

4. $5x + 4y = 1$
$6x + 3y = -6.$

5. $2x + 5y = 7$
$3x + 12y = -3.$

6. $5x - 7y = 9$
$-11x + 5y = 1.$

7. $4z + 3w = 15$
$-z + 4w = 20.$

8. $3A + 2B = 5$
$6A - 8B = 4.$

*★*9. Try to solve the pair of equations $4x - y = 10$, and $8x - 2y = 3$. What seems to be the trouble with these two equations?

*★*10. Show that the pair of equations $4x - y = 10$ and $8x - 2y = 20$ has more than one solution by finding at least two solutions.

11. Now I am 30 years older than my son. In another 5 years I will be 4 times as old as my son. Find our present ages.

12. Mary is now three times as old as John was when John was one half as old as Mary was six years ago. How old are they both now?

13. In a certain chess game there was a lively exchange in which black lost three men, and white lost four men. A kibitzer observed that before the exchange white had twice as many men as black had after the exchange, and that three times the number of white men after the exchange was five more than the number of black men before the exchange. Find the number of men on each side just prior to the exchange.

2.   The general solution of a pair of linear equations in two unknowns.

Let us now solve, once and for all, all systems of two linear equations in two unknowns by developing general formulas for the unknowns. To do this we must replace the particular equations (1) and (2) by general equations in which letters are used for the coefficients in place of numbers. The pair of equations to be considered is

$$a_1 x + b_1 y = c_1, \tag{3}$$

$$a_2 x + b_2 y = c_2, \tag{4}$$

where a_1, b_1, c_1, a_2, b_2, and c_2 are known constants and x and y are the unknowns. Equations (3) and (4) become (1) and (2) when we set $a_1 = 2$, $b_1 = 3$, $c_1 = 12$, $a_2 = 4$, $b_2 = -5$, and $c_2 = 2$.

To solve equations (3) and (4) for x we eliminate y by multiplying (3) by b_2 and (4) by b_1 and subtracting:

$$b_2(a_1 x + b_1 y) = b_2 c_1 \quad \text{or} \quad b_2 a_1 x + b_2 b_1 y = b_2 c_1$$

$$b_1(a_2 x + b_2 y) = b_1 c_2 \quad \text{or} \quad b_1 a_2 x + b_1 b_2 y = b_1 c_2$$

$$\text{Subtracting: } b_2 a_1 x - b_1 a_2 x = b_2 c_1 - b_1 c_2$$

$$(b_2 a_1 - b_1 a_2)x = b_2 c_1 - b_1 c_2.$$

If $b_2 a_1 - b_1 a_2 \neq 0$, then we can divide both sides by this quantity and find

$$x = \frac{b_2 c_1 - b_1 c_2}{b_2 a_1 - b_1 a_2} = \boxed{\frac{c_1 b_2 - b_1 c_2}{a_1 b_2 - b_1 a_2}}. \tag{5}$$

Similarly we can solve equations (3) and (4) for y by eliminating x.   Multiplying (3) by a_2 and (4) by a_1 and subtracting:

$$a_2(a_1x + b_1y) = a_2c_1 \quad \text{or} \quad a_2a_1x + a_2b_1y = a_2c_1$$

$$a_1(a_2x + b_2y) = a_1c_2 \quad \text{or} \quad a_1a_2x + a_1b_2y = a_1c_2$$

Subtracting: $a_2b_1y - a_1b_2y = a_2c_1 - a_1c_2$.

If $a_2b_1 - a_1b_2 \neq 0$, then we can divide both sides by this quantity and find

$$y = \frac{a_2c_1 - a_1c_2}{a_2b_1 - a_1b_2} = \frac{a_1c_2 - c_1a_2}{a_1b_2 - b_1a_2}. \tag{6}$$

The formulas (5) and (6) are the ones we are seeking.   They give the general solution for any pair of linear equations in two unknowns.   However these equations appear to be somewhat complicated and hard to memorize.   In the next section we will see how determinants can be used to give these equations a very simple and pretty form, so that memorization becomes automatic and painless.

3.   Determinants of second order.   A square array of numbers to which a certain numerical value has been attached is called a *determinant*. For convenience the square array is set between vertical lines.   For example the arrays

$$\begin{vmatrix} 1 & 3 \\ 2 & 9 \end{vmatrix}, \quad \begin{vmatrix} 1 & -2 & 7 \\ \sqrt{5} & 6 & -11 \\ -1 & 0 & 1/2 \end{vmatrix}, \quad \begin{vmatrix} \pi & 0 & \sqrt{2} & -7 \\ 0 & 1 & 3 & \sqrt{5} \\ -11 & 19 & 3 & 4 \\ 5 & 19 & 2 & 0 \end{vmatrix}$$

are determinants of second, third, and fourth order respectively.   The *order* of a determinant is the number of numbers in any one row (or column).

How do we attach a numerical value to these arrays?   In this section we will consider the second order determinant, postponing the general case to the next section.

DEFINITION 1.   *The value of a second order determinant is given by the formula*

$$\begin{vmatrix} a_1 & b_1 \\ a_2 & b_2 \end{vmatrix} = a_1b_2 - b_1a_2. \tag{7}$$

The expression on the right is called the expansion of the determinant.

This formula is easy to remember if we observe that we multiply elements on the diagonals and use a plus sign if the diagonal descends from left to right, and a minus sign if the diagonal descends from right to left.

Examples:
$$\begin{vmatrix} 1 & 3 \\ 2 & 9 \end{vmatrix} = 1 \cdot 9 - 3 \cdot 2 = 9 - 6 = 3,$$

$$\begin{vmatrix} 2 & -5 \\ 3 & 7 \end{vmatrix} = 2 \cdot 7 - (-5) \cdot 3 = 14 + 15 = 29,$$

$$\begin{vmatrix} -4 & -3 \\ -6 & \frac{1}{2} \end{vmatrix} = (-4) \cdot \frac{1}{2} - (-3)(-6) = -2 - 18 = -20.$$

We can now use these determinants to put the solution of a pair of linear equations in two unknowns, into a very neat form.

THEOREM 1. *The equation set*

$$a_1 x + b_1 y = c_1 \tag{3}$$

$$a_2 x + b_2 y = c_2 \tag{4}$$

has the solution

$$x = \frac{\begin{vmatrix} c_1 & b_1 \\ c_2 & b_2 \end{vmatrix}}{\begin{vmatrix} a_1 & b_1 \\ a_2 & b_2 \end{vmatrix}}, \quad (8) \qquad y = \frac{\begin{vmatrix} a_1 & c_1 \\ a_2 & c_2 \end{vmatrix}}{\begin{vmatrix} a_1 & b_1 \\ a_2 & b_2 \end{vmatrix}}, \quad (9)$$

provided that the determinant in the denominator is not zero.

It is quite easy to observe the rule for forming the determinants in (8) and (9). The determinant in the denominator is formed by taking the coefficients of x and y in the equation set (3) and (4). The determinant in the numerator of (8) is obtained by replacing the coefficients of x by the constants c_1 and c_2 on the right side of the given equations. In the case of (9) where we are solving for y we replace the coefficients of y by c_1 and c_2 in order to form the numerator. This rule for the formation of the determinants in (8) and (9) is called *Cramer's rule*.

We have already given most of the proof of this theorem in section 2 where we proved that if the equation set (3) and (4) has a solution then

$$x = \frac{c_1b_2 - b_1c_2}{a_1b_2 - b_1a_2}, \quad (5) \quad \text{and} \quad y = \frac{a_1c_2 - c_1a_2}{a_1b_2 - b_1a_2}. \quad (6)$$

But the expressions in (5) and (6) are just the values of the determinants appearing in (8) and (9). To complete the proof, it is necessary to substitute the expressions for x and y given by (8) and (9) (or their equivalents (5) and (6)) back in the original equations (3) and (4) and show that they do indeed satisfy the given equations. This step is left for the reader.

EXAMPLE. Solve the set of equations

$$2x - 3y = 9,$$
$$-x + 9y = -2.$$

Using Cramer's rule (Theorem 1) we have

$$x = \frac{\begin{vmatrix} 9 & -3 \\ -2 & 9 \end{vmatrix}}{\begin{vmatrix} 2 & -3 \\ -1 & 9 \end{vmatrix}} = \frac{9 \cdot 9 - (-3)(-2)}{2 \cdot 9 - (-3)(-1)} = \frac{81 - 6}{18 - 3} = \frac{75}{15} = 5,$$

and

$$y = \frac{\begin{vmatrix} 2 & 9 \\ -1 & -2 \end{vmatrix}}{\begin{vmatrix} 2 & -3 \\ -1 & 9 \end{vmatrix}} = \frac{2(-2) - 9(-1)}{15} = \frac{-4 + 9}{15} = \frac{5}{15} = \frac{1}{3}.$$

As a check we substitute these values for x and y back in the given equation:

$$2 \cdot 5 - 3 \cdot \tfrac{1}{3} = 10 - 1 = 9,$$
$$-5 + 9 \cdot \tfrac{1}{3} = -5 + 3 = -2.$$

EXERCISE 2

1. Solve problems 1 through 8 of Exercise 1 using Cramer's rule and the definition of a determinant.

2. Complete the proof of Theorem 1 by substituting (5) and (6) in equations (3) and (4).

3. Prove that if $b_1 = ka_1$ and $b_2 = ka_2$, then the determinant (7) is zero. In other words if one column is proportional to the other column, then the determinant is zero.

4. Prove that if one row of the determinant (7) is proportional to the other row, then the determinant is zero.

5. Prove that for any constant k

$$\begin{vmatrix} a_1 + kb_1 & b_1 \\ a_2 + kb_2 & b_2 \end{vmatrix} = \begin{vmatrix} a_1 & b_1 \\ a_2 & b_2 \end{vmatrix}.$$

6. Prove that for any constant k

$$\begin{vmatrix} a_1 + ka_2 & b_1 + kb_2 \\ a_2 & b_2 \end{vmatrix} = \begin{vmatrix} a_1 & b_1 \\ a_2 & b_2 \end{vmatrix}.$$

7. Prove that

$$\begin{vmatrix} a_1 & b_1 \\ a_2 & b_2 \end{vmatrix} + \begin{vmatrix} c_1 & b_1 \\ c_2 & b_2 \end{vmatrix} = \begin{vmatrix} a_1 + c_1 & b_1 \\ a_2 + c_2 & b_2 \end{vmatrix}.$$

8. Prove that

$$\begin{vmatrix} a_1 & b_1 \\ a_2 & b_2 \end{vmatrix} = - \begin{vmatrix} b_1 & a_1 \\ b_2 & a_2 \end{vmatrix}.$$

What happens if the rows are interchanged?

4. Third order determinants. We have seen how Cramer's rule helps us to solve quickly any system of two linear equations in two unknowns. If this were the limit of Cramer's rule it would be of little value. The beauty of the rule is that it is applicable to any system of n linear equations in n unknowns. To prove that this is the case we need to develop a theory for determinants of nth order. Let us first consider the third order determinant.

$$D = \begin{vmatrix} a_1 & b_1 & c_1 \\ a_2 & b_2 & c_2 \\ a_3 & b_3 & c_3 \end{vmatrix}. \tag{10}$$

The simplest way to compute D is to repeat the first two columns to the right of the determinant, and then take products along the diagonals as indicated in the following diagram, using a plus sign if the diagonal descends from left to right, and a minus sign if the diagonal descends from right to left.

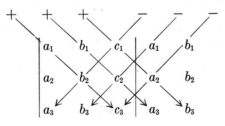

Following this scheme we find for the determinant (10)

$$D = a_1b_2c_3 + a_3b_1c_2 + a_2b_3c_1 - a_3b_2c_1 - a_1b_3c_2 - a_2b_1c_3. \qquad (11)$$

This expression is called the *expansion* of the determinant (10), and gives the *value* of that determinant.   Observe that in (11) we have rearranged the order of the elements in the products so that the letters are in alphabetical order.   The reason for this shuffle will appear later.

EXAMPLE 1.   Evaluate $D = \begin{vmatrix} 3 & 2 & 7 \\ -1 & 5 & 3 \\ 2 & -3 & -6 \end{vmatrix}$.

SOLUTION.   Repeating the first two columns to the right we have

$$D = 3 \cdot 5(-6) + 2 \cdot 3 \cdot 2 + 7(-1)(-3) - 2 \cdot 5 \cdot 7 - (-3)3 \cdot 3 - (-6)(-1)2$$
$$= -90 + 12 + 21 - 70 + 27 - 12 = -112.$$

This method of evaluating a third order determinant does *not* work when the order is greater than three, and for this reason we must introduce an alternate definition that is more complicated but has the advantage of being applicable for determinants of any order.

The *number of inversions* in a permutation of the integers $1, 2, 3, \cdots, n$ is the minimum number of jumps that must be made in order to return the permuted set to the standard position in which the integers are arranged in increasing order.

EXAMPLE 2.   Find the number of inversions in the sequence $(5, 3, 2, 4, 1)$.

SOLUTION.   The jumps are indicated by arrows.

$$(\; 5, 3, 2, 4, 1 \;) \quad \text{gives} \quad (\; 3, 2, 4, 1, 5 \;) \quad \text{in 4 jumps,}$$
$$(\; 3, 2, 4, 1, 5 \;) \quad \text{gives} \quad (\; 1, 3, 2, 4, 5 \;) \quad \text{in 3 jumps,}$$
$$(\; 1, 3, 2, 4, 5 \;) \quad \text{gives} \quad (\; 1, 2, 3, 4, 5 \;) \quad \text{in 1 jump.}$$

Therefore the total number of jumps is $4 + 3 + 1 = 8$ and hence the number of inversions in the sequence $(5, 3, 2, 4, 1)$ is 8.

DEFINITION 2.   *The value of the determinant D given by (10) is the sum of all terms of the form*

$$(-1)^v a_i b_j c_k$$

where in each product one element is selected from each row and one element is selected from each column, and where v is the number of inversions in the sequence of the subscripts (i, j, k).

Using this definition it is easy to see that D is given by equation (11), and hence this definition is consistent with our earlier definition for the value of D.

EXERCISE 3

1. Evaluate each of the following determinants:

a.
$$\begin{vmatrix} 2 & 1 & 3 \\ -4 & -5 & 6 \\ 1 & -9 & 5 \end{vmatrix},$$

b.
$$\begin{vmatrix} -3 & 1 & 2 \\ 5 & 0 & -1 \\ 0 & 3 & 0 \end{vmatrix},$$

c.
$$\begin{vmatrix} \frac{1}{2} & -1 & \frac{1}{3} \\ -6 & 3 & 1 \\ 5 & 2 & -2 \end{vmatrix},$$

d.
$$\begin{vmatrix} 1 & 2 & 3 \\ 4 & 5 & 6 \\ 7 & 8 & 9 \end{vmatrix}.$$

2. Using definition 2 prove that the value of the third order determinant (10) is given by (11).

3. In order to avoid rewriting the first two columns of a determinant the scheme

$$-\quad$$ 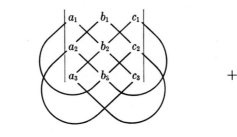 $$\quad+$$

is frequently used. Show that this scheme also gives (11).

4. Find the number of inversions in each of the following sequences $(4, 1, 3, 2)$, $(6, 4, 5, 3, 1, 2)$, $(6, 5, 4, 3, 2, 1)$, and $(8, 2, 4, 6, 1, 5, 3, 7)$.

5. Sometimes the number of inversions in a sequence is defined as the number of times a larger number precedes a smaller one. Thus in our example $(5, 3, 2, 4, 1)$ we see that 5 precedes 4 numbers that are smaller than 5, 3 precedes 2 such numbers, while 2 and 4 each precede 1. Then the number of inversions is $4 + 2 + 1 + 1 = 8$ just as before. This definition is simpler to compute with because it saves

the trouble of making the jumps.   Use this definition to compute the number of inversions in the sequences of problem 4.

5.   Some properties of determinants. The definition of an nth order determinant is analogous to that given in Definition 2 for a third order determinant.

DEFINITION 3.   *An nth order determinant is an array of n^2 numbers in the form*

$$D = \begin{vmatrix} a_1 & b_1 & c_1 & d_1 & \cdots & g_1 \\ a_2 & b_2 & c_2 & d_2 & \cdots & g_2 \\ a_3 & b_3 & c_3 & d_3 & \cdots & g_3 \\ \vdots & \vdots & \vdots & \vdots & \vdots & \vdots \\ a_n & b_n & c_n & d_n & \cdots & g_n \end{vmatrix}.$$

The value of D is the sum of all products of the form

$$(-1)^v a_i b_j c_k d_l \cdots g_q$$

where in each such product one element is taken from each row and one from each column, and where v is the number of inversions in the sequence of subscripts $(i, j, k, l, \cdots, q)$.

The evaluation of an nth order determinant can be quite tedious since there are $n!$ products to be computed, and then added.   However if some of the elements are zero the work may be much easier.   We will develop a few of the elementary properties of determinants and these properties will allow us to convert a given determinant into a determinant with the same value but with many of the elements zero.   All of the theorems and proofs that we give are valid for determinants of any order but for simplicity we will state and prove these theorems for third order determinants.

DEFINITION 4.   *Two determinants are said to be equal, if on evaluation both give the same number.*

$$\text{For example} \quad \begin{vmatrix} 1 & 2 & 3 \\ 0 & 4 & 5 \\ 0 & 0 & 6 \end{vmatrix} = \begin{vmatrix} 4 & 2 & 3 \\ 1 & 2 & 2 \\ 2 & -2 & 3 \end{vmatrix}$$

because on evaluation both yield 24.

THEOREM 2. *If every element in any column is zero, then the determinant is zero.*

PROOF. In the products $a_i b_j c_k$ there is always one element from each column, so each product contains at least one zero. Hence each product is zero, and so also is the sum. Q.E.D.

For example
$$\begin{vmatrix} 3 & -2 & 0 \\ 5 & 7\pi & 0 \\ 9 & \sqrt{53} & 0 \end{vmatrix} = 0.$$

THEOREM 3. *The interchange of any two adjacent columns changes the sign of the determinant.*

PROOF. Suppose that the first two columns are interchanged. We are to prove that

$$\begin{vmatrix} a_1 & b_1 & c_1 \\ a_2 & b_2 & c_2 \\ a_3 & b_3 & c_3 \end{vmatrix} = - \begin{vmatrix} b_1 & a_1 & c_1 \\ b_2 & a_2 & c_2 \\ b_3 & a_3 & c_3 \end{vmatrix}.$$

The determinant on the left is a sum of terms of the form

$$(-1)^v a_i b_j c_k \tag{12}$$

while that on the right is a sum of terms of the form

$$(-1)^w b_j a_i c_k \tag{13}$$

where w is the number of inversions in the sequence (j, i, k). Now the terms $a_i b_j c_k$ of (12) are identical with the terms $b_j a_i c_k$ of (13) and the only difference is the term (-1) to some power out in front. But the sequence (j, i, k) differs from the sequence (i, j, k) by just one jump, so that the number of inversions differs by 1. In symbols $v = w \pm 1$, or $(-1)^v = -(-1)^w$. Therefore the sum of the terms in (12) is the negative of the sum of terms in (13). The same type of argument can be given if the last two columns are interchanged. Q.E.D.

The shuffling of any set of columns can be achieved by interchanging adjacent columns one at a time.   For example

$$
\begin{vmatrix} a_1 & b_1 & c_1 \\ a_2 & b_2 & c_2 \\ a_3 & b_3 & c_3 \end{vmatrix} = - \begin{vmatrix} a_1 & c_1 & b_1 \\ a_2 & c_2 & b_2 \\ a_3 & c_3 & b_3 \end{vmatrix} = -(-1) \begin{vmatrix} c_1 & a_1 & b_1 \\ c_2 & a_2 & b_2 \\ c_3 & a_3 & b_3 \end{vmatrix}
$$

$$
= (-1)^3 \begin{vmatrix} c_1 & b_1 & a_1 \\ c_2 & b_2 & a_2 \\ c_3 & b_3 & a_3 \end{vmatrix} .
$$

COROLLARY.   *The interchange of any two columns changes the sign of the determinant.*

The proof is left as an exercise for the reader.

THEOREM 4.   *If two columns are identical, the determinant is zero.*

For example

$$
\begin{vmatrix} 5 & 12 & 5 \\ -4 & 17 & -4 \\ 181 & -3 & 181 \end{vmatrix} = 0.
$$

PROOF.   Let D denote the value of the given determinant, and let D_1 denote the value of the determinant obtained on interchanging the two identical columns.   Then by the corollary $D = -D_1$.   But since the columns are identical nothing has changed so that D_1 is the same as D. This gives $D = -D$ or $2D = 0$, whence $D = 0$.   Q.E.D.

THEOREM 5.   *If each element of a column is multiplied by a common factor, then the determinant is multiplied by that factor.*

For example

$$
\begin{vmatrix} 5 & 4 & 9 \\ 2 & -1 & 3 \\ 0 & 7 & -12 \end{vmatrix} = 3 \begin{vmatrix} 5 & 4 & 3 \\ 2 & -1 & 1 \\ 0 & 7 & -4 \end{vmatrix} .
$$

PROOF.   Assume that each element in the first column is multiplied by the common factor k. We are to prove that

$$\begin{vmatrix} ka_1 & b_1 & c_1 \\ ka_2 & b_2 & c_2 \\ ka_3 & b_3 & c_3 \end{vmatrix} = k \begin{vmatrix} a_1 & b_1 & c_1 \\ a_2 & b_2 & c_2 \\ a_3 & b_3 & c_3 \end{vmatrix}. \qquad (14)$$

The determinant on the left side of (14) is a sum of terms

$$(-1)^v ka_i b_j c_k \qquad (15)$$

while the determinant on the right side is a sum of terms of the form

$$(-1)^v a_i b_j c_k. \qquad (16)$$

Since each term in (15) is k times the corresponding term in (16), equation (14) is now obvious.

If some other column is under consideration, that column can be moved into the position of the first column, using Theorem 3. The common factor can be removed, by the first part of our proof, and then the column can be returned to its original place, again using Theorem 3.   Q.E.D.

THEOREM 6. *If two columns are proportional then the determinant is zero.*

For example

$$\begin{vmatrix} 11 & -5 & 15 \\ 19 & -1 & 3 \\ 65 & -7 & 21 \end{vmatrix} = 0,$$

because the last two columns are proportional, with -3 as the constant of proportionality. To see this observe that each element in the third column is -3 times the element in the same row and in the second column.

PROOF. Let us suppose that the first two columns are proportional. Using first Theorem 5, and then Theorem 4, we have

$$D = \begin{vmatrix} kb_1 & b_1 & c_1 \\ kb_2 & b_2 & c_2 \\ kb_3 & b_3 & c_3 \end{vmatrix} = k \begin{vmatrix} b_1 & b_1 & c_1 \\ b_2 & b_2 & c_2 \\ b_3 & b_3 & c_3 \end{vmatrix} = k \cdot 0 = 0. \qquad (17)$$

The proof is the same for any two columns.   Q.E.D.

THEOREM 7.   *If two determinants are identical except for the elements of one column, then they may be added by adding the elements in that column in which they differ.   More precisely*

$$
\begin{vmatrix} A_1 & b_1 & c_1 \\ A_2 & b_2 & c_2 \\ A_3 & b_3 & c_3 \end{vmatrix} + \begin{vmatrix} a_1 & b_1 & c_1 \\ a_2 & b_2 & c_2 \\ a_3 & b_3 & c_3 \end{vmatrix} = \begin{vmatrix} A_1 + a_1 & b_1 & c_1 \\ A_2 + a_2 & b_2 & c_2 \\ A_3 + a_3 & b_3 & c_3 \end{vmatrix}. \tag{18}
$$

For example

$$
\begin{vmatrix} 3 & 5 & 7 \\ 2 & 6 & -5 \\ -8 & -9 & -13 \end{vmatrix} + \begin{vmatrix} 4 & 5 & 7 \\ -7 & 6 & -5 \\ -5 & -9 & -13 \end{vmatrix} = \begin{vmatrix} 7 & 5 & 7 \\ -5 & 6 & -5 \\ -13 & -9 & -13 \end{vmatrix},
$$

and since the first and third columns in the sum are identical, in this special case the sum is zero.

PROOF.   The left side of (18) is a sum consisting of two sets of terms of the form

$$
(-1)^v A_i b_j c_k + (-1)^v a_i b_j c_k \tag{19}
$$

and by grouping and factoring, this sum can be written as a sum of terms of the form

$$
(-1)^v (A_i + a_i) b_j c_k. \tag{20}
$$

But the sum of terms of the form (20) is just the determinant on the right side of (18).   Q.E.D.

Obviously this theorem is valid, if the two determinants to be added differ only in the second column, or differ only in the third column.

THEOREM 8.   *If in any determinant the elements of any one column are all multiplied by a common factor k and the result added termwise to some other column, the determinant is unchanged.*

If we assume that the columns in question are the second and first columns respectively, then we are to prove that

$$
\begin{vmatrix} a_1 & b_1 & c_1 \\ a_2 & b_2 & c_2 \\ a_3 & b_3 & c_3 \end{vmatrix} = \begin{vmatrix} a_1 + kb_1 & b_1 & c_1 \\ a_2 + kb_2 & b_2 & c_2 \\ a_3 + kb_3 & b_3 & c_3 \end{vmatrix}. \tag{21}
$$

For example

$$
\begin{vmatrix} 7 & 2 & 17 \\ -15 & -5 & 6 \\ 9 & 3 & 49 \end{vmatrix} = \begin{vmatrix} 1 & 2 & 17 \\ 0 & -5 & 6 \\ 0 & 3 & 49 \end{vmatrix}
$$

because the second determinant can be obtained from the first one by multiplying each element in the second column by -3 and adding it to the first column. In this example the work of evaluating the second determinant is much simpler than the work for the first determinant because of the zeros that have been introduced.

PROOF. We start with the right side of equation (21). By Theorem 7 this is equal to the sum

$$
\begin{vmatrix} a_1 & b_1 & c_1 \\ a_2 & b_2 & c_2 \\ a_3 & b_3 & c_3 \end{vmatrix} + \begin{vmatrix} kb_1 & b_1 & c_1 \\ kb_2 & b_2 & c_2 \\ kb_3 & b_3 & c_3 \end{vmatrix}.
$$

By Theorem 6 (equation 17) the second of these two determinants is zero, so that the sum is just the left side of (21). But this type argument can be given for any two columns.   Q.E.D.

Up to this time we have been concerned only with the columns of the determinants. It is a fact however that if the word "column" is replaced by the word "row" wherever it appears in Theorems 2, 3, 4, 5, 6, 7, and 8, the new statement is also a true theorem. The key to the proof of this remarkable fact lies in

THEOREM 9. *If the rows and columns of a determinant are interchanged, the determinant is unchanged.*

PROOF. If $n = 3$, this states that

$$
\begin{vmatrix} a_1 & b_1 & c_1 \\ a_2 & b_2 & c_2 \\ a_3 & b_3 & c_3 \end{vmatrix} = \begin{vmatrix} a_1 & a_2 & a_3 \\ b_1 & b_2 & b_3 \\ c. & c_2 & c_3 \end{vmatrix}. \tag{22}
$$

We leave it to the reader to prove (22) by showing that both determinants give (11). In case $n > 3$, the proof must be based on Definition (3). The proof is a little complicated, and since no use will be made of this theorem for $n > 3$, we omit the proof.

We will now show how these theorems can be used to simplify the evaluation of a determinant.   If all the elements in some column are zero except one, then we can reduce the order of the determinant.   For example it is easy to see that

$$\begin{vmatrix} a_1 & b_1 & c_1 \\ 0 & b_2 & c_2 \\ 0 & b_3 & c_3 \end{vmatrix} = a_1 \begin{vmatrix} b_2 & c_2 \\ b_3 & c_3 \end{vmatrix} \tag{23}$$

by using (11) and (7), and the fact that $a_2 = a_3 = 0$.

The determinant $\begin{vmatrix} b_2 & c_2 \\ b_3 & c_3 \end{vmatrix}$ is called the *minor* of a_1 in the original determinant.

EXAMPLE 1.   Evaluate the determinant

$$D = \begin{vmatrix} 36 & 18 & 17 \\ 183 & 101 & 78 \\ 45 & 24 & 20 \end{vmatrix}.$$

SOLUTION.   We use our theorems to replace the large numbers in D by smaller ones, and eventually by zeros.

$$D = \begin{vmatrix} 36 & 18 & 17 \\ 183 & 101 & 78 \\ 45 & 24 & 20 \end{vmatrix}$$

(multiplying each element in the last row by -4 and adding to the second row — Theorem 8 for rows)

$$= \begin{vmatrix} 36 & 18 & 17 \\ 3 & 5 & -2 \\ 45 & 24 & 20 \end{vmatrix}$$

(factoring 3 from each element in the first column — Theorem 5)

$$= 3 \begin{vmatrix} 12 & 18 & 17 \\ 1 & 5 & -2 \\ 15 & 24 & 20 \end{vmatrix}$$

(multiplying each element of the last column by -1 and adding to the second column — Theorem 8)

$$= 3 \begin{vmatrix} 12 & 1 & 17 \\ 1 & 7 & -2 \\ 15 & 4 & 20 \end{vmatrix}$$

$$= 3 \begin{vmatrix} 12 & 1 & 17 \\ 1 & 7 & -2 \\ 3 & 3 & 3 \end{vmatrix}$$

(multiplying the first row by -1 and adding to the last row)

$$= 9 \begin{vmatrix} 12 & 1 & 17 \\ 1 & 7 & -2 \\ 1 & 1 & 1 \end{vmatrix}$$

(factoring 3 from the last row)

$$= 9 \begin{vmatrix} 12 & -11 & 5 \\ 1 & 6 & -3 \\ 1 & 0 & 0 \end{vmatrix}$$

(subtracting the first column from the second column, and then subtracting the first column from the third)

$$= 9 \begin{vmatrix} 1 & 0 & 0 \\ 12 & -11 & 5 \\ 1 & 6 & -3 \end{vmatrix}$$

(moving the third row up to the first row — Theorem 3 for rows, applied twice)

$$= 9 \begin{vmatrix} -11 & 5 \\ 6 & -3 \end{vmatrix} = 9 \begin{vmatrix} 1 & -1 \\ 6 & -3 \end{vmatrix} = 9(-3 + 6) = 27.$$

(using equation (23) for rows)

In actual practice it is not necessary to write out the explanation of each step as we have done.

EXERCISE 4

In problems 1 through 6 evaluate the given determinant.

1. $\begin{vmatrix} 1 & 4 & 9 \\ 4 & 9 & 16 \\ 9 & 16 & 25 \end{vmatrix}.$

2. $\begin{vmatrix} 12 & 15 & 11 \\ 6 & 2 & 7 \\ 13 & 16 & 12 \end{vmatrix}.$

3. $\begin{vmatrix} 17 & 4 & 5 \\ 16 & 10 & 9 \\ 8 & 1 & 3 \end{vmatrix}$.

4. $\begin{vmatrix} 2 & 3 & 5 \\ 7 & 11 & 13 \\ 17 & 19 & 23 \end{vmatrix}$.

5. $\begin{vmatrix} 171 & 110 & 60 \\ 141 & 71 & 70 \\ 344 & 221 & 121 \end{vmatrix}$.

6. $\begin{vmatrix} 28 & 30 & -35 \\ -15 & -14 & 19 \\ 6 & 11 & -5 \end{vmatrix}$.

7. Prove that $\begin{vmatrix} a & b & c \\ c & a & b \\ b & c & a \end{vmatrix} = a^3 + b^3 + c^3 - 3abc.$

8. Prove that $\begin{vmatrix} 1 & 1 & 1 \\ x & y & z \\ x^2 & y^2 & z^2 \end{vmatrix} = (z - x)(z - y)(y - x).$

9. Prove that $\begin{vmatrix} b + c & a - c & a - b \\ b - c & c + a & b - a \\ c - b & c - a & a + b \end{vmatrix} = 8abc.$

10. Prove that $\begin{vmatrix} b + c & c & b \\ c & c + a & a \\ b & a & a + b \end{vmatrix} = 4abc.$

In the following problems, reduce the fourth order determinant to a third order determinant by using a method similar to that illustrated by equation (23). Then evaluate.

11. $\begin{vmatrix} 4 & 2 & 2 & 2 \\ 2 & 4 & 2 & 2 \\ 2 & 2 & 4 & 2 \\ 2 & 2 & 2 & 4 \end{vmatrix}$.

12. $\begin{vmatrix} 1 & 1 & 1 & 1 \\ 1 & 2 & 3 & 4 \\ 1 & 3 & 6 & 10 \\ 1 & 4 & 10 & 20 \end{vmatrix}$.

13.
$$\begin{vmatrix} -6 & 1 & 2 & 3 \\ 1 & -6 & 2 & 3 \\ 2 & 1 & -6 & 3 \\ 2 & 1 & 3 & -6 \end{vmatrix}.$$

14.
$$\begin{vmatrix} 2 & -3 & 0 & 4 \\ -4 & 2 & 3 & -5 \\ 2 & 0 & -2 & 4 \\ 3 & -4 & 5 & 2 \end{vmatrix}.$$

15.
$$\begin{vmatrix} 1 & 1 & 1 & 1 \\ 1 & -1 & 1 & -1 \\ 1 & 1 & -1 & -1 \\ 1 & -1 & -1 & 1 \end{vmatrix}.$$

16.
$$\begin{vmatrix} 1 & 2 & 3 & 4 \\ 4 & 1 & 2 & 3 \\ 3 & 4 & 1 & 2 \\ 2 & 3 & 4 & 1 \end{vmatrix}.$$

$\star$**17.** The numbers 228, 589, and 779 are all divisible by 19. Use this fact to prove that the determinant

$$D = \begin{vmatrix} 2 & 2 & 8 \\ 5 & 8 & 9 \\ 7 & 7 & 9 \end{vmatrix}$$

is divisible by 38 without finding the value of D.

6.   The solution of systems of linear equations. Cramer's rule for solving a system of 2 linear equations in 2 unknowns was given in Theorem 1. The rule is also valid for n linear equations in n unknowns, but for simplicity we state the theorem and give the proof for $n = 3$.

THEOREM 10.   *If the system of simultaneous equations*

$$\begin{aligned} a_1x + b_1y + c_1z &= k_1 \\ a_2x + b_2y + c_2z &= k_2 \\ a_3x + b_3y + c_3z &= k_3 \end{aligned} \tag{24}$$

has a solution, and if the determinant of the coefficients

$$D = \begin{vmatrix} a_1 & b_1 & c_1 \\ a_2 & b_2 & c_2 \\ a_3 & b_3 & c_3 \end{vmatrix} \tag{25}$$

is not zero, then the solutions are given by

$$x = \frac{\begin{vmatrix} k_1 & b_1 & c_1 \\ k_2 & b_2 & c_2 \\ k_3 & b_3 & c_3 \end{vmatrix}}{D}, \ y = \frac{\begin{vmatrix} a_1 & k_1 & c_1 \\ a_2 & k_2 & c_2 \\ a_3 & k_3 & c_3 \end{vmatrix}}{D}, \ z = \frac{\begin{vmatrix} a_1 & b_1 & k_1 \\ a_2 & b_2 & k_2 \\ a_3 & b_3 & k_3 \end{vmatrix}}{D}. \ (26)$$

PROOF.   We begin by observing that

$$xD = x \begin{vmatrix} a_1 & b_1 & c_1 \\ a_2 & b_2 & c_2 \\ a_3 & b_3 & c_3 \end{vmatrix} = \begin{vmatrix} a_1x & b_1 & c_1 \\ a_2x & b_2 & c_2 \\ a_3x & b_3 & c_3 \end{vmatrix}. \quad (27)$$

In this last determinant, we multiply the second column by y and add it to the first column, and we multiply the third column by z and add it to the first column.   Then (27) gives

$$xD = \begin{vmatrix} a_1x + b_1y + c_1z & b_1 & c_1 \\ a_2x + b_2y + c_2z & b_2 & c_2 \\ a_3x + b_3y + c_3z & b_3 & c_3 \end{vmatrix}. \quad (28)$$

If now we assume that the equation set (24) has a solution, then we can use those values for x, y, z in (28).   Doing this, the elements in the first column can be replaced termwise by k_1, k_2, and k_3, and hence (28) becomes

$$xD = \begin{vmatrix} k_1 & b_1 & c_1 \\ k_2 & b_2 & c_2 \\ k_3 & b_3 & c_3 \end{vmatrix}. \quad (29)$$

Dividing both sides of (29) by D (which by hypothesis is not zero) we obtain the first of the equations in (26).   The other two equations in that set are obtained similarly starting with yD and zD respectively.   Q.E.D.

The proof of Cramer's rule for n equations in n unknowns is just the same, and just as easy.

We have proved that if the system has a solution then Cramer's rule (equation (26)) gives the solution. It is further true that if $D \neq 0$, then the system has a solution. This is proved by direct substitution of x, y, and z as given by (26) back into the given equations (24). This computation is not easy, and so we omit it. In any numerical problem, the reader should check the answers obtained by substituting them in the given equations.

EXAMPLE 1. Solve the system of simultaneous equations

$$14x + 2y - 6z = 9,$$
$$-4x + y + 9z = 3, \tag{30}$$
$$6x - 4y + 3z = -4.$$

SOLUTION. The denominator D is formed by taking the coefficient of the unknowns x, y, and z. We find that

$$D = \begin{vmatrix} 14 & 2 & -6 \\ -4 & 1 & 9 \\ 6 & -4 & 3 \end{vmatrix} = \begin{vmatrix} 26 & -6 & 0 \\ -22 & 13 & 0 \\ 6 & -4 & 3 \end{vmatrix} = 3 \begin{vmatrix} 26 & -6 \\ -22 & 13 \end{vmatrix} = 3 \begin{vmatrix} 4 & 7 \\ -22 & 13 \end{vmatrix}$$

$$= 3(52 + 154) = 618.$$

For the numerator of x, we replace the coefficients of x by the constants. Thus

$$\begin{vmatrix} 9 & 2 & -6 \\ 3 & 1 & 9 \\ -4 & -4 & 3 \end{vmatrix} = \begin{vmatrix} 1 & -6 & 0 \\ 15 & 13 & 0 \\ -4 & -4 & 3 \end{vmatrix} = 3(13 + 90) = 309.$$

Whence

$$x = \frac{309}{D} = \frac{309}{618} = \frac{1}{2}.$$

Similarly for the numerator of y we find

$$\begin{vmatrix} -14 & 9 & -6 \\ -4 & 3 & 9 \\ 6 & -4 & 3 \end{vmatrix} = \begin{vmatrix} 26 & 1 & 0 \\ -22 & 15 & 0 \\ 6 & -4 & 3 \end{vmatrix} = 3 \begin{vmatrix} 26 & 1 \\ -22 & 15 \end{vmatrix} = 1236.$$

Whence

$$y = \frac{1236}{D} = \frac{1236}{618} = 2.$$

Finally for the numerator of z we have

$$\begin{vmatrix} 14 & 2 & 9 \\ -4 & 1 & 3 \\ 6 & -4 & -4 \end{vmatrix} = 2 \begin{vmatrix} 14 & 2 & 9 \\ -4 & 1 & 3 \\ 3 & -2 & -2 \end{vmatrix} = 2 \begin{vmatrix} 22 & 0 & 3 \\ -4 & 1 & 3 \\ -5 & 0 & 4 \end{vmatrix} = 2 \begin{vmatrix} 22 & 3 \\ -5 & 4 \end{vmatrix}$$

$$= 2(88 + 15) = 206.$$

$$z = \frac{206}{618} = \frac{1}{3}.$$

To check the answers $x = 1/2$, $y = 2$, $z = 1/3$, we substitute in (30), the given equation. We find:

$$14 \times \tfrac{1}{2} + 2 \times 2 - 6 \times \tfrac{1}{3} = 7 + 4 - 2 \quad = 9,$$
$$-4 \times \tfrac{1}{2} + 2 + 9 \times \tfrac{1}{3} \quad\quad = -2 + 2 + 3 = 3,$$
$$6 \times \tfrac{1}{2} - 4 \times 2 + 3 \times \tfrac{1}{3} = 3 - 8 + 1 \quad = -4.$$

EXERCISE 5

In problems 1 through 8 use Cramer's rule to solve the given system of equations for the unknowns.

1. $\quad x + y + z = 6,$
$\quad 2x - y + 3z = 9,$
$\quad 3x - 2y - z = -4.$

2. $\quad 6x + 5y + 4z = 5,$
$\quad 5x + 4y + 3z = 5,$
$\quad 4x + 3y + z = 7.$

3. $\quad x - 2y + 3z = 15,$
$\quad 5x + 7y - 11z = -29,$
$\quad -13x + 17y + 19z = 37.$

4. $\quad x - 3y + 6z = -8,$
$\quad 3x - 2y - 10z = 11,$
$\quad -5x + 6y + 2z = -7.$

5. $\quad 5u + 3v + 5w = 3,$
$\quad 3u + 5v + w = -5,$
$\quad 2u + 2v + 3w = 7.$

6. $\quad 6A + 5B = 1,$
$\quad 7B + 4C = 13,$
$\quad 8A + 3C = 23.$

7. $\quad x + y + z - u = 8,$
$\quad x + y - z + u = 4,$
$\quad x - y + z + u = -2,$
$\quad -x + y + z + u = -6.$

8. $\quad 3p + 5q - 7r = 3,$
$\quad 2p - r + 5s = 5,$
$\quad p - 3q + 2s = -2,$
$\quad q + 2r + 7s = 13.$

★9. According to Euler's formula, in any convex polyhedron, V (the number of vertices), E (the number of edges), and F (the number of faces) must satisfy the equation $V - E + F = 2$. In a certain polyhedron twice the number of edges is three times the number of vertices, and twice the number of faces is one less than the number of edges. Find the number of vertices, edges, and faces for this polyhedron. Sketch one polyhedron that satisfies the conditions of this problem.

10. In a recent basketball game the two guards failed to score for Mussel University. However the center scored twice as many points as the left forward, and five more points than both forwards together. But the center was six points shy of scoring three times as many points as the right forward. What was the score for Mussel University?

N	0	1	2	3	4	5	6	7	8	9
0.0		5.395	6.088	6.493	6.781	7.004	7.187	7.341	7.474	7.592
0.1	7.697	7.793	7.880	7.960	8.034	8.103	8.167	8.228	8.285	8.339
0.2	8.391	8.439	8.486	8.530	8.573	8.614	8.653	8.691	8.727	8.762
0.3	8.796	8.829	8.861	8.891	8.921	8.950	8.978	9.006	9.032	9.058
0.4	9.084	9.108	9.132	9.156	9.179	9.201	9.223	9.245	9.266	9.287
0.5	9.307	9.327	9.346	9.365	9.384	9.402	9.420	9.438	9.455	9.472
0.6	9.489	9.506	9.522	9.538	9.554	9.569	9.584	9.600	9.614	9.629
0.7	9.643	9.658	9.671	9.685	9.699	9.712	9.726	9.739	9.752	9.764
0.8	9.777	9.789	9.802	9.814	9.826	9.837	9.849	9.861	9.872	9.883
0.9	9.895	9.906	9.917	9.927	9.938	9.949	9.959	9.970	9.980	9.990
1.0	0.00000	0995	1980	2956	3922	4879	5827	6766	7696	8618
1.1	9531	*0436	*1333	*2222	*3103	*3976	*4842	*5700	*6551	*7395
1.2	0.1 8232	9062	9885	*0701	*1511	*2314	*3111	*3902	*4686	*5464
1.3	0.2 6236	7003	7763	8518	9267	*0010	*0748	*1481	*2208	*2930
1.4	0.3 3647	4359	5066	5767	6464	7156	7844	8526	9204	9878
1.5	0.4 0547	1211	1871	2527	3178	3825	4469	5108	5742	6373
1.6	7000	7623	8243	8858	9470	*0078	*0682	*1282	*1879	*2473
1.7	0.5 3063	3649	4232	4812	5389	5962	6531	7098	7661	8222
1.8	8779	9333	9884	*0432	*0977	*1519	*2058	*2594	*3127	*3658
1.9	0.6 4185	4710	5233	5752	6269	6783	7294	7803	8310	8813
2.0	9315	9813	*0310	*0804	*1295	*1784	*2271	*2755	*3237	*3716
2.1	0.7 4194	4669	5142	5612	6081	6547	7011	7473	7932	8390
2.2	8846	9299	9751	*0200	*0648	*1093	*1536	*1978	*2418	*2855
2.3	0.8 3291	3725	4157	4587	5015	5442	5866	6289	6710	7129
2.4	7547	7963	8377	8789	9200	9609	*0016	*0422	*0826	*1228
2.5	0.9 1629	2028	2426	2822	3216	3609	4001	4391	4779	5166
2.6	5551	5935	6317	6698	7078	7456	7833	8208	8582	8954
2.7	9325	9695	*0063	*0430	*0796	*1160	*1523	*1885	*2245	*2604
2.8	1.0 2962	3318	3674	4028	4380	4732	5082	5431	5779	6126
2.9	6471	6815	7158	7500	7841	8181	8519	8856	9192	9527
3.0	9861	*0194	*0526	*0856	*1186	*1514	*1841	*2168	*2493	*2817
3.1	1.1 3140	3462	3783	4103	4422	4740	5057	5373	5688	6002
3.2	6315	6627	6938	7248	7557	7865	8173	8479	8784	9089
3.3	9392	9695	9996	*0297	*0597	*0896	*1194	*1491	*1788	*2083
3.4	1.2 2378	2671	2964	3256	3547	3837	4127	4415	4703	4990
3.5	5276	5562	5846	6130	6413	6695	6976	7257	7536	7815
3.6	8093	8371	8647	8923	9198	9473	9746	*0019	*0291	*0563
3.7	1.3 0833	1103	1372	1641	1909	2176	2442	2708	2972	3237
3.8	3500	3763	4025	4286	4547	4807	5067	5325	5584	5841
3.9	6098	6354	6609	6864	7118	7372	7624	7877	8128	8379
4.0	8629	8879	9128	9377	9624	9872	*0118	*0364	*0610	*0854
4.1	1.4 1099	1342	1585	1828	2070	2311	2552	2792	3031	3270
4.2	3508	3746	3984	4220	4456	4692	4927	5161	5395	5629
4.3	5862	6094	6326	6557	6787	7018	7247	7476	7705	7933
4.4	8160	8387	8614	8840	9065	9290	9515	9739	9962	*0185
4.5	1.5 0408	0630	0851	1072	1293	1513	1732	1951	2170	2388
4.6	2606	2823	3039	3256	3471	3687	3902	4116	4330	4543
4.7	4756	4969	5181	5393	5604	5814	6025	6235	6444	6653
4.8	6862	7070	7277	7485	7691	7898	8104	8309	8515	8719
4.9	8924	9127	9331	9534	9737	9939	*0141	*0342	*0543	*0744
5.0	1.6 0944	1144	1343	1542	1741	1939	2137	2334	2531	2728
N	0	1	2	3	4	5	6	7	8	9

Take tabular value—10

N	0	1	2	3	4	5	6	7	8	9
5.0	1.6 0944	1144	1343	1542	1741	1939	2137	2334	2531	2728
5.1	2924	3120	3315	3511	3705	3900	4094	4287	4481	4673
5.2	4866	5058	5250	5441	5632	5823	6013	6203	6393	6582
5.3	6771	6959	7147	7335	7523	7710	7896	8083	8269	8455
5.4	8640	8825	9010	9194	9378	9562	9745	9928	*0111	*0293
5.5	1.7 0475	0656	0838	1019	1199	1380	1560	1740	1919	2098
5.6	2277	2455	2633	2811	2988	3166	3342	3519	3695	3871
5.7	4047	4222	4397	4572	4746	4920	5094	5267	5440	5613
5.8	5786	5958	6130	6302	6473	6644	6815	6985	7156	7326
5.9	7495	7665	7834	8002	8171	8339	8507	8675	8842	9009
6.0	9176	9342	9509	9675	9840	*0006	*0171	*0336	*0500	*0665
6.1	1.8 0829	0993	1156	1319	1482	1645	1808	1970	2132	2294
6.2	2455	2616	2777	2938	3098	3258	3418	3578	3737	3896
6.3	4055	4214	4372	4530	4688	4845	5003	5160	5317	5473
6.4	5630	5786	5942	6097	6253	6408	6563	6718	6872	7026
6.5	7180	7334	7487	7641	7794	7947	8099	8251	8403	8555
6.6	8707	8858	9010	9160	9311	9462	9612	9762	9912	*0061
6.7	1.9 0211	0360	0509	0658	0806	0954	1102	1250	1398	1545
6.8	1692	1839	1986	2132	2279	2425	2571	2716	2862	3007
6.9	3152	3297	3442	3586	3730	3874	4018	4162	4305	4448
7.0	4591	4734	4876	5019	5161	5303	5445	5586	5727	5869
7.1	6009	6150	6291	6431	6571	6711	6851	6991	7130	7269
7.2	7408	7547	7685	7824	7962	8100	8238	8376	8513	8650
7.3	8787	8924	9061	9198	9334	9470	9606	9742	9877	*0013
7.4	2.0 0148	0283	0418	0553	0687	0821	0956	1089	1223	1357
7.5	1490	1624	1757	1890	2022	2155	2287	2419	2551	2683
7.6	2815	2946	3078	3209	3340	3471	3601	3732	3862	3992
7.7	4122	4252	4381	4511	4640	4769	4898	5027	5156	5284
7.8	5412	5540	5668	5796	5924	6051	6179	6306	6433	6560
7.9	6686	6813	6939	7065	7191	7317	7443	7568	7694	7819
8.0	7944	8069	8194	8318	8443	8567	8691	8815	8939	9063
8.1	9186	9310	9433	9556	9679	9802	9924	*0047	*0169	*0291
8.2	2.1 0413	0535	0657	0779	0900	1021	1142	1263	1384	1505
8.3	1626	1746	1866	1986	2106	2226	2346	2465	2585	2704
8.4	2823	2942	3061	3180	3298	3417	3535	3653	3771	3889
8.5	4007	4124	4242	4359	4476	4593	4710	4827	4943	5060
8.6	5176	5292	5409	5524	5640	5756	5871	5987	6102	6217
8.7	6332	6447	6562	6677	6791	6905	7020	7134	7248	7361
8.8	7475	7589	7702	7816	7929	8042	8155	8267	8380	8493
8.9	8605	8717	8830	8942	9054	9165	9277	9389	9500	9611
9.0	9722	9834	9944	*0055	*0166	*0276	*0387	*0497	*0607	*0717
9.1	2.2 0827	0937	1047	1157	1266	1375	1485	1594	1703	1812
9.2	1920	2029	2138	2246	2354	2462	2570	2678	2786	2894
9.3	3001	3109	3216	3324	3431	3538	3645	3751	3858	3965
9.4	4071	4177	4284	4390	4496	4601	4707	4813	4918	5024
9.5	5129	5234	5339	5444	5549	5654	5759	5863	5968	6072
9.6	6176	6280	6384	6488	6592	6696	6799	6903	7006	7109
9.7	7213	7316	7419	7521	7624	7727	7829	7932	8034	8136
9.8	8238	8340	8442	8544	8646	8747	8849	8950	9051	9152
9.9	9253	9354	9455	9556	9657	9757	9858	9958	*0058	*0158
10.0	2.3 0259	0358	0458	0558	0658	0757	0857	0956	1055	1154
N	0	1	2	3	4	5	6	7	8	9

10	2.30259	25	3.21888	40	3.68888	55	4.00733	70	4.24850	85	4.44265
11	2.39790	26	3.25810	41	3.71357	56	4.02535	71	4.26268	86	4.45435
12	2.48491	27	3.29584	42	3.73767	57	4.04305	72	4.27667	87	4,46591
13	2.56495	28	3.33220	43	3.76120	58	4.06044	73	4.29046	88	4.47734
14	2.63906	29	3.36730	44	3.78419	59	4.07754	74	4.30407	89	4.48864
15	2.70805	30	3.40120	45	3.80666	60	4.09434	75	4.31749	90	4.49981
16	2.77259	31	3.43399	46	3.82864	61	4.11087	76	4.33073	91	4.51086
17	2.83321	32	3.46574	47	3.85015	62	4.12713	77	4.34381	92	4.52179
18	2.89037	33	3.49651	48	3.87120	63	4.14313	78	4.35671	93	4.53260
19	2.94444	34	3.52636	49	3.89182	64	4.15888	79	4.36945	94	4.54329
20	2.99573	35	3.55535	50	3.91202	65	4.17439	80	4.38203	95	4.55388
21	3.04452	36	3.58352	51	3.93183	66	4.18965	81	4.39445	96	4.56435
22	3.09104	37	3.61092	52	3.95124	67	4.20469	82	4.40672	97	4.57471
23	3.13549	38	3.63759	53	3.97029	68	4.21951	83	4.41884	98	4.58497
24	3.17805	39	3.66356	54	3.98898	69	4.23411	84	4.43082	99	4.59512

x	e^x	$\text{Log}_{10}(e^x)$	e^{-x}	x	e^x	$\text{Log}_{10}(e^x)$	e^{-x}
0.00	1.0000	0.00000	1.000000	0.50	1.6487	0.21715	0.606531
0.01	1.0101	.00434	0.990050	0.51	1.6653	.22149	.600496
0.02	1.0202	.00869	.980199	0.52	1.6820	.22583	.594521
0.03	1.0305	.01303	.970446	0.53	1.6989	.23018	.588605
0.04	1.0408	.01737	.960789	0.54	1.7160	.23452	.582748
0.05	1.0513	0.02171	0.951229	0.55	1.7333	0.23886	0.576950
0.06	1.0618	.02606	.941765	0.56	1.7507	.24320	.571209
0.07	1.0725	.03040	.932394	0.57	1.7683	.24755	.565525
0.08	1.0833	.03474	.923116	0.58	1.7860	.25189	.559898
0.09	1.0942	.03909	.913931	0.59	1.8040	.25623	.554327
0.10	1.1052	0.04343	0.904837	0.60	1.8221	0.26058	0.548812
0.11	1.1163	.04777	.895834	0.61	1.8404	.26492	.543351
0.12	1.1275	.05212	.886920	0.62	1.8589	.26926	.537944
0.13	1.1388	.05646	.878095	0.63	1.8776	.27361	.532592
0.14	1.1503	.06080	.869358	0.64	1.8965	.27795	.527292
0.15	1.1618	0.06514	0.860708	0.65	1.9155	0.28229	0.522046
0.16	1.1735	.06949	.852144	0.66	1.9348	.28663	.516851
0.17	1.1853	.07383	.843665	0.67	1.9542	.29098	.511709
0.18	1.1972	.07817	.835270	0.68	1.9739	.29532	.506617
0.19	1.2092	.08252	.826959	0.69	1.9937	.29966	.501576
0.20	1.2214	0.08686	0.818731	0.70	2.0138	0.30401	0.496585
0.21	1.2337	.09120	.810584	0.71	2.0340	.30835	.491644
0.22	1.2461	.09554	.802519	0.72	2.0544	.31269	.486752
0.23	1.2586	.09989	.794534	0.73	2.0751	.31703	.481909
0.24	1.2712	.10423	.786628	0.74	2.0959	.32138	.477114
0.25	1.2840	0.10857	0.778801	0.75	2.1170	0.32572	0.472367
0.26	1.2969	.11292	.771052	0.76	2.1383	.33006	.467666
0.27	1.3100	.11726	.763379	0.77	2.1598	.33441	.463013
0.28	1.3231	.12160	.755784	0.78	2.1815	.33875	.458406
0.29	1.3364	.12595	.748264	0.79	2.2034	.34309	.453845
0.30	1.3499	0.13029	0.740818	0.80	2.2255	0.34744	0.449329
0.31	1.3634	.13463	.733447	0.81	2.2479	.35178	.444858
0.32	1.3771	.13897	.726149	0.82	2.2705	.35612	.440432
0.33	1.3910	.14332	.718924	0.83	2.2933	.36046	.436049
0.34	1.4049	.14766	.711770	0.84	2.3164	.36481	.431711
0.35	1.4191	0.15200	0.704688	0.85	2.3396	0.36915	0.427415
0.36	1.4333	.15635	.697676	0.86	2.3632	.37349	.423162
0.37	1.4477	.16069	.690734	0.87	2.3869	.37784	.418952
0.38	1.4623	.16503	.683861	0.88	2.4109	.38218	.414783
0.39	1.4770	.16937	.677057	0.89	2.4351	.38652	.410656
0.40	1.4918	0.17372	0.670320	0.90	2.4596	0.39087	0.406570
0.41	1.5068	.17806	.663650	0.91	2.4843	.39521	.402524
0.42	1.5220	.18240	.657047	0.92	2.5093	.39955	.398519
0.43	1.5373	.18675	.650509	0.93	2.5345	.40389	.394554
0.44	1.5527	.19109	.644036	0.94	2.5600	.40824	.390628
0.45	1.5683	0.19543	0.637628	0.95	2.5857	0.41258	0.386741
0.46	1.5841	.19978	.631284	0.96	2.6117	.41692	.382893
0.47	1.6000	.20412	.625002	0.97	2.6379	.42127	.379083
0.48	1.6161	.20846	.618783	0.98	2.6645	.42561	.375311
0.49	1.6323	.21280	.612626	0.99	2.6912	.42995	.371577
0.50	1.6487	0.21715	0.606531	1.00	2.7183	0.43429	0.367879

x	e^x	$\text{Log}_{10}(e^x)$	e^{-x}	x	e^x	$\text{Log}_{10}(e^x)$	e^{-x}
1.00	2.7183	0.43429	0.367879	**1.50**	4.4817	0.65144	0.223130
1.01	2.7456	.43864	.364219	1.51	4.5267	.65578	.220910
1.02	2.7732	.44298	.360595	1.52	4.5722	.66013	.218712
1.03	2.8011	.44732	.357007	1.53	4.6182	.66447	.216536
1.04	2.8292	.45167	.353455	1.54	4.6646	.66881	.214381
1.05	2.8577	0.45601	0.349938	**1.55**	4.7115	0.67316	0.212248
1.06	2.8864	.46035	.346456	1.56	4.7588	.67750	.210136
1.07	2.9154	.46470	.343009	1.57	4.8066	.68184	.208045
1.08	2.9447	.46904	.339596	1.58	4.8550	.68619	.205975
1.09	2.9743	.47338	.336216	1.59	4.9037	.69053	.203926
1.10	3.0042	0.47772	0.332871	**1.60**	4.9530	0.69487	0.201897
1.11	3.0344	.48207	.329559	1.61	5.0028	.69921	.199888
1.12	3.0649	.48641	.326280	1.62	5.0531	.70356	.197899
1.13	3.0957	.49075	.323033	1.63	5.1039	.70790	.195930
1.14	3.1268	.49510	.319819	1.64	5.1552	.71224	.193980
1.15	3.1582	0.49944	0.316637	**1.65**	5.2070	0.71659	0.192050
1.16	3.1899	.50378	.313486	1.66	5.2593	.72093	.190139
1.17	3.2220	.50812	.310367	1.67	5.3122	.72527	.188247
1.18	3.2544	.51247	.307279	1.68	5.3656	.72961	.186374
1.19	3.2871	.51681	.304221	1.69	5.4195	.73396	.184520
1.20	3.3201	0.52115	0.301194	**1.70**	5.4739	0.73830	0.182684
1.21	3.3535	.52550	.298197	1.71	5.5290	.74264	.180866
1.22	3.3872	.52984	.295230	1.72	5.5845	.74699	.179066
1.23	3.4212	.53418	.292293	1.73	5.6407	.75133	.177284
1.24	3.4556	.53853	.289384	1.74	5.6973	.75567	.175520
1.25	3.4903	0.54287	0.286505	**1.75**	5.7546	0.76002	0.173774
1.26	3.5254	.54721	.283654	1.76	5.8124	.76436	.172045
1.27	3.5609	.55155	.280832	1.77	5.8709	.76870	.170333
1.28	3.5966	.55590	.278037	1.78	5.9299	.77304	.168638
1.29	3.6328	.56024	.275271	1.79	5.9895	.77739	.166960
1.30	3.6693	0.56458	0.272532	**1.80**	6.0496	0.78173	0.165299
1.31	3.7062	.56893	.269820	1.81	6.1104	.78607	.163654
1.32	3.7434	.57327	.267135	1.82	6.1719	.79042	.162026
1.33	3.7810	.57761	.264477	1.83	6.2339	.79476	.160414
1.34	3.8190	.58195	.261846	1.84	6.2965	.79910	.158817
1.35	3.8574	0.58630	0.259240	**1.85**	6.3598	0.80344	0.157237
1.36	3.8962	.59064	.256661	1.86	6.4237	.80779	.155673
1.37	3.9354	.59498	.254107	1.87	6.4883	.81213	.154124
1.38	3.9749	.59933	.251579	1.88	6.5535	.81647	.152590
1.39	4.0149	.60367	.249075	1.89	6.6194	.82082	.151072
1.40	4.0552	0.60801	0.246597	**1.90**	6.6859	0.82516	0.149569
1.41	4.0960	.61236	.244143	1.91	6.7531	.82950	.148080
1.42	4.1371	.61670	.241714	1.92	6.8210	.83385	.146607
1.43	4.1787	.62104	.239309	1.93	6.8895	.83819	.145148
1.44	4.2207	.62538	.236928	1.94	6.9588	.84253	.143704
1.45	4.2631	0.62973	0.234570	**1.95**	7.0287	0.84687	0.142274
1.46	4.3060	.63407	.232236	1.96	7.0993	.85122	.140858
1.47	4.3492	.63841	.229925	1.97	7.1707	.85556	.139457
1.48	4.3929	.64276	.227638	1.98	7.2427	.85990	.138069
1.49	4.4371	.64710	.225373	1.99	7.3155	.86425	.136695
1.50	4.4817	0.65144	0.223130	**2.00**	7.3891	0.86859	0.135335

x	e^x	$Log_{10}(e^x)$	e^{-x}	x	e^x	$Log_{10}(e^x)$	e^{-x}
2.00	7.3891	0.86859	0.135335	**2.50**	12.182	1.08574	0.082085
2.01	7.4633	.87293	.133989	2.51	12.305	1.09008	.081268
2.02	7.5383	.87727	.132655	2.52	12.429	1.09442	.080460
2.03	7.6141	.88162	.131336	2.53	12.554	1.09877	.079659
2.04	7.6906	.88596	.130029	2.54	12.680	1.10311	.078866
2.05	7.7679	0.89030	0.128735	**2.55**	12.807	1.10745	0.078082
2.06	7.8460	.89465	.127454	2.56	12.936	1.11179	.077305
2.07	7.9248	.89899	.126186	2.57	13.066	1.11614	.076536
2.08	8.0045	.90333	.124930	2.58	13.197	1.12048	.075774
2.09	8.0849	.90768	.123687	2.59	13.330	1.12482	.075020
2.10	8.1662	0.91202	0.122456	**2.60**	13.464	1.12917	0.074274
2.11	8.2482	.91636	.121238	2.61	13.599	1.13351	.073535
2.12	8.3311	.92070	.120032	2.62	13.736	1.13785	.072803
2.13	8.4149	.92505	.118837	2.63	13.874	1.14219	.072078
2.14	8.4994	.92939	.117655	2.64	14.013	1.14654	.071361
2.15	8.5849	0.93373	0.116484	**2.65**	14.154	1.15088	0.070651
2.16	8.6711	.93808	.115325	2.66	14.296	1.15522	.069948
2.17	8.7583	.94242	.114178	2.67	14.440	1.15957	.069252
2.18	8.8463	.94676	.113042	2.68	14.585	1.16391	.068563
2.19	8.9352	.95110	.111917	2.69	14.732	1.16825	.067881
2.20	9.0250	0.95545	0.110803	**2.70**	14.880	1.17260	0.067206
2.21	9.1157	.95979	.109701	2.71	15.029	1.17694	.066537
2.22	9.2073	.96413	.108609	2.72	15.180	1.18128	.065875
2.23	9.2999	.96848	.107528	2.73	15.333	1.18562	.065219
2.24	9.3933	.97282	.106459	2.74	15.487	1.18997	.064570
2.25	9.4877	0.97716	0.105399	**2.75**	15.643	1.19431	0.063928
2.26	9.5831	.98151	.104350	2.76	15.800	1.19865	.063292
2.27	9.6794	.98585	.103312	2.77	15.959	1.20300	.062662
2.28	9.7767	.99019	.102284	2.78	16.119	1.20734	.062039
2.29	9.8749	.99453	.101266	2.79	16.281	1.21168	.061421
2.30	9.9742	0.99888	0.100259	**2.80**	16.445	1.21602	0.060810
2.31	10.074	1.00322	.099261	2.81	16.610	1.22037	.060205
2.32	10.176	1.00756	.098274	2.82	16.777	1.22471	.059606
2.33	10.278	1.01191	.097296	2.83	16.945	1.22905	.059013
2.34	10.381	1.01625	.096328	2.84	17.116	1.23340	.058426
2.35	10.486	1.02059	0.095369	**2.85**	17.288	1.23774	0.057844
2.36	10.591	1.02493	.094420	2.86	17.462	1.24208	.057269
2.37	10.697	1.02928	.093481	2.87	17.637	1.24643	.056699
2.38	10.805	1.03362	.092551	2.88	17.814	1.25077	.056135
2.39	10.913	1.03796	.091630	2.89	17.993	1.25511	.055576
2.40	11.023	1.04231	0.090718	**2.90**	18.174	1.25945	0.055023
2.41	11.134	1.04665	.089815	2.91	18.357	1.26380	.054476
2.42	11.246	1.05099	.088922	2.92	18.541	1.26814	.053934
2.43	11.359	1.05534	.088037	2.93	18.728	1.27248	.053397
2.44	11.473	1.05968	.087161	2.94	18.916	1.27683	.052866
2.45	11.588	1.06402	0.086294	**2.95**	19.106	1.28117	0.052340
2.46	11.705	1.06836	.085435	2.96	19.298	1.28551	.051819
2.47	11.822	1.07271	.084585	2.97	19.492	1.28985	.051303
2.48	11.941	1.07705	.083743	2.98	19.688	1.29420	.050793
2.49	12.061	1.08139	.082910	2.99	19.886	1.29854	.050287
2.50	12.182	1.08574	0.082085	**3.00**	20.086	1.30288	0.049787

714

x	e^x	$\text{Log}_{10}(e^x)$	e^{-x}	x	e^x	$\text{Log}_{10}(e^x)$	e^{-x}
3.00	20.086	1.30288	0.049787	**3.50**	33.115	1.52003	0.030197
3.01	20.287	1.30723	.049292	3.51	33.448	1.52437	.029897
3.02	20.491	1.31157	.048801	3.52	33.784	1.52872	.029599
3.03	20.697	1.31591	.048316	3.53	34.124	1.53306	.029305
3.04	20.905	1.32026	.047835	3.54	34.467	1.53740	.029013
3.05	21.115	1.32460	0.047359	**3.55**	34.813	1.54175	0.028725
3.06	21.328	1.32894	.046888	3.56	35.163	1.54609	.028439
3.07	21.542	1.33328	.046421	3.57	35.517	1.55043	.028156
3.08	21.758	1.33763	.045959	3.58	35.874	1.55477	.027876
3.09	21.977	1.34197	.045502	3.59	36.234	1.55912	.027598
3.10	22.198	1.34631	0.045049	**3.60**	36.598	1.56346	0.027324
3.11	22.421	1.35066	.044601	3.61	36.966	1.56780	.027052
3.12	22.646	1.35500	.044157	3.62	37.338	1.57215	.026783
3.13	22.874	1.35934	.043718	3.63	37.713	1.57649	.026516
3.14	23.104	1.36368	.043283	3.64	38.092	1.58083	.026252
3.15	23.336	1.36803	0.042852	**3.65**	38.475	1.58517	0.025991
3.16	23.571	1.37237	.042426	3.66	38.861	1.58952	.025733
3.17	23.807	1.37671	.042004	3.67	39.252	1.59386	.025476
3.18	24.047	1.38106	.041586	3.68	39.646	1.59820	.025223
3.19	24.288	1.38540	.041172	3.69	40.045	1.60255	.024972
3.20	24.533	1.38974	0.040762	**3.70**	40.447	1.60689	0.024724
3.21	24.779	1.39409	.040357	3.71	40.854	1.61123	.024478
3.22	25.028	1.39843	.039955	3.72	41.264	1.61558	.024234
3.23	25.280	1.40277	.039557	3.73	41.679	1.61992	.023993
3.24	25.534	1.40711	.039164	3.74	42.098	1.62426	.023754
3.25	25.790	1.41146	0.038774	**3.75**	42.521	1.62860	0.023518
3.26	26.050	1.41580	.038388	3.76	42.948	1.63295	.023284
3.27	26.311	1.42014	.038006	3.77	43.380	1.63729	.023052
3.28	26.576	1.42449	.037628	3.78	43.816	1.64163	.022823
3.29	26.843	1.42883	.037254	3.79	44.256	1.64598	.022596
3.30	27.113	1.43317	0.036883	**3.80**	44.701	1.65032	0.022371
3.31	27.385	1.43751	.036516	3.81	45.150	1.65466	.022148
3.32	27.660	1.44186	.036153	3.82	45.604	1.65900	.021928
3.33	27.938	1.44620	.035793	3.83	46.063	1.66335	.021710
3.34	28.219	1.45054	.035437	3.84	46.525	1.66769	.021494
3.35	28.503	1.45489	0.035084	**3.85**	46.993	1.67203	0.021280
3.36	28.789	1.45923	.034735	3.86	47.465	1.67638	.021068
3.37	29.079	1.46357	.034390	3.87	47.942	1.68072	.020858
3.38	29.371	1.46792	.034047	3.88	48.424	1.68506	.020651
3.39	29.666	1.47226	.033709	3.89	48.911	1.68941	.020445
3.40	29.964	1.47660	0.033373	**3.90**	49.402	1.69375	0.020242
3.41	30.265	1.48094	.033041	3.91	49.899	1.69809	.020041
3.42	30.569	1.48529	.032712	3.92	50.400	1.70243	.019841
3.43	30.877	1.48963	.032387	3.93	50.907	1.70678	.019644
3.44	31.187	1.49397	.032065	3.94	51.419	1.71112	.019448
3.45	31.500	1.49832	0.031746	**3.95**	51.935	1.71546	0.019255
3.46	31.817	1.50266	.031430	3.96	52.457	1.71981	.019063
3.47	32.137	1.50700	.031117	3.97	52.985	1.72415	.018873
3.48	32.460	1.51134	.030807	3.98	53.517	1.72849	.018686
3.49	32.786	1.51569	.030501	3.99	54.055	1.73283	.018500
3.50	33.115	1.52003	0.030197	**4.00**	54.598	1.73718	0.018316

x	e^x	$\text{Log}_{10}(e^x)$	e^{-x}	x	e^x	$\text{Log}_{10}(e^x)$	e^{-x}
4.00	54.598	1.73718	0.018316	**4.50**	90.017	1.95433	0.011109
4.01	55.147	1.74152	.018133	4.51	90.922	1.95867	.010998
4.02	55.701	1.74586	.017953	4.52	91.836	1.96301	.010889
4.03	56.261	1.75021	.017774	4.53	92.759	1.96735	.010781
4.04	56.826	1.75455	.017597	4.54	93.691	1.97170	.010673
4.05	57.397	1.75889	0.017422	**4.55**	94.632	1.97604	0.010567
4.06	57.974	1.76324	.017249	4.56	95.583	1.98038	.010462
4.07	58.557	1.76758	.017077	4.57	96.544	1.98473	.010358
4.08	59.145	1.77192	.016907	4.58	97.514	1.98907	.010255
4.09	59.740	1.77626	.016739	4.59	98.494	1.99341	.010153
4.10	60.340	1.78061	0.016573	**4.60**	99.484	1.99775	0.010052
4.11	60.947	1.78495	.016408	4.61	100.48	2.00210	.009952
4.12	61.559	1.78929	.016245	4.62	101.49	2.00644	.009853
4.13	62.178	1.79364	.016083	4.63	102.51	2.01078	.009755
4.14	62.803	1.79798	.015923	4.64	103.54	2.01513	.009658
4.15	63.434	1.80232	0.015764	**4.65**	104.58	2.01947	0.009562
4.16	64.072	1.80667	.015608	4.66	105.64	2.02381	.009466
4.17	64.715	1.81101	.015452	4.67	106.70	2.02816	.009372
4.18	65.366	1.81535	.015299	4.68	107.77	2.03250	.009279
4.19	66.023	1.81969	.015146	4.69	108.85	2.03684	.009187
4.20	66.686	1.82404	0.014996	**4.70**	109.95	2.04118	0.009095
4.21	67.357	1.82838	.014846	4.71	111.05	2.04553	.009005
4.22	68.033	1.83272	.014699	4.72	112.17	2.04987	.008915
4.23	68.717	1.83707	.014552	4.73	113.30	2.05421	.008826
4.24	69.408	1.84141	.014408	4.74	114.43	2.05856	.008739
4.25	70.105	1.84575	0.014264	**4.75**	115.58	2.06290	0.008652
4.26	70.810	1.85009	.014122	4.76	116.75	2.06724	.008566
4.27	71.522	1.85444	.013982	4.77	117.92	2.07158	.008480
4.28	72.240	1.85878	.013843	4.78	119.10	2.07593	.008396
4.29	72.966	1.86312	.013705	4.79	120.30	2.08027	.008312
4.30	73.700	1.86747	0.013569	**4.80**	121.51	2.08461	0.008230
4.31	74.440	1.87181	.013434	4.81	122.73	2.08896	.008148
4.32	75.189	1.87615	.013300	4.82	123.97	2.09330	.008067
4.33	75.944	1.88050	.013168	4.83	125.21	2.09764	.007987
4.34	76.708	1.88484	.013037	4.84	126.47	2.10199	.007907
4.35	77.478	1.88918	0.012907	**4.85**	127.74	2.10633	0.007828
4.36	78.257	1.89352	.012778	4.86	129.02	2.11067	.007750
4.37	79.044	1.89787	.012651	4.87	130.32	2.11501	.007673
4.38	79.838	1.90221	.012525	4.88	131.63	2.11936	.007597
4.39	80.640	1.90655	.012401	4.89	132.95	2.12370	.007521
4.40	81.451	1.91090	0.012277	**4.90**	134.29	2.12804	0.007447
4.41	82.269	1.91524	.012155	4.91	135.64	2.13239	.007372
4.42	83.096	1.91958	.012034	4.92	137.00	2.13673	.007299
4.43	83.931	1.92392	.011914	4.93	138.38	2.14107	.007227
4.44	84.775	1.92827	.011796	4.94	139.77	2.14541	.007155
4.45	85.627	1.93261	0.011679	**4.95**	141.17	2.14976	0.007083
4.46	86.488	1.93695	.011562	4.96	142.59	2.15410	.007013
4.47	87.357	1.94130	.011447	4.97	144.03	2.15844	.006943
4.48	88.235	1.94564	.011333	4.98	145.47	2.16279	.006874
4.49	89.121	1.94998	.011221	4.99	146.94	2.16713	.006806
4.50	90.017	1.95433	0.011109	**5.00**	148.41	2.17147	0.006738

x	e^x	$\text{Log}_{10}(e^x)$	e^{-x}	x	e^x	$\text{Log}_{10}(e^x)$	e^{-x}
5.00	148.41	2.17147	0.006738	**5.50**	244.69	2.38862	0.0040868
5.01	149.90	2.17582	.006671	5.55	257.24	2.41033	.0038875
5.02	151.41	2.18016	.006605	5.60	270.43	2.43205	.0036979
5.03	152.93	2.18450	.006539	5.65	284.29	2.45376	.0035175
5.04	154.47	2.18884	.006474	5.70	298.87	2.47548	.0033460
5.05	156.02	2.19319	0.006409	**5.75**	314.19	2.49719	0.0031828
5.06	157.59	2.19753	.006346	5.80	330.30	2.51891	.0030276
5.07	159.17	2.20187	.006282	5.85	347.23	2.54062	.0028799
5.08	160.77	2.20622	.006220	5.90	365.04	2.56234	.0027394
5.09	162.39	2.21056	.006158	5.95	383.75	2.58405	.0026058
5.10	164.02	2.21490	0.006097	**6.00**	403.43	2.60577	0.0024788
5.11	165.67	2.21924	.006036	6.05	424.11	2.62748	.0023579
5.12	167.34	2.22359	.005976	6.10	445.86	2.64920	.0022429
5.13	169.02	2.22793	.005917	6.15	468.72	2.67091	.0021335
5.14	170.72	2.23227	.005858	6.20	492.75	2.69263	.0020294
5.15	172.43	2.23662	0.005799	**6.25**	518.01	2.71434	0.0019305
5.16	174.16	2.24096	.005742	6.30	544.57	2.73606	.0018363
5.17	175.91	2.24530	.005685	6.35	572.49	2.75777	.0017467
5.18	177.68	2.24965	.005628	6.40	601.85	2.77948	.0016616
5.19	179.47	2.25399	.005572	6.45	632.70	2.80120	.0015805
5.20	181.27	2.25833	0.005517	**6.50**	665.14	2.82291	0.0015034
5.21	183.09	2.26267	.005462	6.55	699.24	2.84463	.0014301
5.22	184.93	2.26702	.005407	6.60	735.10	2.86634	.0013604
5.23	186.79	2.27136	.005354	6.65	772.78	2.88806	.0012940
5.24	188.67	2.27570	.005300	6.70	812.41	2.90977	.0012309
5.25	190.57	2.28005	0.005248	**6.75**	854.06	2.93149	0.0011709
5.26	192.48	2.28439	.005195	6.80	897.85	2.95320	.0011138
5.27	194.42	2.28873	.005144	6.85	943.88	2.97492	.0010595
5.28	196.37	2.29307	.005092	6.90	992.27	2.99663	.0010078
5.29	198.34	2.29742	.005042	6.95	1043.1	3.01835	.0009586
5.30	200.34	2.30176	0.004992	**7.00**	1096.6	3.04006	0.0009119
5.31	202.35	2.30610	.004942	7.05	1152.9	3.06178	.0008674
5.32	204.38	2.31045	.004893	7.10	1212.0	3.08349	.0008251
5.33	206.44	2.31479	.004844	7.15	1274.1	3.10521	.0007849
5.34	208.51	2.31913	.004796	7.20	1339.4	3.12692	.0007466
5.35	210.61	2.32348	0.004748	**7.25**	1408.1	3.14863	0.0007102
5.36	212.72	2.32782	.004701	7.30	1480.3	3.17035	.0006755
5.37	214.86	2.33216	.004654	7.35	1556.2	3.19206	.0006426
5.38	217.02	2.33650	.004608	7.40	1636.0	3.21378	.0006113
5.39	219.20	2.34085	.004562	7.45	1719.9	3.23549	.0005814
5.40	221.41	2.34519	0.004517	**7.50**	1808.0	3.25721	0.0005531
5.41	223.63	2.34953	.004472	7.55	1900.7	3.27892	.0005261
5.42	225.88	2.35388	.004427	7.60	1998.2	3.30064	.0005005
5.43	228.15	2.35822	.004383	7.65	2100.6	3.32235	.0004760
5.44	230.44	2.36256	.004339	7.70	2208.3	3.34407	.0004528
5.45	232.76	2.36690	0.004296	**7.75**	2321.6	3.36578	0.0004307
5.46	235.10	2.37125	.004254	7.80	2440.6	3.38750	.0004097
5.47	237.46	2.37559	.004211	7.85	2565.7	3.40921	.0003898
5.48	239.85	2.37993	.004169	7.90	2697.3	3.43093	.0003707
5.49	242.26	2.38428	.004128	7.95	2835.6	3.45264	.0003527
5.50	244.69	2.38862	0.004087	**8.00**	2981.0	3.47436	0.0003355

x	e^x	$Log_{10}(e^x)$	e^{-x}	x	e^x	$Log_{10}(e^x)$	e^{-x}
8.00	2981.0	3.47436	0.0003355	**9.00**	8103.1	3.90865	0.0001234
8.05	3133.8	3.49607	.0003191	9.05	8518.5	3.93037	.0001174
8.10	3294.5	3.51779	.0003035	9.10	8955.3	3.95208	.0001117
8.15	3463.4	3.53950	.0002887	9.15	9414.4	3.97379	.0001062
8.20	3641.0	3.56121	.0002747	9.20	9897.1	3.99551	.0001010
8.25	3827.6	3.58293	0.0002613	**9.25**	10405	4.01722	0.0000961
8.30	4023.9	3.60464	.0002485	9.30	10938	4.03894	.0000914
8.35	4230.2	3.62636	.0002364	9.35	11499	4.06065	.0000870
8.40	4447.1	3.64807	.0002249	9.40	12088	4.08237	.0000827
8.45	4675.1	3.66979	.0002139	9.45	12708	4.10408	.0000787
8.50	4914.8	3.69150	0.0002035	**9.50**	13360	4.12580	0.0000749
8.55	5166.8	3.71322	.0001935	9.55	14045	4.14751	.0000712
8.60	5431.7	3.73493	.0001841	9.60	14765	4.16923	.0000677
8.65	5710.1	3.75665	.0001751	9.65	15522	4.19094	.0000644
8.70	6002.9	3.77836	.0001666	9.70	16318	4.21266	.0000613
8.75	6310.7	3.80008	0.0001585	**9.75**	17154	4.23437	0.0000583
8.80	6634.2	3.82179	.0001507	9.80	18034	4.25609	.0000555
8.85	6974.4	3.84351	.0001434	9.85	18958	4.27780	.0000527
8.90	7332.0	3.86522	.0001364	9.90	19930	4.29952	.0000502
8.95	7707.9	3.88694	.0001297	9.95	20952	4.32123	0.0000477
9.00	8103.1	3.90865	0.0001234	**10.00**	22026	4.34294	0.0000454

TABLE C—A BRIEF TABLE OF INTEGRALS

Note. An arbitrary constant is to be added to the formula for each indefinite integral.

Elementary Integrals

1. $\displaystyle\int c\, f(u)du = c\int f(u)du.$

2. $\displaystyle\int (f(u) + g(u))du = \int f(u)du + \int g(u)du.$

3. $\displaystyle\int u^n du = \frac{u^{n+1}}{n+1}, \qquad n \neq -1.$

4. $\displaystyle\int \frac{du}{u} = \ln|u|.$

5. $\displaystyle\int e^u du = e^u.$

6. $\displaystyle\int a^u du = \frac{a^u}{\ln a}, \qquad a > 0.$

7. $\displaystyle\int \sin u\, du = -\cos u.$

8. $\displaystyle\int \cos u\, du = \sin u.$

9. $\displaystyle\int \tan u\, du = -\ln|\cos u|.$

10. $\displaystyle\int \cot u\, du = \ln|\sin u|.$

11. $\displaystyle\int \sec u\, du = \ln|\sec u + \tan u|.$

12. $\displaystyle\int \csc u\, du = -\ln|\csc u + \cot u| = \ln|\csc u - \cot u|.$

13. $\displaystyle\int \sec^2 u\, du = \tan u.$

14. $\displaystyle\int \csc^2 u\, du = -\cot u.$

15. $\displaystyle\int \sec u \tan u \, du = \sec u.$

16. $\displaystyle\int \csc u \cot u \, du = -\csc u.$

17. $\displaystyle\int \sinh u \, du = \cosh u.$

18. $\displaystyle\int \cosh u \, du = \sinh u.$

19. $\displaystyle\int \frac{du}{a^2 + u^2} = \frac{1}{a} \tan^{-1} \frac{u}{a}.$

20. $\displaystyle\int \frac{du}{a^2 - u^2} = \frac{1}{2a} \ln \left| \frac{a + u}{a - u} \right|.$

21. $\displaystyle\int \frac{du}{u^2 - a^2} = \frac{1}{2a} \ln \left| \frac{u - a}{u + a} \right|.$

22. $\displaystyle\int \frac{du}{\sqrt{a^2 - u^2}} = \sin^{-1} \frac{u}{a}.$

23. $\displaystyle\int \frac{du}{\sqrt{u^2 - a^2}} = \ln|u + \sqrt{u^2 - a^2}|.$

24. $\displaystyle\int \frac{du}{\sqrt{u^2 + a^2}} = \ln(u + \sqrt{u^2 + a^2}).$

Integrand Containing a + bu

25. $\displaystyle\int \frac{u \, du}{a + bu} = \frac{1}{b^2}(a + bu - a \ln|a + bu|).$

26. $\displaystyle\int \frac{u \, du}{(a + bu)^2} = \frac{1}{b^2} \left(\frac{a}{a + bu} + \ln|a + bu| \right).$

27. $\displaystyle\int \frac{u^2 \, du}{(a + bu)^2} = \frac{1}{b^3} \left(a + bu - \frac{a^2}{a + bu} - 2a \ln|a + bu| \right).$

28. $\displaystyle\int \frac{u \, du}{(a + bu)^3} = \frac{1}{b^2} \left(-\frac{1}{a + bu} + \frac{a}{2(a + bu)^2} \right).$

29. $\displaystyle\int \frac{du}{u(a + bu)} = \frac{1}{a} \ln \left| \frac{u}{a + bu} \right|.$

30. $\displaystyle\int \frac{du}{u^2(a + bu)} = -\frac{1}{au} + \frac{b}{a^2} \ln \left| \frac{a + bu}{u} \right|.$

TABLE C—A BRIEF TABLE OF INTEGRALS—Continued   721

31. $\displaystyle\int \frac{du}{u(a + bu)^2} = \frac{1}{a(a + bu)} - \frac{1}{a^2} \ln\left|\frac{a + bu}{u}\right|.$

32. $\displaystyle\int u^m(a + bu)^n du = \frac{u^{m+1}(a + bu)^n}{m + n + 1} + \frac{an}{m + n + 1}\int u^m(a + bu)^{n-1}du.$

Integrand Containing $\sqrt{a + bu}$

33. $\displaystyle\int u\sqrt{a + bu}\, du = -\frac{2(2a - 3bu)(a + bu)^{3/2}}{15b^2}.$

34. $\displaystyle\int u^n\sqrt{a + bu}\, du = \frac{2u^n(a + bu)^{3/2}}{b(2n + 3)} - \frac{2an}{b(2n + 3)}\int u^{n-1}\sqrt{a + bu}\, du.$

35. $\displaystyle\int \frac{u\, du}{\sqrt{a + bu}} = \frac{2(bu - 2a)\sqrt{a + bu}}{3b^2}.$

36. $\displaystyle\int \frac{u^n\, du}{\sqrt{a + bu}} = \frac{2u^n\sqrt{a + bu}}{b(2n + 1)} - \frac{2an}{b(2n + 1)}\int \frac{u^{n-1}\, du}{\sqrt{a + bu}}.$

37. $\displaystyle\int \frac{du}{u\sqrt{a + bu}} = \frac{1}{\sqrt{a}} \ln\left|\frac{\sqrt{a + bu} - \sqrt{a}}{\sqrt{a + bu} + \sqrt{a}}\right|, \qquad a > 0.$

38. $\displaystyle\int \frac{du}{u\sqrt{a + bu}} = \frac{2}{\sqrt{-a}} \tan^{-1}\sqrt{\frac{a + bu}{-a}}, \qquad a < 0.$

39. $\displaystyle\int \frac{du}{u^n\sqrt{a + bu}} = -\frac{\sqrt{a + bu}}{a(n - 1)u^{n-1}} - \frac{b(2n - 3)}{2a(n - 1)}\int \frac{du}{u^{n-1}\sqrt{a + bu}}.$

40. $\displaystyle\int \frac{\sqrt{a + bu}}{u}\, du = 2\sqrt{a + bu} + a\int \frac{du}{u\sqrt{a + bu}}.$

Integrand Containing $\sqrt{a^2 - u^2}$

See also formulas (20) and (22).

41. $\displaystyle\int \sqrt{a^2 - u^2}\, du = \frac{u}{2}\sqrt{a^2 - u^2} + \frac{a^2}{2}\sin^{-1}\frac{u}{a}.$

42. $\displaystyle\int \frac{\sqrt{a^2 - u^2}}{u}\, du = \sqrt{a^2 - u^2} - a\ln\left|\frac{a + \sqrt{a^2 - u^2}}{u}\right|.$

43. $\displaystyle\int \frac{\sqrt{a^2 - u^2}}{u^2}\, du = -\frac{\sqrt{a^2 - u^2}}{u} - \sin^{-1}\frac{u}{a}.$

44. $\displaystyle \int \frac{du}{u\sqrt{a^2 - u^2}} = -\frac{1}{a} \ln\left|\frac{a + \sqrt{a^2 - u^2}}{u}\right|.$

45. $\displaystyle \int \frac{du}{u^2\sqrt{a^2 - u^2}} = -\frac{\sqrt{a^2 - u^2}}{a^2 u}.$

46. $\displaystyle \int \frac{du}{(a^2 - u^2)^{3/2}} = \frac{u}{a^2\sqrt{a^2 - u^2}}.$

47. $\displaystyle \int \frac{u^2\,du}{\sqrt{a^2 - u^2}} = -\frac{u}{2}\sqrt{a^2 - u^2} + \frac{a^2}{2}\sin^{-1}\frac{u}{a}.$

Integrand Containing $\sqrt{u^2 \pm a^2}$

See also formulas (19), (21), (23), and (24).

48. $\displaystyle \int \sqrt{u^2 \pm a^2}\,du = \frac{u}{2}\sqrt{u^2 \pm a^2} \pm \frac{a^2}{2}\ln\left|u + \sqrt{u^2 \pm a^2}\right|.$

49. $\displaystyle \int \sqrt{(u^2 \pm a^2)^n}\,du = \frac{u\sqrt{(u^2 \pm a^2)^n}}{n+1} \pm \frac{na^2}{n+1}\int\sqrt{(u^2 \pm a^2)^{n-2}}\,du, \; n \neq -1.$

50. $\displaystyle \int \frac{du}{\sqrt{u^2 \pm a^2}} = \ln\left|u + \sqrt{u^2 \pm a^2}\right|.$

51. $\displaystyle \int \frac{du}{(u^2 \pm a^2)^{3/2}} = \frac{\pm u}{a^2\sqrt{u^2 \pm a^2}}.$

52. $\displaystyle \int \frac{u^2\,du}{\sqrt{u^2 \pm a^2}} = \frac{u}{2}\sqrt{u^2 \pm a^2} \mp \frac{a^2}{2}\ln\left|u + \sqrt{u^2 \pm a^2}\right|.$

53. $\displaystyle \int \frac{du}{u\sqrt{u^2 + a^2}} = -\frac{1}{a}\ln\left|\frac{a + \sqrt{u^2 + a^2}}{u}\right|.$

54. $\displaystyle \int \frac{du}{u\sqrt{u^2 - a^2}} = \frac{1}{a}\cos^{-1}\frac{a}{u}, \qquad u > a > 0.$

55. $\displaystyle \int \frac{du}{u^2\sqrt{u^2 \pm a^2}} = \mp \frac{\sqrt{u^2 \pm a^2}}{a^2 u}.$

56. $\displaystyle \int \frac{du}{u^3\sqrt{u^2 + a^2}} = -\frac{\sqrt{u^2 + a^2}}{2a^2 u^2} + \frac{1}{2a^3}\ln\left|\frac{a + \sqrt{u^2 + a^2}}{u}\right|.$

TABLE C—A BRIEF TABLE OF INTEGRALS—Continued   723

57. $\displaystyle\int \frac{du}{u^3\sqrt{u^2-a^2}} = \frac{\sqrt{u^2-a^2}}{2a^2u^2} + \frac{1}{2a^3}\cos^{-1}\frac{a}{u}, \qquad u > a > 0.$

58. $\displaystyle\int \frac{\sqrt{u^2+a^2}}{u}\,du = \sqrt{u^2+a^2} - a\ln\left|\frac{a+\sqrt{u^2+a^2}}{u}\right|.$

59. $\displaystyle\int \frac{\sqrt{u^2-a^2}}{u}\,du = \sqrt{u^2-a^2} - a\cos^{-1}\frac{a}{u}, \qquad u > a > 0.$

60. $\displaystyle\int \frac{\sqrt{u^2\pm a^2}}{u^2}\,du = -\frac{\sqrt{u^2\pm a^2}}{u} + \ln\left|u+\sqrt{u^2\pm a^2}\right|.$

Integrand Containing $\sqrt{Ax^2+Bx+C}$

These integrals can be transformed into types considered in formulas (41) through (60) by the following substitutions.

Let $D = B^2 - 4AC$.

Case 1. If $A > 0$ and $D > 0$, let $u = \sqrt{A}x + \dfrac{B}{2\sqrt{A}}$,

and let $a = \sqrt{D/4A}$.

Then $Ax^2 + Bx + C = u^2 - a^2$.

Case 2. If $A > 0$ and $D < 0$, let $u = \sqrt{A}x + \dfrac{B}{2\sqrt{A}}$,

and let $a = \sqrt{-D/4A}$.

Then $Ax^2 + Bx + C = u^2 + a^2$.

Case 3. If $A < 0$ and $D > 0$, let $u = \sqrt{-A}x - \dfrac{B}{2\sqrt{-A}}$,

and let $a = \sqrt{-D/4A}$.

Then $Ax^2 + Bx + C = a^2 - u^2$.

Case 4. If $A < 0$ and $D < 0$ then $\sqrt{Ax^2+Bx+C}$ is imaginary for all real values of x. This case cannot arise in a real integrand.

Integrand Containing Trigonometric Functions

See also formulas (7) through (16).

61. $\displaystyle\int \sin^2 u\,du = \frac{1}{2}u - \frac{1}{4}\sin 2u.$

62. $\displaystyle\int \cos^2 u\ du = \frac{1}{2}u + \frac{1}{4}\sin 2u.$

63. $\displaystyle\int \tan^2 u\ du = \tan u - u.$

64. $\displaystyle\int \cot^2 u\ du = -\cot u - u.$

65. $\displaystyle\int \tan^3 u\ du = \frac{1}{2}\tan^2 u + \ln|\cos u|.$

66. $\displaystyle\int \cot^3 u\ du = -\frac{1}{2}\cot^2 u - \ln|\sin u|.$

67. $\displaystyle\int \sec^3 u\ du = \frac{1}{2}\sec u \tan u + \frac{1}{2}\ln|\sec u + \tan u|.$

68. $\displaystyle\int \csc^3 u\ du = -\frac{1}{2}\csc u \cot u + \frac{1}{2}\ln|\csc u - \cot u|.$

69. $\displaystyle\int \sin^n u\ du = -\frac{\sin^{n-1} u \cos u}{n} + \frac{n-1}{n}\int \sin^{n-2} u\ du.$

70. $\displaystyle\int \cos^n u\ du = \frac{\cos^{n-1} u \sin u}{n} + \frac{n-1}{n}\int \cos^{n-2} u\ du.$

71. $\displaystyle\int \tan^n u\ du = \frac{\tan^{n-1} u}{n-1} - \int \tan^{n-2} u\ du.$

72. $\displaystyle\int \cot^n u\ du = -\frac{\cot^{n-1} u}{n-1} - \int \cot^{n-2} u\ du.$

73. $\displaystyle\int \sec^n u\ du = \frac{\tan u \sec^{n-2} u}{n-1} + \frac{n-2}{n-1}\int \sec^{n-2} u\ du.$

74. $\displaystyle\int \csc^n u\ du = -\frac{\cot u \csc^{n-2} u}{n-1} + \frac{n-2}{n-1}\int \csc^{n-2} u\ du.$

75. $\displaystyle\int \sin au \sin bu\ du = -\frac{\sin(a+b)u}{2(a+b)} + \frac{\sin(a-b)u}{2(a-b)}, a^2 \neq b^2.$

76. $\displaystyle\int \cos au \cos bu\ du = \frac{\sin(a+b)u}{2(a+b)} + \frac{\sin(a-b)u}{2(a-b)}, a^2 \neq b^2.$

77. $\displaystyle\int \sin au \cos bu\ du = -\frac{\cos(a+b)u}{2(a+b)} - \frac{\cos(a-b)u}{2(a-b)}, a^2 \neq b^2.$

78. $\displaystyle\int u \sin u\ du = \sin u - u \cos u.$

TABLE C—A BRIEF TABLE OF INTEGRALS—Continued 725

79. $\int u \cos u \, du = \cos u + u \sin u.$

80. $\int u^n \sin u \, du = -u^n \cos u + n \int u^{n-1} \cos u \, du.$

81. $\int u^n \cos u \, du = u^n \sin u - n \int u^{n-1} \sin u \, du.$

Integrand Containing the Inverse Trigonometric Functions

82. $\int \sin^{-1} u \, du = u \sin^{-1} u + \sqrt{1 - u^2}.$

83. $\int \cos^{-1} u \, du = u \cos^{-1} u - \sqrt{1 - u^2}.$

84. $\int \tan^{-1} u \, du = u \tan^{-1} u - \frac{1}{2} \ln (1 + u^2).$

85. $\int u \sin^{-1} u \, du = \frac{2u^2 - 1}{4} \sin^{-1} u + \frac{u\sqrt{1 - u^2}}{4}.$

86. $\int u \cos^{-1} u \, du = \frac{2u^2 - 1}{4} \cos^{-1} u - \frac{u\sqrt{1 - u^2}}{4}.$

87. $\int u \tan^{-1} u \, du = \frac{u^2 + 1}{2} \tan^{-1} u - \frac{u}{2}.$

88. $\int \frac{\sin^{-1} u}{u^2} \, du = \ln \left| \frac{1 - \sqrt{1 - u^2}}{u} \right| - \frac{\sin^{-1} u}{u}.$

89. $\int \frac{\tan^{-1} u}{u^2} \, du = \ln|u| - \frac{1}{2} \ln (1 + u^2) - \frac{\tan^{-1} u}{u}.$

Integrand Containing Hyperbolic Functions

These integrals can be transformed into types already considered by using the definitions of the hyperbolic functions in terms of the exponential functions, and then making the substitutions $e^u = v$, and $du = dv/v$.

Integrand Containing the Exponential Function

See also formulas (5) and (6).

90. $\int u e^u \, du = (u - 1)e^u.$

91. $\displaystyle\int u^n e^u \, du = u^n e^u - n \int u^{n-1} e^u \, du.$

92. $\displaystyle\int \frac{e^u}{u^n} \, du = -\frac{e^u}{(n-1)u^{n-1}} + \frac{1}{n-1} \int \frac{e^u \, du}{u^{n-1}}.$

93. $\displaystyle\int e^u \ln u \, du = e^u \ln u - \int \frac{e^u}{u} \, du, \quad u > 0.$

94. $\displaystyle\int e^{au} \sin nu \, du = \frac{e^{au} \, (a \sin nu - n \cos nu)}{a^2 + n^2}.$

95. $\displaystyle\int e^{au} \cos nu \, du = \frac{e^{au} \, (a \cos nu + n \sin nu)}{a^2 + n^2}.$

Integrand Containing the Logarithmic Function

Assume $u > 0$ in formulas (96) through (101).

96. $\displaystyle\int \ln u \, du = u \ln u - u.$

97. $\displaystyle\int u^n \ln u \, du = u^{n+1} \left(\frac{\ln u}{n+1} - \frac{1}{(n+1)^2} \right), \, n \neq -1.$

98. $\displaystyle\int \frac{du}{u \ln u} = \ln|\ln u|.$

99. $\displaystyle\int u^n (\ln u)^m \, du = \frac{u^{n+1}}{n+1} (\ln u)^m - \frac{m}{n+1} \int u^n (\ln u)^{m-1} \, du, \, n \neq -1.$

100. $\displaystyle\int \sin(\ln u) du = \frac{u}{2} \left[\sin(\ln u) - \cos(\ln u) \right].$

101. $\displaystyle\int \cos(\ln u) du = \frac{u}{2} \left[\sin(\ln u) + \cos(\ln u) \right].$

Some Definite Integrals

102. $\displaystyle\int_0^\infty x^{n-1} e^{-x} \, dx = \int_0^1 \left(\ln \frac{1}{x} \right)^{n-1} dx = \Gamma(n), \quad n > 0.$

and $\Gamma(n) = (n-1)!$, if n is a positive integer.

103. $\displaystyle\int_0^1 x^{m-1}(1-x)^{n-1} \, dx = \int_0^\infty \frac{x^{m-1} \, dx}{(1+x)^{m+n}} = \frac{\Gamma(m)\Gamma(n)}{\Gamma(m+n)}, \quad m, n > 0.$

104. $\displaystyle\int_0^\infty \frac{x^{p-1}\,dx}{1+x} = \frac{\pi}{\sin p\pi}, \quad 0 < p < 1.$

105. $\displaystyle\int_0^\infty \frac{dx}{(1-x)x^p} = -\pi \cot p\pi, \quad p < 1.$

106. $\displaystyle\int_0^\infty \frac{\sin ax}{x}\,dx = \frac{\pi}{2}, \quad a > 0.$

107. $\displaystyle\int_0^\infty \frac{\tan x}{x}\,dx = \frac{\pi}{2}.$

108. $\displaystyle\int_0^\infty \sin(x^2)\,dx = \int_0^\infty \cos(x^2)\,dx = \frac{1}{2}\sqrt{\frac{\pi}{2}}.$

109. $\displaystyle\int_0^\infty e^{-a^2x^2}\,dx = \frac{\sqrt{\pi}}{2a}.$

110. $\displaystyle\int_0^{\pi/2} \sin^n x\,dx = \int_0^{\pi/2} \cos^n x\,dx.$

$$= \frac{1 \cdot 3 \cdot 5 \cdots (n-1)}{2 \cdot 4 \cdot 6 \cdots n}\frac{\pi}{2}, \quad \text{if } n \text{ is an even positive integer,}$$

$$= \frac{2 \cdot 4 \cdot 6 \cdots (n-1)}{3 \cdot 5 \cdot 7 \cdots n}, \quad \text{if } n \text{ is an odd positive integer.}$$

111. $\displaystyle\int_0^{\pi/2} \sin^m x \cos^n x\,dx, \quad m \text{ and } n \text{ positive integers,}$

$$= \frac{2 \cdot 4 \cdot 6 \cdots (m-1)}{(n+1)(n+3)\cdots(n+m)}, \quad \text{if } m \text{ is odd, } m > 1,$$

$$= \frac{2 \cdot 4 \cdot 6 \cdots (n-1)}{(m+1)(m+3)\cdots(m+n)}, \quad \text{if } n \text{ is odd, } n > 1,$$

$$= \frac{[1 \cdot 3 \cdots (m-1)][1 \cdot 3 \cdots (n-1)]}{2 \cdot 4 \cdot 6 \cdots (m+n)}\frac{\pi}{2}, \quad m \text{ and } n \text{ both even.}$$

ANSWERS TO EXERCISES

Chapter 1. Exercise 1   Page 4

1. $GH + HJ = GJ$, $GJ + JH = GH$,
$HJ + JG = HG$, $HG + GJ = HJ$,
$JG + GH = JH$, $JH + HG = JG$.

2. 5, 11, 13, 5, 3, 7, $\sqrt{5}$.   **3.** −3.   **4.** −5.   **5.** 5.   **6.** $2\sqrt{3}$.
7. (a) Horizontal line six units above the x-axis; (b) Vertical line three units to the left of the y-axis.   **8.** (a) A line through O, makes 45° angle with the positive x-axis; (b) A line through O, makes 135° angle with the positive x-axis; (c) The line of (a) shifted upward one unit; (d) A circle of radius 5, center at O; (e) the two lines of parts (a) and (b).

Chapter 1. Exercise 2   Page 9

1. (a) 9; (b) 9; (c) 9; (d) −9; (e) −9; (f) −9.   **2.** (a) 13; (b) 5; (c) $2\sqrt{5}$; (d) $16\sqrt{2}$.   **3.** (a) Yes, $|PQ| = |RS| = \sqrt{109}$, $|QR| = |SP| = \sqrt{10}$; (b) No, $|PR| = 11 \neq |QS| = \sqrt{117}$.   **5.** $x + 2y = 3$.   **6.** $10y = 8x + 69$.
7. $x^2 + y^2 = 6x - 8y$.   **8.** $x^2 + y^2 + 8x - 10y = 40$.   **9.** $x^2 = 4(y - 1)$.
10. $8x = y^2 - 2y + 17$.

Chapter 1. Exercise 3   Page 13

11. See Fig. 18. Chap. 1.
17. $y = x + 1$.   **18.** $x^2 + y^2 = 9$.   **19.** $y = 0$.   **20.** $x = 3$.   **21.** $x^2 +$
$y^2 - 2x - 4y = 44$.   **22.** $a = 11/5; b = -19/5$.   **23.** $y = x^2 - 3x + 2$.

Chapter 1. Exercise 4   Page 16

1. 1.   **2.** 1/20.   **3.** −3.   **4.** b/a.   **5.** $3b/a$.   **6.** $-b/a$.   **7.** Yes,
$m = -1/2$.   **8.** Yes, $m = 2/5$.   **9.** No, $-3/5 \neq -11/18$.   **10.** No, $8/5 \neq$
13/8.   **11.** Yes, 3/11 and 9/5.   **12.** No, $-5/14 \neq -3/15$.

Chapter 1. Exercise 5   Page 20

1. $y = 3x + 5$.   **2.** $4y + x + 7 = 0$.   **3.** (a) $y = x + 1$; (b) $2y + x = 11$;
(c) $2x - y = 2$; (d) $\sqrt{3}y = x + 4\sqrt{3} - 1$.   **4.** $y = 10x + 5$.   **5.** $6y + 2x = 7$.
6. (a) −2/3, −4/3; (b) 5, −7; (c) 1/3, −3; (d) −3, 6; (e) 0, 10;
(f) $\sqrt{3}$, $4\sqrt{3}$.   **7.** (a) 45°; (b) 45°; (c) 135°; (d) 60°; (e) 30°; (f) 90°;
8. $(-2, 3)$.   **9.** $(1, -1)$.   **10.** No.   **11.** (a) $4x - 5y = 20$; (b) $x + y = 1$;
(c) $7x + 2y = 14$; (d) $6y = 3x + 1$;   **12.** The two lines $x = 2$ and $y = 1$.
13. The lines $y = x + 2$, $y = 3$.   **14.** The lines $y = x + 2$, $y = -x - 2$.

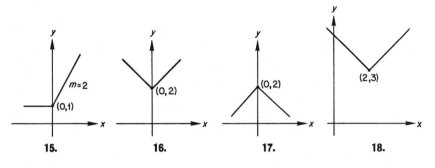

15. **16.** **17.** **18.**

20. (a) (b) above, (c) (d) below.

Chapter 1. Exercise 6   Page 22

   1. $y = x - 10,\quad y = -x.$
   3. $3y = -x,\quad y = 3x.$
   5. $x = 100,\quad y = 200.$

   2. $2y = x + 22,\quad y = -2x + 11.$
   4. $5y = 2x - 3,\quad 2y = -5x - 7.$
   10. $y = 2x + 5,\quad 2y = -x + 30.$

Chapter 1. Exercise 7   Page 25

   1. $x^2 + y^2 = 10x + 24y.$
   2. $x^2 + y^2 = 49.$
   3. $x^2 + y^2 - 2x + 2y = 2.$
   4. $x^2 + y^2 + 8x + 10y + 5 = 0.$
   5. $x^2 + y^2 - 2ax - 4ay = 0.$
   6. $x^2 + y^2 + 9 = 6x + 2by.$
   7. $x^2 + y^2 - 6x - 4y + 9 = 0.$
   8. $4x^2 + 4y^2 + 20x + 12y + 9 = 0.$
   9. $x^2 + y^2 - 10x + 4y = 52.$
   10. $x^2 + y^2 - 2x - 2y = 3.$
   11. Circle center $(2, -1)$, $r = 5$.
   12. Circle center $(-3, -4)$, $r = 1$.
   13. The point $(3, 8)$.
   14. No points.
   15. $x^2 + y^2 - 6x - 4y = 12.$
   16. $x + 2y = 2.$
   17. $(2, 0)$, $(2/5, 4/5)$.

18. P is outside the circle.

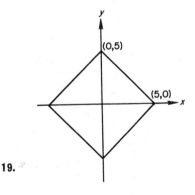

19.

22. 2.   **23.** (a) 3; (b) 5; (c) 6.
24. Yes, the line through their centers.

Chapter 1. Exercise 8   Page 32

   1. (a) $(0, 1)$, $y = -1$; (b) $(0, 1/4)$, $y = -1/4$; (c) $(0, 1/16)$, $y = -1/16$;
(d) $(0, 8)$, $y = -8$.   **4.** (a) $(1, 0)$, $x = -1$; (b) $(0, -1)$, $y = 1$; (c) $(-1, 0)$, $x = 1$;
(d) $(0, -2)$, $y = 2$; (e) $(-1/4, 0)$, $x = 1/4$; (f) $(0, -7/20)$, $y = 7/20$.
5. $8y = x^2 - 8x + 40.$ **6.** $4x = -(y^2 + 14y + 53).$ **8.** $y = x^2 - 2x + 4$ or
$y - 3 = (x - 1)^2.$

10. (a) $\dfrac{x^2}{25} + \dfrac{y^2}{16} = 1$;   (b) $\dfrac{x^2}{100} + \dfrac{y^2}{64} = 1$;

(c) $\dfrac{x^2}{25} + \dfrac{y^2}{1} = 1$;   (d) $\dfrac{x^2}{25} + \dfrac{y^2}{24} = 1$.

12. (a) $2a = 10$, $(\pm 4, 0)$; (b) $2a = 10$, $(\pm 1, 0)$; (c) $2b = 10$, $(0, \pm 4)$; (d) $2a = 10$, $(\pm 3, 0)$; (e) $2a = 4$, $(\pm 1, 0)$; (f) $2a = 10$, $(\pm 3\sqrt{11}/2, 0)$.

14. $\dfrac{x^2}{20} + \dfrac{y^2}{5} = 1$.   **15.** $\dfrac{x^2}{30} + \dfrac{y^2}{10} = 1$.   **16.** P_1 lies inside the ellipse $\dfrac{x^2}{9} + \dfrac{y^2}{4} = 1$.

17. (a) $\dfrac{x^2}{16} - \dfrac{y^2}{9} = 1$;   (b) $\dfrac{x^2}{9} - \dfrac{y^2}{16} = 1$;   (c) $\dfrac{x^2}{4} - \dfrac{y^2}{21} = 1$;   (d) $\dfrac{x^2}{1} - \dfrac{y^2}{24} = 1$;

(e) $4x^2 - \dfrac{4y^2}{99} = 1$; (f) $\dfrac{y^2}{16} - \dfrac{x^2}{9} = 1$.

19. (a) $(\pm 13, 0)$; (b) $(\pm 2, 0)$; (c) $(\pm 13, 0)$; (d) $(\pm 3, 0)$; (e) $(0, \pm 13)$; (f) $(\pm 3, 0)$.

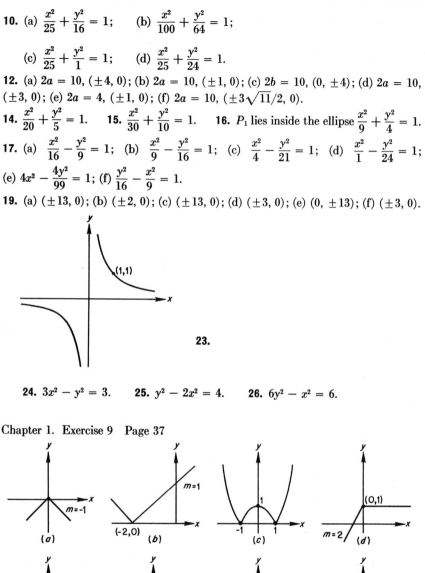

23.

24. $3x^2 - y^2 = 3$.   **25.** $y^2 - 2x^2 = 4$.   **26.** $6y^2 - x^2 = 6$.

Chapter 1. Exercise 9   Page 37

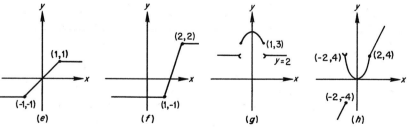

1.

2. (g) $x = \pm 1$; (h) $x = -2$.   **3.** (a) $0 \leqq x \leqq 1$, $2 \leqq x$; (b) all x; (c) $x \leqq -2$, $0 \leqq x \leqq 2$; (d) $0 < x$; (e) all x except $x = 0$, ± 3. (f) $2 < x$ and $x < -2$.
10. $h(3x^2 + 3xh + h^2)$.   **12.** $2/(x + h + 1)(x + 1)$.   **13.** ± 3.

Chapter 1. Exercise 10   Page 40

1. $(1, -2)$.   **2.** $(2, -1)$.   **3.** $(1, 3)$, $(5, 3)$.   **4.** $(1, 10)$, $(4, 1)$.   **5.** $(0, 1)$, $(2, 5)$.   **6.** $(1, 2)$.   **7.** $(-2, -1)$, $(-1, 2)$, $(4, 17)$.   **8.** $(0, 5)$, $(0, 5)$, $(3, 8)$.
9. $(-3/4, 29/2)$, $(1, 11)$, $(3, 7)$.   **10.** $(-1, 1)$, $(3, 3)$.   **11.** $(-3, 1)$, $(1, 3)$.
12. $(\pm 3, \pm 2)$.   **13.** $(1, 0)$, $(0, 1)$.   **14.** none.   **15.** 2.

Chapter 2. Exercise 1   Page 50

1. 0.   **2.** 0.   **3.** -23.   **4.** 66.   **5.** $-3/2$.   **6.** $3/2$.   **7.** 8.   **8.** -8.
9. $2x$.   **10.** $6x^2$.   **11.** $2x$.   **12.** $6x^2$.   **13.** $3x^2$.   **14.** $4v^3$.   **15.** $6x + 2$.
16. $1/4$.   **17.** (a) $3 - 5/x^2$; (b) $1 + 4/x^3$.   **18.** $1/4$.   **19.** ∞.   **20.** 0.
21. $1/2$.   **22.** ∞.   **23.** 0.   **24.** -8.   **25.** 4.   **26.** ∞.   **27.** $-\infty$.

Chapter 2. Exercise 2   Page 53

1. C.   **2.** C.   **3.** C.   **4.** C.   **5.** D at $x = 2$.   **6.** D at $x = 1$.   **7.** No.
8. (a) No; (b) No; (c) Yes, set $f(0) = -2$.   **10.** D for all x.   **11.** $a = 3$, $b = -8$.
12. $A = 3/4$.

Chapter 2. Exercise 3   Page 58

1. $x/2$.   **2.** $x^2/3$.   **3.** $-2x$.   **4.** $2x - 4$.   **5.** $3x^2 - 12$.   **6.** $-7/(x - 5)^2$.
7. $-12x/(1 + x^2)^2$.   **8.** $4(1 - x^2)/(1 + x^2)^2$.

Chapter 2. Exercise 4   Page 61

1. Crit. and low point $(0, 0)$.   **2.** Crit. point $(0, 0)$.   **3.** Crit. and high point $(0, 4)$.   **4.** Crit. and low $(2, -4)$.   **5.** Crit. and high $(-2, 18)$, Crit. and low $(2, -14)$.   **6.** None.   **7.** Crit. and high $(0, 6)$.   **8.** Crit. and high $(1, 2)$, crit. and low $(-1, -2)$.

Chapter 2. Exercise 5   Page 65

1. $24x^5(x^2 - 1)$.   **2.** $5x^4 + 4x^3 + 3x^2 + 2x + 1$.   **3.** $2000x^{199}(x^{800} + 1)$.
4. $12(x^{11} - x^5 + x^2 - x + 1)$.   **5.** -1.   **6.** $24t^5(t^2 - 1)$.   **7.** $24v^5(v^2 - 1)$.
8. $16z - 5$.   **9.** $4\pi r^2$.   **10.** $16\beta - 5$.   **11.** $15(5x + 2)^2$.   **12.** $8(2w - 1)^3$.
13. Low $(-3, -4)$.   **14.** High $(4, 25)$.   **15.** High $(0, 5)$; low $(3, 7/2)$.
16. High $(1, 2)$; low $(-5, -8.8)$.   **17.** High $(-\sqrt{3}, 6\sqrt{3})$; low $(\sqrt{3}, -6\sqrt{3})$.
18. High $(0, 4)$; low $(\pm \sqrt{10}/2, -9/4)$.   **20.** $(-1, -1)$, $(1/3, 13/27)$.
21. $y = 2x^2 - x$.   **22.** $y = x^2 + 2$, $y = 4x - x^2$.   **24.** $2y + x = 6$.
25. $(2, 1)$ $y + x = 3$, $(4, 4)$ $2y + x = 12$.   **26.** $(3, 1)$ $2y + 3x = 11$, $(6, 4)$ $4y + 3x = 34$, $(-9, 9)$ $2y = x + 27$.

Chapter 2. Exercise 6   Page 69

1. $5x^4$.   **2.** $x^4(4x - 5)/(x - 1)^2$.   **3.** $4x(x^2 - 1)$.   **4.** $-4(x + 1)/(x - 1)^3$.
5. $(ad - bc)/(cx + d)^2$.   **6.** $(adx^2 + 2aex + be - cd)/(dx + e)^2$.   **7.** $2z - 2z^{-3}$.
8. $(1 - \theta^2)/(1 + \theta^2)^2$.   **9.** $-8/(7t + 9)^2$.   **10.** $-4t/(t^2 - 1)^2$.   **11.** Low $(1, 3)$.
12. Low $(0, 2)$.   **13.** None.   **14.** Low $(\pm 1, 2)$.   **15.** High $(\sqrt{2}/2, 3\sqrt{2}/4)$,
low $(-\sqrt{2}/2, -3\sqrt{2}/4)$.   **16.** High $(2, -1)$.
20. $y' = t'uvw + tu'vw + tuv'w + tuvw'$.   **21.** $(10, 2/5)$ $(-2, -2)$.   **22.** $(0, 2)$,
$(\pm 1, 1)$.   **23.** $(0, 10\sqrt{5})$, $(\pm 3, \sqrt{5})$.

Chapter 2. Exercise 7   Page 74

1. $30(3x + 5)^9$.   **2.** $4(4x^3 + 3x^2 + 2x)(6x^2 + 3x + 1)$.
3. $7(ad - bc)(ax + b)^6/(cx + d)^8$.   **4.** $10x(5x^2 - 1)(x^2 - 1)^9(x^2 + 1)^{14}$.
5. $28(11x + 4)(7x + 3)^3(4x + 1)^6$.   **6.** $-6x(x + 1)(x^2 + 1)^2/(x^3 - 1)^3$.
7. $8(2x - 1)(x^2 - x - 12)^7$.   **8.** $-(3x^2 + 12x - 7)/(x^3 + 6x^2 - 7x + 8)^2$.

Chapter 2. Exercise 8   Page 77

1. $(3x + 1)/2\sqrt{x}$.   **2.** $8x/7(x^2 - 1)^{3/7}$.   **3.** $-2x/(x^2 + 1)^{1/2}(x^2 - 1)^{3/2}$.
4. $x(13x^3 + 9x - 4)/6(x^2 + 1)^{2/3}(x^3 - 1)^{1/2}$.   **5.** $45(6 + 5\sqrt{x})^8/2\sqrt{x}$.
6. $x(2 - x^2)/(1 - x^2)^{3/2}$.   **7.** $-1/4(4 + \sqrt{4 - x})^{1/2}(4 - x)^{1/2}$.
8. $-1/\sqrt{x}(\sqrt{x} - 1)^2$.   **9.** $-\sqrt{y/x}$.   **10.** $(x^2 - 2y)/(2x - y^2)$.
11. $(2y^2 - 3x^2)/(9y^2 - 4xy)$.   **12.** $-x^2(4x + 3y)/(x^3 + 4y^3)$.
13. $\pm 8x/(x^2 + 4)^{3/2}(x^2 - 4)^{1/2}$.   **14.** $-y^5/x^5$.   **15.** $y/(5x - 4y)$.   **16.** y/x.
18. $y = (49 \pm 20\sqrt{6})x$.

Chapter 2. Exercise 9   Page 81

1. $90(x^8 + x^4)$.   **2.** $3x(4 + x^3)/4(x^3 + 1)^{3/2}$.   **3.** $2(2 + x)/(1 - x)^4$.
4. $-2 + 2/v^3$.   **5.** $2(t - 1)^3(21t^2 - 12t + 1)$.   **6.** $10(2z^2 + 1)(z^2 + 2)^{1/2}$.
7. $(-1)^n n!/(2 + x)^{n+1}$.   **8.** $n! 2^n/(1 - 2x)^{n+1}$.   **9.** $ac^n(-1)^n(n + 1)!/(b + cx)^{n+2}$.
10. $-1 \cdot 3 \cdot 5 \cdots (2n - 3)/2^n(1 - x)^{(2n-1)/2}$ for $n \geq 2$.   **11.** $-b^4/a^2y^3$.
12. $-r^2/y^3$.   **13.** $-2x/y^5$.   **14.** $-p/xy$.   **15.** $a^{1/2}/2x^{3/2}$.
16. $-(n - 1)a^n x^{n-2}/y^{2n-1}$.   **18.** $a = 3$, $b = -2$.   **19.** $u''v + 2u'v' + uv''$,
$u'''v + 3u''v' + 3u'v'' + uv'''$.

Chapter 2. Exercise 10   Page 85

1. $x = (y - 11)/3$.   **2.** $x = (5 \pm \sqrt{1 + 8y})/4$.   **3.** $x = (y - 6)^{1/3}$.
4. $x = \pm\sqrt{1 \pm \sqrt{y + 2}}$.   **5.** $x = (7y + 5)/(y - 3)$.   **6.** $x = (2y + 3)/(7y - 2)$.
7. (1) $3, 1/3$; (2) $-1, -1$; (3) $3, 1/3$; (4) $24, 1/24$; (5) $-26, -1/26$; (6) $-25/144$,
$-144/25$.

Chapter 3. Exercise 1   Page 90

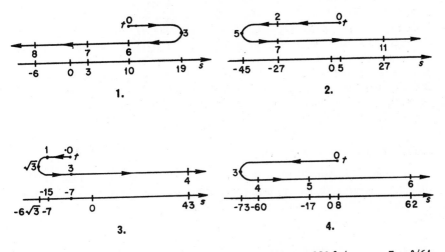

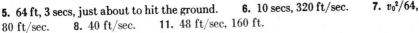

1.   **2.**

3.   **4.**

5. 64 ft, 3 secs, just about to hit the ground.   **6.** 10 secs, 320 ft/sec.   **7.** $v_0^2/64$, 80 ft/sec.   **8.** 40 ft/sec.   **11.** 48 ft/sec, 160 ft.

Chapter 3. Exercise 2   Page 93

1. $4/45\pi$ in/min.   **2.** 6.4 in²/min.   **3.** $((35 - 14t)^2 + 400t^2)^{1/2}$, 106/29 mi/hr.
4. $1/8\pi$ ft/min, $8/\pi$ ft/min.   **5.** $1/4\pi$ ft/min.   **6.** (a) 1.5 ft/sec; (b) 1.5 ft/sec.
7. 5 ft/sec.   **8.** $2\sqrt{5}$ ft/sec.   **9.** (a) $15x^2$; (b) $30x$.   **10.** $2\sqrt{10}$ in³/sec.

Chapter 3. Exercise 3   Page 100

1. $x > -1$, rel. min. $(-1, -6)$.   **2.** $x < -3/2$, rel. max. $(-3/2, 29/2)$.
3. $-\infty < x < -2$, $3 < x < \infty$, rel. max. $(-2, 51)$, rel. min. $(3, -74)$.
4. $-2 < x < -1$, rel. max. $(-1, 6)$, rel. min. $(-2, 5)$.   **5.** $1 < x < 3$, rel. max.
$(3, 5)$, rel. min. $(1, -103)$.   **6.** $1 < x$, rel. min. $(1, -64)$.   **7.** nowhere, no rel.
min. or max.   **8.** everywhere, no rel. min or max.   **9.** nowhere, no rel. min.
or max.   **10.** $-\infty < x < 1, 1 < x < \infty$, no rel. min. or max.   **11.** $-1, -2/3$.
12. 81/82, 100/101.   **13.** 0, 1/2.   **14.** 26/21, 5/3.   **15.** Min. for n even.
16. 7.   **17.** 11.   **18.** 1.   **19.** $x^2 - 2x + 3$.

Chapter 3. Exercise 4   Page 106

2. $f(x)$ is not differentiable at $x = 1$.   **3.** $f(x)$ is not cont. in $1 \leq x \leq 3$.
4. (a) 1; (b) $1 - \sqrt{3}/3$; (c) $1 + \sqrt{3}/3$.   **5.** $-B/2A$.   **6.** (a) $2x^3$; (b) $\frac{1}{8}x^8 - x^5$;
(c) $\frac{1}{6}x^6 + \frac{5}{3}x^3$; (d) $\frac{a}{n + 1}x^{n+1} + \frac{b}{m + 1}x^{m+1}$.   **7.** $x^6 - x^5 + x^4 - x^3 + x^2 - x$ is
zero at $x = 0$ and $x = 1$.   **8.** 2.5.   **9.** 30.25.   **10.** $\sqrt{13/3}$.   **11.** $7 + \sqrt{2}/10$.
12. $7 + \sqrt{2}/100$.   **13.** -2.   **15.** $f'(x)$ cont. in $x_1 \leq x \leq x_2$, differentiable in
$x_1 < x < x_2$.   **16.** $3x^2 + a > 0$ for all x.   **17.** Yes.

Chapter 3. Exercise 5   Page 113

1. Up $x \geqq 0$, Down $x \leqq 0$, Infl. $(0, 0)$.   **2.** Up for all x, no infl. pts.
3. $U.\ x \geqq 1$, $D.\ x \leqq 1$, $I.\ (1, -1)$.   **4.** $U.\ x \leqq 2$, and $x \geqq 4$, $D.\ 2 \leqq x \leqq 4$,
$I.\ (2, 87),\ (4, 231)$.   **5.** $U.\ x \leqq -\sqrt{3}/3$ and $x \geqq \sqrt{3}/3$, $D.\ -\sqrt{3}/3 \leqq x \leqq \sqrt{3}/3$.
$I.\ (\pm\sqrt{3}/3, 3/4)$.   **6.** $U.\ x \geqq 1$ and $-1 \leqq x \leqq 0$, $D.\ x \leqq -1$, and $0 \leqq x \leqq 1$,
$I.\ (0, 0),\ (1, 5/2),\ (-1, -5/2)$.   **7.** $U.\ x > 0$, $D.\ x < 0$. No infl. pts.
8. $U.\ x \leqq -2$ and $x \geqq 2$, $D.\ -2 \leqq x < 0$ and $0 < x \leqq 2$, $I.\ (\pm 2, 8)$.   **9.** $U.$
$2 \leqq x \leqq 4$, and $x \geqq 6$, and $x \leqq 0$, $D.\ 0 \leqq x \leqq 2$ and $4 \leqq x \leqq 6$, $I.\ (0, 0),\ (2, -2^{15})$,
$(4, -2^{15}),\ (6, 0)$.   **10.** $U.\ -1 \leqq x \leqq 0$, and $x \geqq 2$, $D.\ x \leqq -1$ and $0 \leqq x \leqq 2$,
$I.\ (-1, 0),\ (0, 5^{6}),\ (2, 3^{9})$.

Chapter 3. Exercise 6   Page 114

1. None.   **2.** Min. $(0, 0)$.   **3.** R. min. $(3, -17)$, R. max. $(-1, 15)$.   **4.** Min.
$(0, -25)$.   **5.** Max. $(0, 1)$.   **6.** Min. $(-\sqrt{3}/3, -5\sqrt{3}/3)$, Max. $(\sqrt{3}/3, 5\sqrt{3}/3)$.
7. R. max. $(-1, -2)$, R. min. $(1, 2)$.   **8.** None.   **9.** Min. $(3, -3^{10})$.   **10.** R.
max. $(1, 2^{15})$, R. min. $(5, 0)$.

Chapter 3. Exercise 7   Page 119

1. 3 in.   **2.** 5 in.   **6.** R by $\sqrt{3}\ R$.   **7.** 24 in.   **8.** $P^2/16$.   **9.** 10, 10.
10. 2.   **11.** 1.   **12.** 1/2.   **13.** 4.   **14.** $H/3$.   **15.** $2R/\sqrt{3}$.   **16.** $4R/3$.
18. 15, 45.   **19.** 10, 25.   **21.** no solution.   **22.** 8, 8.   **23.** 2, 16.   **24.** $(2, 4)$.
25. $(\pm 2\sqrt{2}, -4),\ 2\sqrt{6}$.   **26.** 100 by 144 ft.   **27.** 60 by 240 ft.   **28.** 60 by
240 ft.   **29.** 1.   **30.** 14 by 21 in.   **31.** $P/(4 + \pi),\ P/(4 + \pi)$.   **32.** 8 mi,
$3\frac{1}{2}$ hrs, 36 min.   **34.** $\sqrt[3]{A}\ L/(\sqrt[3]{A} + \sqrt[3]{B})$ from the source A.   **35.** 32 mi.
36. $\sqrt{2}\ a$ by $\sqrt{2}\ b$.

Chapter 3. Exercise 8   Page 127

1. (a) $6x^2 \Delta x + 6x(\Delta x)^2 + 2(\Delta x)^3$; (b) $(6x + 2\Delta x)(\Delta x)^2$.
2. (a) $(3 - 2x)\Delta x - (\Delta x)^2$; (b) $-(\Delta x)^2$.

3. (a) $\dfrac{-(2x + \Delta x)\Delta x}{x^2(x + \Delta x)^2}$ (b) $\dfrac{(3x + 2\Delta x)(\Delta x)^2}{x^3(x + \Delta x)^2}$.

4. (a) $\dfrac{10\Delta x}{(10 + x)(10 + x + \Delta x)}$ (b) $\dfrac{-10(\Delta x)^2}{(10 + x)^2(10 + x + \Delta x)}$.

5. (a) $6(x + 1)\Delta x + 3(\Delta x)^2$; (b) $3(\Delta x)^2$.   **6.** 10.20.   **7.** 8.063.   **8.** 4.021.
9. 2.005.   **10.** 9.997.   **11.** 11.88.   **12.** 5.150.   **13.** 2.030.   **14.** .1925.
15. 10.55, 10.54.   **17.** 9.6 in^3.

Chapter 4. Exercise 1   Page 134

1. $500x^2 - x^5 + C$.

2. $\dfrac{\pi}{3} x^3 + \dfrac{2}{3} x^{3/2} + C$.

3. $\dfrac{\sqrt{2}}{8} x^8 - \dfrac{1}{2} x^3 - \dfrac{1}{4x^4} + C$.

4. $\dfrac{1}{8} (2x + 7)^4 + C$.

5. $\dfrac{1}{1028}(2x+7)^{514}+C.$

6. $-\dfrac{2}{21}(1-7x)^{3/2}+C.$

7. $\dfrac{1}{77}(3+11x^2)^{7/2}+C.$

8. $\dfrac{-1}{14(11+7t^2)}+C.$

9. $\dfrac{-2}{9(1+u^3)^{3/2}}+C.$

10. $\dfrac{1}{3}(5+z^2)^{3/2}+C.$

11. $\dfrac{2}{9}(y^3+y+55)^{9/2}+C.$

12. $\dfrac{\sqrt{3}}{5}(5w^2+10w+11)^{1/2}+C.$

13. $y=x^3+x^2.$ **14.** $y=x^{-3}-x^{-2}+2.$ **15.** $15y=(4+5x^2)^{3/2}-24.$
16. $2y=m(x^2-1)+2b(x+1).$ **17.** $s=16t^2+5t+100.$ **18.** $y=6/(4-3x^2).$
19. $y^2=(17-2x^2)/(2x^2-19).$ **20.** $y^2-x^2=1.$ **21.** $3u^{1/2}=v^{3/2}+3.$

Chapter 4. Exercise 2 Page 143

1. 20. **2.** 20. **3.** 0. **4.** 64/5. **5.** 1. **6.** 10/3. **7.** $\frac{2}{3}a+2c.$
8. $aB^3/3.$ **9.** 1/3. **10.** 1/5. **11.** 70. **12.** 28/3. **13.** 62/9. **14.** .99.
15. $\sqrt{2}.$ **20.** 32/3. **21.** 9/2. **22.** 8/3. **23.** 27/4. **24.** 4.

Chapter 4. Exercise 3 Page 148

1. (a) $8\frac{1}{3}$; (b) 13. **2.** (a) -69; (b) 75. **3.** (a) 6; (b) $7\frac{1}{3}$. **4.** (a) $7\frac{1}{2}$; (b) $9\frac{5}{6}$.
5. (a) $\frac{4}{3}$; (b) 4. **6.** (a) 0; (b) $12\sqrt{3}$.

Chapter 4. Exercise 4 Page 151

2. $T.$ **3.** $T.$ **4.** $T.$ **5.** $T.$ **6.** $F.$ **7.** $T.$ **8.** $F.$ **9.** $F.$ **10.** $T.$
11. $T.$ **12.** $T.$ **13.** $T.$ **14.** $T.$ **15.** $T.$ **16.** $T.$ **24.** The sum of the
cubes of the first n positive integers is the square of the sum of the first n positive
integers.

Chapter 4. Exercise 5 Page 160

4. $Cb^3/3.$

Chapter 5. Exercise 1 Page 169

1. $10\frac{2}{3}.$ **2.** $4\frac{1}{2}.$ **3.** $10\frac{2}{3}.$ **4.** $4\frac{1}{2}.$ **5.** 4/15. **6.** 1/2. **7.** $6\frac{3}{4}.$ **8.** $3\frac{1}{12}.$
9. $6\frac{1}{8}.$

Chapter 5. Exercise 2 Page 175

1. $500\pi/3.$ **2.** $128\pi/7.$ **3.** $4\pi/3.$ **4.** $512\pi/15.$ **5.** $392\pi/3.$ **6.** $422\pi/5.$
7. $128\pi/3.$ **8.** $16\pi/3.$ **9.** $64\pi/15.$ **10.** $5\pi/14.$ **11.** $192\pi/55.$ **15.** $4\pi ab^2/3.$
16. $4\pi a^2 b/3, a=b.$ **17.** $16r^3/3.$ **18.** $4r^3\sqrt{3}/3.$ **19.** 2000/3 cu. in. **20.** $16r^3/3.$

Chapter 5. Exercise 3 Page 181

1. 4500 lbs. **2.** 3000 lbs. **3.** 4125 lbs. **4.** 66,670 tons. **5.** 12,500 lbs.
6. 25,000 lbs. **7.** 14.06 lbs. **8.** 12.5 lbs. **9.** 83,330 tons. **10.** 100 $wB/3.$

11. $(15H + 50)w$.   **12.** $wAB(3H + 2A)/6$.   **16.** 100 ft-lbs.   **17.** (a) 10 in-lbs;
(b) 30 in-lbs; (c) 50 in-lbs.   **18.** $2500w\pi$ ft-lbs.   **19.** $576w\pi$ ft-lbs.
20. $108w\pi$ ft-lbs.

Chapter 5. Exercise 4   Page 185

    1. $8(10^{3/2} - 1)/27$.   **2.** 45.   **3.** 12.   **4.** $21\frac{3}{16}$.   **5.** 14/3.   **6.** $3a/2$.
7. 146/27.

Chapter 5. Exercise 5   Page 189

    1. $56\pi/3$.   **2.** $16\pi(8\sqrt{3} - 9)$.   **3.** 7π.   **4.** $\pi m(b^2 - a^2)\sqrt{1 + m^2}$.
5. $515\pi/64$.   **6.** 3π.   **7.** $\pi B^2/4$.   **8.** 168π.   **11.** $\left(\dfrac{515}{64} + \dfrac{59}{12} C\right)\pi$.   **12.** $8\sqrt{2}\pi$.

Chapter 6. Exercise 1   Page 195

    1. P. $(3, 2)$, $(1, 2)$, $x = -1$.   **2.** E. $(1, 3)$, $(9, 3)$; $(0, 3)$, $(10, 3)$, $(5, 0)$, $(5, 6)$;
$x = 5$, $y = 3$.   **3.** H. $(-3, 7)$, $(-3, -3)$; $(-3, 5)$, $(-3, -1)$; $x = -3$, $y = 2$.
4. $P.(-1, -6), (-1, -2), y = 2$.   · **5.** $E.(1, -2 \pm \sqrt{15}/2)$; $(\frac{1}{2}, -2), (\frac{3}{2}, -2), (1, 0)$,
$(1, -4)$; $x = 1$, $y = -2$.   **6.** P. $(-7\frac{1}{80}, -1)$, $(-7, -1)$, $x = -6\frac{79}{80}$ **7.** H.
$(-2, 5 \pm \sqrt{2})$; $(-2, 6)$, $(-2, 4)$; $x = -2$, $y = 5$.   **8.** E. $(-2, 9)$, $(-2, 3)$;
$(-2, 11)$, $(-2, 1)$, $(-6, 6)$, $(2, 6)$; $x = -2$, $y = 6$.   **9.** H. $(-7 \pm \sqrt{21}, -3)$;
$(-7 \pm \sqrt{15}, -3)$; $x = -7, y = -3$.   **10.** P. $(90, -74.5)$, $(90, -75)$, $y = -75.5$.
11. $\left(-\dfrac{B}{2A}, C + \dfrac{1 - B^2}{4A}\right)$.   **12.** $-1/4A^2$, ∞, C.   **13.** $1/B^2\sqrt{B^2 - 1}$,
$(0, \pm\infty)$, $(\pm 1, 0)$.   **14.** $1/\sqrt{2K}$, $(0, 0)$, $(\pm\infty, 0)$. No.

Chapter 6. Exercise 2   Page 202

    1. $x = 3, y = 7$.   **2.** $x = -5, y = 2$.   **3.** $x = -1, y = -2$.   **4.** $y = -6$,
$x = 7$.   **5.** $y = 2$, $x = 0$.   **6.** $x = 0$, -2, $y = 5$.   **7.** $x = 2$, -5, $y = 4$.
8. $x = 0$, -4, $y = -6$.   **9.** $x = 3/2$, $y = x + 1$.   **10.** $y = x$, $x = \pm 1$.
11. $x = 0, y = \frac{1}{2}x - 3$.   **12.** $y = -x + 2$.   **13.** none.   **14.** $y = x/2, x = -2$.
18. No.

Chapter 6. Exercise 3   Page 207

    3. $y > 1$ and $y < 0$.   **4.** x-axis, y-axis, origin.   **5.** x-axis. $2 < x < 5$.
6. x-axis, $x < -\sqrt[3]{4}$.   **7.** x-axis, $x < 0$ and $3 < x < 6$.   **8.** x-axis, y-axis,
origin, $x < -1$ and $x > 1$.   **9.** x-axis, $0 < x < 1$.   **11.** (c) is not symmetrical
about $y = x$, (a), (b), and (d) are.

Chapter 6. Exercise 4   Page 213

    1. $1/2$, $(\pm 3, 2)$, $x = \pm 12$.   **2.** $3/5$, $(-4, 2)$, $(-4, 8)$, $y = 40/3, y = -10/3$.
3. 3, $(1, -1)$, $(-5, -1)$, $x = -7/3$, $x = -5/3$, $y = \pm 2\sqrt{2}(x + 2) - 1$.
4. $5/4$, $(3, 9)$, $(3, -1)$, $y = 36/5$, $y = 4/5$, $3y = 4x$, $3y = -4x + 24$.   **5.** $\sqrt{3}$,

$(-2, 3 \pm 2\sqrt{3})$, $y = 3 \pm 2\sqrt{3}/3$, $\sqrt{2}(y - 3) = \pm(x + 2)$.   **6.** 1/2, $(1, -3)$,
$(1, 1)$, $y = 7$, $y = -9$.   **7.** At $(-4, 0)$, $(0, 5)$.   **8.** At $(3, 0)$.   **10.** $5x^2 + 9y^2 = 45$.
11. $80x^2 + 81y^2 = 6480$.   **12.** $x^2 - 4y^2 = 80$.   **13.** $24y^2 - x^2 = 2400$.
14. $5x^2 - 4y^2 = 20$.   **15.** $169x^2 + 25y^2 = 3600$.   **16.** $5x^2 + 9y^2 = 180$.
17. $8x^2 + 3y^2 = 35$.   **18.** $x^2 - 4y^2 = 4$.   **20.** The line segment $-1 \leqq x \leqq 1$.

Chapter 6. Exercise 5   Page 216

1. 1/7.   **2.** $-3/4$.   **3.** 1/21.   **4.** -1.   **5.** $-2, 2/25$.   **6.** $-3, 1/5, -3/11$.

Chapter 6. Exercise 6   Page 220

1. All st. lines through $(3, 2)$.   **2.** All lines with slope 1/2 and nonnegative
y-intercept.   **3.** All circles with radius 4 and center on the line $x = 3$.   **4.** All
pairs of lines through the origin with the coordinate axes as angle bisectors.
5. All parabolas with vertex at $(2, 0)$ and axis $x = 2$.   **6.** All parabolas tangent
to x-axis with directrix $y = -1$.   **7.** All hyperbolas with foci at $(\pm 1, 0)$.
8. All ellipses with foci at $(\pm 1, 0)$.   **9.** $x + y = 1$.   **10.** $21x + 38y = 50$.
11. $y = 3x + 4$.   **12.** $y = mx + m + 1$.   **13.** All lines parallel to the given
lines.   **15.** $11x + 4y = 114$.   **16.** $3x^2 + 3y^2 - 154x - 56y + 1296 = 0$.
17. $x^2 + y^2 - 44x - 16y + 356 = 0$.   **18.** $8x^2 + 9y^2 = 72$.   **19.** $4y = 2Cx - C^2$.
20. $\pm\sqrt{1 - C^2y} + 2Cx = 2$.   **21.** $y(C - 2)^2 + x = 2C - 2$.

Chapter 6. Exercise 7   Page 227

1. $(-1, 1)$, $y = x - 2$.   **2.** $(\sqrt{3}, 1)$ $(-\sqrt{3}, -1)$, $\sqrt{3}x + y = \pm 16$.
3. $(-3\sqrt{2}/2, 3\sqrt{2}/2)$, $(3\sqrt{2}/2, -3\sqrt{2}/2)$, $y = x \pm \sqrt{2}/3$, $y = (9 \pm 4\sqrt{2})x/7$.
4. $(3, 1)$, $(-3, -1)$, $3x + y = \pm 4$, $y = (1 \pm 2\sqrt{6}/3)x$.   **5.** $(-3, \sqrt{3})$,
$(3, -\sqrt{3})$, $y = \sqrt{3}x \pm 16/\sqrt{3}$.   **6.** $(3, -6)$, $2y = x + 15$.   **7.** $(4, 1)$, $x + y = 1$.
8. $(4, 3)$, $(2, 1)$, $x + y = 6$, $x + y = 4$, $x = 3$, $y = 2$.   **9.** $(0, 3)$, $(2, 0)$, $3y = 2x + 15$, $3y = 2x - 10$.   **10.** (a) $x^2 - 4 = 0$; (b) $(x - 1)(y - 2) = 0$; (c)
$x - 3 = 0$; (d) $x^2 + y^2 = 0$; (e) $x^2 + y^2 + 1 = 0$.

Chapter 7. Exercise 1   Page 232

1. $2 \cos 5x - \sin 2x \sin 3x$.   **2.** $\sin x \cos^2 x(2 - 5 \sin^2 x)$.

3. $6 \sin 3x \cos x/\cos^4 2x$.   **4.** $\dfrac{3 \sin x \cos x (\sin x \cos x - \sin x - \cos x)}{2(1 - \sin^3 x)^{1/2}(1 - \cos^3 x)^{3/2}}$

5. $\sin^2(3t^2 + 5) + 6t^2 \sin(6t^2 + 10)$.   **6.** $2\theta \sin^2(5\theta - 1) + (5\theta^2 + 10) \sin(10\theta - 2)$.

7. $-\dfrac{1}{u^4}\left(u^2 \sin \dfrac{1}{u^2} + 2 \cos \dfrac{1}{u^2}\right)$.   **8.** $6 \cos 4x(\sin 2x + \cos 2x)$.

11. $(-1)^n 3^{2n} \sin 3x$.   **12.** $(-1)^{n+1} 5^{2n-1} \cos 5x$.   **13.** $(-1)^n 2^{2n} \cos 2x$.   **14.** 1/4.
15. $\sqrt{3}/10$.   **16.** 2/3.   **17.** $\sin(t^2 + t + 5) + C$.   **18.** $\frac{1}{3}\cos^3 \theta - \cos \theta + C$.
19. $\frac{1}{3}(\sin \theta - \cos \theta)(5 + \sin 2\theta) + C$.   **20.** $\frac{2}{3}\sin x^{3/2} + C$.   **21.** $-5 \cos 2\sqrt{x} + C$.
22. $-\cos^{n+1}ax/a(n + 1) + C$.   **23.** $-1/bc(n - 1)(a + b \sin cx)^{n-1}$.   **24.** $((2n + 1)\pi$,
$(2n + 1)\pi)$, $n = 0$, ± 1, ± 2, $\cdots$ **27.** Max. at $(\beta + 2n\pi, 5)$, min. at
$(\beta + (2n + 1)\pi, -5)$ where $\beta = \tan^{-1}(3/4)$.   **28.** Max. at $(r\pi + \pi/2, 1)$, min.

at $(n\pi, 0)$.   **29.** Rel. min. at $(2n\pi + \pi/3, 2n\pi + \pi/3 - \sqrt{3})$, rel. max. at $(2n\pi - \pi/3, 2n\pi - \pi/3 + \sqrt{3})$.   **30.** Min. at $(n\pi, 0)$, max. at $(n\pi + \pi/2, 1)$. **32.** (a) .530, (b) .695, (c) .515.   **33.** 2/3.   **34.** 1/3.   **35.** $\pi^2/4$.   **36.** $2\sqrt{2}$. **37.** $\tan \varphi = 1/3$ at $(2n\pi, 0)$, $\tan \varphi = -3$ at $((2n + 1)\pi, 0)$, $(\pi/3 + 2n\pi, \sqrt{3}/2)$ and $(-\pi/3 + 2n\pi, -\sqrt{3}/2)$.

Chapter 7. Exercise 2   Page 236

1. $\sin x(1 + \sec^2 x)$.   **2.** $15\cos x \cos 4x$.   **3.** $3\sec^4 t$.   **4.** $3\cot^4 \theta$. **5.** $2 \sec^3 x \csc^2 x - 3 \sec x \csc^4 x$.   **6.** $-\csc^2 \theta$. **7.** $-[2 \sec 2x + (2x \sec 2x + 1)(\sec 2x - \tan 2x)]/(x + \tan 2x)^2$. **8.** $1/(\cos x - 1)$.   **9.** $2 \sec^2 x(3 + 6x \tan x + 2x^2 \tan^2 x + x^2 \sec^2 x)$. **10.** $4x \sec x^2(3 \tan^2 x^2 + 3 \sec^2 x^2 + 2x^2 \tan^3 x^2 + 10x^2 \sec^2 x^2 \tan x^2)$. **11.** $8 \sin 2x(6 \sec^4 2x - \sec^2 2x - 1)$.   **12.** $\sec x \tan x (\tan^2 x + 5 \sec^2 x)$. **14.** $\frac{1}{20} \tan^4 5x + C$.   **15.** $-\frac{1}{30} \csc^5 6x + C$.   **16.** $\frac{1}{15} \tan (5x^3 + 7) + C$. **17.** $2 \tan x - x + C$.   **18.** $-\frac{1}{8} \cot 4\theta^2 + C$.   **19.** $\frac{1}{2} \tan^2 y + C$. **20.** $2 \tan z + 2 \sec z - z + C$.   **21.** $\frac{1}{3} \tan^3 \theta + \tan \theta + C$.   **22.** $(\pi/4, 2)$. **25.** (a) 1.063; (b) .969; (c) 1.940; (d) 1.143.   **26.** 1.   **27.** π.   **28.** $\pi - \pi^2/4$. **29.** $4\pi/3$.   **30.** 1.   **31.** $(\sin x \sin y + 1)/(\cos x \cos y - 1)$. **32.** $-(\sec y + y \sec^2 x)/(\tan x + x \sec y \tan y)$.   **33.** $(\sin x + y)/(\cos y - x)$. **34.** -1.   **36.** $5\sqrt{5}$ ft.

Chapter 7. Exercise 3   Page 242

1. 0.   **2.** $-\pi/6$.   **3.** $\pi/2$.   **4.** $3\pi/4$.   **5.** $\pi/3$.   **6.** $-\pi/6$.   **7.** $2\pi/3 \cdot$ **8.** $5\pi/6$.   **9.** $-\pi/3$.   **10.** (a) 4/5; (b) 4/5; (c) $-\sqrt{3}/2$; (d) 1/2. **11.** (a) $(9\sqrt{3} - 8\sqrt{5})/11$; (b) $-(3\sqrt{2} + \sqrt{14})/8$; (c) $41\sqrt{2}/58$.   **12.** T. **13.** T.   **14.** T.   **15.** F. Set $x = -1/2$.   **16.** F. $u = -1$.   **17.** T.   **18.** F. $w = 1$.   **19.** T.   **20.** T.   **21.** F. $y = -1/2$.   **22.** F. $m = n = \sqrt{3}$. **23.** $0 \le y \le 1$.   **24.** If $|\tan^{-1} m + \tan^{-1} n| < \pi/2$, for example if $|m| < 1$ and $|n| < 1$.

Chapter 7. Exercise 4   Page 247

1. $-5/\sqrt{1 - 25x^2}$.   **2.** $4t^3/(1 + t^8)$.   **3.** $1/2\sqrt{x(1 - x)}$. **4.** $\cot^{-1}(1 + t^2) - 2t^2/(2 + 2t^2 + t^4)$.   **5.** $-(1 + y^2)/(1 - y^2 + y^4)$.   **6.** $-1/(1 + t^2)$. **7.** $-2t/\sqrt{1 - t^4}$.   **8.** $t^2/(1 - t^2)^{3/2}$.   **9.** $2x \sin^{-1} (x/2)$.   **10.** $\sqrt{Ax - B^2}/2x$. **11.** $\pi/2$.   **12.** $\pi/2$.   **13.** No.   **14.** $y = \pi/2$ for $x > 0$, and $y = -\pi/2$ for $x < 0$, y is not defined at $x = 0$.   **15.** 4 ft.   **16.** 24 ft.   **17.** (a) .132 rad/sec; (b) .066 rad/sec; (c) $\theta = 0$.   **18.** $\tan \varphi = 2\sqrt{2}$.   **20.** $\frac{1}{2} \sin^{-1} (2x/5) + C$.

21. $\dfrac{1}{12} \tan^{-1} (y/3) + C$.   **22.** $\dfrac{1}{2\sqrt{10}} \tan^{-1}(2z^2/\sqrt{10}) + C$.

23. $-\sin^{-1}\left(\dfrac{\cos x}{\sqrt{10}}\right) + C$.   **24.** $\sin^{-1}\left(\dfrac{x - 2}{3}\right) + C$.

25. $\dfrac{7}{8} \tan^{-1}\left(\dfrac{2x - 3}{4}\right) + C$.   **26.** $\dfrac{10}{3} \tan^{-1}\left(\dfrac{\sqrt{t}}{3}\right) + C$.

27. $\sin^{-1}\left(\dfrac{3y+2}{3}\right)+C.$ **28.** $\tan^{-1}M,\ \pi/2.$ **29.** $\sin^{-1}M,\ \pi/2.$

Chapter 8. Exercise 1 Page 252

3. 0. **4.** $-\infty.$

Chapter 8. Exercise 2 Page 258

1. $6x(x^4+1)/(x^6+3x^2+1).$ **2.** $3/(x+1).$ **3.** $3/(x+1).$ **4.** $2/x.$

5. $\dfrac{2}{x}\ln x.$ **6.** $2x\tan x^2.$ **7.** $x(1+2\ln x).$ **8.** $2\ln x.$ **9.** $(2x^2+4)/x(x^2+4).$

10. $\dfrac{1}{x}\ln(1-x)+\dfrac{1}{(x-1)}\ln x.$ **11.** 0. **12.** $4x/(1-x^4).$ **13.** $4\tan^{-1}2x.$

14. $2\cos\ln x.$ **15.** $2\sqrt{x^2-5}.$ **16.** $(2x^3+x)/\sqrt{(x^2-1)(x^2+2)}.$
17. $(x^2+4x+1)/((x-1)(x+2)(x+5))^{2/3}.$ **18.** $(6x+1)/(3x+2)^{1/2}(2x+1)^{4/3}.$
19. $6(35-x^4)/x^7(x^2-5)^{1/2}(x^2+7)^{3/2}.$ **22.** $\frac{1}{2}\ln(x^2+4)+C.$ **23.** $\frac{1}{3}\ln$
$(5-3\cos x)+C.$ **24.** $-\frac{1}{2}\ln|\cos x^2|+C.$ **25.** $\frac{1}{5}\ln|\sec 5x+\tan 5x|+C.$

26. $\dfrac{1}{2}\ln(x^2+4)+\dfrac{3}{2}\tan^{-1}\left(\dfrac{x}{2}\right)+C.$ **27.** $2\tan^{-1}\sqrt{x}+C.$ **28.** $-\dfrac{1}{2}\ln|\csc x^2$
$+\cot x^2|+C.$ **29.** $\frac{1}{4}\ln|\sin x^4|+C.$ **30.** $\frac{1}{2}\ln^2 x+C.$ **31.** $\ln|\ln x|+C.$
32. $\frac{1}{3}\ln 6\approx.358.$ **33.** $\frac{1}{2}\ln 2\approx.347.$ **34.** (a), (b), (c), $\ln 7\approx 1.946.$
35. $\pi\ln 7\approx 6.11.$ **36.** (a) $\ln(1+\sqrt{2})\approx.881;$ (b) $127.5+\ln 2\approx 128.193.$
37. No infl. pts. min. $(2,4-8\ln 2)\approx(2,-1.545).$ **38.** 0.

Chapter 8. Exercise 3 Page 262

1. $(2-3x)xe^{-3x}.$ **2.** $\dfrac{-2e^{1/x^2}}{x^3}.$ **3.** $5\sin 10xe^{\sin^2 5x}.$ **4.** $5e^x/(1+5e^x).$
5. $(x^2+2xe^x-x^2e^x)/(x+e^x)^2.$ **6.** $6e^{3x}/(1-e^{6x}).$ **7.** $x^{\sin x}(\cos x\ln x+\dfrac{1}{x}\sin x).$

8. $(\sin x)^x(\ln\sin x+x\cot x).$ **9.** $(1+3x)^{1/x}\left(\dfrac{3}{x(1+3x)}-\dfrac{\ln(1+3x)}{x^2}\right).$
10. $(\cos x^2)^{x^3}(3x^2\ln\cos x^2-2x^4\tan x^2).$ **11.** $-x^5e^{-x}.$ **12.** $(-1)^{n+1}(n-1)!/x^n.$
13. $(-1)^{n-1}5(n-1)!/(1+x)^n.$ **14.** $e^x.$ **15.** $7^n e^{7x}.$ **16.** $(x+n)e^x.$
17. $y'=x+2x\ln x,\ y''=3+2\ln x,\ y^{(n)}=(-1)^{n+1}2(n-3)!/x^{n-2}$ for $n>2.$
18. $-\frac{1}{4}e^{-4x}+C.$ **19.** $7e^{x^2}+C.$ **20.** $e^{\tan x}+C.$ **21.** $6\tan^{-1}e^x+C.$
22. $3\ln(1+e^{3x})+C.$ **23.** $x+\ln(1-e^{-2x})+C.$ **24.** Max $(0,1),$ infl. pt.
$(\pm1/\sqrt{2},\ e^{-1/2})\approx(\pm.707,.607).$ **25.** Min. $(0,2).$ **26.** Infl. pt. $(0,0).$
27. Min. $(-3,-3/e)\approx(-3,-1.104),$ infl. pt. $(-6,-6/e^2)\approx(-6,-.812).$
28. Rel. max. $(\theta,\ \sqrt{2}/2e^\theta),\ \theta=2n\pi+7\pi/4,$ rel. min. at $(\alpha,-\sqrt{2}/2e^\alpha),$
$\alpha=2n\pi+3\pi/4,$ infl. pts. $(n\pi,(-1)^ne^{-n\pi}),\ n=0,\pm 1,\pm2,\cdots.$
29. $b=\sqrt{2},\ h=1/\sqrt{e}.$ **30.** $a+e^{2a}.$ **31.** $-\ln 3.$ **32.** $(e^a-e^{-a})/2.$
33. $\pi(e^{2a}-e^{-2a}+4a)/4.$

Chapter 8. Exercise 4 Page 268

14. $5/3,4/5,5/4,3/5,3/4.$ **15.** (a) $\frac{1}{2}\ln\dfrac{1+x}{1-x},\ -1<x<1;$ (b) $\frac{1}{2}\ln\dfrac{x+1}{x-1},$

$|x| > 1$; (c) $\ln \dfrac{1 + \sqrt{1 - x^2}}{x}$, $0 < x \le 1$; (d) $\ln \dfrac{1 \pm \sqrt{1 + x^2}}{x}$, $x \gtrless 0$.

Chapter 8. Exercise 5   Page 271

2. $3^{2n} \cosh 3x$.   **3.** $(1 - 2 \operatorname{sech}^2 x) \operatorname{sech} x$.   **4.** $|x| < \ln(1 + \sqrt{2})$.
5. $(\ln \sqrt{3},\ 4)$.   **8.** If $x < 0$, then $\sqrt{x^2} = -x$ and $y' = -1/\sqrt{x^2 + 1}$.
9. $3x^2 \coth x^3$.   **10.** e^{2x}.   **11.** $-1/x\sqrt{1 - x^2}$.   **12.** $-2/x\sqrt{1 + x^4}$.
13. $\frac{1}{6} \cosh^6 x - \frac{1}{4} \cosh^4 x + C$.   **14.** $\frac{1}{3} \operatorname{sech}^3 x - \operatorname{sech} x + C$.   **15.** $\frac{1}{2}x + \frac{1}{4} \sinh 2x + C$.
16. $\frac{1}{5} \ln |\sinh 5x| + C$.   **17.** $2 \tan^{-1} e^x + C$.   **18.** $\frac{1}{3} \cosh x^3 + C$.
19. $\frac{1}{2} \ln(2x + \sqrt{1 + 4x^2}) + C$.   **20.** $3 \ln(x^2 + \sqrt{x^4 - 1}) + C$.
21. $\ln(x + 3 + \sqrt{x^2 + 6x + 25}) + C$.   **22.** $2 \ln(x^2 + 3 + \sqrt{x^4 + 6x^2 + 5}) + C$.

Chapter 8. Exercise 6   Page 275

3. (a) $\sin x^2$; (b) $3x^2 e^{x^6}$; (c) $2x \ln \cosh x^2$; (d) $2x\sqrt{1 + x^{10}} - \sqrt{1 + x^5}$.
4. $-2 \le x \le 2$.   **5.** $0 \le x \le 3$ and $x \le -3$.

Chapter 9. Exercise 1   Page 285

Add a constant of integration to the answer to each indefinite integral in this chapter.

1. $4\sqrt{x} - \ln(1 + 4\sqrt{x})$.   **2.** $4x^{1/4} - 4 \ln(1 + x^{1/4})$.
3. $2x^{1/2} - 3x^{1/3} + 6x^{1/6} - 6\ln(1 + x^{1/6})$. **4.** $2x^{1/2} - \frac{10}{3}x^{3/10} + 10x^{1/10} - 10 \tan^{-1} x^{1/10}$.
5. $2(x + 5)^{5/2} - 20(x + 5)^{3/2} + 2(x + 5)^{1/2}$.   **6.** $\frac{1}{5}(x^2 - 4)^{5/2} - 16(x^2 - 4)^{1/2}$.
7. $\frac{1}{2} \tan^{-1} (1 + \frac{1}{2}\sqrt{2x - 3})$.   **8.** $(2x - 5)(8\sqrt{2x - 5} + 15)/6$.   **9.** $34/3$.
10. $(3\pi - 8)/6$.   **11.** $-18 + 48 \ln (3/2)$.   **12.** $8 + 3\sqrt{3}\,\pi/2$.
13. $2\sqrt{M} - 2 \ln(1 + \sqrt{M})$.   **14.** $2\pi \ln(\sqrt{M} + 1) - 2\pi\sqrt{M}/(\sqrt{M} + 1)$.
15. $2\pi(2M^{3/2} - 3M + 6M^{1/2} - 6 \ln(M^{1/2} + 1))/3$.   **16.** $2\pi M/(1 + M^{1/2})$.

Chapter 9. Exercise 2   Page 288

1. $-\cos \theta (15 - 10 \cos^2 \theta + 3 \cos^4 \theta)/15$.   **2.** $\sin^3 y (5 - 3 \sin^2 y)/15$.
3. $(12x - 3 \sin 4x + 4 \sin^3 2x)/192$.   **4.** $(20x - \sin 20x)/160$.
5. $(1 - 6 \cos^2 x - 3 \cos^4 x)/3 \cos^3 x$.   **6.** $-\cot^3 3x(3 \cot^2 3x + 5)/45$.
7. $-(\cos 5x + 5 \cos x)/10$. **8.** $\frac{1}{4}(x + \frac{1}{8} \sin 4x - \frac{1}{6} \sin 6x - \frac{1}{10} \sin 10x + \frac{1}{32} \sin 16x)$.
9. $-\frac{1}{6} \cot 6x$.   **10.** $\frac{1}{5}(\tan 5x - \cot 5x - 2 \ln|\csc 10x + \cot 10x|)$.   **11.** $\pi^2/2$.
12. π.   **13.** $\pi(4 - \pi)/8$.   **14.** $3\pi^2/16$.   **16.** π.
18. $(1 - \cos 2\theta)^{3/2} = 2\sqrt{2}|\sin \theta|^3 \ne 2\sqrt{2} \sin^3 \theta$ when $\pi < \theta < 2\pi$.   **19.** $16\sqrt{2}/3$.

Chapter 9. Exercise 3   Page 292

1. $x/9\sqrt{9 - x^2}$.   **2.** $\sqrt{y^2 - 6}/6y$.   **3.** $\dfrac{1}{250}\left(\tan^{-1}\dfrac{y}{5} + \dfrac{5y}{25 + y^2}\right)$.
4. $-3 \ln \left|\dfrac{3 + \sqrt{9 - x^2}}{x}\right| + \sqrt{9 - x^2}$.   **5.** $x/5\sqrt{x^2 + 5}$.

6. $-\sqrt{4-y^2}/y - \sin^{-1}(y/2)$.   **7.** $-\sqrt{a^2-u^2}(a^2+2u^2)/3a^4u^3$.

8. $\sqrt{u^2-a^2}(a^2+2u^2)/3a^4u^3$.   **9.** $\sqrt{x^2+2x-3} - 2\cos^{-1}(2/(x+1))$.

10. $3\sqrt{x^2+4x+5} + \ln(x+2+\sqrt{x^2+4x+5})$. **12.** $3 - \sqrt{2} + \ln(1+\sqrt{2}/2)$.

14. $\pi r^2/2 - r^2\sin^{-1}(b/r) - b\sqrt{r^2-b^2}$.   **15.** $\pi(8 - 2\ln 5)$.

16. $4\pi^2/3 + \pi\sqrt{3}/2$.   **17.** $2\pi^2 Rr^2$.

Chapter 9. Exercise 4   Page 297

1. $\ln|(x-1)/(x+1)|$.   **2.** $\ln|(x-1)^3(x+2)^2|$.   **3.** $\frac{1}{2}\ln|(x+5)(x-1)^3|$.
4. $x + \ln|(x+4)^3/(x-3)^4|$.   **5.** $\ln x^2(x+2)^4 (x-2)^6$.
6. $\ln|(x+1)(x+2)^3/(x-2)|$.   **7.** $\frac{1}{2}\ln|(x+1)^3(x+3)^{13}/(x+2)^{14}|$.
8. $\ln|(x-3)/(x+5)^2|$.   **9.** $x^2 - 3x + \ln|(x+1)(x+3)/(x+2)(x+4)|$.
10. $2x + \ln|(x-2)(x-3)^3/(x+2)^2(x+3)^4|$.   **11.** $\ln(3/2)$.

12. $\frac{1}{2}\ln\dfrac{3M+3}{M+3}$, $\frac{1}{2}\ln 3$.   **13.** $\pi\ln(3/2)$.   **14.** $\pi(8\ln 2 - 4\ln 3)$.   **15.** The
denominator is 0 at $x=2$ and $x=3$.   **16.** No, see problem 15 of Exercise 4
Chapter 8.

Chapter 9. Exercise 5   Page 301

1. $\dfrac{1}{x} + \ln\left(\dfrac{x-4}{x}\right)^2$.   **2.** $\dfrac{3}{x-3} + \ln\dfrac{x^2}{(x-3)^4}$.   **3.** $\dfrac{4}{x-2} + \ln\dfrac{|x-2|^3}{x^2}$.

4. $\dfrac{2}{x} - \dfrac{10}{x-1}$.   **5.** $\dfrac{6}{x+2} - \dfrac{3}{(x+2)^2} + \ln|x-1|$.   **6.** $\dfrac{5}{1-x} + \ln(x+3)^2$.

7. $-(x+5)/(x^2-9)$.   **8.** $\ln x^2 - \frac{13}{3}\tan^{-1}(x/3)$.   **9.** $\tan^{-1}(x/3) - 3x/(x^2+9)$.
10. $2x^4/(x^2+1)^2$.   **11.** $\ln|x| + 2/x + 2\tan^{-1}x + (4x-3x^2)/2(1+x^2)$.

Chapter 9. Exercise 6   Page 304

1. $\sin x - x\cos x$.   **2.** $(3\theta\sin 3\theta + \cos 3\theta)/9$.   **3.** $\frac{1}{6}x(4x+5)^{3/2} - \frac{1}{60}(4x+5)^{5/2}$.

4. $x^2(x^2+2)^{3/2} - \frac{2}{5}(x^2+2)^{5/2}$.   **5.** $(3x^3\ln x - x^3)/9$.

6. $\dfrac{1}{n+1}x^{n+1}\ln x - \dfrac{x^{n+1}}{(n+1)^2}$.   **7.** $x\sin^{-1}2x + \frac{1}{2}\sqrt{1-4x^2}$.

8. $\frac{1}{2}(1+x^2)\tan^{-1}x - \dfrac{x}{2}$.   **9.** $(2x^3\tan^{-1}x + \ln(1+x^2) - x^2)/6$.

10. $(2y\sin 2y + \cos 2y - 2y^2\cos 2y)/4$.   **11.** $(3x-1)e^{3x}/9$.
12. $(25y^2 - 10y + 2)e^{5y}/125$.   **13.** $(\sin 2x - 2\cos 2x)e^x/5$.
14. $e^{ax}(b\sin bx + a\cos bx)/(a^2+b^2)$.   **15.** $\frac{3}{8}(\ln|\sec x + \tan x| + \sec x\tan x) + \frac{1}{4}\tan x\sec^3 x$.
16. $(32x^3\sin 4x + 24x^2\cos 4x - 12x\sin 4x - 3\cos 4x)/128$.   **17.** $2\pi(1 - 3/e^2)$.
18. $2\pi^2$.   **19.** $2\pi(\sqrt{2} + \ln(1+\sqrt{2}))$.

Chapter 9. Exercise 7   Page 307

1. $\frac{1}{2}\ln|\tan(x/2)| - \frac{1}{4}\tan^2(x/2)$.   **2.** $\frac{1}{6}\ln|1 + \tan 3x|$.   **3.** $\frac{1}{3}\tan^{-1}(\frac{1}{3}\tan\theta)$.
4. $\frac{1}{5}\ln|2 + \tan(x/2)| - \frac{1}{5}\ln|-1 + 2\tan(x/2)|$.

5. $\ln|1 + \tan(x/2)| - \ln|3 + \tan(x/2)|$.   **6.** $-\dfrac{\theta}{3} + \dfrac{5}{6}\tan^{-1}(2\tan(\theta/2))$.

Chapter 9. Exercise 8   Page 308

10. $1/3, -4/9, 4/9, -8/27, 8/81$.   **11.** $1/3, -1/3, 2/9, -2/27$.   **12.** $1/5$, $3/25, -6/125, -6/625$.   **13.** $1/7, 6/35, 8/35, 16/35$.   **14.** $-1/15, -4/45$, $-8/45$.   **15.** $1/6, 5/24, 5/16, 5/16$.

Chapter 9. Exercise 9   Page 309

1. $4\tan^{-1}x + \frac{3}{2}\ln(1 + x^2) - 3\ln|x| - 1/x$.   **2.** $1/(1 + x^2) + \ln(x^2/(1 + x^2))$.
3. $-\ln|\cot 2x + \csc 2x|$.   **4.** $\frac{2}{3}x^{3/2} - x + 2x^{1/2} - 2\ln(1 + x^{1/2})$.   **5.** $\frac{1}{2}\ln|1 - e^{-2x}|$.
6. $-2\sqrt{1 + \cos x}$.   **7.** $-\tan^{-1}\cos x$.   **8.** $\frac{1}{12}\sinh 3x + \frac{3}{4}\sinh x$.   **9.** $-2\cos\sqrt{x}$.
10. $\frac{1}{4}\ln|\sec 2\theta|$.   **11.** $-\tan^{-1}\cos\theta$.   **12.** $-(25x^2 + 10x + 2)e^{-5x}/125$.
13. $x\cot^{-1}2x + \frac{1}{4}\ln(1 + 4x^2)$.   **14.** $x\ln^2 x - 2x\ln x + 2x$.   **15.** $\frac{1}{8}\ln^8 x$.
16. $\ln(2 + \sin x) - \ln(3 - \sin x)$.   **17.** $-\ln(1 + e^{-x})$.   **18.** $\frac{1}{3}\tan^{-1}(3\tan x)$.
19. $\frac{1}{24}\cosh 6x - \frac{3}{8}\cosh 2x$.   **20.** $x\cosh x - \sinh x$.   **21.** $\frac{1}{4}\cos 2x - \frac{1}{6}\cos 3x$.
22. $\ln|\ln x|$.   **23.** $e^{\tan y}$.   **24.** $-\frac{2}{3}\cos^{3/2}x + \frac{4}{7}\cos^{7/2}x - \frac{2}{11}\cos^{11/2}x$.

25. $\frac{1}{3}\tan^{-1}e^{3x}$.   **26.** $\ln(9x^2 + 6x + 5) - \tan^{-1}\dfrac{3x + 1}{2}$.   **27.** $-2(1 - \sin\theta)^{1/2}$.

28. $(6x^3 - 3)e^{2x^3}$.   **29.** $5x\ln(x^2 + a^2) - 10x + 10a\tan^{-1}(x/a)$.
30. $-\frac{1}{2}\ln(1 + \cos^2 t)$.   **31.** $2(\sec y)^{1/2}$.   **32.** $2\sin\sqrt{x} - 2\sqrt{x}\cos\sqrt{x}$.
33. $\frac{1}{20}\sin 10x + \frac{1}{8}\sin 4x$.   **34.** $\frac{1}{2}z + \frac{1}{4}\ln\left|\dfrac{1 + \tan z}{1 - \tan z}\right|$.

35. $-2e^{3x} - 3e^{2x} - 6e^x - 6\ln|e^x - 1|$.   **36.** $\ln((1 + e^x)/(3 - e^x))^2$.
37. $\theta\tan\theta + \ln|\cos\theta|$.   **38.** $-2(1 + \cos\theta)^{1/2}$.   **39.** $-\ln|\ln\cos x|$.
40. $\dfrac{3}{8}\sin\dfrac{4x}{3} - \dfrac{1}{4}\sin 2x$.   **41.** $(\sin x\cosh x - \cos x\sinh x)/2$.
42. $x^5(25\ln^2 x - 10\ln x + 2)$.   **43.** $\tan\theta - \cot\theta$.   **44.** $e^{ax}(a\sin bx - b\cos bx)/(a^2 + b^2)$.
45. $\ln(x^6|x^2 - 4|/(x^2 - 1)^4)$.   **46.** $(\tan^{-1}y)^3/3$.   **47.** $x(\cos\ln x + \sin\ln x)/2$.
48. $-\frac{1}{2}\sin^2\theta + \ln(1 + \sin^2\theta)$.   **49.** $x - 2\tan^{-1}x$.
50. $\frac{1}{10}e^{2x}(2\cos x + \sin x) - \frac{1}{2}\sin x$.

Chapter 10. Exercise 1   Page 317

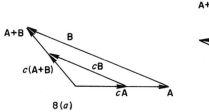

8 (a)

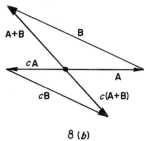

8 (b)

Chapter 10. Exercise 2   Page 321

1. (a) $4\mathbf{i} - 3\mathbf{j}$; (b) $-7\mathbf{i} + 9\mathbf{j}$; (c) $-2\mathbf{i} - 7\mathbf{j}$; (d) $-4\mathbf{i} + 4\mathbf{j}$; (e) $7\mathbf{i} - 8\mathbf{j}$;
(f) $25\mathbf{i} - 19\mathbf{j}$; (g) $-8\mathbf{i} + 6\mathbf{j}$; (h) $\mathbf{0}$.   **2.** $\sqrt{5}$, $\sqrt{34}$, $\sqrt{113}$, $3\sqrt{10}$.   **3.** $7\pi/4$,
$2\pi/3$, π, $\pi/2$.   **4.** $2\sqrt{2}(\cos(7\pi/4)\mathbf{i} + \sin(7\pi/4)\mathbf{j})$, $8(\cos(2\pi/3)\mathbf{i} + \sin(2\pi/3)\mathbf{j})$,
$25(\cos\pi\mathbf{i} + \sin\pi\mathbf{j})$, $\pi(\cos(\pi/2)\mathbf{i} + \sin(\pi/2)\mathbf{j})$.   **5.** (a) $-8\mathbf{i} + 6\mathbf{j}$, 10; (b) $30\mathbf{i} + 40\mathbf{j}$,
50; (c) $-12\mathbf{i} - 5\mathbf{j}$, 13; (d) $12\mathbf{i} - 8\mathbf{j}$, $4\sqrt{13}$.   **6.** $(3\mathbf{i} + 4\mathbf{j})/5$, $(8\mathbf{i} - 15\mathbf{j})/17$,
$(-21\mathbf{i} + 20\mathbf{j})/29$, $(4\mathbf{i} - 7\mathbf{j})/\sqrt{65}$, $-(2\mathbf{i} + \mathbf{j})/\sqrt{5}$.   **9.** (a) $(7, 11)$; (b) $(7, -7)$;
(c) $(1, 2)$; (d) $(\sqrt{2}, \pi + e)$.   **10.** $y = x^2 - 2$.   **13.** $\left(\dfrac{a_1 + 2b_1}{3}, \dfrac{a_2 + 2b_2}{3}\right)$.

Chapter 10. Exercise 3   Page 326

1. The line segment joining $(0, 1)$ and $(1, 0)$.   **2.** $x^2 + y^2 = 25$.   **3.** The
line segment joining $(0, 5)$ and $(5, 0)$ covered four times.   **4.** The upper half of
the ellipse $25x^2 + 9y^2 = 225$.   **5.** The part of the parabola $y = 1 - 2x^2$ between
$(0, 1)$ and $(1, -1)$ doubly covered.   **6.** The right branch of the hyperbola
$x^2 - y^2 = 1$.

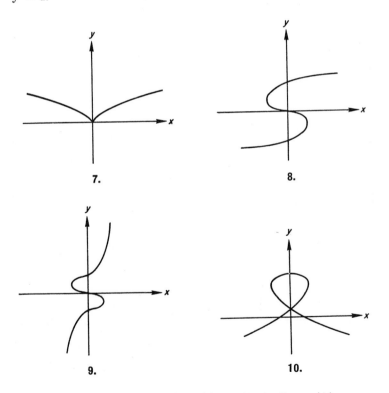

7.

8.

9.

10.

11. $x = a_1 + t(a_2 - a_1)$, $y = b_1 + t(b_2 - b_1)$.   **12.** (a, b), $r = |k|$.
13. $\mathbf{R} = (b + b^2 \sec^2\theta)\mathbf{i} + b \tan\theta\,\mathbf{j}$, $y^2 = x - (b + b^2)$.

14. $\mathbf{R} = (b + 4b \sec \theta)\mathbf{i} + b \tan \theta\mathbf{j}$, $(x - b)^2 - 16y^2 = 16b^2$.
15. $\mathbf{R} = 2 \cos^2 \theta\mathbf{i} + \cos \theta \sin \theta\mathbf{j}$, $(x - 1)^2 + 4y^2 = 1$.
16. $\mathbf{R} = a(\cos \theta + \theta \sin \theta)\mathbf{i} + a(\sin \theta - \theta \cos \theta)\mathbf{j}$.
17. $\mathbf{R} = 2a \cos^2 \theta\mathbf{i} + 2a \tan \theta\mathbf{j}$, $y^2 x = 4a^2(2a - x)$.
20. $\mathbf{R} = a \cos \theta\mathbf{i}$.   **21.** A spiral.

Chapter 10. Exercise 4   Page 336

1. $\sec^2 t\mathbf{i} + \sec t \tan t\mathbf{j}$.   **2.** $(\cos u - u \sin u)\mathbf{i} + (1 + \ln u)\mathbf{j}$.

3. $(2v^3 + 3v^2)e^{2v}\mathbf{i} + (2v - 3v^2)e^{-3v}\mathbf{j}$.   **4.** $\dfrac{\mathbf{i}}{\sqrt{1 - w^2}} + \dfrac{\mathbf{j}}{1 + w^2}$.

5. (a) $\mathbf{A} = 10 \cos 2t(-\mathbf{i} + \mathbf{j})$, $|\mathbf{V}| = 5\sqrt{2}|\sin 2t|$; (b) $(5, 0)$, $(0, 5)$; (c) none.
6. (a) $\mathbf{A} = -\mathbf{R}$, $|\mathbf{V}| = \sqrt{9 + 16 \cos^2 t}$; (b) nowhere; (c) $(0, \pm 5)$ and $(\pm 3, 0)$.
7. (a) $\mathbf{A} = -\sin t\,\mathbf{i} - 4 \cos 2t\,\mathbf{j}$,
$|\mathbf{V}| = |\cos t|\sqrt{1 + 16 \sin^2 t}$; (b) $(\pm 1, -1)$; (c) $(0, 1)$.
8. (a) $\mathbf{A} = 6t\mathbf{i} + 2\mathbf{j}$, $|\mathbf{V}| = |t|\sqrt{4 + 9t^2}$; (b) $(0, 0)$; (c) $(0, 0)$.
9. (a) $\mathbf{A} = 6t\mathbf{i}$, $|\mathbf{V}| = \sqrt{9t^4 - 18t^2 + 10}$; (b) nowhere; (c) $(-2, 1)$, $(2, -1)$.
10. (a) $\mathbf{A} = 6t\mathbf{i} - 2\mathbf{j}$, $|\mathbf{V}| = \sqrt{9t^4 - 14t^2 + 9}$; (b) nowhere; (c) $(0, 4)$, $(\pm 2, 3)$.

11. $|\mathbf{V}| = a\dfrac{d\varphi}{dt} \sqrt{2 - 2 \cos \varphi}$, $\max|\mathbf{V}| = 2a\left|\dfrac{d\varphi}{dt}\right|$.   **12.** $((2n + 1)\pi a, 2a), (2n\pi a, 0)$.

Chapter 10. Exercise 5   Page 339

1. 10,000 ft.   **2.** 670 ft.   **3.** $V_0^2/32$.   **4.** 3290 ft/sec.   **5.** $V_0^2 \sin^2 \alpha/64$.
7. $y = -gx^2/2V_0^2 \cos^2 \alpha + x \tan \alpha$.   **8.** 12.5 secs, 4,400 ft.   **9.** 54.5 mi/hr.
10. 43.0 ft upward $m \approx 1.132$.

Chapter 10. Exercise 6   Page 345

1. 0.   **2.** $2/(4x^2 + 8x + 5)^{3/2}$.   **3.** $e^x/(1 + e^{2x})^{3/2}$.   **4.** $2/(1 + 4y)^{3/2}$.
5. $-9 \sin 3x/(1 + 9 \cos^2 3x)^{3/2}$.   **6.** $\cos y$.   **7.** $-1/4a|\sin(\varphi/2)|$.   **8.** $1/b|\theta|$.
9. $2/5\sqrt{5}$.   **10.** Arc length is measured in the opposite direction.   **11.** $\rho = 2$ at
$(0, 0)$.   **12.** $3\sqrt{3}/2$ at $x = \sqrt{2}/2$.   **13.** $9/7\sqrt[6]{28}$ at $x = \pm(2/7)^{1/6}$.

Chapter 10. Exercise 7   Page 350

1. $(-n\mathbf{i} + m\mathbf{j})/\sqrt{m^2 + n^2}$.   **2.** $-(\cos t\mathbf{i} + \sin t\mathbf{j})$.
3. $(-b \cos t\mathbf{i} - a \sin t\mathbf{j})/\sqrt{a^2 \sin^2 t + b^2 \cos^2 t}$.   **4.** $(-t\mathbf{i} + \mathbf{j})/\sqrt{1 + t^2}$.
5. $(2t\mathbf{i} + (t^2 - 1)\mathbf{j})/(1 + t^2)$.   **6.** $((e^{-t} - e^t)\mathbf{i} + 2\mathbf{j})/(e^t + e^{-t})$.
7. $\sin(t/2)(-\cos(t/2)\mathbf{i} + \sin(t/2)\mathbf{j})/|\sin(t/2)|$.   **8.** $-\sin u\mathbf{i} + \cos u\mathbf{j}$.
9. $x = a + ms/\sqrt{m^2 + n^2}$, $y = b + ns/\sqrt{m^2 + n^2}$.   **10.** $x = a + r \cos(s/r)$,
$y = b + r \sin(s/r)$.   **11.** $x = 2(\cos \sqrt{s} + \sqrt{s} \sin \sqrt{s})$,
$y = 2(\sin \sqrt{s} - \sqrt{s} \cos \sqrt{s})$.   **12.** $x = \dfrac{1}{\sqrt{2}}(s + 1)\cos \ln(s + 1)$,

$y = \dfrac{1}{\sqrt{2}}(s + 1)\sin \ln(s + 1)$.   **13.** $x = \frac{2}{3}(1 - s)^{3/2}$, $y = \frac{2}{3}s^{3/2}$.   **14.** $8a$.

15. $s = \frac{1}{2}e^{2t} + t - \frac{1}{2}$, $P_0(2, 1/2)$. **16.** $s = \int_0^t \sqrt{9 + 7 \sin^2 u} \; du$.

Chapter 10. Exercise 8 Page 354

1. 7.64 r.p.m. **2.** 27 r.p.m. **4.** 17,600 lbs. **5.** 5.5. **7.** 33 tons.
8. 29.67 lbs, 19.67 lbs, 27 r.p.m. **9.** (a) 1.42 W; (b) 3.42 W. **12.** 5.16 mi/sec;
89.2 minutes.

Chapter 11. Exercise 1 Page 361

1. $\pi/4$. **2.** $\pi/4$. **3.** $\pi/2$. **4.** $\pi/6$. **5.** 3. **6.** 14/9. **7.** $\pm\sqrt{3}$.
8. 1/3.

Chapter 11. Exercise 2 Page 364

1. 2/7. **2.** $-4/3$. **3.** $-\pi/2$. **4.** 1. **5.** 2/3. **6.** -2. **7.** $1/\pi^2$.
8. 16. **9.** $-1/3$. **10.** ∞. **11.** ∞. **12.** 0. **13.** $\ln(b/a)$. **14.** $-5/\pi$.
15. 0. **16.** 2. **17.** 1/36. **18.** 2. **19.** 1/2. **20.** 1. **21.** 3. **22.** 1/16.

Chapter 11. Exercise 3 Page 366

1. 0. **2.** 0. **3.** 1/2. **4.** ∞. **5.** 3. **6.** 0. **7.** 1. **8.** 0. **12.** No.

Chapter 11. Exercise 4 Page 369

1. 0. **2.** 1/2. **3.** 0. **4.** 0. **5.** 0. **6.** 0. **7.** 1. **8.** ∞. **9.** e^4.
10. 1. **11.** 1. **12.** 1. **13.** e. **14.** $1/e$. **15.** 1. **16.** 1/3. **17.** 1.
18. 1. **20.** e^{-k}. **22.** 0.

Chapter 11. Exercise 5 Page 372

1. 1. **2.** D. **3.** 2. **4.** D. **5.** D. **6.** 3. **7.** $1/2e^2$. **8.** D. **9.** π.
10. 4π. **11.** 3/2. **12.** 0. **13.** D. **14.** $\sqrt{2}(\ln 4 - 4)$. **15.** D. **16.** π.
17. D. **18.** D. **19.** 1/2. **20.** 0. **21.** D. **22.** D. **24.** $1/(1 - k)$ if
$k < 1$, D. if $k \geq 1$. **25.** $0! = 1$. **26.** $32\pi/9$. **28.** The derivative of
$-2\sqrt{1 - \sin x}$ is $\cos x \sqrt{1 + \sin x}/|\cos x| = \epsilon\sqrt{1 + \sin x}$, where $\epsilon = \pm 1$ according as $\cos x > 0$ or $\cos x < 0$. At $x = 2n\pi + \pi/2$, the function $-2\sqrt{1 - \sin x}$
does not have a derivative.

Chapter 12. Exercise 1 Page 377

1. (4, 0). **2.** $(-3, 0)$. **3.** (5, 0). **4.** (0, 2). **5.** $(0, -4)$. **6.** $(\sqrt{3}, -1)$.
7. $(-4\sqrt{2}, 4\sqrt{2})$. **8.** $(4\sqrt{2}, 4\sqrt{2})$. **9.** $(-3, 3\sqrt{3})$.

In problems 10 through 18, n is any integer.

10. $(\sqrt{2}, \; 2n\pi + \pi/4)$, $(-\sqrt{2}, \; 2n\pi + 5\pi/4)$. **11.** $(\sqrt{6}, \; 2n\pi + 3\pi/4)$,
$(-\sqrt{6}, 2n\pi - \pi/4)$. **12.** $(4, 2n\pi - \pi/3)$, $(-4, 2n\pi - 4\pi/3)$.
13. $(-5, 2n\pi + \pi/2)$, $(5, 2n\pi - \pi/2)$. **14.** $(3\sqrt{2}, 2n\pi + 5\pi/4)$,

$(-3\sqrt{2},\ 2n\pi + \pi/4)$.　**15.** $(4,\ (2n+1)\pi),\ (-4,\ 2n\pi)$.　**16.** $(5,\ 2n\pi + \alpha)$, $(-5,\ (2n+1)\pi + \alpha)$, where $\alpha = \tan^{-1}(4/3)$.　**17.** $(13,\ 2n\pi + \beta)$, $(-13,\ (2n+1)\pi + \beta)$, where $\beta = \cos^{-1}(-5/13)$.　**18.** $(\sqrt{5},\ 2n\pi + \gamma)$, $(-\sqrt{5},\ (2n+1)\pi + \gamma)$, where $\gamma = \sin^{-1}(-1/\sqrt{5})$.　**21.** Sym. w. r. to origin. **22.** Sym. w. r. to y-axis. **23.** Sym. w. r. to x-axis. **24.** Sym. w. r. to the line $y = x$.

Chapter 12. Exercise 2　Page 381

　1. Circle.　**2.** Ray.　**3.** St. line $x = 5$.　**4.** St. line $y = 3$.　**5.** Cardioid. **6.** Limaçon.　**7.** Reciprocal spiral.　**8.** Four-leafed rose.　**9.** Lemniscate (figure eight).　**10.** Three-leafed rose.　**13.** $r = 2B \sin \theta$.　**14.** $(2\sqrt{2},\ \pi/4)$, $(2\sqrt{2},\ 3\pi/4)$.　**15.** $(4,\ -\pi/3)$.　**16.** $(a,\ \pm\cos^{-1}(1/4))$.　**17.** O, $(a\sqrt{2}/2,\ \pi/4)$. **18.** $(1/2,\ \pm\pi/3)$.　**19.** $(2,\ \pm\pi/3),\ (-1,\ \pi)$.　**20.** O, $(-1,\ \pm\pi/3)$.　**21.** $(a/2,\ \pm\pi/6)$.　**22.** If $r = a \cos \theta$ is the given circle, the new curve is $r = \frac{1}{2} a \cos \theta$, also a circle.　**23.** $r = a \sin 2\theta$, a four-leafed rose (see Fig. 8).

Chapter 12. Exercise 3　Page 384

　1. $\theta = 0$.　**2.** $\theta = \pi/2$.　**3.** $\theta = \pi/2$.　**4.** $\theta = 0$.　**5.** $\theta = \pi/4$. **6.** $\theta = \pi/2$.　**7.** $\theta = 0$.　**8.** $\theta = 0$.　**9.** $\theta = \pi/2$.　**10.** $\theta = n\pi/4,\ n = 0, 1, 2, 3$. **12.** $\sqrt{A^2 + B^2},\ (B,\ A)$.　**13.** $r = 1 + 6 \sin \theta$.　**14.** $r^2 = 2 \sin 2\theta$. **15.** $r = \sin^2 \theta/\cos \theta \cos 2\theta$.　**16.** $r = 4 \sin 2\theta/(\sin^3 \theta + \cos^3 \theta)$. **17.** $r = a \cos \theta(\tan^2 \theta - 1)$. **18.** $r = 2 \sin 3\theta$.　**19.** $y^2 = x^3/(2 - x)$. **20.** $y^2 = 16(x + 4)$.　**21.** $y^3 = x(x^2 + y^2)^2$.　**22.** $(x^2 + y^2)^2 = a^2(x^2 - y^2)$.

Chapter 12. Exercise 4　Page 387

　1. P. 1, 7.　**2.** H. 3, 5/3.　**3.** E. 3/4, 10/3.　**4.** H. 4/3, 5/2.　**5.** (a) $r = ep/(1 + e \cos \theta)$; (b) $r = ep/(1 + e \sin \theta)$; (c) $r = ep/(1 - e \sin \theta)$. **6.** E. $e = 1/2$, directrix horizontal, 12 units above O.　**7.** (a) $(ep/(1 + e),\ \pi)$; (b) $(ep/(1 - e),\ 0)$.　**8.** $2ep/(1 - e^2),\ (e^2p/(1 - e^2),\ 0)$.　**10.** $\theta_0 = \cos^{-1} e$, $(ep/(1 - e^2),\ \pm\cos^{-1} e),\ 2ep/\sqrt{1 - e^2}$.　**12.** $(12, 0),\ (4, \pi),\ (8,\ \pm\pi/3),\ 16,\ 8\sqrt{3}$. **13.** $(a, 0)$.　**14.** $2/ep$.　**15.** For $\theta = 0$, $1/d_1 + 1/d_2 = 8/15$, for $\theta = \pi/3$ the sum is $4/15$.

Chapter 12. Exercise 5　Page 392

　1. $(a/2, \pi/6),\ (a/2, 5\pi/6),\ (2a, 3\pi/2)$.　**2.** $(a, \pi/2)$.　**3.** $\alpha = 2\theta$ if $0 \leq \theta < \pi/2$; $\psi = \theta$ if $0 \leq \theta < \pi$.　**5.** $\tan \psi = 1/b$.　**7.** $r_1 r_2 = -\dfrac{dr_1}{d\theta}\dfrac{dr_2}{d\theta}$.　**9.** $(a, 1),\ (-a, -1)$. **10.** (a) $(58\sqrt{29} - 16)/3$; (b) $a\sqrt{1 + b^2}(e^{b\pi} - 1)/b$; (c) $3\pi a/2$; (d) $a(4^3\sqrt{10^3} - 5^3)/12^3$.　**11.** $\sqrt{5} - \sqrt{2} + \ln(2\sqrt{2} + 2) - \ln(1 + \sqrt{5})$. **13.** $\displaystyle\int 2\pi r \sin \theta\sqrt{r^2 + (dr/d\theta)^2}\ d\theta$.　**14.** $2\pi a^2(2 - \sqrt{2})$.　**15.** $32\pi a^2/5$. **16.** $4\pi\sqrt{2}e^{2\pi}/5$.　**17.** $2\pi a^2\sqrt{2}$.　**18.** $\pi^2 a^2$.

Chapter 12. Exercise 6　Page 395

　1. $\pi a^2/4$.　**2.** 11π.　**3.** 11π.　**4.** $19\pi/8$.　**5.** $(2a^2 + b^2 + c^2)\pi/2$.

6. $a^2\pi/4n$.   **7.** a^2.   **8.** $\pi - 3$.   **9.** $a^2/2$.   **10.** $a^2(4 - \pi)/8$.   **11.** $(e^2 - 1)/4$.
12. $a^2(8 - \pi)/4$.   **13.** $a^2(2\pi + 3\sqrt{3})/6$.   **14.** Same as problem 13.
15. $a^2(2\pi - 6 + 3\sqrt{3})/3$.   **16.** $(\pi a^2 + 2(b^2 - a^2)\tan^{-1}(a/b) - 2ab)/8$.
17. The area swept out by the radial line $r = e^\theta$ as θ runs from 0 to 2π is counted twice in the answer.

Chapter 13. Exercise 1   Page 400

1. 2.   **2.** D.   **3.** $1/2$.   **4.** 2.   **5.** D.   **6.** $\pi^2/6 \approx 1.645$.   **7.** $e \approx 2.718$.
8. 3.   **9.** $1/9$.   **10.** D.   **11.** D.   **12.** D.   **13.** $\ln 2 \approx .693$.   **14.** $\pi \approx 3.14$.
15. $1/n^2$.   **16.** $1/(3n + 1)$.   **17.** $1/(n^2 + 3)$.
18. $1/(2n - 1)(2n + 1) = 1/(4n^2 - 1)$.   **19.** $(2n + 1)/2^n$.   **20.** $n/(n^2 + 2)$.
21. $(n + 5)^2/n^n$.   **22.** $(n + 2)/2^n$.   **23.** $6/(1 + n^2)$.   **24.** $2n/(n + 1)(n + 2)(n + 3)$.

Chapter 13. Exercise 2   Page 403

1. $1, 3, 4, 9, 11$.   **2.** 4.   **3.** 5.   **4.** $6/11$.   **5.** $8/11$.   **6.** D.
7. $(75 + 40\sqrt{3})/11$.   **8.** $6/7$.   **9.** $40/27$.   **10.** D.   **11.** D.   **12.** $2/15$.
13. $5/18$.   **14.** $11/18$.   **15.** $3/11$.   **16.** $28/33$.   **17.** $34/37$.   **18.** 70 ft.
20. $\sqrt{H}(1 + \sqrt{r})/4(1 - \sqrt{r})$secs, 11.01 secs.

Chapter 13. Exercise 3   Page 406

1. $4 + 6(x - 1) + 4(x - 1)^2 + (x - 1)^3$.
2. $36 + 72(x - 3) + 48(x - 3)^2 + 12(x - 3)^3 + (x - 3)^4$.
3. $5 - 57(x + 2) + 76(x + 2)^2 - 40(x + 2)^3 + 10(x + 2)^4 - (x + 2)^5$.
4. $95 - 57(x + 5) + 7(x + 5)^2$.   **5.** $\frac{3}{2} + 14(x - \frac{1}{2}) + 42(x - \frac{1}{2})^2 + 32(x - \frac{1}{2})^3$.
6. $18(x + \frac{3}{2}) - 24(x + \frac{3}{2})^2 + 8(x + \frac{3}{2})^3$.   **7.** $2 + 30x^2 + 30x^4 + 2x^6$.   **8.** See
problem 1.   **9.** $1 + 5(x - 2) - 4\sqrt{3}(x - 2)^2 + 8\pi(x - 2)^3$.   If $n > 3$, there
are infinitely many polynomials.   If $n = 3$, there is only one.
11. $1 - 12(x + 1) + 60(x + 1)^2 - 160(x + 1)^3 + 240(x + 1)^4 - 192(x + 1)^5 + 64(x + 1)^6$.

Chapter 13. Exercise 4   Page 410

1. $\sum_{k=0}^{\infty} \dfrac{2^k x^k}{k!}$.

2. $\sum_{k=0}^{\infty} \dfrac{(-1)^k x^{2k+1}}{(2k + 1)!}$.

3. $\sum_{k=0}^{\infty} \dfrac{(-1)^k x^{2k}}{(2k)!}$.

4. $\sum_{k=1}^{\infty} \dfrac{(-1)^{k+1} x^k}{k}$.

5. $\sum_{k=1}^{\infty} \dfrac{x^k}{k}$.

6. $\sum_{k=0}^{\infty} 5(4x)^k$.

7. $\sum_{k=0}^{\infty} \dfrac{(k + 2)(k + 1)}{2} 3^k x^k$.

8. $\sum_{k=0}^{\infty} \dfrac{(2k)! x^k}{4^k (k!)^2}$.

9. $\sum_{k=1}^{\infty} \dfrac{x^k}{(k - 1)!}$.

10. $1 - \sum_{k=1}^{\infty} \dfrac{(2k - 2)! x^k}{2^{2k-1} k! (k - 1)!}$.

11. 6 terms gives 2.717.   **12.** .0349.

13. $\displaystyle\sum_{k=1}^{\infty} \frac{2x^{2k-1}}{2k-1}.$ **14.** $\displaystyle\sum_{k=0}^{\infty} \frac{e^2(x-2)^k}{k!}$ **15.** $\displaystyle\sum_{k=0}^{\infty} \frac{(-1)^k(x-3)^k}{3^{k+1}}.$

16. $\displaystyle\sum_{k=0}^{\infty} \frac{(-1)^k(x-\pi/6)^{2k}}{2(2k)!} + \sum_{k=0}^{\infty} \frac{(-1)^k\sqrt{3}(x-\pi/6)^{2k+1}}{2(2k+1)!}.$

17. $\displaystyle\ln 3 + \sum_{k=1}^{\infty} \frac{(-1)^{k+1}(x-3)^k}{k3^k}.$ **18.** $x + 2x^2 + 3\underline{x}^3.$

19. $1 - x + \dfrac{3}{2}x^2.$ **20.** $x + x^2 + \dfrac{1}{3}x^3.$

21. $x + \dfrac{x^3}{3} + \dfrac{2}{15}x^5.$ **22.** .5150.

Chapter 13. Exercise 5 Page 413

1. $\displaystyle\sum_{k=1}^{\infty} \frac{x^{2k}}{(2k-1)!}.$ **2.** $\displaystyle\sum_{k=0}^{\infty} \frac{(-1)^k x^{4k+2}}{(2k+1)!}$

3. $\displaystyle\sum_{k=0}^{\infty} \frac{(k+3)(k+2)(k+1)}{6}x^k.$ **4.** $1 + 2\displaystyle\sum_{k=1}^{\infty} x^k.$

5. $\displaystyle\sum_{k=0}^{\infty} \frac{(-1)^k x^{k+1}}{(2k)!}.$ **6.** $\displaystyle\sum_{k=1}^{\infty} \frac{(-1)^{k+1} x^k}{k}.$

7. $\displaystyle\sum_{k=0}^{\infty} (-1)^k x^{2k}.$ **8.** $\displaystyle\sum_{k=1}^{\infty} kx^k.$ **9.** $\displaystyle\sum_{k=0}^{\infty} \frac{(-1)^k x^{2k+1}}{2k+1}.$

10. $1 + 5\displaystyle\sum_{k=1}^{\infty} (-1)^k 2^{k-1} x^k.$ **11.** $\displaystyle\sum_{k=0}^{\infty} \left(\frac{(-1)^{k+1}}{2^k} - \frac{2}{3^{k+1}} \right) x^k.$

12. $4\displaystyle\sum_{k=0}^{\infty} \frac{(-1)^k}{2k+1}.$ **13.** .234.   **14.** .255.   **15.** .217.

16. .006.   **17.** $(x + x^2)/(1 - x)^3.$ **19.** $1 - x + x^3 - x^4 + x^6.$ **20.** $-\sin x.$

Chapter 13. Exercise 6 Page 419

1. 0.   **2.** 0.   **3.** D.   **4.** 2.   **5.** D.   **6.** 0.   **7.** D.   **8.** $\sqrt{2}/2.$
9. 2500.   **10.** 5/2.   **11.** $-1.$ **12.** D.   **13.** 3.   **15.** Dec.   **16.** Inc.
17. Inc.   **18.** Dec.   **19.** Inc.

Chapter 13. Exercise 7 Page 426

1. C.   **2.** C.   **3.** D.   **4.** C.   **5.** C.   **6.** C.   **7.** D.   **8.** C.   **9.** D.
10. C.   **11.** C.   **12.** C.   **13.** C.   **14.** C.   **15.** D.   **18.** (a) D; (b) C;
(c) C; (d) D.

Chapter 13. Exercise 8 Page 430

1. C.   **2.** C.   **3.** D.   **4.** C.   **5.** C.   **6.** C.   **7.** D.   **8.** D.   **9.** C.
10. C.   **11.** C.   **12.** C.   **13.** D   **14.** C.

Chapter 13. Exercise 9   Page 434

1. $-1 < x < 1$.   **2.** $-1/2 \leqq x \leqq 1/2$.   **3.** $-1 \leqq x < 1$.   **4.** $-5 < x \leqq 5$.
5. $-\infty < x < \infty$.   **6.** $-\infty < x < \infty$.   **7.** $x = 0$.   **8.** $2 < x < 4$.
9. $-7 \leqq x < -3$.   **10.** $7/2 \leqq x < 9/2$.   **11.** $1 \leqq x < 3$.   **12.** $-7 \leqq x < -4$.
13. $-7/3 \leqq x \leqq 1$.   **14.** $-1 \leqq x \leqq 1$.   **15.** $x > 1$ or $x < -1$.   **16.** $x > 1$ or
$x \leqq -1$.   **17.** $5 \leqq x \leqq 8$.   **18.** $3 < x < 9$.   **19.** $-1 \leqq x < 11$.
20. $12/5 < x < 22$.   **21.** $x \leqq -1$, or $x > 1$.   **22.** $-\infty < x < -1$.   **23.** D.
for all x.   **24.** $-1 < x < 1$.   **25.** C. for all x.   **26.** $-\infty < x < \infty$.
29. $1 < |x| < 3$, $(x^2 - 5)/(9 - x^2)$.   **31.** All x except $x = 1$.

Chapter 13. Exercise 10   Page 440

In these problems n is the exponent in the last term needed in the computation.
6. 1.0488, $n = 3$.   **7.** 1.2214, $n = 4$.   **8.** $.1823$, $n = 5$.   **9.** $.0523$, $n = 3$.
10. $.9986$, $n = 3$.   **11.** 5.196, $n = 2$.   **12.** 4.642, $n = 3$.   **13.** $.545$, $n = 2$.

Chapter 13. Exercise 12   Page 446

9. $\sum_{n=0}^{\infty} \dfrac{(n + 1)(n + 2)\cdots(n + k - 1)}{(k - 1)!} x^n$.   **11.** $.6931$.
12. $.4055$.   **13.** 1.0986.   **14.** $.5108$, 1.6094.   **15.** 3.1416.

16. $\sum_{n=0}^{\infty} \dfrac{(-1)^n}{(4n + 1)(2n)!}$.   **17.** $\sum_{n=0}^{\infty} \dfrac{(-1)^n}{(2n + 1)(2n + 1)!}$.

18. $\sum_{n=1}^{\infty} \dfrac{(-1)^n}{n \, 2^n \, n!}$.   **19.** $1 - \sum_{n=1}^{\infty} \dfrac{(2n - 2)!}{(3n + 1)2^{2n-1}n!(n - 1)!}$.

20. $y = x^{1/3}$ does not have a derivative at $x = 0$, while a convergent Maclaurin series does.

Chapter 13. Exercise 14   Page 451

1. C.   **2.** C.   **3.** C.   **4.** D.   **5.** C.   **6.** C.   **7.** D.   **8.** C.   **9.** C.
10. D.   **11.** (a) D; (b) C to $-\ln 2$.   **12.** $-1 < x < 1$.   **13.** Set $x = 1/(2M + 1)$.
15. $\ln a + \sum_{n=1}^{\infty} \dfrac{(-1)^{n+1}x^n}{na^n}$.   **16.** $\ln 2 + \sum_{n=1}^{\infty} \dfrac{(-1)^{n+1}(x - 2)^n}{n \, 2^n}$.

18. $\sum_{n=0}^{\infty} \dfrac{(-1)^n ca^n}{b^{n+1}} x^n$.   **19.** $\sum_{n=0}^{\infty} 7\left(\dfrac{1}{2^n} - \dfrac{1}{3^n}\right) x^n$.

20. $-\sum_{n=0}^{\infty} (-1)^n \left(\dfrac{x - 3}{2}\right)^n$.   **21.** $1 + 3x + 6x^2 + 10x^3 + 15x^4$.
23. $x \geqq 1/2$.   **30.** $.0124$.   **31.** $.0048$.   **32.** $.4613$.   **33.** $.9317$.   **34.** $-1/2$.
35. $-1/6$.   **36.** 2.   **37.** $-1/3$.   **38.** $55/3$.

Chapter 14. Exercise 1   Page 458

3. All possible combinations with $x = 2$ or 7, $y = 3$ or 10, $z = 4$ or -3.
4. $(5, 0, 1)$, $(0, 6, 0)$.   **5.** $(7, 0, 0)$, $(0, 2, 7)$.   **6.** $(4, 0, 8)$, $(0, 4, 6)$.
7. $(3, 0, -5)$, $(0, 7.5, 10)$.   **13.** $x^2 + y^2 + z^2 = 25$.   **14.** $\sqrt{123}$.

Chapter 14. Exercise 2   Page 463

2. (a) $5\mathbf{i} - \mathbf{j} + 2\mathbf{k}$; (b) $7\mathbf{i} + 7\mathbf{j} + \mathbf{k}$; (c) $-8\mathbf{i} - 2\mathbf{j} - 17\mathbf{k}$; (d) $8\mathbf{i} + 7\mathbf{j} + 39\mathbf{k}$.
4. $\{2/3, 1/3, -2/3\}$, $\{6/7, -3/7, 2/7\}$, $\{1/\sqrt{3}, 1/\sqrt{3}, 1/\sqrt{3}\}$,
$\{-1/\sqrt{5}, 6/5\sqrt{5}, 8/5\sqrt{5}\}$.   **5.** (a) 6; (b) 12; (c) $5\sqrt{3}$; (d) $13\sqrt{2}$.
6. $\sin^2\theta + \cos^2\theta = 1$.   **8.** $m = 2, n = 1/2, p = -3$.
10. $x^2 + y^2 + z^2 - 4x + 6y - 12z = 0$.   **11.** $-x + 6y + 9z = 3$.   **12.** (a)
$2x+2y-2z = 1$;(b)$ax+by+cz = a^2+b^2+c^2$.   **14.** $(x-a)^2+(y-b)^2+(z-c)^2 = r^2$.
15. (a) $(-2, 0, 3)$, $\sqrt{13}$; (b) $(-6, 3, -2)$, 7; (c) $(5, -3, -4)$, 6; (d) $(1/6, 5/6, 2/3)$,
$\sqrt{11/6}$.   **16.** $(0, 6, 0)$, 2.   **17.** (a) $\sqrt{t^2 + u^2}$; (b) $\sqrt{s^2 + u^2}$; (c) $\sqrt{s^2 + t^2}$;
(d) $|s - 2|$; (e) $\sqrt{(t + 3)^2 + (u - 5)^2}$.

Chapter 14. Exercise 3   Page 467

1. $\dfrac{x - 1}{3} = \dfrac{y - 2}{4} = \dfrac{z - 3}{-12}$.   **2.** $\dfrac{x}{1} = \dfrac{y + 5}{11} = \dfrac{z - 8}{-6}$.

3. $\dfrac{x - 2}{3} = \dfrac{y - 1}{-5} = \dfrac{z + 3}{10}$.   **4.** $x = -2 + 4t, y = 6, z = 8 - 16t$.
5. $(0, 2/3, 7)$.   **6.** $(-1, -16, 14)$.   **7.** No.   **8.** $(13/8, 13/8, -17/4)$,
$(14/5, -1/3, -1/3)$, $(29/7, -18/7, 29/7)$.   **9.** $\mathbf{R} = 2\mathbf{j} + 7\mathbf{k} + t(-7\mathbf{i} + 2\mathbf{j} + 7\mathbf{k})$.
10. $\mathbf{R} = \mathbf{i} + 5\mathbf{j} + 5\mathbf{k} + t(-2\mathbf{i} + 5\mathbf{j} + 10\mathbf{k})$.   **11.** $\mathbf{R} = 3\mathbf{i} - 4\mathbf{k} + t(20\mathbf{i} + 15\mathbf{j} + 12\mathbf{k})$.
12. Same as problem 9.   **13.** $(7, 10, -21)$.   **14.** $(13, -8, -1)$.   **15.** $(52, -9, 43)$.
16. $(5, 2, 6)$.   **18.** $x = y = z$.   **19.** $(8, 11, 0)$.   **21.** (a) $(1, -1, 5)$;
(b) $(3, -2, -1)$; (c) $(AD/R^2, BD/R^2, CD/R^2)$ where $R^2 = A^2 + B^2 + C^2$.

Chapter 14. Exercise 4   Page 472

1. (a) -23; (b) 3; (c) 0; (d) -1.   **2.** (a) $-23/\sqrt{29}\sqrt{62}$; (b) $3/2\sqrt{31}\sqrt{55}$;
(c) 0; (d) $-1/2\sqrt{61}\sqrt{97}$.   **3.** $-14/3$.   **4.** $1/5\sqrt{2}$, $4/\sqrt{65}$, $9/\sqrt{130}$.
5. $1/2, 1/2, 1/2$.   **6.** $1/2, 1/2, 1/2$.   **13.** If the two vectors $a_1\mathbf{i} + a_2\mathbf{j} + a_3\mathbf{k}$ and
$b_1\mathbf{i} + b_2\mathbf{j} + b_3\mathbf{k}$ are parallel or if one of them is zero.   **14.** $\sqrt{2/3}$.   **15.** $9/11$.
17. $6\mathbf{i} + 4\mathbf{j} + 5\mathbf{k}$.

Chapter 14. Exercise 5   Page 477

1. (a) $3(2\mathbf{i} - 11\mathbf{j} - 4\mathbf{k})$; (b) $7(-3\mathbf{i} + 7\mathbf{j} - 9\mathbf{k})$; (c) $-71\mathbf{i} + 50\mathbf{j} - 18\mathbf{k}$;
(d) $113\mathbf{i} + 17\mathbf{j} - 103\mathbf{k}$.   **2.** (a) $3\sqrt{141}/\sqrt{29}\sqrt{62}$; (b) $7\sqrt{139}/2\sqrt{31}\sqrt{55}$;
(c) 1; (d) $7\sqrt{21}\sqrt{23}/2\sqrt{61}\sqrt{97}$.   **4.** $(\mathbf{i} - \mathbf{j} + \mathbf{k})/\sqrt{3}$.   **6.** (a) $13/2$; (b) 17;
(c) $3\sqrt{6}/2$; (d) $\sqrt{222}/2$.   **7.** When the three points are collinear.   **8.** (a)
$42\mathbf{i} + 19\mathbf{j} - 17\mathbf{k}$; (b) $19\mathbf{i} + 5\mathbf{j} - 10\mathbf{k}$.

Chapter 14. Exercise 6   Page 482

1. (a) $\sqrt{5}$; (b) $\sqrt{397}/7$; (c) $3\sqrt{2}/11$; (d) 0.   **2.** (a) $35/\sqrt{230}$; (b) $\sqrt{11/30}$;
(c) 0; (d) $2\sqrt{6}/3$.   **4.** Cyclic permutation of the rows in a third order det. does
not change the value of the det.   **5.** (a) 5; (b) 18; (c) 0; (d) 20.   **6.** (a) $\sqrt{2}$;
(b) $17/5\sqrt{6}$; (c) 0; (d) $2\sqrt{3}$.   **7.** $4/\sqrt{3}$.   **8.** $\sqrt{3/14}$, $\sqrt{83/14}$.   **9.** If **AB**
and **CD** are parallel.

Chapter 14. Exercise 7 Page 486

1. (a) $x - y + z = 7$; (b) $3x + 2y - z = -10$; (c) $2x - 5y - 7z = 0$;
(d) $bcx + cay + abz = abc$; (e) $bcx + cay + abz = 2abc$. **2.** $3x + 5y - 7z = -44$.
3. (a) $7/\sqrt{3}$; (b) $10/\sqrt{14}$; (c) 0; (d) $|abc|/\sqrt{b^2c^2 + c^2a^2 + a^2b^2} = \left(\dfrac{1}{a^2} + \dfrac{1}{b^2} + \dfrac{1}{c^2}\right)^{-1/2}$;
(e) $2\left(\dfrac{1}{a^2} + \dfrac{1}{b^2} + \dfrac{1}{c^2}\right)^{-1/2}$. **4.** (a) $1/\sqrt{3}$; (b) $6/\sqrt{14}$; (c) $9/\sqrt{78}$. **7.** 2.
8. $\dfrac{x + 9}{2} = \dfrac{y - 4}{6} = \dfrac{z - 3}{9}$, $Q(-105/11, 26/11, 6/11)$. **9.** 3.
10. $x - 3 = y + 1 = z - 6$. **11.** (a) $-x = y - 2 = z + 2$; (b) $\dfrac{x + 5}{13} = \dfrac{y - 5}{-5} = \dfrac{z + 2}{4}$;
(c) $x - 4 = y - 1 = 2 - z$. **12.** (a) $x - z = 0$; (b) $3x - 2y + 3z = 20$;
(c) $x - 9y - z = 49$. **14.** $9/2\sqrt{39}$, 0, $5/2\sqrt{133}$. **15.** (a) $8/21$; (b) $20/33$;
(c) 0; (d) 1. **16.** $2x + 2y + 2z = 3$.

Chapter 14. Exercise 8 Page 492

1. $5a \cos 5t\mathbf{i} - 5a \sin 5t\mathbf{j} + 3\mathbf{k}$, $-25a(\sin 5t\mathbf{i} + \cos 5t\mathbf{j})$.
2. $a \cos t\mathbf{i} - a \sin t\mathbf{j} + 4 \cos 2t\mathbf{k}$, $-a \sin t\mathbf{i} - a \cos t\mathbf{j} - 8 \sin 2t\mathbf{k}$. **3.** $3\mathbf{i} - 5\mathbf{j} - \mathbf{k}$, 0.
4. $\mathbf{i} + 2t\mathbf{j} + 3t^2\mathbf{k}$, $2\mathbf{j} + 6t\mathbf{k}$. **5.** $2t\mathbf{i} + (3t^2 - 6t)\mathbf{j} + 5\mathbf{k}$, $2\mathbf{i} + 6(t - 1)\mathbf{j}$.
6. $(t - 1)e^{-t}\mathbf{i} - t^{-2}\mathbf{j} + t^{-2}(1 - \ln t)\mathbf{k}$, $(2 - t)e^{-t}\mathbf{i} + 2t^{-3}\mathbf{j} - t^{-3}(3 - \ln t)\mathbf{k}$.
10. $(-1, 0, 0)$ at $t = 0$, $(3, -4, 10)$ at $t = 2$. **11.** $P_\infty(1, 5, 0)$, $\mathbf{V}_\infty = 0$, $\mathbf{A}_\infty = 0$.
12. No. Consider $\mathbf{R} = t^{-1} \sin t^2 \mathbf{i}$. **14.** 267 mi/hr. **15.** 147 mi/hr.

Chapter 14. Exercise 9 Page 497

1. $y = z = 0, x = 0$. **2.** $x = \sqrt{2}(y - 1) = -\sqrt{2}(z - 1)$, $\sqrt{2}x + y - z = 0$.
3. $\mathbf{R} = t\mathbf{j} + \sqrt{3}t\mathbf{k}$, $y + \sqrt{3}z = 0$. **4.** $\mathbf{R} = t\mathbf{i} + \mathbf{j}$, $x = 0$.
5. $3x = 3y = z + 9$, $x + y + 3z = 72$. **6.** $s = t^3 + 6t$, $s = e^t - e^{-t}$,
$s = \frac{1}{2}t\sqrt{4 + t^2} + 2 \ln(t + \sqrt{4 + t^2}) - 2 \ln 2$, $s = 2(1 + t)^{3/2} - 2$,
$s = [2(t + 2)^{3/2} - 4\sqrt{2}]/3$. **7.** $\sqrt{2}/(e^t + e^{-t})^2$. **8.** $\sqrt{2}/6(1 + t^2)^2$.
9. $1/3a(1 + t^2)^2$. **10.** $18/5\sqrt{38}$. **11.** $24/65$.
13. $[-(\sin t + \cos t)\mathbf{j} + (\cos t - \sin t)\mathbf{k}]/\sqrt{2}$.
14. $(-\sin t\mathbf{i} + \sin 2t\mathbf{j} - \cos 2t\mathbf{k})/\sqrt{1 + \sin^2 t}$.
15. $[-2t\mathbf{i} + (2 - t^2)\mathbf{j} + 2t\mathbf{k}]/(2 + t^2)$.

Chapter 14. Exercise 10 Page 502

1. (a) $f(x, -y, z) = f(x, y, z)$; (b) $f(-x, y, z) = f(x, y, z)$;
(c) $f(x, -y, -z) = f(x, y, z)$; (d) $f(-x, -y, z) = f(x, y, z)$; (e) $f(y, x, z) = f(x, y, z)$.
2. It is a cyl. perp. to the xz-plane, sym. $w. r.$ to the y-axis and $w. r.$ to the origin.
3. $x_0 = \pm a$. **4.** $z_0 = 0$. **13.** $\dfrac{z^2}{a^2} + \dfrac{x^2}{b^2} + \dfrac{y^2}{b^2} = 1$. **15.** $x^2 + (y - 2)^2 = 4$.
16. $(x + 1)^2 + y^2 = 9$. **17.** $x = \pm y$, $|x| \leq 2$. **18.** $x^2 - y^2 = 5$, $|x| \leq 3$.
19. $y = 2x$. **20.** $2y = (A \pm \sqrt{A^2 - 16})x$. **21.** $x^2 + y^2 + xy = 2A(x + y)$.
25. $c^2 = a^3 + 2b^4$, yes $(0, 0, 0)$. **26.** $(x^2 + y^2 + z^2 + A^2 - a^2)^2 = 4A^2(x^2 + y^2)$

Chapter 14. Exercise 11   Page 505

1. $(0, 3, 5)$.   **2.** $(0, -3, -5)$.   **3.** $(-2, 2\sqrt{3}, 1)$.   **4.** $(1, 0, 6)$.
5. $(3\sqrt{2}, -3\sqrt{2}, 19)$.   **6.** $(-1.665, 3.637, 1)$.   **7.** $(\sqrt{2}, \pi/4, 1)$.
8. $(2\sqrt{2}, 7\pi/4, -2)$.   **9.** $(6, 5\pi/6, 6)$.   **10.** $(4\sqrt{2}, 3\pi/4, -7)$.   **11.** $(16, 4\pi/3, \pi)$.
12. $(10, 0, -10)$.   **13.** $r^2 + z^2 = 16$.   **14.** $z = r^3 \cos 3\theta$.   **15.** $z^2 = \tan 2\theta$.
16. $r(A \cos \theta + B \sin \theta) + Cz = D$.   **17.** $x^2 + y^2 = 4x$.   **18.** $(x^2 + y^2)^3 = z^3 y^3$.
19. $(x^2 + y^2)^{5/2} = 4xyz$.   **20.** $x^2 - y^2 = z^3$.

Chapter 14. Exercise 12   Page 507

1. $(2\sqrt{2}, 2\sqrt{2}, 4\sqrt{3})$.   **2.** $(2, 2\sqrt{3}, 0)$.   **3.** $(-4\sqrt{2}, -4\sqrt{2}, 8\sqrt{3})$.
4. $(0, 0, 7)$.   **5.** $(0, 0, -\pi)$.   **6.** $(0, 0, 0)$.   **7.** Sphere $\rho = 8 \cos \varphi$.   **8.** Paraboloid of revolution $\rho^2 \sin^2 \varphi + \rho \cos \varphi = 10$.   **9.** A distorted torus $\rho = \sin^2 \varphi$.
10. $\rho = \cos^2 \theta$. Each plane containing the z-axis intersects this surface in a circle with center at 0 and radius $\cos^2 \theta$. When $x = 0$ and $y = 0$, z is indeterminate.
12. Plane $z = -7$.   **13.** Sphere $(x - 2)^2 + y^2 + (z - 1)^2 = 5$.   **14.** Cyl. $x^2 + y^2 = 100$.   **15.** $x^2(x^2 + y^2 + z^2) = 4y^2$. Each plane containing the z-axis intersects the surface in a circle of radius $2 \tan \theta$, except the plane $x = 0$, and except for pts on the z-axis.   **16.** $r = \rho \sin \varphi$, $\theta = \theta$, $z = \rho \cos \varphi$.
17. (a) $r^2 + z^2 + A^2 - a^2 = 2rA$; (b) $a^2 = \rho^2 + A^2 - 2\rho A \sin \varphi$.
18. (a) $\rho = 2A \sin \varphi \cos \theta$; (b) $\rho = 2A \cos \varphi$.

Chapter 15. Exercise 1   Page 511

1. $63, 84, (4, 3), 0$.   **2.** $40, 40, (2, 2), -20$.   **3.** $22, 46, (23/6, 11/6), -14$.
4. $26, -15, (-3/2, 13/5), -4$.   **5.** $60, 80, (4, 3), 0$.   **6.** 9.   **10.** $\bar{P}$ can be put at any point in the interior of $\Delta P_1 P_2 P_3$ by a proper selection of the three weights.
12. $2/3$.

Chapter 15. Exercise 2   Page 516

1. $(1, 1, 1)$.   **2.** (a, b, c).   **3.** (a, b, c).   **4.** $(1, 32/21, 2/21)$.   **5.** $(1, 2, 3)$.

Chapter 15. Exercise 3   Page 518

1. .70 lbs/ft².   **2.** 1.35 lbs/ft².   **3.** .045 lbs/ft.   **4.** .007 lbs/ft.   **5.** .0031 lbs/in².   **6.** .004 in².   **7.** 7.5 lbs.   **8.** 14/3 lbs.   **10.** $n3^{n-1}/2$.   **11.** 55 lbs.
12. $8\pi(8 \ln \frac{3}{2} - 3)$lbs.   **13.** Yes, 8π lbs.   **14.** $(a + \frac{1}{2} \sinh 2a)$lbs.

Chapter 15. Exercise 4   Page 524

2. $(1, 1)$.   **3.** $(a/3, b/3)$.   **4.** $(14/5, 12/5)$.   **5.** $(3/2, 6/5)$.   **6.** $(32/7, 4/5)$.
7. $(93/35, 45/56)$.   **8.** $(0, 83/70)$.   **9.** $(5/9, 5/27)$.   **10.** $(16/15, 64/21)$.

11. $(4, 2)$.   **12.** $(0, 4a/3\pi)$.   **13.** $(\pi/2, \pi/8)$.   **14.** $\left(\dfrac{e^2 + 1}{e^2 - 1}, \dfrac{e^2 + 1}{4}\right)$.

15. $(1, e^2/4)$.   **16.** $1/2$.   **17.** $1/6$.   **18.** $(2, 1/5)$.   **19.** 360 lbs-ft, 272 lbs-ft $(34/15, 3)$.   **20.** $(20/13, 24/13)$.

CHAPTER 15. Exercise 5. Page 527

1. $a\,(b_2{}^3 - b_1{}^3)\,/3$, no. **2.** $27/4,\,27/4$. **3.** $ab^3/12,\,ba^3/12$. **4.** $252,\,340$.
5. $2^7/21,\,2^5/5$. **6.** $32/3,\,1536/5$. **7.** $62/15,\,254/7$. **8.** $934/105,\,26/15$.
9. $27/1820,\,3/28$. **10.** $4/9,\,\pi^2 - 4$. **11.** $(e^6 - 1)\,/9,\,2e^2 - 2$. **12.** $\tfrac{1}{3} < p \le \tfrac{1}{2}$,
$1/3(3p - 1)$. **13.** $p > 3$. **14.** $2^9/7$.

Chapter 15. Exercise 6 Page 531

1. $(0,\,0,\,3R/8)$. **2.** $(0,\,0,\,2/3)$. **3.** $(0,\,0,\,3)$. **4.** $(0,\,0,\,1/3)$. **5.** $(0,\,0,\,5/6)$.
6. $(0,\,0,\,(\pi^2 + 4)/32)$. **7.** $4\pi R^5/15,\,\pi/6,\,192\pi/7,\,\pi/3,\,2^{11}\pi/9,\,3\pi(\pi^2 - 8)/2$.
8. $n > 1/4,\,\pi/2(4n - 1)$. **9.** $n > 1,\,\pi/2(n - 1)$.

Chapter 15. Exercise 7 Page 532

1. $(2R/\pi,\,2R/\pi)$. **2.** $(R/2,\,R/2,\,R/2)$. **3.** $\pi R^3/4$. **4.** $\pi R^4/3$. **5.** $(A/3,\,0,\,0)$.
6. $\pi B^3\sqrt{A^2 + B^2}/2$. **7.** $(2A/5,\,2A/5)$. **8.** $15\pi A/256$. **9.** $(\pi A,\,4A/3)$.
10. $(a\operatorname{csch} a + \cosh a)/2$. **11.** $(a^2 + a\sinh 2a - \sinh^2 a)/4(a\sinh a - \cosh a + 1)$.
12. $(R(\pi + 4)/(2\pi + 4),\,3R/(\pi + 2))$.

Chapter 15. Exercise 8 Page 535

1. $AB(2R + A)\pi,\,2(A + B)(2R + A)\pi$. **2.** $64\pi R/3$. **3.** $BH(3R + H)\pi/3$,
$2(B + H + \sqrt{B^2 + H^2})(3R + H)\pi/3$. **4.** $BH(3R - H)\pi/3$,
$2(B + H + \sqrt{B^2 + H^2})(3R - H)\pi/3$. **5.** $(4r/3\pi,\,0)$. **6.** $(2r/\pi,\,0)$.
7. $(3\pi R + 4r)\pi r^2/3$. **8.** $(3\pi R - 4r)\pi r^2/3$. **9.** Yes.

Chapter 15. Exercise 9 Page 536

1. 4500 lbs. **2.** 3000 lbs. **3.** 4240 lbs. **4.** 25,000 lbs. **5.** 5000 lbs.

Chapter 15. Exercise 10 Page 538

1. $9/4$. **2.** $164\tfrac{1}{4}$. **3.** (a) $2/5$; (b) $2^8/15$. **4.** $27\tfrac{4}{5}$. **5.** 62. **6.** 168.
7. It must pass through the centroid of the region. **8.** $3\pi R^4 H/2$. **9.** $28\pi R^5/15$.
10. 4.

Chapter 16. Exercise 1 Page 544

1. $2xy - y^3,\ x^2 - 3xy^2,\ 2x - 3y^2$. **2.** $e^{xy}[y\sin(x + 2y) + \cos(x + 2y)]$,
$e^{xy}[x\sin(x + 2y) + 2\cos(x + 2y)],\ e^{xy}[(xy - 1)\sin(x + 2y) + (x + 2y)\cos(x + 2y)]$.
3. $\sec 2y(\tan 3x + 3x\sec^2 3x),\ 2x\sec 2y\tan 2y\tan 3x,\ 2\sec 2y\tan 2y(\tan 3x + 3x\sec^2 3x)$.
4. $1/x,\ -4y\csc 2y^2,\ 0$. **5.** $-y/(x^2 + y^2),\ x/(x^2 + y^2),\ (y^2 - x^2)/(x^2 + y^2)^2$.
6. Same as problem 5. **7.** $\cos\theta,\ -r\sin\theta,\ -\sin\theta$. **8.** $1/4(s^{3/2} + st^{1/2})^{1/2}$,
$1/4(ts^{1/2} + t^{3/2})^{1/2},\ -1/16(st)^{1/2}\,(s^{1/2} + t^{1/2})^{3/2}$. **9.** $x + x\ln(x^2 + y^2 + z^2)$,
$y + y\ln(x^2 + y^2 + z^2),\ z + z\ln(x^2 + y^2 + z^2)$. **10.** $1/y^2 - t^4/x^2,\ -2x/y^3 + 2y/z^3$,
$-3y^2/z^4 + 3z^2/t^4,\ -4z^3/t^5 + 4t^3/x$. **17.** $\delta = 1/30$, or any smaller positive
number. **18.** $\delta = \epsilon/3$. **19.** $\delta = 1/40$. **20.** 0.

Chapter 16. Exercise 2   Page 546

1. $-4, 10$.   **2.** $16\pi, 216\pi$.   **3.** $-8/9, 24/49$.   **4.** $-1/2\sqrt{30}, -1/3\sqrt{78}$.
5. $y^4 + 2x$, $3x^2y^4 \sin \pi xy^2 + \pi x^3y^6 \cos \pi xy^2$, $4xy^2/(y^2 - x^2)^2$, $-y^2/2x\sqrt{8x^2 + xy^2}$.

Chapter 16. Exercise 3   Page 550

1. $2x + 4y + z = 15$, $\mathbf{R} = (1 - 2t)\mathbf{i} + (2 - 4t)\mathbf{j} + (5 - t)\mathbf{k}$.
2. $12x - 12y - z = 6$, $\mathbf{R} = (3 + 12t)\mathbf{i} + (2 - 12t)\mathbf{j} + (6 - t)\mathbf{k}$.
3. $6x + 3y + 2z = 18$, $\mathbf{R} = (1 + 6t)\mathbf{i} + (2 + 3t)\mathbf{j} + (3 + 2t)\mathbf{k}$.
4. $z = -\pi e^2(y - 1)$, $\mathbf{R} = 2\mathbf{i} + (1 - \pi e^2t)\mathbf{j} - t\mathbf{k}$.
5. $3x + 3y - z = 4$, $\mathbf{R} = (1 + 3t)\mathbf{i} + (1 + 3t)\mathbf{j} + (2 - t)\mathbf{k}$.
6. $6x + 7y + 6z = 121$, $\mathbf{R} = 6(1 + t)\mathbf{i} + 7(1 + t)\mathbf{j} + 6(1 + t)\mathbf{k}$.
7. $\cos \theta = \pm\sqrt{26}/22$.   **10.** $H(1 + A)/\sqrt{A}$.
11. $\dfrac{ax^2}{(1 + 2aH)^2} + \dfrac{by^2}{(1 + 2bH)^2} = H$.

Chapter 16. Exercise 4   Page 552

1. Open.   **2.** Closed.   **3.** Open.   **4.** Open.   **5.** Closed.   **6.** Open.
7. Neither.   **8.** Open.   **9.** Closed.   **10.** Closed.   **11.** Neither.   **12.** Open.
13. Open.   **14.** Neither.   **15.** Neither.   **16.** 11, 12, 13, 14, 15.

17. $(x - x_0)^2 + (y - y_0)^2 + (z - z_0)^2 < r^2, r > 0$.   **18.** $\left\{ \sum\limits_{k=1}^{n} (y_k - x_k)^2 \right\}^{1/2}$.

Chapter 16. Exercise 5   Page 557

1. $2(\Delta x)^2 + 3(\Delta y)^2$.   **2.** $(3x + \Delta x)(\Delta x)^2 + 2y(\Delta x)(\Delta y) + (x - 3y + \Delta x - \Delta y)(\Delta y)^2$.
3. $\Delta y(-y\Delta x + x\Delta y)/y^2(y + \Delta y)$.   **4.** $3x^2(\Delta y)^2 + 3y^2(\Delta x)^2 + 3(\Delta x)(\Delta y)[4xy + 2x\Delta y + 2y\Delta x + (\Delta x)(\Delta y)]$.   **5.** $.142$ ft, $.075\%$.   **6.** 7.28 ft, 1.48%.   **7.** 140 ft^2,
1.4 ft.   **8.** 4.4π in^3.   **9.** 10.8.   **10.** -1.2.   **11.** 2%.   **12.** $.25$ cm.   **13.** 1.92.
14. $.0538$.   **17.** f_x and f_y are not continuous in a neighborhood of $(0, 0)$.

Chapter 16. Exercise 6   Page 562

1. 0.   **2.** $1/(1 + t^2)$.   **3.** $(6t^2 + 2t^3)e^t + (6t^2 - 2t^3)e^{-t}$.   **4.** $4(4 - t^2)/(4 + t^2)^2$.
5. $4/t$.   **6.** $\ln 2(t^2 + u^2) + 2t(t + u)/(t^2 + u^2)$, $\ln 2(t^2 + u^2) + 2u(t + u)/(t^2 + u^2)$.

7. $10te^{5t^2} \sin 5u^2$, $10ue^{5t^2} \cos 5u^2$.   **8.** $r \sin 2\theta$, $r^2 \cos 2\theta$.
9. $\pi l^3(2 \sin \theta \cos^2 \theta - \sin^3 \theta)/3$, $\pi l^2 \sin^2 \theta \cos \theta$.   **11.** In 9, V_h is computed with r
held constant, and in 11, V_h is computed with θ held constant.   In 9, V_θ is computed with l held constant and in 11 V_θ is computed with h held constant.   A drawing will show that there is no reason to expect equality among these quantities.

Chapter 16. Exercise 7   Page 568

1. Dir. der. of f with $\theta = \pi$ and $\theta = 3\pi/2$ resp.

Chapter 16. Exercise 8 Page 570

1. (a) $(f_x\mathbf{i} + f_y\mathbf{j}) \cdot (\cos\,\theta\mathbf{i} + \sin\,\theta\mathbf{j})$; (b) $\nabla f = f_x\mathbf{i} + f_y\mathbf{j}$; (c) In Theorem 7 replace $f(x, y, z)$ by $f(x, y)$. **2.** $\sqrt{2}$. **3.** 0. **4.** $-\pi/\sqrt{5}$. **5.** $-60/7$. **6.** $15/\sqrt{14}$. **7.** $12\pi/11$. **8.** The cyl. $y = \sin x$. **9.** No. **10.** The line $x = 3 - 2t,\ \ y = 1 + 2t,\ \ z = -5 + t$. **11.** The line $y = 2x,\ \ z = 3x$. **12.** $y = 1/3,\ 3z = 1 + \pi\sqrt{3}x$. **13.** The circles $x^2 + y^2 = |\nabla f|^2/5$. **14.** The points on each of the lines $(0, 0, z)$, $(0, y, -5/2)$, $(2/3, y, -5/2)$ or on the curve $(x, 0, -5/3x)$. **18.** f is constant in $\Re$. **19.** $f = ax + by + cz + d$ in $\Re$.

Chapter 16. Exercise 9 Page 576

1. $2\mathbf{i} + 5\mathbf{j}$, $\mathbf{u} = (5\mathbf{i} - 2\mathbf{j})/\sqrt{29}$. **2.** $2\mathbf{i} - \mathbf{j}$, $\mathbf{u} = (\mathbf{i} + 2\mathbf{j})/\sqrt{5}$; $-2\mathbf{i} - \mathbf{j}$, $\mathbf{u} = (\mathbf{i} - 2\mathbf{j})/\sqrt{5}$. **3.** $6\mathbf{i} - 8\mathbf{j}$, $\mathbf{u} = (4\mathbf{i} + 3\mathbf{j})/5$; $-10\mathbf{i} + 24\mathbf{j}$, $\mathbf{u} = (12\mathbf{i} + 5\mathbf{j})/13$. **4.** $8\mathbf{i} + 8\mathbf{j}$, $\mathbf{u} = (\mathbf{i} - \mathbf{j})/\sqrt{2}$; $-6\mathbf{j}$, $\mathbf{u} = \mathbf{i}$. **5.** $\mathbf{i} + \mathbf{j}$, $\mathbf{u} = (\mathbf{i} - \mathbf{j})/\sqrt{2}$; $4\mathbf{i} + \mathbf{j}$, $\mathbf{u} = (\mathbf{i} - 4\mathbf{j})/\sqrt{17}$. **6.** $\mathbf{0}$, $\mathbf{u} = (\mathbf{i} - \mathbf{j})/\sqrt{2}$. **7.** $\mathbf{i}$, $\mathbf{u} = \mathbf{j}$; $\mathbf{i} - 4\mathbf{j}$, $\mathbf{u} = (4\mathbf{i} + \mathbf{j})/\sqrt{17}$. **8.** $\mathbf{0}$, no tangent vector; $8\mathbf{i}$, $\mathbf{u} = \mathbf{j}$. **9.** $2x + y - 5z = 30$. **10.** $11x + 2y - 5z = 0$. **11.** $2ex - \pi y + (e + \pi)z = 3e$. **12.** $2x + 2y + z = 2$. **15.** $\dfrac{x - 1}{5} = \dfrac{y - 2}{11} = \dfrac{z + 1}{7}$. **16.** $\dfrac{x - 2}{1} = \dfrac{y - 1}{4} = \dfrac{z + 1}{-2}$. **20.** $(x - 1) = 17(1 - y)/7 = 17(z - 1)$. **21.** $3\pi(x - 2) = y - 1,\ z = 3$. **23.** $(-Az - Cx)/(Cy + Bz),\ (Bx - Ay)/(Cy + Bz)$. **24.** $(x^2(z - y) + z^2(y - x))/D$, $(x^2(z - y) + y^2(x - z))/D$, where $D = y^2(x - z) + z^2(y - x)$.

Chapter 16. Exercise 11 Page 586

1. 14 at $(\pm\sqrt{3}/2, 1/2)$, 4 at $(0, -1/2)$. **2.** 425 at $(-4, 3)$ and $(4, -3)$, -200 at $(3, 4)$, and $(-3, -4)$, saddle pt. at $(0, 0)$. **3.** $17r^2$ at $(-4r/5, 3r/5)$ and $(4r/5, -3r/5)$, $-8r^2$ at $(3r/5, 4r/5)$ and $(-3r/5, -4r/5)$. **4.** 275 at $(0, 5)$, 0 at $(0, 0)$, saddle pt. at $(0, -4)$. **5.** 640 at $(8, 8)$, $(8, -4)$ and $(-4, 8)$; -1408 at $(-8, -8)$; rel. min. -8 at $(2, 2)$; saddle pt. at $(0, 0)$. **6.** 2 at $(1/2, 1/2)$, -1 at $(-1, -1)$. **7.** Max $= (1 + 2\sqrt{2}r)/(1 + r^2)$, Min $= (1 - 2\sqrt{2}r)/(1 + r^2)$. **8.** $3\sqrt{3}/2$. **9.** 3^52^4. **10.** $(5, 3, 5/3)$. **11.** $V = d^3/27abc$ at $(d/3a, d/3b, d/3c)$. **13.** $V = 8abc/3\sqrt{3}$. **14.** (a) $7/\sqrt{3}$; (b) $10/\sqrt{14}$. **15.** (a) $\sqrt{2}$; (b) $2\sqrt{3}$; (c) 0; (d) 13. **16.** $(6, 3, 4)$. **17.** $(10/3, 20, 8/3)$. **18.** $R^4,\ R^4/3$. **19.** $(\pm\sqrt{6}, \pm\sqrt{6}, 3)$. **20.** $x = y = z = 5$ in. **21.** 2 ft by 2 ft glass face, 3 ft deep. **22.** $1/30e^3$. **23.** 5 at $(6, 3, -1)$. **24.** If $x = y = 0$, $G = -27z^2 + 14$ (no min); if $y = z = 0$, $G = x^2 + 14$ (no max.). **26.** $\pm\left(\sum\limits_{k=1}^{n} a_k^2\right)^{1/2}$.

Chapter 17. Exercise 1 Page 591

1. $0 < y < 4,\ 0 < x < \sqrt{4 - y}$. **2.** $0 < y < 4,\ |x| < \sqrt{4 - y}$. **3.** $0 < y < e^4 - 1,\ \ln(y + 1) < x < 4$. **4.** $1/2 < y < 1,\ \sin^{-1}y < x < \pi/2$. **5.** $1 < y < 2,\ \ 3 + 2\sqrt{y - 1} < x < 5$. **6.** $2/5 < y < 2,\ \ 0 < x < \ln(2/y)$. **7.** If $-3 < y < 0$ then $|x| < 1$, if $0 \le y < 1$, then $\sqrt[4]{y} < |x| < 1$. **8.** $1 < y < 2,\ 2 - 2\sqrt{2 - y} < x < 2\sqrt[3]{y - 1}$. **9.** $|x| < 3,\ |y| < 4\sqrt{1 - x^2/9}$.

10. $0 < y$, $|x| < 2\sqrt{y}$. **11.** If $0 < y \leq 1$ then $|x| < 2\sqrt{y}$, if $1 \leq y < 4$ then $2y - 4 < x < 2\sqrt{y}$. **12.** $|y| < 4$, $10 - \sqrt{65 - y^2} < x < \sqrt{25 - y^2}$.
13. If $0 < y \leq 16$ then $|x| < y^{1/4}$, if $16 \leq y < 20$ then $|x| < \sqrt{20 - y}$.
14. If $0 < y < 12$ then $|x| < y^{1/4}$, if $12 \leq y < 16$ then $\sqrt{y - 12} < |x| < y^{1/4}$.
15. $\mathfrak{R}_1 : -1 \leq x \leq 1$, $\sqrt{1 - x^2} \leq y \leq \sqrt{4 - x^2}$; $\mathfrak{R}_2 : -1 \leq x \leq 1$, $-\sqrt{4 - x^2} \leq y \leq -\sqrt{1 - x^2}$; $\mathfrak{R}_3 : -\sqrt{3} \leq y \leq \sqrt{3}$, $1 \leq x \leq \sqrt{4 - y^2}$; $\mathfrak{R}_4 : -\sqrt{3} \leq y \leq \sqrt{3}$, $-\sqrt{4 - y^2} \leq x \leq -1$.

Chapter 17. Exercise 2 Page 595

1. 5. **2.** 10/3. **3.** 128/15. **4.** 32. **5.** 8/3. **6.** $(e^8 - 9)/4$.
7. $3\sqrt{3} - \pi$. **8.** 5/12. **9.** π. **10.** $abc/6$. **11.** 2. **12.** 8. **13.** $2 - \ln 3$.
14. 61/210. **15.** $(e^4 - 1)/4$. **16.** 128/3. **17.** 153/2.

Chapter 17. Exercise 3 Page 600

7. is false. Let $\mathfrak{R}$ be the square $0 \leq x \leq 2$, $0 \leq y \leq 2$, and set $f(x)g(y) = xy$. The left side is 4 and the right side is 16.

Chapter 17. Exercise 4 Page 603

1. 9/2. **2.** $15/2 - 8 \ln 2$. **3.** 9. **4.** $8 - 6 \ln 3$. **5.** (55/36, 7/4), 135/4, 87/4. **6.** (13/20, 29/20), 76/5, 16/5. **7.** (2/5, 2/5), 1/60, 1/60.
8. 111/2, 92/5, 1/30. **9.** (6/5, 96/35). **10.** 512/35, 32/15. **11.** 64/21.
12. $((12 - \pi^2)/3(4 - \pi), \pi/6(4 - \pi))$. **13.** $(A^2 + 5A + 10)/3(A + 1)(A + 6)$.
14. The region is not convex.

Chapter 17. Exercise 5 Page 607

1. $9(1 + b^2 + c^2)^{1/2}$. **2.** 38. **3.** 104/3. **4.** $9 - (8 + e^{-6})^{3/2}/3$. **5.** $10\sqrt{2}$.
6. $2a^2$. **7.** $\frac{1}{3}(2\sqrt{2} - 1)$. **8.** ∞. **9.** $7\sqrt{13}/2$. **10.** $2a^2$. **11.** $8a^2$.
13. $1, \frac{\pi}{2} - 1$.

Chapter 17. Exercise 6 Page 612

1. $a^2\sqrt{3}/8$. **2.** 3π. **3.** $19\pi/2$. **4.** $(4 - \pi)/8$. **5** $\left(\dfrac{9\sqrt{3}}{2} - \pi\right) a^2$.
6. $7\pi^3/192$. **7.** 8π, $32\pi/3$, $\pi(17\sqrt{17} - 1)/6$. **8.** πa^3, $a/4$, $5a/8$, $\pi a^5/2$.
9. $\pi a(2a^2 + 3b^2)/3$. **10.** $(b - a) \ln (\sqrt{2} + 1)$, $\frac{1}{2}(b^2 - a^2) \ln (\sqrt{2} + 1)$, $(b^2 - a^2)(\sqrt{2} - 1)$, $\pi(\ln b - \ln a)/8$. **11.** 16/105. **12.** $2a^3(3\pi - 4)/9$.
13. $a^2(\pi - 2)$. **15.** $\delta r \sin \theta$, $\delta r \cos \theta$, $\delta r^2 \sin^2 \theta$, $\delta r^2 \cos^2 \theta$, δr^2. **16.** $\pi a^4/4$.
17. $(4a/3\pi, 0)$. **18.** $\bar{x} = -20/9\pi^{5/3}$, $\bar{y} = 10/9\pi^{2/3}$. **19.** $(5a/6, 0)$.
20. $(\pi a/2, 0)$. **21.** $(2(a^2 - b^2)^{3/2}/3(a^2 \cos^{-1} (b/a) - b\sqrt{a^2 - b^2}), 0)$.
23. $2b(5a^2 + b^2)/5(3a^2 + b^2)$. **24.** $b(5a^2 + 3b^2)/5(a^2 + b^2)$. **25.** $5\pi/64$, $\pi/64$.
26. $3\pi/32$. **27.** $a^4/3$, $a^4/6$, $a^4/2$. **29.** $\pi/4$.

Chapter 17. Exercise 7 Page 619

1. $a^2b^3c^4$. **2.** 512/7. **4.** 4. **5.** 64. **6.** 16/3. **7.** $32\sqrt{2}\pi$. **8.** $\pi/2$

9. 8π.　**10.** $k/2$.　**11.** $kab^2c/2$.　**12.** $abc + ka^2b^3c^4$.　**13.** $256k/15$.　**14.** $13/72$.
15. $(\ln 4)^3/6$.　**17.** (a) $(1/2, 2/3, 1/2)$; (b) $(a/2, 2b/3, c/2)$;

$$\text{(c)} \quad \left(\frac{a}{d} \left(\frac{1}{2} + \frac{2}{3} q \right), \frac{b}{d} \left(\frac{1}{2} + \frac{3}{4} q \right), \frac{c}{d} \left(\frac{1}{2} + \frac{4}{5} q \right) \right) \quad \text{where}$$

$q = kab^2c^3$, and $d = 1 + q$; (d) $(372/455, 258/455, 7/26)$.　**18.** (a) $5k/12, k/3$;
(b) $kab^2c(3b^2 + 2c^2)/12, kab^2c(a^2 + c^2)/6$; (c) $abc(b^2 + c^2)/3 + ka^2b^3c^4(9b^2 + 10c^2)/15$,
$abc(a^2 + c^2)/3 + ka^2b^3c^4(3a^2 + 4c^2)/6$; (d) $209/2400, 349/2400$.　**19.** $(a/4, b/4, c/4)$.
20. $abc(b^2 + c^2)/60$.

Chapter 17.　Exercise 8　Page 622

1. (a) z; (b) $r \cos \theta$; (c) $z^2 + r^2 \sin^2 \theta$; (d) $z^2 + r^2 \cos^2 \theta$.　**2.** $2\pi \rho_0^3(1 - \cos \varphi_0)/3$.
4. $(0, 0, 3H/4)$.　**5.** $4\pi(8\sqrt{2} - 7)/3$.　**6.** $7/(8\sqrt{2} - 7)$.　**7.** $\pi/32$.
8. $(0, 1/2, 5/12)$.　**9.** $3\pi R^4H/2$, $\pi R^2H(3R^2 + 4H^2)/12$.　**10.** $\pi HR^4/10$,
$\pi R^2H(3R^2 + 2H^2)/60$.　**11.** π.　**12.** $32k(2 - \sqrt{2})/15, 5(2 + \sqrt{2})/16$,
$5(\pi - 2)(2 + \sqrt{2})/32$.　**13.** $\pi(4Ha^2 + 2Hb^2 + 4ma^2b + mb^3)/4$.　**14.** $\pi Q/2$,
$\bar{x} = \bar{y} = 2[2 - (2 + 2R + R^2)e^{-R}]/\pi Q$, $\bar{z} = [1 - (1 + 2R)e^{-2R}]/8Q$ where $Q = 1 - (1 + R)e^{-R}$.　**15.** $(4/\pi, 4/\pi, 1/8)$.

Chapter 17.　Exercise 9　Page 625

3. (a) $\rho \cos \varphi$; (b) $\rho \sin \varphi \sin \theta$; (c) $\rho^2(\sin^2 \varphi \sin^2 \theta + \cos^2 \varphi)$;
(d) $\rho^2(\sin^2 \varphi \cos^2 \theta + \cos^2 \varphi)$; (e) $\rho^2 \sin^2 \varphi$.　**4.** $\frac{4}{3}\pi R^3, \frac{8}{15}\pi R^5$.
5. $(0, 0, 3(B^4 - A^4)/8(B^3 - A^3))$.　**6.** $I_z = I_x = 4\pi(B^5 - A^5)/15$.
7. $2\pi R^3(1 - \cos \gamma)/3, 3R(1 + \cos \gamma)/8, 2\pi R^5(2 - 3 \cos \gamma + \cos^3 \gamma)/15$,
$\pi R^5(4 - 3 \cos \gamma - \cos^3 \gamma)/15$.　**9.** $\pi^2A^3/4$.　**10.** $\pi^2A^3/3$.　**11.** $(B^4 - A^4)/(B^3 - A^3)$.
12. $B, 4B/3$.　**13.** $\pi A^3(4B - 3A)/6B$.　**14.** $\pi A^3/6$.　**15.** $2\pi kR^{3-n}/(3 - n)$, if $n < 3$.
16. $\pi kR^{4-n}/(4 - n)$ if $n < 4$, $\bar{z} = (3 - n)R/2(4 - n)$ if $n < 3$, $3 \leqq n < 4$.
17. $4\pi kR^{5-n}/3(5 - n), n < 5$.　**18.** Yes.

Chapter 17.　Exercise 10　Page 629

2. $F_1 = -\gamma M/(b^2 - a^2)$.　**3.** $F_2 = -\gamma M/b\sqrt{a^2 + b^2}$.　**4.** $F_2 = -2\gamma\delta/b$.
5. $F_3 = -2\gamma M(\sqrt{a^2 + R^2} - a)/R^2\sqrt{a^2 + R^2}$.　**7.** $F_3 = 2\pi H\gamma\delta(1 - \cos \alpha)$
where $\tan \alpha = R/H$.　**8.** $F_3 = \pi \gamma kH^2 \ln \sec \alpha$.
9. $F_3 = 2\pi\gamma kH^{n+1}(\sec^{n-1} \alpha - 1)/(n^2 - 1)$.

Chapter 18.　Exercise 1　Page 633

1. $y\, dx - x\, dy = 0$.　**2.** $2y\, dx + (1 - x)dy = 0$.　**3.** $(y^2 - 5)dx - xy\, dy = 0$.
4. $(x^2 - y^2)dx + 2xy\, dy = 0$.　**5.** $(y^4 - 2yx^3)dx + (x^4 - 2xy^3)dy = 0$.
6. $(y - x^2 + 2x \tan x)dx - \tan x\, dy = 0$.　**7.** $y'' - y = 0$.　**8.** $y'' + y' - 6y = 0$.
9. $(2x^2y + 1)y'' + (4xy' + 2y)(y - xy') = 0$.
10. $(1 + \tan x)y'' - 2y' + (1 - \tan x)y = 0$.　**11.** $2dx - dy = 0$.
12. $2xy\, dx + (y^2 - x^2)dy = 0$.　**13.** $(x^2 + 2xy - y^2)dx + (y^2 + 2xy - x^2)dy = 0$.
14. $2x(y - 1)dx + (y^2 - x^2 - 2y + 1)dy = 0$.　**15.** $x^2(dx)^2 + 2xy\, dx\, dy - x^2(dy)^2 = 0$.
16. $xy\, dx + (1 - x^2)dy = 0$.　**17.** $x(y')^2 - (x + y - 10)y' + y = 0$.

18. $2xy\,dx + (y^2 - x^2 + 1)\,dy = 0$.   **19.** $yy'' + (y')^2 = 0$.
20. $(x^2 + y^2)y'' - 2x(y')^3 + 2y(y')^2 - 2xy' + 2y = 0$.   **22.** $(y')^2 - 4xy' + 4y = 0$.

Chapter 18. Exercise 2   Page 636

1. $xy^3 e^y = C$.   **2.** $r\cos^4\theta = C$.   **3.** $6e^x + e^{3y^2} = C$.   **4.** $y = Cx/(x+3)^2$.
5. $C = (x+y)/(1 - xy)$.   **6.** $4y - x^2 + 2x^2\ln x - 4\ln y = C$.   **7.** $y = Cx$.
8. $y = C/x^2$.   **9.** $y^2 - 3x^2 = C$.   **10.** $2y^3 + (C + 3x^2)y + 4 = 0$.
11. $2y^2 = \ln x^2 + C$.   **12.** $2y^2 = C + x^2(1 - \ln x^2)$.   **13.** If we solve
$y^2(y'')^2 + 2xyy' - y^2 = 0$ for y' the product of the roots is -1.   **14.** As in 13 the
product of the roots of $xy(y')^2 + (x^2 - y^2 - 1)y' - xy = 0$ is -1.   **15.** $x^2 + y^2 = r^2$,
$x^2 + y^2 = 25$.   **16.** $xy = C$, $xy = 3$.   **17.** $(x + C)^2 + y^2 = L^2$,
$[x - (2L \pm L)]^2 + y^2 = L^2$.   **18.** $y^2 = \pm 2Ax + C$, $y^2 = \pm 2A(x - 4) + 1$.
19. $y = x/(1 + Cx)$, $y = x$.   **20.** $y = Kx/(1 + Cx)$, $y = 2Kx/[2 + (K - 1)x]$.

Chapter 18. Exercise 3   Page 639

1. $x^3(x^3 + 2y^3) = C$.   **2.** $(y - 3x)(y + 3x)^2 = C$.   **3.** $\sin\dfrac{y - x}{x} = Cx$.
4. $y + 3xe^{y/x} = C$.   **5.** $y = x\sin(\frac{1}{2}\ln|C/x|)$.   **6.** $x(\sec(y/x) + \tan(y/x))^3 = C$.
7. $\ln(5x^2 + 4xy + y^2) = C + 4\tan^{-1}(2 + y/x)$.   **8.** $x^2 - y^2 = Cx$.
9. $Cx^3(x + 2y) = e^{2y/x}$.   **12.** No.   There are no solutions in 5 if $|y/x| > 1$.

Chapter 18. Exercise 4   Page 642

1. $2x^3 + 5xy^2 = C$.   **2.** $x^3y^2 + x^2y^4 + y = C$.   **3.** $r^2\sin\theta + r\cos\theta = C$.
4. $y^2 e^{x/y} = C$.   **5.** $x^2 - y = Cy^3$.   **6.** $x^2\sin xy^2 + \cos y^2 = C$.
7. $\mathscr{F}_1 : a(x^2 - y^2) - 2bxy = C_1, \mathscr{F}_2 : b(x^2 - y^2) + 2axy = C_2$.   **8.** $\mathscr{F}_1 : x^3 - 3xy^2 = C_1$,
$\mathscr{F}_2 : 3x^2y - y^3 = C_2$.   **11.** $x^2/y + y/x = C$.   **12.** $e^x(xy + x - y) = C$.
13. $x + \ln(x^2 + y^2) - 3\tan^{-1}(x/y) = C$.   **14.** $2xy + x^2/y^2 = C$.
15. (a) $3x + x^3y = Cy$; (b) $x^2y + y^2 = C$.

Chapter 18. Exercise 5   Page 644

1. $3y = e^{2x} + Ce^{-x}$.   **2.** $yx^3 = x^6 + C$.   **3.** $xy = \sin x - x\cos x + C$.
4. $y = x + 4 + Ce^{-x}$.   **5.** $y = 1 + x^2 + C\sqrt{1 + x^2}$.
6. $(1 + x)^2(2 + y + xy) = C$.   **7.** $y\sin^2 x = 2\sin^3 x + C$.
8. $(x - 1)(x - 2)^2 y = x^2(x - 3) + C$.
10. $y^3 = 8x^6/(C - 3x^8)$.   **11.** $\sqrt{y} = x(3x^2 + C)$.
12. $x = y(x\cos x - \sin x + C)$.   **13.** $y^6x^6 = 2x^3 - x^6 + C$.

Chapter 18. Exercise 6   Page 649

1. $y = C_1 e^x + C_2 e^{3x}$.   **2.** $y = C_1 e^{13x} + C_2 e^{-x}$.   **3.** $y = C_1 + C_2 e^{-16x}$.
4. $y = e^{-4x}(C_1 + C_2 x)$.   **5.** $y = C_1\cos 4x + C_2\sin 4x$.
6. $y = e^{-4x}(C_1\cos x + C_2\sin x)$.   **7.** $y = e^{-x}(C_1\cos 4x + C_2\sin 4x)$.
8. $y = C_1 + C_2 e^{\pi x}$.   **9.** $s = e^t(C_1\cos 2t + C_2\sin 2t)$.   **10.** $r = C_1 e^{-3\theta} + C_2 e^{-19\theta}$.
11. $x = e^{3t}(C_1 + C_2 t)$.   **12.** $u = C_1\sin\sqrt{2}\,v + C_2\cos\sqrt{2}\,v$.   **13.** $y = 11e^x - 7e^{2x}$.

14. $y = [(r_2A - B)e^{r_1x} - (r_1A - B)e^{r_2x}]/(r_2 - r_1)$.   **15.** $y = e \sin(x/2)$.
16. $y = C_1e^{2x} + C_2e^{5x} + C_3$.   **17.** $y = C_1e^{-2x} + C_2xe^{-2x} + C_3x + C_4$.   **22.** If u
and v are solutions then $y = C_1u + C_2v$ is also a solution.   **23.** Yes, if $q(x) = 0$.
No otherwise.

Chapter 18. Exercise 7   Page 652

1. $y = C_1e^{3x} + C_2 - 4e^{2x}$.   **2.** $y = C_1 \cos x + C_2 \sin x + x^2 - 2$.
3. $y = C_1 \cos 2x + C_2 \sin 2x - \frac{1}{5} \sin 3x + x/2$.
4. $y = C_1e^{5x} + C_2e^{-3x} + 3x^2 + 4x/5 - 22/75$.
5. $y = e^{2x}(C_1 \cos x + C_2 \sin x) + x^3 + x^2 + 2x/5 - 2/25$.
6. $y = C_1 \cos 2x + C_2 \sin 2x + \frac{1}{3}x \sin x - \frac{2}{9} \cos x$.
7. $y = e^x(C_1 \cos \sqrt{3}x + C_2 \sin \sqrt{3}x) + (7x + 4)e^{-x}/49$.
8. $y = (C_1 + C_2x)e^{-x} + 5x - 10 + \pi e^{-2x}$.   **9.** $y = C_1e^x + C_2e^{3x} - 3xe^x$.
10. $y = C_1e^x + C_2 - x^3 - 3x^2 - 6x$.   **11.** $y = (C_1 - x)e^{3x} + (C_2 + x)e^{4x}$.
12. $(C_1 + C_2x + 4x^2)e^x$.   **13.** $y = C_1 \cos 2x + (C_2 + x/4)\sin 2x$.
14. $y = (C_1 + 2x)e^{3x} + C_2e^{-4x} - x/2 - 1/24$.
15. $y = C_1e^{10x/3} + C_2 - \frac{1}{4}x^4 + \frac{1}{2}x^3 + x^2 + x$.   **16.** $y = (C_1 + C_2x + 5x^2)e^{-3x} + 10$.
18. $y = x^4/12$.   **19.** $y = 4e^x + 2e^{2x} - 3e^{3x}$.   **20.** $y = 4e^x(1 - e^x)^2$.   **21.** $4xe^{2x}$.

Chapter 18. Exercise 8   Page 654

1. $C_1e^x + C_2e^{-x} + C_3 \cos x + C_4 \sin x$.

2. $e^{\sqrt{2}x}(C_1 \cos \sqrt{2}x + C_2 \sin \sqrt{2}x) + e^{-\sqrt{2}x}(C_3 \cos \sqrt{2}x + C_4 \sin \sqrt{2}x)$.
3. $e^{x/2}(C_1 + C_2x + C_3x^2)$.   **4.** $C_1e^{2x} + C_2e^{-2x} + C_3 \cos \sqrt{3}x + C_4 \sin \sqrt{3}x$.
5. $C_1 \cos 2x + C_2 \sin 2x + C_3 + 2e^x$.   **6.** $C_1 \cos 3x + C_2 \sin 3x + C_3 - \frac{1}{5} \cos 2x$.
7. $C_1e^{-x} + C_2e^{-2x} + C_3e^{-3x} + 3e^{2x}$.
8. $C_1e^x + C_2e^{-x} + e^{2x}(C_3 \cos 3x + C_4 \sin 3x) - 2x^2 - 3x - 4$.
9. $(C_1 + C_2x)\cos x + (C_3 + C_4x)\sin x + 2x + e^x + 2e^{-x}$.
10. $C_1e^{5x} + C_2 + C_3x - \frac{3}{10}x^2 - \frac{1}{2}x^3 - \frac{5}{8}e^{4x}$.
11. $y = C_1e^{4x} + C_2e^{-3x} + C_3 + x(e^{4x} - 1)/4$.
12. $(C_1 + C_2x + C_3x^2 + 20x^3 + 3x^5)e^{-x}/60$.   **13.** $y = \frac{1}{2}(1 + e^{-2x} - 2e^{-x})$.
14. $y = Ae^x(\cos \sqrt{3}x - \sqrt{3} \sin \sqrt{3}x) - Ae^{-2x}$.

Chapter 18. Exercise 9   Page 658

1. $y = Cx^2$.   **2.** $y = C \sum_{n=0}^{\infty} \frac{x^{2n}}{n!} = Ce^{x^2}$.

3. $y = -3 + C \sum_{n=0}^{\infty} \frac{x^{2n}}{n!} = -3 + Ce^{x^2}$.   **4.** $y = -x + Ce^{2x}$.

5. $y = C(3x^2 + 2x^3)$.   **6.** $y = C \sum_{n=0}^{\infty} \frac{x^n}{n!} + \sum_{n=0}^{\infty} \frac{x^{n+1}}{n!} = (C + x)e^x$.

7. $y = A\left(1 + \frac{x^3}{2 \cdot 3} + \frac{x^6}{2 \cdot 3 \cdot 5 \cdot 6} + \frac{x^9}{2 \cdot 3 \cdot 5 \cdot 6 \cdot 8 \cdot 9} + \cdots\right)$

$$+ B\left(x + \frac{x^4}{3 \cdot 4} + \frac{x^7}{3 \cdot 4 \cdot 6 \cdot 7} + \frac{x^{10}}{3 \cdot 4 \cdot 6 \cdot 7 \cdot 9 \cdot 10} + \cdots\right).$$

8. $y = A(1 - x^2) + B\left(x - \dfrac{x^3}{1 \cdot 3} - \dfrac{x^5}{3 \cdot 5} - \dfrac{x^7}{5 \cdot 7} - \dfrac{x^9}{7 \cdot 9} - \cdots\right).$

9. $y = A\left(1 + \dfrac{x^3}{3} + \dfrac{x^6}{3 \cdot 6} + \dfrac{x^9}{3 \cdot 6 \cdot 9} + \cdots\right)$

$$+ B\left(x + \dfrac{x^4}{4} + \dfrac{x^7}{4 \cdot 7} + \dfrac{x^{10}}{4 \cdot 7 \cdot 10} + \cdots\right).$$

10. $y = A \sum\limits_{n=0}^{\infty} \dfrac{1}{2^n n!} x^{2n} + B \sum\limits_{n=0}^{\infty} \dfrac{2^n n!}{(2n + 1)!} x^{2n+1}.$

11. $y = A\left(1 - \dfrac{1}{2} x^2 + \dfrac{1 \cdot 3}{2 \cdot 4} x^4 - \dfrac{1 \cdot 3 \cdot 5}{2 \cdot 4 \cdot 6} x^6 + \cdots\right)$

$$+ B\left(x - \dfrac{2}{3} x^3 + \dfrac{2 \cdot 4}{3 \cdot 5} x^5 - \dfrac{2 \cdot 4 \cdot 6}{3 \cdot 5 \cdot 7} x^7 + \cdots\right).$$

12. $y = A\left(1 + \dfrac{3}{2!} x^2 + \dfrac{3 \cdot 7}{4!} x^4 + \dfrac{3 \cdot 7 \cdot 11}{6!} x^6 + \cdots\right)$

$$+ B\left(x + \dfrac{5}{3!} x^3 + \dfrac{5 \cdot 9}{5!} x^5 + \dfrac{5 \cdot 9 \cdot 13}{7!} x^7 + \cdots\right).$$

13. $y = (A + Bx)/(1 + x^2).$

14. $y = Ae^{(x^5)/5} + B\left(x + \dfrac{x^6}{6} + \dfrac{x^{11}}{6 \cdot 11} + \dfrac{x^{16}}{6 \cdot 11 \cdot 16} + \cdots\right).$

15. $y = A \sum\limits_{n=0}^{\infty} \dfrac{x^{2n}}{4^n (n!)^2}.$

16. $y = A\left(1 - \sum\limits_{n=1}^{\infty} \dfrac{x^{2n}}{2n(2n - 2)!}\right) + \dfrac{B}{2} \sum\limits_{n=1}^{\infty} \dfrac{x^{2n+1}}{(2n + 1)(2n - 1)!}.$

17. At $x = 0$, such a solution would make the left side of the diff. equ. finite and the right side infinite, and this is impossible. **19.** $y = x^3/7.$

20. $y = 1 + \dfrac{x^2}{2} + \dfrac{x^4}{24} - \dfrac{x^5}{60} + \cdots.$ **21.** Same as 20.

22. $y = x + \dfrac{x^3}{6} - \dfrac{7x^5}{120} - \dfrac{19x^7}{5040} + \cdots.$ **23.** $y = 2x + \dfrac{x^2}{2} + \dfrac{x^3}{6} + \dfrac{x^4}{3} + \cdots.$

24. $y = 1 + 3x + \dfrac{x^3}{2} + \dfrac{3x^4}{4} + \cdots.$ **25.** $y \equiv 0$, there are no nonzero terms.

Chapter 18. Exercise 10   Page 662

1. 1981, 1993. **2.** 4.24%. **3.** 30 years. **5.** 6.49%. **6.** 11.5 min, 27.7 min. **7.** 16.2 min, 43.9 min. **8.** 15 hrs, 1000 gal.
9. $Q = \frac{3}{4}(100 + t) + 225 \times 10^6/(100 + t)^3$, 1 lb/gal, 73.2 min. **10.** .075%, .045%. **11.** $x = g(e^{-ct} - 1 + ct)/c^2$ where the resistance is cWv/g. **14.** 37 ft/sec $\approx$ 25.2 mi/hr. **15.** $g(W_2 - W_1)/(W_2 + W_1)$, $2W_1W_2/(W_1 + W_2)$.
17. 6.93 mi/sec. **19.** 5.4 lbs/in². **20.** $x = C \cos \omega t$, $\omega = \sqrt{gk/W}$.

21. $\pi/8$ secs.   **22.** $\dfrac{\sqrt{2}}{4}\,\ln(4+\sqrt{15})$ secs.   **23.** $C_1\cos\omega t + C_2\sin\omega t$.

24. $C_1\cos\omega t + C_2\sin\omega t + \dfrac{\alpha E_0}{L(\omega^2-\alpha^2)}\cos\alpha t$.

25. $C_1 e^{-10t} + C_2 e^{-20t} + .33\sin 10t + .11\cos 10t$.

26. $E_0(R\sin\omega t - \omega L\cos\omega t + \omega L e^{-Rt/L})/(R^2+\omega^2 L^2)$.   **27.** $r = r_0 - Ct$.

28. 34 days.   **29.** $Q = Q_0 e^{-kt} + M(1-e^{-kt})$.   **30.** 2 hrs 54 min.

32. $32 + 4\sqrt{2} \approx 37.66$ min.   **33.** 899 days.

ANSWERS FOR APPENDICES

Appendix 1. Page 670

1. $a = 1$.   **2.** $2a = 5b$.   **3.** $c = d$.   **4.** $c = d$.   **5.** $a = b$.   **6.** $a = b$.
7. $x = 2y$.   **8.** $x = y = z$.   **9.** $c = d$.   **10.** $a = 3b$.   **11.** $c = d$.
12. $A = D,\ B = C$.   **13.** 4, 6, 7, 8, 9.   **14.** $\sqrt{19} + \sqrt{21}$.   **15.** $\sqrt{11} - \sqrt{8}$.
16. $5\sqrt{7}$.   **17.** $\sqrt[3]{23}$.   **20.** $x < -2$.   **21.** $x > 1/3$.   **22.** $x < 0$ or $x > 1$.
23. $1 < x < 8$.   **24.** $3 < x < 5$.   **25.** $1/4 < x < 3$.   **28.** (a) $2 < x < 2.01$;
(b) $1.99 < x < 2.01,\, x \neq 2$; (c) $4.8 < x < 5.2,\, x \neq 5$; (d) $(1-\sqrt{362})/2 < x < -9$
or $10 < x < (1+\sqrt{362})/2$.

Appendix 2. Page 677

15. $n = 1$ or $n \geq 5$.   **16.** $n = 1$ or $n \geq 10$.

Appendix 5. Exercise 1   Page 688

1. $x = 5, y = 6$.   **2.** $x = 7, y = 4$.   **3.** $x = 3, y = 8$.   **4.** $x = -3, y = 4$.
5. $x = 11, y = -3$.   **6.** $x = -1, y = -2$.   **7.** $z = 0, w = 5$.   **8.** $A = 4/3$,
$B = 1/2$.   **9.** There is no solution. These are the equations of parallel lines.
10. $x = 3,\ y = 2;\ x = 5,\ y = 10$.   **11.** 35, 5.   **12.** 18, 12.
13. $W = 8,\ B = 7$.

Appendix 5. Exercise 3   Page 695

1. (a) 207; (b) 21; (c) -6; (d) 0.   **4.** 4, 13, 15, 14.   **5.** 4, 13, 15, 14.

Appendix 5. Exercise 4   Page 703

1. -8.   **2.** -1.   **3.** 133.   **4.** -78.   **5.** 1.   **6.** 113.   **11.** 80.   **12.** 1.
13. 0.   **14.** 104.   **15.** 16.   **16.** -160.

Appendix 5. Exercise 5   Page 708

1. $x = 1,\ y = 2,\ z = 3$.   **2.** $x = 3,\ y = -1,\ z = -2$.   **3.** $x = 3,\ y = 0$,
$z = 4$.   **4.** $x = 10, y = 7, z = 1/2$.   **5.** $u = -5, v = 1, w = 5$.   **6.** $A = 1$,
$B = -1,\ C = 5$.   **7.** $x = 4,\ y = 2,\ z = -1,\ u = -3$.   **8.** $p = -3,\ q = 1$,
$r = -1,\ s = 2$.   **9.** $V = 10,\ E = 15,\ F = 7$.   **10.** 79.

INDEX

INDEX

INDEX OF SPECIAL SYMBOLS

STEVEN L. SENDERS